P9-DEB-725

All the tools you need to achieve greater math success.

PRENTICE HALL

EACHING
ODAY'S
UDENTS

PRENTICE HALL
MIDDLE GRADES
MATH
TOOLS FOR SUCCESS
Course 1

PRENTICE HALL
MIDDLE GRADES
MATH
TOOLS FOR SUCCESS
Course 2

PRENTICE HALL
MIDDLE GRADES
MATH
TOOLS FOR SUCCESS
Course 3

To achieve success in today's middle grades classroom, you need to connect to
students think. And only one program—**Prentice Hall Middle Grades Ma**s
you meet this need head-on. This new program draws on students' prior knond
relates math to their everyday lives.

Building MATH SKILLS **Checking** UNDERSTANDING

But connecting is only the first part of the pro&t,
Middle Grades Math helps students build stro.
It achieves this through an exclusive and contir;ess
of *building* math skills and *checking* understanding. Then students *immedi*
these skills to real-world, problem-solving situations.

This emphasis on connecting with the way students think, on building skills, a
continuously checking understanding is what makes **Prentice Hall
Middle Grades Math** stand apart.

**Relating to
their world**

**Building
on prior
knowledge**

r math success

way tudents think.

Asking the
right
question
at the
right time

Checking for immediate
understanding

Listening to
student feedback

Encouraging
different
approaches

- Building on prior knowledge

- Pacing content in manageable parts

- Building stronger skills through student-friendly step-by-step instruction

---

DATA ANALYSIS Connection

1-3 Mean, Median, and Mode

What You'll Learn

▼ To find the mean

▼ To find the median or mode

...And Why

You can find the median length of comedy movies or discover which hobby is most popular.

Here's How

Look for questions that
- build understanding
- ✔ check understanding

Work Together
Finding Averages

Is your name longer than average? Let nd out!

1. Write the names of the students in r class on strips of graph paper as shn.

2. Find the average length of the namof the students in your group. Describe hcour group found this number.

3. ⬥*Analyze* Compare your work wither groups. Did everyone find the averalength of the names the same way? Explair

Uri
Gregory
Daria
Miki
Angela

THINK AND DISCUSS

▼ **Finding the Mean**

You are probably familiar with the word *erage*. In mathematics, an average is called a meaThe **mean** is the sum of the data divided by the number of datems.

■ **EXAMPLE 1** *Real-World Prcem Solving*

Airplanes Use the data table at the le Find the mean wingspan of the jet airliners.

Step 1: Find the sum of the data.

Step 2: Divide the sum by the number oata items.

Method 1: Paper and Pencil

① 60
45
44
58
+ 43
250

② $5\overline{)250}$
$-25\downarrow$
000

Methd 2: Calculator

① 60 ⊞ 45 ⊞ 44 ⊞
58 ⊞ 43 ▤ 250

② 250 ⊞ 5 ▤ 50

The mean wingspan of the jet airliners is0 meters.

Wingspan of Jet Airliners

Type	Wingspan (meters)
Airbus A330	60
McDonnell Douglas DCB Super 63	45
Boeing 707	44
Ilyushin IL-96-300	58
Ilyushin IL-62	43

Source: *The Cambridge Factfinder*

skills and check understanding

...sessment success.

EXCLUSIVE FEATURE

✔ **Try It Out**
provides students with
immediate skill check.

4. The wingspan of the Concorde is 26 meters. Suppose you include this value with the set of data in Example 1.
   a. ▪ *Estimation* Estimate the mean. Do you think the mean will be greater than or less than 50?
   b. ✔ *Try It Out* Find the mean.

5. ✔ *Try It Out* Find the mean of each data set.
   a. 23, 25, 19, 20, 21, 23, 23   b. 6, 3, 4, 6, 4, 5, 6, 4, 7

• Asking the right questions at the right time to immediately assess understanding

② *Finding the Median or Mode*

If the data set has an extreme high or low value, the median is a better measure to use. The **median** is the middle number in a set of ordered data.

Order the data.

18 3 20 17 22 20 19 → 3 17 18 19 20 20 22

↑
median

6. *Temperature* The daily temperatures (°F) at noon for one week are 86, 78, 92, 79, 87, 91, and 77.
   a. Order the data values.
   b. ✔ *Try It Out* Find the median.

When there is an even number of data items, you can find the median by adding the two middle numbers and dividing by 2.

■ **EXAMPLE 2**   *Real-World Problem Solving*

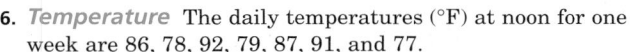

Entertainment Find the median length of the comedy movies at the right.

Lengths of 10 Comedy Movies (min)

111 105 100 101 101
92   87   96   92   95

111 105 100 101 101 92 87 96 92 95 ⟵ List the data.

87 92 92 95 96 100 101 101 105 111 ⟵ Order the data.

⟶ Identify the middle numbers.

$\frac{96 + 100}{2} = 98$ ⟵ Add and divide by 2.

The median is 98.

• Applying skills right away in a problem-solving context

7. ✔ *Try It Out* Find the median of each data set.
   a. 78, 90, 88, 76, 102, 79, 80   b. 10, 5, 7, 13, 14, 12, 12, 10

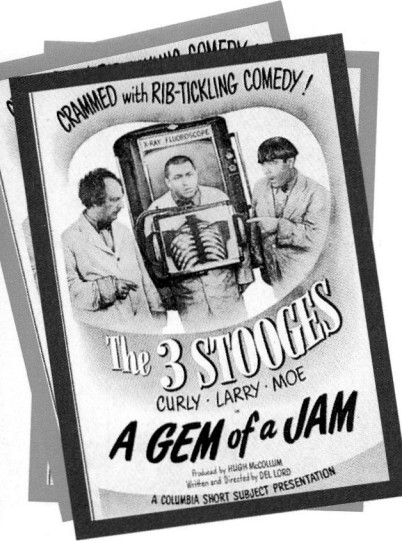

In the 1930s and early 1940s, the Three Stooges became popular in short films that played for 15–20 minutes before each feature film.

Building MATH SKILLS & Checking UNDERSTANDING

Solid preparation for future algebra and geometry study.

- **Middle Grades Math** provides a <u>solid foundation in fundamental middle grades topics,</u> including fractions, decimals, ratios, proportions, and percents.

- Readying students for future math study, **Middle Grades Math** integrates <u>key algebra, geometry, and data analysis topics</u> through-out the three-book series.

ALGEBRA Connection

6-10 Using Proportions with Percents

What You'll Learn

1. To find what percent one number is of another

2. To find a number when you know a percent and a part

...And Why

Business people use percents to advertise sales.

Here's How

Look for questions that
- build understanding
- ✔ check understanding

THINK AND DISCUSS

1 Finding a Percent

You can use models to understand the relationship of one number to another. You can use your model to write a proportion to express the relationship as a percent.

■ **EXAMPLE 1**   *Real-World Problem Solving*

Hiking Eighteen students in a class of 25 students plan to go on a class hiking trip. What percent of the students plan to go on the trip?

Model the relationship.

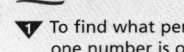

Hint: Divide your model into rectangles that are helpful to you.

0% — 0
n% — 18 ← part
100% — 25 ← whole

Write a proportion.
$$\frac{n}{100} = \frac{18}{25}$$

Solve the proportion.

$\frac{n}{100} = \frac{18}{25}$ ← Simplify by multiplying each side by 100.

$n = \frac{1800}{25}$ ← Divide.

$n = 72$

72% of the class plan to go on the trip.

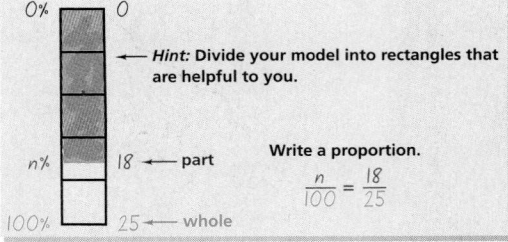

1. **Look Back** The model in Example 1 has five equal rectangles. What percent does each rectangle represent?

2. ✔**Try It Out** Draw a model for each problem. Then solve.
   a. What percent of 90 is 36?
   b. What percent of 60 is 15?

6-10 Using Proportions with Percents   **271**

Comprehensive approach to assessment leads to greater success on standardized tests.

The **Interactive Student Tutorial** CD-ROM has been developed to help students perform better on tests. It uses innovative self tests and provides helpful hints, lesson & lab tutorials, and instant scoring.

Assessment Success Kits give you the most comprehensive collection of assessment preparation resources available for middle grades math.
Each kit contains:

- Assessment Success Booklet
- Interactive Student Tutorial CD-ROM
- Resource Pro® CD-ROM with Planning Express® —an exclusive lesson planning tool containing all teaching resources

More opportunities than ever to assess progress throughout the course.

PRENTICE HALL EXCLUSIVES

- **Think & Discuss questions** <u>within the lesson</u> build understanding as concepts are presented.
- **Try It Out questions** <u>within the lesson</u> provide an immediate skill check after each worked-out example.

ADDITIONAL ASSESSMENT OPTIONS

- Checkpoint quizzes
- Wrap Up chapter review
- On Your Own exercises
- Mixed Review
- Chapter Assessments
- Cumulative Reviews
- Journal
- Portfolio
- Chapter Projects with rubrics
- Problem Solving Practice pages
- Pre-Course Skills Assessment
- Mid-Course Assessment
- End-of-Course Assessment
- Student Self-Assessment Survey
- Skills Handbook

Computer Item Generator with Standardized Test Prep on CD-ROM allows you to easily customize practice sheets and tests to meet local, state, and national assessment objectives.

Includes Dial-A-Test™

Resources to better connect with your students and more effectively manage your time.

For connecting with your students

- Student Edition with Practice Workbook
- Teaching Transparencies
- Interdisciplinary Units
- Manipulatives Kit
- Calculator Packages
- ✔ Multimedia Math Hot Pages
- ✔ Math Tools Software
- ✔ Interactive Student Tutorial

✔ = PRENTICE HALL EXCLUSIVES

PRENTICE HALL
Simon & Schuster Education Group

For more information call:
1-800-848-9500

For managing your time

- Teacher's Edition
- Solution Key
- Teaching Resources
- ✔ Chapter Support Files organized by chapter
  - Multiple-Use Classroom Resources
  - Spanish Resources
- ✔ Computer Item Generator with Dial-A-Test
  - Cumulative Assessment
  - Tools for Studying Smarter
- ✔ Resource Pro with Planning Express
- ✔ Assessment Success Kits
- Professional Development book

See us on the Internet   http://www.phschool.com

Teacher's Edition

PRENTICE HALL

MIDDLE GRADES
MATH
TOOLS FOR SUCCESS

Course 1

AUTHORS

Suzanne H. Chapin

Theodore J. Gardella

Mark Illingworth

Marsha S. Landau

Joanna O. Masingila

Leah McCracken

CONSULTING AUTHORS

Sadie Chavis Bragg

Bridget A. Hadley

Vincent O'Connor

Anne C. Patterson

Edwardo Reyna

PRENTICE HALL
Needham, Massachusetts
Upper Saddle River, New Jersey

We are grateful to our reviewers, who advised us in the development stages and provided invaluable feedback, ideas, and constructive criticism to help make this program one that meets the needs of middle grades teachers and students.

REVIEWERS

All Levels
Ann Bouie, Ph.D., Multicultural Reviewer, Oakland, California
Dorothy S. Strong, Ph.D., Chicago Public Schools, Chicago, Illinois

Course 1
Darla Agajanian, Sierra Vista School, Canyon Country, California
Rhonda Bird, Grand Haven Area Schools, Grand Haven, Michigan
Gary Critselous, Whittle Springs Middle School, Knoxville, Tennessee
Rhonda W. Davis, Durant Road Middle School, Raleigh, North Carolina
Leroy Dupee, Bridgeport Public Schools, Bridgeport, Connecticut
Jose Lalas, Ph.D., California State University, Dominguez Hills, California
Richard Lavers, Fitchburg High School, Fitchburg, Massachusetts
Lavaille Metoyer, Houston Independent School District, Houston, Texas

Course 2
Raylene Bryson, Alexander Middle School, Huntersville, North Carolina
Susan R. Buckley, Dallas Public Schools, Dallas, Texas
Sheila Cunningham, Klein Independent School District, Klein, Texas
Natarsha Mathis, Hart Junior High School, Washington, D.C.
Jean Patton, Clements Middle School, Covington, Georgia
Judy Trowell, Arkansas Department of Higher Education, Little Rock, Arkansas

Course 3
Michaele F. Chappell, Ph.D., University of South Florida, Tampa, Florida
Bettye Hall, Math Consultant, Houston, Texas
Joaquin Hernandez, Barbara Goleman Senior High, Miami, Florida
Steven H. Lapinski, Henrico County Public Schools, Richmond, Virginia
Dana Luterman, Lincoln Middle School, Kansas City, Missouri
Loretta Rector, Leonardo da Vinci School, Sacramento, California
Elias P. Rodriguez, Leander Middle School, Leander, Texas
Anthony C. Terceira, Providence School Department, Providence, Rhode Island

STAFF CREDITS

The people who made up the *Middle Grades Math* team—representing editorial, design, marketing, page production, editorial services, production, manufacturing, technology, electronic publishing, and advertising and promotion—and their managers are listed below. Bold type denotes core team members.

Barbara A. Bertell, Bruce Bond, Therese Bräuer, Christopher Brown, **Judith D. Buice**, Kathy Carter, Linda M. Coffey, Noralie V. Cox, Sheila DeFazio, Edward de Leon, Christine Deliee, Gabriella Della Corte, Jo DiGiustini, Robert G. Dunn, Audra Floyd, David B. Graham, Maria Green, Kristen Guevara, Jeff Ikler, Mimi Jigarjian, Elizabeth A. Jordan, Russell Lappa, Joan McCulley, Paul W. Murphy, Cindy A. Noftle, Caroline M. Power, Olena Serbyn, Dennis Slattery, Martha G. Smith, Kira Thaler Marbit, Robin Tiano, **Christina Trinchero, Stuart Wallace, Cynthia A. Weedel, Jeff Weidenaar, Mary Jane Wolfe,** Stewart Wood

We would like to give special thanks to National Math Consultants Ann F. Bell and Brenda Underwood for all their help in developing this program.

PRENTICE HALL
Simon & Schuster Education Group

Copyright © 1999 by Prentice-Hall, Inc., Upper Saddle River, New Jersey 07458. All rights reserved. No part of this book may be reproduced or transmitted in any form or by any means, electronic or mechanical, including photocopying, recording, or by any information storage and retrieval system, without permission in writing from the publisher.

Printed in the United States of America.

ISBN: 0-13-434686-6

1 2 3 4 5 6 7 8 9 10   04 03 02 01 00 99 98

AUTHORS

Suzanne H. Chapin, Ed.D., is Professor of Mathematics Education at Boston University. Dr. Chapin also directs all mathematics professional development in a landmark Boston University/Chelsea Public Schools Partnership program, working closely with teachers, administrators, and parents to provide opportunities for all students to learn mathematics. *Proportional Reasoning and Probability strands and Tools for Problem Solving*

Theodore J. Gardella, formerly of the Bloomfield Hills Public Schools, Bloomfield Hills, Michigan, was awarded the Michigan Presidential Award for Excellence in Science and Mathematics Teaching. Mr. Gardella is also an originator of the "Tune in Mathematics and Science" project, delivering satellite video courses for students and staff development sessions for teachers. *Algebra strand*

Mark Illingworth is a classroom teacher in the Hollis Public Schools, Hollis, New Hampshire. He was awarded the New Hampshire Presidential Award for Excellence in Science and Mathematics Teaching. Mr. Illingworth's original formal training was as a mechanical engineer, a profession that by definition applies mathematics and science to solving real-world problems. One of his greatest interests is in making math meaningful and interesting to young learners. *Graphing strand and projects*

Marsha S. Landau, Ph.D., formerly of National Louis University in Evanston, Illinois, is an active workshop leader in city and suburban school districts on such topics as preparing middle school students for success on standardized tests. Dr. Landau also is a leader in the Center for Talent Development at the School of Education and Social Policy at Northwestern University in programs for academically talented urban and suburban students. *Algebra, Functions, and Computation strands*

Joanna O. Masingila, Ph.D., is an Associate Professor of Mathematics and Mathematics Education at Syracuse University and a Fulbright Scholar in the department of Education Communication and Technology at Kenyatta University in Nairobi, Kenya. Dr. Masingila is also a coach and member of the Inquiry Leadership Team, working with teachers in two schools in the Syracuse City School District. *Geometry strand*

Leah McCracken is a teacher at Lockwood School District in Billings, Montana, and an educational technologies instructor at Montana State University in Billings. Ms. McCracken is a very active member of and speaker for the Montana Council of Teachers of Mathematics and a recipient of numerous teaching awards, including the Montana Teacher of the Year. *Data Analysis strand*

PRENTICE HALL

MIDDLE GRADES
MATH
TOOLS FOR SUCCESS

Course 1

About the Cover:

The images on the cover—the in-line skate and the math graphics—appeal to students and emphasize the connection of mathematics to the real world and students' interests. The cover was produced by merging photographs electronically.

PRENTICE HALL

MIDDLE GRADES MATH
TOOLS FOR SUCCESS

CONTENTS

Contents

The "Tools for Problem Solving" section, which appears before Chapter 1, helps students review their problem solving skills and can be used before or with Chapter 1. At the end of the book, there are a number of useful resources. Extra Practice pages for each chapter contain additional exercises correlated to each lesson. The Skills Handbook provides an in-text tutorial of math skills that students may need to review. The skills covered in this section are the same as the skills tested in the Precourse test. The Glossary/Study Guide provides not only a definition with a page reference but also an example of most vocabulary terms.

Problem Solving and Connections

...and More!

CHAPTER PROJECT

Theme: Surveys
On Your Own Time

Students review and build upon their fifth-grade math skills, while learning to display and organize data in tables and graphs. Data analysis is explored early so that tables and graphs can be applied throughout the year. Students use whole number operations to find means, medians, modes, and ranges. They are given an opportunity to explore technology.

CHAPTER 2 Patterns and Algebraic Thinking

Problem Solving and Connections

Bicycle Designer 60
Fund-raising 62
Space 63
Health 66
Algebra 72
Hockey 73
Air Quality 76

...and More!

CHAPTER PROJECT

Theme: Patterns
Stepping Stones

Build a Fort 43
Project Links 47, 64, 76
Finishing the Chapter Project 77
Web Extension

Students look for patterns and develop number sense and algebraic reasoning while continuing to analyze data. They learn basic concepts, such as the order of operations, and are introduced to variables so that they can write and model expressions and equations in their work throughout the year. They solve simple equations using addition, subtraction, multiplication, and division.

Problem Solving and Connections

...and More!

ASSESSMENT

CHAPTER PROJECT

Theme: Consumer Issues
Name That Tune

Chapter 3 introduces students to decimals through the use of models. Students learn to read, write, compare, and order whole numbers and decimals. Whole numbers and decimals are based on powers of 10, so decimals are explored before fractions. Students review and apply the basic metric units for length, mass, and capacity.

Problem Solving and Connections

CHAPTER PROJECT

x

In Chapter 4, students build upon their work in Chapter 3 and learn to multiply and divide decimals. They then solve simple one-step equations using decimals. Students apply this knowledge to the metric system as they learn to convert measurements from one metric unit to another.

CHAPTER 5
Investigating Fractions

Problem Solving and Connections

Chess 219
Geometry 185
Pilot 191
Weather 194
Design 204
Astronomy 207
Construction 214

...and More!

CHAPTER PROJECT

Theme: Sports
Home Court Advantage

As students continue to use models, they learn about equivalent fractions, mixed numbers, and improper fractions. The fraction calculator is introduced. Students then use least common multiples to compare and order fractions. In Lesson 5-9, students learn about the relationship between fractions and decimals.

CHAPTER 6 Using Fractions

CHAPTER PROJECT

Seeing Is Believing
Theme: Proofs

Building on the lessons in Chapter 5, Chapter 6 begins with estimating sums and differences of fractions. Then students use fraction models to add and subtract fractions with like and unlike denominators. They solve equations using fractions and mixed numbers. Students review the customary system of measurement and learn to convert measurements to and from the customary system.

Ratios, Proportions, and Percents

**Problem Solving
and Connections**

Camp   *278*
School Supplies   *286*
Geometry   *292*
Earth Science   *301*
Fitness   *309*
Internet Help
  Provider   *313*
Environment   *315*

...and More!

**CHAPTER
PROJECT**

Theme: Astronomy
Planet of the Stars
Make a Scale Model   *277*
Project Links   *284, 288, 295*
Finishing the Chapter Project   *319*
   Web Extension

Students first apply proportional reasoning to explore the meaning of ratio and write equal ratios. Using their skills in solving equations, they solve proportions and geometry-related problems with scale drawings.

Students explore the relationships among percents, fractions, and decimals. They learn to estimate percents and to find percents of a number using percent models and technology.

Problem Solving and Connections

...and More!

CHAPTER PROJECT

Theme: Puzzles
Puzzling Pictures

Chapter 8 introduces students to the basics of geometry. Students learn to measure and estimate angles and to classify polygons. They use their estimation and measurement skills to explore congruent and similar figures. Then students learn about transformations of geometric figures in a hands-on manner.

CHAPTER 9 Geometry and Measurement

Students build on their measurement and geometry skills to explore perimeters and areas of two-dimensional figures. They use technology to explore pi. Students find circumferences and areas of circles.

Students also identify three-dimensional figures and use algebra skills to find surface area and volume.

T23

10 Algebra: Integers and Graphing

Problem Solving and Connections

...and More!

CHAPTER PROJECT

xvi

Students use a number line to build on their understanding of integers. They model integers with algebra tiles and use these models to add and subtract integers. Using geometry skills, students graph on the coordinate plane. Using data analysis, students graph functions and apply what they know about integers to graphs.

CHAPTER

11 Exploring Probability

**Problem Solving
and Connections**

**Board Game
 Designer** **507**
Games **480**
Consumer Issues **501**
Data Analysis **502**
Music **508**
Track and Field **509**
Tourism **512**

...and More!

**CHAPTER
PROJECT**

Theme: Statistics
Now Playing!
Design a Three-Choice System *479*
Project Links *491, 496, 506*
Finishing the Chapter Project *517*
 Web Extension

Since students now have the prerequisite skills, they can successfully explore probability with hands-on activities. Students decide the fairness of a game and perform simulations of a problem. They explore theoretical probability, tree diagrams, and independent events. Using data analysis, students make predictions.

Of Special Interest

Real-World Problem Solving

A variety of applications that pique the interests of middle grades students provides settings for students to apply problem solving skills

Problem Solving Strategies

Real-World Applications

Math Integration

Woven throughout: strands of algebra, geometry, data analysis, measurement, statistics, probability, patterns, and number sense

Algebra

Geometry

Data Analysis/Statistics

Math at Work

Introducing students to a wide range of career possibilities that highlight how mathematics is applied in these careers

Technology

To provide students with meaningful experiences to utilize technology

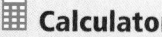 **Calculator**

 Computer

Building Student Success Every Step of the Way

Opportunities to build on students' experiences and check their skills, ensuring that students thoroughly grasp a concept before moving on

Building Skills through Student Experiences

Helping students build the skills they need to succeed by providing just the right mixture of experiences and probing questions to guide their thinking

Work Together

Activities that provide students with hands-on learning opportunities, working cooperatively

Activities to Begin Lesson

Discovery Activities, 14, 12, 72, 134, 189, 314, 337, 392, 403, 463
Finding a Pattern, 51, 66, 151, 202, 206, 344, 418
Activating Prior Knowledge, 61, 143, 182, 185
Data Gathering, 109, 118, 262, 492, 507, 514
Hands-on Activity, 12, 99, 113, 123, 148, 213, 241, 253, 300, 340, 349, 356, 370

Activities to Complete Lesson

Reinforcing Skills, 24, 158, 161, 415, 444, 450

Extending Skills, 45, 85, 328, 383, 410, 489
Applying Skills, 29, 230, 298, 361, 389, 459

Building Understanding

Analyze, 12, 22, 28, 33, 51, 56, 61, 92, 97, 99, 100, 109, 113, 123, 186, 203, 207, 215, 298, 316, 337, 344, 356, 370, 392, 398, 399, 409, 444, 463, 469, 499, 502
Data Collection, 278, 480, 507, 514
Draw a Conclusion, 4, 33, 66, 161, 165, 182, 190, 202, 263, 285, 399, 409, 439, 443, 449, 480
Estimation, 13, 45, 230, 258, 298, 403
Explain, 19, 85, 151, 185, 189, 198, 259, 292, 314, 315, 365, 382, 387, 392, 399, 400, 405, 435, 444, 482, 492, 493, 514
Go a Step Further, 62, 161, 237, 328, 382, 493, 504, 514
Look Back, 5, 14, 19, 22, 23, 27, 28, 68, 73, 93, 106, 171, 247, 259, 268, 306, 331, 340, 394, 481, 502, 513
Mental Math, 57, 67, 72, 73, 74, 183, 209, 210, 286

Modeling, 84, 85, 92, 99, 149, 157, 185, 197, 210, 228, 254, 262, 314, 356, 360, 389, 439, 482, 488, 507
Number Sense, 149, 152, 189, 228, 253, 262, 267, 388, 399
Open-Ended, 24, 115, 124, 234, 279, 297, 327, 333, 349, 382, 415, 418, 435, 458
Patterns, 44, 161, 165, 392, 418, 458
Predict, 410, 507
Reasoning, 4, 24, 27, 33, 674, 88, 96, 109, 113, 114, 118, 123, 125, 134, 141, 143, 153, 158, 164, 165, 172, 183, 185, 186, 193, 202, 203, 213, 228, 262, 263, 281, 286, 292, 297, 300, 310, 331, 332, 341, 349, 350, 356, 357, 361, 364, 365, 371, 372, 387, 401, 415, 420, 436, 442, 443, 465, 481, 489, 492, 493, 499, 508
Spatial Reasoning/Visual Thinking, 341, 399, 410, 500
Summarize, 51, 151, 418, 470, 486
Think About It, 61, 100, 148, 229, 306, 327, 341, 350, 399, 400, 415, 480, 489, 493, 503, 508, 513
What If..., 19, 22, 62, 113, 210, 328, 388, 393, 439, 481, 492, 514

Assessing Student Understanding

Traditional and alternative assessment opportunities to evaluate student understanding

Ongoing Assessment within Instruction

✔ Try It Out
To check understanding or provide immediate practice and reinforcement
Chapter 1, 5, 13, 14, 19, 22, 23, 24, 28, 29, 34
Chapter 2, 51, 52, 56, 57, 58, 61, 62, 67, 68, 72, 73
Chapter 3, 85, 89, 90, 93, 100, 104, 105, 106,, 108, 109, 114, 119, 120, 124, 125
Chapter 4, 134, 140, 141, 143, 145, 149, 151, 152, 153, 157, 158, 161, 163, 164, 172, 173
Chapter 5, 183, 186, 187, 189, 190, 193, 194, 197, 198, 204, 206, 207, 209, 210, 211, 213, 214, 215

Chapter 6, 228, 229, 232, 233, 236, 237, 241, 242, 243, 247, 248, 254, 255, 258, 259, 263, 264, 267, 268
Chapter 7, 279, 281, 282, 285, 286, 301, 306, 309, 310, 316
Chapter 8, 326, 327, 331, 332, 333, 337, 338, 346, 350, 357, 361, 364, 365, 371, 372
Chapter 9, 382, 383, 388, 389, 393, 394, 399, 400, 404, 405, 408, 415, 419, 420
Chapter 10, 434, 435, 436, 439, 443, 449, 450, 458, 464, 465, 470
Chapter 11, 481, 482, 489, 493, 500, 503, 509, 513, 514

Informal Assessment

Chapter Projects (with rubrics)
Surveys: Create A Survey, 2–3
Patterns: Build a Fort, 42–43

Consumer Issues: Do a Price Comparison, 82–83
Planning: Plan a Celebration, 132–133
Sports: Compare Basketball Statistics, 180–181
Proofs: Design a Demonstration, 226–227
Astronomy: Make a Scale Model, 276–277
Puzzles: Create a Puzzle, 324–325
Technology: Design a Home Page, 380–381
History: Draw a Time Line, 432–433
Statistics: Design a Three-Choice System, 478–479

Formal Assessment

Standardized Test Prep

Within Lessons, 15, 20, 29, 59, 63, 68, 75, 94, 107, 110, 137, 158, 161, 165, 173, 184, 195, 204, 208, 211, 244, 248, 255, 265, 302, 335, 352, 358, 366, 384, 390, 395, 401, 411, 416, 420, 421, 441, 460, 466, 471, 483, 490, 504

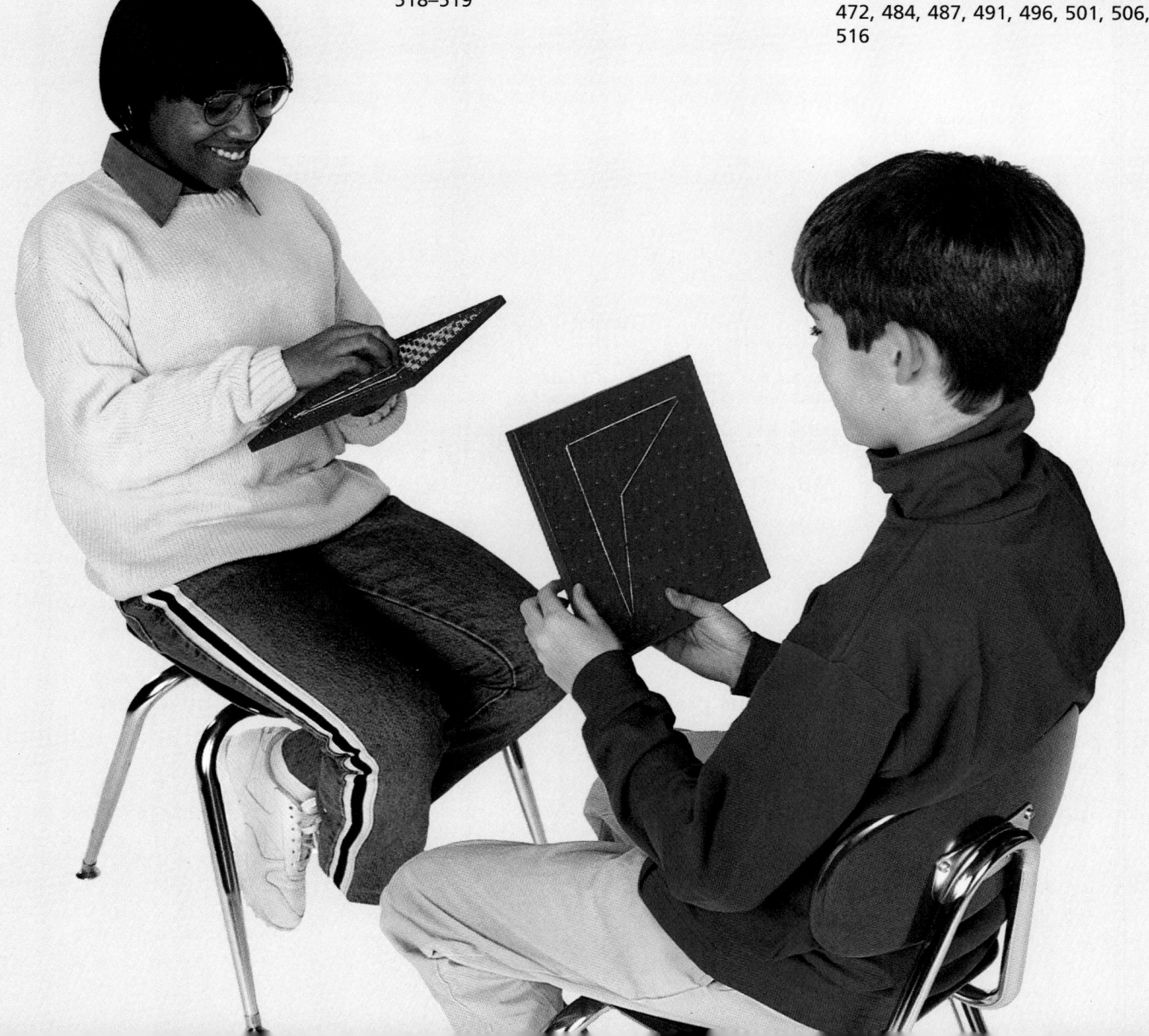

Pacing Guide for Prentice Hall Middle Grades Math

This chart is provided merely as a guide to help you customize your course. To accommodate flexible scheduling, many lessons are subdivided into parts. In your Teacher's Edition, these parts are indicated in red by the symbol ▼. The Assignment Options in each lesson indicate which practice exercises in the Student Edition correspond to the parts of each lesson.

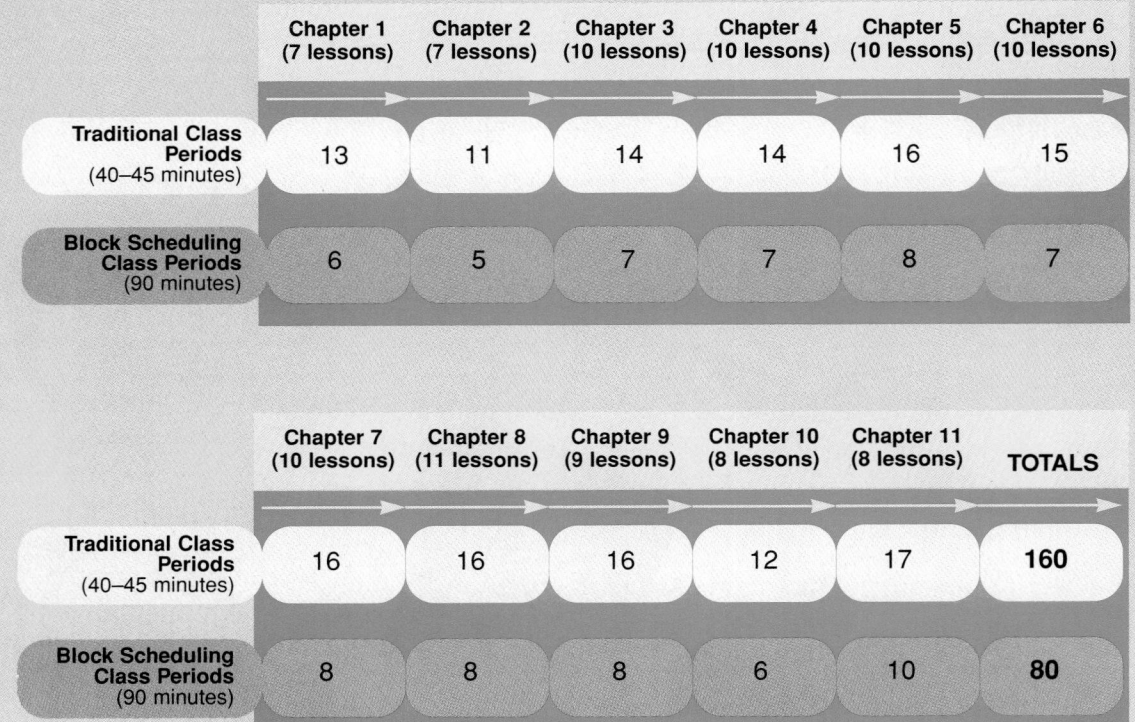

	Chapter 1 (7 lessons)	Chapter 2 (7 lessons)	Chapter 3 (10 lessons)	Chapter 4 (10 lessons)	Chapter 5 (10 lessons)	Chapter 6 (10 lessons)
Traditional Class Periods (40–45 minutes)	13	11	14	14	16	15
Block Scheduling Class Periods (90 minutes)	6	5	7	7	8	7

	Chapter 7 (10 lessons)	Chapter 8 (11 lessons)	Chapter 9 (9 lessons)	Chapter 10 (8 lessons)	Chapter 11 (8 lessons)	TOTALS
Traditional Class Periods (40–45 minutes)	16	16	16	12	17	160
Block Scheduling Class Periods (90 minutes)	8	8	8	6	10	80

Detailed Chapter Pacing Options precede each chapter and give you lesson-by-lesson pacing suggestions for that specific chapter.

Teaming—Working with Teachers in Other Disciplines

Making Connections

Have you ever heard the following questions from your students? "Does the math I use in math class have anything to do with science? With social studies?" Students don't always make connections. Forming a multidisciplinary team of teachers can help students see these connections.

Teaming . . . Getting Started

- Form a team of core subject teachers with a common planning period.

- Display all the content area courses of study on a common school year calendar. Look for overlapping topics or common themes to use as a starting point. Choose one of these topics or themes for a possible unit.

- Look for links to other disciplines. What math skills will your students use in the study of this topic? Can you connect this to a language arts skill? How does this topic relate to science? to social studies?

- Organize your brainstorming in a web. Use lines to connect the topic to each discipline. Continue the webbing by adding skills and topics from the curriculum of each discipline.

- Use your web and your curriculum calendar to plan an interdisciplinary unit. Don't be too ambitious at first. Start with two disciplines and add others later. An example of a two-discipline web is shown

- By becoming involved in all subject areas, you and your students will see how math relates to the real world. You will have a better understanding of your students, since you will see a more complete picture of everything they are studying.

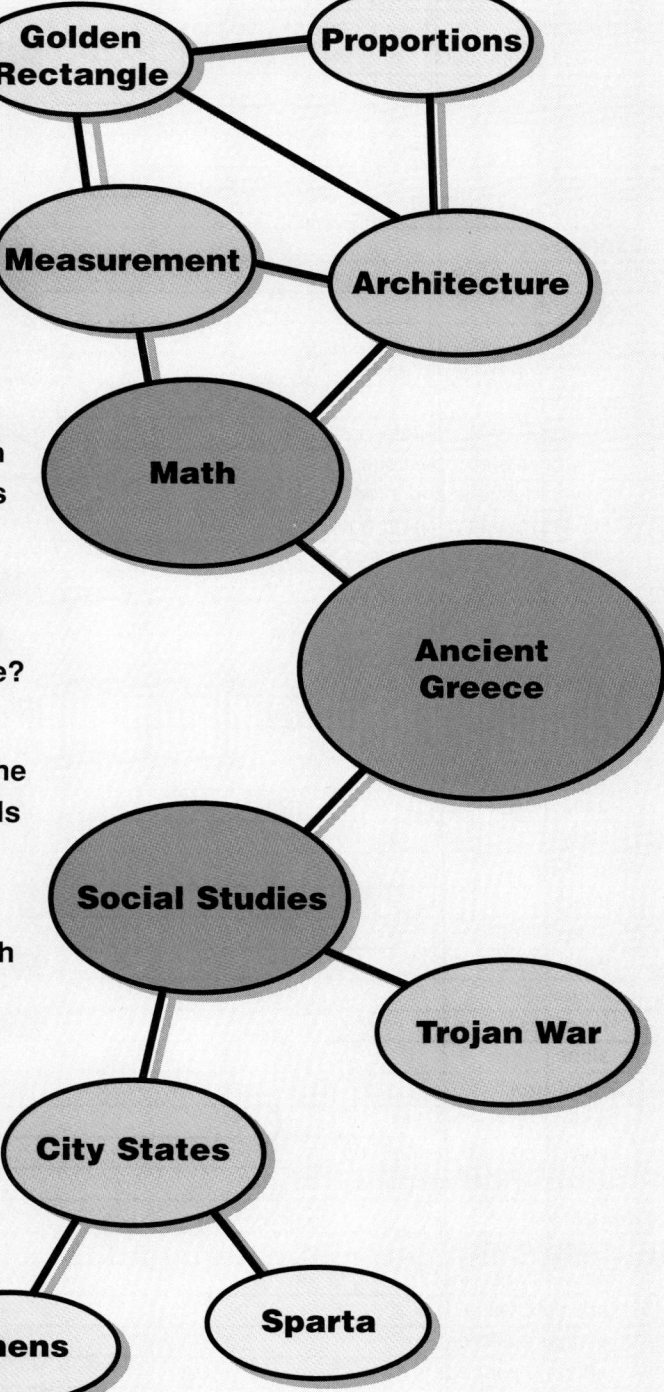

Scope and Sequence for Prentice Hall Middle Grades Math

Algebra and Algebraic Thinking

	Course	1	2	3
Properties				
of whole numbers		◼	◼	
communicative			◼	
associative			◼	
distributive			◼	
of integers			◼	◻
of rational numbers				◼
Expressions				
order of operations		◼	◼	◼
evaluate		◼	◼	
simplify		◼	◼	
write from word phrases		◼	◼	
Equations				
solve one-step equations		◻	◼	◼
solve two-step equations			◼	◼
solve equations and integer solutions				◼
solve systems of linear equations				◼
write from word sentences		◻	◼	◻
formulas		◼	◼	◼
Functions				
write a rule		◻	◼	◼
look for a pattern strategy		◼	◼	◻
input-output tables		◼	◼	
linear			◻	◼
quadratic				◼
absolute value				◼
step				
Graphing				
integers			◼	◻
inequalities				◼
ordered pairs		◼	◼	◼
equations			◼	◼
functions		◼	◼	◻
slope				◼
Inequalities				
write				◼
solve one-step inequalities				◼
solve two-step inequalities				◼
Integers				
read and write			◼	◻
on a number line			◼	◻
absolute value			◼	◻
compare and order			◼	◻
add and subtract			◼	◻
multiply and divide			◼	◻

Algebra and Algebraic Thinking (cont.)

	Course	1	2	3
equations				◼
Polynomials				
simplify				◼
add and subtract				◼
multiply				◼
Rational numbers				
simplify				◼
compare and order			◻	◼
add and subtract			◻	◼
multiply and divide			◻	◼
equations				◼
Irrational numbers				◼
Real numbers				◼

Communication

	Course	1	2	3
Create written and oral problems		◼	◼	◼
Evaluate effectiveness of different representations		◼	◼	◼
Interpret mathematical ideas through discussing, listening, modeling, questioning, reading, viewing, and writing		◼	◼	◼
Make convincing arguments using mathematical ideas		◼	◼	◼
Relate mathematical language to everyday language		◼	◼	◼
Relate topics to the history of mathematics		◼	◼	◼
Use writing to clarify ideas		◼	◼	◼
Verbalize and define concepts		◼	◼	◼
Work in groups		◼	◼	◼

Decimals

	Course	1	2	3
Read and write		◼	◻	
Place value		◼	◻	
Compare and order		◼	◻	
Equivalent decimals		◼	◻	
Add and subtract		◼	◻	
Multiply and divide				
decimals by whole numbers		◼	◻	
two decimals		◼	◻	
decimals by powers of 10		◼	◻	
Estimate				
rounding		◼	◻	
operations		◼	◻	
Convert decimals to fractions		◼	◻	

Legend: ◻ Introduce ◼ Develop ◻ Maintain and Apply

Decimals (cont.)

	1	2	3
Convert decimals to percents	●	●	●
Terminating and repeating	●	●	●
Scientific notation	○	●	●

Estimation

	1	2	3
Decimals			
value	●	●	○
operations	●	●	
Dimensional analysis			●
Fractions			
proper, improper, and mixed numbers	●	●	○
operations	●	●	
Geometry			
angle measure	●		
length	○		
area	●	●	●
volume		○	○
Integers			
sums and differences		○	●
products and quotients			●
Number lines	●	○	
Percents	●	●	○
Precision			○
Proportions			
Reasonableness of estimates	○	●	●
Significant digits			
Solutions of equations		●	●
Square roots		○	●
Strategies			
choose the computation method	●	●	○
clustering	●	●	
compatible numbers	●	●	
front-end	●	●	
rounding	●	●	
Whole numbers			
whole number values	○	○	
operations	○	○	

Fractions

	1	2	3
Equivalent fractions	●	●	○
Simplest form	●	●	
Mixed numbers and improper fractions	●	●	
Compare and order	●	●	○
Add and subtract			
like denominators	●	○	
unlike denominators	●	●	○
mixed numbers	●	●	
Reciprocal	●		
Multiply and divide			
whole numbers and fractions	●	○	
fractions and fractions	●	●	●
whole numbers and mixed numbers	●	●	●

Fractions (cont.)

	1	2	3
fractions and mixed numbers	●	●	●
mixed numbers	●	●	
Estimate			
rounding	●	●	○
operations			
Convert fractions to decimals			●
Convert fractions to percents	●	●	●

Geometry and Spatial Reasoning

	1	2	3
Angles			
classify	●	●	
measure			
estimate measure	●	○	
Constructions			
congruent segments			○
parallel lines			●
perpendicular lines			●
perpendicular bisectors		●	●
angle bisectors			●
congruent angles			●
Polygons			
identify	●	●	
classify triangles	●	●	○
different viewpoints			
Pythagorean theorem		○	●
classify quadrilaterals	●	●	
Congruence	●	●	●
Nets	●		
Similarity	●	●	●
Symmetry	●	●	●
Tessellations	●		
Transformations			
translations		●	●
reflections		●	●
rotations		●	●
dilations			●
Three-dimensional figures	●	○	○
Coordinate geometry	○	○	
Spatial visualization	●	●	○

Measurement

	1	2	3
Customary system			
use customary units of length, area, volume, weight, and capacity	●	●	○
choose appropriate units	●	●	
convert within customary system	○	●	
Metric system			
use metric units of length, area, volume, weight, and capacity	●	●	○
choose appropriate units	●	●	
convert within metric system	●	○	
Length			
estimate	○		

Course	1	2	3

Measurement (cont.)

Topic	1	2	3
perimeter	Develop	Maintain	
radius, diameter, and circumference	Develop	Develop	

Area
Topic	1	2	3
estimate area of irregular figures	Develop		Develop
of squares and rectangles	Develop		
of parallelograms and rhombuses	Develop		
of triangles	Develop		
of trapezoids	Develop		
of circles	Develop		
of composite figures	Introduce/Develop		Develop

Surface area
Topic	1	2	3
of prisms		Develop	Develop
of cylinders			Develop

Volume
Topic	1	2	3
estimate		Develop	Maintain
of prisms	Develop	Develop	
of cylinders		Develop	
of cones and pyramids			Develop
of spheres			Introduce

Indirect measurement
Topic	1	2	3
scale drawing		Develop	Maintain
Pythagorean theorem			Develop
using similar triangles		Develop	
ratios in right triangles		Develop	
trigonometric ratios			Introduce

Topic	1	2	3
Relate perimeter and area	Maintain		
Relate perimeter, area, and volume		Maintain	Develop
Temperature	Maintain		

Time
Topic	1	2	3
convert units of time	Maintain		
estimate	Develop	Develop	
elapsed time	Develop		
time zones	Maintain		

Mental Math

Topic	1	2	3
Divisibility	Develop	Develop	
Solving equations	Develop		

Strategies
Topic	1	2	3
choose the computation method	Develop	Develop	
compatible numbers	Develop		
patterns	Develop		
use properties	Develop		Maintain

Modeling and Manipulatives

Topic	1	2	3
Decimals	Develop	Maintain	
Distributive property	Develop	Develop	

Equations
Topic	1	2	3
one-step	Develop	Develop	Develop
two-step		Develop	Develop

Topic	1	2	3
Exponents	Introduce/Develop	Develop	
Factors	Develop	Develop	Develop
Fractions	Develop	Develop	Develop

Modeling and Manipulatives (cont.)

Geometry
Topic	1	2	3
area	Develop	Maintain	Develop
squares and square roots		Maintain	Develop
surface area	Develop	Develop	
volume	Develop	Develop	

Integers
Topic	1	2	3
absolute value	Develop	Develop	Maintain
add and subtract	Develop	Develop	Develop
opposites	Develop	Develop	Develop
zero	Develop	Develop	Develop

Manipulatives
Topic	1	2	3
algebra tiles		Develop	
area models		Develop	
centimeter cubes/counters	Maintain		
compasses			Maintain
decimal models	Maintain		
fraction models	Maintain		
graph paper			Maintain
paper folding			Maintain
pattern blocks			Maintain
percent models		Develop	
protractors			Maintain
rulers (metric and customary)			Maintain
spinners			Maintain
tangrams			Maintain

Topic	1	2	3
Number line models	Develop		
Number patterns	Develop	Maintain	
Percent	Develop	Maintain	

Probability
Topic	1	2	3
outcomes	Develop	Develop	Develop
simulations	Develop	Maintain	Develop

Topic	1	2	3
Problem Solving	Develop		
Pythagorean theorem			Develop
Ratios	Introduce/Develop	Develop	Develop
Rational numbers			
Tree diagrams		Develop	Maintain
Variable expressions	Introduce/Develop	Develop	Develop
Venn diagrams	Develop		Develop

Number Sense and Quantitative Reasoning

Topic	1	2	3
Read and write numbers	Develop	Maintain	

Place value
Topic	1	2	3
whole number	Develop	Develop	
decimal	Develop	Develop	Maintain

Compare and order
Topic	1	2	3
whole numbers	Develop		
decimals	Develop	Maintain	
fractions	Develop	Develop	Develop
integers	Introduce/Develop	Develop	
rationals			Develop

T34

Legend: ░ Introduce   ■ Develop   ▥ Maintain and Apply

Number Sense and Quantitative Reasoning (cont.)

	1	2	3
irrationals			◣
Number theory			
divisibility rules	●	●	●
factors	●	●	●
prime and composite numbers	●	●	●
prime factorization	●	●	
greatest common factor	●	●	
multiples	●	◐	●
least common multiple	●	●	
Exponents			
positive	●	●	
negative			◐
Scientific notation	◐	◣	●
Square numbers and square roots		◣	●

Patterns and Functions

	1	2	3
Geometric patterns	◐	●	●
Pascal's triangle		◣	
Sequences			
recognize and complete	●	●	●
arithmetic	◣	●	
geometric		◣	●
Fibonacci sequence		●	
Strategy: look for a pattern	●	●	
Tessellations	●	◐	
Functions			
linear	◐	●	●
quadratic			●
other nonlinear			
absolute value			●
step			
graph	●	●	●
interpret graphs	◣	●	●
multiple representations	◐	●	●
write a rule	◣	●	
input-output tables	●	●	●

Probability

	1	2	3
Simple probability	●	●	●
Counting principle	●	●	●
Tree diagrams/sample spaces	●	●	●
Odds		◣	●
Independent and dependent events		●	●
Experimental probability	●	●	
Theoretical probability	◐	◐	●
Probability of complements	◐	◣	●
Conduct experiments			
use samples to predict	●	●	●
random samples	●	◣	
random numbers	●	●	●
simulate a problem	●	●	●

Probability (cont.)

	1	2	3
conduct a survey	●	●	●
fair and unfair games	●	●	●
use a computer	●	●	●
Factorial notation			◣
Permuations		◐	●
Combinations			●
Pascal's triangle			◣

Problem Solving

	1	2	3
Analyze and make decisions	●	●	●
find and classify data	●	●	●
interpret data	●	●	●
determine trends from data	●	●	●
make predictions from data	●	●	●
decide how to present data	●	●	●
Strategies			
draw a diagram	●	●	●
guess and test	●	●	●
look for a pattern	●	●	●
make a model	●	◐	●
make a table	●	●	●
simulate the problem	●	●	●
solve a simpler problem	●	●	●
too much or too little information	●	●	●
use logical reasoning	●	◐	●
use multiple strategies	●	●	●
use a proportion			◣
work backward	●	●	●
write an equation	●	◣	●
Use a calculator	●	●	●
Use a computer	●	●	●
Use estimation	●	●	●
Use formulas	●	●	●
Use graphs	●	●	●

Proportional Reasoning

	1	2	3
Ratios	●	●	●
read and write	●	●	◐
equal ratios		◣	●
Rate			
unit rate	●	●	●
unit price	●	◐	
distance, rate, time problems	●	●	●
dimensional analysis			◣
Proportions			
solve proportions	◣	●	●
estimate solutions to proportions			◣
reason with proportions	◐	◣	●
Proportionals in similar figures			
find missing parts		◣	●
scale drawings	◣	●	
scale factors			◣

Proportional Reasoning (cont.)

	1	2	3
ratio of sides and areas		Develop	Develop
ratio of sides and volumes		Maintain and Apply	Develop
indirect measurement			Develop
Sine, cosine, and tangent			Develop
Percents			
understand concept	Develop	Develop	Maintain and Apply
write as ratio and decimal	Develop	Develop	Maintain and Apply
greater than 100		Develop	Develop
less than 1		Develop	Develop
estimate	Develop	Develop	Maintain and Apply
modeling		Develop	Develop
find using a proportion		Develop	Develop
find using an equation			Develop
find percent of a number		Develop	Develop
find percent one number is of another		Develop	Develop
find number when percent is known		Develop	Develop
percent of change		Develop	Develop
Applications of percents			
markup			Develop
discount		Introduce	Maintain and Apply
commission			Develop
sales tax		Develop	Develop
simple interest			Develop
compound interest			Develop

Reasoning

	1	2	3
Construct Venn diagrams	Develop	Develop	Maintain and Apply
Justify answers	Develop	Develop	Maintain and Apply
Make and test conjectures	Develop	Develop	Maintain and Apply
Make generalizations	Develop	Develop	Maintain and Apply
Reason from graphs		Develop	Develop
Reason with proportions		Develop	Develop
Recognize patterns	Introduce	Develop	Maintain and Apply
Use logical reasoning	Develop	Develop	Maintain and Apply
Use spatial visualization	Develop	Develop	Maintain and Apply

Statistics

	1	2	3
Analyze data			
mean, median, and mode	Develop	Develop	Maintain and Apply
range		Develop	Develop
quartile			Develop
outlier			Develop
Collect data from a variety of sources	Develop	Develop	Maintain and Apply
Conduct surveys			
analyze questions			Develop
population		Develop	Develop
sample	Develop	Develop	Maintain and Apply
random sample		Develop	Develop
Organize and display data			
tables and charts	Develop	Develop	Maintain and Apply
frequency tables		Develop	Develop
line plots	Develop	Develop	Maintain and Apply

Statistics (cont.)

	1	2	3
histograms		Develop	Develop
bar graphs	Develop	Maintain and Apply	Maintain and Apply
double bar graphs			Develop
stacked bar graphs			Develop
sliding bar graphs			Develop
line graphs	Develop	Maintain and Apply	Maintain and Apply
multiple line graphs			Develop
circle graphs			Develop
scatter plots			Develop
stem-and-leaf plots		Develop	Develop
back-to-back stem-and-leaf plots			Maintain and Apply
box-and-whisker plots		Develop	Develop
draw and compare different representations			Develop
Choose an appropriate graph or statistic	Develop	Develop	Maintain and Apply
Identify misleading graphs and statistics		Develop	Develop
Reason from graphs		Develop	Develop
Make predictions from graphs			Develop

Technology

	1	2	3
Use a calculator			
for computation	Develop	Develop	Maintain and Apply
for problem solving	Develop	Develop	Maintain and Apply
for algebra		Develop	Develop
for fractions		Develop	Develop
from geometry and measurement	Develop	Develop	Maintain and Apply
for graphing functions			Develop
for statistics	Develop	Develop	Maintain and Apply
to evaluate square roots		Develop	Develop
to evaluate trigonometric functions			Develop
special keys	Develop	Develop	Maintain and Apply
Use a computer			
to create a spreadsheet	Develop	Develop	Maintain and Apply
to display data in graphs	Develop	Develop	Maintain and Apply
to draw and measure geometric figures	Develop	Develop	Maintain and Apply
to graph equations			Develop
to generate random numbers			Develop
to simulate problems			Develop

Whole Numbers

	1	2	3
Place value	Maintain and Apply		
Number lines	Maintain and Apply		
Add, subtract, multiply, and divide	Maintain and Apply		
Determine reasonableness of answers	Introduce	Develop	
Rounding	Maintain and Apply		
Multiplying and dividing by powers of 10		Develop	

Introduce   Develop   Maintain and Apply

PRENTICE HALL

MIDDLE GRADES MATH
TOOLS FOR SUCCESS

Course 1

*Prentice Hall dedicates
this mathematics program
to all mathematics educators
and their students.*

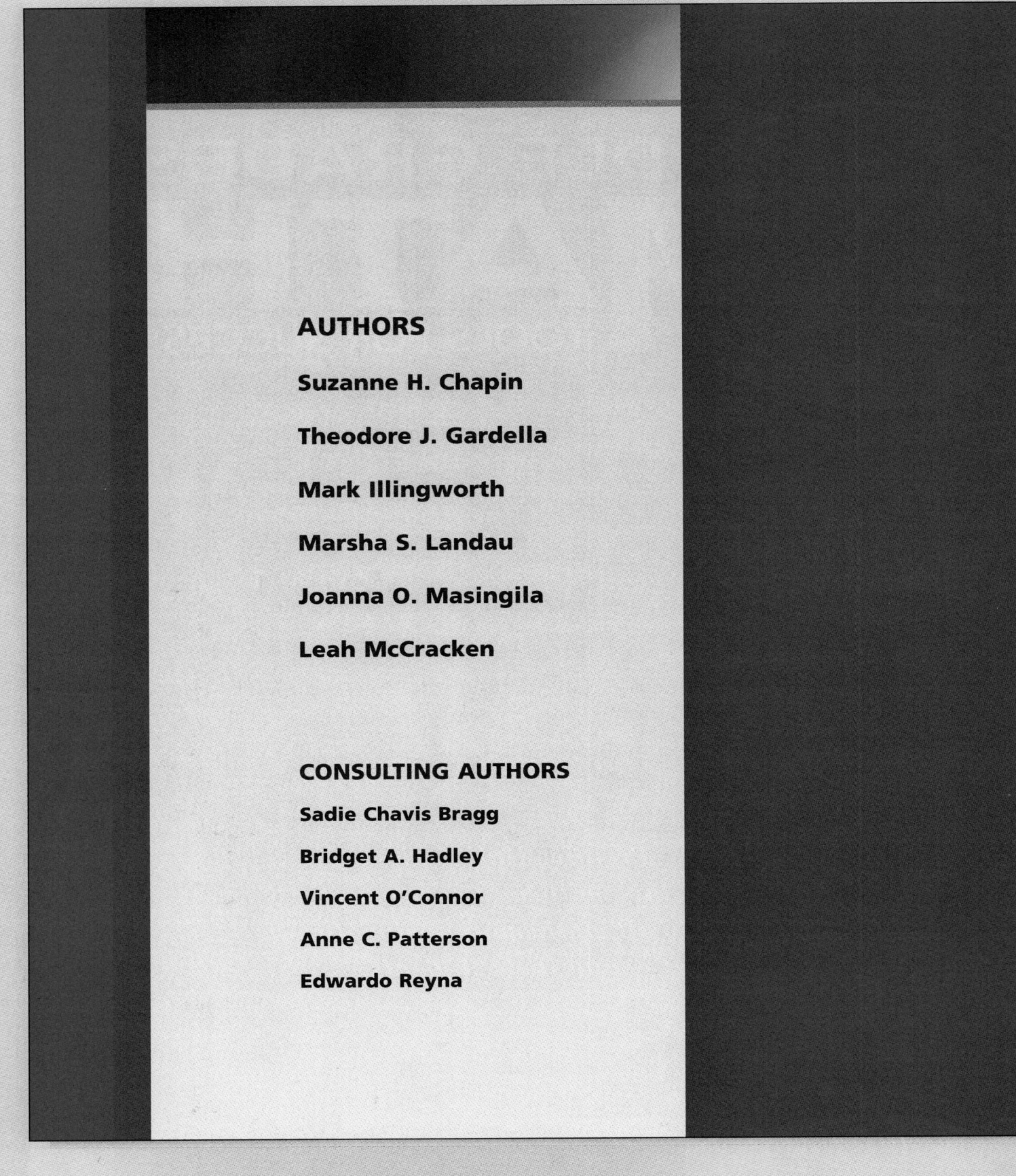

AUTHORS

Suzanne H. Chapin

Theodore J. Gardella

Mark Illingworth

Marsha S. Landau

Joanna O. Masingila

Leah McCracken

CONSULTING AUTHORS

Sadie Chavis Bragg

Bridget A. Hadley

Vincent O'Connor

Anne C. Patterson

Edwardo Reyna

PRENTICE HALL

MIDDLE GRADES
MATH
TOOLS FOR SUCCESS

Course 1

PRENTICE HALL
Needham, Massachusetts
Upper Saddle River, New Jersey

AUTHORS

Suzanne H. Chapin, Ed.D., Boston University, Boston, Massachusetts
Proportional Reasoning and Probability strands, and
Tools for Problem Solving

Theodore J. Gardella, Formerly, Bloomfield Hills Public Schools, Bloomfield Hills, Michigan
Algebra strand

Mark Illingworth, Hollis Public Schools, Hollis, New Hampshire
Graphing strand

Marsha S. Landau, Ph.D., Formerly, National Louis University, Evanston, Illinois
Algebra, Functions, and Computation strands

Joanna O. Masingila, Ph.D., Syracuse University, Syracuse, New York
Geometry strand

Leah McCracken, Lockwood School District, Billings, Montana
Data Analysis strand

CONSULTING AUTHORS

Sadie Chavis Bragg, Ed.D., Borough of Manhattan Community College, The City University of New York, New York, New York

Bridget A. Hadley, Mathematics Curriculum Specialist, Hopkinton, Massachusetts

Vincent O'Connor, Formerly, Milwaukee Public Schools, Milwaukee, Wisconsin

Anne C. Patterson, Volusia County Schools, Daytona Beach, Florida

Edwardo Reyna, McAllen Independent School District, McAllen, Texas

PRENTICE HALL
Simon & Schuster Education Group

Copyright © 1999 by Prentice-Hall, Inc., a Viacom Company, Upper Saddle River, New Jersey 07458. All rights reserved. No part of this book may be reproduced or transmitted in any form or by any means, electronic or mechanical, including photocopying, recording, or by any information storage and retrieval system, without permission in writing from the publisher.

Printed in the United States of America.

ISBN: 0-13-434682-3

1 2 3 4 5 6 7 8 9 10   04 03 02 01 00 99 98

We are grateful to our reviewers, who advised us in the development stages and provided invaluable feedback, ideas, and constructive criticism to help make this program one that meets the needs of middle grades teachers and students.

REVIEWERS

All Levels
Ann Bouie, Ph.D., Multicultural Reviewer, Oakland, California
Dorothy S. Strong, Ph.D., Chicago Public Schools, Chicago, Illinois

Course 1
Darla Agajanian, Sierra Vista School, Canyon Country, California
Rhonda Bird, Grand Haven Area Schools, Grand Haven, Michigan
Gary Critselous, Whittle Springs Middle School, Knoxville, Tennessee
Rhonda W. Davis, Durant Road Middle School, Raleigh, North Carolina
Leroy Dupee, Bridgeport Public Schools, Bridgeport, Connecticut
Jose Lalas, Ph.D., California State University, Dominguez Hills, California
Richard Lavers, Fitchburg High School, Fitchburg, Massachusetts
Lavaille Metoyer, Houston Independent School District, Houston, Texas

Course 2
Raylene Bryson, Alexander Middle School, Huntersville, North Carolina
Susan R. Buckley, Dallas Public Schools, Dallas, Texas
Sheila Cunningham, Klein Independent School District, Klein, Texas
Natarsha Mathis, Hart Junior High School, Washington, D.C.
Jean Patton, Clements Middle School, Covington, Georgia
Judy Trowell, Arkansas Department of Higher Education, Little Rock, Arkansas

Course 3
Michaele F. Chappell, Ph.D., University of South Florida, Tampa, Florida
Bettye Hall, Math Consultant, Houston, Texas
Joaquin Hernandez, Barbara Goleman Senior High, Miami, Florida
Steven H. Lapinski, Henrico County Public Schools, Richmond, Virginia
Dana Luterman, Lincoln Middle School, Kansas City, Missouri
Loretta Rector, Leonardo da Vinci School, Sacramento, California
Elias P. Rodriguez, Leander Middle School, Leander, Texas
Anthony C. Terceira, Providence School Department, Providence, Rhode Island

STAFF CREDITS

The people who made up the *Middle Grades Math* team—representing editorial, design, marketing, page production, editorial services, production, manufacturing, technology, electronic publishing, and advertising and promotion—and their managers are listed below. Bold type denotes core team members.
Barbara A. Bertell, Bruce Bond, Therese Bräuer, Christopher Brown, **Judith D. Buice**, Kathy Carter, Linda M. Coffey, Noralie V. Cox, Sheila DeFazio, Edward de Leon, Christine Deliee, Gabriella Della Corte, Jo DiGiustini, Robert G. Dunn, Barbara Flockhart, Audra Floyd, David B. Graham, Maria Green, Kristen Guevara, Jeff Ikler, Mimi Jigarjian, Elizabeth A. Jordan, Russell Lappa, Joan McCulley, Paul W. Murphy, Cindy A. Noftle, Caroline M. Power, Olena Serbyn, Dennis Slattery, Martha G. Smith, Kira Thaler Marbit, Robin Tiano, **Christina Trinchero**, **Stuart Wallace**, **Cynthia A. Weedel**, **Jeff Weidenaar**, **Mary Jane Wolfe**, Stewart Wood

We would like to give special thanks to National Math Consultants Ann F. Bell and Brenda Underwood for all their help in developing this program.

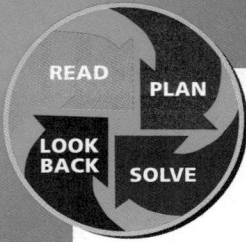

READ PLAN
LOOK BACK SOLVE

Tools for Problem Solving... An Overview

CONTENTS

The four "mini-lessons" in this Overview focus on the big picture of problem solving. They introduce students to the four-step problem solving plan, problem solving strategies, cooperative learning, and standardized tests.

To the Student:

The key to your success in math is your ability to use math in the real world—both now and in the future. To succeed you need math skill and some problem solving tools too. In this Problem Solving Overview, you'll learn how to use a four-step plan for problem solving, how to choose strategies for solving problems, how to best work in groups, and how to apply strategies to standardized tests.

As you work through the book, you'll find plenty of opportunities to improve your problem solving skills. The more you build on a skill, the better you'll get. And the better you get, the more confident you'll become. So keep at it!

Problem Solving Strategies

Draw a Diagram
Guess and Test
Look for a Pattern
Make a Model
Make a Table
Simulate a Problem
Solve a Simpler Problem
Too Much or Too Little
 Information
Use Logical Reasoning
Use Multiple Strategies
Work Backward

The "mini-lessons" can be covered in any order and at any time throughout the year, but they're especially well suited for use at the beginning of the course. You could spend from a couple of days to a week on the Overview. Each "mini-lesson" contains a portion to be discussed in class followed by Exercises that students can work on individually or in groups.

The Four-Step Approach

You solve problems every day. Some problems are easy to solve. Others require good problem solving skills.

How you approach a problem can determine whether or not you solve it. Here is a four-step approach that many successful problem solvers use.

THE FOUR-STEP APPROACH

1. Read and understand the problem.
2. Plan how to solve the problem.
3. Solve the problem.
4. Look back.

As you follow each of the four steps, ask yourself questions about the problem.

SAMPLE PROBLEM...............

Sports A soccer field is 110 yards by 80 yards. A volleyball court is 20 yards by 10 yards. How many volleyball courts could you fit on a soccer field?

....

The four-step approach gives students a simple yet effective path to problem solving success. Most students have used this approach (or a similar one) in earlier courses. By reviewing it at the beginning of the year, they can get into the "problem solving" mode as they approach word problems, which they will find in every lesson in this book.

READ

Read for understanding.
Summarize the problem.

Read the problem again. What information is given? What information is missing? Ask yourself: "What am I being asked to find or do?"

You can summarize the given information in the form of short notes like those below. You can also summarize what is being asked.

> • soccer field — 110 yd × 80 yd
> • volleyball court — 20 yd × 10 yd
> • 1 soccer field = ? volleyball courts

 PLAN

Decide a strategy.

Consider the strategies you know. Can you use one of them? Have you solved a similar problem before? If so, try the same approach.

This problem involves visualization. To see how many volleyball courts fit on a soccer field, you can draw a diagram.

 SOLVE

Try the strategy.

Make a sketch and find how many volleyball courts fit.

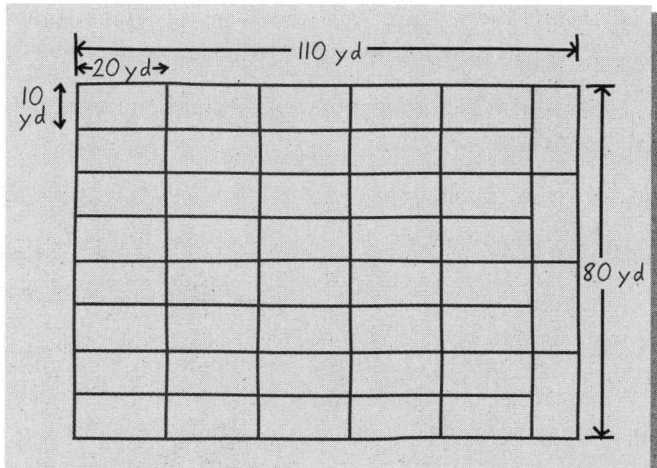

Eight volleyball courts fit down.

Five volleyball courts fit across.

Four more volleyball courts fit in the strip at the end of the soccer field.

$5 \times 8 + 4 = 44$

Therefore, 44 volleyball courts fit in the area of a soccer field.

Students should remember the key words "Read," "Plan," "Solve," and "Look Back." You may want to discuss each step of the Sample Problem as a class or in small groups.

LOOK BACK
Think about how you solved the problem.

This is an important step in solving a problem. Check that you answered the question. Does your answer make sense? Is there a different way to solve the problem?

Another way to solve the problem is to divide the area of a soccer field by the area of a volleyball court.

Area = length × width

Area of soccer field = 110 yd × 80 yd = 8,800 square yards

Area of volleyball court = 20 yd × 10 yd = 200 square yards

8,800 ÷ 200 = 44

This confirms that 44 volleyball courts can fit on a soccer field.

EXERCISES *On Your Own*

Use the four-step approach to solve each problem.
Remember that there are many ways to solve problems.

1. Juan, Lewin, and Ken arrive at the lunch line at the same time. In how many different orders can they stand in line?

2. *Patterns* Chandre made the arrangements below using pennies.

Following this pattern, Chandre used 55 pennies to make a triangle. How many pennies were in the bottom row of this large triangle?

3. *Home Improvement* Suppose you want new carpeting for a hallway 18 feet long and 1 yard wide. Each square yard of carpeting costs $25. Installation costs $55. Find the total cost of the new carpet.

4. *Jobs* Paulette and Camila rake leaves and mow lawns on Saturdays. Paulette charges $5 per hour and Camila charges $4 per hour. One day they worked for a combined total of 9 hours and together made $40. How much did each girl earn?

As suggested earlier, you might want to assign the Exercises for homework or have students work on them in groups in class. Encourage students to use the four-step approach to solve each Exercise.

Using Strategies

A strategy can give you a head start in solving a problem. Some strategies you may have already learned include *Draw a Diagram, Make a Table, Look for a Pattern,* and *Guess and Test.*

There are many ways to solve problems. As you learn more about problem solving strategies, you can choose the ones that work best for you.

SAMPLE PROBLEM..

Design A landscape architect was asked to sketch some designs for a reflecting pool to go in front of the new city courthouse. Here are his first three sketches.

A pool 1 foot long needs 4 square tiles. A pool 2 feet long needs 6 square tiles. A pool 8 feet long needs 12 square tiles.

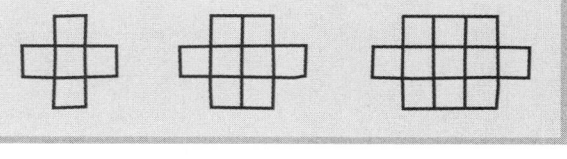

Suppose the pool is 6 feet long and follows the pattern in the drawings above. How many square tiles are needed?

....

The solutions that follow use three different strategies to solve the problem. As you consider the solutions, ask yourself, "Which strategy would I use?"

This section shows students that there is often more than one way to succeed at solving a problem and reviews familiar problem solving techniques. Not all the strategies are included here, but students will add to their repertoire of problem solving techniques as the year progresses.

Solution 1

STRATEGY: *Draw a Diagram*

The *Draw a Diagram* strategy helps you see the relationships in a problem. Sketch a simple picture that shows the information.

You may want to sketch several pictures. In this problem, for example, you could draw the next four pools in the pattern. Or just draw the pool that is 6 feet long.

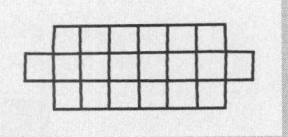

A 6-foot pool needs 14 square tiles.

Solution 2

STRATEGY: *Make a Table*

The *Make a Table* strategy is useful for organizing information so you can analyze it. Put the numbers in the problem into an ordered list like the one below.

Length of Pool	Number of Tiles
1	4
2	6
3	8
4	10
5	12
6	?

Solution 3

STRATEGY: *Look for a Pattern*

Patterns are all around us. They often occur in problems where there is a progression of data. You can find a rule that creates the pattern. Then use the rule to solve the problem.

The *Look for a Pattern* strategy often works well combined with the *Make a Table* strategy.

Encourage students to solve the Sample Problem before looking at the strategies used in the book. Then they can compare their solutions to those presented. You could ask students to give solutions that differ from those in the book.

Length of Pool	Number of Tiles
1	4
2	4 + 2
3	4 + 2 + 2
4	4 + 2 + 2 + 2
5	4 + 2 + 2 + 2 + 2
6	4 + 2 + 2 + 2 + 2 + 2 = 14

The rule here is *add* 2.

The answer is the same. A 6-foot pool needs 14 square tiles.

EXERCISES *On Your Own*

1. *Zoology* The Stone Zoo has two cobras in its reptile collection. One is 8 inches longer than the other. The sum of their lengths is 152 inches. How long is each snake?

2. *Money* Suppose you have dimes, nickels, and pennies in your pocket. You reach in and pull out three coins. What different amounts of money could you could be holding?

3. *Sports* The officials of a soccer league make sure that all the players are called when games are canceled. They use a "telephone tree" to make the calls in rounds. The first person makes 2 phone calls. In the second round, 4 phone calls are made. In the third round, 8 phone calls are made. How many phone calls are made in the sixth round of calls?

4. *Design* If the pattern below continues, how many blocks are needed to make the tenth design in the sequence?

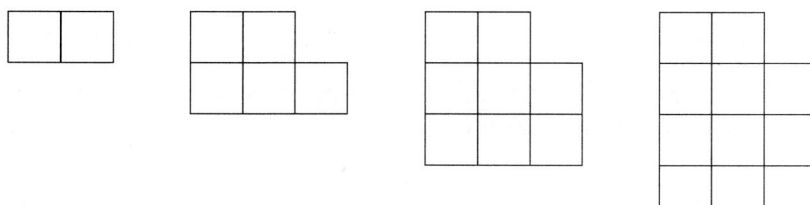

You might want to assign the Exercises for homework or have students work on them in groups in class. Encourage students to use any one strategy. You could ask some students or groups to solve one or more of the Exercises using as many different strategies as possible. Students should not be limited to the strategies used in the lesson.

Working Together

Sometimes you may be asked to work in a cooperative group during math class. Sharing ideas and strategies with your classmates can help you become a better problem solver.

Solving problems in a group involves responsibility and cooperation. Usually classrooms have individual and group rules.

Here are some rules for individuals.

- You are responsible for your own work.
- You are responsible for your own behavior.

Here are some rules for groups.

- You must be willing to help other group members.
- All members should contribute to the solution.
- Group members should try to answer questions themselves before asking a teacher.

Part of working together is empowering one of your group members to speak for the entire group.

People know that working together and valuing others is paramount, especially in today's workplace. There are many opportunities throughout the program where students will be asked to work together to solve a problem, to gather data, or to make conclusions. This lesson provides the framework for working together.

In a cooperative learning group, members work together to solve problems. Some members of the group may also have specific, individual responsibilities.

- The **recorder** takes notes and records information.

- The **researcher** finds necessary information that has not already been provided.

- Each member of the group should have general supplies such as paper and pencil, a calculator, and a ruler. The **organizer** makes sure that any unusual items, such as a stopwatch or masking tape, are also available.

- The **presenter** explains the group's strategies and solution to the rest of the class.

Though members of your group may have different roles, each must contribute if you are to come up with the best solution to the problem.

EXERCISES *On Your Own*

Solve each problem with your small group. Assign a role to each member of your group. Rotate the role assignments with each new exercise.

1. *Distance* What is the average number of paces taken by a member of your group when you walk a distance of 100 yards together?

2. *Geography* Suppose a planet has two hemispheres. In each hemisphere there are three continents. On each continent there are four countries. In each country there are five states. How many states are there on the planet?

3. *Time* In the morning, the school bell rings at 8:20, 9:05, 9:50, and 10:35. If this pattern continues, will the bell also ring at 11:20? At 12:35?

4. *Money* Eighty people went on the class trip to the local museum. Entrance fees were $2 for students and $3 for adults. The entrance fees totaled $168. How many people on the trip were students?

These Exercises can provide students with the opportunity to practice working in groups successfully, especially if you plan to have students work in groups throughout the year.

Preparing for Standardized Tests

Many standardized tests have multiple choice questions. You can use problem solving skills to answer multiple choice questions. Eliminating answers that don't make sense can help you choose the correct answer.

SAMPLE PROBLEM 1..

Baking A recipe calls for $2\frac{2}{3}$ cups of sugar. To make half as much as the recipe calls for, how many cups of sugar should you use?

A. $5\frac{1}{3}$ **B.** $4\frac{2}{3}$ **C.** $1\frac{7}{8}$ **D.** $1\frac{1}{3}$ **E.** Not Here

....

Read and Understand If you make half the recipe, is the amount of sugar you need more than or less than $2\frac{2}{3}$ cups?

Why can you eliminate choices A and B?

Plan You can use the *Draw a Diagram* strategy to see relationships and find the answer.

Solve

     Half of $2\frac{2}{3}$ is $1\frac{1}{3}$.

1   1 $\frac{2}{3}$

The correct answer is D.

Look Back Check your answer by adding $1\frac{1}{3} + 1\frac{1}{3} = 2\frac{2}{3}$.

This section boosts students' preparation for standardized tests. Throughout the text— in lessons, Mixed Reviews, Problem Solving Practice pages, and Cumulative Reviews— students will continue to practice standardized test-type problems. Encourage students to add other helpful hints they might be able to apply when taking mathematics tests.

SAMPLE PROBLEM 2 ....

Zack gets his household chores done by paying his little brother Mike to do them. Zack gives Mike 1¢ on Monday, 2¢ on Tuesday, 4¢ on Wednesday, and 8¢ on Thursday. According to this pattern, how much will Mike get on Sunday?

A. 64¢   **B.** 32¢   **C.** 10¢   **D.** 4¢   **E.** Not Here

....

Day	Pay
Mon	1¢
Tue	2¢
Wed	4¢
Thu	8¢
Fri	16¢
Sat	32¢
Sun	64¢

Make a table and look for a pattern.

Eliminate C and D because they don't follow the doubling pattern.

Find Mike's pay for Sunday.

The correct answer is A.

EXERCISES *On Your Own*

Use problem solving strategies and eliminate answers to find the correct answer.

1. Find the missing number in the sequence 1, 4, 9, 16, __, 36.
   A. 32   **B.** 25   **C.** 5   **D.** 3   **E.** Not Here

2. How many square brownies 2 inches on a side can be cut from a square pan 8 inches on a side?
   A. 64   **B.** 16   **C.** 4   **D.** 2   **E.** Not Here

3. Elizabeth bought milk for $1.10, carrots for $.69, cottage cheese for $1.29, and kidney beans for $.59. There was no tax. What was the bill for these items?
   A. $4.76   **B.** $3.76   **C.** $3.67   **D.** $2.48   **E.** Not Here

4. A rectangular garden is 30 feet by 25 feet. How many fence posts do you need to place one every 5 feet?
   A. 24   **B.** 22   **C.** 13   **D.** 6   **E.** Not Here

You might want to assign the Exercises for homework or have students work on them in groups. Have students discuss which answers they eliminated first, and why, or any other helpful test-taking hints they wish to share with their classmates.

Precourse Skills Assessment

A broad range of assessment tools are available to reach a variety of learners. Options for Formal and Informal Assessment appear on the **Assessing Progress** pages that precede each chapter.

Computer Item Generator

With the Computer Item Generator, you can customize assessment tests and create customized practice worksheets.

Standardized Test Preparation

You may wish to take advantage of the Standardized Test Preparation component that is available on the Computer Item Generator and the Resource Pro™ CD-ROM. With this component, you can generate tests to help students prepare for these standardized tests:

CATS California Achievement Test, 5th Edition
ITBS Iowa Test of Basic Skills, Form B
MAT 7 Metropolitan Achievement Test, 7th Edition
SAT9 Stanford Achievement Test, 9th Edition
CTBS/5 (Terra Nova) Comprehensive Test of Basic Skills, 5th Edition

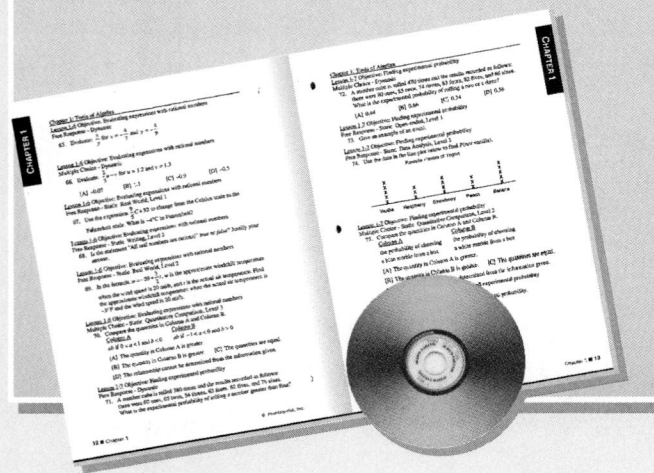

Precourse Skills Assessment

The Precourse Skills Assessment, available in the *Cumulative Assessment* booklet in the Teaching Resources, covers the 11 skills addressed in the **Skills Handbook** at the back of the Student Edition.

Structure The Precourse Skills Assessment is a three-page test. There are four, free-response test items for each of the 11 skills covered in the Skills Handbook at the back of the Student Edition.

Scoring Usually three out of four responses correct (75%) should demonstrate that the student has sufficient mastery of the skill to be able to succeed in this program. However, you may wish to set your own criteria.

Progress and Remediation Chart To assist you in assessing the skill level of your students, a Progress and Remediation Chart appears with the Precourse Skills Assessment. This chart identifies the skills assessed, student achievement on the assessment test, and suggests where remediation help, if necessary, will be found within the *Prentice Hall Middle Grades Math* program.

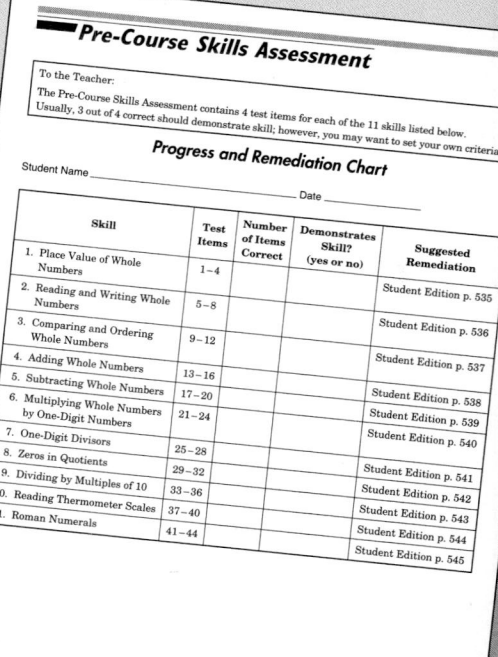

Pre-Course Skills Assessment

To the Teacher:
The Pre-Course Skills Assessment contains 4 test items for each of the 11 skills listed below. Usually, 3 out of 4 correct should demonstrate skill; however, you may want to set your own criteria.

Progress and Remediation Chart

Student Name _____ Date _____

Skill	Test Items	Number of Items Correct	Demonstrates Skill? (yes or no)	Suggested Remediation
1. Place Value of Whole Numbers	1–4			Student Edition p. 535
2. Reading and Writing Whole Numbers	5–8			Student Edition p. 536
3. Comparing and Ordering Whole Numbers	9–12			Student Edition p. 537
4. Adding Whole Numbers	13–16			Student Edition p. 538
5. Subtracting Whole Numbers	17–20			Student Edition p. 539
6. Multiplying Whole Numbers by One-Digit Numbers	21–24			Student Edition p. 540
7. One-Digit Divisors	25–28			Student Edition p. 541
8. Zeros in Quotients	29–32			Student Edition p. 542
9. Dividing by Multiples of 10	33–36			Student Edition p. 543
10. Reading Thermometer Scales	37–40			Student Edition p. 544
11. Roman Numerals	41–44			Student Edition p. 545

■ *Pre-Course Skills Assessment*

Skill 1: Place Value of Whole Numbers

1. Write the place of the underlined digit in 318,420,657.

    1. <u>ten millions</u>

2. Write the value of the underlined digit in 907,428,615.

    2. <u>7 million</u>

3. Write the value of the 4 in 1,492.

    3. <u>400</u>

4. Write the value of the 8 in 385,206,591.

    4. <u>80 million</u>

Skill 2: Reading and Writing Whole Numbers

Complete each statement.

5. 4,830,600 = ■ million, ■ thousand, ■

    5. <u>4; 830; 600</u>

6. 745,000,521,200 = ■ billion, ■ thousand, ■

    6. <u>745; 521; 200</u>

Write each number in standard form.

7. 104 billion, 936 thousand

    7. <u>104,000,936,000</u>

8. 3 billion, 41 million, 702 thousand

    8. <u>3,041,702,000</u>

Skill 3: Comparing and Ordering Whole Numbers

Use > or < to compare the numbers.

9. 37,007 ■ 37,604

    9. <u><</u>

10. 258,303 ■ 258,103

    10. <u>></u>

Write the numbers in order from least to greatest.

11. 2,478; 2,568; 2,858; 2,480

    11. <u>2,478; 2,480; 2,568; 2,858</u>

Use > or < to make true sentences.

12. 43,561 ■ 44,679 ■ 44,697

    12. <u>43,561 < 44,679 < 44,697</u>

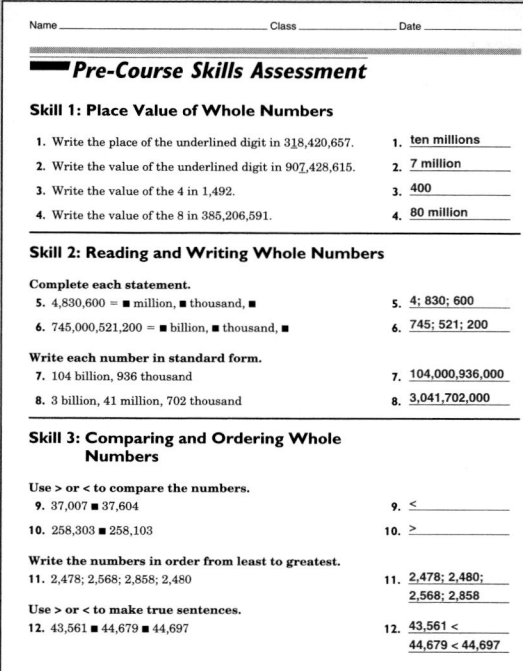

Skill 4: Adding Whole Numbers

Add.

13.   58
  + 27

14.   3,605
  + 2,749

15. 316 + 64

16. 865 + 3,079

  13. <u>85</u>
  14. <u>6,354</u>
  15. <u>380</u>
  16. <u>3,944</u>

Skill 5: Subtracting Whole Numbers

Subtract.

17.   62
  − 39

18.   893
  − 465

19. 354 − 89

20. 631 − 497

  17. <u>23</u>
  18. <u>428</u>
  19. <u>265</u>
  20. <u>134</u>

Skill 6: Multiplying Whole Numbers by One-Digit Numbers

Multiply.

21.   47
  × 4

22.   786
  × 5

23. 9 × 233

24. 547 × 8

  21. <u>188</u>
  22. <u>3,930</u>
  23. <u>2,097</u>
  24. <u>4,376</u>

Skill 7: One-Digit Divisors

Divide.

25. 9⟌38

26. 8⟌257

27. 80 ÷ 6

28. 734 ÷ 5

  25. <u>4 R2</u>
  26. <u>32 R1</u>
  27. <u>13 R2</u>
  28. <u>146 R4</u>

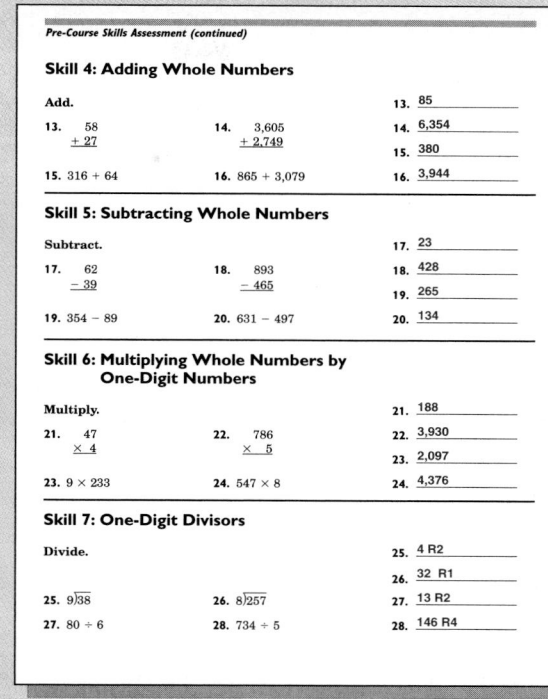

Skill 8: Zeros in Quotients

Divide.

29. 8⟌246

30. 87⟌285

31. 1,016 ÷ 5

32. 1,756 ÷ 29

  29. <u>30 R6</u>
  30. <u>3 R24</u>
  31. <u>203 R1</u>
  32. <u>60 R16</u>

Skill 9: Dividing by Multiples of 10

Find each quotient.

33. 354 ÷ 1,000

34. 720 ÷ 10

35. 63.9 ÷ 10

36. 0.081 ÷ 100

  33. <u>0.354</u>
  34. <u>72</u>
  35. <u>6.39</u>
  36. <u>0.00081</u>

Skill 10: Reading Thermometer Scales

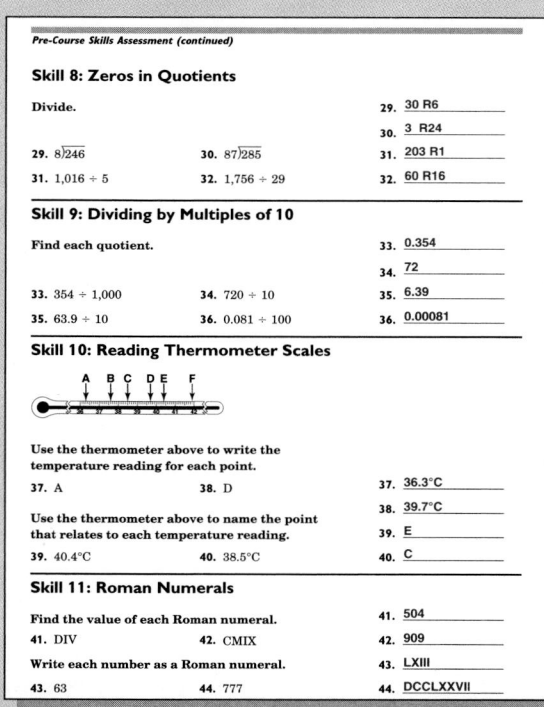

Use the thermometer above to write the temperature reading for each point.

37. A

38. D

  37. <u>36.3°C</u>
  38. <u>39.7°C</u>

Use the thermometer above to name the point that relates to each temperature reading.

39. 40.4°C

40. 38.5°C

  39. <u>E</u>
  40. <u>C</u>

Skill 11: Roman Numerals

Find the value of each Roman numeral.

41. DIV

42. CMIX

Write each number as a Roman numeral.

43. 63

44. 777

  41. <u>504</u>
  42. <u>909</u>
  43. <u>LXIII</u>
  44. <u>DCCLXXVII</u>

1 Using Statistics to Analyze Data

CHAPTER OVERVIEW

To accommodate flexible scheduling, most lessons are divided into parts. Assignment Options are given in the Teacher's Edition for each lesson.

Pages 4–7	**Lesson 1-1** **Organizing and** **Displaying Data**
NCTM 1, 2, 3, 4, 5, 7, 10, 13	**Part 1** Making Frequency Tables **Part 2** Using Line Plots and Finding the Range **Key terms:** frequency table, line plot, range **Alternative Activity** 1-1 ▼ **Project Link**

Pages 8–10	**Lesson 1-2** **Problem Solving Strategy**
NCTM 1, 3, 5	**Make a Table**

Pages 12–16	**Lesson 1-3** **Data Analysis:** **Mean, Median, and Mode**
NCTM 1, 2, 5, 7, 13	**Part 1** Finding the Mean **Part 2** Finding the Median or Mode **Key terms:** average, mean, median, mode **Journal** ▼ **Project Link** ☑ **Checkpoint 1**

Pages 33–36	**Lesson 1-7** **Misleading Graphs**
NCTM 1, 2, 3, 7, 13	**Part 1** Misleading Line Graphs **Part 2** Misleading Bar Graphs ▼ **Project Link**

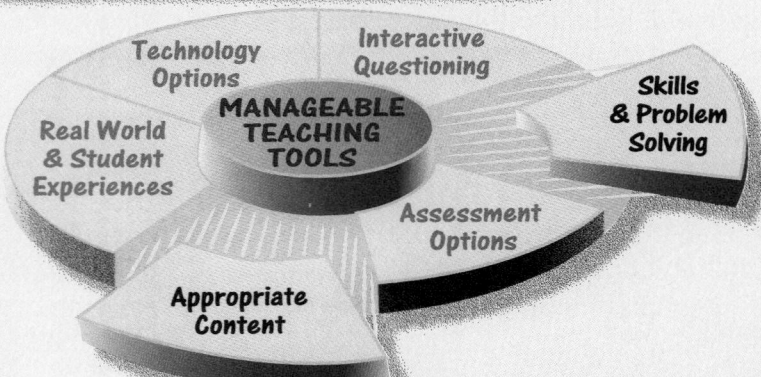

Pacing Options

This chart suggests pacing only for the core lessons and their parts. It is provided merely as a possible guide. It will help you determine how much time you have in your schedule to cover other features, such as the Chapter Project, Math Toolboxes, Wrap Up, and Assessment.

	1 Class Period	1 Class Period	1 Class Period
Traditional (40–45 min class periods)	1–1 1–1 ▼1 ▼2	1–2 ▼	1–3 1–3 ▼1 ▼2
Block Scheduling (90 min class periods)	1–1 1–1 ▼1 ▼2	1–2 1–3 ▼1	1–3 1–4 1–4 ▼1 ▼1 ▼2

CHAPTER PROJECT

Friendly Favorites

Goal: Learn how to collect, analyze, and present data to find answers.

THEME:
Surveys

NCTM STANDARDS

1 Problem Solving	**6** Number Systems and Number Theory	**10** Statistics
2 Communication	**7** Computation and Estimation	**11** Probability
3 Reasoning	**8** Patterns and Functions	**12** Geometry
4 Mathematical Connections	**9** Algebra	**13** Measurement
5 Number and Number Relationships		

Pages 18–21	**Lesson 1-4 Technology: Using Spreadsheets to Organize Data**
NCTM 1, 2, 3, 5, 9	**Part 1** Using Spreadsheets **Part 2** Creating Formulas **Key terms:** spreadsheet, cell, formula **Alternative Activity** 1-4 **Journal**

Pages 22–26	**Lesson 1-5 Algebra: Reading and Understanding Graphs**
NCTM 1, 2, 3, 4, 5, 13	**Part 1** Reading Bar and Line Graphs **Part 2** Reading Circle Graphs **Key terms:** bar graph, line graph, circle graph **Journal** **Math at Work**

Pages 27–31	**Lesson 1-6 Making Bar and Line Graphs**
NCTM 1, 2, 3, 4, 13	**Part 1** Making Bar Graphs **Part 2** Making Line Graphs **Alternative Activity** 1-6 ✓ **Checkpoint 2**

Optional Materials and Manipulatives

graph paper (1-1, 1-2, 1-6, 1-7)
calculator (1-3, 1-4, 1-5)
computer (1-4)

spreadsheet software (1-4)
dot paper (1-5)
index cards (1-5)

Optional calculator use is integrated throughout the courses.

1 Class Period	1 Class Period	1 Class Period	1 Class Period	1 Class Period	1 Class Period	1 Class Period	1 Class Period	1 Class Period	1 Class Period

1–5
1–6
1–6
1–7 1–7

1–7

MEETING INDIVIDUAL NEEDS

Accommodating Diverse Learning Styles

In your Teacher's Edition, you will find suggestions as to how you can help students complete mathematical tasks in Chapter 1 by meeting individual needs and supporting various learning styles. Here are some examples:

VISUAL LEARNING
sketching a bar graph *(p. 27)*

TACTILE LEARNING
making a table using play money *(p. 8)*

AUDITORY LEARNING
reading spreadsheet cell names aloud *(p. 20)*

KINESTHETIC LEARNING
lying on butcher paper to model graph bars *(p. 30)*

EARLY FINISHERS
Performance-Based Project, MathBlaster® Mystery, Interdisciplinary Units

GIFTED AND TALENTED
making misleading graphs from a class survey *(p. 34)*

DIVERSITY using graphs from foreign language publications *(p. 29)*

ACQUIRING ENGLISH PROFICIENCY (AEP)
making a personal glossary of new terms *(p. 4)*

ASSESSING PROGRESS

A broad range of assessment tools are available to reach a variety of learners.

INFORMAL ASSESSMENT

Informal assessments provide day-to-day feedback to help give you a picture of conceptual understanding and skill development.

ONGOING ASSESSMENT is built into lesson instruction and the Teaching Notes of the Teacher's Edition.

In the Teacher's Edition
Lesson Quiz for every lesson

In the Student Edition
On Your Own, Mixed Review, Journal, Portfolio, Project Link, Chapter Wrap Up

Look for **Interactive Questions** within lessons that

- **BUILD UNDERSTANDING** with labels such as **Analyze, Reasoning, Estimation, Writing, and Summarize**
- ✔ **CHECK UNDERSTANDING** with the **Try It Out** label.

FORMAL ASSESSMENT

Formal assessment can occur before and after the chapter, as well as at natural breaking points in the chapter.

Checkpoints
Two forms of each self-assessment Checkpoints are available: one in the Student Edition and another in the Chapter Support File in the Teaching Resources box.

- Mid-Chapter Checkpoint 1, page 16
- End-of-Chapter Checkpoint 2, page 31

Chapter 1 Assessment, page 40.
Two alternative forms are available in the Chapter Support File. They may be used after a chapter has been completed, or as a pre-test and post-test comparison.

Cumulative Review, page 41.
Assesses skills and concepts in Chapter 1.
An alternative form is available in Chapter Support File.

Computer Item Generator for Chapter 1
Customized tests can be generated for each lesson and for mid-chapter and end-of-chapter assessments, and for pre- and post-test comparisons of achievement.

Interactive Questioning

Technology Options

MANAGEABLE TEACHING TOOLS

Real World & Student Experiences

Skills & Problem Solving

Appropriate Content

Assessment Options

CHAPTER PROJECT

The Chapter Project in the student edition provides a real-world connection to the math context of the chapter. The Teacher's Edition contains a scoring rubric.

Another performance-based Chapter Project with a scoring rubric can be found in the Chapter Support File in the Teaching Resources Box.

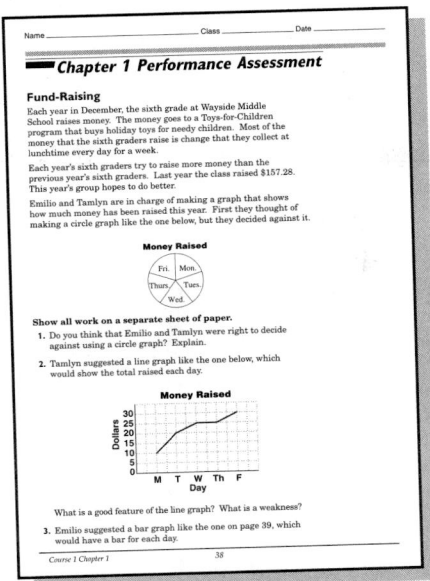

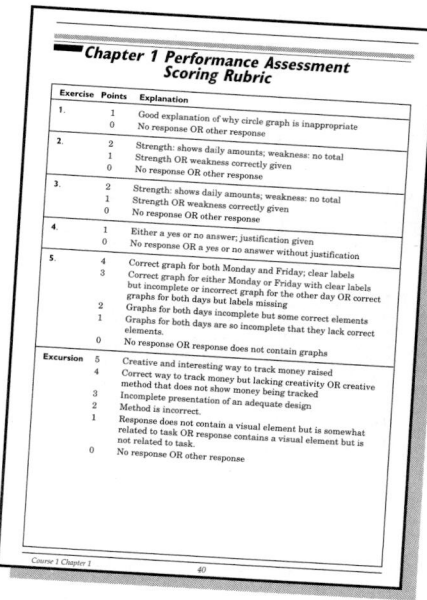

Correlation to Standardized Tests

Lesson		STANDARDIZED TEST ITEMS					
		CAT5	CTBS/5 Terra Nova	ITBS	MAT7	SAT9	Your Local Test
1-1	Organizing and Displaying Data	■	■	■	■	■	
1-2	Problem Solving Strategy: Make a Table	■		■	■	■	
1-3	Data Analysis: Mean, Median, and Mode			■		■	
1-4	Technology: Using Spreadsheets to Organize Data			■	■		
1-5	Algebra: Reading and Understanding Graphs	■	■	■	■	■	
1-6	Making Bar and Line Graphs	■	■	■	■	■	
1-7	Misleading Graphs	■	■	■	■	■	

CAT5 California Achievement Test, 5th Edition
CTBS/5 Comprehensive Test of Basic Skills, 5th Edition

ITBS Iowa Test of Basic Skills, Form B
MAT 7 Metropolitan Achievement Test, 7th Edition

SAT9 Stanford Achievement Test, 9th Edition

MAKING CONNECTIONS

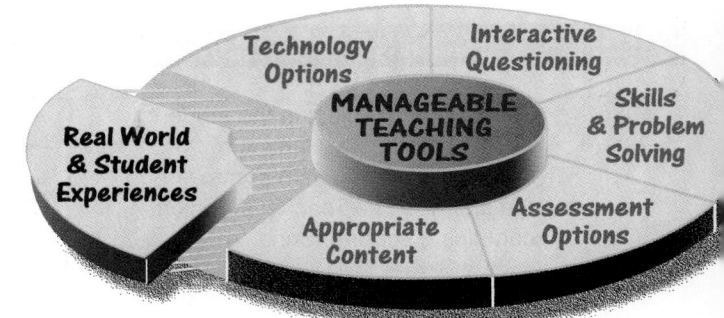

Technology Options
Interactive Questioning
MANAGEABLE TEACHING TOOLS
Skills & Problem Solving
Real World & Student Experiences
Assessment Options
Appropriate Content

TEAM TEACHING WITH PRENTICE HALL MATERIALS

MIDDLE GRADES MATH INTERDISCIPLINARY UNITS

- **Consumer Awareness:** Activities 2, 4, 9, & 12
- **Sports:** Activities 1, 6, 9, & 12
- **Travel and Geography:** Activities 9 & 11

INTERDISCIPLINARY EXPLORATIONS

- *SOAP* pp. 7 & 8
- *India Beyond the Golden Age* pp. 33 & 35
- *Wagons West* p. 16

SCIENCE EXPLORER
L Life Science **E** Earth Science **P** Physical Science

L Lab p. 528 (graphing data)
E Sec. 1-2 Recording and Analyzing Data
Lab p. 202 (change in temperature)
Lab p. 550 (graphing climate information)

Lesson	Interdisciplinary Connections	Real World Connections	Math Integration
1-1	Art Geography Social Studies Literature	Entertainment Sports	Data Analysis
1-2	Statistics Science	Carnival Ride Newspapers Games Transportation Jewelry	Patterns
1-3	Music Nutrition	Airplanes Temperature Entertainment Sports	Estimation Patterns
1-4	Computer Science	Music Temperature	Algebra Number Sense
1-5	Music Geography	Recycling In-line Skating Food Recreation Education Sports	Data Analysis
1-6	Environmental Science	Animal Studies Population Education Architecture Hobbies	Data Analysis
1-7	Government	Entertainment Car Sales	Data Analysis Mental Math

School to Home

MATERIALS:

newspaper
scissors
tape
paper
pencil

English and Spanish versions are available in the Teacher's Communication Kit, Teacher's Resource box.

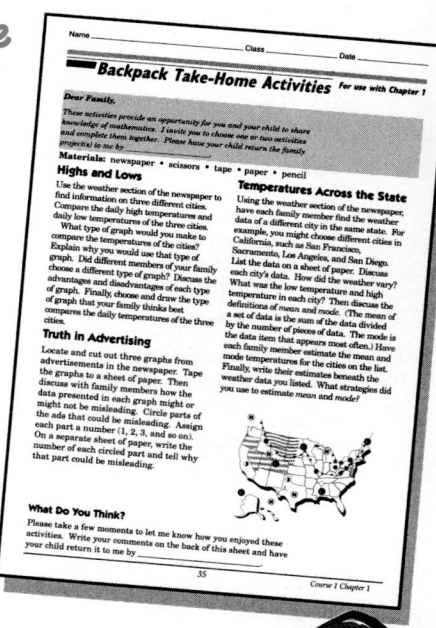

Name _____ Class _____ Date _____

Backpack Take-Home Activities *for use with Chapter 1*

Dear Family,

These activities provide an opportunity for you and your child to share knowledge of mathematics. I invite you to choose one or two activities and complete them together. Please have your child return the family project(s) to me by _____.

Materials: newspaper • scissors • tape • paper • pencil

Highs and Lows

Use the weather section of the newspaper to find information on three different cities. Compare the daily high temperatures and daily low temperatures of the three cities.

What type of graph would you make to compare the temperatures of the cities? Explain why you would use that type of graph. Did different members of your family choose a different type of graph? Discuss the advantages and disadvantages of each type of graph. Finally, choose and draw the type of graph that your family thinks best compares the daily temperatures of the three cities.

Truth in Advertising

Locate and cut out three graphs from advertisements in the newspaper. Tape the graphs to a sheet of paper. Then discuss with family members how the data presented in each graph might or might not be misleading. Circle parts of the ads that could be misleading. Assign each part a number (1, 2, 3, and so on). On a separate sheet of paper, write the number of each circled part and tell why that part could be misleading.

Temperatures Across the State

Using the weather section of the newspaper, have each family member find the weather data of a different city in the same state. For example, you might choose different cities in California, such as San Francisco, Sacramento, Los Angeles, and San Diego. List the data on a sheet of paper. Discuss each city's data. How did the weather vary? What was the low temperature and high temperature in each city? Then discuss the definitions of *mean* and *mode*. (The mean of a set of data is the sum of the data divided by the number of pieces of data. The mode is the data item that appears most often.) Have each family member estimate the mean and mode temperatures for the cities on the list. Finally, write their estimates beneath the weather data you listed. What strategies did you use to estimate *mean* and *mode*?

What Do You Think?

Please take a few moments to let me know how you enjoyed these activities. Write your comments on the back of this sheet and have your child return it to me by _____.

35   Course 1 Chapter 1

USING TECHNOLOGY TO ENHANCE INSTRUCTION

FOR THE STUDENT

Multimedia Math Hot Pages™
This interactive software and video package on CD-ROM integrates solid math content through a variety of media.

- Hot Page™ 1 (1-3)
- Hot Page™ 2 (1-5)
- Hot Page™ 3 (1-7)

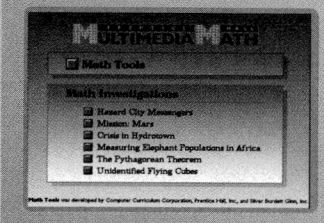

Multimedia Math Investigations
These in-depth interactive activities on CD-ROM develop real-world applications of mathematics. They allow students the opportunity to reinforce key concepts.

- Hazard City Messengers
- Mission: Mars

MathBlaster® Mystery
This award-winning, interactive software program on CD-ROM can be used to maintain skills or to accommodate early finishers.

- Level: Earn 2 coins; Pay 6 coins
- Mission Mode (all lessons)
- Kitchen Comparisons (1-3, 1-7)
- Number Guesser (1-1)
- Equation Maker (1-4, 1-6)
- Word Problems (1-2, 1-5, Problem Solving Practice)

Math Labs
This software, available on both diskette and CD-ROM, includes on-screen Math Lab activities. Students use linkable, interactive tools to explore math concepts.

- Math Lab: Bar and Line Graphs (1-6)

Interactive Student Tutorial
Available on CD-ROM, this test preparation program contains self-tests with questions in standardized test format. Software includes electronic versions of the text lessons and the Math Tools and Math Labs.

Internet Connection

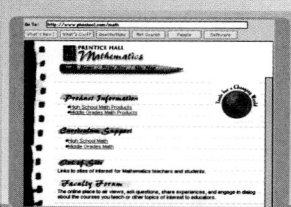

For Students
Support for the Chapter Project
A career-oriented link for Math at Work feature

www.phschool.com/math

For teachers
Curriculum Support
Product Information
Regional Support Information

FOR THE TEACHER

Computer Item Generator
Available on both CD-ROM and diskette, this software generates customized practice sheets, quizzes, and tests. It generates an unlimited supply of questions with varying levels of difficulty.

The Resource Pro™
Available on CD-ROM, this software can be used to customize and plan lessons.

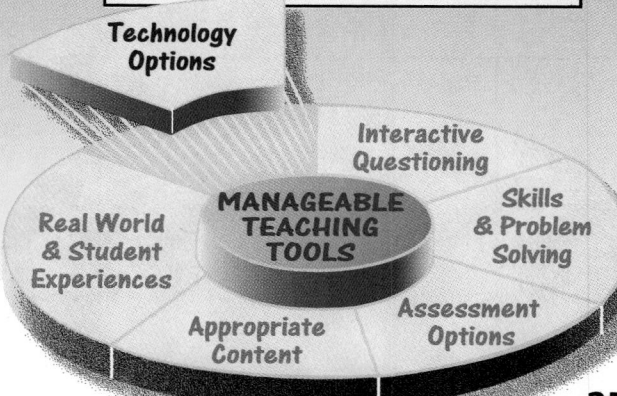

Technology Options

MANAGEABLE TEACHING TOOLS

- Interactive Questioning
- Skills & Problem Solving
- Assessment Options
- Appropriate Content
- Real World & Student Experiences

USING STATISTICS TO ANALYZE DATA

CONNECTING TO PRIOR LEARNING Ask students what they think the word *data* means. Have students give examples of data they use in day-to-day life. Discuss the different forms data can take, from a table of monthly high temperatures in an almanac, to a bar graph comparing yearly sales of CDs by type of music.

CULTURAL CONNECTIONS A favorite activity of students may be listening to music.

Encourage students to research the origins and elements of the types of music they enjoy. Their findings may surprise them. For example, the increasingly popular Tejano music incorporates the accordion. Have students share their findings.

INTERDISCIPLINARY CONNECTIONS Ask students to investigate how scientists use graphs in their work. Possibilities include

recording research findings and displaying the results of experiments.

ABOUT THE PROJECT The Chapter Project will give students an opportunity to gather and analyze data and display the information in a graph. The Project Link questions will help students understand and complete the process.

Internet • For information and activities related to the Chapter Project, visit the Prentice Hall site at www.phschool.com/mgm1/ch1

Using Statistics to Analyze Data

WHAT YOU WILL LEARN IN THIS CHAPTER	• How to gather, display, and graph data	• How to find and use the range, mean, median, and mode	• How to use spreadsheets to analyze data

LAUNCHING THE CHAPTER PROJECT

PROJECT NOTEBOOK Encourage students to keep all project-related materials in a separate folder or notebook.

Ask students: *Do you know what a market survey is? How can a market survey help a company make or improve their products?*

TRACKING THE PROJECT You may wish to have students read Finishing the Chapter Project on page 37 to help them get an overview of the project. Set benchmark deadlines for students to show you their work in progress.

ON YOUR OWN TIME

CHAPTER PROJECT

THEME: SURVEYS

RING!!! The last bell of the day has rung. You and your classmates will soon head in different directions. Some of your classmates are on the same team or in the same club as you. Some of them are not. Can you name your classmates' favorite activities? You could guess the answers to the last question, but a more accurate method of finding the answers would be to collect real data.

Conduct a Survey For the chapter project you will survey 25 of your friends and classmates. You can choose the survey subject, such as your favorite afterschool activity. You will organize and graph the data. Then you will make a presentation to your class to display your results.

Steps to help you complete the project:

p. 7   **Project Link:** *Collecting Data*
p. 16   **Project Link:** *Analyzing Data*
p. 36   **Project Link:** *Making a Decision*
p. 37   ***Finishing the Chapter Project***

• How to solve problems by making tables

SCORING RUBRIC

3 You correctly used three different display methods to show the data you collected. Your displays are attractive and self-explanatory. You identified both the best display method and the best averaging method. You gave reasons to support your choices.

2 You created three displays of your data and calculated the mean, median, and mode. Either your displays or your explanations are not as complete or neat as they could be.

1 Your survey data is complete, but you only completed two displays of the data. Either your displays are not self-explanatory, or you neglected to compare display methods or averaging techniques.

0 Either your survey was not thorough or complete, or you left out important parts of your presentation.

1 Focus

CONNECTING TO PRIOR KNOWLEDGE Ask students to give examples of data that are organized and have them identify the source of the data. Ask why data might need to be organized. **to make it easier to understand and use the data** Then challenge students to think of some specific types of data

Prerequisite Skills
• gathering, recording, and organizing data (precourse)

Vocabulary/Symbols
frequency table, line plot, range

Materials/Manipulatives
• graph paper

Resources

 Student Edition

Skills Handbook, p. 536
Extra Practice, p. 522
Glossary/Study Guide

Teaching Resources

Chapter Support File, Ch. 1
• Lesson Planner 1-1
• Practice 1-1, Reteaching 1-1
• Alternative Activity 1-1
• Answer Masters 1-1
Teaching Aids Master 1
Glossary, Spanish Resources

Transparencies

1, 30–35, 78 Minds on Math 1-1

Warm Up

Evaluate each of the following expressions for $n = 6$.
Multiply n by 4 and add 6. **30**
Multiply n by 9 and add 12. **66**

---

organization that they have seen used, such as tables, graphs, and charts.

2 Teach

Work Together

ERROR ALERT! Students may lose track of which classmates they have questioned.
Remediation: Have students develop a method for tracking classmates as they question them, such as writing their names.

KINESTHETIC LEARNING As you name each color, have students stand to indicate that color is their favorite.

AEP Students with limited English proficiency can benefit from sitting near the front of the classroom or where there is a minimum of distraction. Encourage students to start a personal glossary for the meaning of terms that are new to them.
Example 1 When finished organizing

1-1 Organizing and Displaying Data

What You'll Learn

1. To organize data into frequency tables
2. To make a line plot and find the range of data

...And Why

You can use frequency tables and line plots to collect and display data.

Here's How

Look for questions that
- build understanding
- check understanding

Blue is the favorite color of most Americans. In order, their next most favorite colors are red, green, purple, orange, and yellow.

Source: 3-2-1 Contact

Work Together ——— *Organizing Data in a Table*

Art What's your favorite color? Suppose you want to find out the most popular color among students in your math class. Use the colors in the color wheel at the left below.

1. Record the favorite color of each student in a table.
1–2. Check students' work.
2. Which color was the most popular? How many students picked each of the other colors?

3. ⚑ *Draw a Conclusion* Describe how your table helps you organize the data.
Answers may vary. Sample: The table lists all the data in one place.

THINK AND DISCUSS

1. *Making Frequency Tables*

A **frequency table** shows the number of times each type of answer occurs. Here's a sample of possible favorite color data.

■ **EXAMPLE 1** *Real-World Problem Solving*

Organize responses to favorite color in a frequency table.

List the color choices.　Make a tally mark, |, to record the data.　Count the tally marks and record the frequency.

Favorite Color	Tally	Frequency
blue	⊞⊞ IIII	9
purple	⊞⊞ II	7
red	III	3
orange	I	1
yellow	II	2
green	⊞⊞	5

4. ⚑ *Reasoning* How many people responded in Example 1? Describe two ways you can find this number. **27; you can count all the tally marks or add all the frequencies.**

Example 1 When finished organizing responses, have students arrange frequencies in descending order. This will help them when they get to *range*.

Question 6 Ask students: *Would a line plot be a good way to display the number of videos rented in a week or a month?* **probably not** *Why or why not?* **There might be too many Xs to count easily.**

■ **ADDITIONAL EXAMPLES**

FOR EXAMPLE 1

The favorite lunch for ten students was: pizza, pizza, chicken, hamburger, chicken, pizza, chicken, pizza, pizza, pizza. Have students organize this data in a frequency table.

Lunch	Tally	Frequency
hamburger	I	1
pizza	⊦⊦⊥ I	6
chicken	I I I	3

FOR EXAMPLE 2

Have students make a line plot of the data in Additional Example 1. Find the range of the data. **5**

Favorite Lunch
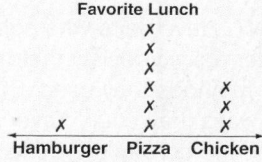

5. **Student Eye Color**

Color	Frequency
brown	4
blue	1
hazel	3
green	2

5. ✔ *Try It Out* The eye colors of ten students are brown, brown, blue, hazel, green, brown, green, hazel, hazel, and brown. Organize the eye color data in a frequency table.

Now you may assign Exercises 1–8, 22.

❷ *Using Line Plots and Finding the Range*

A **line plot** displays data using a number line.

■ **EXAMPLE 2** *Real-World Problem Solving*

Entertainment Suppose you work at Video Village. One night you kept track of the number of videos each customer rented. Make a line plot of the data given.

3, 5, 1, 2, 2, 1, 4, 1, 4, 2, 3, 3, 4, 1, 5, 2, 6, 2, 2, 4, 3, 1, 1, 2, 4, 2

Number of Videos Rented at Video Village

① Write a title describing the data.

③ Mark an x for each response.

② Draw a number line with the choices below it.

6. ■ *Look Back* How many customers rented videos at Video Village? How did you find this number?
26; add the total for each stack.

7. ✔ *Try It Out* Make a line plot for the following set of data.
Ring sizes: 7, 5, 6, 6, $6\frac{1}{2}$, 8, 8, $5\frac{1}{2}$, $6\frac{1}{2}$, 9, 8, 5, $8\frac{1}{2}$, 7

7. **Ring Sizes**

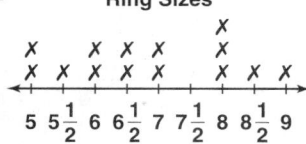

$5 \ 5\frac{1}{2} \ 6 \ 6\frac{1}{2} \ 7 \ 7\frac{1}{2} \ 8 \ 8\frac{1}{2} \ 9$

The **range** is the difference between the greatest and the least values in a set of numerical data. In Example 2, the range of the number of videos each customer rents is $6 - 1$, or 5 videos.

8. *Geography* In 1852, surveyors made these six measurements of Mt. Everest to determine its height.

28,990 ft	28,992 ft	28,999 ft
29,002 ft	29,005 ft	29,026 ft

a. What was the greatest height measured? The least height measured? **29,026 ft; 28,990 ft**

b. ✔ *Try It Out* Find the range of the measurements. **36 ft**

Now you may assign Exercises 9–21, 23–24.

Technology Options

Prentice Hall Technology

💾 💿 **Software for Learners**

- Math Blaster® Mystery*
- Interactive Student Tutorial, Chapter 1*

💾 💿 **Teaching Resource Software**

- Computer Item Generator 1-1
- Resource Pro™ Chapter 1*

🔄 **Internet** • For related mathematics activities, visit the Prentice Hall site at www.phschool.com/math

Available on CD-ROM only

Assignment Options for Exercises On Your Own

To provide flexible scheduling, this lesson can be subdivided into parts.

▼❶ **Core** 1–8
Extension 22

▼❷ **Core** 9–15, 17–21, 23
Extension 16, 24

Use Mixed Review to maintain skills.

CONNECTION TO SPORTS Students can discuss the use of frequency tables for sports data. **baseball–charting balls and strikes thrown; football–tackles made and passes received**

ASSESSMENT Have pairs who completed the Work Together activity review their work and evaluate the methods they used. Students might name ways they could have accomplished the activity more efficiently. As students talk to each other, circulate and identify those who demonstrate understanding as well as those who need further help.

3 Practice/Assess

EXERCISES *On Your Own*

RESEARCH **Exercise 16a** Have a map of the United States available to help students locate these states.

REASONING **Exercise 22a** Ask students to explain when they think it is best to use a line plot to display data rather than a frequency table.

WRAP UP

IDENTIFYING THE BIG IDEA Ask students what *frequency tables* and *line plots* are. Have students describe when to use them.

PROJECT LINK Survey topics might include favorite sports, hobbies, musical groups, foods, or pets.

---

pages 6–7 On Your Own

3.
Cost	Frequency
$122	3
$125	3
$135	1
$138	1

4.
Number of Letters	Frequency
2	4
3	4
4	5
5	3
6	3
7	1
8	1
11	1

5.
Number of Days	Frequency
28	1
30	4
31	7

6.
Result	Frequency
TT	4
TH	6
HH	2

7.
Number Absent	Frequency
0	7
1	8
2	4
3	1
6	2

8.
Goals	Frequency
0	6
1	9
2	4
3	3
4	1
5	1

EXERCISES *On Your Own*

1. *Social Studies* A town in Wales is named Llanfairpwllgwyngyllgogerychwyrndrobwllllantysiliogogogoch.
   a. Copy and complete the frequency table using the name of the Welsh town.
   b. *Writing* Describe the data recorded in your frequency table. **Answers may vary. Sample: There are 6 *o*'s, 3 each of *a*'s and *i*'s, 1 *e*, and no *u*.**

Letter	Tally	Frequency
a	I I I	3
e	I	1
i	I I I	3
o	⫞⫞⫞⫞ I	6
u		0

Wales

2. *Literature* The number of letters in each of the first 25 words of the book *The Story of Amelia Earhart* is shown below. Make a frequency table. **See back of book.**

6 3 4 2 3 5 3 7 3 4 3 3 4 3 3 3 6 6 3 5 3 2 3 7 5

Make a frequency table for each set of data. 3–8. See margin.

3. cost of a CD player in several stores: $125, $122, $138, $135, $125, $122, $122, $125

4. lengths of words in a sentence: 5, 6, 3, 7, 4, 2, 3, 4, 6, 3, 4, 6, 2, 11, 5, 2, 5, 2, 4, 4, 3, 8

5. days in each month (nonleap year): 31, 28, 31, 30, 31, 30, 31, 31, 30, 31, 30, 31

6. results of tossing two coins: TT, TH, TT, HH, TH, TH, TH, HH, TT, TH, TH, TT

7. students absent from class: 2, 0, 1, 1, 1, 0, 2, 3, 6, 2, 1, 0, 0, 0, 0, 6, 1, 1, 1, 1, 2, 0

8. goals in soccer games: 3, 2, 0, 0, 2, 2, 1, 3, 1, 1, 5, 1, 1, 0, 0, 1, 0, 1, 1, 3, 2, 0, 1, 4

Make a line plot for each set of data. 9–12. See back of book.

9. test scores: 85, 80, 85, 90, 90, 80, 75, 80, 75, 95, 85, 80, 75, 70, 80, 70, 90

10. heights of plants (in.): 10, 12, 15, 11, 12, 15, 13, 9, 14, 12, 11, 13, 10, 11, 11, 9, 12

11. speeds of runners (mi/h): 7, 7, 8, 8, 7, 9, 7, 7, 8, 9, 7, 7, 8, 8, 8, 9, 7, 8, 7, 9, 9, 8, 8, 7

12. shoe sizes: 6, 7, $4\frac{1}{2}$, $5\frac{1}{2}$, 5, 6, $8\frac{1}{2}$, 6, 4, $7\frac{1}{2}$, 8, $5\frac{1}{2}$, 9, 6, 4, 5, $6\frac{1}{2}$, 5, 6, 8, $5\frac{1}{2}$, 7

Find the range of each data set.

13. 4, 5, 3, 4, 5, 5, 5, 4, 5, 0 **5**

14. 80, 87, 85, 85, 82, 92, 80 **12**

15. $4\frac{1}{2}$, $5\frac{1}{2}$, 5, 6, 6, 4, $7\frac{1}{2}$, 8, $5\frac{1}{2}$, 7 **4**

16. a. *Research* Name the 8 states that begin with the letter *M*.
    b. *Data Collection* Ask 20 people to name as many states that begin with the letter *M* as they can. Record the states that each person correctly names in a frequency table.
    c. Display your results in a line plot.
    d. *Writing* Describe the results of your survey. What state was most often missed? **b–d. Check students' work.**

a. **Maine, Maryland, Massachusetts, Michigan, Minnesota, Mississippi, Missouri, Montana**

1. Make a frequency table for the data of the number of cats in each household.
1 1 2 0 2 0 1 1 1 0 2 1 0

cats	tally	frequency
0	IIII	4
1	THL I	6
2	III	3

2. Make a line plot for the data of the dinner hours for 7 families.
5 7 6 6 8 7 6

```
        X
        X       X
  X     X   X
  X     X   X   X
 ←——————————————————→
  5     6   7   8
```

Use the line plot at the right for Exercises 17–19.

17. What information is displayed in the line plot?
grades on a science test

18. How many test grades are recorded in the line plot?
16 grades

19. How many students received a grade of C or better?
13 students

Science Test Grades

```
        X
        X
  X     X
  X     X   X
  X     X   X   X
  X     X   X   X   X
 ————————————————————
  A     B   C   D   F
```

20. *Sports* The prices of tickets available for a Texas Rangers' baseball game are $20, $18, $16, $12, $9, $10, $10, $9, $8, $6, and $4. Find the range. **$16**

21. *Social Studies* The birth states of the first 41 Presidents of the United States are shown at the right.
a. Make a line plot of the data. **See back of book.**
b. In what four states were the most Presidents born?
Virginia, Ohio, New York, and Massachusetts

22. a. *Reasoning* When would you use a frequency table?
b. Why do you think it is called a *frequency table?*
a–b. See below.

23. *Writing* How are frequency tables and line plots alike? How are they different?
Answers may vary. See below right for sample.

24. *Calculator* To the nearest inch, NASA requires that an astronaut be at least 59 in. and at most 76 in. tall. Find the height range. **17 in.**

22a. You use a frequency table to record numerical data from a list.

Presidential Birth States

State	Tally	State	Tally
VA	THL III	NJ	I
MA	IIII	IA	I
SC	I	MO	I
NY	IIII	TX	II
NC	II	CA	I
NH	I	NE	I
PA	I	GA	I
KY	I	IL	I
OH	THL II	AR	I
VT	II		

22b. Answers may vary. Sample: You record the *frequency* of each outcome.

Mixed Review

Find each answer. *(Previous Course)*

25. 243 + 43 + 817 + 36 **1,139**   **26.** 592 − 418 **174**

27. 23,427 − 4,798 **18,629**

28. 1,585 − 371 + 19 **1,233**   **29.** 15,904 − 6,086 **9,818**

30. 18 + 39 + 22 + 7 + 11 **97**

31. *Choose a Strategy* Jemika has six coins that total 52¢. What coins, and how many of each, does she have?
2 pennies, 1 nickel, 2 dimes, 1 quarter

23. Frequency tables and line plots each show how many times each item occurs. Line plots display the information graphically. Frequency tables display it numerically.

CHAPTER PROJECT

PROJECT LINK: COLLECTING DATA

Choose a survey topic. Identify seven or eight responses for students to choose. Decide how to organize the responses of your 25 friends or classmates. Collect and record the data in a table or chart. **Check student's work.**

Practice 1-1 *Organizing and Displaying Data*

1. Choose a page from a book you are reading. Choose 50 words on that page. Using these 50 words, complete the frequency table. **Answers will vary.**

Letter	Tally	Frequency
t		
s		
r		
n		
d		

2. Make a line plot for your frequency table.
See students' line plots. Line plots should show the letters *t, s, r, n,* and *d* as labels on the horizontal line with the appropriate number of *X*'s for each letter.

3. Which letter occurred most frequently in your sample? least frequently? **Answers will vary.**

Use the line plot at the right to answer Exercises 4–7.

4. What information is displayed in the line plot?
time spent on homework last night

5. How many students spent time doing homework last night?
24 students

6. How many students spent at least a half hour on homework?
9 students

7. What is the range of time spent on homework last night?
25 min

Time Spent Doing Homework Last Night (min)

```
            X
  X         X           X
  X X       X       X   X
  X X   X   X   X   X   X
 ——————————————————————————
 15  20  25  30  35  40
```

8. A kennel is boarding dogs that weigh the following amounts (in pounds).

5	62	43	48	12	17	29	74
8	15	4	11	15	26	63	

a. What is the range of the dogs' weights? **70 lb**
b. How many of the dogs weigh under 50 lb? **12 dogs**

In copymaster and workbook formats

Reteaching 1-1 *Organizing and Displaying Data*

Sixteen students were asked to name their favorite school day. A **frequency table** can be used to organize their responses.

Favorite School Day	Tally	Frequency
Monday	III	3
Tuesday	II	2
Wednesday	III	3
Thursday	IIII	4
Friday	IIII	4

To make a frequency table:
① List all the choices.
② Mark a tally for each student's response.
③ Total the tallies for each choice.

Students compared the number of books they carry to school. A **line plot** can be used to show this data. Each *X* represents one student.

Number of Books Carried to School

```
            X
    X   X   X
  X X   X   X   X
 ——————————————————
 1  2  3  4  5  6
```

To use a line plot to find the **range:**
① Subtract the least value from the greatest value along the horizontal line.
② The range is 6 − 1 or 5 books.

Make a frequency table for each set of data.

1. first letters of students' names: A, A, B, D, F, F, H, J, J, J, J

First Letter	Tally	Frequency
A	II	2
B	I	1
D	I	1
F	II	2
H	I	1
J	IIII	4

2. birthday months: March, May, April, June, July, June, May, May, May, July, March, May

Month	Tally	Frequency
March	II	2
April	I	1
May	THL	5
June	II	2
July	II	2

Make a line plot for each set of data. Find the range.

3. ages of middle school students: 11, 12, 12, 12, 12, 12, 13, 13, 13, 13, 13, 13, 14, 14, 14

Students' Ages
```
        X
    X   X
    X   X
    X   X
  X X   X   X
 ———————————————
 11 12  13  14
```
The range is **3**.

4. questions answered correctly on a quiz: 9, 9, 8, 7, 10, 9, 6, 7, 9, 9, 10, 8, 8, 8, 7, 6, 10, 10

Questions Answered Correctly
```
            X
        X   X   X
    X   X   X   X
    X   X   X   X
 ———————————————————
  6   7   8   9   10
```
The range is **4**.

Minds on Math Transparency

1-1

Each member of a team wears a T-shirt with a different consecutive number starting with one. The team members work in 6 pairs on a warm-up exercise. The sum of the numbers on the T-shirts of every pair of students is the same. Reynold is wearing a T-shirt with the number 5 on it. What is the number on his partner's T-shirt?

8

See *Solution Key* for worked-out answers.

---

1 Focus

CONNECTING TO PRIOR KNOWLEDGE Ask students to think of a situation in which they might need to organize information in a logical way. For instance, when ordering pizzas for a group of people, how could they determine the number of ways to pick two toppings from a list of eight toppings?

Lesson Planning Options

Prerequisite Skills
• making a table (precourse)

Materials/Manipulatives
• graph paper

Resources

 Student Edition

Skills Handbook, p. 535
Extra Practice, p. 522
Glossary/Study Guide

 Teaching Resources

Chapter Support File, Ch. 1
• Lesson Planner 1-2
• Practice 1-2, Reteaching 1-2
• Answer Masters 1-2
Glossary, Spanish Resources

 Transparencies
Minds on Math 1-2

Warm Up

Choose the appropriate graph:
1. You own a fish store. You want to compare one week's sales of salmon and swordfish. **bar graph**
2. You have examined your diet and want to show what parts of the food you have consumed belong to each of the four basic food groups. **circle graph**

8

---

2 Teach

THINK AND DISCUSS

ERROR ALERT! Questions 1–11 Some students may leave out possible solutions when they make their tables. **Remediation:** Help students work in a logical manner. For example, they can use the greatest number of the coin with the greatest value first. Then use one fewer of those coins for the next combination and so on.

AEP Review the names and values of coins in the table. Have students practice naming and telling the value of play dimes, nickels, and pennies.

TACTILE LEARNING Encourage students to draw the table on a large sheet of paper. Students can put play coins under each column to show and check numbers in the table.

PROBLEM SOLVING STRATEGY

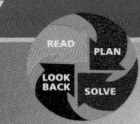

1-2 Make a Table

Problem Solving Strategies
Draw a Diagram
Guess and Test
Look for a Pattern
Make a Model
✓ Make a Table
Simulate a Problem
Solve a Simpler Problem
Too Much or Too Little Information
Use Logical Reasoning
Use Multiple Strategies
Work Backward

 READ

Read for understanding. Summarize the problem.

 PLAN

Decide on a strategy.

SOLVE

Try the strategy.

Dimes	Nickels	Pennies
1	0	8
1	1	3
0	3	3
0	2	8
0	1	13
0	0	18

THINK AND DISCUSS

Sometimes you need to make a table to help you solve a problem. Use a table to list information in a logical way. Then you don't skip or leave out important parts of the answer.

SAMPLE PROBLEM..

Robert has a pocket full of coins. With just these coins, he can show you all possible ways to make 18¢.
How many ways can Robert show you?

....

Think about the information you are given and what you are asked to find.

1. What does the problem ask you to find?
   the number of different coin combinations that total 18¢
2. What types of coins must Robert have in his pocket? What is the value of each of these coins?
   pennies, nickels, dimes; 1¢, 5¢, 10¢

You can make a table to help you organize the possible ways to make 18¢.

3. Suppose Robert shows you only dimes and pennies. How many of each coin is needed to make 18¢?
   1 dime and 8 pennies
4. Suppose Robert shows you one dime and one nickel. How many pennies are needed to make 18¢? **3 pennies**

You can form an organized list of all possible ways to make 18¢.

Dimes	Nickels	Pennies
1	0	8
⋮	⋮	⋮
0	0	18

5. Copy and complete the table above.

■ **ADDITIONAL PROBLEM**

The math club is having a picnic. Members make sandwiches for lunch by picking two of these extra ingredients to go with their ham: sprouts, lettuce, avocado, and tomato. How many different kinds of sandwiches can a student make? **6**

3 Practice/Assess

EXERCISES *On Your Own*

VISUAL LEARNING Have students draw pictures of the coins.

AEP Students having difficulty with word problems might work in small groups with other students who can help with vocabulary.

ASSESSMENT Exercise 1 Have students examine the table they made. Ask students to evaluate their work based on the following.

• *Is the table clear and well organized?*

• *Did you list all possible types of coins that can be used to make the amount?*

• *Did you work in a logical manner to list all possible combinations?*

• *Did you list any combinations twice?*

6. Why does the number 2 not appear in the *Dimes* column?
   You have more than 18 ¢ with 2 dimes.
7. How many ways can Robert make 18¢? Check your answer for reasonableness. **6 ways**

➤ **LOOK BACK**

Think about how you solved the problem.

8. You can replace 1 dime with 2 nickels, 1 nickel and 5 pennies, or 10 pennies. You can replace 1 nickel with 5 pennies.

You can use the table you made to answer many other questions.

8. Find and describe any patterns in the numbers that appear in your table. **Answers may vary. See left for sample.**

9. What is the minimum number of coins needed to make 18¢?
   5 coins
10. What is the maximum number of coins needed to make 18¢?
    18 coins
11. Ten coins total 18¢. Name the ten coins. **2 nickels and 8 pennies**

Now you may assign Exercises 1–11.

EXERCISES *On Your Own*

Make a table to solve each problem.

1. How many possible ways are there to make 28¢?
   13 ways   **2a. nickels and pennies**
2. There is 16¢ in a bag. There are more nickels than pennies.
   a. What types of coins are in the bag?
   b. How many of each type of coin are in the bag?
      3 nickels and 1 penny
3. *Rides* The carnival has two types of children's rides. Each race car seats 4 children and each tugboat seats 6 children. Altogether there are 28 race cars and tugboats that seat a total of 136 children. How many of each ride are there?
   16 race cars and 12 tugboats

Use any strategy to solve each problem. Show all your work.

   20 Sunday and 40 daily papers
4. *Newspapers* Michael has a paper route. He earns 15¢ for each daily paper and 35¢ for each Sunday paper he delivers. Michael delivers twice as many daily papers each week as Sunday papers. How many of each type of paper does he deliver if he earns $13 each week?

Technology Options

Prentice Hall Technology

Software for Learners

• Math Blaster® Mystery*
• Interactive Student Tutorial, Chapter 1*

Teaching Resource Software

• Computer Item Generator 1-2
• Resource Pro™ Chapter 1*

Internet • For related mathematics activities, visit the Prentice Hall site at www.phschool.com/math.

*Available on CD-ROM only

Assignment Options for Exercises On Your Own

Core 1–5, 7, 8, 11
Extension 6, 9, 10

Use Mixed Review to maintain skills.

PRACTICE

Practice 1-2 *Problem-Solving Strategy: Make a Table*

Make a table to solve each problem.

1. How many ways are possible to make change for 36¢?
   24 ways

2. Tom has a $20 bill, a $10 bill, a $5 bill, and a $1 bill. List the total costs possible for items he could buy if he receives no change.
   $1, $5, $6, $10, $11, $15, $16, $20, $21, $25, $26, $30, $31, $35, $36

3. A club began with 4 members. At each meeting every member must bring 2 new people. These new people become members. How many members will there at the fourth meeting?
   108 members

4. Colleen is making raffle tickets for the school's give-away drawing. She wants to use the digits 2, 5, 7, and 8 to make three-digit numbers. How many different three-digit numbers can she make if she can use each digit any number of times?
   64 numbers

Use any strategy to solve each problem. Show all your work.

5. Gavin sells popcorn at basketball games. A large box costs $.75, and a small box costs $.40. One night he sold 45 boxes and collected a total of $25. How many large and how many small boxes of popcorn did Gavin sell?
   20 large, 25 small boxes

6. Find the total number of triangles in the figure. **27 triangles**

7. How many squares are contained in the floor tile below? **14 squares**

8. Find the smallest number that meets all of the following criteria. **58**
   - when you divide the number by 5 there are 3 left over
   - when you divide the number by 8 there are 2 left over
   - when you divide the number by 9 there are 4 left over

In copymaster and workbook formats

RETEACHING

Reteaching 1-2 *Problem-Solving Strategy: Make a Table*

Some problems contain many pieces of data.

Read A stadium sells buttons, pins, and pennants. The prices are $1.25 for a button, $.54 for a pin, and $4.39 for a pennant. Audrey wants to buy an equal number of each. What is the greatest number she can buy without spending more than $20.00?

Plan To solve the problem, it may help to put the data into a table.

	1	2	3	4
Buttons	$1.25	$2.50	$3.75	$5.00
Pins	$.54	$1.08	$1.62	$2.16
Pennants	$4.39	$8.78	$13.17	$17.56
Total	$6.18	$12.36	$18.54	$24.72

Solve Read the totals from the table. Audrey can buy 3 of each without spending more than $20.00.

Look Back You can estimate to check whether your answer is reasonable. $4 + $2 + $13 is less than $20.

Solve. Use the information from the table above.

1. How much would it cost to buy 9 pins? There are several ways to find the total in the table.
   a. $9 \times \$.54 = $ **$4.86**
   b. $3 \times \$1.62 = $ **$4.86**
   c. $2 \times \$2.16 + \$.54 = $ **$4.86**

2. How much more do 4 pennants cost than 4 buttons?
   a. Cost of 4 pennants: **$17.56**
   b. Cost of 4 buttons: **$5.00**
   c. Subtract: $17.56 − $5.00 = **$12.56**

3. Suppose Audrey has $35.00 to spend. What is the greatest number of items she can buy if she buys an equal number of each?
   15 items; 5 of each

4. How much will it cost to buy 30 pennants?
   $131.70

5. Pins are packed 12 to a box. Pennants are packed 10 to a carton.
   a. How much will 3 boxes of pins cost? **$19.44**
   b. How much will 2 boxes of pins and 1 carton of pennants cost? **$56.86**

Reteaching

ENRICHMENT

Minds on Math Transparency

1-2

I am a 2-digit number. The difference between the product of me and myself and the sum of me and myself is 99. What number am I?

11

See Solution Key for worked-out answers.

10

CONNECTION TO SCIENCE Encourage students to discuss how they might use tables to organize, compare, or show results from experiments in science classes.

WRAP UP

IDENTIFYING THE BIG IDEA Ask students to explain how *tables* can help them solve problems.

LESSON QUIZ

Ask students to make a table to solve each problem.

1. You have five coins that total 42¢. Two coins are the same. Describe the number and types of coins that you have. **1 quarter, 1 nickel, 1 dime, and 2 pennies**

2. You have quarters, nickels, and pennies. How many ways can you make 32¢? **9**

---

5. *Games* Chris's favorite game uses three Velcro darts and a Velcro board like the one at the right. When a dart lands on a line, the higher value is counted. What possible scores can Chris get if all three darts hit the board?
   45, 40, 35, 30, 25, 20, 15

6. *Fruits* Six apples weigh the same as two grapefruits and two kiwis. A grapefruit weighs the same as eight kiwis. How many kiwis weigh as much as one apple? **3 kiwis**

7. *Transportation* Buses leave Boston for New York every 40 min. The first bus leaves at 5:10 A.M. What is the departure time closest to 12:55 P.M.? **1:10 P.M.**

8. *Supplies* Carlos spent $13 on pens, pencils, and notebooks. Pens cost $2. Pencils cost $1. Notebooks cost $4. How many combinations of school supplies could Carlos have bought?
   6 combinations

9. *Jewelry* You want to make a single length of chain from the links shown below. Find the least number of links that must be opened and then closed to do this.
   2 links

10. Sue, Kelly, and Carmen earned degrees in engineering, nursing, and law. Sue and the engineer plan to share an apartment. The nurse helps Carmen pack. Kelly's law firm specializes in corporate law. Who is the engineer?
    Carmen

11. *Clothes* Ken has a blue shirt, a yellow shirt, a white shirt, a pair of black pants, and a pair of jeans. How many different outfits does Ken have to choose from? **6 outfits**

12. | Student Heights | Frequency |
    |-----------------|-----------|
    | 52 | 1 |
    | 53 | 3 |
    | 54 | 1 |
    | 55 | 3 |
    | 57 | 1 |
    | 60 | 1 |

Mixed Review

Use the following data. *(Lesson 1-1)*
Student heights (inches): 53, 55, 60, 53, 57, 55, 52, 54, 53, 55

12. Make a frequency table.
    See above right.

13. Make a line plot.
    See back of book.

14. Find the range.
    8 in.

15. *Book Club* Andrés is starting a book club. He is the only member now, but he plans to have each member find an additional 3 new members each month. How many members does Andrés expect to have after 6 months? *(Previous Course)*
    4,096 members

In Lesson 1-3, students find the mean of a set of data. This toolbox reviews whole number division, which students use to find the mean for each set of data. Later in this course, students will learn to write remainders as decimals or fractions.

ERROR ALERT! Students may have difficulty estimating a quotient before they begin

dividing. **Remediation:** Remind students to round the divisor and dividend to compatible numbers when estimating. Compatible numbers are easy to divide because they divide without a remainder. The most convenient compatible numbers are often multiples of 10 and 100.

ASSESSMENT Exercise 1 Have pairs of students compare their steps for Exercise 1 with the example steps. Circulate among students as they discuss why their steps are the same as or different from those of the

example. Ask students also to explain their choices of compatible numbers when making an estimate.

■ **ADDITIONAL PROBLEM**

Divide 9)270. Check your answer. **30**

SKILLS REVIEW

WHOLE NUMBER DIVISION

Before Lesson 1-3

Division is the opposite of multiplication. So you multiply the divisor by your estimate for each digit in the quotient. Then subtract. You repeat this step until you have a remainder that is less than the divisor.

■ **EXAMPLE**

Divide 23)1,158.

Step 1: Estimate the quotient.

$1{,}158 \div 23$ ⟵ The dividend is 1,158. The divisor is 23.

$1{,}200 \div 20 \approx 60$ ⟵ Mentally round 1,158 to the nearest hundred. Mentally round 23 to the nearest ten.

Step 2:

$$\begin{array}{r} 6 \\ 23\overline{)1158} \\ -138 \end{array}$$ ⟵ Try 6 tens.

⟵ $6 \times 23 = 138$
You cannot subtract so 6 tens is too much.

Step 3:

$$\begin{array}{r} 5 \\ 23\overline{)1158} \\ -115 \\ \hline 0 \end{array}$$ ⟵ Try 5 tens.

⟵ $5 \times 23 = 115$
⟵ Subtract.

Step 4:

$$\begin{array}{r} 50 \text{ R8} \\ 23\overline{)1158} \\ -115 \downarrow \\ \hline 08 \\ -0 \\ \hline 8 \end{array}$$

⟵ Bring down 8.
⟵ $0 \times 23 = 0$
⟵ Subtract. The remainder is 8.

Step 5: Check your answer.

First compare your answer to your estimate.
Since 50 R8 is close to 60, the answer is reasonable.
Then find $50 \times 23 + 8$.

Divide. Check your answer.

1. 7)212 **30 R2**
2. 9)376 **41 R7**
3. 3)280 **93 R1**
4. 8)541 **67 R5**
5. 6)483 **80 R3**

6. $1{,}058 \div 5$ **211 R3**
7. $3{,}018 \div 6$ **503**
8. $5{,}072 \div 7$ **724 R4**
9. $1{,}718 \div 4$ **429 R2**
10. $3{,}767 \div 6$ **627 R5**

11. $3{,}372 \div 67$ **50 R22**
12. 19)1,373 **72 R5**
13. 62)2,129 **34 R21**
14. $4{,}165 \div 59$ **70 R35**
15. 41)4,038 **98 R20**

16. $2{,}612 \div 31$ **84 R8**
17. 34)1,609 **47 R11**
18. $1{,}937 \div 48$ **40 R17**
19. 54)1,350 **25**
20. $1{,}850 \div 82$ **22 R46**

21. *Writing* Describe how to estimate a quotient. Use the words *dividend* and *divisor* in your description.
Round the dividend and the divisor to two numbers that are easy to divide mentally.

Teaching Notes

1 Focus

CONNECTING TO PRIOR KNOWLEDGE Ask students to give examples of when they have seen averages. **average grade for a course, batting averages** Have students name ways to find an average.

Lesson Planning Options

Prerequisite Skills

- adding and dividing whole numbers (precourse)
- ordering whole numbers (precourse)
- reading line plots (1-2)

Vocabulary/Symbols

average, mean, median, mode

Materials/Manipulatives

- calculator

Resources

 Student Edition

Skills Handbook, p. 541
Extra Practice, p. 522
Glossary/Study Guide

 Teaching Resources

Chapter Support File, Ch. 1
- Lesson Planner 1-3
- Practice 1-3, Reteaching 1-3
- Answer Masters 1-3
Teaching Aids Masters 1, 2
Glossary, Spanish Resources

 Transparencies

1, Minds on Math 1-3

Warm Up

Express each fraction as a decimal and then find their sum.
$\frac{1}{2}, \frac{1}{4}, \frac{1}{8}, \frac{1}{8}$
$0.5 + 0.25 + 0.125 + 0.125 = 1$

2 Teach

Work Together

Have students work in groups of five or six. Each student can start a list with his or her name. Then pass the lists around the group for every member to sign until all name lists are complete.

ALTERNATIVE METHOD An alternative method for finding the mean is to move letters from longer names to shorter names until all the names contain the same number of letters. Group together any left-over letters. Count the left-over letters, then divide by the number of names to get a fraction. Add this fraction to the new equal length for the names.

DIVERSITY This is a good opportunity to celebrate the diversity of students' names in spelling, sound, and origins.

DATA ANALYSIS Connection

1-3 Mean, Median, and Mode

What You'll Learn

1 To find the mean
2 To find the median or mode

...And Why

You can find the median length of comedy movies or discover which hobby is most popular.

Here's How

Look for questions that
- build understanding
✓ check understanding

Work Together

Finding Averages

Is your name longer than average? Let's find out!

1. Write the names of the students in your class on strips of graph paper as shown.

2. Find the average length of the names of the students in your group. Describe how your group found this number.

1–3. **Check students' work.**

3. **Analyze** Compare your work with other groups. Did everyone find the average length of the names the same way? Explain.

uri
Gregory
Daria
Miki
Angela

THINK AND DISCUSS

1 *Finding the Mean*

You are probably familiar with the word *average*. In mathematics, an average is called a mean. The **mean** is the sum of the data divided by the number of data items.

EXAMPLE 1 *Real-World Problem Solving*

Airplanes Use the data table at the left. Find the mean wingspan of the jet airliners.

Step 1: Find the sum of the data.

Step 2: Divide the sum by the number of data items.

Wingspan of Jet Airliners

Type	Wingspan (meters)
Airbus A330	60
McDonnell Douglas DCB Super 63	45
Boeing 707	44
Ilyushin IL-96-300	58
Ilyushin IL-62	43

Source: *The Cambridge Factfinder*

Method 1: Paper and Pencil

① 60
45
44
58
+ 43
___
250

②
```
   50
5)250
 - 25
 ___
  000
```

Method 2: Calculator

① 60 ⊞ 45 ⊞ 44 ⊞ 58 ⊞ 43 ⊟ *250*

② 250 ⊞ 5 ⊟ *50*

The mean wingspan of the jet airliners is 50 meters.

THINK AND DISCUSS

ESTIMATION Question 4a Remind students that they already know the sum of the wingspans of five other jets. They just need to add the new wingspan to the previous sum before dividing. Some students may also forget and divide by 5 again. Ask: *How many planes are in the new data set?* **6**

Question 6 Ask students to describe how a median number is like the median line on a highway. **Both are in the middle.**

■ ADDITIONAL EXAMPLES

FOR EXAMPLE 1
Margarita's test scores are 78, 85, 94, 88, and 90. Find the mean test score. **87**

FOR EXAMPLE 2
Tickets to a basketball game cost $12, $7, $50, $60, or $25, depending on where the seats are located and if the tickets are for an adult or a child. Find the median price of the basketball tickets. **$25**

FOR EXAMPLE 3
Students were surveyed about their favorite primary color. Their answers were blue, red, blue, yellow, yellow, blue, red, blue, yellow, blue, red, yellow. Find the mode. **blue**

Example 3 Mention to students that survey takers frequently use mode when reporting data on preferences or purchases.

VISUAL LEARNING Let students with a visual learning style create line plots to show the mode.

4. The wingspan of the Concorde is 26 meters. Suppose you include this value with the set of data in Example 1.
   a. ⬛*Estimation* Estimate the mean. Do you think the mean will be greater than or less than 50? **less than 50**
   b. ✔ *Try It Out* Find the mean. **46 m**

5. ✔ *Try It Out* Find the mean of each data set.
   a. 23, 25, 19, 20, 21, 23, 23 **22**   b. 6, 3, 4, 6, 4, 5, 6, 4, 7 **5**

Now you may assign Exercises 1–9, 34.

❷ *Finding the Median or Mode*

If the data set has an extreme high or low value, the median is a better measure to use. The **median** is the middle number in a set of ordered data.

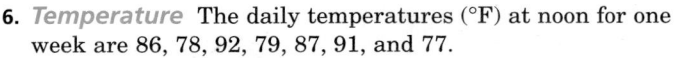

Order the data.

18 3 20 17 22 20 19   ⟶   3 17 18 **19** 20 20 22

median

6. *Temperature* The daily temperatures (°F) at noon for one week are 86, 78, 92, 79, 87, 91, and 77.
   a. Order the data values. **77, 78, 79, 86, 87, 91, 92**
   b. ✔ *Try It Out* Find the median. **86**

When there is an even number of data items, you can find the median by adding the two middle numbers and dividing by 2.

■ EXAMPLE 2   *Real-World Problem Solving*

Entertainment Find the median length of the comedy movies at the right.

Lengths of 10 Comedy Movies (min)
| 111 | 105 | 100 | 101 | 101 |
| 92 | 87 | 96 | 92 | 95 |

111 105 100 101 101 92 87 96 92 95 ⟵ List the data.

87 92 92 95 96 100 101 101 105 111 ⟵ Order the data.

⟶ Identify the middle numbers.

$\frac{96 + 100}{2} = 98$ ⟵ Add and divide by 2.

The median is 98.

7. ✔ *Try It Out* Find the median of each data set.
   a. 78, 90, 88, 76, 102, 79, 80   b. 10, 5, 7, 13, 14, 12, 12, 10
   80   **11**

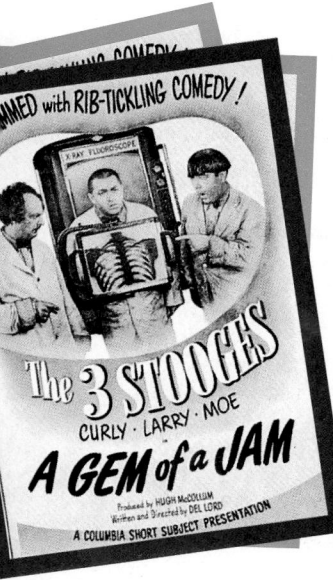

In the 1930s and early 1940s, the Three Stooges became popular in short films that played for 15–20 minutes before each feature film.

Technology Options

Prentice Hall Technology

 Software for Learners

- Hot Page™ 1*
- Math Blaster® Mystery*
- Interactive Student Tutorial, Chapter 1*

 Teaching Resource Software

- Computer Item Generator 1-3
- Resource Pro™ Chapter 1*

🔄 **Internet** • For related mathematics activities, visit the Prentice Hall site at www.phschool.com/math

*Available on CD-ROM only

Assignment Options for Exercises On Your Own

To provide flexible scheduling, this lesson can be subdivided into parts.

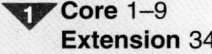**Core** 1–9
Extension 34

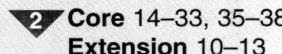**Core** 14–33, 35–38
Extension 10–13

Use Mixed Review to maintain skills.

Have a discussion about how means are used. You may want to start with these examples:

- **Media** describing an average consumer or voter concern, averaging reader profiles for marketing purposes
- **Household** averaging bill payments, salary, and expenses to plan a budget
- **Business** finding average sales to estimate business trends, comparing stocks, comparing employees' efficiency and wages

ERROR ALERT! Students may use the words *median* and *mode* incorrectly. **Remediation:** It might be helpful for students to use associations to keep the meanings clear: *medi*an means *mid*dle (median of a road), *mo*de sounds like *mo*st.

ASSESSMENT Ask students: *A baseball player recorded the number of hits she got in each game. Her record was 1, 3, 0, 1, 3, 2, 2, 1, 4, 3. Find the mean, median, and mode(s).* 2; 2; 1 and 3

EXTENSION If you have extended class periods or block scheduling, students may want to explore using a spreadsheet to help find mean, median, and mode. Students can enter a formula to find mean, can use the internal function to average, and can use the "sort" option to order data for finding median and mode.

---

pages 14–16   On Your Own

10. favorite month of year: June, July, December, July, July, September, August, December

11. player's scoring in basketball games: 15, 12, 9, 15, 32, 21, 23, 19, 22

12. hourly wages of bakery employees: $5.75, $5.75, $5.75, $5.75, $5.50, $6.50, $12

Data can also be described by the *mode*. The **mode** is the data value that appears most often. The mode is most helpful when the data are not numerical.

■ **EXAMPLE 3**   *Real-World Problem Solving*

The line plot shows the items collected by a group of students. Find the mode.

Collectibles

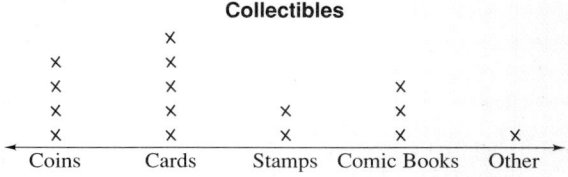
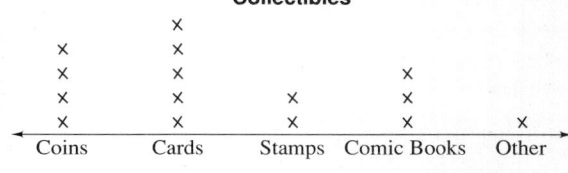

The mode is cards because it appears most often.

A set of data can have more than one mode. There is no mode when all the data items occur the same number of times.

Aja Henderson has a collection of over 1,000 books! Aja lends them out to neighborhood kids who can't get to the public library.

8. ▪*Look Back* Refer to Example 3. Suppose a student who collects stamps collects coins instead. Find the mode.
   coins and cards

9. What would a line plot look like if the data set had no mode?
   All stacks would have different heights.

10. ✔*Try It Out* Find the mean, median, and mode of each data set. 16; 16; no mode
   a. 15 12 20 13 17 19
   b. 95 80 92 91 98 94 94
      92; 94; 94

Now you may assign Exercises 10–33, 35–38.

EXERCISES *On Your Own*

Find the mean of each data set.

1. 12, 9, 11, 8, 9, 12, 9 10
2. 6, 5, 7, 5, 7, 6 6
3. 3, 2, 0, 2, 2, 3, 3, 1 2

4. 14, 18, 22, 19, 22, 9, 15 17
5. 18, 21, 19, 17, 19, 20 19
6. 125, 95, 115, 90, 100 105

7. 25, 13, 29, 26, 20, 19 22
8. 112, 112, 115, 109, 107 111
9. 0, 5, 25, 50, 75, 100, 25 40

Open-ended **Create a data set that is best described with the given measure. Then describe the data set.**

10. mode
11. mean
12. median
10–12. See margin for samples.

14

3 Practice/Assess

EXERCISES *On Your Own*

Exercises 10–12 If some students are having trouble getting started, ask them to think of everyday situations in which they see data reported in one of these forms.

Exercise 32 Ask students if they can also find the mean and the median of this data.

no Explain. You only find mean and median for numerical data.

CONNECTION TO SPORTS Exercise 34
Challenge students to research for other ways mean, median, or mode are used in sports.

WRAP UP

IDENTIFYING THE BIG IDEA Have students tell how to decide if the *mean*, *median*, or *mode* is most appropriate for a given situation.

PROJECT LINK Have students rephrase the questions using the terms from this lesson.

JOURNAL Have students include instructions and examples on how to find mean, median, and mode. Be sure they include finding the median for both an even number of data items and an odd number of data items.

---

13. *Music* The line plot shows the number of songs on 30 recently released CDs.

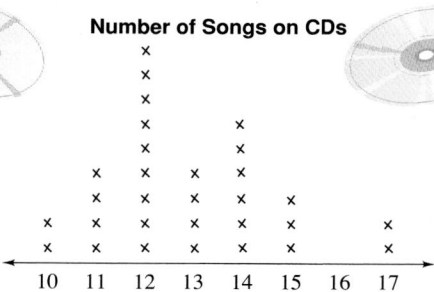

Number of Songs on CDs

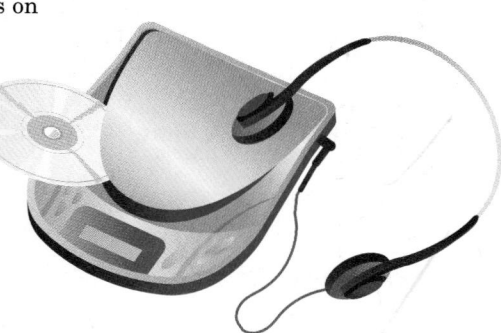

a. Find the median and mode. **12.5; 12**
b. *Writing* Would it make sense to use the mean to describe these data? Why or why not? **Answers may vary. Sample: No; the extreme values should not affect the rest of the data.**

Find the median of each data set.

14. 5, 7, 8, 7, 7, 5, 8 **7**

15. 14, 20, 24, 16, 20, 18 **19**

16. 88, 93, 87, 90, 88 **88**

17. 50, 52, 48, 52, 48, 52 **51**

18. 500, 450, 475, 450, 500 **475**

19. 820, 800, 775, 850 **810**

20. 350, 190, 40, 110, 230, 70 **150**

21. 17, 17, 17, 17, 17, 17 **17**

22. 5, 9, 5, 9, 5, 9 **7**

Find the mode of each data set.

23. 3, 2, 5, 2, 2, 5, 4, 3, 2 **2**

24. 100, 100, 100 **100**

25. 0, 1, 1, 1, 0, 1, 1, 0, 0, 0 **0 and 1**

26. 87, 92, 90, 89, 87, 91 **87**

27. 9, 10, 12, 9, 12, 11 **9 and 12**

28. 31, 28, 31, 30, 31, 30 **31**

29. 31, 31, 30, 31, 30, 31 **31**

30. T, H, T, T, H, H, H, T **T and H**

31. 5, 6, 9, 8, 4, 7, 10, 3, 11 **no mode**

32. fish, beef, vegetarian, chicken, chicken, beef, chicken **chicken**

33. **Choose A, B, C, or D.** Marc's teacher allows students to decide whether to record the mean, median, or mode of their test scores as their test score. Marc's score will be highest if he uses the mean. Which set of grades is Marc's? **C**
   A. 74, 80, 92, 82, 92 B. 74, 80, 74, 82, 85 C. 74, 80, 92, 85, 74 D. 74, 80, 70, 71, 80

34. *Sports* In Major League baseball, a baseball is used for an average of five pitches before it is replaced. Find seven numbers that have a mean of 5. **Sample: 2, 3, 4, 5, 6, 7, 8**

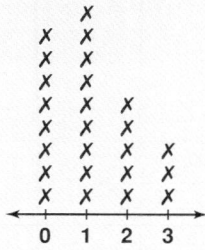

CHECKPOINT 1

Name _____ Class _____ Date _____

Checkpoint 1 *Lessons 1-1 through 1-3*

The Hickory Hill Hockey Club team had the following scores during its last season.

4 1 4 3 2 0 2 4 5 3 2
3 3 4 0 5 4 1 2 4 1 1 3

1. Make a frequency table for this set of data.
2. Make a line plot for this set of data.

Number	Tally	Frequency
0	II	2
1	IIII	4
2	IIII	4
3	IIII	5
4	IIII I	6
5	II	2

Use the data in the table for Exercises 3–5.

3. Find the mean. **33**
4. Find the median. **32**
5. Find the mode. **25**

Exercise Time

Day	Minutes Spent
Monday	32
Tuesday	47
Wednesday	25
Thursday	36
Friday	25

page 16   Checkpoint

4.

Grams of Fat	Frequency
0	8
1	9
2	5
3	3

5. Fat in Cereals (g)

Practice 1-3 Mean, Median, and Mode

Find the mean, median, and mode for each set of data.

1. 85, 91, 76, 85, 93 **86, 85, 85**

2. 72, 76, 73, 74, 75 **74, 74, no mode**

3. 5, 7, 9, 10, 9, 9, 10, 5 **8, 9, 9**

4. 129, 156, 118, 147, 131, 129 **135, 130, 129**

5. 86, 87, 95, 96, 88, 94, 98 **92, 94, no mode**

Use the tables for Exercises 6–11.

6. What is the mean height of the active volcanoes listed? (Find the mean to the nearest foot.)
   10,470 ft

7. What is the median height of the active volcanoes listed?
   9,705 ft

8. What is the mode of the heights of the active volcanoes listed?
   no mode

Active Volcanoes	
Name	**Height Above Sea Level (ft)**
Camaroon Mt.	13,354
Mount Erebus	12,450
Asama	8,300
Gerde	9,705
Sarychev	5,115
Ometepe	5,106
Fogo	9,300
Mt. Hood	11,245
Lascar	19,652

Source: The Universal Almanac

9. What is the mean of the wages listed?
   $11.57

10. What is the median of the wages listed?
    $14.41

11. What is the mode of the wages listed?
    no mode

Hourly Wages of Production Workers 1991 (includes benefits)	
Country	**Wage**
Austria	$17.47
Brazil	$2.55
Finland	$20.57
France	$15.26
Hong Kong	$3.58
Japan	$14.41
Mexico	$2.17
Spain	$12.65
United States	$15.45

Source: The Universal Almanac

Each student in a class has taken five tests. The teacher allows the students to pick the mean, median, or mode for each set of scores. Which average should each student pick in order to have the highest average?

12. 100, 87, 81, 23, 19 **median**

13. 90, 80, 74, 74, 72 **mean**

14. 80, 80, 70, 67, 68 **mode**

15. 75, 78, 77, 70, 70 **median**

16. 100, 47, 45, 32, 31 **mean**

17. 86, 86, 77, 14, 12 **mode**

18. 79, 78, 77, 76, 85 **mean**

19. 86, 80, 79, 70, 70 **median**

In copymaster and workbook formats

Reteaching 1-3 Mean, Median, and Mode

• The **mean** is the average of a set of numbers.
  74 + 77 + 80 + 81 + 85 + 87 + 94 + 94 = 672
  672 ÷ 8 = 84
  The mean math test grade is 84.

Math Test Grades	
Sharon	81
Rashid	94
Durrin	77
Nicole	80
Terry	74
Mei-lin	94
Kevin	87
Carlos	85

• **Median** means "middle." When the grades are arranged in order from least to greatest, there are two middle numbers.
  74, 77, 80, 81, 85, 87, 94, 94
  To find the median, add the two middle numbers and divide the total by 2.
  81 + 85 = 166
  166 ÷ 2 = 83
  The median grade is 83.

• The **mode** is the number that appears most often. For this data, 94 is the mode.

Find the mean of each data set.

1. 8, 6, 5, 9, 7, 13 **8**

2. 12, 10, 16, 14, 8, 24 **14**

3. 9, 12, 14, 6, 8, 5 **9**

4. 104, 126, 128, 100, 97 **111**

5. 86, 68, 70, 48, 66, 76 **69**

6. 65, 50, 95, 35, 75, 100 **70**

Find the median of each data set.

7. 5, 4, 7, 9, 8 **7**

8. 12, 16, 19, 14, 14, 18 **15**

9. 9, 19, 21, 13 **16**

10. 46, 38, 22, 48, 61 **46**

11. 60, 57, 53, 78, 44, 51 **55**

12. 8, 6, 6, 5, 8, 9 **7**

Find the mode of each data set.

13. 3, 4, 5, 5, 3, 5, 4, 2 **5**

14. 1, 2, 1, 1, 2, 2, 3, 1 **1**

15. 6, 8, 3, 8, 3, 9, 3 **3**

16. 33, 35, 34, 33, 35, 33 **33**

17. 98, 97, 98, 98, 97 **98**

18. 110, 121, 121, 110, 115, 117, 119 **110, 121**

Minds on Math Transparency

1-3

Two dogs stood on a hill. The little dog was the big dog's son, but the big dog wasn't the little dog's father. How is this possible?

The big dog was the little dog's mother.

See Solution Key for worked-out answers.

LESSON QUIZ

Find the mean.

1. 17, 27, 11, 8, 21, 15, 13 **16**

2. 117, 105, 99, 100, 94 **103**

Find the median.

3. 24, 31, 35, 27, 30, 29, 21 **29**

4. 300, 298, 405, 348, 411 **348**

Find the mode.

5. 24, 31, 29, 27, 30, 29, 21 **29**

6. red, blue, blue, pink, black, pink, yellow, white **blue and pink**

Which measure—mean, median, or mode—best describes the data set? Explain your reasoning.

Median; 114 affects the mean too much.

See below right.

35. 54, 63, 47, 114, 51

36. 40, 50, 45, 30, 35

37. blue, red, blue, blue, white
Mode; the data are not numeric.

38. 80, 80, 80, 55, 80
Mode; almost all the data items are the same.

JOURNAL
Describe mean, median, and mode. Provide an example for each description.

36. Mean; the extreme values are not that much different from the other data.

Mixed Review

Find each answer. (Previous Course)

39. 2,057 − 569 **1,488**

40. 114 × 12 **1,368**

41. 248 ÷ 8 **31**

42. 37 × 27 **999**

43. 1,001 ÷ 13 **77**

44. *Patterns* At one point on a mountain road, the elevation is 4,000 ft. Two miles up the road, the elevation is 5,200 ft. Suppose this pattern continues. Predict the elevation six miles up the road from the starting point. (Lesson 1-2) **7,600 ft**

CHAPTER PROJECT

PROJECT LINK: ANALYZING DATA

Order the responses of your classmates by popularity. Find the mean, median, and mode of the data. Determine which measure is more typical of the responses. Explain why.

Check students' work.

✓ CHECKPOINT 1

Communications Use the table at the right.

1. Find the mean number of stations. **20**

2. Find the median. **20**   3. Find the mode. **15**

Nutrition Use the data below for Exercises 4 and 5.
Grams of fat per serving for 25 popular breakfast cereals:
0, 1, 1, 3, 1, 1, 2, 2, 0, 3, 1, 3, 2, 0, 1, 0, 2, 1, 1, 0, 0, 0, 2, 1, 0

4. Make a frequency table.   5. Make a line plot.
   4–5. See margin p. 15.

6. How many possible ways are there to make $1 without using pennies? **29 ways**

States with the Most Public Radio Stations

State	Number of Stations
Alaska	15
California	23
Illinois	15
Michigan	20
Minnesota	17
New York	33
Ohio	20
Texas	15
Wisconsin	22

Source: The Top 10 of Everything

PROBLEM SOLVING PRACTICE ★★

This page provides problems for students to solve using their knowledge of measurement, rates, graphs, average, and three-dimensional figures. Allow students to use any method they find helpful.

Exercise 4 Encourage students to draw a diagram of the box or use a cube to help them determine the number of sides it has.

Exercise 5 To help students decide which operation to choose, ask them if the number of roses in each group is greater than or less than 48. **less than** Then ask which operations with whole numbers result in smaller answers. **subtraction and division**

USING MANIPULATIVES Exercise 5 Have students use counters to model the roses.

COOPERATIVE GROUPS Exercise 8 Have students work in small groups. Group members can discuss the choices and work together to choose the correct answer.

PROBLEM SOLVING PRACTICE ★★★★★

Choose the best answer.

1. Arturo played three games of miniature golf. His scores were 89, 84, and 94. What was his mean (average) score for the 3 games? **B**

   A. 84   B. 89   C. 94   D. 287

2. Which measurement is most reasonable for the height of a refrigerator? **H**

   F. 2 inches   G. 2 feet
   H. 2 yards   J. 2 miles

3. If Jeremy grows 3 more inches, he will be 6 feet tall. How tall is Jeremy now? **C**

   A. 57 inches   B. 63 inches
   C. 69 inches   D. 75 inches

4. An ordinary shoe box has the top removed so that it is an open-topped box. How many sides does the box have after the top is removed? **H**

   F. 3   G. 4   H. 5   J. 6

5. Forty-eight roses are to be split into 8 equal groups. Which number sentence would you use to find the number of roses in each group? **D**

   A. 48×8 B. $48 + 6$
   C. $48 - 8$ D. $48 \div 8$

Please note that items 6–9 have *five* answer choices.

6. A public library lent the following numbers of books each day for a week. Find the median. **H**

   12 29 14 18 26 26 22

   F. 18   G. 21   H. 22   J. 26   K. Not Here

7. Melitha can make a silk bouquet in 15 to 20 minutes. What is a reasonable number of bouquets she can make in 240 minutes? **C**

   A. less than 8
   B. between 8 and 11
   C. between 12 and 16
   D. between 17 and 20
   E. more than 20

8. The graph shows the number of laps Mackenzie swam each day.

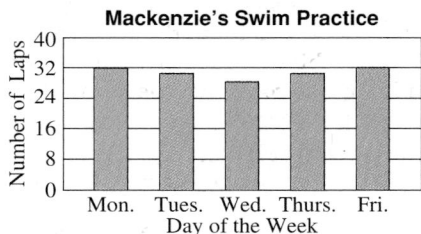

Mackenzie's Swim Practice

How many total laps did Mackenzie swim? **J**

   F. 32   G. 30
   H. 142   J. 152
   K. Not Here

9. Paul is taking a trip. His plane ticket will cost $198. His hotel will cost $65 per night. He budgets $35 per day for food and extras. He has saved $1,200. What else do you need to know to find if he has saved enough? **C**

   A. the cost of luggage
   B. the number of rooms available
   C. the length of the vacation stay
   D. the number of flights per day
   E. the cost of plays he will attend

1 Focus

CONNECTING TO PRIOR KNOWLEDGE Ask students who are familiar with spreadsheets to share ideas about the purpose of spreadsheets.

Lesson Planning Options

Prerequisite Skills

- finding the mean (1-4)

Vocabulary/Symbols
spreadsheet, cell, formula

Materials/Manipulatives
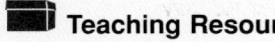
- calculator
- computer
- spreadsheet
  software

Resources

Student Edition

Skills Handbook, p. 538
Extra Practice, p. 522
Glossary/Study Guide

Teaching Resources

Chapter Support File, Ch. 1
- Lesson Planner 1-4
- Practice 1-4, Reteaching 1-4
- Alternative Activity 1-4
- Answer Masters 1-4
Teaching Aids Master 5
Glossary, Spanish Resources

Transparencies

4, 5, Minds on Math 1-4

Warm Up

Coach Brown bought six t-shirts for her volleyball players for $47.88. What was the price per shirt?
$7.98

2 Teach

THINK AND DISCUSS

Use the spreadsheet table to help students understand these points.

- You describe cells by naming the column letter and row number. Every cell in column D has D and a number in its name. Every cell in row 2 has a letter and 2 in its name.

- The cells in the left column identify the type of music. The cells in the top row identify the disk number.

AEP Many students confuse *columns* and *rows*. Have students find pictures of buildings with columns. Also have them find pictures of items in rows, such as stadium seats or kernels on a corn cob.

TACTILE LEARNING **Question 1** Have students use their index fingers to trace column D and row 4 at the same time. Then

---

1-4 Using Spreadsheets to Organize Data

What You'll Learn
1. To organize data in a spreadsheet
2. To create formulas for spreadsheets

...And Why
Spreadsheets can help you organize data about CDs.

Here's How
Look for questions that
- build understanding
- check understanding

THINK AND DISCUSS

1 Using Spreadsheets

A compact disc can hold nearly 80 minutes of music. Do some types of CDs contain more music than other types?

You can use a **spreadsheet** to organize and analyze data. A **cell** is the spreadsheet box where a row and a column meet.

■ **EXAMPLE 1** *Real-World Problem Solving*

Music The spreadsheet below shows the lengths of 15 CDs from five different categories. Identify the value of cell B5.

column B

	A	B	C	D	E
1	Music Type	Disk 1 (min)	Disk 2 (min)	Disk 3 (min)	Mean Length (min)
2	Rock/Pop	40	44	45	43
3	Rap	48	53	55	52
4	Country	32	34	30	32
5	Classical	45	54	51	50
6	Jazz	41	53	44	46

row 5 → (cell B5)

The value in cell B5 is 45.

have pairs of students give each other cell names to trace and find.

ERROR ALERT! **Questions 1 and 2**
Students may try to use the letters A–F and numbers 1–6 as data. **Remediation:** Make sure students understand that these letters and numbers identify columns and rows.

■ **ADDITIONAL EXAMPLES**

FOR EXAMPLE 1
a. Name the value of cell B2. **40**

b. Which type of music has the greatest mean length. **classical** In which cell is that value recorded? **E5**

FOR EXAMPLE 2
Write a formula to find the mean length of all the CDs in the Disk 2 column.
(C2+C3+C4+C5+C6)/6

Question 3 Explore the fact that a spreadsheet uses cell names. If you change the data in the cell, the spreadsheet recalculates the formula using the new data.

Question 4b Remind students that mean length is the mean of the CD playing times.

CONNECTING TO THE STUDENTS' WORLD
Encourage students to create a spreadsheet using their own CDs or tapes. Make sure they choose a manageable number of CDs or tapes. Have students work with a partner to determine different categories.

CONNECTION TO CAREERS Have students add to the list of how spreadsheets may be used in the following jobs.

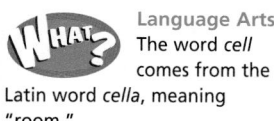
Language Arts
The word *cell* comes from the Latin word *cella*, meaning "room."

Source: *The Oxford Dictionary of English Etymology*

1. a.  **Try It Out** What is the value of cell D4 in Example 1? What does this number mean?
 b. What cells are in row 2? **rock/pop CDs**
1a. 30 min; country disk 3 is 30 min long.
2. a. **Look Back** Which cell in Example 1 contains the greatest value? The least value? **C5; D4**
 b. What type of music is on the CD that contains the greatest amount of music? The least amount of music?
 rap; country

Now you may assign Exercises 1–8, 15–20, 29.

2 **Creating Formulas**

A computer automatically fills in the values for a cell of a spreadsheet if you tell it what calculations to do. A **formula** is a statement of a mathematical relationship. You can use a formula to tell the computer what to do.

■ **EXAMPLE 2**

Use the spreadsheet shown in Example 1.
a. Describe how to calculate the value of E2 without using a computer.

Without using a computer, find the mean of the values in row 2.

$$\frac{40 + 44 + 45}{3} = \frac{129}{3} = 43$$

The mean of the values in row 2 is 43.

b. *Algebra* Write the formula for cell E2.

To write the formula, use cell names instead of values.

Enter =(B2+C2+D2)/3 into cell E2.

4a. = (B3 + C3 + D3) / 3;
 = (B4 + C4 + D4) / 3;
 = (B5 + C5 + D5) / 3;
 = (B6 + C6 + D6) / 3

TECHNOLOGY HINT
You can substitute appropriate values into each cell to see what happens to the value in cell E4.

3. ⁞*Explain* Why are cell names used instead of numbers?
Answers may vary. Sample: The values in the cells may change.
4. Use the spreadsheet in Example 1.
 a. ✔ *Try It Out* Write the formulas for cells E3 through E6.
 b. Find the mean lengths for each of the five types of music.
 43; 52; 32; 50; 46
5. ⁞*What If . . .* Explain what will happen to the value in E4 if each of the following occurs.
 a. the value in cell C4 increases **increases**
 b. the value in cell B4 decreases **decreases**
 c. the value in cell B3 increases **does not change**

Now you may assign Exercises 9–14, 21–28.

Technology Options

Prentice Hall Technology

Software for Learners
- Math Blaster® Mystery*
- Interactive Student Tutorial, Chapter 1*

Teaching Resource Software
- Computer Item Generator 1-4
- Resource Pro™ Chapter 1*

Internet • For related mathematics activities, visit the Prentice Hall site at www.phschool.com/math

Available on CD-ROM only

Assignment Options for Exercises On Your Own

To provide flexible scheduling, this lesson can be subdivided into parts.

▼ **Core** 1–8, 15–20
 Extension 29

▼ **Core** 9–12, 21–28
 Extension 13, 14

Use Mixed Review to maintain skills.

- Storekeeper record and average sales
- Teacher record and average grades

EXTENSION If you have block scheduling or extended class periods, let students use a computer spreadsheet application. Encourage students to organize and calculate data from science class, sports score reports, or class surveys.

3 Practice/Assess

EXERCISES *On Your Own*

AUDITORY LEARNING Tell students to read the cell names aloud to themselves as they move through the spreadsheet.

ASSESSMENT Have students explain why the cells in row 1 or column A for each of the spreadsheets do not have values. **These cells label the rows and columns.**

Exercise 14 Have students use cell values of 80 or greater to see what happens to the mean score.

WRAP UP

IDENTIFYING THE BIG IDEA Ask: *How can spreadsheets help you work with data?*

JOURNAL Suggest that students make a sample spreadsheet in their journals to refer to when they need it.

---

pages 20–21 On Your Own

21. Subtract B2 from C2.

22. Multiply the value in D2 by 6.

23. Multiply the value in D6 by 6, or add E2, E3, E4, and E5.

24. Divide the value in D6 by 4.

25. Subtract B5 from C5.

26. Multiply the value in D7 by 6, or divide the value in E6 by 4.

27. $= C2 - B2; = C3 - B3; = C4 - B4; = C5 - B5; = D2 + D3 + D4 + D5; = D6 / 4; = D2 * 6; = D3 * 6; = D4 * 6; = D5 * 6; = D6 * 6; = D7 * 6;$

EXERCISES *On Your Own*

Use the spreadsheet below for Exercises 1–14.

Each group of students created a video and received scores for originality, effort, and quality. Suppose their teacher entered all the data, but a "bug" in the program erased some of the data.

	A	B	C	D	E	F		E
1	Group	Originality	Effort	Quality	Total	Mean Score		Total
2	Red	90	85	80		85		255
3	Orange	90	90	60		80		240
4	Yellow	95	100	75		90		270
5	Green	65	80	80		75		225
6	Blue	85	85	85		85		255

Identify the cell or cells that indicate each category.

1. Effort
   column C

2. Mean Score
   column F

3. Mean Score for Red
   F2

4. Green
   row 5

5. Total for Yellow
   E4

6. Originality
   column B

7. Quality for Blue
   D6

8. Effort for Orange
   C3

9. Write the formulas that the teacher could have used to determine the values for cells E2 through E6.
   $= B2 + C2 + D2; = B3 + C3 + D3; = B4 + C4 + D4; = B5 + C5 + D5; = B6 + C6 + D6$

10. **Choose A, B, or C.** Which formula could the teacher *not* have used to find the value for cell F2? **B**
    A. $=E2/3$
    B. $=(B2+B3+B4)/3$
    C. $=(B2+C2+D2)/3$

11. *Writing* Explain how to find the value in cell D3.
    Multiply the mean in cell F3 by 3. Then subtract the values in B3 and C3.

12. a. *Technology* Copy and complete the spreadsheet above. **See above.**
    b. Which group created the most original video? **yellow**
    c. Which group put the least effort into creating their video? **green**
    d. Which group did the best job overall? Explain.
       Yellow; yellow has the highest mean score.

13. *Reasoning* Was it necessary to include column E in the spreadsheet to determine the mean score for each group? Explain. **No; you could use the formulas for the mean directly in column F.**

14. *Number Sense* Why does the value in cell B5 have to be less than 80? **Each of the other scores is 80 and the mean is less than 80.**

LESSON QUIZ

Have students use the spreadsheet on page 20 to answer these questions.

1. The value for E2 is 255. Which formula can help you find the value of C2? **b.**
   a. 255−(B2−D2)
   b. 255−(B2+D2)
   c. 255+(B2+D2)

2. The value of E5 is 225. What formula would not help you find the value of B5? **c.**
   a. 225−(C5+D5)
   b. 225−(D5+C5)
   c. 225−(D5−C5)

3. What value should cell D3 contain if the orange group mean is not 80 but 75? **45**

Use the spreadsheet below for Exercises 15–29.

Suppose a student works a part-time job and makes $6 per hour. The spreadsheet below shows a typical schedule for a week.

	A	B	C	D	E
1	Day	Time In (P.M.)	Time Out (P.M.)	Hours Worked	Amount Earned
2	9/15	3	5	2	12
3	9/17	4	6	2	12
4	9/19	3	6	3	18
5	9/20	1	6	5	30
6			Total:	12	72
7			Mean:	3	18

Write the value for the given cell.

15. C2 5   **16.** C5 6   **17.** B4 3   **18.** B2 3   **19.** C3 6   **20.** B5 1

Describe how to calculate the value of the given cell.   21–26. See margin p. 20.

21. D2   **22.** E2   **23.** E6   **24.** D7   **25.** D5   **26.** E7

27. Write the formulas for the cells in columns D and E.
   See margin p. 20.

28. a. *Computer* Make a spreadsheet like the one above. Enter formulas in columns D and E. **See Exercise 27 for formulas.**
   b. Copy or print the completed spreadsheet.
      See above.

29. a. How much does this student earn in a typical week? **$72**
   b. Which cell tells you this? **E6**

> **JOURNAL**
> Summarize what you know about spreadsheets. Include instructions for writing formulas using cells.

Mixed Review

Use the data 37, 11, 15, 16, 19, 11, 13, 20, and 11 to find the following. *(Lessons 1-1 and 1-3)*

30. range 26   **31.** mean 17   **32.** median 15   **33.** mode 11

34. *Temperature* At 9:00 P.M., the temperature was 42°F. By midnight, it had dropped 8 degrees. By 10:00 A.M., it had risen 15 degrees. Find the temperature at 10:00 A.M.
(Previous Course) **49°F**

PRACTICE

Practice 1-4 *Using Spreadsheets to Organize Data*

Gervase works after school and on weekends at a pet store, where he is paid $5 per hour. He uses the following spreadsheet to keep track of the time he works and the money he earns.

	A	B	C	D	E
1	Day	Time In (P.M.)	Time Out (P.M.)	Hours Worked	Amount Earned
2	Monday	4	7		
3	Tuesday	4	7		
4	Thursday	4	8		
5	Saturday	1	9		
6			Total		

1. How can the value of cell D2 be calculated?
   =C2−B2

2. How can the value of cell E2 be calculated?
   =5*D2

3. Write the formula to find the value of cell D6.
   =D2+D3+D4+D5

4. Write the formula to find the value of cell E6.
   =5*D6 or =E2+E3+E4+E5

5. How many hours does Gervase work in a week?
   18 h

6. How much does Gervase earn in a week?
   $90

7. Determine Gervase's weekly earnings if he receives a $1 per hour raise.
   $108

8. Determine Gervase's weekly earnings if he receives a $1 per hour raise and works 4 hours on Friday night.
   $132

9. Rosaria, Alphonse, John, and Nancy went together to buy a car for $6,000. John paid half as much as the other three paid altogether. Rosaria paid one-third as much as the other three paid. Alphonse paid one-fourth as much as the other three paid. How much did each person pay? Make a spreadsheet as needed to help you solve the problem.
   John $2,000; Rosaria $1,500; Alphonse $1,200; Nancy $1,300

In copymaster and workbook formats

RETEACHING

Reteaching 1-4 *Using Spreadsheets to Organize Data*

Party Pals has party equipment for rent. The company uses a **spreadsheet** to keep track of the number of hours its equipment is rented.

	A	B	C	D	E	F
1	Machine	Fri.	Sat.	Sun.	Total	Mean Rental Time
2	Party Popcorner	4	8	6		
3	Juice Fountain	0	3	3		
4	Soft Ice Cream Machine	8	9	4		
5	Pretzel Oven	1	6	5		

- A **cell** is the name for the box where a column and row meet. In column C, you find the cells C1, C2, C3, and so on. C2 shows 8. Its value is 8 hours.

- Missing values can be found by telling the spreadsheet what calculation to do. The value for cell E3 can be found by using the formula =B3+C3+D3.

Identify the cell or cells that indicate each category.

1. machines rented
   A2–A5

2. rental times for Saturday
   C2–C5

3. total rental hours for the Popcorner
   E2

4. mean rental time for the pretzel oven
   F5

Write the value for the given cell.

5. B5   **6.** C4   **7.** D3   **8.** B3   **9.** D5
   1 hour   9 hours   3 hours   0 hours   5 hours

Solve.

10. How can you calculate the value of cell E4?
   Add B4 + C4 + D4.

11. Write the formula to find the value of cell E5.
   =B5+C5+D5

12. Write the formula to find the value of cell E2.
   =B2+C2+D2

13. Write the formula to find the value of cell F5.
   =E5/3 or =B5+C5+D5/3

ENRICHMENT

Minds on Math Transparency   1-4

I am a 3-digit palindrome. I do not change when my digits are reversed. My first digit is twice my middle digit. The sum of my digits is 10. What palindrome am I?

424

See *Solution Key* for worked-out answers.

21

1-5 Teaching Notes

Answers may vary. Sample: to help you understand data more quickly

graph represent? dollars per ton of recyclable paper

1 Focus

CONNECTING TO PRIOR KNOWLEDGE Ask students to describe graphs they have seen. **Answers may vary. Sample: graphs of budget, height graphs, and other examples of bar, line, or circle graphs** Then ask students to tell the purpose of the graphs.

2 Teach

THINK AND DISCUSS

Example 1 Ask students:

• *What information is at the bottom of the graph?* **types of recyclable paper**

• *What do the numbers on the left side of the*

VISUAL LEARNING Example 1 Ask which bar in the graph is the shortest and which is the longest. **newspaper; white** Ask students to estimate how many of the short bars it would take to form the longest bar. **about 18** Ask students to explain how they solved this problem.

AUDITORY LEARNING Example 2 Have students read the labels and title on the line graph aloud to help them understand the graph.

Lesson Planning Options

Prerequisite Skills
• understanding percentages (precourse)

Vocabulary/Symbols
bar graph, line graph, circle graph

Materials/Manipulatives
• calculator   • dot paper
• index cards

Resources

 Student Edition

Skills Handbook, p. 536
Extra Practice, p. 522
Glossary/Study Guide

 Teaching Resources

Chapter Support File, Ch. 1
• Lesson Planner 1-5
• Practice 1-5, Reteaching 1-5
• Answer Masters 1-5
Teaching Aids Masters 1, 2
Glossary, Spanish Resources

 Transparencies
1, Minds on Math 1-5

Warm Up

Mari packaged 14 seashells in a box. If she had 360 seashells, how many full boxes did she have? How many shells were left over after all the boxes had been filled? **25; 10**

22

ALGEBRA Connection

1-5 Reading and Understanding Graphs

What You'll Learn

▼1 To read and understand bar and line graphs

▼2 To read and understand circle graphs

...And Why

Reading graphs can help you discover information about recycling, in-line skating, and playing an instrument.

Here's How

Look for questions that
⠿ build understanding
✔ check understanding

 Paper has been made from recycled materials since early times. The Chinese invented paper in A.D. 105, using discarded rags and fishing nets. Trees were not cut down for paper-making until the 1850s.

Source: Origins of Everything Under, and Including, the Sun

THINK AND DISCUSS

▼1 *Reading Bar and Line Graphs*

You can display data using graphs. The type of graph you choose depends on the type of data you have collected and the idea you want to communicate. A **bar graph** is used to compare amounts.

■ **EXAMPLE 1** *Real-World Problem Solving*

Recycling Use the bar graph below. How much money is earned by recycling newspapers?

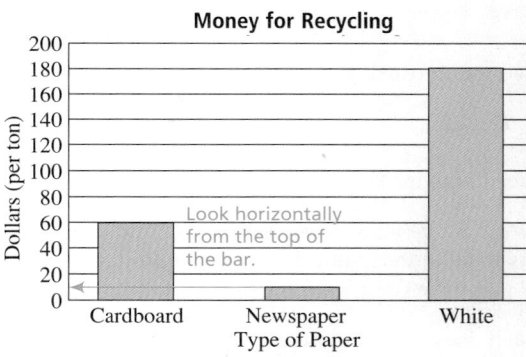

Money for Recycling

Look horizontally from the top of the bar.

Recycling newspapers earns $10 per ton.
white, cardboard, newspaper

1. **a.** ⠿*Look Back* Refer to Example 1. Order the types of paper from highest to lowest dollar amount per ton.
   b. How does the bar graph allow you to make these comparisons quickly? **Order the bars from tallest to shortest.**
   c. ⠿*Analyze* Describe the relationship between the heights of the bars and the dollars per ton of paper. **The taller the bar, the greater the amount.**

2. ✔*Try It Out* How much is cardboard worth? How much is white paper worth? **$60 per ton; $180 per ton**

3. ⠿*What If . . .* Refer to Example 1. A neighborhood collected 15 tons of newspaper. How much money will they earn? **$150**

Question 4 Explain that the line graph makes the trend more apparent than does a table of data.

■ ADDITIONAL EXAMPLES

FOR EXAMPLE 1

If a club collects 3 tons of white ledger paper, how much money will they receive? **$540**

If they collect half a ton of cardboard boxes, how much money will they receive? **$30**

FOR EXAMPLE 2

Between what two years was there the smallest increase in the number of in-line skaters? **1995 and 1996**

FOR EXAMPLE 3

Estimate the percentage of amateur musicians who are guitar players. **about 25%**

CONNECTION TO SOCIAL STUDIES Discuss how social scientists use graphs in areas such as geography and government. Start with these examples: displaying census information, describing a budget, displaying categories of government spending, comparing populations, comparing types of land in different regions, and tracking population growth.

A **line graph** shows how an amount changes over time.

■ **EXAMPLE 2**   *Real-World Problem Solving*

In-Line Skating Use the line graph below. How many in-line skaters were there in 1994?

5a. 10 million skaters
 b. 15 million skaters
 c. 27 million skaters
 d. 31 million skaters

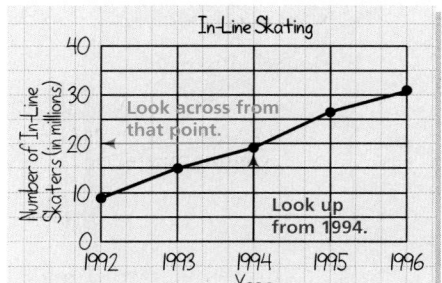

Source: IISA

There were about 20 million in-line skaters in 1994.

4. ⬛*Look Back* What trend does the line graph above show? Explain. **The number of in-line skaters increases every year.**
5a–d. See above left.
5. ✔ *Try It Out* Use the line graph in Example 2. Estimate how many in-line skaters there were in the year given.
   a. 1992   **b.** 1993   **c.** 1995   **d.** 1996
Now you may assign Exercises 1–3, 6–9, 16–18.

▼**2** *Reading Circle Graphs*

A **circle graph** compares parts to a whole. The entire circle represents the whole. Each wedge represents a part of the whole.

■ **EXAMPLE 3**   *Real-World Problem Solving*

Music Use the circle graph at the right. What instrument do more amateur musicians play than any other?

More amateur musicians play the piano than any other instrument.

Instruments Played by Amateurs

Source: *USA Today*

Technology Options

Prentice Hall Technology

 Software for Learners

• Hot Page™ 2*
• Math Blaster® Mystery*
• Interactive Student Tutorial, Chapter 1*

Teaching Resource Software

• Computer Item Generator 1–5
• Resource Pro™ Chapter 1*

Internet • For related mathematics activities, visit the Prentice Hall site at www.phschool.com/math.

*Available on CD-ROM only

Assignment Options for Exercises On Your Own

To provide flexible scheduling, this lesson can be subdivided into parts.

▼**1** **Core** 1–3, 6–9, 16, 17
   Extension 18

▼**2** **Core** 4, 10–15
   Extension 5

Use Mixed Review to maintain skills.

ASSESSMENT Have pairs of students work together. Each pair is to pick a different type of graph (bar, line, circle, etc.). The group then acts as salespersons for the graph they have picked by explaining:

- the components of the graph
- what this type of graph looks like
- why one would want to use this graph
- examples of this type of graph

Work Together

ERROR ALERT! Questions 8 and 9
Students may have trouble understanding when to use a bar graph or a line graph.
Remediation: Point out to students that both graphs display amounts. However, the focus of the bar graph is to compare total amounts. The line graph connects the amounts so you can see more easily the increase or decrease.

OPEN-ENDED Question 9 Have students tell why they chose a particular graph for the situation.

3 Practice/Assess

EXERCISES *On Your Own*

Exercise 2 Ask students if it is necessary to know the exact area in square miles to answer the question. Explain. **No; you only need to look at the bars to find two values that are about the same.**

 Angel Falls is the highest waterfall in the world. It is located in Venezuela and is about 1,000 m high.

Source: *The Information Please Almanac*

6. ✔ *Try It Out* Use the circle graph in Example 3. What instrument do the fewest amateur musicians play? **drums**

7. ⚫*Reasoning* Describe the relationship between the size of the circle wedges and the number of musicians in Example 3.
The more musicians, the wider the wedge.

Work Together — *Choosing the Most Appropriate Graph*

Work with a partner.

8a. Circle graph; students from each grade are parts of the whole chorus.

b. Line graph; graph shows change over time.

c. Bar graph; you use the graph to compare quantities.

8. ⚫*Reasoning* Choose the most appropriate type of graph to display each set of data. Support your answer.
  a. students from each grade that are in the chorus
  b. school enrollment for each year from 1995 to the present
  c. heights of the ten highest waterfalls in the world

9. ⚫*Open-ended* Describe two situations that would best be displayed by each type of graph. Write each description on a separate index card. Then ask your partner to identify the most appropriate graph for each situation.
  a. bar graph **b.** line graph **c.** circle graph
  a–c. Check students' work.

Now you may assign Exercises 4–5, 10–15.

EXERCISES *On Your Own*

Geography **Use the bar graph at the right.**

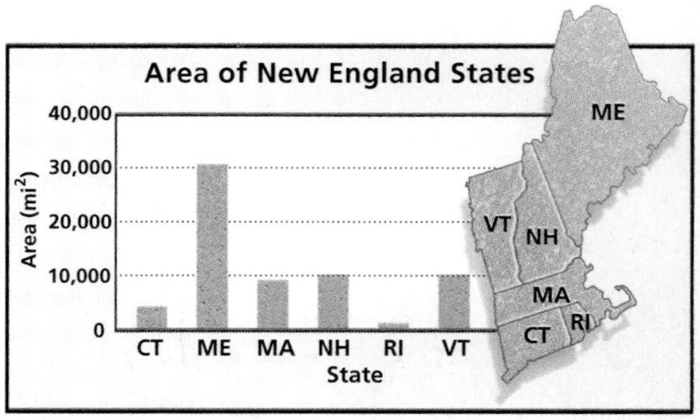

1. Which New England state has the greatest amount of land? The least amount of land? **ME; RI**

2. Which New England states have about the same amount of land?
NH and VT

3. Compare the amount of land in Maine to the amount of land in Vermont.
Maine has about 3 times as much land as Vermont.

Area of New England States

ME
VT NH
MA RI
CT

(bar graph: Area (mi²) vs State; values 40,000, 30,000, 20,000, 10,000, 0; CT, ME, MA, NH, RI, VT)

Food **Use the circle graph at the right.**

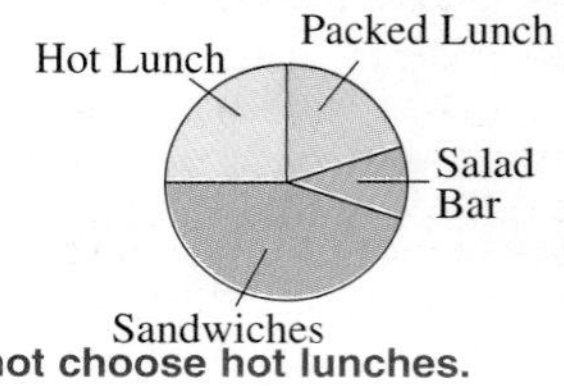

4. What is the least popular lunch choice for students? How do you know by looking at the circle graph?
Salad bar; look for the smallest wedge.

5. Why is a circle graph a good graph to use to convince this school's cafeteria to improve their hot-lunch program?
Answers may vary. Sample: The graph shows that most students do not choose hot lunches.

Lunch Choices
Hot Lunch Packed Lunch Salad Bar Sandwiches

VISUAL LEARNING **Exercises 12–15**
Students could make a sketch of the graph
they pick to see if it makes sense.

Exercise 16 Ask students if a line graph would
also be appropriate for displaying this kind of
data. **no** Why or why not? **The data in this
graph does not reflect change over time.**

WRITING Exercise 17 Ask students to first
describe any relationships in lengths of the
bars before they look at the dollar amounts.
**Answers may vary. Sample: The Gold bar
is twice as long as the Bronze bar.**

WRAP UP

IDENTIFYING THE BIG IDEA Ask students to
explain how to read graphs. Then ask students
how they determine the most appropriate
graph to use to represent a set of data.

JOURNAL Ask students to write a letter to
an imaginary friend who wants to learn how to
make and use graphs.

Math at Work

If you have block scheduling or extended
class periods, consider having students
research the amount of rainfall received in
one of your state parks over a ten-year
period. Organize students in groups and let
them decide which type of graph would best
display the information. Then have them make
the graph.

Recreation **For Exercises 6–9, use the line graph below.**

The Albuquerque International Balloon Fiesta

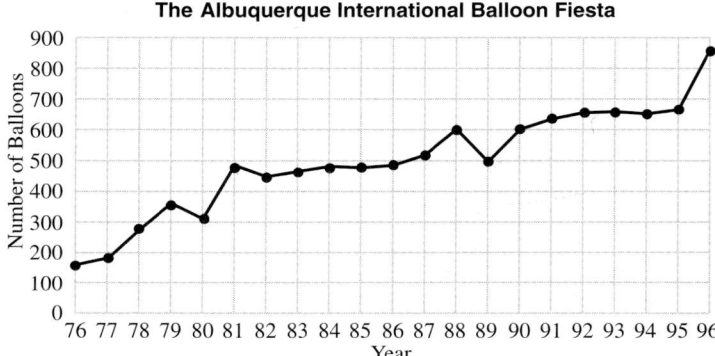

6. What overall trend does the line graph show?
   The number of participants increases over time.

7. During what periods did the number of balloons
   taking part in the Fiesta remain about the same?
   1983–1986 and 1992–1994

8. During what years did the number of balloons
   taking part in the Fiesta increase the most?
   from 1980 to 1981 and from 1995 to 1996

9. How many balloons took part in the Fiesta in the
   year given?

   a. 1992   b. 1996   c. your birth year
      650 balloons   **850 balloons**   **Check students' work.**

Education **Use the circle graph at the right.**

**Number of Teachers
for the Typical
Middle Grade Student**

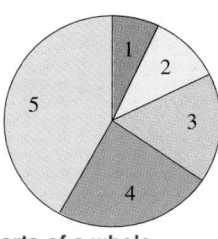

10. How many teachers do most middle grade students have?
    5 teachers

11. Do about the same number of middle grade students have
    one teacher as have four teachers? Explain. **No; the wedge
    for 4 teachers is much larger than the wedge for 1 teacher.**

**Choose the most appropriate type of graph to display
each set of data. Explain your reasoning.**

12. the number of left-handed students and the number of right-
    handed students in your math class
    Bar graph; the graph allows you to compare data that are not all parts of a whole.

13. the number of cases of chicken pox in the United States for
    the years 1935, 1945, 1955, 1965, 1975, 1985, and 1995
    Line graph; the graph shows change in time.

14. the life spans of selected animals
    Bar graph; the graph allows you to compare data that are not changing over time.

15. the average annual temperature from 1990 to the present
    Line graph; the graph shows change in time.

PRACTICE

Practice 1-5 *Reading and Understanding Graphs*

Use the circle graph for Exercises 1–3.

Major Elements Found in the Body

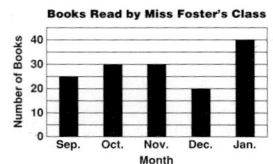

1. Which element is found in greatest quantity in the body?
   oxygen

2. What are the three elements named?
   oxygen, carbon, hydrogen

3. Why might there be a portion labeled "other"?
   There are other elements in quantities too small to be labeled individually.

Use the bar graph for Exercises 4–6.

Nuclear Reactors in Operation

4. Which part of the world has the greatest number of operating nuclear reactors?
   Western Europe

5. Which two parts of the world have the least active nuclear reactors?
   Middle East, Africa

6. Which part of the world has about twice as many nuclear reactors in operation as the Far East?
   North America

Use the line graph for Exercises 7 and 8.

Percent of Men Aged 25–29 Who Have Never Married

7. What overall trend does the line graph show?
   A greater percentage of men are reaching ages 25–29 without having married.

8. During which 10-year period did the percent of unmarried men, ages 25–29, decrease?
   1960 to 1970

Circle A, B, C, or D. Which type of graph—circle, bar, or line—would be most appropriate to display the data?

9. the height of a child from ages 1 to 6
   A. circle graph B. bar graph C. line graph D. any graph

In copymaster and workbook formats

RETEACHING

Reteaching 1-5 *Reading and Understanding Graphs*

A **bar graph** helps to compare data. To read the graph at the right, first read the horizontal axis. Then read from the top of a bar to the vertical axis. This graph shows that in September, Miss Foster's class read 25 books.

Books Read by Miss Foster's Class

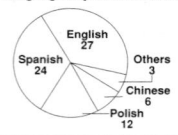

A **circle graph** shows how parts compare to a whole. The graph at the right shows that 27 people in the survey speak English at home.

Languages Spoken at Home

Use the bar graph for Exercises 1–4.

1. How many books were read in December?
   20 books

2. In which month did students read the most books?
   January

3. How many more books were read in January than in October?
   10 books

4. In which 2 months did students read the same number of books?
   October and November

Use the circle graph for Exercises 5–8.

5. Which 2 languages did most people surveyed speak?
   English and Spanish

6. How many people spoke Polish?
   12 people

7. How many more people spoke Spanish than Polish?
   12 people

8. Did more people speak Polish or Chinese?
   Polish

ENRICHMENT

Minds on Math Transparency

1-5

Draw the figure shown below without lifting your pencil from the paper and without retracing any line. Answers may vary. Sample: Start in the bottom right hand corner and follow the numbers in order.

See *Solution Key* for worked-out answers.

26

LESSON QUIZ

1. Would a line graph be appropriate for the recycling data? **no** Why or why not? **The data does not reflect change over time.**

2. Would a bar graph be appropriate for the in-line skater data? **no** Why or why not? **You can use a bar graph to compare the amounts shown, but a line graph is more helpful to see the trend.**

3. Would a line graph be appropriate for the amateur musician data? **no** Why or why not? **A line graph does not compare parts to a whole.**

Go for the Gold !

Beginning in 1994, Olympic winners received money as well as medals. The amount is based on the type of medal won.

The U.S. Olympic Committee says the awards provide "a way to pay for training, to stay in the sport longer."

Olympic Awards

Sports Use the article above for Exercises 16 and 17.

16. How much money does an Olympic gold medalist receive? A silver medalist? A bronze medalist?
    $15,000; $10,000; $7,500

17. *Writing* Describe the relationship between the length of the bar and the award amount for each type of Olympic medal.
    The longer the bar, the more money it represents.

18. *Data Analysis* What type of data is best displayed on a line graph?
    A line graph is best to represent data that show a change over time.

JOURNAL
Summarize what you know about bar, line, and circle graphs. Explain when each type of graph is the most appropriate to use.

Mixed Review

Find the mean, median, and mode. *(Lesson 1-3)*

19. 156, 159, 151, 155, 157, 155, 152
    155; 155; 155

20. 10, 60, 18, 98, 54, 25, 67, 84
    52; 57; no mode

21. *Choose a Strategy* Find two consecutive positive numbers whose product is 462. **21 and 22**

Math at Work

PARK RANGER

Do you enjoy working outdoors? Are you interested in history? If so, maybe a career as a park ranger is for you! Park rangers use mathematics to predict the number of visitors, measure rainfall and tree growth, plan trails, solve problems involving acid rain or deforestation, and construct time lines.

Visit the National Park Service Web site www.nps.gov/ for more information.

1 Focus

CONNECTING TO PRIOR KNOWLEDGE Ask students to describe types of graphs they have studied so far. Have students give examples of graphs they have seen outside school. Ask students to share which graphs they think would be the easiest and the hardest to make.

2 Teach

THINK AND DISCUSS

VISUAL LEARNING Question 1 Sketch a horizontal bar graph so that students can compare the picture with the verbal descriptions.

REASONING Question 2 If students have difficulty imagining the graph, encourage them to draw the graph with units of five marked on the vertical axis.

ERROR ALERT! Students may confuse *horizontal* and *vertical*. **Remediation:** Explain that a horizontal line is flat, like the horizon. A vertical line goes straight up, and at the top you get *vertigo*.

EXTENSION Encourage students to research species of endangered animals in their state. Suggest that students work together to evaluate which data to include on a graph. Have students create relevant graphs to share with the class.

ALGEBRA Connection

1-6 Making Bar and Line Graphs

What You'll Learn

▼ To make bar graphs
▼ To make line graphs

...And Why

You can make bar and line graphs to show trends in wildlife data.

Here's How

Look for questions that
- build understanding
- check understanding

U.S. Endangered Animals

Type of Animal	Number of Species
Mammals	55
Birds	74
Reptiles	14
Amphibians	7
Fish	65

Source: U.S. Fish and Wildlife Service

THINK AND DISCUSS

▼ Making Bar Graphs

Many animals face the danger of disappearing forever. The main causes are human activities like hunting and pollution and environmental changes.

■ **EXAMPLE 1** *Real-World Problem Solving*

Animal Studies Make a bar graph to display the data shown in the table at the left.

Draw and label the horizontal and vertical axes.

Choose an appropriate title.

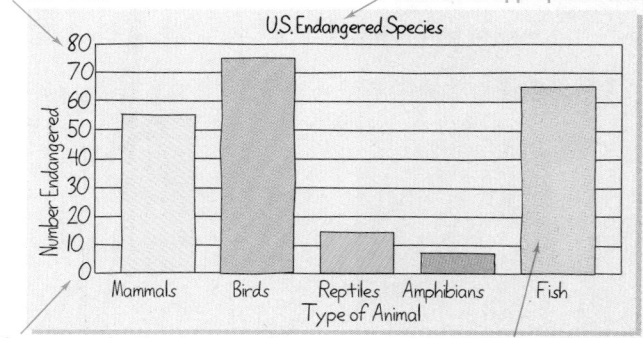

Choose a scale. The data goes from 7 to 74. Mark 0 to 80 in units of 10.

Draw bars of equal widths. The heights will vary.

1. **Look Back** Refer to Example 1. How would you display this data in a bar graph where the bars are horizontal? **Exchange the axes.**

2. **Reasoning** Suppose the vertical axis were marked in units of five. List an advantage and a disadvantage of using units of five instead of ten. **See margin p. 29.**

3a–c. **Answers may vary. See margin p. 29 for samples.**
3. Choose a scale for the given data.
   a. 6, 3, 11, 14, 7   b. 125, 160, 52, 75, 180
   c. the average speeds of five animals ranging from 25 mi/h to 60 mi/h

Now you may assign Exercises 1–6, 9–11.

Now you may assign Exercises 1–6, 9–11.

Lesson Planning Options

Prerequisite Skills
- identifying bar and line graphs (1-6)

Materials/Manipulatives
- graph paper

Resources

📖 **Student Edition**

Skills Handbook, p. 537
Extra Practice, p. 522
Glossary/Study Guide

▭ **Teaching Resources**

Chapter Support File, Ch. 1
- Lesson Planner 1-6
- Practice 1-6, Reteaching 1-6
- Alternative Activity 1-6
- Answer Masters 1-6
Teaching Aids Masters 1, 2
Glossary, Spanish Resources

Transparencies
1, 36–41, 79, Minds on Math 1-6

Warm Up

What combination of two bills and three coins can be used to make $15.45? **one $10 bill, one $5 bill, one quarter, and two dimes**

ASSESSMENT Ask students to draw a vertical bar graph that shows the numbers of endangered animal species from least to greatest. Graphs should show the bars in this order: amphibians, reptiles, mammals, fish, and birds.

■ **ADDITIONAL EXAMPLES**

FOR EXAMPLE 1
Describe how to display the data in this table as a vertical bar graph.

1990 Population Per Square Mile of the Most Populous States

State	Population
California	190
New York	380
Texas	65
Florida	239
Pennsylvania	265

Answers may vary. Sample:
- Draw horizontal and vertical axes.
- Put the name of each state on the horizontal axis.
- Choose a scale. The data goes from 65 to 380. Use units of 50 to draw a scale from 0 to 400.
- Draw a bar to show the number of people per square mile in each state.
- Label the axes. Label the graph.

Technology Options

Prentice Hall Technology

  Software for Learners
- Math Lab: Bar and Line Graphs
- Math Blaster® Mystery*
- Interactive Student Tutorial, Chapter 1*

  Teaching Resource Software
- Computer Item Generator 1-6
- Resource Pro™ Chapter 1*

Internet • For related mathematics activities, visit the Prentice Hall site at www.phschool.com/math

Available on CD-ROM only

Assignment Options for Exercises On Your Own

To provide flexible scheduling, this lesson can be subdivided into parts.

▼ **1 Core** 1–6, 10–11
Extension 9

▼ **2 Core** 7, 8, 12–23, 25
Extension 24

Use Mixed Review to maintain skills.

28

---

2 Making Line Graphs

When you make a line graph, you use points instead of bars. These points are connected to show changes over time.

■ **EXAMPLE 2** *Real-World Problem Solving*

Population Make a line graph to display the changing population of Cleveland.

Population of Ohio Cities

Year	Cleveland	Columbus
1950	914,808	375,901
1960	876,050	471,316
1970	751,000	540,000
1980	574,000	565,000
1990	505,616	632,958

Source: Bureau of the Census

Draw and label the axes.

Choose an appropriate title

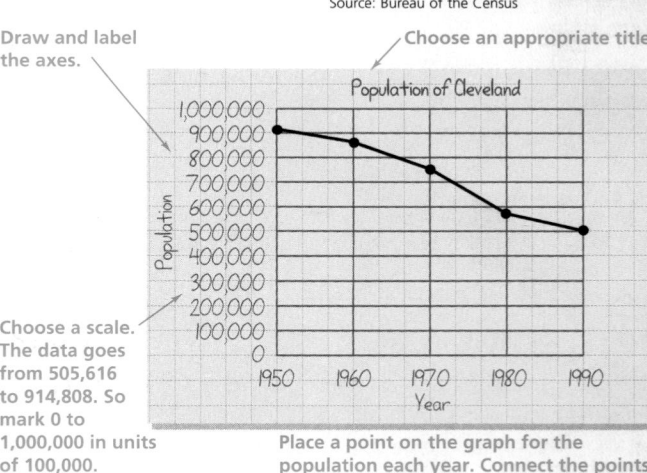

Choose a scale. The data goes from 505,616 to 914,808. So mark 0 to 1,000,000 in units of 100,000.

Place a point on the graph for the population each year. Connect the points.

4a. The population of Cleveland has decreased over time.

4. a. ▪*Look Back* What trend does the line graph in Example 2 show?
  b. Would changing the numbers marked on the vertical axis affect the trend? Explain. No; the trend does not depend on the choice of scales and labels.
5a–b. See margin p. 29 for graphs.

5a. The population of Columbus increases over time.

5c. The bar graph shows differences between years. The line graph shows growth or decline in population from year to year.

5. a. ✔*Try It Out* Make a line graph to display the population of Columbus. Use the data in Example 2. Describe the trend shown in the line graph.
  b. Make a bar graph to display the population of Columbus.
  c. ▪*Analyze* Compare the graphs of parts (a) and (b).

FOR EXAMPLE 2

What would happen if in the year 2000 the population of Cleveland was 525,321 and the population of Columbus was 595,000? **Each trend would reverse itself.**

AEP **Example 2** Explain the words *trend*, *horizontal*, *vertical*, and *scale*. Have students copy the graph and use these words to label its parts.

Ask students:

- *Why might you misunderstand the data after looking at one of the graphs?* Answers may vary. Sample: The scale may not start at 0.

- *How did you make your bar graph easier to read?* Answers may vary. Sample: I started the scale at 0, made each bar width the same, and spaced grid lines evenly.

3 Practice/Assess

EXERCISES *On Your Own*

DIVERSITY If a student receives a foreign language publication at home that contains a graph, ask the student to bring the publication to class.

WRITING **Exercise 9** Have students think of the numerical data they want to include to support their answer.

---

6. The vertical scale does not start at 0; the bars have different widths; the horizontal grid lines are not evenly spaced.

7.

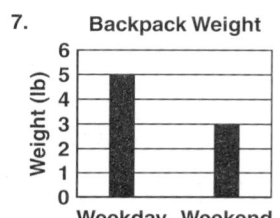

Backpack Weight

Work Together _____   *Identifying Graph Errors*

Each graph below displays the same data. All three graphs are drawn incorrectly.

Weight of Your Backpack

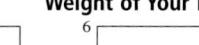
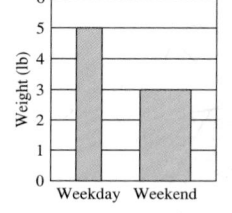
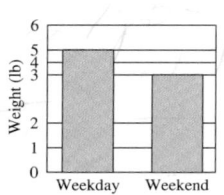

6. Analyze each graph and describe the error.
6–7. See left.

7. ✔ *Try It Out* Make a bar graph using the same data. Be sure your graph is drawn correctly.

Now you may assign Exercises 7–8, 12–25.

EXERCISES *On Your Own*

Suppose you graphed the given data. Should you use units of 5, 10, 100, 1,000, or 5,000 for the scale? Explain.

1. 10,275 ft; 12,383 ft; 19,904 ft; 1,575 ft

2. $153, $215, $499, $385, $260, $428

3. 10,122 lb; 25,875 lb; 9,673 lb; 37,111 lb

4. 999, 56, 87, 156, 484, 525

5. 15 s, 27 s, 49 s, 8 s, 35 s, 59 s, 18 s, 33 s
1–6. See margin p. 30.

6. $10,000; $17,000; $19,500; $15,900

Education **Use the table at the right.**

7. Choose A, B, or C. How would you best mark the scale used to graph the data? **C**
A. units of 10 B. units of 100 C. units of 1,000
8a–b. See back of book.

8. a. *Data Analysis* Make a line graph to display the number of schools with CD-ROMs.

b. Make a line graph to display the number of schools with satellite dishes. Use the same scale you used in part (a). **c.** The numbers in each graph increase over time.

c. Describe the trend(s) shown in your line graphs.

d. Which type of technology has increased at a higher rate? How is this shown on the graph? **Satellite dishes; the line for satellite dishes rises much faster.**

Technology in Schools

Year	Number of CD-ROMs	Schools With Satellite Dishes
1992	5,706	1,129
1993	11,021	8,812
1994	24,526	12,580
1995	31,501	14,290

Source: Quality Education Data, Inc.

---

pages 27–28   Think and Discuss

2. You can estimate the number of each type of animal better; the unit marks would be too close together or the graph would be much taller.

3. Answers may vary.

a. Sample: Use the scale 0 to 16 and mark units of 2.

b. Sample: Use the scale 0 to 200 and mark units of 25.

c. Sample: Use the scale 0 to 60 mi/h and mark units of 10.

5a.

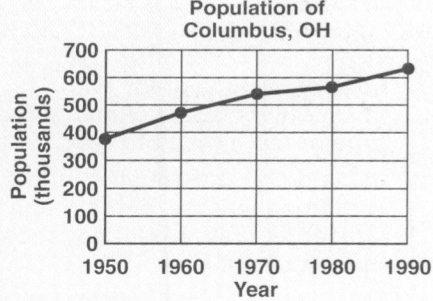

b.

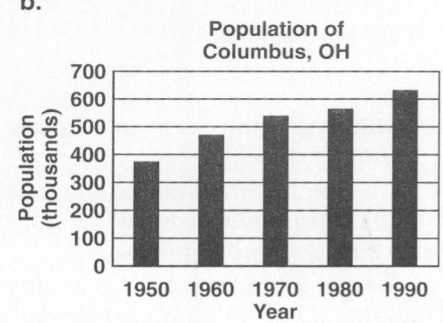

KINESTHETIC LEARNING Ask groups of students to draw a bar graph on butcher paper to show the heights of each group member. Have each student in the groups lie on the butcher paper to model graph bars. Have groups share and compare graphs.

Exercise 32 Discuss possible categories for this data such as none, one a week, two a week, etc.

Exercise 33 Make sure students understand the graph will show the amount of rain for each month.

WRAP UP

IDENTIFYING THE BIG IDEA Ask students to explain how to construct bar and line graphs. Ask them when to use each.

LESSON QUIZ

1. Would you use a scale unit of five or ten to graph the following data: 36, 53, 18, 10, 70? Explain. **Answers may vary. Sample: Ten; this unit lets you show the range of data with the fewest grid lines.**

2. How do you decide which scale unit to use to graph a data set? **Answers may vary. Sample: Compare the range of the data.**

CHECKPOINT 2

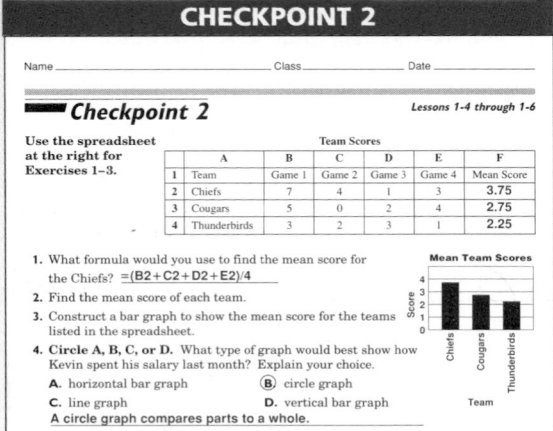

Name _____ Class _____ Date _____

■ **Checkpoint 2**   Lessons 1-4 through 1-6

Use the spreadsheet at the right for Exercises 1–3.

	A	B	C	D	E	F
	Team	Game 1	Game 2	Game 3	Game 4	Mean Score
1	Team	Game 1	Game 2	Game 3	Game 4	Mean Score
2	Chiefs	7	4	1	3	3.75
3	Cougars	5	0	2	4	2.75
4	Thunderbirds	3	2	3	1	2.25

1. What formula would you use to find the mean score for the Chiefs? =(B2+C2+D2+E2)/4

2. Find the mean score of each team.

3. Construct a bar graph to show the mean score for the teams listed in the spreadsheet.

4. Circle A, B, C, or D. What type of graph would best show how Kevin spent his salary last month? Explain your choice.
   A. horizontal bar graph   Ⓑ circle graph
   C. line graph   D. vertical bar graph
   A circle graph compares parts to a whole.

---

pages 29–31   On Your Own

1. 1,000 or 5,000; a graph with smaller units would either be too large or too difficult to read.

2. 100; a graph with smaller units would be too large, and a graph with larger units would not show enough detail.

3. 5,000; a graph with smaller units would either be too large or too difficult to read.

4. 10; a graph with smaller units would be too large, and a graph with larger units would not show enough detail.

5. 5; a graph with larger units would not show enough detail.

6. 1,000 or 5,000; a graph with smaller units would either be too large or too difficult to read.

25c. Answers may vary. Sample: A line graph better displays changes over time.

Architecture **Use the table at the right.**

9. *Writing* Would you use the same scale to graph the number of stories as the height? Why or why not? **See below.**

10. Make a bar graph to display the number of stories in New York City's five tallest buildings.
10–11. See back of book.

11. Make a bar graph to display the height in feet of New York City's five tallest buildings.

9. No; the number of stories and the height use different units.

Choose a scale for the given data.   12–20. Answers may vary. Samples are given.

12. 8, 17, 12, 8, 7, 15, 13, 9
    0 to 18 by 2's

13. 8, 17, 25, 6, 49, 56, 64, 68
    0 to 70 by 10's

14. 121, 152, 123, 147, 164, 188
    0 to 200 by 20's

15. 68, 69, 70, 82, 99, 129, 56
    0 to 130 by 10's

16. 9, 11, 13, 10, 9, 9, 19, 12, 9
    0 to 20 by 2's

17. 12,235; 12,383; 18,911
    0 to 20,000 by 2,000's

18. 122, 199, 175, 196, 127
    0 to 200 by 25's

19. 15, 128, 75, 53, 90, 46, 2, 7
    0 to 135 by 15's

20. 36; 216; 1,296; 1,776; 842
    0 to 1,800 by 200's

Find the error in each graph.
The vertical scale does not start at 0.

21. **Field Goals**

22. **U.S. Population**

23. **Cereal Prices**

The bars have unequal width.

23. The horizontal gridlines are unevenly spaced.

24. a. *Hobbies* Would you use a bar graph or a line graph to display the data in the table at the right? Explain your choice.
    b. Graph the data. **See back of book.**
24a. Bar graph; there is no change in time.

25. a. *Technology* Display the data in the spreadsheet below as a line graph.
    b. Display the data as a bar graph. **a–b. See back of book.**
    c. Is the line graph or bar graph a better display of the data? Explain. **See margin.**

	A	B	C	D	E	F
1	Year	1950	1960	1970	1980	1990
2	U.S. Population (per square mile)	43	51	58	64	70

Five Tallest Buildings in New York City

Building	Stories	Height
World Trade Center (North)	110	1,368 ft
World Trade Center (South)	110	1,362 ft
Empire State Building	102	1,250 ft
Chrysler Building	77	1,046 ft
American International Building	67	950 ft

Source: *World Almanac*

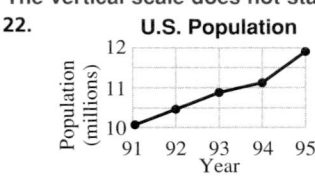

Top-Selling Stamp Sets

Stamp Set	Sales in Millions
The Civil War	46.6
Legends of The West	46.5
World War II	32.5
Jazz Musicians	26.5
Great Lakes Lighthouses	26.2

Source: The Associated Press

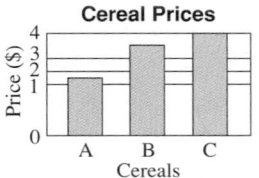

3. If you want to show the population of an animal species over time, would you use a bar graph or line graph to record data? Explain. **Answers may vary. Sample: Line graph; it shows trends over time.**

4. Explain why it is important to label the axes of graphs. **You cannot explain what the data shows without labels.**

Mixed Review

Make a line plot of the data. *(Lesson 1-1)*   **26–31. See back of book.**

26. A, C, C, D, A, A, B, A, F   **27.** 16, 18, 18, 20, 18, 16, 17   **28.** 29, 36, 25, 29, 36, 29, 36, 26

29. S, L, XL, M, L, L, XL, L   **30.** 93, 87, 95, 87, 94, 95, 90   **31.** 1, 6, 6, 2, 5, 3, 1, 6, 4, 3, 6

Name the type of graph that would be most appropriate. Explain your choice. *(Lessons 1-1, 1-5, and 1-6)*

32. frequency with which students rent movie videos
circle graph

33. average monthly rainfall in Seattle, Washington
bar graph

34. home prices from 1990 to the present
line graph

✓ CHECKPOINT 2   *Lessons 1-4 through 1-6*

Use the spreadsheet below for Exercises 1 and 2.

	A	B	C	D	E	F
1	Student	Test 1	Test 2	Test 3	Test 4	Mean Score
2	Justin	80	78	94	88	
3	Elizabeth	64	78	82	80	
4	Naomi	94	84	88	82	

1. Choose A, B, or C. What formula could you use to determine the value in cell F4? **C**
A. =(B2+B3+B4)/3   **B.** =(A4+B4+C4+D4+E4)/5   **C.** =(B4+C4+D4+E4)/4

2. Make a bar graph to display the mean scores for the students listed in the spreadsheet.   **See back of book.**

Use the circle graph at the right.

3. Which branch of the U.S. armed forces received the most Medals of Honor for service in the Vietnam War?
Army

4. How many Medals of Honor were awarded for service in the Vietnam War? **239 medals**

Vietnam Medals of Honor
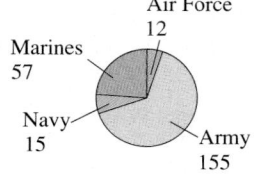
Air Force 12
Marines 57
Navy 15
Army 155

PRACTICE

Practice 1-6 *Making Bar and Line Graphs*

Use the table below to answer Exercises 1–3.

All-Time Favorite Sports Figures

Sports Figure	Number of Votes
Babe Ruth	29
Babe Didrikson Zaharias	22
Jackie Robinson	18
Billie Jean Moffitt King	17
Muhammad Ali	14
Jim Thorpe	13

Source: *The Book of Lists #3, The People's Almanac*

1. What would you label the horizontal axis for a bar graph of the data?
names of the athletes

2. What interval would you use for the vertical axis for the bar graph?
Answers may vary. Sample: 5

3. Construct a bar graph displaying the number of votes for all-time favorite sports figures.

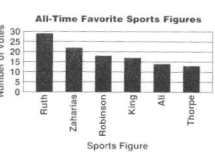

Use the table below to answer Exercises 4 and 5.

Daily Use of Petroleum in the U.S. (millions of barrels)

Year	Number
1950	6.5
1955	8.5
1960	9.8
1965	11.5
1970	14.7
1975	16.3
1980	17.1
1985	15.7
1990	16.9

Source: *U.S. Dept. of Energy, Annual Energy Review*

4. Construct a line graph for the amount of petroleum used daily in the U.S.

5. What overall trend does the line graph show?
Daily use of petroleum has increased since 1950.

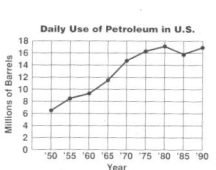

In copymaster and workbook formats

RETEACHING

Reteaching 1-6 *Making Bar and Line Graphs*

To make bar graphs and line graphs from data, follow these steps:

① Give the graph a title. Decide what information to show on each axis.

Number of Apples Picked	
Week	Apples
1	21
2	34
3	29

② Draw and label the horizontal and vertical axes.

③ Choose a scale. Think about which intervals of 5, 10, 100, or 1,000 would work best.

Amount Earned from After-School Job	
Week	Amount
1	$10.00
2	$9.00
3	$12.00
4	$15.00

④ Draw each bar, or plot the data and connect the points to form a line graph.

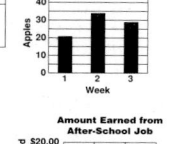

Would the best scale for the given data be fives, tens, hundreds, or thousands?

1. 83 ft, 49 ft, 66 ft, 73 ft
tens

2. $12, $22, $18, $26, $6
fives

3. 1,000 mi; 2,500 mi; 4,000 mi
thousands

4. 320 lb, 179 lb, 240 lb, 119 lb
hundreds

5. 6 days, 10 days, 4 days, 9 days
fives

6. 66 gal, 34 gal, 71 gal, 59 gal
tens

Use the tables at the right for Exercises 7 and 8.

7. Would you use a bar graph or line graph to display the data in the table? Explain your choice.
Bar graph; data shows amounts, but not changes over time.

Favorite Sports

Sport	Number Answering
Wrestling	290
Football	50
Basketball	520
Baseball	130

8. Would you use a bar graph or line graph for the data? Explain.
Line graph; data shows change over time.

Population of Springdale

Year	Population
1970	45,000
1980	62,000
1990	68,000

Reteaching

ENRICHMENT

Minds on Math Transparency

1-6

How many 4-digit numbers can you make using the digits 1, 4, 6, and 9 if you use each digit only once in each number?

24 numbers

See *Solution Key* for worked-out answers.

In Lesson 1-6, students learned how to construct bar and line graphs. In this toolbox, students explore other methods of displaying data, stem-and-leaf plots and box-and-whisker plots.

ERROR ALERT! Students may have trouble understanding box-and-whisker plots.
Remediation: It is important for students to understand that different representations of data have different functions. Have students tell what a box-and-whisker plot does and what it does not do.

ASSESSMENT Have pairs of students discuss the data in each plot. Challenge students to work with their partners to write descriptions in their own words of how each plot displays its data. Have pairs compare their descriptions.

■ **ADDITIONAL PROBLEM**

Which plot would you use to compare the time it takes you to get ready for school with the time it takes other students to do the same? **Answers may vary. Sample: box-and-whisker plots because they group the data for comparison**

---

pages 33–34 Think and Discuss

1. The first graph; the increase seems to be gradual. The other graph seems to show a steep rise in rates.

2b. The greater the range of the scale, the shallower the graph. The graph with the shorter scale seems to show more drastic changes.

3. When the data items on the horizontal scale are spaced further apart, the graph seems not to rise as fast as when the data are closer together.

4.
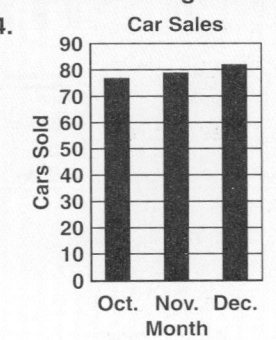

MATH TOOLBOX

EXPLORATION

Other Methods of Displaying Data

After Lesson 1-6

You can use a *stem-and-leaf plot* or a *box-and-whisker plot* to display data. For example, the data shows the number of minutes it takes 27 students to get ready for school.

47 28 78 47 58 93 34 76 35 72 45 53 23
43 75 27 23 87 33 43 25 35 49 35 48 37 28

A **stem-and-leaf plot** orders the data and lets you see the values and frequencies.

stem ⟶ 5 8 ⟵ leaf

Time to Get Ready

2	3 3 5 7 8 8
3	3 4 5 5 5 7
4	3 3 5 7 7 8 9
5	3 8
6	
7	2 5 6 8
8	7
9	3

Key: 2/3 means 23 min

A **box-and-whisker plot** shows you how the data are distributed and identifies only certain values.

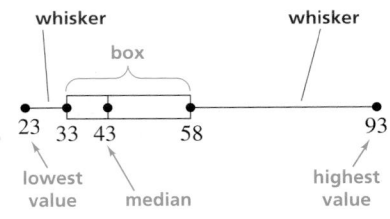

33 and 58 are the middle values of the bottom and top halves of the data, respectively.

Use the stem-and-leaf plot above for Exercises 1–3.

1. What does the stem 4 and leaf 7 represent?
   47 min

2. How many students took more than 50 minutes?
   8 students

3. a. *Reasoning* How would you use the stem-and-leaf plot to find the median and the mode of the data? **See above.**

   b. What is the median? The mode?
   43 min; 35 min

3a. **Count only the leaves. The middle leaf counting from top to bottom and from left to right is the median. The leaf that appears most often on a single stem is the mode.**

Use the box-and-whisker plot at the right.

4. Find the median. **32**

5. Find the highest and lowest values. **49; 27**

27 29 32 40 49

6. *Writing* What does 29 represent?
   29 is the median of the lower half of the data.

7. *Analyze* The right side of the box is wider. What does this tell you about the spread of the data? **The data above the median are spread out more than the data below the median.**

2 Teach

1 Focus

CONNECTING TO PRIOR KNOWLEDGE Ask students to share any advertisements they have seen that they thought were misleading. Ask if there is any other time they may have heard or seen misleading data. **Answers may vary. Sample: political campaigns**

THINK AND DISCUSS

REASONING **Question 1** Before answering the question, have students determine the cable company's purpose in using a graph. **Answers may vary. Sample: to show that past price increases have not been great**

VISUAL LEARNING **Questions 2 and 3** Have students sketch changes in the different

axes. Have them make several sketches to see the pattern as they change each axis. Also, ask students to bring in graphs that they think display information clearly or poorly. As a group, critique the graphs.

DIVERSITY Have students look for a wide variety of publications outside of class with examples of graphs. Emphasize that publications unfamiliar to most students or written in languages other than English would be of greatest interest. Have students discuss the graphs' similarities and differences.

1-7 Misleading Graphs

What You'll Learn

▼**1** To recognize misleading line graphs

▼**2** To recognize misleading bar graphs

...And Why

Misleading graphs are often used to persuade consumers.

Here's How

Look for questions that
- ♣ build understanding
- ✔ check understanding

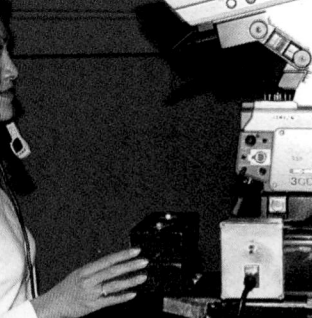

THINK AND DISCUSS

▼**1** *Misleading Line Graphs*

Sometimes people display data in a way that persuades you to see things their way for their own purposes. Even graphs that are correctly drawn can mislead the reader.

Both graphs below display recent basic monthly rates for Quality Cable Company.

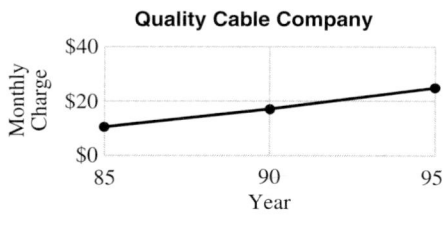 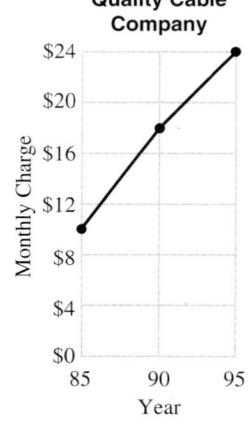

1. ♣*Reasoning* Which graph above is the cable company more likely to use to persuade you that an increase is justified? Explain. **See margin p. 32.**

2a. $0 to $40 and $0 to $24

2. **a.** What is the vertical scale of each graph above?

   b. ♣*Analyze* How does a change in the vertical scale affect the appearance of the data in the line graph? Explain.

2b, 3. See margin p. 32.

3. ♣*Drawing Conclusions* In the first graph above, data items on the horizontal scale are spaced farther apart. How does this change the appearance of the data in the line graph?

Now you may assign Exercises 1–3, 10–12, 15.

Lesson Planning Options

Prerequisite Skills
- reading bar and line graphs (1-6)
- determining scale (precourse)

Materials/Manipulatives
- graph paper

Resources

📖 **Student Edition**

Skills Handbook, p. 537
Extra Practice, p. 522
Glossary/Study Guide

📦 **Teaching Resources**

Chapter Support File, Ch. 1
- Lesson Planner 1-7
- Practice 1-7, Reteaching 1-7
- Answer Masters 1-7
Teaching Aids Masters 1, 2
Glossary, Spanish Resources

💻 **Transparencies**
1, Minds on Math 1-7

Warm Up

Find three numbers between 400 and 410 that are divisible by 3. **402, 405, 408**

■ **ADDITIONAL EXAMPLE**

FOR EXAMPLE

Suppose you wanted to boost the morale of the sales staff. How would you make the graph? **Answers may vary. Sample: Do not break the vertical axis.**

ERROR ALERT! Students' first response to Additional Example 1 may not be their best answer. **Remediation:** Encourage students to draw rough sketches first.

CONNECTION TO BUSINESS Have a discussion about how businesses and consumers might find graphs useful. Begin with these examples: review sales trends or expenses, compare products.

EXTENSION Ask students to take a class survey. Then use the information to create two graphs. One of the graphs should mislead students and the other should be an accurate a representation.

ASSESSMENT Have students list what they have learned about misleading graphs. Challenge students to think of ways they could apply this knowledge.

Technology Options

Prentice Hall Technology

 Software for Learners

- Hot Page™ 3*
- Math Blaster® Mystery*
- Interactive Student Tutorial, Chapter 1*

 Teaching Resource Software

- Computer Item Generator 1-7
- Resource Pro™ Chapter 1*

Internet • For related mathematics activities, visit the Prentice Hall site at www.phschool.com/math

*Available on CD-ROM only

Assignment Options for Exercises On Your Own

To provide flexible scheduling, this lesson can be subdivided into parts.

▼**1 Core** 1–3, 10–12
Extension 15

▼**2 Core** 4–9, 13
Extension 14

Use Mixed Review to maintain skills.

2 *Misleading Bar Graphs*

Bar graphs can be misleading. Gaps in the scale make differences between the bar heights appear greater than they really are.

■ **EXAMPLE** *Real-World Problem Solving*

Car Sales A company claims that it has dramatically increased its sales over the past three months. One of its advertisements shows the graph below. What is wrong with the company's claim? Explain.

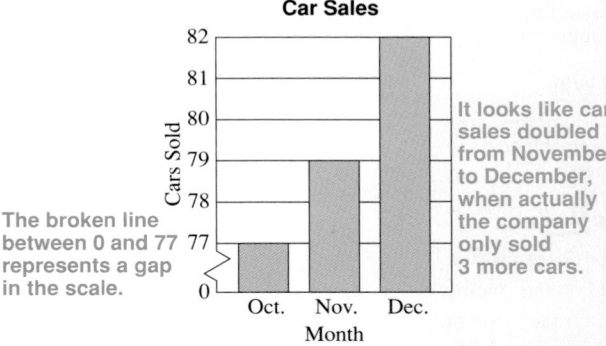

The broken line between 0 and 77 represents a gap in the scale.

It looks like car sales doubled from November to December, when actually the company only sold 3 more cars.

The graph is misleading because large portions of the bars are missing.

4. ✔ Try It Out Suppose the company wants to show that car sales have been constant over the past three months. Redraw the bar graph to support this claim. See margin p. 32.

Now you may assign Exercises 4–9, 13–14.

EXERCISES *On Your Own*

Decide if each line graph appears misleading. Explain.
1–3. Answers may vary. See margin p. 35 for samples.

1. 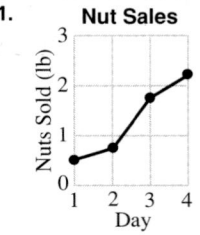 Nut Sales

2. 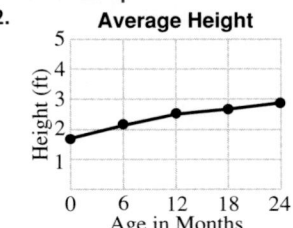 Average Height

3. 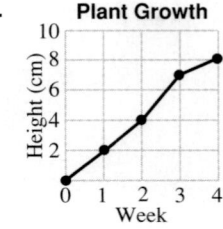 Plant Growth

EXERCISES *On Your Own*

WRITING Exercise 12 Have students tell how they wanted the lines to look, and what they tried to do to make that happen.

OPEN-ENDED Exercise 15 Remind students that as the intervals on the axis increase or decrease, the appearance of the graph changes.

WRAP UP

IDENTIFYING THE BIG IDEA Ask students to describe how to analyze the effects of different scales and intervals on graph data. Have them explain how to recognize misleading graphs.

PROJECT LINK Help students recall the different reasons for using each type of graph.

PORTFOLIO Share with students the criteria you will use to assess their work in portfolios, as well as how you plan to use the results. Students should understand how the rubrics are used to assess their work, how each piece in the portfolio counts, and how the scores they get in their portfolios will affect their overall evaluation.

Decide if each bar graph appears misleading. Explain. Then redraw any misleading graph.

4–6. Answers may vary. Samples are given.

4.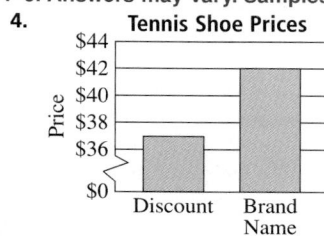

Tennis Shoe Prices

See margin.

5.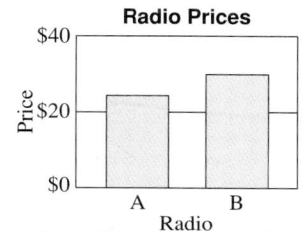

Radio Prices

Not misleading; the graph allows you to compare radio prices directly.

6.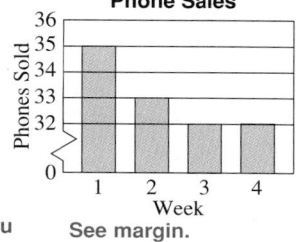

Phone Sales

See margin.

Government **Each graph below came from one of the sources given in Exercises 7–9. Match each graph with its most likely source. Explain your choices.**

i.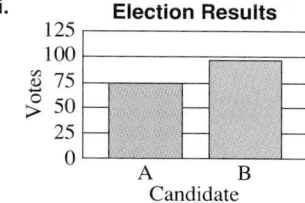

Election Results

ii.

Election Results

iii.

Election Results

7. ii; the gap in the scale makes B's margin appear much greater.

9. i; the wider bar directs attention to candidate A.

7. Candidate B's ad

8. the school newspaper
8. iii; the graph shows the exact distribution of votes.

9. Candidate A's ad
See above.

Data Analysis **Use the table at the right.**

10. Draw a line graph showing that the money pledged increased greatly from 1988 to 1997.
10–11. See back of book.

11. Draw a line graph showing that the money pledged increased slowly from 1988 to 1997.

12. *Writing* Explain how you drew the graphs in Exercises 10 and 11 to get the desired results. See below.

13. How is a gap in the scale of a graph represented?
Use the broken line or zig-zag symbol to represent a gap in the scale.

14. How does a gap in the scale of a graph affect the appearance of the data? A gap in the scale distorts the differences between the data items.

12. Use a gap in the scale to show that the amount increased greatly. Use a wide range and more horizontal space between data points to show that the amount increased little.

Money Pledged During a National Telethon

Year	Dollars Pledged
1988	30,691,627
1989	32,074,566
1990	33,181,652
1991	34,096,773
1992	39,021,723
1993	41,132,113
1994	42,209,727
1995	44,172,186
1996	45,071,857
1997	45,759,368

pages 33–34 On Your Own

1. Misleading; the scale makes it appear that the sales are increasing rapidly.
2. Misleading; the vertical scale includes too many values.
3. Not misleading; the graph accurately represents plant growth.
4–5. Answers may vary. Samples are given.
4. Misleading; brand name sneakers appear twice as expensive as the discount pair.

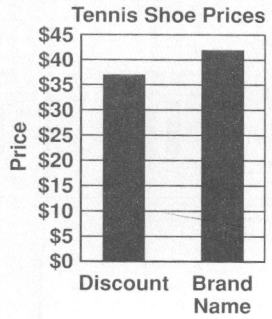

Tennis Shoe Prices

6. Misleading; the gap in the scale makes the differences between the bars appear greater than they are.

6.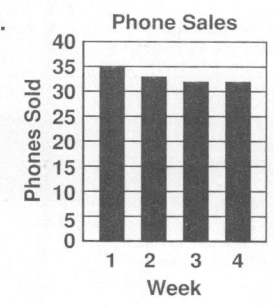

Phone Sales

36

PRACTICE

Practice 1-7 *Misleading Graphs*

There are only two used car dealers in Auto City, Junkers and Clunkers. Monthly auto sales for January, February, and March are shown for Clunkers.

Clunker's Monthly Auto Sales	
January	15
February	14
March	13

1. Draw a bar graph that Junkers could use to show that Clunkers' business is really falling off.

Sample: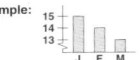

2. Draw a line graph that Clunkers could use to show that business has been stable.

Sample: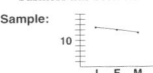

3. What is the actual decline in auto sales for Clunkers?
2 cars

4. Using data from the first three months of the year, can you determine if sales for the whole year will be bad? Explain.
Probably not; car sales vary greatly and information from the first three months is not necessarily indicative of the whole year.

Use the line graph for Exercises 5 and 6.

5. What is wrong with the way the graph is drawn?
The vertical axis changes units; the graph continues through a break.

6. What impression does the graph try to present?
The number of people who prefer Yummy Cereal is increasing sharply.

In copymaster and workbook formats

RETEACHING

Reteaching 1-7 *Misleading Graphs*

Data can be displayed on graphs in ways that are misleading.

The horizontal scales make these graphs seem different. As the numbers are moved farther apart, it appears that the change over time is less.

These graphs may seem different because of how the vertical scales are drawn.

The break in the vertical scale makes the differences seem greater than they really are.

Use the graphs above to answer Exercises 1–6.

1. Which graph might be used to convince someone that the price of pizza has risen too quickly over the years?
graph A

2. Which graph might be used to convince someone that pizza makers should raise their prices?
graph B

3. Name 2 ways in which the pizza graphs differ.
The years on the horizontal axis are spaced differently; graph A seems to rise more steeply than graph B.

4. Which graph would Car Company X use to show that its cars last longer than the competition?
graph D

5. Which graph of cars still on the road after 10 years would Car Company Z prefer?
graph C

6. Name 2 ways in which graphs C and D differ.
vertical scale is unbroken on one, and broken on the other; difference in the bars seems greater on graph D

ENRICHMENT

Minds on Math Transparency

1-7

Perry said he is thinking of a number that is as much greater than 36 as it is less than 94. What is Perry's number?

65

See *Solution Key* for worked-out answers.

LESSON QUIZ

1. Describe what makes the line graph misleading. **large spaces between the lines on the vertical axis**

2. Describe what makes the bar graph accurate. **proper scale, no gaps**

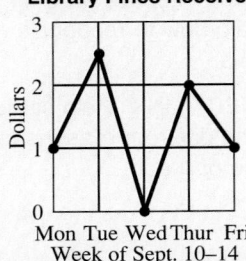

Library Fines Received

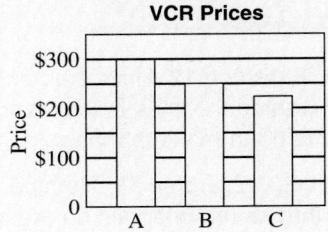

VCR Prices

---

15. *Open-ended* How might you redraw the graph below to show that recreation costs have increased dramatically?

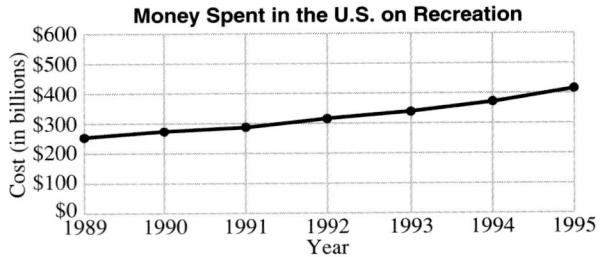

Source: *World Almanac*

Answers may vary. Sample: Use a gap up to $200 and a scale up to $450. Narrow the horizontal space.

Mixed Review

Mental Math **Add, subtract, multiply, or divide.** *(Previous Course)*

16. $300 + 700$
1,000

17. $10 + 110$
120

18. $100 - 10$
90

19. $1100 + 111$
1,211

20. $10 + 100 - 11$
99

21. $10,000 \div 10$
1,000

22. $100 \times 1,000$
100,000

23. $100 \div 10$
10

24. $10,000 \div 100$
100

25. $1,000 \times 1,000$
1,000,000

26. *Data Analysis* Draw a bar graph to display the data at the right. *(Lesson 1-6)*
26–27. See margin p. 37.

27. *Data Analysis* Draw a pictograph to display the data at the right. *(Hint:* For help see "pictograph" in the Glossary/Study Guide.) *(Previous Course)*

28. *Choose a Strategy* Sumi earns $4.50 per hour baby-sitting. How many hours will she have to baby-sit to earn enough money to buy a portable CD player that costs $89.95? **20 h**

Snowiest Cities	
City	**Average Snowfall**
Albany, NY	about 65 in.
Boston, MA	about 40 in.
Juneau, AK	about 100 in.
Omaha, NE	about 30 in.

PORTFOLIO

For your portfolio, select one or two items from your work for this chapter. Consider the following:
• corrected work
• tables, data displays, graphs
Explain why you have included each selection.

CHAPTER PROJECT

PROJECT LINK: DISPLAYING THE RESULTS

Display the data from your survey in three different ways.
• Consider different graphs as well as some type of table or chart.
• Which method do you think expresses the information the best? Why? **Check students' work.**

Extra Practice, Lesson 1-7, page 522

PROJECT DAY You may wish to plan a project day on which students share their completed projects. Encourage students to explain their processes as well as their products.

PROJECT NOTEBOOK Have students review their methods for gathering data, making graphs, and analyzing data for the projects.

SCORING RUBRIC

3 You correctly used three different display methods to show the data you collected. Your displays are attractive and self-explanatory. You identified both the best display method and the best averaging method. You gave reasons to support your choices.

2 You created three displays of your data and calculated the mean, median, and mode. Either your displays or your explanations are not as complete or neat as they could be.

1 Your survey data is complete, but you only completed two displays of the data. Either your displays are not self-explanatory, or you neglected to compare display methods or averaging techniques.

0 Either your survey was not thorough or complete, or you left out important parts of your presentation.

FINISHING THE CHAPTER PROJECT

CHAPTER PROJECT

ON YOUR OWN TIME

Conduct a Survey The Project Link questions on pages 7, 16, and 36 should help you complete your project. Here is a checklist to help you gather the parts of your project together.

✓ your chosen topic, the choices, and the data you collected

✓ the mean, median, and mode of your data

✓ three different methods of displaying the data

Make a presentation to the class that displays the information neatly and accurately. Explain which display of information you feel is best and why you feel that way.

Reflect and Revise

Review your project with a friend or someone at home. Are your graphs complete and accurate? Would a different type of graph be more appropriate? Are any of your graphs misleading? How might the information you collected and graphed be used? If necessary, make changes to improve your project.

Web Extension

Prentice Hall's Internet site contains information you might find helpful as you complete your project. Visit www.phschool.com/mgm1/ch1 for some links and ideas related to surveys.

Materials/Manipulatives

• graph paper

page 36 Mixed Review

26.

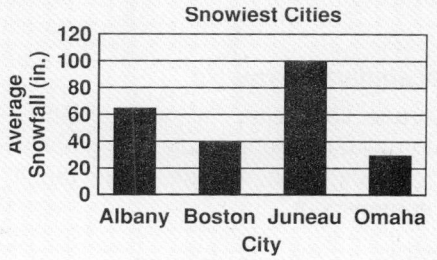

Snowiest Cities

27.

Snowiest Cities	
Albany, NY	❄ ❄ ❄ ⸰
Boston, MA	❄ ❄
Juneau, AK	❄ ❄ ❄ ❄ ❄
Omaha, NE	❄ ⸰
	Key: ❄ = 20 in.

STUDENT SELF-ASSESSMENT SURVEY

Chapter 1 Student Self-Assessment Survey

1. Now that you have finished this chapter, think about what you have learned about representing data. Check each topic that you feel confident you understand.
   _____ use a frequency table and a line plot to organize data (1-1)
   _____ solve problems by making a table (1-2)
   _____ find the mean, median, and mode (1-3)
   _____ decide which average to use in a given situation (1-3)
   _____ use a spreadsheet to organize data (1-4)
   _____ create formulas for a spreadsheet (1-4)
   _____ read and understand bar and line graphs (1-5)
   _____ read and understand circle graphs (1-5)
   _____ make bar graphs and line graphs (1-6)
   _____ recognize misleading bar and line graphs (1-7)

2. Before the Chapter Assessment, I need to review _____

3. a. Check one. In general, I thought this chapter was
   ____ a snap ____ easy ____ average ____ hard ____ a monster
   b. Why do you feel this way?

4. In this chapter, I did my best work on _____

5. In this chapter, I had trouble with _____

6. List three places outside the classroom where people use graphs to represent data. _____

7. Did you use a spreadsheet on the computer? _____ If so, did you find the computer helpful? _____ Explain.

Assessment

Vocabulary/Symbols

average, bar graph, cell, circle graph, formula, frequency table, line graph, line plot, mean, median, mode, range, spreadsheet

Materials/Manipulatives

• graph paper

Resources

 Student Edition

Extra Practice, p. 522
Glossary/Study Guide

 Teaching Resources

Chapter Support File, Ch. 1
• Student Self-Assessment Survey
Glossary, Spanish Resources
Tools for Studying Smarter

38

WRAP UP

Exercises 1 and 2 You may want to suggest that students count the vowels and words in the given paragraph more than once, and perhaps in more than one order, to ensure an accurate count.

Exercises 6 and 7 Have students work in groups to decide what row and column headings to use in their tables. Circulate among students and help if needed.

Exercises 8–10 Remind students to compute the mean by adding the data values and then dividing the total by the number of data values.

Exercises 14–17 Review with students how to label cells on a spreadsheet.

ASSESSMENT Exercises 18 and 19 Ask students to discuss how to make the graphs accurate and not misleading.

1 WRAP UP

Organizing and Displaying Data 1-1

A **frequency table** lists data and shows the number of times each type of answer occurs. A **line plot** displays data on a horizontal line. The **range** is the difference between the greatest and the least values in a set of numerical data. 1–2. See back of book.

1. Make a frequency table showing the number of times each vowel appears in the paragraph above.

2. Make a line plot showing the number of times the words *the*, *and*, *a*, and *are* appear in the paragraph above.

Find the range of each data set.

3. 7, 8, 10, 6, 5, 7, 9, 4, 6
   6

4. 90, 76, 88, 94, 81, 77, 80, 87
   18

5. 4, 2, 12, 7, 3, 2, 10, 9, 6, 4
   10

Problem Solving Strategies 1-2

You can make a table to organize possible solutions to a problem.

6. *Money* In how many ways can you make 21¢? **9 ways**

7. *Clothes* Kayla spent $48 on gym clothes. She bought at least one of each item. Shorts cost $16. T-shirts cost $8. Socks cost $2 a pair. How many ways could Kayla have bought gym clothes?
   12 ways

8. *Money* Suppose you have six coins that total $1. How many quarters do you have? **3 quarters**

Mean, Median, and Mode 1-3

The **mean** is the sum of the data divided by the number of pieces of data. The **median** is the middle number in a set of ordered data. When there is an even number of data items, you can find the median by adding the two middle numbers and dividing by 2. The **mode** is the data value that appears most often.

Find the mean and median of each data set.

9. 34, 49, 63, 43, 50, 50, 26
   45; 49

10. 3, 7, 1, 9, 9, 5, 8
    6; 7

11. 14, 13, 16, 17, 24, 12, 13, 19
    16; 15

Find the mode of each data set.

12. M, S, XL, XL, M, L, M, L
    M

13. 18, 18, 18, 18, 18, 18, 18
    18

14. 8, 7, 10, 5, 6, 6, 8, 9, 5, 8
    8

Remind students that the definitions of new mathematical terms for this chapter are in the Student Study Guide/Glossary in the back of the textbook.

Using Spreadsheets to Organize Data 1-4

You use a **spreadsheet** to organize and analyze data. A **cell** is the spreadsheet box where a row and column meet. A **formula** is a set of instructions.

	A	B	C	D	E
1	Date	Kite Sales ($)	String Sales ($)	Book Sales ($)	Total Sales ($)
2	9/9/98	500	85	145	▦
3	9/10/98	750	65	125	▦

15. Which cells indicate kite sales? **B2 and B3** **16.** What is the value of cell C3? **$65**

17. Write the formula for cell E2.
= B2 + C2 + D2

18. What is the value of cell E3?
$940

Reading and Making Graphs 1-5, 1-6, 1-7

A **bar graph** is used to compare amounts. A **line graph** shows how an amount changes over time. A **circle graph** compares parts to a whole.

19. Make a line graph to display the cost of tickets shown in the table at the right.
19–20. See back of book.

20. Make a bar graph to display the data you collected in the frequency table in Exercise 1.

Ticket Prices

Year	Ticket Cost
1970	$10.00
1975	$15.00
1980	$20.00
1985	$25.00
1990	$30.00

Choose the most appropriate type of graph to display each set of data. Explain your reasoning.

21. your height on each birthday from birth to the present
Line graph; the graph shows change over time.

22. the sales of different types of lunches in the cafeteria
Circle graph; the data are parts of a whole.

Decide if each graph appears misleading. Explain.

23.
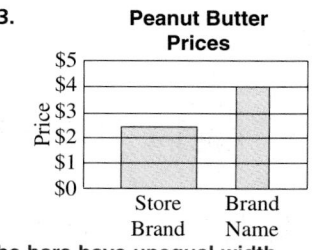
The bars have unequal width.

24.
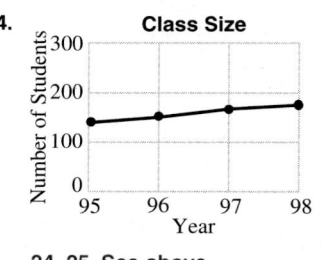
24–25. See above.

25.
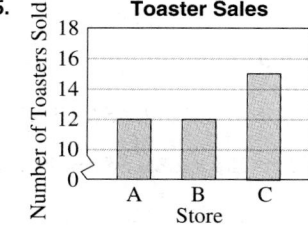

24. The range of the vertical scale is too great. The graph appears flat.

25. The gap in scale makes it appear that toaster C sold much better.

Chapter 1 Assessment • Form A

Answers

1. A number cube was thrown 15 times. The results were as follows.
1, 6, 3, 4, 6, 1, 5, 2, 3, 4, 6, 5, 5, 3, 3
What is the median of this data?

1. 4

2. What is the mode of the data in Exercise 1?

2. 3

3. Make a frequency table of the data in Exercise 1.

3.

Number	Tally	Frequency
1	//	2
2	/	1
3	////	4
4	//	2
5	///	3
6	///	3

4. What number was seen the fewest times on the number cube?

4. 2

5. Make a line plot for the following set of quiz scores.
6, 7, 10, 7, 8, 8, 9, 6, 7, 8, 10, 8.

5.
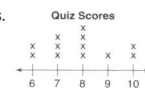

Use the spreadsheet below for Exercises 6–8.

	A	B	C	D	E	F
1	Name	Test I	Test II	Test III	Test IV	Mean
2	Anderson, J.	95	90	91	84	90
3	Baker, V.	68	75	73	74	
4	Bradley, K.	75		74	80	78
5	Burroughs, S.	92	85	89	90	

6. What formula could be used to determine the value of cell F3?

6. = (B3+C3+D3+E3)/4

Chapter 1 Assessment • Form A (continued)

7. Test II score for K. Bradley was erased. What formula could be used to calculate the value of cell C4?

7. = (4*F4)−B4−D4−E4

8. Find the mean test score for S. Burroughs.

8. 89

9. Use the information in the table below to make a bar graph.

Pairs of Shoes Sold

Running	200
Tennis	350
Cross-training	500

9.
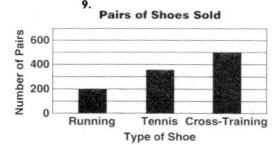

10. Suppose you were to make a bar graph for the following sales in one week.
$575, $826, $604, $281, $132, $617
Would you use 5, 10, 100, or 1,000 for the scale? Explain your reasoning.

10. 100; the data round to hundreds.

Choose A, B, C, or D.

11. What is the mode of the following data set?
97, 90, 91, 92, 89, 90, 95, 94, 96, 91, 92, 94, 90, 89
A. 92 B. 91
C. 90 D. 97 − 89

11. C

Choose a Strategy

12. In how many ways can you make $.40 from combining quarters, dimes, and nickels? Show all your work.

12. 7 ways. Sample shown.

Q	1	1	0	0	0	0	0
D	1	0	4	3	2	1	0
N	1	3	0	2	4	6	8

Writing

13. When is the most appropriate time to use a circle graph? What do the wedges represent?
Use a circle graph when you want to compare parts to a whole. Each wedge is part of the whole.

Chapter 1 Assessment • Form B

Choose the best answer. Circle A, B, C, or D.

1. Two number cubes were thrown 20 times. The total points from both number cubes were as follows: 2, 4, 5, 3, 4, 6, 12, 10, 9, 10, 7, 12, 3, 5, 9, 7, 5, 2, 8, 6. What is the mode of this data?
   (A) 5   **B.** 6   **C.** 8   **D.** 11

2. Which is the median of the data in Exercise 1?
   (A) 6   **B.** 6.45   **C.** 6.5   **D.** 6.8

Use the spreadsheet below for Exercises 3–5.

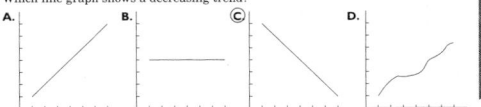

Total Rainfall

	A	B	C	D	E	F	G	H
1	Name	Mon.	Tues.	Wed.	Thurs.	Fri.	Total	Mean
2	Nickeltown	1.2	0.0	0.05	1.1	1.3		
3	Linville	0.10	0.20	1.00	0.0	0.0		
4	Bergtown	0.0	0.0	0.1	0.0	0.0		
5	Burrland	1.2	2.1	0.0	0.0	1.0		
6	Lassville	0.0	0.0	0.0	1.0	0.1		

3. Which formula could be used to calculate the value of cell G2?
   A. = (B2+C2+D2+E2+F2)/5   **(B)** = B2+C2+D2+E2+F2
   C. = B2+B3+B4+B5+B6   **D.** = (D2+D3+D4+D5+D6)/5

4. Which formula could be used to calculate the value of cell H5?
   A. = (B3+C3+D3+E3+F3)/5   **B.** = B5+C5+D5+E5+F5
   (C) = (B5+C5+D5+E5+F5)/5   **D.** = (D2+D3+D4+D5+D6)/5

5. The place with the most rainfall for the 5 days shown is ____.
   A. Nickeltown   **B.** Linville   **C.** Bergtown   **(D)** Burrland

6. Which line graph shows a decreasing trend?
   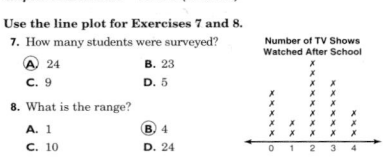
   A.   **B.**   **(C)**   **D.**

Chapter 1 Assessment • Form B (continued)

Use the line plot for Exercises 7 and 8.

7. How many students were surveyed?
   (A) 24   **B.** 23
   C. 9   **D.** 5

Number of TV Shows Watched After School

8. What is the range?
   A. 1   **(B)** 4
   C. 10   **D.** 24

9. What is the mean of the following data set?
   97, 90, 91, 92, 89, 90, 90, 95, 94, 96, 91, 92, 94, 90, 89
   (A) 92   **B.** 91   **C.** 90   **D.** 97 − 89

10. The most appropriate type of graph to display the set of data in Exercise 9 is what type?
    A. circle graph   **B.** line graph   **C.** spreadsheet   **(D)** line plot

11. Shawn saves money from the different incomes he has. He saves the least from which income?

Savings

    A. mowing lawns   **B.** allowance   **(C)** odd jobs   **D.** baby-sitting

12. To create a bar graph for the following data, which value would be most appropriate to use for the scale?
    12, 47, 58, 83, 52, 99, 104, 24, 63, 88
    A. 5   **(B)** 10   **C.** 100   **D.** 1,000

Choose a Strategy

13. In how many ways can you make $.37 from quarters, dimes, nickels, and at most 9 pennies?
    A. 6 ways   **(B)** 11 ways   **C.** 15 ways   **D.** 18 ways

 Teaching Resources

Chapter Support File, Ch. 1, and Spanish Resources

 Teacher's Edition

See pp. 2C–D for Assessment Options.

 Teaching Resource Software

• Computer Item Generator, Ch. 1

Exercises 1 and 8 Review with students the definitions and differences of frequency tables, line plots, and line graphs.

WRITING EXERCISES allow students to describe how they understand the concepts they have learned. **Exercise 5c** is a writing exercise.

OPEN-ENDED PROBLEMS allow for more than one solution. Students must give their own responses instead of choosing from possible answers. Reading these responses will help you determine the depth of student understanding and any possible areas of difficulty. **Exercise 11** is an open-ended problem. Make sure the students support their answers.

---

1 ASSESSMENT

1. The numbers of children in 15 families are 1, 3, 2, 1, 3, 1, 2, 6, 2, 3, 3, 4, 3, 4, and 5.
   a. Make a frequency table.
   b. Make a line plot.
   a–b. See back of book.

2. Find the mean, median, mode, and range of each set of data.
   a. 9, 8, 6, 6, 8, 1, 8, 2 **6; 7; 8; 8**
   b. 31, 20, 31, 51, 27 **32; 31; 31; 31**

3. How many ways can you have $1.05 with only dimes, nickels, and quarters?
   22 ways

4. **Choose A, B, or C.** If all the numbers in a set of data occur the same number of times, then the set has no __?__. **C**
   A. median   **B.** mean   **C.** mode

5. Use the circle graph at the right.
   a. What method do students use *most* to commute to school? **bus**
   b. What method do students use *least*? **bicycle**

   How Students Get to School

   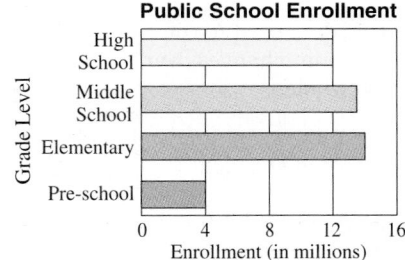

   c. *Writing* Why is a circle graph better for displaying these data than a bar graph? **The data are parts of a whole.**

Use the spreadsheet below.

	A	B	C	D	E
1	Student	Quiz 1	Quiz 2	Quiz 3	Average
2	Yori	81	95	88	
3	Sarah	78	81	87	

6. What is the value of cell C3? **81**
7. = B2 + C2 + D2; = B3 + C3 + D3
7. Write the formulas for cells E2 and E3.
8b. **The trend is positive. The population increased steadily.**

8. *History*
   Use the data in the table at the right.
   a. Display the data in a line graph.
   b. Describe the trend. **See below left.**

Population of the American Colonies

Year	Population
1700	250,900
1710	331,700
1720	466,200
1730	629,400
1740	905,600

9. Create a data set with six numbers. The data set should have a mean of 40, a median of 41, and a range of 18.
   Answers may vary. Sample: 31, 34, 40, 42, 44, 49

10. Use the bar graph below.

    Public School Enrollment

    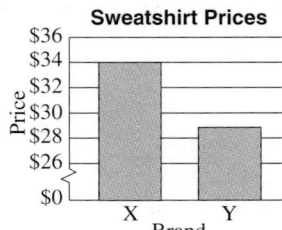

    Source: U.S. Department of Education
    a. preschool   b. elementary
    a. Which grade level has the *least* number of students enrolled?
    b. Which grade level has the *most*?
    c. Estimate the range. **10 million**

11. Why is the graph below misleading?

    Sweatshirt Prices

    The gap in scale makes brand B appear much more expensive than brand C.

Item	Review Topic	Ch	Item	Review Topic	Ch
1, 6, 8	Kinds of measures	1	4	Estimating	Precourse
2, 7	Number problem	1	5	Finding range	1
3, 9	Analyzing graphs	Precourse	10	Constructing graphs	1

1 CUMULATIVE REVIEW

Choose the best answer.

1. Which measure is the greatest for these data? 81, 70, 95, 73, 74, 91, 86, 74 **A**

   A. mean
   B. median
   C. mode
   D. range

2. *Number Sense* When a number is divided by 13, the quotient is 15 and the remainder is less than 4. Which could be the number? **A**

   A. 198   B. 200   C. 190   D. 206

3. *Data Analysis* What information does the bar graph shown *not* give you? **C**

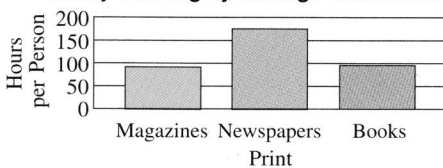

Yearly Reading by Average Americans

   A. Americans spend more time reading newspapers than books.
   B. Americans spend about the same time reading magazines as books.
   C. Most Americans read the Sunday newspaper.
   D. Americans spend twice as much time reading newspapers as books.

4. *Estimation* Which product gives the best estimate of the product 519 × 36? **C**

   A. 500 × 30   B. 550 × 40
   C. 500 × 40   D. 550 × 30

5. A business had weekly profits of $5,000, $3,000, $2,000, $2,500, and $5,000. Which measure might be misleading? **C**

   A. mean   B. median
   C. mode   D. none of these

6. *Number Sense* The mean of three numbers is 19. The median is 22. What do you know about the other numbers? **D**

   A. They are both between 19 and 22.
   B. The numbers must be 17 and 18.
   C. At least one of the numbers is between 19 and 22.
   D. If a number is 24, another must be 11.

7. Grapefruit juice is priced at three cans for $2.39. To the nearest cent, what is the cost of one can? **C**

   A. $.08   B. $.79   C. $.80   D. $1.20

8. In one store portable radios sell for $90, $109, $79, and $60. Find the range. **C**

   A. $60   B. $109   C. $49   D. $19

Use the line graph below for Exercises 9 and 10.

Who Buys Hot Lunch?

9. Estimate the median number of students buying hot lunch. **B**

   A. 70   B. 140   C. 150   D. 120

10. How could you redraw the graph so it appears that about the same number of students buy lunch each day? **C**

    A. Begin the vertical scale at 50.
    B. Use units of 10 instead of 50.
    C. Use units of 100 instead of 50.
    D. Display the data in a circle graph.

Chapter 1 Cumulative Review

Choose the best answer. Circle A, B, C, or D.

1. Find two numbers that have a sum of 45 and a product of 450.
   A. 10, 35   B. 20, 25
   C. 12, 33   **D.** 15, 30

2. Find the product of 37 × 55.
   A. 1,925   B. 2,037
   C. 2,035   D. 3,035

3. Find the sum of 55 + 64 + 36 + 40.
   A. 195   B. 200
   C. 100   D. 155

4. Find the quotient of 654 ÷ 6.
   A. 118   B. 3,924
   C. 55   **D.** 109

5. Find the difference of 63,540 − 7,641.
   A. 55,800   B. 55,799
   C. 55,899   D. 71,181

6. Carlita has 8 coins that total $.58. How many dimes does she have?
   A. 0 dimes   B. 1 dime
   C. 2 dimes   D. 3 dimes

7. Find two consecutive integers whose product is 156.
   A. 13, 14   **B.** 12, 13
   C. 2, 78   D. 6, 26

8. According to the circle graph shown, what is the most preferred way to prepare eggs?

   Preferred Preparation of Eggs

   34% Scrambled
   31% Fried
   23% Boiled
   5% Omelets
   4% Other
   3% Poached

   A. fried   **B.** scrambled
   C. boiled   D. omelets

9. What is the total percentage that do not like their eggs fried or scrambled?
   A. 4%   B. 12%
   C. 23%   **D.** 35%

10. On his grandfather's farm, Mark counted 80 legs and 25 animals. There were only cows and chickens on the farm. How many cows were there on the farm?
    A. 10 cows   **B.** 15 cows
    C. 20 cows   D. 25 cows

11. Find the range of the following data set.
    56, 62, 55, 57, 56, 63, 56, 58, 60, 62
    A. 8   B. 15
    C. 56   D. 63

Assessment

Chapter 1 Cumulative Review (continued)

12. Which of the following line plots represents the data from Exercise 11?

    A.
    ```
        x
        x  x  x  x  x  x
     55 56 57 58 60 63
    ```

    B.
    ```
           x
        x  x  x  x  x
     55 56 57 58 59 60
    ```

    C.
    ```
                          x
        x  x  x  x     x  x  x
     55 56 57 58 59 60 61 62 63
    ```

    D.
    ```
        xxxxxxx  xxx
     55       60       65
    ```

Use the data below for Exercises 13–15.
37, 45, 50, 35, 41, 43, 54, 41, 38, 46

13. Find the mean.
    A. 10   B. 41
    C. 42   **D.** 43

14. Find the median.
    A. 10   B. 41
    C. 42   D. 43

15. Find the mode.
    A. 10   **B.** 41
    C. 42   D. 43

Use the spreadsheet below for Exercises 16–18.

	A	B	C	D	E
1	Day	Time In	Time Out	Total Hours	Amount Earned
2	Sat.	1	6		
3	Mon.	2	8		
4	Tues.	2	8		
5	Wed.	1	8		
6	Thurs.	1	8		
7			Weekly Total		

16. Riki works a summer job for $5.75 an hour. The spreadsheet shows a typical workweek. How much does she earn in a typical week?
    A. $178.25   B. $172.50
    C. $166.75   D. $189.75

17. What would not be a formula for calculating the value of cell E7?
    A. =E2+E3+E4+E5+E6
    B. =5.75*D7
    C. =(D2+D3+D4+D5+D6)*5.75
    D. =(E2+E3+E4+E5+E6)*5.75

18. For how many weeks will Riki have to save in order to take a $878.00 one-week trip to Disneyland?
    A. about 4 weeks   **B.** about 5 weeks
    C. about 6 weeks   D. about 7 weeks

Resources

Teaching Resources

Chapter Support File, Ch. 1
• Cumulative Review

Teacher's Edition

See also pp. 2C-D for Assessment Options.

2 Patterns and Algebraic Thinking

CHAPTER OVERVIEW

To accommodate flexible scheduling, most lessons are divided into parts. Assignment Options are given in the Teacher's Edition for each lesson.

Pages 44–47	**Lesson 2-1** **Data Analysis: Patterns and Number Sense**
NCTM 1, 2, 3, 4, 6, 13	Part 1 Extending Patterns Part 2 Writing Rules for Number Patterns **Key term:** terms ▼ **Project Link**

Pages 48–50	**Lesson 2-2** **Problem Solving Strategy**
NCTM 1, 6, 7	**Look for a Pattern**

Pages 51–54	**Lesson 2-3** **The Order of Operations**

NCTM
1, 2, 5, 7, 9
	Part 1 Using the Order of
	              Operations
	Part 2 Comparing Values of
	              Expressions
	Key term: expression, order of operations
	
	☑ **Checkpoint 1**

Pages 72–76	**Lesson 2-7** **Modeling Equations That Use Multiplication or Division**

NCTM
1, 2, 3, 7, 9, 12
	Part 1 Solving Equations Using
	              Modeling
	Part 2 Solving Using a Calculator or
	              Mental Math
	Key terms: identity properties, commutative properties, associative properties
	
	▼ **Project Link**

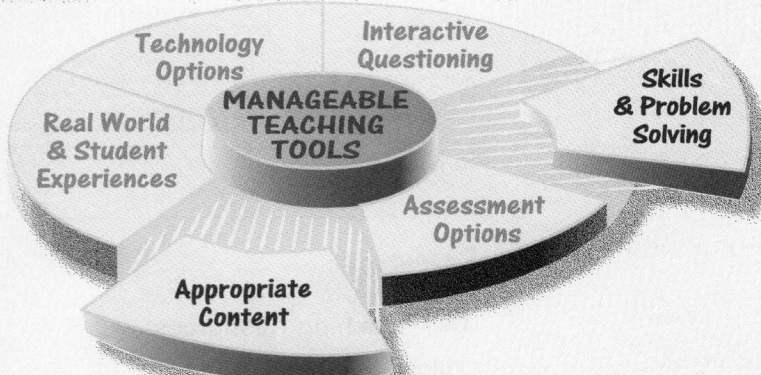

Real World & Student Experiences · Technology Options · Interactive Questioning · MANAGEABLE TEACHING TOOLS · Skills & Problem Solving · Assessment Options · Appropriate Content

Pacing Options

This chart suggests pacing only for the core lessons and their parts. It is provided merely as a possible guide. It will help you determine how much time you have in your schedule to cover other features, such as the Chapter Project, Math Toolboxes, Wrap Up, and Assessment.

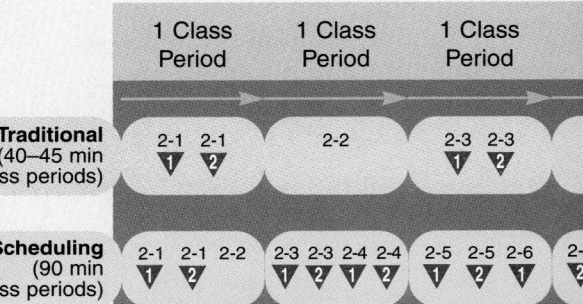

	1 Class Period	1 Class Period	1 Class Period	
Traditional (40–45 min class periods)	2-1 ▼1 2-1 ▼2	2-2	2-3 ▼1 2-3 ▼2	
Block Scheduling (90 min class periods)	2-1 ▼1 2-1 ▼2 2-2	2-3 ▼1 2-3 ▼2 2-4 ▼1 2-4 ▼2	2-5 ▼1 2-5 ▼2 2-6	2-

Stepping Stories

Goal: Model and describe patterns, record data, and write variable expressions to describe a calculation

THEME: PATTERNS

NCTM STANDARDS

1 Problem Solving
2 Communication
3 Reasoning
4 Mathematical Connections
5 Number and Number Relationships
6 Number Systems and Number Theory
7 Computation and Estimation
8 Patterns and Functions
9 Algebra
10 Statistics
11 Probability
12 Geometry
13 Measurement

Pages 56–60	**Lesson 2-4** **Variables and Expressions**
NCTM **1, 2, 3,** **6, 7, 9,** **12**	**Part 1** Modeling Variable Expressions **Part 2** Evaluating Variable Expressions **Key terms:** magic square, variable, numerical expression, variable expression **Journal** **Math at Work**

Pages 61–64	**Lesson 2-5** **Writing Variable Expressions**
NCTM **1, 2, 3,** **4, 5, 9**	**Part 1** Describing Variable Expressions **Part 2** Writing Variable Expressions **Alternative Activity** 2-5 ▼ **Project Link**

Pages 66–70	**Lesson 2-6** **Modeling Equations That Use Addition or Subtraction**
NCTM **1, 2, 7,** **9, 13**	**Part 1** Defining Equations **Part 2** Solving Equations **Key terms:** equation, solve, solution, isolate the variable **Journal** ☑ **Checkpoint 2**

Optional Materials and Manipulatives

graph paper (2-1)
calculator (2-3, 2-4, 2-6, 2-7)

algebra tiles (2-4, 2-6, 2-7)

Optional calculator use is integrated throughout the course.

s	1 Class Period	1 Class Period	1 Class Period	1 Class Period	1 Class Period	1 Class Period	1 Class Period	1 Class Period	1 Class Period	1 Class Period
-5 ▼2	2-6 ▼1	2-6 ▼2	2-7 ▼1	2-7 ▼2						

MEETING INDIVIDUAL NEEDS

Accommodating Diverse Learning Styles

In your Teacher's Edition, you will find suggestions as to how you can help students complete mathematical tasks in Chapter 2 by meeting individual needs and supporting various learning styles. Here are some examples:

VISUAL LEARNING
drawing dots to visualize number patterns *(p. 45)*

TACTILE LEARNING
drawing squares and rectangles to represent tiles *(p. 57)*

AUDITORY LEARNING
sharing students' mnemonics *(p. 52)*

KINESTHETIC LEARNING
solving a problem about numbers of handshakes by acting it out *(p. 49)*

EARLY FINISHERS
Performance-Based Project, MathBlaster® Mystery, Interdisciplinary Units

GIFTED AND TALENTED
creating magic squares *(p. 58)*

DIVERSITY inviting students to explain Hanukkah *(p. 50)*

ACQUIRING ENGLISH PROFICIENCY (AEP)
relating isolating variables to isolated islands *(p. 67)*

ASSESSING PROGRESS

A broad range of assessment tools are available to reach a variety of learners.

INFORMAL ASSESSMENT

Informal assessments provide day-to-day feedback to help give you a picture of conceptual understanding and skill development.

ONGOING ASSESSMENT is built into lesson instruction and the Teaching Notes of the Teacher's Edition.

In the Teacher's Edition
Lesson Quiz for every lesson

In the Student Edition
On Your Own, Mixed Review, Journal, Portfolio, Project Link, Chapter Wrap Up

Look for **Interactive Questions** within lessons that

BUILD UNDERSTANDING with labels such as Analyze, Reasoning, Estimation, Writing, and Summarize

✔ **CHECK UNDERSTANDING** with the Try It Out label.

FORMAL ASSESSMENT

Formal assessment can occur before and after the chapter, as well as at natural breaking points in the chapter.

Checkpoints
Two forms of each self-assessment Checkpoints are available: one in the Student Edition and another in the Chapter Support File in the Teaching Resources box.
- Mid-Chapter Checkpoint 1, page 54
- End-of-Chapter Checkpoint 2, page 70

Chapter 2 Assessment, page 80.
Two alternative forms are available in the Chapter Support File. They may be used after a chapter has been completed, or as a pre-test and post-test comparison.

Cumulative Review, page 81.
Assesses skills and concepts in Chapters 1–2.
An alternative form is available in Chapter Support File.

Computer Item Generator for Chapter 2
Customized tests can be generated for each lesson and for mid-chapter and end-of-chapter assessments, and for pre- and post-test comparisons of achievement.

Interactive Questioning

Technology Options

MANAGEABLE TEACHING TOOLS

Skills & Problem Solving

Real World & Student Experiences

Appropriate Content

Assessment Options

CHAPTER PROJECT

The Chapter Project in the student edition provides a real-world connection to the math context of the chapter. The Teacher's Edition contains a scoring rubric.

Another performance-based Chapter Project with a scoring rubric can be found in the Chapter Support File in the Teaching Resources Box.

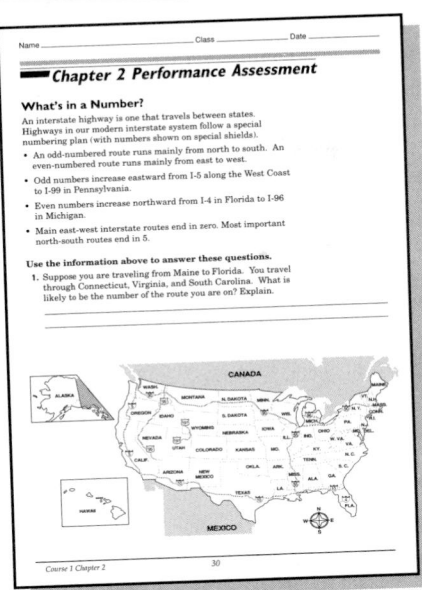

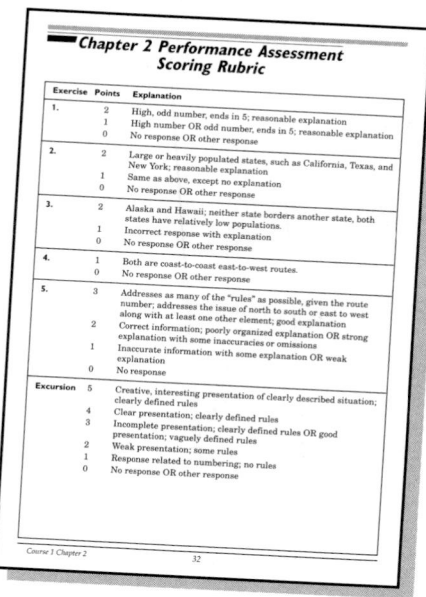

Correlation to Standardized Tests

		STANDARDIZED TEST ITEMS					
Lesson		CAT5	CTBS/5 Terra Nova	ITBS	MAT7	SAT9	Your Local Test
2-1	Data Analysis Patterns and Number Sense	■	■	■	■	■	
2-2	Problem Solving Strategy: Look for a Pattern		■	■	■	2	
2-3	The Order of Operations	■				■	
2-4	Variables and Expressions				■		
2-5	Writing Variable Expressions				■		
2-6	Modeling Equations That Use Addition or Subtraction	■		■	■		
2-7	Modeling Equations That Use Multiplication or Division	■		■	■		

CAT5 California Achievement Test, 5th Edition
CTBS/5 Comprehensive Test of Basic Skills, 5th Edition
ITBS Iowa Test of Basic Skills, Form B
MAT 7 Metropolitan Achievement Test, 7th Edition
SAT9 Stanford Achievement Test, 9th Edition

MAKING CONNECTIONS

MANAGEABLE TEACHING TOOLS
- Technology Options
- Interactive Questioning
- Skills & Problem Solving
- Assessment Options
- Appropriate Content
- Real World & Student Experiences

TEAM TEACHING WITH PRENTICE HALL MATERIALS

MIDDLE GRADES MATH INTERDISCIPLINARY UNITS

- Space Exploration: Activities 3 & 5

INTERDISCIPLINARY EXPLORATIONS

- *Riddles of the Pharaohs* p. 24
- *The Power of Patterns* p. 9
- *Sleuth's Supper* p. 32

SCIENCE EXPLORER

L Life Science **E** Earth Science **P** Physical Science

L Sec. 1-3 Metric System
E Sec. 1-3 Metric System
　Sec. 8-3 Mapping the Earth's Surface
P Sec. 1-3 Metric System

Lesson	Interdisciplinary Connections	Real World Connections	Math Integration
2-1	Biology	Astronomy	Data Analysis
2-2	Speech Music	Savings Jobs Cars Holidays	Data Analysis
2-3	Sports	Consumer Issues	Algebra
2-4	Sports	Concerts Bicycles	Algebra Geometry
2-5	Music Health	Fund-raising Food Amusement Rides Space Flight	Algebra
2-6	Language Arts Science Sports	Sailing Consumer Issues Advertising	Data Analysis Algebra
2-7	Sports	Volleyball Hockey Swimming Pollution Calendar	Algebra Geometry

School to Home

MATERIALS:
pad of paper
pencil

English and Spanish versions are available in the Teacher's Communication Kit, Teacher's Resource box.

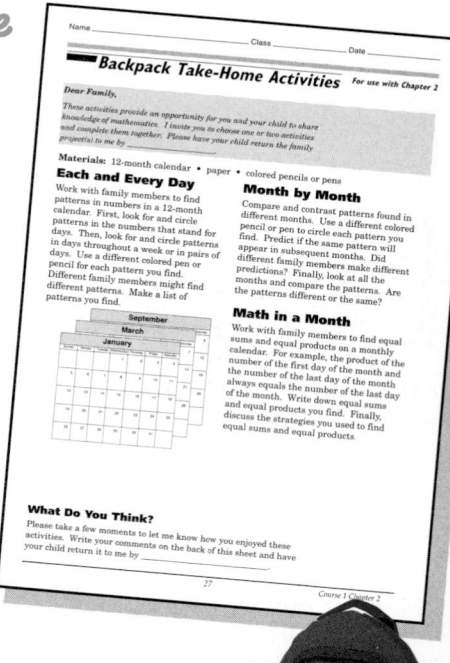

Backpack Take-Home Activities *For use with Chapter 2*

Dear Family,

These activities provide an opportunity for you and your child to share knowledge of mathematics. I invite you to choose one or two activities and complete them together. Please have your child return the family project(s) to me by ___.

Materials: 12-month calendar • paper • colored pencils or pens

Each and Every Day
Work with family members to find patterns in numbers in a 12-month calendar. First, look for and circle patterns in the numbers that stand for days. Then, look for and circle patterns in days throughout a week or in pairs of days. Use a different colored pen or pencil for each pattern you find. Different family members might find different patterns. Make a list of patterns you find.

Month by Month
Compare and contrast patterns found in different months. Use a different colored pencil or pen to circle each pattern you find. Predict if the same pattern will appear in subsequent months. Did different family members make different predictions? Finally, look at all the months and compare the patterns. Are the patterns different or the same?

Math in a Month
Work with family members to find equal sums and equal products on a monthly calendar. For example, the product of the number of the first day of the month and the number of the last day of the month always equals the number of the last day of the month. Write down equal sums and equal products you find. Finally, discuss the strategies you used to find equal sums and equal products.

What Do You Think?
Please take a few moments to let me know how you enjoyed these activities. Write your comments on the back of this sheet and have your child return it to me by ___.

USING TECHNOLOGY TO ENHANCE INSTRUCTION

FOR THE STUDENT

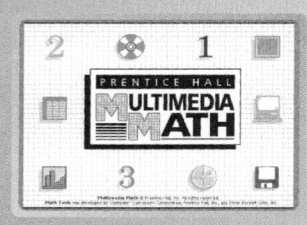

Multimedia Math Hot Pages™
This interactive software and video package on CD-ROM integrates solid math content through a variety of media.
- Hot Page™ 4 (2-1)
- Hot Page™ 5 (2-5)
- Hot Page™ 6 (2-7)

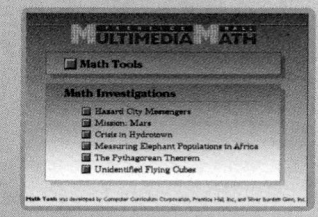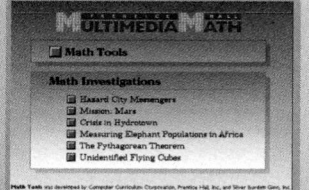

Multimedia Math Investigations
These in-depth interactive activities on CD-ROM develop real-world applications of mathematics. They allow students the opportunity to reinforce key concepts.
- Unidentified Flying Cubes

MathBlaster® Mystery
This award-winning, interactive software program on CD-ROM can be used to maintain skills or to accommodate early finishers.
- Level: Earn 2 coins; Pay 6 coins
- Mission Mode (all lessons)
- Kitchen Comparisons (2-4, 2-6)
- Number Guesser (2-1, 2-7)
- Equation Maker (2-3, 2-5, 2-7)
- Word Problems (2-2, Problem Solving Practice)

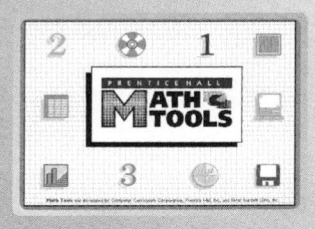

Math Labs
This software, available on both diskette and CD-ROM, includes on-screen Math Lab activities. Students use linkable, interactive tools to explore math concepts.
- Math Lab: Modeling Addition and Subtraction Equations (2-6)

Interactive Student Tutorial
Available on CD-ROM, this test preparation program contains self-tests with questions in standardized test format. Software includes electronic versions of the text lessons and the Math Tools and Math Labs.

For Students
Support for the Chapter Project
A career-oriented link for Math at Work feature

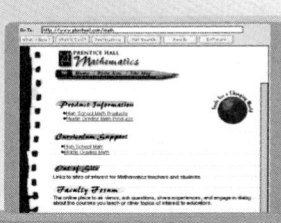

www.phschool.com/math

For teachers
Curriculum Support
Product Information
Regional Support Information

FOR THE TEACHER

Computer Item Generator
Available on both CD-ROM and diskette, this software generates customized practice sheets, quizzes, and tests. It generates an unlimited supply of questions with varying levels of difficulty.

The Resource Pro™
Available on CD-ROM, this software can be used to customize and plan lessons.

Technology Options

Interactive Questioning

Skills & Problem Solving

MANAGEABLE TEACHING TOOLS

Real World & Student Experiences

Appropriate Content

Assessment Options

PATTERNS AND ALGEBRAIC THINKING

CONNECTING TO PRIOR LEARNING Discuss with students where they may have seen or used patterns. Some examples may include counting nickels and dimes, colored tiles in a pattern, counting off for sports teams, brick patterns in buildings, numbers of kinds of stitches to form patterns in knitting (i.e., 2 knit, 3 pearl).

INTERDISCIPLINARY CONNECTIONS Have students research this historic Mexical temple. Challenge them to find other examples of patterns in architecture.

CULTURAL CONNECTIONS Farmers and gardeners often time the planting and harvesting of crops with the patterns in the phases of the moon. These people can use the Farmer's Almanac to tell them which phase of the moon is best for which activity. The belief that the moon has an influence on agriculture is thousands of years old.

ABOUT THE PROJECT The Chapter Project gives students an opportunity to apply their knowledge of patterns and equations to building a fort.

Internet • For information and activities related to the Chapter Project, visit the Prentice Hall site at www.phschool.com/mgm1/ch2

Patterns and Algebraic Thinking

2

| **WHAT YOU WILL LEARN IN THIS CHAPTER** | • How to model patterns and exponents | • How to model and write expressions and equations | • How to solve equations using one of the operations |

Have students practice designing a fort using cubes. Ask students:

- *If your foundation is rectangular, what are all the combinations of foundation lengths and widths that use exactly 30 cubes?* **3 and 10, 2 and 15, 1 and 30**

- *Have students imagine building a wall of cubes on the perimeter of each of these rectangular foundations. Which of these combinations makes a fort with walls and an interior room?* **3 and 10**

PROJECT NOTEBOOK Encourage students to keep all project-related materials in a separate folder or notebook.

Ask students: *Have you ever noticed patterns in a building? Describe some.*

TRACKING THE PROJECT You may wish to have students read Finishing the Chapter Project on page 77 to help them get an overview of the project. Set benchmark deadlines for students to show you their work in progress.

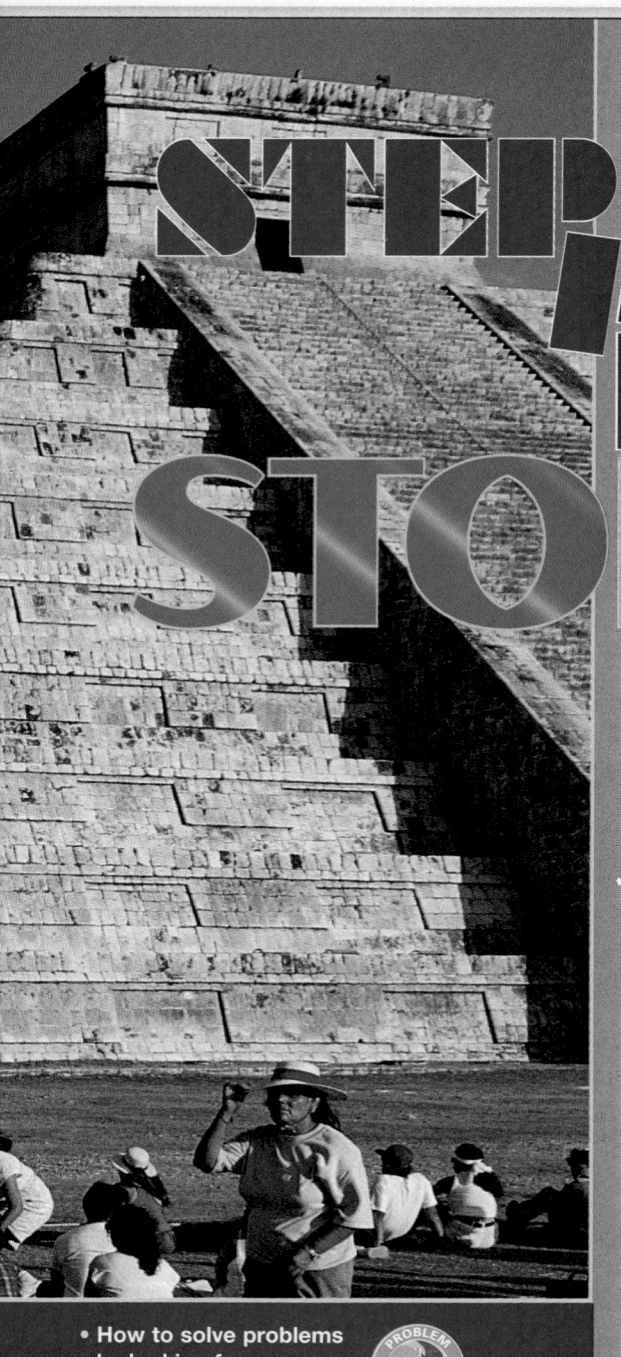

- **How to solve problems by looking for a pattern**

CHAPTER PROJECT

THEME: PATTERNS

STEPPING STONES

Do you see a pattern in the layers of this historic Mayan temple? How many pieces of material do you think were needed at the bottom of the structure compared to the top? Many buildings have mathematical patterns to their designs.

Building a Fort For this project you will build a model of a simple fort. You will record the changing value of the fort as you build up the walls layer by layer. You will look for patterns and write equations to describe the patterns.

Steps to help you complete the project:

p. 47   **Project Link:** *Modeling*
p. 64   **Project Link:** *Recording Data*
p. 76   **Project Link:** *Calculating*
p. 77   *Finishing the Chapter Project*

SCORING RUBRIC

3 Your numerical expressions and equation accurately and clearly describe the reasons for the pattern in the data. Your data, equations, diagrams, and explanations are all organized to give a clear and interesting picture of the pattern you discovered.

2 Your numerical expression and equation correctly describe the pattern, and the total value is within the 200¢ budget. Your work is complete and neat.

1 Your data tables, numerical expressions, and equations are complete, but there are some errors in the equations or data.

0 Diagrams, data tables, numerical expressions, or equations are not complete.

2-1 Teaching Notes

1 Focus

CONNECTING TO PRIOR KNOWLEDGE Start a discussion about number patterns with your students. Ask:

• *Name the first five odd numbers.* **1, 3, 5, 7, 9**

• *What is the pattern in the numbers?* **Start with 1 and add 2 repeatedly.**

Have students create other number patterns and describe them.

2 Teach

THINK AND DISCUSS

DIVERSITY and TACTILE LEARNING
Questions 1–3 Students who experience difficulty with fine motor skills could use a set of tiles instead of graph paper. Students lay

tiles on a piece of paper to create the patterns rather than draw them.

AEP Some students may not understand the word *pattern.* Bring in samples of textile patterns that repeat. Books about quilts or Indian rugs are good sources. Relate the repetition in the designs to the repetition in the number patterns.

Lesson Planning Options

Prerequisite Skills
• ordering whole numbers, fractions, and decimals (precourse)
• using frequency tables and line plots (1-1)

Vocabulary/Symbols
terms

Materials/Manipulatives
• graph paper

Resources

 Student Edition

Skills Handbook, pp. 538, 539
Extra Practice, p. 523
Glossary/Study Guide

 Teaching Resources

Chapter Support File, Ch. 2
• Lesson Planner 2-1
• Practice 2-1, Reteaching 2-1
• Answer Masters 2-1
Teaching Aids Masters 1, 2
Glossary, Spanish Resources

 Transparencies
1, Minds on Math 2-1

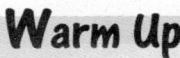 **Warm Up**

Express 3 y and 1 ft in inches. **120 in.**

44

DATA ANALYSIS Connection

2-1 Patterns and Number Sense

What You'll Learn

▼ To find the next term in a number pattern

▼ To write rules for number patterns

...And Why

You can explore patterns concerning animals and astronomy.

Here's How

Look for questions that
▪ build understanding
✔ check understanding

THINK AND DISCUSS

▼ Extending Patterns

The first three designs in a pattern are shown at the right.

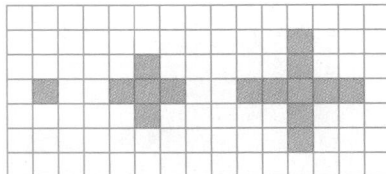

a, c. See back of book.

1. a. ▪ *Patterns* Sketch the fourth and fifth designs.
   b. How many shaded squares are in the fourth design? The fifth design? **13; 17**
   c. Imagine the sixth design. Describe the design in words.

You can form a number pattern from the design pattern above.

terms

1, 5, 9, . . . ← The three dots indicate that the pattern continues without end.

2. Each term in the number pattern represents the number of squares in the corresponding design.

2. How are the first, second, and third terms in the number pattern related to the first, second, and third designs above? **See left.**

3. What are the fourth and fifth terms in the number pattern? **13; 17**

To extend a number pattern, identify the number and operation used to get from one term to the next.

▪ **EXAMPLE 1**   *Real-World Problem Solving*

Patterns Use 50, 46, 42, 38, . . . to find the next three terms.

50, 46, 42, 38, . . . ← Subtract 4 from each term
$\underbrace{\quad}_{-4}\underbrace{\quad}_{-4}\underbrace{\quad}_{-4}$ to get the next term.

50, 46, 42, 38, <u>34</u>, <u>30</u>, <u>26</u> ← Continue the pattern to
$\underbrace{}_{-4}\underbrace{}_{-4}\underbrace{}_{-4}\underbrace{}_{-4}\underbrace{}_{-4}\underbrace{}_{-4}$ find the next three terms.

The next three numbers in the pattern are 34, 30, 26.

Now you may assign Exercises 3–14, 16.

VISUAL LEARNING Question 5a Students may want to draw a picture of the pattern: 4 dots, 7 dots, 10 dots, and 13 dots. Then they can use the picture to find the rule.

Work Together _____

Question 5b Remind students that you multiply or add to go from one number to a greater number. Also, you divide or subtract to go from one number to a lesser number.

■ **ADDITIONAL EXAMPLES**

FOR EXAMPLE 1
Use 67, 107, 147, 187, . . . to find the next three terms. **227, 267, 307**

FOR EXAMPLE 2
Find the next three terms in the number pattern 3, 9, 27, 81, ... **243; 729; 2,187**
Write a rule to describe the number pattern.
Start with 3 and multiply by 3 repeatedly.

EXTENSION Ask students where they have seen patterns. **Answers may vary. Sample: art designs, growth patterns, traffic light intervals, bank interest**

▼2 *Writing Rules for Number Patterns*

To describe the number pattern 1, 5, 9, 13, . . . use the following rule: *Start with the number 1, and add 4 repeatedly.*

Need Help? For practice with multiplying, see Skills Handbook page 540.

■ **EXAMPLE 2**

Patterns Find the next three terms in the number pattern 1, 3, 9, 27, ... Write a rule to describe the number pattern.

$$1, \quad 3, \quad 9, \quad 27, \ldots$$
$$\ \times3\ \ \times3\ \ \times3$$
← *Multiply by 3 to get the next term.*

$$1, \quad 3, \quad 9, \quad 27, \quad \underline{81}, \quad \underline{243}, \quad \underline{729}$$
$$\ \times3\ \times3\ \times3\ \times3\ \times3\ \times3$$
← *Continue the pattern to find the next three terms.*

The next three terms are 81, 243, 729. The rule is *Start with the number 1, and multiply by 3 repeatedly.*

a. 16, 19, 22; start with 4 and add 3 repeatedly.

4. ✓*Try It Out* Find the next three terms in each number pattern. Write a rule to describe each number pattern.
   a. 4, 7, 10, 13, . . .   **b.** 5, 20, 80, 320, . . .

b. 1,280; 5,120; 20,480; start with 5 and multiply by 4 repeatedly.

Work Together _____   *Graphing Number Patterns*

Kangaroo Hopping Speeds

Speed (km/h)	Length of Hop (m)
10	1.2
15	1.8
20	2.4
25	3.0
■ 30	■ 3.6

Biology At times you can predict the length of a kangaroo's hop.
b, d. See back of book.
5. a. Copy and complete the table at the left.
   b. Write two rules for the table: one to describe speed entries and one to describe length of hop entries.
   c. About how far does a kangaroo hop when it reaches a speed of 35 km/h? **4.2 m**
   d. ▪*Estimation* Make a line graph to display the data. Estimate how far a kangaroo hops when it reaches the speed of 27 km/h. **Now you may assign Exercises 1–2, 15, 17–26.**

Technology Options

Prentice Hall Technology

🖫 💿 **Software for Learners**
- Hot Page™ 4*
- Math Blaster® Mystery*
- Interactive Student Tutorial, Chapter 2*

🖫 💿 **Teaching Resource Software**
- Computer Item Generator 2-1
- Resource Pro™ Chapter 2*

Internet • For related mathematics activities, visit the Prentice Hall site at www.phschool.com/math

Available on CD-ROM only

Assignment Options for Exercises On Your Own

To provide flexible scheduling, this lesson can be subdivided into parts.

▼1 **Core** 3–13
   Extension 14, 16

▼2 **Core** 1, 2, 15, 17–25
   Extension 26

Use Mixed Review to maintain skills.

3 Practice/Assess

ERROR ALERT! Exercises 5–13 Students may have difficulty finding a rule for the patterns. **Remediation:** Have them take the first number and find all the ways they can get to the second number. Then take the second number and find all the ways to get to the third number. Have them continue until they

find the one way that is common to all steps in the pattern. For example:

$$2, \quad 6, \quad 18, \quad 54, \ldots$$
$$\times 3 \quad \times 3 \quad \times 3$$
$$+ 4 \quad + 12 \quad + 36$$

The rule is start with the number 2, and multiply by 3 repeatedly.

ASSESSMENT and OPEN-ENDED Exercise 26 Have students exchange their designs with a partner. Have them draw the next three figures in the pattern on a separate piece of paper. They should state the rule and check with their partner to see if their rules match.

WRAP UP

IDENTIFYING THE BIG IDEA Ask students to explain what a pattern is and give several examples.

---

pages 46–47 On Your Own

1d. In the first number pattern, you start with 1 and *multiply by* 2 repeatedly. In the second number pattern, you start with 1 and *add* 2 repeatedly.

3.

17. 486; 1,458; 4,374; start with 6 and multiply by 3 repeatedly.

18. 256; 1,024; 4,096; start with 1 and multiply by 4 repeatedly.

19. 42, 52, 62; start with 2 and add 10 repeatedly.

20. 35, 42, 49; start with 7 and add 7 repeatedly.

21. 60, 45, 30; start with 120 and subtract 15 repeatedly.

22. 126, 138, 150; start with 78 and add 12 repeatedly.

23. 103, 97, 91; start with 127 and subtract 6 repeatedly.

24. 1,250; 6,250; 31,250; start with 2 and multiply by 5 repeatedly.

25. 18, 6, 2; start with 1,458 and divide by 3 repeatedly.

EXERCISES *On Your Own*

1. **a.** Sketch the fifth and sixth designs in the pattern at the right. **See below right.** **b.** 1, 2, 4, 8, 16, 32, . . .
   b. Use the designs to form a number pattern.
   c. Write a rule to describe the number pattern.
   d. How is this rule different from the one that describes the number pattern 1, 3, 5, 7, . . . ? **See margin.**
   c. Start with 1 and multiply by 2 repeatedly.

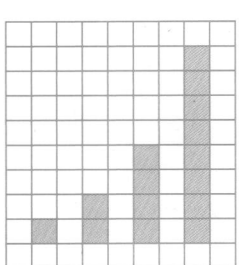

2. Write the first five terms in the following number pattern: *Start with the number 1, and multiply by 4 repeatedly.* 1, 4, 16, 64, 256

Sketch the next three designs in each pattern.

3.
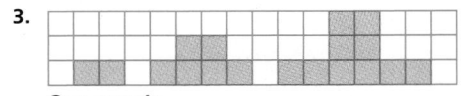
See margin.

4.

See back of book.

Find the next three terms in each number pattern.

5. 2, 4, 6, 8, 10, . . .
12, 14, 16

6. 1, 7, 49, 343, . . .
2,401; 16,807; 117,649

7. 2, 8, 14, 20, . . .
26, 32, 38

8. 8, 16, 24, 32, . . .
40, 48, 56

9. 13, 19, 25, 31, . . .
37, 43, 49

10. 24, 21, 18, 15, . . .
12, 9, 6

11. 64, 32, 16, 8, . . .
4, 2, 1

12. 1; 9; 81; 729; 6,561; . . .
59,049; 531,441; 4,782,969

13. 25, 50, 75, 100, . . .
125, 150, 175

14. *Astronomy* Edmund Halley (1656–1742) first saw the comet named for him in 1682. He correctly predicted that it would return about every 76 years.
   a. *Calculator* Based on Halley's calculations, when was the last time the comet appeared? **1986**
   b. When is the comet expected to return next? About how old will you be? **2062; check students' work for age.**
   c. *Writing* Did Edmund Halley see the comet a second time? Explain. **No; he died in 1742, before the comet returned.**

15. *Writing* Why is it important to tell what number to start with when describing the rule of a number pattern? Give an example. **Number patterns may vary. Sample: Number patterns starting with different numbers may not be the same; 1, 3, 5, 7, . . . and 2, 4, 6, 8, ...**

16. *Reasoning* The Difference Engine is a computer designed by Charles Babbage (1791–1871). If you feed it a list of numbers, it will look for a pattern and continue the list. Why do you think the computer was given this name? **Answers may vary. Sample: The machine looks for patterns in the differences between the numbers in the pattern.**

1a.

Answers may vary. Sample: A real foundation is much bigger and more expensive. A penny foundation has gaps.

LESSON QUIZ

Find the next three terms in each number pattern.

1. 3, 6, 12, 24, . . . **48, 96, 192**

2. 11, 22, 33, 44, . . . **55, 66, 77**

Find the next three terms in each number pattern. Write a rule to describe the pattern.

3. 6, 12, 18, 24, . . . **30, 36, 42; start with 6 and add 6 repeatedly.**

4. 100, 85, 70, 55, . . . **40, 25, 10; start with 100 and subtract 15 repeatedly.**

Find the next three terms in each number pattern. Write a rule to describe each number pattern. 17–25. See margin p. 46.

17. 6, 18, 54, 162, . . .

18. 1, 4, 16, 64, . . .

19. 2, 12, 22, 32, . . .

20. 7, 14, 21, 28, . . .

21. 120, 105, 90, 75, . . .

22. 78, 90, 102, 114, . . .

23. 127, 121, 115, 109, . . .

24. 2, 10, 50, 250, . . .

25. 1,458; 486; 162; 54; . . .

26. *Open-ended* Draw three figures in a design that follow a pattern. State the rule of the pattern using numbers or words. **Check students' work.**

Mixed Review

Organize the data in a frequency table and in a line plot.
(Lessons 1-1 & 1-3) **27–28. See back of book.**

27. ages: 16 15 9 10 9 13 9 12 15 11 8 20

28. points: 8.5 8.8 8.4 8.4 8.5 9 8.6 8.1 8.5 9

29. Find the mean, median, and mode of each set of data in Exercises 27 and 28. **12.25; 11.5; 9**

30. Forty-six members of the hiking club are going camping. Each tent can hold four people. How many tents do they need to take with them? *(Previous Course)* **12 tents**

CHAPTER PROJECT

PROJECT LINK: MODELING

Start by planning a foundation for a fort like the one shown here. You can choose the shape and size of your foundation, but use no more than 30 objects. Suppose each object is worth 1 cent. Find the value of your foundation layer. Now add your first layer of the walls by stacking an object on top of each of the objects along the outer edge. What is the value of your fort with one layer in the wall? **Check students' work.**

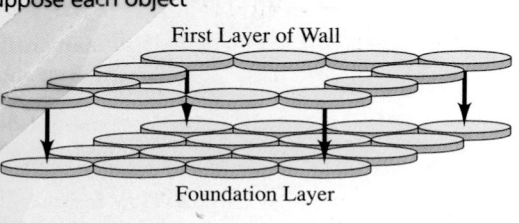

First Layer of Wall

Foundation Layer

Extra Practice, Lesson 2-1, page 523

2-1 Patterns and Number Sense **47**

PRACTICE

47

Practice 2-1 *Patterns and Number Sense*

Sketch the next two designs in each pattern.

1.

2.

Find the next three terms in each number pattern.

3. 3, 5, 7, 9, **11, 13, 15**

4. 34, 31, 28, 25, **22, 19, 16**

5. 2, 6, 18, 54, **162, 486, 1,458**

6. 12, 20, 28, 36, **44, 52, 60**

7. 54, 53, 52, 51, **50, 49, 48**

8. 7, 8, 10, 13, **17, 22, 28**

Find the next three terms in each number pattern. Write a rule to describe each number pattern.

9. 4, 7, 10, 13, ■, ■, ■
16, 19, 22; Start with the number 4 and add 3 repeatedly.

10. 2, 4, 8, 16, ■, ■, ■
32, 64, 128; Start with the number 2 and multiply by 2 repeatedly.

11. 19, 29, 39, 49, ■, ■, ■
59, 69, 79; Start with the number 19 and add 10 repeatedly.

12. 8, 11, 14, 17, ■, ■, ■
20, 23, 26; Start with the number 8 and add 3 repeatedly.

13. 135, 125, 115, 105, ■, ■, ■
95, 85, 75; Start with the number 135 and subtract 10 repeatedly.

14. 5, 10, 20, 40, ■, ■, ■
80, 160, 320; Start with the number 5 and multiply by 2 repeatedly.

15. Write the first five terms in a number pattern starting with the number 6. Write the rule that describes your pattern.
Answers may vary.

In copymaster and workbook formats

RETEACHING

Reteaching 2-1 *Patterns and Number Sense*

Find the next three numbers in the pattern.
  3, 9, 15, 21, ?, ?, ?

Look at how the second number can be found from the first.

  3, 9, 15, 21 or 3, 9, 15, 21
  × 3 (3 × 3 = 9) + 6 (3 + 6 = 9)

Look at how the third number can be found from the second.

  3, 9, 15, 21 or 3, 9, 15, 21
  × 3 (9 × 3 is not 15) + 6 + 6 (9 + 6 = 15)

Try adding 6 to the third number.

  3, 9, 15, 21
  + 6 + 6 + 6 (15 + 6 = 21)

Now you can write a rule to describe the pattern. The rule is *Start with the number 3 and add 6 repeatedly.*
  3, 9, 15, 21, 27, 33, 39
  + 6 + 6 + 6 + 6 + 6 + 6

The next three numbers in the pattern are 27, 33, and 39.

Find the next three numbers in each number pattern. Write a rule to describe each pattern.

1. 2, 5, 8, 11, **14**, **17**, **20**
Start with 2 and add 3 repeatedly.

2. 3, 6, 12, 24, **48**, **96**, 192
Start with 3 and multiply by 2 repeatedly.

3. 9, 18, 27, 36, **45**, **54**, **63**
Start with 9 and add 9 repeatedly.

4. 64, 56, 48, 40, **32**, **24**, 16
Start with 64 and subtract 8 repeatedly.

5. 1, 4, 16, 64, **256**, **1,024**, **4,096**
Start with 1 and multiply by 4 repeatedly.

6. 75, 70, 65, 60, **55**, **50**, 45
Start with 75 and subtract 5 repeatedly.

7. 90, 81, 72, 63, **54**, **45**, 36
Start with 90 and subtract 9 repeatedly.

8. 4, 8, 16, 32, **64**, **128**, 256
Start with 4 and multiply by 2 repeatedly.

ENRICHMENT

Minds on Math Transparency

2-1

Draw as many different lines as possible that pass through any two of the points below. How many different lines are possible?

10

See Solution Key for worked-out answers.

1 Focus

CONNECTING TO PRIOR KNOWLEDGE Ask students for examples of patterns in their lives. **Answers may vary. Sample: When traffic lights turn green, you go; when it is very cold outside, you wear a coat.** Tell students that recognizing patterns can help them solve some kinds of problems.

Lesson Planning Options

Prerequisite Skills
• constructing diagrams from written information (precourse)

Resources

 Student Edition

Skills Handbook, p. 536
Extra Practice, p. 523
Glossary/Study Guide

 Teaching Resources

Chapter Support File, Ch. 2
• Lesson Planner 2-2
• Practice 2-2, Reteaching 2-2
• Answer Masters 2-2
Glossary, Spanish Resources

 Transparencies
80, Minds on Math 2-2

Warm Up

Ask students to use this data to answer the following questions:
June   13 yr, 10 mo
Kari   15 yr, 5 mo
Steve   15 yr, 9 mo
Who is the oldest? **Steve** How much older is Kari than June? **1 yr 7 mo**

---

2 Teach

THINK AND DISCUSS

KINESTHETIC LEARNING Questions 3–6
Students can act out the phone connections using string or rope.

ASSESSMENT Question 7b Before students answer part (b), ask them if the following statement is true: the number of calls $= \frac{1}{2}$ the number of students. **false**

ERROR ALERT! Question 8 Students might assume since 15 members of the club are calling each other, there are 15×14 calls. **Remediation:** Remind students the phone call connecting the first student to the second student is the same as the second student calling the first. This means there is half as many calls. Have students look back through the simpler problems to find the pattern, students $\times$ (students $- 1$) $\div 2$.

PROBLEM SOLVING STRATEGY

2-2 Look for a Pattern

Problem Solving Strategies
Draw a Diagram
Guess and Test
✓ Look for a Pattern
Make a Model
Make a Table
Simulate a Problem
Solve a Simpler Problem
Too Much or Too Little Information
Use Logical Reasoning
Use Multiple Strategies
Work Backward

THINK AND DISCUSS

Patterns are everywhere! You use patterns every day to predict and plan.

Sample Problem ······················
For practice, the speech coach asks each of the 15 members of the speech club to give a speech over the phone to every other member. What is the least number of phone calls needed?

 READ
Read for understanding. Summarize the problem.

Think about the given information and what you are asked to find.

1. How many members belong to the speech club? **15 members**

2. What does the problem ask you to find?

 PLAN
Decide on a strategy.

2. the least number of phone calls needed for every member to speak to every other member

You could draw diagrams and look for patterns in simpler cases. Record the minimum number of phone calls needed for each case.

3. How many calls are needed between 2 members? **1 call**

4. How many calls are needed among 3 members? **3 calls**

5. How many calls are needed among 4 members? **6 calls**

6. How many calls are needed among 5 members? **10 calls**

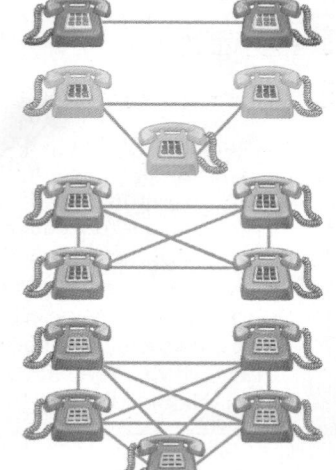

48

■ **ADDITIONAL PROBLEM**

Eight teams are in a basketball league. Each team will play one game against each of the other teams. How many games will be played? **28**

3 Practice/Assess

EXERCISES *On Your Own*

KINESTHETIC LEARNING Exercise 1 Act out the problem with different numbers of students. Organize the handshaking to avoid miscounting.

Exercise 1 Tell students to imagine the people are numbered 1–12. Ask:

- *If number 1 shook hands with numbers 2–12, how many handshakes will there be altogether?* **11**

- *If number 2 shook hands with numbers 3–12 (1 and 2 have already met), how many handshakes will there be altogether?* **10**

Help students write a question whose result is 9. **Answers may vary. Sample: If number 3 shook hands with numbers 4–12, how many handshakes will there be altogether?**

Exercises 3–8 Encourage students to use blocks, tiles, or other manipulatives to model a problem. If students cannot show all their work, have them explain what they did in writing.

➡ **SOLVE**
Try the strategy.

Record the information in a table like the one shown below. Look for a pattern.

Number of Members	Number of Calls
2	1
3	3
4	6
5	10
6	
7	

+2
+3
+4

7. **a.** How many calls are needed among 6 members? **15 calls**
   Among 7 members? **21 calls**

   b. Describe the pattern.   **Each successive number of phone calls increases by a number 1 greater than the preceding increase.**

8. Continue the pattern. Find the number of calls needed among all 15 members of the speech club. **105 calls**

➡ **LOOK BACK**
Think about how you solved the problem.

You could have used *Guess and Test* to find the number of calls needed.

9. Do you think *Guess and Test* would have been a good strategy to use to answer the problem? Why or why not?
   Answers may vary. Sample: No; you would probably need a lot of guesses.

Now you may assign Exercises 1–8.

EXERCISES *On Your Own*

Use *Look for a Pattern* to solve each problem.

1. Twelve people are at a party. Suppose each person shakes hands with each of the others exactly once. How many handshakes will there be altogether? **66 handshakes**

2. *Savings* Germaine plans to save $1 the first week, $2 the second week, $4 the third week, $8 the fourth week, and $16 the fifth week. If Germaine can continue this pattern, how much money will he save the twelfth week? **$2,048**

Technology Options

Prentice Hall Technology

💾 💿 **Software for Learners**

- Math Blaster® Mystery*
- Interactive Student Tutorial, Chapter 2*

💾 💿 **Teaching Resource Software**

- Computer Item Generator 2-2
- Resource Pro™ Chapter 2*

Internet • For related mathematics activities, visit the Prentice Hall site at www.phschool.com/math

*Available on CD-ROM only

Assignment Options for Exercises On Your Own

▽ **Core** 1–6, 8
   Extension 7

Use Mixed Review to maintain skills.

Practice 2-2 Problem-Solving Strategy:
Look for a Pattern

Use Look for a Pattern to solve each problem.

1. A radio station held a contest to give away concert tickets. On the first day, the first caller won. On the second day, the second caller won. On the third day, the fourth caller won. On the fourth day, the seventh caller won. Assuming that this pattern continued, did the thirtieth caller ever win?
no

2. Three drawings are shown. What would the next three look like?

Use any strategy to solve each problem. Show all your work.

3. Find two numbers with a product of 72 and a sum of 17.
9 and 8

4. Juana is one year younger than her husband, Leo. The product of their ages is 650. How old is each?
Juana: 25; Leo: 26

5. A carpenter charges a basic fee of $25, plus $22 per hour. How much will she charge Ms. Lin if she works for 18 hours?
$421

6. The product of two numbers is 442. The sum of the two numbers is 43. Find the two numbers.
26 and 17

7. There are 42 students who signed up for youth camp and 56 students who signed up for family camp. There are 15 students who are signed up for both camps. What is the total number of students who are signed up for camp?
83 students

8. Marquetta charged the Lees a basic fee of $35, plus $25 per hour for repairing their washing machine. What did the Lees pay if it took Marquetta 2.5 hours to finish the job?
$97.50

In copymaster and workbook formats

Reteaching 2-2 Problem-Solving Strategy:
Look for a Pattern

Stony Hollow School District has a softball playoff each spring for its 8 schools. Each school plays 1 game against every other school. The winner is the school with the greatest number of victories. How many playoff games are played in all?

Read What does the problem ask you to find? *You need to find the total number of playoff games.*
How many times will one school play any other school? *1 time*

Plan How can you simplify the problem? *Draw a diagram for a few schools. Look for a pattern.*

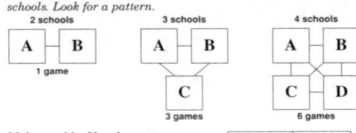

Solve Make a table. Use the pattern you discovered to extend the table to 8 schools.

28 games must be played.

Number of Schools	Number of Games	
2	1	+2
3	3	+3
4	6	+4
5	10	+5
6	15	+6
7	21	+7
8	28	

Look Back Does the pattern make sense? *Yes. Each school added to the table plays each of the other schools once. So the number of games added is 1 less than the total number of schools.*

Use Look for a Pattern to solve each problem.

1. School C won the Stony Hollow School District softball tournament. How many games did School C play in all?
7 games

2. If the Stony Hollow School District had 10 schools, how many playoff games would there be in all?
45 games

3. Each umpire is paid $25 per game. There are 2 umpires for each game. What is the total amount paid to umpires for an 8-team playoff?
$1,400

4. Suppose one team wins all of its games. Why is it impossible for there to be a tie for the championship?
Every other team has lost at least 1 game.

Minds on Math Transparency

2-2

Move one circle in the figure below to make four rows of two circles each.

Move circle 1 below circle 2.

See *Solution Key* for worked-out answers.

DIVERSITY Exercise 8 Ask a student who celebrates Hanukkah to bring a menorah to class. Ask the student to tell the class more about the holiday.

WRAP UP

IDENTIFYING THE BIG IDEA Ask students: *How are patterns useful in problem solving?*

Choose any strategy to solve each problem.

1. How many different pairs can six people make? **15**

2. One day you deposit $1 in the bank. The next day you deposit $3. On the third day, you deposit $5. If you continue the pattern each day, how much money will you have deposited at the end of seven days? **$49**

Choose any strategy to solve each problem. Show all your work.

3. *Jobs* Kieron wants to take his mother, father, and younger sister to the school play. Adults' tickets cost $6.00 and children's tickets cost $2.00. Kieron earns $3.50 per hour babysitting. How many hours will he have to work to buy two adults' and two children's tickets? **5 h**

4. The student council is selling white, pink, and red carnations. The order slip at the right was accidentally torn. How many different combinations could have been ordered?
6 combinations

white	
pink	
red	1
TOTAL	6

5. *Cars* Suppose a car dealer sells at least 3 cars a day. On Monday morning, 50 cars are on the lot. By Friday evening of that week, what is the maximum number of cars the dealer can expect to have left? **35 cars**

6. There are 32 students in the chorus and 44 students in the band. There are 8 students who are in both the chorus and the band. How many students in all are enrolled in these two programs? **68 students**

7. You open a book. The product of the page numbers you see is 600. What are the page numbers? **pages 24 and 25**

8. Hanukkah is a Jewish festival that lasts eight days. Two candles are lit on the first night of Hanukkah. Every night after that these candles are replaced and one more is added. How many candles have been used by the time Hanukkah ends? **44 candles**

Mixed Review

9. *Choose a Strategy* Don expects a grade above 80 in both English and math. How many possible ways are there for him to obtain an average grade of 93? **15 ways**

Find each answer. (*Previous Course*)

10. $918 + 79$
997

11. $160 \div 8$
20

12. $4,809 + 795$
5,604

13. $1,287 \div 3$
429

14. $695 \div 5$
139

15. Suppose you ask 100 people whether they prefer blueberry, raspberry, or vanilla yogurt. What type of graph would be appropriate to display your results? Explain. (*Lesson 1-5*) **Answers may vary.**
Sample: Circle graph; the answers are parts of a whole.

1 Focus

CONNECTING TO PRIOR KNOWLEDGE Ask: *What do people do at a traffic signal?* **They stop on red, prepare to stop on yellow, and go on green.** *What would happen if there was no rule about what the colors mean?* **Answers may vary. Sample: There would be more collisions, especially at busy** intersections. *If everyone decided to stop on yellow, go on red, and prepare to stop on green would that work?* **yes** Encourage students to list other situations where rules and order are important, such as in courtrooms, legislatures, and games.

2 Teach

DIVERSITY Discuss how different countries and cultures have different rules from the United States. In some other countries, they drive on the left side of the road. **England, Australia, Japan** Some languages are read from right to left or up and down. **Arabic and Hebrew; Chinese** Ask student for other examples.

Work Together

Question 1 You may want to pair students and have one student use paper and pencil, the other use a calculator. Note: Some calculators perform operations in the order the students enters, rather than using order of operations.

2-3 The Order of Operations

What You'll Learn

▼ To find the value of expressions using the order of operations

▼ To compare values of expressions

...And Why

You can apply the order of operations to give you the mathematically correct answer for an expression.

Here's How

Look for questions that
 build understanding
 ✔ check understanding

Even soccer equipment—shoes with cleats, socks, and shin guards—needs to be put on in a certain order.

Work Together _____ _Experimenting with Order of Operations_

Which operation does your calculator do first? Let's find out. An **expression** is a mathematical phrase.

Calculator answers may vary.

1. **≡ Calculator** Compute the value of each expression below twice. First use paper and pencil. Then use a calculator.
   a. $18 + 12 \times 6$ b. $15 - 12 \div 3$ c. $(6 + 18) \div 3 \times 6$
      90; 90   11; 11   48; 48

2. a. **Analyze** Compare your results in Question 1. Were the answers in each pair the same? **Check students' work.**
   b. Is it possible to get two different values? Explain.
   c. How might getting two values for one expression cause problems? **Check students' work.**   b. See margin p. 53.

3. **Summarize** Look at each calculator result. Decide which operation the calculator performed first for each expression.
   $\times; \div; +; -$

THINK AND DISCUSS

▼ Using the Order of Operations

The order in which you calculate numbers matters. The **order of operations** gives you a set of rules to follow.

ORDER OF OPERATIONS

1. Do all operations within parentheses first.
2. Multiply and divide in order from left to right.
3. Add and subtract in order from left to right.

4. **✔ Try It Out** Use the expression $3 + 2 \times 5 \times 4$.
   a. What would you do first? Why? **Multiply 2 and 5.**
   b. Write the expression you have after the first step.
   c. What would you do next? **Multiply 10 and 4.**
   d. What is the last step? **Add 3 and 40**
   e. Find the final value. **43**
   b. $3 + 10 \times 4$

Lesson Planning Options

Prerequisite Skills
• using whole numbers (precourse)

Vocabulary/Symbols
expression order of operations

Materials/Manipulatives
• calculator

Resources

 Student Edition

Skills Handbook, p. 540
Extra Practice, p. 523
Glossary/Study Guide

 Teaching Resources

Chapter Support File, Ch. 2
• Lesson Planner 2-3
• Practice 2-3, Reteaching 2-3
• Answer Masters 2-3
Glossary, Spanish Resources

 Transparencies
19, Minds on Math 2-3

Warm Up

Determine a rule for a pattern. Make the pattern using a set of three drawings using squares. Have the first drawing for the pattern be one square. Use your rule for your pattern to determine how to make drawings two and three.

ERROR ALERT! Questions 5–7 Students may have difficulty remembering the order of operations. **Remediation:** Encourage students to create mnemonics for remembering the order of operations. Each mnemonic device should use the letters *P* (parenthesis), *M* (multiply), *D* (divide), *A* (add), and *S* (subtract).

■ **ADDITIONAL EXAMPLES**

FOR EXAMPLE 1

Find the value of each expression.
a. 34 ÷ 2 + (4 × 3) **29**

b. 24 − 6 × 3 **6**

FOR EXAMPLE 2

Replace ■ with <, >, or =.
Use (24 + 8) ÷ 4 − 0 ■ 24 + 8 ÷ 4. **<**

Example 2 Remind students of the meaning of the inequality signs. Tell them the arrow points to the smaller number.

AUDITORY LEARNING Have students share aloud their mnemonic devices and explain what they mean.

ASSESSMENT Have students evaluate the expression 3 + (6 − 2) × 5 with a partner. Have students discuss what they did in each step. **23**

Technology Options

Prentice Hall Technology

 Software for Learners

- Math Blaster® Mystery*
- Interactive Student Tutorial, Chapter 2*

 Teaching Resource Software

- Computer Item Generator 2-3
- Resource Pro™ Chapter 2*

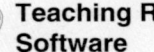 **Internet** • For related mathematics activities, visit the Prentice Hall site at www.phschool.com/math

Available on CD-ROM only

Assignment Options for Exercises On Your Own

To provide for flexible scheduling, this lesson can be split into parts.

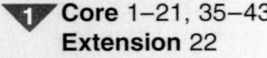 **Core** 1–21, 35–43
Extension 22

Core 23–34, 44–46
Extension 47

Use Mixed Review to maintain skills.

■ **EXAMPLE 1**

Find the value of the expression 30 − (6 + 2) × 3.

$$30 - \underbrace{(6 + 2)} \times 3 \quad \longleftarrow \text{Write the expression.}$$
$$30 - \underbrace{8 \times 3} \quad \longleftarrow \text{Add within the parentheses.}$$
$$30 - \underbrace{24} \quad \longleftarrow \text{Multiply 8 and 3.}$$
$$6 \quad \longleftarrow \text{Subtract 24 from 30.}$$

5. ✓*Try It Out* Find the value of each expression.
a. 17 − 4 × 2   **b.** 3 + 5 × 2 − 6   **c.** 10 ÷ 2 + 3 × 8
    9   **7**   **29**

Most calculators use the order of operations. To find the value of 18 + 6 ÷ 3 and 3 × (5 + 2), use the keystrokes shown.

18 ⊞ 6 ⊟ 3 ⊟ *20*

3 ⊠ (5 ⊞ 2) ⊟ *21*

CALCULATOR HINT

Some calculators perform operations strictly from left to right. If your calculator does not use the order of operations, you may need to insert parentheses. For example, enter 18 + 6 ÷ 3 as 18 ⊞ (6 ⊟ 3).

6. ▪*Calculator* Find the value of each expression.
a. 24 − 10 ÷ 2 **19**   **b.** 15 + 5 × 2 **25**   **c.** 18 ÷ (3 − 1) **9**
d. 16 ÷ 4 × (13 − 9) × 7 **112**   **e.** (69 − 13) + 60 ÷ 5 **68**

Now you may assign Exercises 1–22, 35–43.

2 Comparing Values of Expressions

Use the order of operations to compare values of expressions.

■ **EXAMPLE 2**

Replace ■ with <, >, or =.
Use (12 − 4) + 6 ÷ 2 ■ 12 − (4 + 6) ÷ 2.

$$\underbrace{(12 - 4)} + 6 \div 2 \quad ■ \quad 12 - \underbrace{(4 + 6)} \div 2 \quad \longleftarrow \text{Do operations within parentheses.}$$
$$8 + \underbrace{6 \div 2} \quad ■ \quad 12 - \underbrace{10 \div 2} \quad \longleftarrow \text{Divide on both sides.}$$
$$\underbrace{8 + 3} \quad ■ \quad \underbrace{12 - 5} \quad \longleftarrow \text{Add and subtract.}$$
$$11 \quad ■ \quad 7 \quad \longleftarrow \text{Compare sides.}$$
$$11 > 7$$

7. ✓*Try it Out* Replace ■ with <, >, or =.
a. (18 + 8) ÷ 2 + 4 ■ 18 + 8 ÷ 2 + 4   **<**
b. (24 + 11) ÷ (5 + 2) ■ (24 + 11) ÷ 5 + 2   **<**

8. Replace ■ with <, >, or =.
a. 5 + 0 ■ 5 (addition property of zero)   **=**
b. 5 × 0 ■ 0 (multiplication property of zero)   **=**

Now you may assign Exercises 23–34, 44–47.

KINESTHETIC LEARNING If you have block scheduling or extended class periods, have students suggest and act out a series of three actions that must be done in a certain order. **Answers may vary. Sample: (1) Put on socks. (2) Put on shoes. (3) Tie shoes.** Students may act out their series in the wrong order to show why order matters to achieve the correct result.

EXTENSION Ask students how they would solve the expression: $(9 \times 3 + 3) \div 10$. **Perform the order of operations within the parentheses first. Multiply 9×3, then add 3, then divide by 10.**

3 Practice/As

EXERCISES *On Your Own*

REASONING Exercise 19 Have students write an example. **Answers may vary. Sample: $(4 + 2) \times 3$**

WRITING Exercise 20 Have each student write the explanations in the form of instructions. Then have another student follow the instructions to solve the problem.

EXERCISES *On Your Own*

Which operation would you perform first?

1. $8 - 2 \times 3$ $\times$

2. $(40 - 16) \div 4$ $-$

3. $15 \times 8 \div 3$ $\times$

4. $12 - 2 \times 3 \div 5$ $\times$

5. $63 \div 7 \times (5 - 2)$ $-$

6. $12 - 9 \div 3 - 2$ $\div$

Find the value of each expression.

7. $6 - 2 + 4 \times 2$ **12**

8. $3 + 3 \times 2$ **9**

9. $33 - (14 + 6)$ **13**

10. $4 \times 3 + 20 \div 5$ **16**

11. $6 \times (2 \times 5)$ **60**

12. $26 + 4 - 4 \times 2$ **22**

13. $400 \div (44 - 24)$ **20**

14. $12 + 8 \times 6$ **60**

15. $13 - (7 + 4)$ **2**

16. $45 \div 9 + 6 \times 3$ **23**

17. $7 \times (4 + 6) \times 3$ **210**

18. $13 + 5 \times 12 - 4$ **69**

19. *Reasoning* When would you add before multiplying?
If addition is in parenthesis, you add before multiplying

20. *Writing* Explain the steps you would use to find the value of the expression $8 \div 4 \times 6 + (7 - 5)$. **See margin.**

21. a. Find the value of each expression.
   i. $(4 + 5) \times 5$ **45**   **ii.** $4 + (5 \times 5)$ **29**   **iii.** $4 + 5 \times 5$ **29**
   b. What do you notice about the values in part (a)?
the values of expressions (ii) and (iii) are the same, yet different from (i).

22. The price of the apples at the right will be reduced by 20 cents. Next week the reduced price will double.
   a. To find next week's price, should you use $79 - 20 \times 2$ or $(79 - 20) \times 2$? Explain. **See margin.**
   b. Find the price of apples next week. **$1.18**

79¢ Per lb

Replace 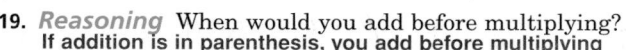 **with <, >, or =.**

23. $(3 + 9) \times 4$ $\overset{>}{\blacksquare}$ $3 + 6 \times 4$

24. $(8 - 2) \times (6 + 1)$ $\overset{>}{\blacksquare}$ $(8 - 2) \times 6$

25. $2 + (12 \div 3)$ $\overset{=}{\blacksquare}$ $2 + 12 \div 3$

26. $7 - 2 \times 0$ $\overset{>}{\blacksquare}$ $(7 - 2) \times 0$

27. $2 \times (15 - 3)$ $\overset{<}{\blacksquare}$ $2 \times 15 - 3$

28. $62 - 37 + 8$ $\overset{>}{\blacksquare}$ $62 - (37 + 8)$

Place parentheses in each equation to make it true.

29. $12 + 6 \div 2 - 1 = 8$
$(12 + 6) \div 2 - 1 = 8$

30. $14 \div 2 + 5 - 1 = 1$
$14 \div (2 + 5) - 1 = 1$

31. $1 + 2 \times 15 - 4 = 33$
$(1 + 2) \times (15 - 4) = 33$

32. $11 - 7 \div 2 = 2$
$(11 - 7) \div 2 = 2$

33. $14 - 3 - 2 \times 3 = 11$
$14 - (3 - 2) \times 3 = 11$

34. $5 \times 6 \div 2 + 1 = 10$
$5 \times 6 \div (2 + 1) = 10$

CHECKPOINT 1

Name _____ Class _____ Date _____

▄▄▄ *Checkpoint 1*   *Lessons 2-1 through 2-3*

1. Write the first five terms in the following number pattern: Start with the number 3. Multiply by 3 and add 1 repeatedly.
   3, 10, 31, 94, 283

2. A bus comes to the bus stop at 7:40, 8:15, 8:50, and 9:25 each morning. If this pattern continues, when will the next three stops be?
   10:00 A.M., 10:35 A.M., 11:10 A.M.

Find the value of the expression.

3. $4 + 4 \times 2$ **12**

4. $36 \div 9 + (4 \times 2)$ **12**

Write <, >, or =.

5. $5 + (16 \div 4)$ $\boxed{=}$ $5 + 16 \div 4$

6. $(7 - 4) \times (8 + 1)$ $\boxed{>}$ $(7 - 4) \times 8$

page 51   Work Together
  2b. Yes; some calculators perform operations as soon as you enter them.

pages 53–54   On Your Own
  20. First, subtract 5 from 7. Then, divide 8 by 4 and multiply the result by 6. Last, add 12 and 2.

  21b. The values of expressions (ii) and (iii) are the same, yet different from (i).

  22a. $(79 - 20) \times 2$; you must use parentheses to show that subtraction comes first.

PRACTICE

Practice 2-3 *The Order of Operations*

Which operation would you perform first?

1. $4 + 6 \times 9$
   6×9
2. $(7 - 5) \times 3$
   $(7 - 5)$
3. $14 \div 2 \times 3$
   $14 \div 2$

4. $18 - 5 + 3$
   $18 - 5$
5. $5 \times 2 + 6$
   5×2
6. $(9 + 14) - 8 \div 2$
   $(9 + 14)$

Find the value of the expression.

7. $8 - 3 \times 1 + 5$
   10
8. $(43 - 16) \times 5$
   135
9. $14 \times 6 \div 3$
   28

10. $100 \div (63 - 43)$
    5
11. $9 \times (3 \times 5)$
    135
12. $7 \times (8 + 6)$
    98

13. $15 - (5 + 7)$
    3
14. $(12 - 9) \times (6 + 1)$
    21
15. $(9 - 3) \times 2$
    12

16. $8 - 3 \times 2 + 7$
    9
17. $(9 - 4) \times 6$
    30
18. $35 - 5 \times 3$
    20

Compare. Use <, >, or = to complete each statement.

19. $5 - 3 \times 1 \;\boxed{=}\; (5 - 3) \times 1$
20. $(4 + 8) \times 3 \;\boxed{>}\; 4 + 8 \times 3$

21. $3 \times (8 - 2) \;\boxed{<}\; 3 \times 8 - 2$
22. $(7 + 2) \times 4 \;\boxed{>}\; 7 + 2 \times 4$

23. $4 + (20 \div 4) \;\boxed{>}\; (4 + 20) \div 4$
24. $42 - (35 + 4) \;\boxed{<}\; 42 - 35 + 4$

25. $(9 - 2) \times 3 \;\boxed{>}\; 9 - 2 \times 3$
26. $55 + 10 - 7 \;\boxed{=}\; 55 + (10 - 7)$

Place parentheses in each equation to make it true.

27. $6 + 7 \times 4 - 2 = 26$
    $(6 + 7) \times (4 - 2) = 26$
28. $14 - 5 + 3 = 3$
    $(14 - 5) \div 3 = 3$

29. $27 \div 4 + 5 - 1 = 2$
    $27 \div (4 + 5) - 1 = 2$
30. $6 \times 7 + 2 - 1 = 53$
    $6 \times (7 + 2) - 1 = 53$

In copymaster and workbook formats

RETEACHING

Reteaching 2-3 *The Order of Operations*

To find the value of an expression follow the **order of operations**.
First, do all operations inside parentheses.
Next, multiply and divide from left to right.
Then, add and subtract from left to right.

Find the value of
$$6 + (3 + 4) \times 2.$$

① Work inside parentheses. → $(3 + 4) = 7$
   $$6 + 7 \times 2$$

② Skip over the addition. Multiply next. → $7 \times 2 = 14$
   $$6 + 14$$

③ Then, add.
   $$6 + 14 = 20$$

Compare $10 - (6 \div 2) + 1$ and $(10 - 6) \div 2 + 1$.

First, find the value of each expression.   Then, use <, >, or = to compare.

$10 - (6 \div 2) + 1$	$(10 - 6) \div 2 + 1$	$8 > 3$
$10 - 3 + 1$	$4 \div 2 + 1$	So,
$7 + 1$	$2 + 1$	$10 - (6 \div 2) + 1 > (10 - 6) \div 2 + 1$.
8	3	

Find the value of the expression.

1. $3 + (4 + 1) \times 2$
   a. $4 + 1 = \underline{5}$
   b. $\underline{5} \times 2 = \underline{10}$
   c. $3 + \underline{10} = \underline{13}$

2. $24 \div (5 + 3) - 2$
   a. $5 + 3 = \underline{8}$
   b. $24 \div \underline{8} = \underline{3}$
   c. $\underline{3} - 2 = \underline{1}$

3. $2 + 6 \times 3 \div 3 = \underline{8}$
4. $(6 + 2) \times 3 + 4 = \underline{6}$
5. $7 + 5 \times 2 - 6 = \underline{11}$
6. $12 \div 3 \times 5 - 6 = \underline{14}$

Compare. Use <, >, or = to complete each statement.

7. $9 + 3 \times 4 \;\boxed{=}\; 9 + (3 \times 4)$
8. $(12 - 4) \times 3 \;\boxed{>}\; 12 - (4 \times 3)$

9. $6 \div 3 + 4 \times 2 \;\boxed{=}\; (6 \div 3) + 4 \times 2$
10. $3 \times (12 - 5) + 2 \;\boxed{<}\; 3 \times 12 - (5 + 2)$

11. $15 - (12 \div 3) \;\boxed{>}\; (15 - 12) + 3$
12. $8 + 2 \times (9 - 7) \;\boxed{<}\; 8 + (2 \times 9) - 7$

13. $10 + (10 \div 5) \;\boxed{=}\; 10 + 10 \div 5$
14. $20 - (2 \times 6) \;\boxed{<}\; (20 - 2) \times 6$

ENRICHMENT

Minds on Math Transparency

2-3

Write the letters A, B, C, D, and E in the squares so that the same letter is not used more than once in any row, column, or diagonal.

A	E	D	B	C
B	C	E	D	A
C	D	B	A	E
D	A	C	E	B
E	B	A	C	D

Answers may vary. Sample is shown.

See *Solution Key* for worked-out answers.

54

Exercises 35–43 Have students check their answers by doing each problem two ways.

WRAP UP

IDENTIFYING THE BIG IDEA Ask students to explain how to use the order of operations, and tell why these rules are necessary.

LESSON QUIZ

Find the value of the expression.
1. $8 \times (5 - 3)$ **16**

Replace ■ with <, >, or =.
2. $(6 + 9) \div 3 \;\blacksquare\; 7 \times (8 - 8)$ **>**

Place parentheses in the equation to make it true.
3. $12 + 8 \div 4 - 2 = 3$
$(12 + 8) \div 4 - 2 = 3$

Choose Use a calculator, paper and pencil, or mental math to find each answer.

35. $5 + 2 \times 0$ **5**
36. $(63 + 37) \div 5$ **20**
37. $160 \div (25 - 5)$ **8**

38. $4 \times (13 - 6)$ **28**
39. $(12 - 7) \times 5 + 1$ **26**
40. $13 \times (46 - 46)$ **0**

41. $(63 - 48) \times 1$ **15**
42. $(16 \times 4) \div (42 - 34)$ **8**
43. $18 \div 6 - (5 - 4)$ **2**

Insert operation symbols to make each equation true.

44. $(6 \;\overset{+}{\blacksquare}\; 9) \;\overset{\times}{\blacksquare}\; 4 \;\overset{\div}{\blacksquare}\; 6 = 10$
45. $(12 \;\overset{-}{\blacksquare}\; 8) \;\overset{\times}{\blacksquare}\; (5 \;\overset{\times}{\blacksquare}\; 1) = 20$
46. $14 \;\overset{\div}{\blacksquare}\; 7 \;\overset{+}{\blacksquare}\; 2 \;\overset{+}{\blacksquare}\; 3 = 7$

47. *Open-ended* Write three expressions that equal 8, 9, and 10, respectively. Use the numbers 1, 2, 5, and 6, operation symbols, and the order of operations. **Samples:** $6 \times 2 - (5 - 1); 5 - 2 \times 1 + 6; (5 \times 6) \div (1 + 2)$

Mixed Review

48. Will has 2 copies of a *Batman* comic book valued at $35 each and an *Amazing Spiderman* comic valued at $170. Find the value of his comic collection. *(Previous Course)* **$240**

49. *Choose a Strategy* The lockers in the sixth-grade hallway are numbered 100 to 275. How many lockers are there? **176 lockers**

✓ CHECKPOINT 1

Lessons 2-1 through 2-3

Find the value of each expression.

1. $8 + 13 \times 2$ **34**
2. $66 \div (2 + 4)$ **11**
3. $(1 + 12 - 7) \div 3$ **2**

Find the next three terms in each number pattern.

4. $9; 45; 225; 1,125; \ldots$
   5,625; 28,125; 140,625
5. $54, 49, 44, 39, \ldots$
   34, 29, 24
6. $0, 7, 14, 21, \ldots$
   28, 35, 42

7. *Open-ended* Create a number pattern. List at least five terms. Then write a rule to describe the number pattern. **Sample: 12, 17, 22, 27, 32; start with 12 and add 5 repeatedly.**

8. *Choose a Strategy* A bus can hold 44 passengers. It starts out empty and picks up 1 passenger at the first stop, 2 at the second stop, 3 at the third stop, and so on. If no one gets off of the bus, at which stop will the bus become full? **The bus will be full before the last passenger at stop 9 can get on.**

PROBLEM SOLVING PRACTICE ★★

This page provides problems for students to solve using their knowledge of patterns, mean, expressions, and addition and subtraction. Allow students to use any method they find helpful.

Problem 4 Ask students first to write a description of the pattern in the form of a rule, such as: *Add 8 to the previous number.* Then students can apply their rules to find the missing number in the pattern.

USING MANIPULATIVES **Problems 6 and 7** Students may want to use base-ten blocks to model the addition and subtraction in these problems.

Problem 8 Encourage students to write their own expression for the problem. Have them find an expression in the answer choices that means the same as the expression they wrote.

PROBLEM SOLVING PRACTICE ★★★★★

Choose the best answer.

1. Dennis works as a waiter. On five days he earned $25, $35, $45, $40, and $35 in tips. What was the mean (average) amount he earned each day? **C**

   A. $34   B. $35
   C. $36   D. $180

2. For 4 days, Juanita kept a record of the number of laps she jogged around the school track. The numbers she recorded were 7, 11, 15, and 19. If she continues in the same pattern, how many laps will she jog on the fifth day? **J**

   F. 20   G. 21
   H. 22   J. 23

3. Zachary is going to buy a new computer monitor that costs $392. He has already saved $295. How much more does he need to save? **D**

   A. $687   B. $197
   C. $103   D. $97

4. Suki kept the following record of the number of sit-ups she did for 5 days in a row: 10, 18, 26, 34, 42. If she continues in the same pattern, how many sit-ups will she do on the sixth day? **H**

   F. 44   G. 46
   H. 50   J. 52

5. Jill walks her dog three times every day. Each walk lasts from 10 to 20 minutes. How many times does she walk her dog in 1 year (365 days)? **D**

   A. 375   B. 385
   C. 985   D. 1,095

Please note that items 6–9 have *five* answer choices.

6. Eric bought a stove costing $572 and a refrigerator costing $679. What was the total cost? **J**

   F. $107
   G. $1,141
   H. $1,151
   J. $1,251
   K. Not Here

7. Marvella wants to save $1,000 to attend computer camp. So far she has saved $718. How much more does she need to save? **C**

   A. $382
   B. $318
   C. $282
   D. $218
   E. Not Here

8. At an amusement park, each person pays $5 to enter plus $2 for each ride. Suppose each person pays for 9 rides. Which expression represents the total amount spent? **F**

   F. $5 + 9 \times 2$
   G. $(5 + 9) \times 2$
   H. $(5 \times 9) + 2$
   J. $5 \times 9 \times 2$
   K. Not Here

9. A carton is packed with 24 cans that weigh 14 ounces each. What is the total weight of all the cans? **D**

   A. 38 ounces
   B. 136 ounces
   C. 236 ounces
   D. 336 ounces
   E. Not Here

1 Focus

CONNECTING TO PRIOR KNOWLEDGE Have students give examples of ways they have used to hold their place. **Answers may vary. Sample: A friend holds a place in line, a backpack saves a seat in the lunchroom.** Tell students that sometimes there is a number either missing or unknown in a math

expression. Ask students to name ways they could save a place for a number in an equation. **Answers may vary. Sample: Use letters or another symbol such as a box.**

2 Teach

THINK AND DISCUSS

Question 1 Tell students they must first find a column, row, or diagonal that contains only

numbers. Point out that students can use the diagonal from the bottom left to the top right of the magic square to find that the sum of each row, column, and diagonal is 15.

AEP Relate the word *variable* to the word *vary*. A variable's value can vary or change.

MENTAL MATH Question 4a Ask students to explain how they found their answers. Ask:

Lesson Planning Options

Prerequisite Skills
- using whole numbers (precourse)
- using decimals (precourse)

Vocabulary/Symbols
magic square, variable, numerical expression, variable expression

Materials/Manipulatives
- algebra tiles
- calculator

Resources

 Student Edition

Skills Handbook, p. 541
Extra Practice, p. 523
Glossary/Study Guide

 Teaching Resources

Chapter Support File, Ch. 2
- Lesson Planner 2-4
- Practice 2-4, Reteaching 2-4
- Answer Masters 2-4

Teaching Aids Master 27
Glossary, Spanish Resources

 Transparencies
81, Minds on Math 2-4

Warm Up

Ask the students to find the product of the numbers in each line.
1, 2 **2**
1, 2, 3 **6**
1, 2, 3, 4 **24**

2-4 Variables and Expressions

What You'll Learn

▼ To model variable expressions

▼ To evaluate variable expressions

...And Why

You can use models and algebra to evaluate expressions and solve an ancient puzzle.

Here's How

Look for questions that
- build understanding
- ✔ check understanding

THINK AND DISCUSS

▼ Modeling Variable Expressions

A **magic square** is a special arrangement of numbers in a square. The rows, columns, and diagonals all have the same sum.

Magic Square

a	7	2
1	5	b
8	c	4

1. Find the magic square sum above. Explain how you found it. **15; use the diagonal 8-5-2 and add the numbers, 8 + 5 + 2.**

A **variable** is a symbol, usually a letter, that stands for an unknown number.

2. ✔ *Try It Out* Name the variables in the magic square above. **a, b, c**

A **numerical expression** contains only numbers and operation symbols.

$$8 + 5 + 2$$

A **variable expression** contains at least one variable.

a. the sum of the diagonal with entries 8, 5, and 2 $a + 7 + 2$

3. a. What does the numerical expression $8 + 5 + 2$ represent?

b. What does the variable expression $a + 7 + 2$ represent?

c. ▪*Analyze* What is true about the values of both expressions? **The value of each expression is 15.**

b. the sum of the top row with entries *a*, 7, and 2

Art In 1514, artist Albrecht Dürer included a 4-by-4 magic square in this mysterious and complex engraving.

Source: *Mathematical Puzzles & Diversions*

- *Did you use a row, column, or diagonal?*

- *Do you think one way is easier to do mentally?* **Answers may vary. Sample: No; it is just as easy to add 7 + 2, as it is to add 8 + 1 or 5 + 4.**

TACTILE LEARNING Some students may prefer to draw the squares and rectangles representing the tiles.

ERROR ALERT When using the algebra tiles, alert students not to assume $x = 5$ just because the green tile looks about five times

the length of the yellow tile. **Remediation:** Tell students to say the words *some number* whenever they see a variable. The green tile represents a variable, so it represents *some number*. The tile is meant to be a visual representation of an unknown value.

■ **ADDITIONAL EXAMPLES**

FOR EXAMPLE 1

Model the expression $4y + 2$ with algebra tiles. **Students should show 4 green tiles and 2 yellow tiles.**

FOR EXAMPLE 2

Use algebra tiles to evaluate $3x + 2$ for $x = 4$. **14**

FOR EXAMPLE 3

Evaluate $8a - 3$ for $a = 3$. **21**

ERROR ALERT! **Example 3b** Students might believe r and s are equal just because they are both variables. **Remediation:** Point out that different letters used for variables in the same problem have different values. The

4. a. ▪*Mental Math* What is the value of a in the magic square at the top of page 56? **6**

   b. Name another variable expression that you could use to find the value of a. $a + 1 + 8$ or $a + 5 + 4$

5. a. In the magic square at the top of page 56, what variable expressions could you use to determine the value of b? Of c?

   b. ▪*Mental Math* What is the value of b? Of c? **9; 3**
   5a. $1 + 5 + b$ or $2 + b + 4$; $8 + c + 4$ or $7 + 5 + c$

You can model numerical and variable expressions with tiles. Yellow tiles represent ones. Green tiles represent variables.

Expression		Model
$2 + 3$	$\longrightarrow$	
$4x$ (means $4 \times x$)	$\longrightarrow$	
$2x + 3$	$\longrightarrow$	

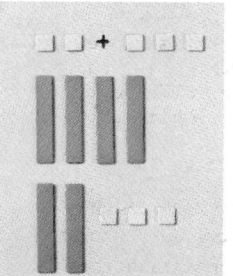

■ **EXAMPLE 1**

Modeling Model the expression $3x + 1$ with algebra tiles.

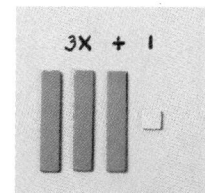

Model $3x$ with 3 green tiles and model 1 with 1 yellow tile.

6. ✓*Try It Out* Model each expression with algebra tiles.
   a. $2x$ **b.** $4 + 1$ **c.** $x + 4$ **d.** $5x + 2$

   Now you may assign Exercises 1–10, 30, 36–37.

❷ *Evaluating Variable Expressions*

You can evaluate a variable expression using algebra tiles.

6a.

b.

c.

d.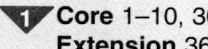

Technology Options

Prentice Hall Technology

Software for Learners

- Math Blaster® Mystery*
- Interactive Student Tutorial, Chapter 2*

Teaching Resource Software

- Computer Item Generator 2-4
- Resource Pro™ Chapter 2*

Internet • For related mathematics activities, visit the Prentice Hall site at www.phschool.com/math

*Available on CD-ROM only

Assignment Options for Exercises On Your Own

To provide flexible scheduling, this lesson can be subdivided into parts.

❶ Core 1–10, 30
   Extension 36, 37

❷ Core 11–29, 31–35
   Extension 38

Use Mixed Review to maintain skills.

same letters used for variables in the same problem must have the same value.

ASSESSMENT Have students evaluate the expression $2a + 3b$ for $a = 2$ and $b = 5$, showing each step. **19** Have them exchange their work with a partner. Next to each step, the partner writes what operation was performed.

EXTENSION Tell students:

- A *term* is a variable, a variable and a number multiplied together, or a number by itself. **t, $3x$, 2**

- A *coefficient* is a number in a term that is written in front of a variable. **4 in $4z$**

- A *constant* is a term that is a number only. **8**

Write the expression $2x + 1$. Have students identify the terms, coefficient, and constant. **terms: $2x$, 1; coefficient: 2, constant: 1**

3 Practice/Assess

EXERCISES *On Your Own*

Exercises 1–4 Make sure students understand they may choose any letter or symbol to use as a variable. Discuss why they might avoid using certain variables like *o* and *z*. *o* and *z* look like the numbers 0 and 2. Ask students for other examples. **Answers may vary. Sample: *l* and 1, *s* and 5**

■ EXAMPLE 2

Modeling Use algebra tiles to evaluate $2x + 1$ for $x = 3$.

Model the expression $2x + 1$.   Replace each green tile with 3 yellow tiles.

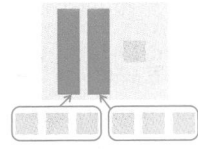 

The value of $2x + 1$ for $x = 3$ is 7.

7. ✓*Try It Out* Use algebra tiles to evaluate $6 + 3t$ for $t = 2$.
12

You can evaluate a variable expression with numbers. Replace each variable with a number. Then follow the order of operations.

■ EXAMPLE 3

a. Evaluate $7b - 11$ for $b = 6$.
$$7b - 11 = 7(6) - 11 \quad \longleftarrow \text{Replace } b \text{ with 6.}$$
$$= 42 - 11 \quad \longleftarrow \text{Multiply 7 and 6.}$$
$$= 31 \quad \longleftarrow \text{Subtract 11 from 42.}$$

b. Evaluate $r(36 - s)$ for $r = 4$ and $s = 8$.
$$r(36 - s) = 4(36 - 8) \quad \longleftarrow \text{Replace } r \text{ with 4 and } s \text{ with 8.}$$
$$= 4(28) \quad \longleftarrow \text{Subtract 8 from 36.}$$
$$= 112 \quad \longleftarrow \text{Multiply 4 and 28.}$$

8. ✓*Try It Out* Evaluate each expression.
a. $56 - 7x$ for $x = 5$ **21**   **b.** $a(1 + 2b)$ for $a = 5$ and $b = 3$
35

Now you may assign Exercises 11–29, 31–35, 38.

EXERCISES *On Your Own*

Modeling **Write a variable expression for each model.**

1–4. Variable labels may vary. Samples are given.

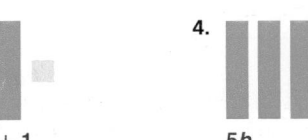

1. $4a + 1$ 2. $b + 4$ 3. $2a + 1$ 4. $5b$

EXTENSION **Exercises 11–16** Have students choose another value for *x* and re-evaluate each expression.

EXTENSION **Exercise 30** Have students work in pairs to create their own magic squares.

CONNECTION TO TECHNOLOGY **Exercises 31–34** Have students check their answers with a spreadsheet program. Enter the *x*-values in column A. In column B, use the expression to define a formula.

WRITING **Exercise 36** Tell students to use examples in their explanations.

CONNECTION TO GEOMETRY **Exercise 38** Help students discover where the formula for perimeter of a rectangle comes from. Remind them that a rectangle has opposite sides that are equal, so two lengths are equal (2*l*), and two widths are equal (2*w*).

WRAP UP

IDENTIFYING THE BIG IDEA Have students discuss what variables are and how they are used.

JOURNAL Students can look at word problems in the text for example ideas.

pages 58–60   On Your Own

5.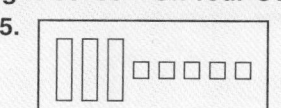

6.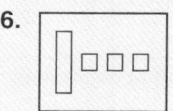

7.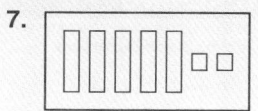

8.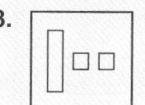

9.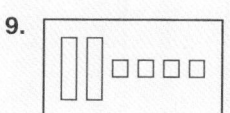

10.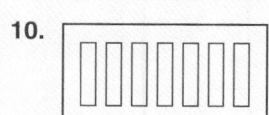

Modeling **Model each variable expression with tiles.**   5–10. See margin.

5. $3x + 5$ **6.** $c + 3$ **7.** $5b + 2$ **8.** $x + 2$ **9.** $4 + 2x$ **10.** $7x$

Mental Math **Evaluate each expression for $x = 8$.**

11. $x + 12$ 20   **12.** $80 \div x$ 10   **13.** $7x$ 56   **14.** $10 + 2x$ 26   **15.** $x \div 2$ 4   **16.** $2(x - 3)$ 10

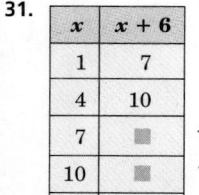 *Choose* **Use a calculator, mental math, or paper and pencil to evaluate each expression.**

17. $24 \div d$ for $d = 3$ 8   **18.** $p + 8$ for $p = 6$ 14   **19.** $3r - 2$ for $r = 65$ 193

20. $8b - 12$ for $b = 6$ 36   **21.** $n \div 10$ for $n = 30$ 3   **22.** $75s$ for $s = 20$ 1,500

23. $3(2c)$ for $c = 3$ 18   **24.** $8 - 3y$ for $y = 2$ 2   **25.** $6a + 8$ for $a = 7$ 50

26. $6n - (m + 8)$ for $m = 20$ and $n = 15$ 62   **27.** $5x - y$ for $x = 12$ and $y = 14$ 46

28. $2r + st$ for $r = 7$, $s = 30$, and $t = 5$ 164   **29.** $2abc$ for $a = 35$, $b = 3$, and $c = 10$ 2,100

30. Copy and complete the magic square shown at the right. Find the values of r, s, and t.

	4	9	*r*	8
11	*s*	7	3	
	6	5	*t*	10

Copy and complete each table by evaluating the expression for the given values of x.

31.

x	*x* + 6	
1	7	
4	10	
7	▨	13
10	▨	16
14	▨	20

32.

x	7*x*	
2	▨	14
4	▨	28
6	▨	42
8	▨	56
10	▨	70

33.

x	100 − *x*	
20	▨	80
35	▨	65
50	▨	50
72	▨	28
88	▨	12

34.

x	3*x* + 4	
0	▨	4
1	▨	7
2	▨	10
5	▨	19
10	▨	34

35. **Choose A, B, C, D, or E.** Use the expression $9x - 4$. Which value of x gives you a result of 50?   **D**

   A. 10   **B.** 45   **C.** 5   **D.** 6   **E.** 7

36. *Writing* What is the difference between a numerical expression and a variable expression?   **A numerical expression contains only numbers and operations. A variable expression also contains at least one variable.**

PRACTICE

Practice 2-4 *Variables and Expressions*

Write a variable expression for each model. Squares represent ones.
Shaded rectangles represent variables. Sample answers given.

1.
   _3 + 2x_

2.
   _3x + 6_

3.
   _2x + 5_

Choose a calculator, mental math, or paper and pencil
to evaluate each expression.

4. $56 \div b$ for $b = 7$
   _8_

5. $3m$ for $m = 9$
   _27_

6. $8n$ for $n = 9$
   _72_

7. $4y + 6$ for $y = 18$
   _78_

8. $v + 16$ for $v = 9$
   _25_

9. $2t - 8$ for $t = 21$
   _34_

10. $2(4e)$ for $e = 5$
    _40_

11. $12 - 2g$ for $g = 3$
    _6_

12. $3pq$ for $p = 3$ and $q = 5$
    _45_

13. $7n - (m + 18)$ for $n = 4$ and $m = 10$
    _0_

14. $9r + 16$ for $r = 8$
    _88_

15. $s(58 + t)$ for $s = 2$ and $t = 7$
    _130_

16. $24 - 4t$ for $t = 4$
    _8_

17. $3v + 5k$ for $v = 3$ and $k = 6$
    _39_

18. $5d - (h + 9)$ for $d = 3$ and $h = 5$
    _1_

Complete each table by evaluating the expression
for the given values of x.

19.
x	$x + 7$
2	9
5	12
8	15
11	18
14	21

20.
x	$5x$
3	15
6	30
9	45
12	60
15	75

21.
x	$125 - x$
15	110
30	95
45	80
60	65
75	50

22.
x	$6x + 5$
2	17
4	29
6	41
8	53
10	65

In copymaster and workbook formats

RETEACHING

Reteaching 2-4 *Variables and Expressions*

Numerical expressions are made up of numbers and operation symbols.

Examples:
$6 + 3$ $9 \times 2 + 1$

Variable expressions contain one or more variables. A **variable** is a letter that stands for an unknown number.

Examples:
$x + 4 \times 2$ $a - b$

You can model variable expressions using objects.

 ▢▢▢▢

The 3 paper clips represent 3 of the same variable.

$3p + 4$

You can evaluate the variable expression $3p + 4$ if you know a value for p.

① Think of each paper clip as having a value of 6.

$3p + 4$ for $p = 6$ means $3 \times 6 + 4$

② Then use the order of operations to evaluate.

$3p + 4 = 3 \times 6 + 4$
$= 18 + 4$
$= 22$

Write a variable expression for each model. Answers may vary.

1.
   _p + 2_

2.
   _2p_

3.
   _3p + 6_

Evaluate each expression.

4. $3t - 4$ for $t = 8$
   $3 \times \underline{8} - 4 = \underline{20}$

5. $7c$ for $c = 6$
   $7 \times \underline{6} = \underline{42}$

6. $k \div 2$ for $k = 20$
   $\underline{20} \div 2 = \underline{10}$

7. $15 + m$ for $m = 6$
   _21_

8. $2x + 1$ for $x = 3$
   _7_

9. $5y - 10$ for $y = 6$
   _20_

10. $4m + 8$ for $m = 5$
    _28_

11. $3(4h)$ for $h = 2$
    _24_

12. $9 - 3r$ for $r = 2$
    _3_

13. $a - b$ for $a = 5$ and $b = 4$
    _1_

14. $3ab$ for $a = 3$ and $b = 4$
    _36_

15. $x + 2y$ for $x = 3$ and $y = 2$
    _7_

Reteaching

ENRICHMENT

Minds on Math Transparency

2-4

The number on Julie's softball jacket has 2 digits.
Her number is a multiple of 3, 4, 5, and 6. What
is Julie's number?

60

See *Solution Key* for worked-out answers.

60

Math at Work

If you have block scheduling or extended class periods, ask students who have a mountain bike, road bike, or hybrid to bring their bicycles to class. Ask students to investigate the differences in the bicycles. You may want to ask a bicycle designer or mechanic to visit the class.

37. *Reasoning* Why is the symbol $\times$ used to show multiplication in numerical expressions but not in variable expressions? **See below right.**

38. *Geometry* The formula for the perimeter of a rectangular swimming pool is $2\ell + 2w$. The length ℓ of the pool is 24 ft and the width w is 12 ft. Find the perimeter. **72 ft**

Mixed Review

Find the next three terms in each number pattern.
(Lesson 2-1)

39. 1, 4, 16, 64, . . .
    256; 1,024; 4,096

40. 32, 35, 38, 41, . . .
    44, 47, 50

41. 2,187; 729; 243; 81; . . .
    27, 9, 3

42. Would you find the mean, median, or mode to discover the favorite pizza topping of the students in your class? Explain.
    (Lesson 1-3) **Mode; you use the mode when the data are not numerical.**

43. Margarite is standing in the middle of a line to buy concert tickets. There are 47 people in front of her. How many people are in the line? *(Previous Course)* **95 people**

JOURNAL
Describe a variable in your own words. Where have you seen variables used before? Give an example of a situation where a variable could be useful.

37. **Answers may vary. Sample: The symbol $\times$ can be easily confused with a variable x.**

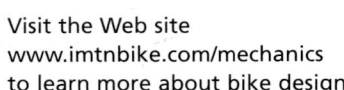

BICYCLE DESIGNER

What kind of bicycle would you like to own? With so many different types of bicycles to choose from, it could be a difficult decision. A bicycle designer combines mathematical, visual, and artistic skills to make special bicycle designs.

Bicycle designers use mathematical patterns to find the size and shape of the wheels, the number of gears, and how well these parts will work together for the cyclist. They also use math skills to find the size, shape, weight, and cost of materials.

Visit the Web site
www.imtnbike.com/mechanics
to learn more about bike design.

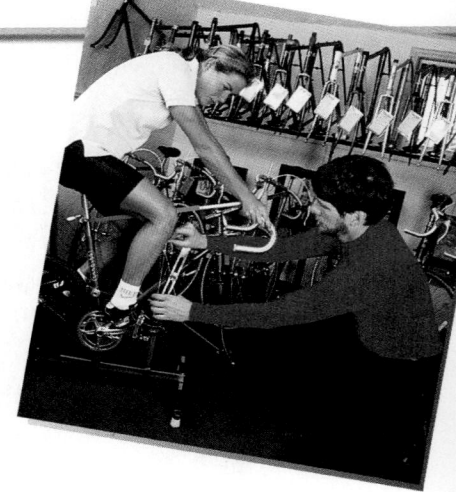

LESSON QUIZ

Evaluate each expression for $x = 7$.

1. $x + 13$ **20**

2. $9 + 3x$ **30**

Evaluate each expression.

3. $16 \div a$ for $a = 4$ **4**

4. $7b - 10$ for $b = 5$ **25**

5. $12c - 3c$ for $c = 9$ **81**

6. $3d + e$ for $d = 5$ and $e = 2$ **17**

Teaching Notes

1 Focus

CONNECTING TO PRIOR KNOWLEDGE Ask students for word phrases for these expressions:

3 + 2 three plus two; the sum of three and two

2 × 4 two times four; the product of two and four, twice four

5 − 3 five minus three; three less than five

2 Teach

Work Together

ERROR ALERT! Students may have trouble distinguishing the small difference in the word phrases *5 less than a number* and *5 is less than a number*. **Remediation** *Is* means *equals* in math. Always circle the *is*. This will help students remember to write < where they would usually write =.

THINK AND DISCUSS

VISUAL LEARNING Write the word phrases on the board. Draw brackets and arrows from the words to the symbols.

22	more than	a number
22	1	n

2-5 Writing Variable Expressions

What You'll Learn

❶ To describe variable expressions with word phrases

❷ To write variable expressions

...And Why

You can use variable expressions to describe fund-raising, food, and space flight situations.

Here's How

Look for questions that
❖ build understanding
✔ check understanding

a. the sum of *b* and 15; 15 more than a number

b. the difference of *m* and *n*; *n* less than *m*

c. 6 times *x*; the product of 6 and *x*

d. the quotient of 18 and *p*; 18 divided by *p*

Work Together ___ *Exploring How to Write Expressions*

1. ❖*Think About It* Make a list of all the words or phrases you can think of that describe each operation: addition, subtraction, multiplication, and division.

2. ❖*Analyze* Use your list to describe each numerical expression in as many different ways as you can.
   a. 5 + 8   b. 10 − 4   c. 10 × 3   d. 18 ÷ 6

1–2. Check students' work.

THINK AND DISCUSS

❶ *Describing Variable Expressions*

You can use a word phrase to describe a variable expression. Here are some examples.

Word Phrase	Variable Expression
the sum of *m* and 45	$m + 45$
22 more than a number	$n + 22$
w less than 55	$55 - w$
the product of *w* and 10	$10w$
the quotient of *r* and *s*	$r \div s$

a–d. Answers may vary. Samples are given.

3. ✔*Try It Out* Write two word phrases for each variable expression.
   a. $b + 15$ b. $m - n$ c. $6x$ d. $18 \div p$

   Now you may assign Exercises 1–21.

❷ *Writing Variable Expressions*

You can write a variable expression using a word phrase.

4. ✔*Try It Out* Write a variable expression for each word phrase.
   a. five plus *y*
      $5 + y$
   b. 6 times *q*
      $6q$
   c. 2 less than *x*
      $x - 2$

Lesson Planning Options

Prerequisite Skills
• using whole numbers (precourse)

Resources

📖 **Student Edition**

Skills Handbook, p. 536
Extra Practice, p. 523
Glossary/Study Guide

📔 **Teaching Resources**

Chapter Support File, Ch. 2
• Lesson Planner 2-5
• Practice 2-5, Reteaching 2-5
• Alternative Activity 2-5
• Answer Masters 2-5
Teaching Aids Master 27
Glossary, Spanish Resources

📺 **Transparencies**
Minds on Math 2-5

Warm Up

Ask students to write the following numbers as the sum of two primes.

50 19 + 31; or 3 + 47; or 7 + 43; or 13 + 37

36 7 + 29; or 5 + 31; or 13 + 23; or 17 + 19

44 13 + 31; or 3 + 41; or 7 + 37

Question 4b Students may use × to indicate multiplication. Suggest they use parentheses, (6)(*q*), nothing between, 6*q*, or a multiplication dot, 6 · *q*, to avoid confusing the multiplication symbol × with the variable *x*.

AUDITORY LEARNING Write 2*m* on the board. Ask students to name the variable and tell what it represents. **_m_; money raised at last year's car wash** Encourage students to form the habit of saying aloud, or to themselves, what variables represent.

Question 5 Ask students to explain why they chose the word phrases. **Answers may vary. Sample: I looked for the numbers in the dialogue.** Ask students if word phrases expressing mathematical ideas always contain a number written as a word. Explain. **No; they could contain the words _only_ or _double_. These words are not numbers, but they represent numbers.**

■ ADDITIONAL EXAMPLE

FOR EXAMPLE
Write two word phrases for the expression 10 + *n*. **the sum of 10 and _n_; 10 more than _n_**

CONNECTING TO THE STUDENTS' WORLD
Discuss word phrases for variable expressions found in everyday life. **Answers may vary. Sample: Sam is 3 in. taller than Mike for _m_ + 3.**

Technology Options

Prentice Hall Technology

 Software for Learners

- Hot Page™ 5*
- Math Blaster® Mystery*
- Interactive Student Tutorial, Chapter 2*

 Teaching Resource Software

- Computer Item Generator 2-5
- Resource Pro™ Chapter 2*

Internet • For related mathematics activities, visit the Prentice Hall site at www.phschool.com/math

*Available on CD-ROM only

Assignment Options for Exercises On Your Own

To provide flexible scheduling, this lesson can be subdivided into parts.

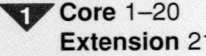 **1** **Core** 1–20
Extension 21

2 **Core** 22–36, 38, 39
Extension 37, 40–43

Use Mixed Review to maintain skills.

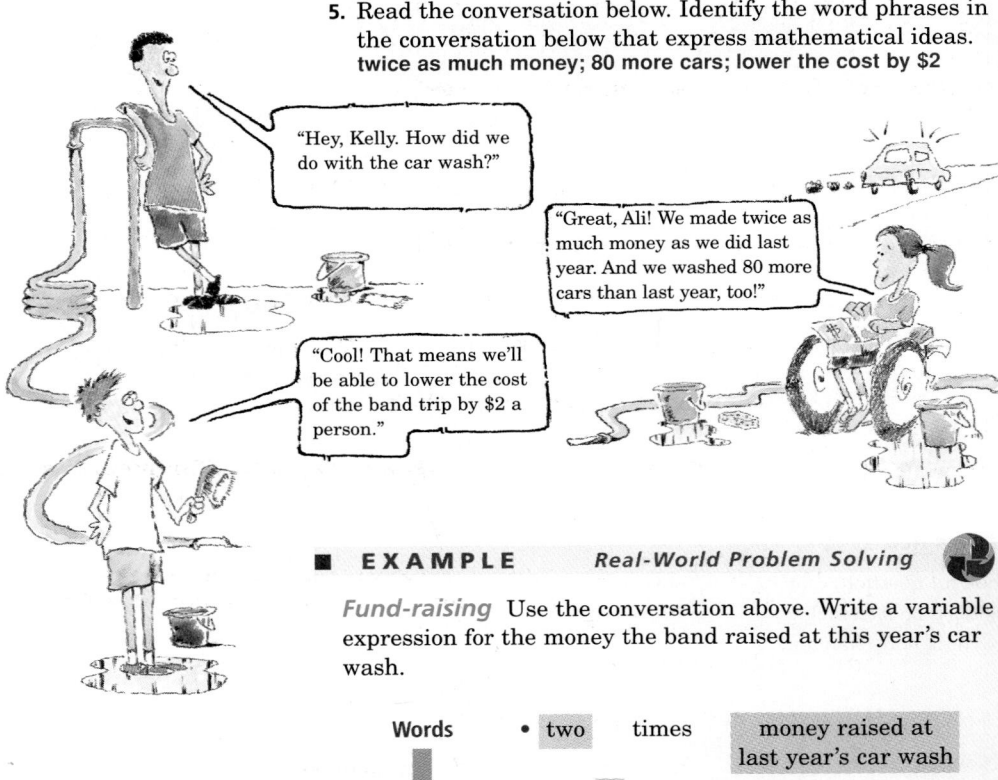

5. Read the conversation below. Identify the word phrases in the conversation below that express mathematical ideas. **twice as much money; 80 more cars; lower the cost by $2**

"Hey, Kelly. How did we do with the car wash?"

"Great, Ali! We made twice as much money as we did last year. And we washed 80 more cars than last year, too!"

"Cool! That means we'll be able to lower the cost of the band trip by $2 a person."

■ EXAMPLE   *Real-World Problem Solving*

Fund-raising Use the conversation above. Write a variable expression for the money the band raised at this year's car wash.

Words	•	two	times	money raised at last year's car wash

• Let *m* = money raised

Expression	•	2	×	*m*

A variable expression for the money raised this year is 2*m*.

6. ⬧*What If . . .* Suppose the band raised $240 at last year's car wash. Evaluate the expression in the Example to find the money raised at this year's car wash. **$480**

7. a. ✓*Try It Out* Write a variable expression for the number of cars the band washed this year. **_n_ + 80**
  b. Suppose the band washed 50 cars last year. Find the number of cars washed at this year's car wash. **130**

8. ⬧*Go a Step Further* Suppose *t* was the cost per person for the band trip before the car wash. Write a variable expression for the cost of the trip after the car wash. **_t_ − 2**

Now you may assign Exercises 22–43.

EXERCISES *On Your Own*

ASSESSMENT Exercises 1–10 Give students the expression $n + 8$. Have pairs write down as many word phrases as they can think of. **Answers may vary. Sample: *n* plus 8, the sum of *n* and 8, 8 more than *n*, the total of 8 and *n*, 8 increased by *n*** All pairs should come up with at least two phrases on their own. Have the pair with the

most phrases share them with the class. Carefully critique the phrases. Have other pairs add to the list.

TACTILE LEARNING Exercise 22 If you have block scheduling or extended class periods, have partners make a proportional model using clay or a piece of paper. Then scratch into the clay or write on the paper the variable expression for each side.

REASONING Exercise 37b Remind students their expression must represent the time in minutes, not in seconds. Ask them how they could make their expression represent the time in hours. **Divide by 60.**

WRITING Exercise 38 Ask students to decide when the order of words in a variable expression is important. **Order is important in subtraction and division.**

EXERCISES *On Your Own*

Write two word phrases for each variable expression.

1. $z + 24$ 2. $y - x$ 3. $7s$ 4. $g \div h$ 5. $7 - x$

6. $t + 6$ 7. $18 - h$ 8. ab 9. $21 \div m$ 10. $4n$

1–10. Answers may vary. See margin for samples.

What operation does the given word or phrase indicate?

11. more than $+$ 12. quotient $\div$ 13. increased by $+$ 14. total $+$ 15. product $\times$

16. plus $+$ 17. less than $-$ 18. times $\times$ 19. divided by $\div$ 20. difference $-$

21. **Choose A, B, C, or D.** Which word phrase does *not* describe the expression $36 - x$? **B**

   A. 36 minus x B. 36 less than x C. 36 decreased by x D. a difference of 36 and x

22. *Food* The length of the largest lasagna in the United States was ten times its width.
   a. Write a variable expression for the length of the lasagna. **Let *w* = width; 10w.**
   b. Why is w a good variable to use to represent the width? ***w* is the first letter of "width."**
   c. The lasagna measured 7 ft wide. Evaluate the expression to find the length of the lasagna. **70 ft**

Write a variable expression for each word phrase.

23. 34 less than k
   $k - 34$
24. 8 multiplied by x
   8x
25. d more than 50
   $50 + d$
26. 23 times q
   23q
27. 7 increased by b
   $7 + b$
28. r less than 13
   $13 - r$
29. h times 150
   $h \times 150$ or 150h
30. 4 added to e
   $e + 4$
31. eight less than s
   $s - 8$
32. six more than a number
   $6 + n$
33. two inches taller than you
   $h + 2$
34. b divided by 3
   $b \div 3$
35. the sum of r and s
   $r + s$
36. the product of three and m
   $3m$

37. *Amusement Rides* Suppose you ride one roller coaster all day. The ride lasts 45 seconds.
   a. Let t represent the number of times you go on the ride. Write a variable expression for the number of seconds you spend riding the roller coaster. **45t**
   b. *Reasoning* Write a variable expression for the number of minutes you spend riding the roller coaster. **$\frac{3}{4}t$**

38. *Writing* Do the phrases *twenty-two less than x* and *x less than twenty-two* result in the same variable expression? Explain.
   No; *twenty-two less than x* is $x - 22$, but *x less than twenty-two* is $22 - x$.

pages 63–64   On Your Own
1. the sum of z and 24; 24 more than a number
2. the difference of y and x; x less than y
3. 7 times s; the product of 7 and s
4. the quotient of g and h; g divided by h
5. the difference of 7 and x; x less than 7
6. the sum of t and 6; 6 more than a number
7. the difference of 18 and h; h less than 18
8. a times b; the product of a and b
9. the quotient of 21 and m; 21 divided by m
10. 4 times n; the product of 4 and n

PRACTICE

Practice 2-5 *Writing Variable Expressions*

Write two word phrases for each variable expression. Answers may vary.

1. $5m$
five times m,
the product of
five and m

2. $8 + b$
b more than 8,
the sum of 8
and b

3. $15q$
fifteen times a
number, the product
of 15 and a number

4. $c - 10$
c minus 10,
10 less than a
number

5. $18 \div a$
18 divided by a,
the quotient of
18 and a

6. $27 - m$
a number less
than 27,
27 minus a number

7. $v \div 21$
a number divided
by 21, the quotient
of a number and 21

8. $8r$
eight times r,
the product of 8
and r

9. $t + 17$
17 more than a
number, the sum of
a number and 17

Choose A, B, C, or D.

10. Which word phrase does *not* describe the expression $24 - x$?
A. 24 decreased by x **B.** a difference of 24 and x
C. 24 minus x (**D.**) 24 less than x

11. Which word phrase does *not* describe the expression $36r$?
A. 36 times r **B.** the product of 36 and r
(**C.**) 36 added to r **D.** 36 multiplied by r

Write a variable expression for each word phrase.
Answers may vary.

12. nine less than t
$t - 9$

13. eleven more
than a number
$n + 11$

14. 700 divided by a
number
$700 \div n$

15. two times the number
of windows
$2w$

16. b divided by seven
$b \div 7$

17. 81 increased by n
$81 + n$

18. twelve times the
number of muffin pans
$12m$

19. $15 times the
number of hours
$15h$

20. 8 less than a number
$n - 8$

In copymaster and workbook formats

RETEACHING

Reteaching 2-5 *Writing Variable Expressions*

These terms are used to describe mathematical operations.

Addition	Subtraction	Multiplication	Division
sum more than increased by total added to	difference less than fewer than decreased by	product times multiplied by	quotient of divided by

You can use the terms above to write variable expressions for
word phrases.

Word Phrase		Variable Expression
the sum of m and 17	→	$m + 17$
the difference of x and 12	→	$x - 12$
3 times w	→	$3w$
the quotient of q and 6	→	$q \div 6$

Write two word phrases for each variable expression. Answers may vary.

1. $t - 3$
3 less than t, t decreased by 3

2. $5w$
5 times w, the product of 5 and w

3. $18 + r$
18 plus r, r more than 18

4. $36 \div g$
36 divided by g, the quotient of 36 and g

5. $9 - x$
9 minus x, x less than 9

6. mn
m times n, the product of m and n

Write a variable expression for each word phrase.

7. 6 increased by y
$6 + y$

8. the quotient of 8 and e
$8 \div e$

9. the difference of h and 3
$h - 3$

10. 4 times w
$4w$

11. the difference of s and 8
$s - 8$

12. r divided by 2
$r \div 2$

13. five more than n
$n + 5$

14. the product of six and m
$6m$

ENRICHMENT

Minds on Math Transparency

2-5

Find the missing digits in the number below if the number is
the product of two equal factors.

2,[0] [2] 5

See *Solution Key* for worked-out answers.

64

WRAP UP

IDENTIFYING THE BIG IDEA Ask students:
*How do you change word phrases to variable
expressions? variable expressions to word
phrases?*

PROJECT LINK Challenge students to
describe the pattern with a word phrase. Then
have them write the phrase as a variable
expression.

LESSON QUIZ

Write a word phrase for each variable
expression.

1. $15 \div x$ fifteen divided by x

2. $n + 18$ n plus eighteen

Write a variable expression for each word
phrase.

3. 58 less than y $y - 58$

4. 8 times a number $8n$

39. *Space* At the end of a space flight, an astronaut's height can
temporarily be 2 inches more than normal.
  a. Write a variable expression to describe an astronaut's
  height after flight. Variable labels may vary. Sample: $h + 2$
  b. What variable did you use? What does it represent?
  For sample in part (a): h; astronaut's normal height

Write a variable expression for the rule in each table.

40. $3x$

x	■
1	3
2	6
3	9
4	12

41. $a + 3$

a	■
2	5
5	8
6	9
7	10

42. $m - 3$

m	■
5	2
10	7
15	12
20	17

43. $p \div 2$

p	■
0	0
4	2
8	4
12	6

Before
68 in.

After
70 in.

In the absence of gravity,
the cartilage disks in the
spine expand. So an
astronaut is temporarily
2 inches taller.

Mixed Review

44. President Eisenhower was born October 14, 1890, and died
March 28, 1969. How old was he when he died? *(Previous Course)*
78 years old

Use the spreadsheet below for Exercises 45 and 46. *(Lesson 1-4)*

	A	B	C
1	Title/Artist	Year	Weeks at No. 1
2	One Sweet Day/Mariah Carey and Boys II Men	1995	16
3	I Will Always Love You/Whitney Houston	1992	14
4	End of the Road/Boys II Men	1992	13
5	Hey Jude/Beatles	1968	9

Source: *The Top Ten of Everything*

45. What value is in cell B4?
1992

46. What cells are in column C?
number of weeks a song spent at no. 1

CHAPTER PROJECT

PROJECT LINK: RECORDING DATA

Continue adding layers to your fort. The final value must
be within a budget of $2. Record the number of layers
and the value of the fort. Describe the pattern. Write a
numerical expression to relate layers to fort value.

Check
students'
work.

In Lesson 2-6, students learn to solve equations. This toolbox helps students review subtracting with zeros, which they may use when solving equations.

ERROR ALERT! Students may lose track of digits after they regroup more than once to subtract a number. **Remediation:** Direct students to describe aloud their steps as they strike through a digit and decrease by 1 when regrouping. Describing the steps to themselves helps students catch careless errors they might make when regrouping.

ASSESSMENT Have students work with a partner and choose a problem that was difficult. Each student writes instruction for finding the difference. Then partners trade instructions and try to work the problem according to the directions.

■ **ADDITIONAL PROBLEM**

Ask students how they might solve Exercise 11 mentally. **Add 5 ones, 6 tens and 3 hundreds (365) to reach 800.**

SKILLS REVIEW

Subtracting with Zeros

Before Lesson 2-6

When you subtract from a number with zeros, you may need to regroup more than once. Start by lining up the digits in the correct columns.

■ **EXAMPLE 1**

Subtract 3,020 − 86.

Step 1

$$\begin{array}{r} {\scriptstyle 110} \\ 3,02\cancel{0} \\ -\ 86 \\ \hline 4 \end{array}$$

Step 2

$$\begin{array}{r} {\scriptstyle 9\ 11} \\ {\scriptstyle 2\ \cancel{10}\ \cancel{1}\ 10} \\ 3,02\cancel{0} \\ -\ 86 \\ \hline 34 \end{array}$$

Step 3

$$\begin{array}{r} {\scriptstyle 9\ 11} \\ {\scriptstyle 2\ \cancel{10}\ 110} \\ 3,02\cancel{0} \\ -\ 86 \\ \hline 2,934 \end{array}$$

■ **EXAMPLE 2**

Find each difference.

a. 908 − 273

$$\begin{array}{r} {\scriptstyle 8\ 10} \\ 9\cancel{0}8 \\ -\ 273 \\ \hline 635 \end{array}$$

b. 602 − 174

$$\begin{array}{r} {\scriptstyle 9} \\ {\scriptstyle 5\ \cancel{10}\ 12} \\ 6\cancel{0}\cancel{2} \\ -\ 174 \\ \hline 428 \end{array}$$

c. 5,002 − 1,247

$$\begin{array}{r} {\scriptstyle 9\ 9} \\ {\scriptstyle 4\ \cancel{10}\ \cancel{10}\ 12} \\ 5,00\cancel{2} \\ -\ 1,247 \\ \hline 3,755 \end{array}$$

Subtract.

1. 806 − 174 = 632	2. 240 − 63 = 177	3. 707 − 361 = 346	4. 5,060 − 3,221 = 1,839	5. 6,000 − 1,830 = 4,170	6. 8,000 − 5,274 = 2,726

7. 609 − 274 **335** **8.** 403 − 122 **281** **9.** 760 − 405 **355** **10.** 901 − 65 **836** **11.** 800 − 435 **365**

12. 459 − 78 **381** **13.** 222 − 151 **71** **14.** 680 − 47 **633** **15.** 301 − 260 **41** **16.** 425 − 406 **19**

17. 7,820 − 1,608 **6,212** **18.** 9,071 − 6,407 **2,664** **19.** 3,003 − 1,998 **1,005** **20.** 8,044 − 2,111 **5,933**

21. 6,508 − 2,147 **4,361** **22.** 5,300 − 1,771 **3,529** **23.** 7,004 − 1,512 **5,492** **24.** 8,000 − 4,337 **3,663**

25. a. *Writing* Explain what is meant by *regrouping*. **You replace one larger unit with 10 smaller units.**
   b. When is regrouping necessary? **You need regrouping when subtracting a greater number of units from a smaller one.**

1 Focus

CONNECTING TO PRIOR KNOWLEDGE Give students the statement: "A robin is a bird." Ask them to substitute variables for the nouns. *r* is *b* Replace is with an equal sign. *r = b* Ask students how this differs from a variable expression. **Variable expressions do not have equal signs.**

Lesson Planning Options

Prerequisite Skills
- writing variable expressions (2-5)
- using whole numbers and decimals (precourse)

Vocabulary/Symbols
equation, solve, solution, isolate the variable

Materials/Manipulatives
- algebra tiles
- calculator

Resources

 **Student Edition**

Skills Handbook, pp. 538, 539
Extra Practice, p. 523
Glossary/Study Guide

Teaching Resources

Chapter Support File, Ch. 2
- Lesson Planner 2-6
- Practice 2-6, Reteaching 2-6
Teaching Aids Master 27
Glossary, Spanish Resources

Transparencies
13, Minds on Math 2-6

Warm Up

Ask students to estimate the following:
19.055 − 4.41 **15**
12.89 − 5.24 **8**
4.63 + 7.71 **12**

2 Teach

Work Together

CONNECTION TO SCIENCE Some students may want to know more about their bones. Have them research questions that interest them. Some suggestions are: *How many bones are there in your hand and foot? Where is your largest bone? your smallest bone?* Have students write numerical expressions combining the facts they find. Have them share the information with the class.

THINK AND DISCUSS

AEP Help students distinguish between the terms *expression* and *equation* by asking them to write examples of each under each term. Then circle the equal sign in the equations.

2-6 Modeling Equations That Use Addition or Subtraction

What You'll Learn
▼ **1** To define equations
▼ **2** To solve equations

...And Why
You can solve equations about anatomy.

Here's How
Look for questions that
- build understanding
✔ check understanding

Work Together *Writing Numerical Expressions*

Use the table at the right.

1. a. Write a numerical expression for the total number of bones in your arm and chest. **32 + 25**
   b. Write a numerical expression for the total number of bones in your leg and spine. **31 + 26**
   c. ▪Draw a Conclusion What do you notice about the value of the expressions in parts (a) and (b)? **The values are equal.**

Bones in Your Body

Body Part	Number of Bones
Arm	32
Leg	31
Skull	29
Spine	26
Chest	25

THINK AND DISCUSS

▼ **1** *Defining Equations*

An **equation** is a mathematical sentence that contains an equal sign, =, read "is equal to." The equation acts like a balance scale.

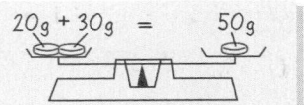 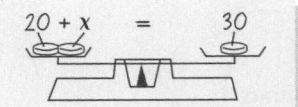

To **solve** an equation, replace the variable with a number that makes the equation true. This number is a **solution.**

■ **EXAMPLE 1**

State whether 29 is a solution to the equation $x - 15 = 12$.

$$x - 15 = 12$$
$$29 - 15 \stackrel{?}{=} 12 \quad \longleftarrow \text{Replace } x \text{ with 29.}$$
$$14 \neq 12 \quad \longleftarrow \text{Subtract. (} \neq \text{ means "is not equal to.")}$$

The equation is false, so 29 is *not* a solution to $x - 15 = 12$.

TACTILE LEARNING Let students use a balance-beam scale to model the equation $m + 4 = 7$. Ask: If you have 7 tiles on the right side of the scale and 4 tiles on the left side, how many tiles would you add to the left side to balance the scale? **3**

■ **ADDITIONAL EXAMPLES**

FOR EXAMPLE 1
State whether $x = 20$ is a solution to the equation $x - 6 = 14$. **yes**

FOR EXAMPLE 2
Use algebra tiles to solve $s - 4 = 11$.
$s = 15$

FOR EXAMPLE 3
Solve each equation using a calculator.
a. $14,095 = t + 5,432$ $t = 8,663$
b. $r - 342 = 31$ $r = 373$

AEP Relate the word *isolate* to the English word *island* and its equivalent in other languages. Tell students that when they isolate the variable, they separate it from the rest of the numbers by an equal sign. This is similar to an island being separated from other islands by water.

2. ✓*Try It Out* State whether the given number is a solution to the equation.
a. $y - 6 = 24$; 18 **no**   **b.** $20 = p + 4$; 16 **yes**
c. $150 = k - 50$; 200 **yes**   **d.** $j + 30 = 70$; 100 **no**

Now you may assign Exercises 1–16,

❷ *Solving Equations*

You can use algebra tiles to find the solution to an equation. To *isolate the variable*, get the variable alone on one side of the equal sign.

■ **EXAMPLE 2**

Use algebra tiles to solve $x + 2 = 6$.

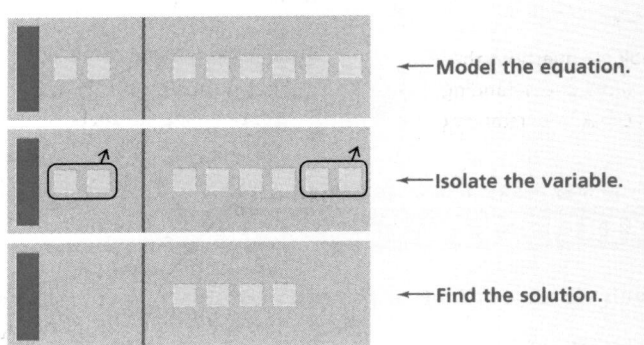

←——Model the equation.

←——Isolate the variable.

←——Find the solution.

The solution to $x + 2 = 6$ is 4.

3. a. What did you do to isolate the variable in Example 2? **2 unit tiles were removed from each side.**
b. What operation does this action represent? **subtraction**

4. ✓*Try It Out* Use algebra tiles to solve each equation.
a. $m + 4 = 7$ **3**   **b.** $6 + k = 11$ **5**   **c.** $9 = h + 3$ **6**

You can use mental math to solve equations involving addition or subtraction.

5. In the equation $r + 8 = 15$, what is the value of r? **7**

6. In the equation $m - 4 = 10$, what is the value of m? **14**

7. ⚬*Mental Math* Solve each equation.
a. $8 = 3 + h$ **5**   **b.** $a + 5 = 8$ **3**   **c.** $m - 2 = 10$ **12**
d. $15 = g - 5$ **20**   **e.** $5 = n - 10$ **15**   **f.** $8 = k + 7$ **1**

Technology Options

Prentice Hall Technology

Software for Learners
• Math Lab: Modeling Addition and Subtraction Equations
• Math Blaster® Mystery*
• Interactive Student Tutorial, Chapter 2*

Teaching Resource Software
• Computer Item Generator 2-6
• Resource Pro™ Chapter 2*

Internet • For related mathematics activities, visit the Prentice Hall site at www.phschool.com/math

Available on CD-ROM only

Assignment Options for Exercises On Your Own

To provide flexible scheduling, this lesson can be subdivided into parts.

▼❶ **Core** 1–15
   Extension 16

▼❷ **Core** 17–50
   Extension 51, 52

Use Mixed Review to maintain skills.

 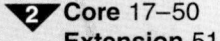

ERROR ALERT! Question 6 Students may try to find the answer by subtracting 4 from 10 instead of adding. **Remediation:** Remind students to ask themselves: *What number can replace the variable and make the equation true?* Always have them check their work.

MENTAL MATH Question 7 Have students check their answers by replacing each variable with the solution of the equation.

EXTENSION Have students solve the following.

Michelle bought a CD through the mail. The CD cost $11.50. Her bill, including shipping and handling, was $15. Find how much shipping and handling she paid.
$11.50 + s = 15$; $3.50

may vary. Sample: Change $9 - 3 = 2$ to $9 - 3 = 6$.

ASSESSMENT Exercises 6–14 Have students find the correct solution for each equation that is not true.

Exercise 16 Have students give an example of an equation and a sentence to illustrate their answers.

TACTILE LEARNING Exercises 17–22 Let students use algebra tiles to model and solve the given equations.

3 Practice/Assess

EXERCISES *On Your Own*

Exercises 1–4 Have students rewrite the false equations so they are true. **Answers**

---

pages 68–70   On Your Own

15. The statement $4 + 6 = 10$ is true because the sum of 4 and 6 is equal to 10. The statement $3 + 7 = 12$ is false because the sum of 3 and 7 is not equal to 12.

Sometimes it is not convenient to solve an equation using algebra tiles or mental math. Then you can use paper and pencil or a calculator.

■ **EXAMPLE 3**

Calculator Solve each equation using a calculator.

a. $x + 3{,}687 = 5{,}543$
5543 ⊟ 3687 ⊟ *1856*
The solution is 1,856.

b. $x - 4{,}621 = 1{,}347$
1347 ⊞ 4621 ⊟ *5968*
The solution is 5,968.

8. *Look Back* Check the solution to Example 3a by replacing x with 1,856. Is the solution reasonable?
$1{,}856 + 3{,}687 = 5{,}543$; yes

9. ✓*Try It Out* When you solve the equation $x + 567 = 739$ using a calculator, what operation key do you use? ⊟

10. *Calculator* Solve each equation. Then check your solution.
a. $y - 432 = 127$ 559
b. $12{,}597 = h + 6{,}954$ 5,643
c. $183 = 119 + b$ 64
d. $189 = p - 24$ 213

Now you may assign Exercises 17–52.

EXERCISES *On Your Own*

Is each statement *true* or *false*?

1. $5 + 10 = 15$
   true
2. $9 - 3 = 2$
   false
3. $24 = 6 + 18$
   true
4. $19 - 7 = 5 + 4$
   false

5. **Choose A, B, C, or D.** Which value of x is a solution for the equation $x - 4 = 5$? **C**

   A. 6   B. 10   C. 9   D. 1

State whether the given number is a solution to the equation.

6. $h + 6 = 14$; 7   no
7. $k + 5 = 16$; 11   yes
8. $p - 10 = 20$; 20   no

9. $18 = m - 4$; 22 yes
10. $25 = 14 + y$; 11 yes
11. $t - 5 = 25$; 15 no

12. $15 + x = 57$; 32 no
13. $c - 7 = 14$; 7 no
14. $r + 16 = 42$; 26 yes

15. *Writing* Explain why the statement $4 + 6 = 10$ is true and the statement $3 + 7 = 12$ is false. **See margin.**

16. *Language* How is an equation like a sentence? **Check students' work.**

68

Exercises 17–22 Ask students to write the equations shown in each of the models. Have them check by replacing the variables with their solutions.

Exercises 31–42 Have students solve each of the equations twice, using two different methods to check their work.

CONNECTING TO THE STUDENTS' WORLD
Exercise 44 Ask students: *What do you dream of doing some day? What would you have to do to accomplish your dreams?*

OPEN-ENDED Exercise 51 Have students trade their equations with a partner to solve. Then trade back the equations to check the solutions. If a solution is incorrect, pairs work together until a solution is agreed upon.

EXTENSION and REASONING Exercise 52
Use this exercise to prepare students for the next lesson. Ask: *What other operations undo each other?* multiplication and division

CONNECTION TO SPORTS Ask: *A football player made 35 yd on a pass play. The quarterback threw the ball 13 yd to him. Use the equation $13 + r = 35$ to find how far the player ran after he caught the pass.* **22 yd**

Modeling **Solve the equation shown in each model.**

17.
3
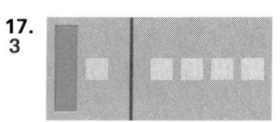

18.
2
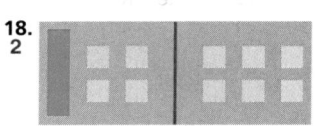

19.
2

20.
1
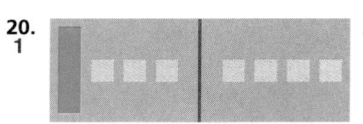

21.
0
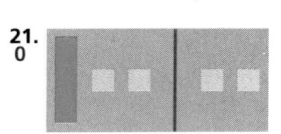

22.
8

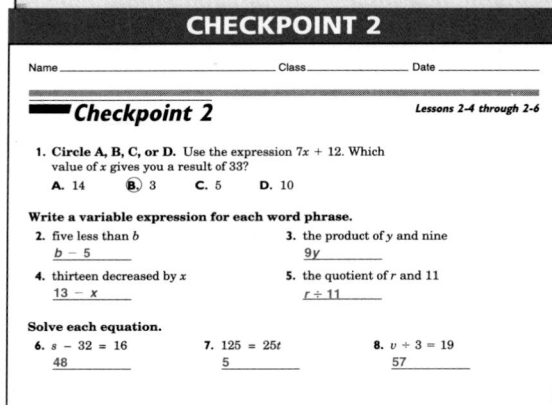

CHECKPOINT 2

Name _____ Class _____ Date _____

Checkpoint 2 Lessons 2-4 through 2-6

1. **Circle A, B, C, or D.** Use the expression $7x + 12$. Which value of x gives you a result of 33?
   A. 14 **B.** 3 **C.** 5 **D.** 10

Write a variable expression for each word phrase.
2. five less than b $b - 5$
3. the product of y and nine $9y$
4. thirteen decreased by x $13 - x$
5. the quotient of r and 11 $r \div 11$

Solve each equation.
6. $s - 32 = 16$ 48
7. $125 = 25t$ 5
8. $v \div 3 = 19$ 57

Mental Math **Solve each equation mentally.**

23. $x + 2 = 7$ 5 **24.** $c - 7 = 22$ 29 **25.** $16 = k + 7$ 9 **26.** $w - 7 = 10$ 17

27. $6 + w = 9$ 3 **28.** $20 = m - 66$ 86 **29.** $x + 4 = 12$ 8 **30.** $26 - p = 7$ 19

Choose **Use algebra tiles, mental math, or a calculator to solve each equation. Check for reasonable solutions.**

31. $33 = k + 17$ 16 **32.** $152 = p + 64$ 88 **33.** $g + 8 = 84$ 76 **34.** $437 + y = 512$ 75

35. $62 + r = 83$ 21 **36.** $y - 265 = 124$ 389 **37.** $a - 64 = 65$ 129 **38.** $6 + w = 9$ 3

39. $x + 3 = 9$ 6 **40.** $42 + h = 52$ 10 **41.** $42 = 51 - m$ 9 **42.** $45 = d + 28$ 17

52. When one number is *added* to another, you can get the first number back by *subtracting* the second number from the result. Similarly, when a number is *subtracted* from another number, *adding* the subtracted number to the result gives you the second number.

Use the article below for Exercises 43 and 44.

A DREAM COME TRUE

Dwight Collins was ten years old when he first thought about crossing the Atlantic Ocean. Twenty-six years later, he set a record by pedaling his boat, Tango, from Newfoundland to London in just 40 days—14 days faster than the previous record. Can you imagine pedaling 2,250 miles across the ocean? Not even a storm could stop Dwight Collins from making his dream come true!

43. Use the equation $r - 14 = 40$. Find the previous record r in days. **54 days**

44. After the storm, Dwight still had 1,200 miles of pedaling to do. Use the equation $p + 1,200 = 2,250$. Find the number of miles Dwight had pedaled p before he sailed into the storm. **1,050 mi**

Practice 2-6 Modeling Equations That Use Addition or Subtraction

State whether the number given is a solution to the equation.

1. $m + 7 = 18; m = 11$
yes

2. $14 = 9 + v; v = 6$
no

3. $19 = 17 + y; y = 3$
no

4. $w - 17 = 24; w = 41$
yes

5. $93 = b - 43; b = 146$
no

6. $53 = m - 14; m = 67$
yes

7. $n - 53 = 69; n = 122$
yes

8. $78 = b + 19; b = 59$
no

9. $47 + a = 153; a = 104$
no

Choose a calculator, paper and pencil, or mental math to solve each equation.

10. $t + 19 = 47$
28

11. $v + 14 = 76$
62

12. $94 = y + 32$
62

13. $86 = a + 29$
57

14. $w - 53 = 76$
129

15. $53 = z - 19$
72

16. $112 = x - 74$
186

17. $49 = c + 19$
30

18. $b + 24 = 52$
28

19. $117 = 69 + a$
48

20. $e - 84 = 79$
163

21. $62 = g - 27$
89

If possible, write an equation and solve each problem. If it is not possible to solve, explain why.

22. Some brown eggs and 8 white eggs make a dozen. How many brown eggs are there?
4 brown eggs

23. Tomás ran 6 mi. How long will it take him to run 10 mi?
Can't solve. There is no information on how fast Tomás runs.

24. Zack lost 5 pounds to reach a trim 89 pounds. How heavy had he been?
94 pounds

25. It took Bekka 12 min to walk to school. How long will it take her to walk to the store?
Can't solve. There is no information on how far she walks in 12 min, or how far the store is.

In copymaster and workbook formats

Reteaching 2-6 Modeling Equations That Use Addition or Subtraction

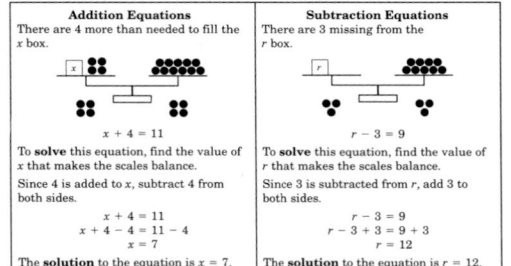

Addition Equations	**Subtraction Equations**
There are 4 more than needed to fill the x box.	There are 3 missing from the r box.

$x + 4 = 11$

$r - 3 = 9$

To **solve** this equation, find the value of x that makes the scales balance.
Since 4 is added to x, subtract 4 from both sides.

$x + 4 = 11$
$x + 4 - 4 = 11 - 4$
$x = 7$

The **solution** to the equation is $x = 7$.

To **solve** this equation, find the value of r that makes the scales balance.
Since 3 is subtracted from r, add 3 to both sides.

$r - 3 = 9$
$r - 3 + 3 = 9 + 3$
$r = 12$

The **solution** to the equation is $r = 12$.

State whether the number given is a solution to the equation.

1. $t - 9 = 15; t = 24$
yes

2. $w + 4 = 12; w = 16$
no

3. $y + 13 = 20; y = 7$
yes

4. $6 + x = 18; x = 24$
no

5. $23 = m - 4; m = 27$
yes

6. $q - 8 = 16; q = 8$
no

Solve each equation.

7. $a + 15 = 31$
$a + 15 - 15 = 31 - 15$
$a = 16$

8. $5 = x - 20$
$5 + 20 = x - 20 + 20$
$25 = x$

9. $19 + t = 51$
32

10. $p - 11 = 12$
23

11. $60 = n + 30$
30

12. $71 = b - 29$
100

13. $86 + m = 107$
21

14. $w + 349 = 761$
412

15. $50 - y = 30$
20

16. $d - 125 = 75$
200

Reteaching

Minds on Math Transparency

2-6

How many different rectangles can you find in the figure below?

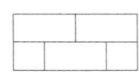

10 rectangles

See **Solution Key** for worked-out answers.

WRAP UP

IDENTIFYING THE BIG IDEA Have students explain how to solve an addition and subtraction equation containing a variable.

JOURNAL You may want to extend beyond modeling with algebra tiles and show students how to use a balance-beam scale to solve an equation.

LESSON QUIZ

Solve each equation.

1. $44 = a - 16$ $a = 60$

2. $59 + d = 72$ $d = 13$

3. $y - 65 = 5$ $y = 70$

4. $g + 9 = 45$ $g = 36$

5. $72 = e - 28$ $e = 100$

6. $x + 19 = 19$ $x = 0$

▦ Calculator Solve and check each equation.

45. $f + 1,478 = 3,652$
2,174

46. $10,006 = k - 67,948$
77,954

47. $z - 11,897 = 34,954$
46,851

48. $50,876 + s = 877,942$
827,066

49. $x - 6,781 = 10,384$
17,165

50. $18,943 = x - 11,256$ 30,199

51. *Open-ended* Give an example of an equation that contains a variable. Then solve the equation.   Sample: $a + 37 = 51$; 14

52. *Reasoning* Explain what is meant by the statement *"addition and subtraction undo each other."*
See margin p. 69.

JOURNAL
How can models help you evaluate expressions and solve equations? Give examples.

Mixed Review

53. *Data Analysis* About how many more people own color sets than own black and white sets? *(Previous Course)*
about 88 million people

54. *Choose a Strategy* A bookstore advertised the following sale: *Buy 3 books, get 1 book free!* How many books do you have to buy to get 4 free books?   12 books

Find the value of each expression. *(Lesson 2-3)*

55. $24 \div 3 - 2 \times 4$
0

56. $(63 + 87) - 6 \times 2$
138

How Many Own Televisions?

Type	Number of People
Color	90,258,000
Black and white	1,842,000
2 or more sets	59,865,000
1 set	32,235,000
Any type of set	92,100,000

Source: *Information Please Almanac*

✓ CHECKPOINT 2

Lessons 2-4 through 2-6

Evaluate each expression for $x = 7$.

1. $3x + 12$
33

2. $56 \div x$
8

3. $10 - x + 3$
6

4. $3(4 + x)$
33

5. $9x$
63

Write a variable expression for each word phrase.

6. 12 more than y
$12 + y$

7. b increased by 5
$b + 5$

8. 6 times w
$6w$

9. r less than 20
$20 - r$

Solve each equation.

10. $b + 25 = 75$
50

11. $256 = m - 129$
385

12. $6 = 4 + y$
2

13. $22 - p = 13$ 9

14. **Choose A, B, C, or D.** Which expression has a value of 10 for $x = 8$? D

A. $2x - 3$

B. $22 + x \div 3$

C. $3x - 22$

D. $3x - 14$

In Lesson 2-7, students learn how to solve equations using mental math. This toolbox allows students to review multiplying whole numbers, which they will use to solve equations.

ERROR ALERT! Students may forget to begin with a zero in the ones place when they multiply by the tens. **Remediation:** Have

students make sure the second partial product always ends with zero. Students may want to include this as a check in Step 2.

ASSESSMENT Exercise 1 Ask students to write a short paragraph explaining how they multiplied 312 × 53. Then organize the students in small groups to compare their explanations. Each group should decide which explanation is correct and the most clear and concise.

■ **ADDITIONAL PROBLEM**

Is 80 × 50 greater than, less than, or equal to 800 × 5? Explain. **They are equal. In both, you multiply 8 × 5, then write two zeros on the end.**

Resources

📦 **Teaching Resources**
Teaching Aids Master 1

▨ **Transparencies**
1, 13

page 71   Math Toolbox
39b. **The product has the same number of zeros as the sum of zeros in the factors.**

SKILLS REVIEW

Multiplying Whole Numbers

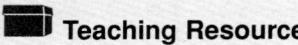 Before Lesson 2-7

When you multiply by a two-digit number, first multiply by the ones. Then multiply by the tens. Add the products. Remember zero times any number is zero.

■ **EXAMPLE**

Multiply 48×327.

Step 1: Multiply the ones.

$$\begin{array}{r} {}^{2\,5} \\ 327 \\ \times\ 48 \\ \hline 2{,}616 \end{array}$$

Step 2: Multiply the tens.

$$\begin{array}{r} {}^{1\,2} \\ 327 \\ \times\ 48 \\ \hline 2{,}616 \\ +\ 13{,}080 \end{array}$$

Step 3: Add the products.

$$\begin{array}{r} 327 \\ \times\ 48 \\ \hline 2{,}616 \\ +\ 13{,}080 \\ \hline 15{,}696 \end{array}$$

Multiply.

1. $\begin{array}{r}312\\ \times\ 53\\ \hline 16{,}536\end{array}$	**2.** $\begin{array}{r}456\\ \times\ 71\\ \hline 32{,}376\end{array}$	**3.** $\begin{array}{r}906\\ \times\ 20\\ \hline 18{,}120\end{array}$	**4.** $\begin{array}{r}915\\ \times\ 27\\ \hline 24{,}705\end{array}$	**5.** $\begin{array}{r}808\\ \times\ 60\\ \hline 48{,}480\end{array}$	**6.** $\begin{array}{r}409\\ \times\ 70\\ \hline 28{,}630\end{array}$
7. $\begin{array}{r}25\\ \times\ 46\\ \hline 1{,}150\end{array}$	**8.** $\begin{array}{r}601\\ \times\ 63\\ \hline 37{,}863\end{array}$	**9.** $\begin{array}{r}62\\ \times\ 88\\ \hline 5{,}456\end{array}$	**10.** $\begin{array}{r}430\\ \times\ 80\\ \hline 34{,}400\end{array}$	**11.** $\begin{array}{r}87\\ \times\ 31\\ \hline 2{,}697\end{array}$	**12.** $\begin{array}{r}970\\ \times\ 40\\ \hline 38{,}800\end{array}$
13. $\begin{array}{r}54\\ \times\ 26\\ \hline 1{,}404\end{array}$	**14.** $\begin{array}{r}780\\ \times\ 62\\ \hline 48{,}360\end{array}$	**15.** $\begin{array}{r}881\\ \times\ 77\\ \hline 67{,}837\end{array}$	**16.** $\begin{array}{r}440\\ \times\ 67\\ \hline 29{,}480\end{array}$	**17.** $\begin{array}{r}68\\ \times\ 46\\ \hline 3{,}128\end{array}$	**18.** $\begin{array}{r}82\\ \times\ 17\\ \hline 1{,}394\end{array}$

19. 415×76 31,540
20. 500×80 40,000
21. 320×47 15,040
22. 562×18 10,116
23. 946×37 35,002

24. 76×103 7,828
25. 32×558 17,856
26. 371×84 31,164
27. 505×40 20,200
28. 620×19 11,780

29. 607×50 30,350
30. 601×42 25,242
31. 400×26 10,400
32. 109×60 6,540
33. 298×70 20,860

34. 58×41 2,378
35. 30×600 18,000
36. 94×77 7,238
37. 163×47 7,661
38. 458×32 14,656

39. a. Multiply.
1,500   1,500   1,500   15,000
15,000 **i.** 500×30 **ii.** 50×30 **iii.** 500×3 **iv.** 5×300 **v.** 50×300

   b. *Writing* How does the number of zeros in the numbers you multiply relate to the number of zeros in each product? See margin.

   c. *Reasoning* Does the product 500×40 fit the rule you found in part (b)? Why or why not?
   No; there is an extra 0 in the product because $5 \times 4 = 20$.

71

1 Focus

CONNECTING TO PRIOR KNOWLEDGE Tell students to pretend they are inviting friends over to eat breakfast. Ask:

• *How would you decide how much food to make?* **Answers may vary. Sample: Multiply the number of people by the** amount of food you think one person will eat.

• *If you had a limited amount of food, how would you decide how many people you can invite?* **Answers may vary. Sample: Divide the amount of food you have by the amount you think one person will eat.**

Lesson Planning Options

Prerequisite Skills
• writing variable expressions (2-5)
• multiplying and dividing whole numbers and decimals (precourse)

Vocabulary/Symbols
identity properties, commutative properties, associative properties

Materials/Manipulatives
• algebra tiles   • calculator

Resources

 Student Edition

Skills Handbook, p. 540
Extra Practice, p. 523
Glossary/Study Guide

 **Teaching Resources**

Chapter Support File, Ch. 2
• Lesson Planner 2-7
• Practice 2-7, Reteaching 2-7
• Answer Masters 2-7
Teaching Aids Master 27
Glossary, Spanish Resources

 Transparencies
Minds on Math 2-7

Warm Up

Ask students to write the next three multiples for each.
3, 6, 9, . . . **12, 15, 18**
12, 24, 36, . . . **48, 60, 72**
14, 28, 42, . . . **56, 70, 84**

2 Teach

Work Together

KINESTHETIC LEARNING Question 1a Have students model the volleyball teams by organizing 30 students into equal groups of 6. If there are not 30 students in the class, use chairs to represent the missing students.

TACTILE LEARNING Question 1 Give students 30 counters to represent the 30 students. Have them form the counters into

---

2-7 Modeling Equations That Use Multiplication or Division

What You'll Learn
1 To solve equations using models
2 To solve equations using a calculator or mental math

...And Why
You can solve equations about sports teams.

Here's How
Look for questions that
▪ build understanding
✔ check understanding

1b. $6t = 30$; $6t$ and 30 each describe the total number of students on all teams.

Work Together ——— *Writing Equations from Data*

Use the table shown at the right.

1. **a.** ▪ *Mental Math* How many volleyball teams t can be formed with 30 students? **5 teams**
   b. ▪ *Algebra* Does $6t = 30$ or $30t = 6$ describe this situation? Explain. **See below.**
   c. Write equations for the number of basketball teams and the number of soccer teams. **$5t = 30$; $11t = 30$**

Number of Players in Starting Lineup

Sport	Number of Players
Baseball	9
Basketball	5
Soccer	11
Volleyball	6

THINK AND DISCUSS

1 *Solving Equations Using Modeling*

You can use algebra tiles to solve an equation with a whole number multiplied by a variable on one side.

▪ **EXAMPLE 1**

Modeling Use algebra tiles to solve the equation $3x = 12$.

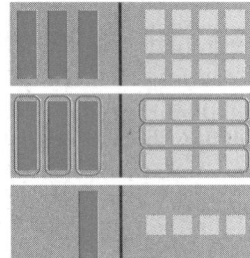

←—Model the equation.

←—Divide each side into 3 equal parts.

←—Keep one part on each side.

The solution is 4.

2. ✔*Try It Out* Use algebra tiles to solve each equation.
   a. $2x = 8$ **4**   **b.** $2x = 10$ **5**   **c.** $4x = 12$ **3**

Now you may assign Exercises 1–3, 10–19.

groups to find the number of volleyball or basketball teams. They can also explore how to form the baseball or soccer teams.

THINK AND DISCUSS

ERROR ALERT! **Question 6b** Students may try to solve by dividing 30 by 2.
Remediation: Remind students that multiplication undoes division. Students may want to put a large X over any operation signs that they are to undo. This may help them to

remember not to perform that operation in the problem. Have students check their solutions by substituting them into the equation.

■ ADDITIONAL EXAMPLES

FOR EXAMPLE 1
Use algebra tiles to solve the equation $4x = 24$. **x = 6**

FOR EXAMPLE 2
Solve each equation using a calculator.
a. $145y = 435$ **y = 3**
b. $y \div 537 = 259$ **y = 139,083**

FOR EXAMPLE 3
Josie invited some friends for breakfast Saturday morning. She made 48 muffins. She is expecting 12 people to come. How many muffins did she make for each person? **4**

✌ *Solving Using a Calculator or Mental Math*

At times it is impractical to solve an equation using algebra tiles. You could use paper and pencil or a calculator instead.

■ EXAMPLE 2

▦ *Calculator* Solve each equation using a calculator.

a. $125x = 1,875$

1875 125 *15*

The solution is 15.

b. $x \div 21 = 85$

85 21 *1785*

The solution is 1,785.

3. ⬩*Look Back* Check the solution to Example (2a) by replacing x with 15. Is the solution reasonable?
125 × 15 = 1,875; yes

4. ✓*Try It Out* When you solve the equation $x \div 429 = 6,864$, what operation key do you use? ⊠

▦ **5.** ✓*Try It Out* Solve and check each equation. **4,432,344**
a. $125v = 2,750$ **22**
b. $t \div 588 = 7,538$
c. $2,256 = g \div 1,111$
2,506,416
d. $3,456n = 41,472$ **12**

Sometimes you can solve equations mentally.

■ EXAMPLE 3   *Real-World Problem Solving*

Hockey A school spent $75 on chin straps for the hockey team. Each costs $3. How many straps did the school buy?

Words • | total cost | equals | cost of one chin strap | times | number of straps |

• Let c = number of chin straps bought

Equation • | 75 | = | 3 | × | c |

$75 = 3c$ ⟵ Ask yourself "What number times 3 equals 75?"

$75 = 3 \times 25$ ⟵ Use mental math.

The school bought 25 chin straps.

6. ⬩*Mental Math* Solve each equation. Check your solution.
a. $5c = 35$ **7**
b. $n \div 2 = 30$ **60**
c. $100 = k \div 20$
d. $150 = 5h$ **30**
e. $11m = 121$ **11**
f. $b \div 10 = 1,000$
6c. 2,000
6f. 10,000

Technology Options

Prentice Hall Technology

💾 💿 **Software for Learners**

• Hot Page™ 6*
• Math Blaster® Mystery*
• Interactive Student Tutorial, Chapter 2*

💾 💿 **Teaching Resource Software**

• Computer Item Generator 2-7
• Resource Pro™ Chapter 2*

🌐 **Internet** • For related mathematics activities, visit the Prentice Hall site at www.phschool.com/math

*Available on CD-ROM only

Assignment Options for Exercises On Your Own

To provide flexible scheduling, this lesson can be subdivided into parts.

▼ **Core** 1–3, 10–18
Extension 19

▼ **Core** 4–9, 40–49
Extension 39, 50

Use Mixed Review to maintain skills.

ASSESSMENT Organize students in groups of three. Have each student choose a property and write one example using addition and one example using multiplication. Ask each student to share their examples and explain the property they chose to the others in their group.

CONNECTING TO THE STUDENTS' WORLD Ask the athletic director at your school how much money the school spent on basketballs last season. Find out how much one basketball costs. Use this information to have the students find how many basketballs the school purchased last season.

3 Practice/Assess

EXERCISES *On Your Own*

TACTILE LEARNING Exercises 1–3 Let students model these exercises using algebra tiles, then draw the solutions on their paper.

Exercises 4–9 When the number given is not a solution to the equation, have the student find the solution.

---

pages 74–76   On Your Own

1.
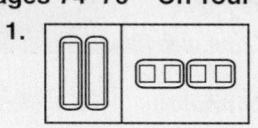

2.
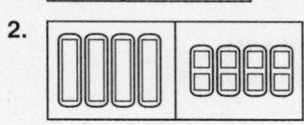

3.
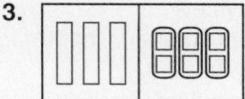

Certain algebraic properties can help you calculate mentally.

> **ALGEBRAIC PROPERTIES**
>
> **Identity Properties**
> The sum of 0 and any number is that number.
> Examples: $0 + 121 = 121$; $a + 0 = a$
> The product of 1 and any number is that number.
> Examples: $1 \times 75 = 75$; $x \times 1 = x$
>
> **Commutative Properties**
> Changing the order of addends or factors does not change the sum or product.
> Examples: $7 + 8 = 8 + 7$; $9 \times 5 = 5 \times 9$
>
> **Associative Properties**
> Changing the grouping of numbers does not change a sum or product.
> Examples: $16 + (4 + 8) = (16 + 4) + 8$
> $(7 \times 5) \times 2 = 7 \times (5 \times 2)$

7. The sum $16 + 4$ is 20, which is easy to work with.
7. ⚎*Reasoning* Why do you think it would be easier to find $(16 + 4) + 8$ mentally than $16 + (4 + 8)$?
8. Think $25 \times 42 \times 4 = 25 \times 4 \times 42 = 4,200$.
8. ⚎*Mental Math* Use the commutative property to find $25 \times 42 \times 4$ mentally.

Now you may assign Exercises 4–9, 20–50.

EXERCISES *On Your Own*

Modeling Show the next step needed to solve the equation in each model.   1–3. See margin.

1.

2.

3.

74

Exercises 10–17 To show their work, or if tiles are unavailable, students can draw rectangles and squares on their paper. Have students check their solutions with mental math.

Exercises 20–38 After students have completed these exercises, have them make a general statement about when they use algebra tiles, mental math, or a calculator. **Answers may vary. Sample: I use algebra tiles when the numbers are small and I have enough tiles. I use mental math when**

I can divide or multiply the numbers in my head. I use a calculator the rest of the time.

VISUAL LEARNING Exercise 49 Have students use graph paper to model their solution. Make sure they label their drawing.

CONNECTION TO HISTORY Exercise 53 This exercise works only for calendars organized in seven-day weeks. Have students research for calendars that are organized in other ways.

WRAP UP

IDENTIFYING THE BIG IDEA Ask students to explain how to solve multiplication and division equations. Ask them to make a general statement about how to solve multiplication, division, addition, and subtraction equations.

State whether the given number is a solution to the equation.

4. $6h = 60$; 10 **yes**

5. $g \div 8 = 7$; 64 no

6. $r \div 6 = 13$; 78 **yes**

7. $15 = 5p$; 3 **yes**

8. $36 = m \div 3$; 12 **no**

9. $8c = 450$; 50 **no**

Modeling **Use algebra tiles to solve each equation.**

10. $3x = 9$ **3**

11. $2m = 14$ **7**

12. $6x = 24$ **4**

13. $3x = 24$ **8**

14. $4x = 12$ **3**

15. $7x = 14$ **2**

16. $20 = 4x$ **5**

17. $5x = 25$ **5**

18. *Modeling* Use the model at the right.
   a. Write an equation for the model. $3x + 1 = 4$
   b. *Reasoning* Use algebra tiles to solve the equation. **1**

19. *Writing* Suppose you model and solve the equation $2x = 14$. Why do you divide each side of the equation into two equal parts? **You divide each side of the equation into the number of parts equal to the number of variable tiles.**

Choose **Use algebra tiles, mental math, or a calculator to solve each equation.**

20. $3m = 15$ **5**

21. $g \div 5 = 25$ **125**

22. $805 = 7b$ **115**

23. $6g = 24$ **4**

24. $25h = 450$ **18**

25. $10 = k \div 20$ **200**

26. $y \div 43 = 1{,}204$ **51,772**

27. $n \div 3 = 14$ **42**

28. $16 = 4h$ **4**

29. $525c = 86{,}625$ **165**

30. $h \div 20 = 9$ **180**

31. $90 = 6v$ **15**

32. $e \div 2 = 88$ **176**

33. $75 = 15c$ **5**

34. $56d = 112$ **2**

35. $12 = r \div 9$ **108**

36. $18{,}750 = 1{,}250k$ **15**

37. $d \div 1{,}000 = 100$ **100,000**

38. $400 = y \div 50$ **20,000**

39. **Choose A, B, C, or D.** Luchia participated in a swim-a-thon. Mr. Brown pledged $2.00 per lap. Luchia asked Mr. Brown for $44.00. Choose the equation that represents the number of laps Luchia swam. **B**

   A. $2(44) = s$
   B. $2s = 44$
   C. $2 \div s = 44$
   D. $2 = 44s$

Practice 2-7 *Modeling Equations That Use Multiplication or Division*

State whether the number given is a solution to the equation.

1. $8c = 80; c = 10$
yes

2. $b \div 7 = 8; b = 56$
yes

3. $9m = 108; m = 12$
yes

4. $y \div 9 = 17; y = 163$
no

5. $9r = 72; r = 7$
no

6. $14b = 56; b = 4$
yes

7. $48 = y \div 4; y = 12$
no

8. $32 = y \div 8; y = 256$
yes

9. $17a = 41; a = 3$
no

10. $w \div 21 = 17; w = 357$
yes

11. $21c = 189; c = 8$
no

12. $52 = y \div 6; y = 302$
no

Choose a calculator, paper and pencil, or mental math to solve each equation.

13. $905 = 5a$
181

14. $6v = 792$
132

15. $12 = y \div 12$
144

16. $b \div 18 = 21$
378

17. $80 = 16b$
5

18. $19m = 266$
14

19. $d \div 1,000 = 10$
10,000

20. $g \div 52 = 18$
936

21. $672 = 21f$
32

22. $z \div 27 = 63$
1,701

23. $43h = 817$
19

24. $58 = j \div 71$
4,118

Solve.

25. Lea drove 420 mi and used 20 gal of gas. How many miles per gallon did her car get? 21 mi/gal

26. Ty spent $15.00 on folders that cost $3.00 each. How many folders did he buy?
5 folders

27. Bob pays a $2.00 toll each way when going to and from work. How much does he pay in four weeks, working five days a week? $80.00

28. Julia wants to buy copies of a book to give as presents. How many books can she buy if they are on sale for $12 each, and she has $100 to spend? 8 books

In copymaster and workbook formats

Reteaching 2-7 *Modeling Equations That Use Multiplication or Division*

What value of w makes the scales balance?

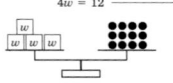

$4w = 12$

To solve the multiplication sentence, use division.
$4w = 12$
$4w \div 4 = 12 \div 4$ ← Divide both sides by 4.
$w = 3$
The solution is $w = 3$.

To solve a division sentence, use multiplication.
$y \div 3 = 7$
$y \div 3 \times 3 = 7 \times 3$ ← Multiply both sides by 3.
$y = 21$
The solution is $y = 21$.

State whether the number given is a solution to the equation.

1. $3g = 36; g = 12$
yes

2. $t + 8 = 2; t = 4$
no

3. $h \div 7 = 21; h = 3$
no

4. $18 = 3m; m = 6$
yes

5. $6a = 18; a = 3$
yes

6. $36 = r \div 9; r = 4$
no

Solve each equation.

7. $12 = 4y$
$12 \div 4 = 4y \div 4$
$3 = y$

8. $n \div 9 = 4$
$n \div 9 \times 9 = 4 \times 9$
$n = 36$

9. $23n = 115$
5

10. $z \div 9 = 9$
81

11. $48 = 12h$
4

12. $10w = 150$
15

13. $34 = t + 14$
476

14. $105 = 21t$
5

15. $64 = e \div 9$
576

16. $8v = 32$
4

Minds on Math Transparency

2-7

What single-digit numbers do ◯, ▢, and △ represent in the expressions below?

$▢ - △ = 3$
$◯ \times △ = 30$
$◯ + △ + ▢ = 20$

◯ = 5
▢ = 9
△ = 6

See *Solution Key* for worked-out answers.

PORTFOLIO Share with students the criteria you will use to assess their work in portfolios, as well as how you plan to use the results. Students should understand how the rubrics are used to assess their work, how each piece in the portfolio counts, and how the scores they get in their portfolios will affect their overall evaluation.

▽ **PROJECT LINK** To prompt students, ask: *How many layers have the same number of coins? How can you show this in a mathematical expression?*

Practice

Use algebra tiles to solve.

1. $6m = 18$ $m = 3$

2. $25 = 5x$ $x = 5$

Solve each equation using a calculator or mental math.

3. $36h = 108$ $h = 3$

4. $1,000 = p \div 10$ $p = 10,000$

5. $458c = 100,302$ $c = 219$

▦ *Calculator* **Solve and check each equation.**

40. $x \div 23 = 56$ 1,288

41. $4,731 = 57g$ 83

42. $125p = 4,250$ 34

43. $p \div 287 = 64,685$
18,564,595

44. $105,042 = 2,562s$ 41

45. $s \div 62,409 = 289$
18,036,201

Match each equation below with the property it illustrates.

46. $47 \times 1 = 47$ **B**

47. $56 + 93 = 93 + 56$ **C**

48. $(9 \times 5) \times 2 = 9 \times (5 \times 2)$ **A**

A. Associative

B. Identity

C. Commutative

49. *Geometry* The area of a playground is given by the equation $A = w \times \ell$. The width w is 20 ft and the area A is 680 ft^2. Find the length of the playground. **34 ft**

50. *Pollution* A 9-gallon tank of gasoline produces about 180 pounds of carbon dioxide when it is burned.
a. Write an equation to describe how much carbon dioxide one gallon of gasoline produces. **9g = 180**
b. Solve the equation. **20 lb**

Mixed Review

A record club sells CDs for **$15.99 each plus a $2.38 shipping charge per order.** *(Lesson 1-6)*

51. Make a table showing the cost of ordering 1, 2, 3, 4, or 5 CDs.
See above right.

52. Graph the data in your table.
See margin p. 77.

53. *Calendar* A year has two months in a row with a Friday the thirteenth. What months must they be? *(Previous Course)*
February and March

Extra Practice, Lesson 2-7, page 523

PORTFOLIO
For your portfolio, choose one or two items from your work for this chapter. Here are some possibilities:
• a journal entry
• corrected work
• part of your project
Explain why you have included each selection.

51.
Number of CDs	Cost ($)
1	18.37
2	34.36
3	50.35
4	66.34
5	82.33

CHAPTER PROJECT

PROJECT LINK: CALCULATING

Write a sentence to describe how to calculate the value of the walls of your fort if you know the number of layers. Then write an equation to find the value of the fort.

Check students' work.

PROJECT DAY You may wish to plan a
project day on which students share their
completed projects. Encourage students to
explain their process as well as their product.

PROJECT NOTEBOOK Ask students to
review their project work and bring their
notebooks up to date.

SCORING RUBRIC

3 Your numerical expressions and equation
accurately and clearly describe the
reasons for the pattern in the data. Your
data, equations, diagrams, and
explanations are all organized to give a
clear and interesting picture of the pattern
you discovered.

2 Your numerical expression and equation
correctly describe the pattern, and the total
value is within the 200¢ budget. Your work
is complete and neat.

1 Your data tables, numerical expressions,
and equations are complete, but there are
some errors in the equations or data.

0 Diagrams, data tables, numerical
expressions, or equations are not
complete.

FINISHING THE CHAPTER PROJECT

**CHAPTER
PROJECT**

STEPPING STONES

Building a Fort The Project Link questions on pages 47, 64,
and 76 should help you to complete your project. Here is a
checklist to help you gather the parts of your project together.

✔ determining the size of your foundation and the value of
your fort with one layer in the wall

✔ a table, a description, and a numerical expression that
fits your pattern

✔ a sentence describing how to calculate the value of your
fort and an equation to find its value

Your final product will be a visual presentation of your fort,
including a report with a diagram, a table, and calculations.
You need to convince your teacher and the other members of
the class that your fort is appropriate and within budget.

Be sure your work is neat and clear. Show your data and
calculations. Write any explanations you think are necessary.

Reflect and Revise

Review your project with a friend or family member. Is your
fort a reasonable size and shape? Is it within the $2 budget?
Are your numerical expression and equation correct? If
necessary, revise your project before presenting it to the class.

Web Extension
Prentice Hall's Internet site contains
information you might find helpful as
you complete your project. Visit
www.phschool.com/mgm1/ch2 for some
links and ideas related to patterns.

page 76 **Mixed Review**
52.

Cost of CDs

page 76 Mixed Review graph: Cost (y-axis $0 to $100) vs Number of CDs (x-axis 1 to 5)

STUDENT SELF-ASSESSMENT SURVEY

■ Chapter 2 Student Self-Assessment Survey

1. Now that you have finished this chapter, think about what you have learned about patterns, functions, and equations. Check each topic that you feel confident you understand.
   - _____ find terms in number patterns (2-1)
   - _____ write number patterns in words (2-1)
   - _____ solve problems by looking for a pattern (2-2)
   - _____ find values of expressions using the order of operations (2-3)
   - _____ compare values of expressions (2-3)
   - _____ model variable expressions such as 3y + 2 (2-4)
   - _____ evaluate variable expressions (2-4)
   - _____ write variable expressions and word phrases (2-5)
   - _____ solve equations using one of the operations + or − (2-6)
   - _____ solve equations using models, a calculator, or mental math (2-7)

2. Before the Chapter Assessment, I need to review _____

3. a. Check one. In general, I thought this chapter was
   - _____ a snap _____ easy _____ average _____ hard _____ a monster
   b. Why do you feel this way? _____

4. In this chapter, I did my best work on _____

5. In this chapter, I had trouble with _____

6. Check each one that applies. Now that I've spent some time studying number patterns, I think they are
   - _____ important _____ boring _____ useful _____ fun
   - _____ a waste of time _____ confusing _____ tricky _____ interesting

7. Did you use a computer spreadsheet or graphing software to help you graph data? _____ If yes, did you have any problems using it? _____ If yes, explain. _____

Assessment

Vocabulary/Symbols

associative properties, commutative properties, equation, identity properties, isolate the variable, magic square, numerical expression, order of operations, solution, solve, terms, variable, variable expression

Resources

 Student Edition

Extra Practice, p. 523
Glossary/Study Guide

 **Teaching Resources**

Chapter Support File, Ch. 2
• Student Self-Assessment Survey
Glossary, Spanish Resources
Tools for Studying Smarter

78

WRAP UP

TACTILE/VISUAL LEARNING Exercises 1–4 Provide materials such as tiles and graph paper for students to use to find the patterns.

Exercises 7–14 Remind students to use their mnemonic devices to help them remember the order of operations.

Exercise 21 Remind students that you multiply two variables that are written next to each other.

ERROR ALERT! Exercise 23 Students may not be sure whether to write $5 - x$ or $x - 5$. **Remediation:** Tell students to ask themselves which term is greater, 5 or x. The greater term should be written first in a subtraction problem with positive numbers only.

ASSESSMENT Exercises 28–35 Have students write a variable expression for the left side of each equation.

2 WRAP UP

Patterns and Number Sense · 2-1

Each number in a number pattern is called a term. You can describe a number pattern with a rule. A rule tells you the first term and what to do to get each of the following terms.

Find the next three terms in each number pattern.

1. 2, 6, 18, 54, . . .
   162; 486; 1,458

2. 7, 19, 31, 43, . . .
   55, 67, 79

3. 75, 65, 55, 45, . . .
   35, 25, 15

4. 7, 14, 28, 56, . . .
   112, 224, 448

5. Write the first five terms in the following number pattern:
   Start with the number 5, and add 7 repeatedly.
   5, 12, 19, 26, 33

Problem Solving Strategies · 2-2

One strategy for solving a problem is to *Look for a Pattern*.

6. The cost of a 1-min call from Brookfield to the neighboring town Carnstown is 7 cents. The cost of a 2-min call is 15 cents, and a 3-min call is 23 cents. If this pattern continues, what would be the cost of a 5-min call?
   39 cents

The Order of Operations · 2-3

The **order of operations** is a set of rules used in mathematics. You use these rules to find the value of numerical expressions.

- Do all operations within parentheses first.
- Multiply and divide in order from left to right.
- Add and subtract in order from left to right.

Find the value of each expression.

7. $2 \times 20 + 24 \div 4$
   46

8. $5 + 4 \times 11$
   49

9. $5 + 3 \times 12 - 4$
   37

10. $(4 + 12) \div 4$
    4

11. $21 \div 3 + 4 \times 2$
    15

12. $8 \times (3 + 7) \times 3$
    240

13. $45 \div 5 + 24 \div 6$
    13

14. $16 \div (14 - 6)$
    2

Replace each ■ with <, >, or =.

15. $2 \times (12 - 3) \; \overset{<}{■} \; 2 \times 12 - 3$

16. $(18 - 2) \times (6 - 2) \; \overset{>}{■} \; 18 - 2 \times 6 - 2$

Remind students that the new mathematical terms in this chapter are defined in the Glossary/Study Guide in the back of the book.

Variables and Variable Expressions 2-4, 2-5

A **variable** is a symbol that stands for an unknown number. A **numerical expression** contains only numbers and operation symbols. A **variable expression** contains at least one variable. To evaluate a variable expression, replace each different variable with a number and then simplify.

Evaluate each expression.

17. $48 \div x$ for $x = 6$
8

18. $c - 7$ for $c = 56$
49

19. $14b$ for $b = 3$
42

20. $x \div 12$ for $x = 72$
6

21. $2ab + 3$ for $a = 4$ and $b = 3$
27

22. $h + 3k - 1$ for $h = 7$ and $k = 4$
18

Write a variable expression for each phrase.

23. 5 less than x
$x - 5$

24. y divided by p
$y \div p$

25. b more than 20
$20 + b$

26. h times 4
$h \times 4$ or $4h$

27. The drama club sold twice as many tickets on Saturday as on Friday. Write a variable expression for the number of tickets sold on Saturday. **$2t$**

Modeling Equations 2-6, 2-7

An **equation** is a mathematical sentence that contains an equal sign. To **solve** an equation, replace the variable with a number that makes the equation true. The number that makes the equation true is a **solution**.

Solve each equation.

28. $x + 7 = 12$
5

29. $m + 348 = 781$
433

30. $r - 1,078 = 4,562$
5,640

31. $t \div 4 = 32$
128

32. $78x = 4,368$
56

33. $m - 8 = 15$
23

34. $4a = 32$
8

35. $x + 3 = 8$
5

36. Choose A, B, C, or D. Chandrelle bought a calculator for x dollars. She gave the clerk $40. She received $7 back. Which equation could you use to find the cost of the calculator? **D**

  A. $7x = 40$
  B. $x - 40 = 7$
  C. $x \div 7 = 40$
  D. $x + 7 = 40$

37. *Writing* Describe in your own words the difference between an expression and an equation. **An expression is made up of numbers, variables, and operations, but no equal sign. An equation has an expression on either side of the equal sign.**

▬ Chapter 2 Assessment • Form A

Answers

1. Find the next three terms in this number pattern.
9, 16, 23, 30, . . .
1. 37, 44, 51

2. Write a rule to describe this number pattern.
6, 12, 24, 48, . . .
2. Start with the number 6 and multiply by 2 repeatedly.

3. Evaluate the expression $23 + 6 \div 2$.
3. 26

4. Evaluate the expression $5 \times (3 + 1) \times 4$.
4. 80

5. Use mental math to evaluate $4(x - 7)$ for $x = 10$.
5. 12

6. Write the equation $36 \div 9 + 3 \times 2 = 6$ with parentheses to make it true.
6. $36 \div (9 + 3) \times 2 = 6$

7. Replace ■ with $<$, $>$, or $=$.
$8 - 3 \times 2$ ■ $(8 - 3) \times 2$
7. $<$

8. Write two word phrases for the variable expression $a + 23$.
8. Sample: 23 more than a number, the sum of a and 23

9. State whether $y = 5$ is a solution to the equation $5 - y = 0$.
9. yes

10. Solve $8 - x = 2$.
10. 6

11. Solve $13 = 9 + y$.
11. 4

12. State whether $p = 0$ is a solution to the equation $9 \times p = 9$.
12. no

13. Solve $18n = 108$.
13. 6

Chapter 2 Assessment • Form A (continued)

14. Solve $30 = k \div 3$.
14. 90

15. Evaluate the expression $3a + 6$ for $a = 6$.
15. 24

16. Solve $43 + j = 61$.
16. 18

Choose A, B, C, or D.

17. Which numerical expression has a value closest to 125?
  A. $(22 + 3) \times 6$
  B. $5 \times 9 + 50$
  C. $205 - 9 \times 9$
  D. $200 \div 5 + 75$
17. C

18. Which variable expression shows twelve less than a number?
  A. $12 - n$
  B. $n - 12$
  C. $\frac{12}{n}$
  D. $12n$
18. B

Choose a Strategy

19. Annie agreed to wash the car each week if she could get paid 1 cent the first week, 2 cents the second week, 4 cents the third week, 8 cents the fourth week, and so on for 15 weeks. How much money will she have at the end of 15 weeks?
19. $327.67

Writing

20. Explain why $(2 + 3) \times 4$ is not equal to $2 + 3 \times 4$.
Using the correct order of operations, $(2 + 3) \times 4 = 20$ and $2 + 3 \times 4 = 14$. The expressions are not equal.

■Chapter 2 Assessment • Form B

Choose the best answer. Circle A, B, C, or D.

1. What are the next three numbers in the number pattern
53, 48, 43, 38?
   A. 33, 28, 25
   B. 33, 23, 13
   Ⓒ 33, 28, 23
   D. 28, 23, 18

2. Which rule describes the number pattern
125, 25, 5, 1?
   A. subtract twenty-five
   B. add twenty-five
   Ⓒ divide by five
   D. multiply by five

3. Evaluate the expression $54 \div 6 + 4 \times 2$.
   Ⓐ 17
   B. 26
   C. 68
   D. 80

4. Use mental math to evaluate $4 \times (5 - 3)$.
   A. 60
   Ⓑ 8
   C. 19
   D. 32

5. Use mental math to evaluate $5(12 - y)$ for $y = 3$.
   A. 67
   B. 60
   Ⓒ 45
   D. 9

6. Which numerical expression has a value closest to 95?
   Ⓐ $5 \times 20 - 4$
   B. $4 \times 30 - 15$
   C. $60 \div 3 \times 5$
   D. $(2 + 3) \times 20$

7. Which variable expression shows ten less than a number?
   A. $10 - n$
   B. $10 + n$
   Ⓒ $n - 10$
   D. $\frac{n}{10}$

8. Which word phrase does *not* describe the expression $43 + c$?
   A. 43 plus c
   B. 43 increased by c
   Ⓒ a difference of 43 and c
   D. 43 more than c

9. Which value of x is a solution for the equation
$8 - x = 8$?
   A. 16
   B. 8
   C. 1
   Ⓓ 0

10. Solve $4 + m = 24$.
    A. 28
    Ⓑ 20
    C. 6
    D. 4

11. Solve $5 = 17 - q$.
    A. 22
    B. 17
    Ⓒ 12
    D. 5

Chapter 2 Assessment • Form B (continued)

12. Which value of k is a solution for the equation
$10 \div k = 1$?
    A. 100
    Ⓑ 10
    C. 1
    D. 0

13. Solve $200 = 50x$.
    A. 10,000
    B. 250
    C. 40
    Ⓓ 4

14. Solve $63 \div z = 7$.
    A. 441
    B. 70
    C. 56
    Ⓓ 9

15. Which of the following is *not* equal to $3 + 4 \times 5$?
    Ⓐ $(3 + 4) \times 5$
    B. $3 + (4 \times 5)$
    C. $3 + 5 \times 4$
    D. $5 \times 4 + 3$

16. Evaluate $3(x - 2)$ for $x = 5$.
    A. 3
    Ⓑ 9
    C. 13
    D. 21

17. Which would you use in $6 \times 3 - 2 \blacksquare 6 - 3 \times 2$?
    Ⓐ >
    B. <
    C. =
    D. +

18. What would you do first if you had to evaluate the expression
$5(9 - 4)$?
    A. 5×9
    B. 5×4
    Ⓒ $(9 - 4)$
    D. $5 \times 9 - 5 \times 4$

19. Wendy participated in a jog-a-thon to raise money. She raised
$51.00 in all. She jogged 17 laps. Choose the equation Wendy
could use to find how much she raised per lap.
    Ⓐ $51 = 17l$
    B. $17 = 51l$
    C. $17 \div l = 51$
    D. $51(17) = l$

Choose a Strategy

20. Carla wanted to raise money toward the cost of summer
camp. She agreed to walk the neighbor's dog every day if she
could get paid 5 cents the first week, 10 cents the second
week, 20 cents the third week, 40 cents the fourth week, and
so on. How much money will Carla have at the end of
12 weeks?
    A. $.60
    B. $120.00
    C. $3.20
    Ⓓ $204.75

 Teaching Resources

Chapter Support File, Ch. 2, and Spanish
Resources

 Teacher's Edition

See pp. 42C–D for Assessment Options.

  **Teaching Resource
Software**

• Computer Item Generator, Ch. 2

ASSESSMENT

ENHANCED MULTIPLE CHOICE QUESTIONS
are more complex than traditional multiple
choice questions, which assess only one skill.
Enhanced multiple choice questions assess
the processes that students use as well as
the end result. The wording of the questions
encourages students to use more than one
strategy to solve problems. The National
Council of Teachers of Mathematics (NCTM)
encourages the use of multiple strategies in
problem solving. **Exercise 6** is an enhanced
multiple choice question.

Exercise 6 Whatever answer students
choose, ask them to explain their reasoning.
You may want to extend this exercise by
having students describe the rule for the
patterns in answers A, B, and C.

WRITING EXERCISES allow students to
describe how they think about and understand
the concepts they have learned. **Exercise 23**
is a writing exercise.

---

② ASSESSMENT

1. **a.** Sketch the fourth and fifth designs in
   the pattern below.

   b. Use the designs to form a number
   pattern. 1, 3, 5, 7, 9, . . .
   c. Write a rule to describe the number
   pattern. **Start with 1 and add 2 repeatedly.**
   d. Predict the number of triangles in the
   tenth design. **19 triangles**

**Find the next three terms in each
number pattern. Write a rule to
describe each number pattern.**
2–5. See back of book for rules.

2. 6, 10, 14, 18, . . .
   22, 26, 30

3. 64, 32, 16, 8, . . .
   4, 2, 1

4. 78, 69, 60, 51, . . .
   42, 33, 24

5. 4, 12, 36, 108, . . .
   324; 972; 2,916

6. **Choose A, B, C, or D.** Which number
   pattern can be described by this rule:
   *Start with the number 3, and add 7
   repeatedly?* **D**

   A. 3, 21, 147, . . .
   B. 7, 10, 13, . . .
   C. 1, 3, 7, . . .
   D. 3, 10, 17, . . .

7. Carol is training for a swim meet. She
   swims 4 laps per day the first week,
   8 laps per day the second week, 12 laps
   per day the third week, and 16 laps per
   day the fourth week. She continues this
   pattern. How many laps per day will
   Carol swim in the eighth week? **32**

8. Replace ■ with <, >, or =.
   a. $3 + 2 \times 2 \blacksquare 3 + (2 \times 2)$ **=**
   b. $6 + 14 \div 2 \blacksquare (6 + 14) \div 2$ **>**

9. Evaluate $2a + b$ for $a = 5$ and $b = 18$. **28**

10. *Mental Math* Solve each equation.
    a. $14 = y - 8$ **22**
    b. $2m = 26$ **13**

11. Write a variable expression for each
    model.
    a.
    b.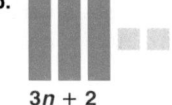

    a. $2x + 4$
    b. $3n + 2$

Find the value of each expression.

12. $500 + (12 - 8)$ **504**
13. $3 + 3 \times 4$ **15**

14. $8 \div 4 - 2$ **0**
15. $8 + 4 \div 2$ **10**

16. Write a variable expression for each
    word phrase.
    a. 8 less than d **$d - 8$**
    b. twice q **2q**
    c. c less than four **$4 - c$**
    d. six times x **6x**

17. Solve the equation shown in each model.
    a.  **3**

    b. **4**

Solve each equation.

18. $25 + b = 138$ **113**
19. $n - 46 = 84$ **130**

20. $140 = 10y$ **14**
21. $k \div 12 = 3$ **36**

22. State whether the given number is a
    solution to the equation.
    a. $x + 15 = 32; 16$ **no**
    b. $21 - b = 13; 8$ **yes**

23. *Writing* How would you use a calculator
    to solve $x - 562 = 1,455$?
    Use the ⊞ key to add 1,455 and 562.

Item	Review Topic	Ch
1	Measure of central tendency	1
2	Number patterns	2
3	Multiplying whole numbers	Precourse

Item	Review Topic	Ch
4, 7	Writing expressions	2
5, 9	Dividing whole numbers	Precourse
6	Analyzing graphs	1
8	Solving expressions	2

---

2 CUMULATIVE REVIEW

Choose the best answer.

1. In a set of data, what name is given to the number found by subtracting the lowest number from the highest? **D**

A. mean
B. median
C. mode
D. range

2. Which rule best describes the number pattern 4, 8, 12, 16, . . . ? **B**

A. Add 4 repeatedly.
B. Start with 4, and add 4 repeatedly.
C. Start with 4, and multiply by 2.
D. Start with 4, and multiply by 2 repeatedly.

3. For a lake cruise, each of 127 people will pay $20 for a ticket. What is the total cost of all the tickets? **D**

A. $147
B. $154
C. $2,440
D. $2,540

4. At a school play, adult tickets cost $7 and student tickets cost $4. The Baray family consists of 3 adults and 5 students. Which number sentence could be used to find T, the total cost in dollars for the family's tickets? **C**

A. $T = (4 \times 7) \times (5 \times 3)$
B. $T = (4 \times 7) + (5 \times 3)$
C. $T = (3 \times 7) + (5 \times 4)$
D. $T = (3 + 7) \times (5 + 4)$

5. For a class project, 23 students have collected 925 golf balls that are being put into 23 wire baskets. Each basket will have the same number of balls. What is the greatest number of balls each basket can contain? **C**

A. 4
B. 39
C. 40
D. 41

6. The circle graph below shows how Malinda budgets her income.

Malinda's Budget

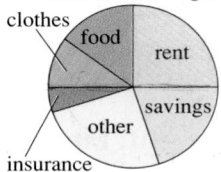

Which statement is true? **B**

A. The biggest budget item is food.
B. The amount for food and clothing is the same as for rent.
C. She budgets more for insurance than for savings.
D. The amount for savings is more than the amount for rent.

7. At a theme park each adult pays $20 and each student pays $12. Let R represent the total receipts for the day. Which sentence shows the total receipts for 320 adults and 578 students? **B**

A. $R = 20 + 12 + 320 + 578$
B. $R = (20 \times 320) + (12 \times 578)$
C. $R = 20 \times 320 \times 12 \times 578$
D. $R = (20 + 350) \times (12 + 578)$

8. What is the value of $79 - 5 \times (3 + 10)$? **A**

A. 14
B. 70
C. 232
D. 962

9. Hank earns $25 each week on his paper route. So far he has earned $2,625. For how many weeks has he had the paper route? **A**

A. 105
B. 15
C. 65,625
D. 2,600

CUMULATIVE REVIEW
Chapter 2 Cumulative Review

Choose the best answer. Circle A, B, C, or D.

1. Find the next three terms in the number pattern.
0, 3, 7, 12, __, __, __

A. 18, 24, 32
B. 18, 25, 32
C. 17, 23, 30
D. 18, 25, 33

2. Evaluate $4 \times (3 + 7)$.

A. 19
B. 14
C. 43
D. 40

3. What is the median of the following data set?
22, 18, 16, 27, 24,
19, 24, 21, 23, 17, 19

A. 17
B. 19
C. 21
D. 24

4. Of 28 students, four read both *The Red Pony* and *The Hobbit*. Fifteen read the first book, but not the second. Five students read neither book. How many read only *The Hobbit*?

A. 8 students
B. 5 students
C. 4 students
D. 7 students

5. Which word phrase best describes the expression $x + y$?

A. a number plus itself
B. twice a number
C. a number more than two
D. a number plus another number

6. Use mental math to solve $k - 4 = 9$.

A. 5
B. 9
C. 13
D. 36

7. In which equation is the value of y the same as in the equation $y \times 19 = 95$?

A. $95 \div y = 5$
B. $y + 5 = 19$
C. $95 \div 19 = y$
D. $95 - 19 = y$

8. Which is the value of $64 - 4 \times (2 + 13)$?

A. 4
B. 34
C. 47
D. 900

9. What formula could be used to find the value of cell C5?

Trash Collected

	A	B	C
1		Fri.	Sat.
2	Oak	16	17
3	Elm	13	11
4	Ash	14	15
5	Total		

A. =(C2+C3+C4)/3
B. =B2+C2
C. =C2+C3+C4
D. =3(B4+B5)

CUMULATIVE REVIEW
Chapter 2 Cumulative Review (continued)

10. Use mental math to evaluate $4x - 9$ for $x = 6$.

A. 14
B. 15
C. 33
D. 37

11. Janet paid x for a cassette tape. She gave the clerk a $20 bill. She received $7 in change. Which equation would you use to find the cost of the tape?

A. $7x = 20$
B. $20 = x + 7$
C. $x - 20 = 7$
D. $x + 7 = 20$

12. Multiply 110×43.

A. 4,530
B. 770
C. 4,510
D. 4,730

13. Use mental math to evaluate $(24 + 86) \times 10$.

A. 1,000
B. 1,010
C. 1,100
D. 1,110

14. Which operations will make the two expressions equal?
$2 + (12 \div 3) = 2 \_ 12 \_ 3$

A. +, +
B. −, −
C. ÷, ×
D. +, ÷

15. Evaluate $9 \times 9 - 6 \div 6$.

A. 4.5
B. 12.5
C. 45
D. 80

Use the bar graph below for Exercises 16 and 17.

Ice Cream Sold

16. Which list orders the months according to how much ice cream was sold from least to greatest?

A. Sept., June, July, Aug.
B. June, July, Aug., Sept.
C. July, June, Aug., Sept.
D. July, Aug., June, Sept.

17. About how many more gallons of ice cream were sold in August than in June?

A. 20 gal
B. 30 gal
C. 10 gal
D. 40 gal

Choose a Strategy

18. Elena bought 8 cans of juice. She gave the clerk $5.00 and received $1.80 in change. Each can of juice costs the same. Which equation could you use to find the cost of 1 can of juice?

A. $8y + 1.80 = 5.00$
B. $8y - 5.00 = 1.80$
C. $y + 1.80 = 5.00$
D. $y - 5.00 = 1.80$

Resources

Teaching Resources

Chapter Support File, Ch. 2
• Cumulative Review

Teacher's Edition

See pp. 42C–D for Assessment Options.

CHAPTER OVERVIEW

To accommodate flexible scheduling, most lessons are divided into parts. Assignment Options are given in the Teacher's Edition for each lesson.

Pages 84–87	**Lesson 3-1** **Geometry: Exploring Decimal Models**
NCTM 1, 2, 3, 5, 7	Part 1 Modeling Decimals Part 2 Exploring Equivalent Decimals **Key terms:** one tenth, one hundredth, equivalent **Math at Work**

Pages 88–91	**Lesson 3-2** **Reading and Writing Whole Numbers and Decimals**
NCTM 1, 2, 3, 4, 5, 13	Part 1 Reading and Writing Whole Numbers Part 2 Reading and Writing Decimals **Key terms:** standard form, expanded form, mill **Alternative Activity** 3-2

Pages 92–95	**Lesson 3-3** **Comparing and Ordering Decimals**
NCTM 1, 2, 3, 4, 5, 13	Part 1 Comparing Decimals Using Models Part 2 Ordering Decimals Using Place Value **Alternative Activity** 3-3 ▼ **Project Link** ☑ **Checkpoint 1**

Pages 108–111	**Lesson 3-7** **Algebra: Adding and Subtracting Decimals**
NCTM 1, 2, 3, 4, 5, 6, 7, 9, 13	Part 1 Adding Decimals Part 2 Subtracting Decimals **Alternative Activity** 3-7

Pages 113–117	**Lesson 3-8** **Measurement: Metric Units of Length**
NCTM 1, 2, 3, 4, 7, 12, 13	Part 1 Using Metric Units of Length Part 2 Choosing Appropriate Units **Key terms:** standard unit, metric system, meter ☑ **Checkpoint 2**

Pages 118–121	**Lesson 3-9** **Measurement: Metric Units of Mass and Capacity**
NCTM 1, 2, 3, 5, 13	Part 1 Metric Units of Mass Part 2 Metric Units of Capacity **Key terms:** mass, gram, capacity, liter **Journal** ▼ **Project Link**

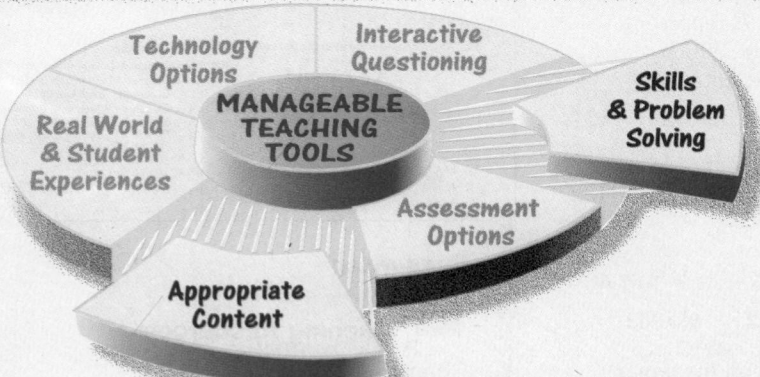

MANAGEABLE TEACHING TOOLS — Technology Options, Interactive Questioning, Skills & Problem Solving, Assessment Options, Appropriate Content, Real World & Student Experiences

Pacing Options

This chart suggests pacing only for the core lessons and their parts. It is provided merely as a possible guide. It will help you determine how much time you have in your schedule to cover other features, such as the Chapter Project, Math Toolboxes, Wrap Up, and Assessment.

	1 Class Period	1 Class Period	1 Class Period	1
Traditional (40–45 min class periods)	3–1 3–1 ▼1 ▼2	3–2 3–2 ▼1 ▼2	3–3 3–3 ▼1 ▼2	
Block Scheduling (90 min class periods)	3–1 3–1 3–2 3–2 ▼1 ▼2 ▼1 ▼2	3–3 3–3 3–3 3–4 ▼1 ▼2 ▼1	3–5 3–5 3–6 3–6 ▼1 ▼2 ▼1 ▼2	3–7 ▼1

Name That Tune

Goals: Compare prices, round and estimate to evaluate costs of CDs

THEME: CONSUMER ISSUES

NCTM STANDARDS

1 Problem Solving	6 Number Systems and Number Theory
2 Communication	7 Computation and Estimation
3 Reasoning	8 Patterns and Functions
4 Mathematical Connections	9 Algebra
5 Number and Number Relationships	

10 Statistics
11 Probability
12 Geometry
13 Measurement

Pages 96–98

Lesson 3-4
Problem Solving Strategy

NCTM 1, 3, 4, 5, 13

Guess and Test

Key term: guess and test

Pages 99–102

Lesson 3-5
Modeling the Addition and Subtraction of Decimals

NCTM 1, 2, 3, 5, 7

Part 1 Modeling Addition of Decimals

Part 2 Modeling Subtraction of Decimals

Journal

▼ **Project Link**

Pages 104–107

Lesson 3-6
Data Analysis: Rounding and Estimating Data

NCTM 1, 2, 3, 4, 5, 7, 13

Part 1 Rounding Data

Part 2 Estimating Sums and Differences

Key term: front end estimation

Pages 123–126

Lesson 3-10
Measurement: Measuring Elapsed Time

NCTM 1, 2, 3, 4, 13

Part 1 Adding and Subtracting Measures of Time

Part 2 Reading, Using, and Making Schedules

Key terms: second, elapsed time

Optional Materials and Manipulatives

graph paper (3-1, 3-3, 3-5)
calculator (3-6, 3-7)

metric ruler (3-8)
newspaper (3-9)

Optional calculator use is integrated throughout the course.

---

ss d	1 Class Period	1 Class Period	1 Class Period	1 Class Period	1 Class Period	1 Class Period	1 Class Period	1 Class Period	1 Class Period	1 Class Period	1 Class Period

-5 ▼ | 3–6 ▼1 3–6 ▼2 | 3–7 ▼1 3–7 ▼2 | 3–8 ▼1 | 3–8 ▼2 | 3–9 ▼1 | 3–9 ▼2 | 3–10 ▼1 3–10 ▼2 | | | |

-9 ▼ | 3–9 ▼2 3–10 ▼1 3–10 ▼2 | | | | | | | | | |

MEETING INDIVIDUAL NEEDS

Accommodating Diverse Learning Styles

In your Teacher's Edition, you will find suggestions as to how you can help students complete mathematical tasks in Chapter 3 by meeting individual needs and supporting various learning styles. Here are some examples:

VISUAL LEARNING
drawing figures to solve problems *(p. 115)*

TACTILE LEARNING
modeling money exercises using coins *(p. 94)*

AUDITORY LEARNING
reading decimal numbers out loud for partners to write *(p. 89)*

KINESTHETIC LEARNING
forming human decimal numbers by holding digits and standing in a line *(p. 89)*

EARLY FINISHERS
Performance-Based Project, MathBlaster® Mystery, Interdisciplinary Units

GIFTED AND TALENTED
creating word problems *(p. 97)*

DIVERSITY saying numbers in Portuguese and Spanish *(p. 92)*

ACQUIRING ENGLISH PROFICIENCY (AEP)
comparing the prefixes *kilo-, centi-,* and *milli-* to words in other languages *(p. 114)*

ASSESSING PROGRESS

A broad range of assessment tools are available to reach a variety of learners.

INFORMAL ASSESSMENT

Informal assessments provide day-to-day feedback to help give you a picture of conceptual understanding and skill development.

ONGOING ASSESSMENT is built into lesson instruction and the Teaching Notes of the Teacher's Edition.

In the Teacher's Edition
Lesson Quiz for every lesson

In the Student Edition
On Your Own, Mixed Review, Journal, Portfolio, Project Link, Chapter Wrap Up

Look for **Interactive Questions** within lessons that

BUILD UNDERSTANDING with labels such as Analyze, Reasoning, Estimation, Writing, and Summarize

✔ **CHECK UNDERSTANDING** with the Try It Out label.

FORMAL ASSESSMENT

Formal assessment can occur before and after the chapter, as well as at natural breaking points in the chapter.

Checkpoints
Two forms of each self-assessment Checkpoints are available: one in the Student Edition and another in the Chapter Support File in the Teaching Resources box.
- Mid-Chapter Checkpoint 1, page 94
- End-of-Chapter Checkpoint 2, page 116

Chapter 3 Assessment, page 130.
Two alternative forms are available in the Chapter Support File. They may be used after a chapter has been completed, or as a pre-test and post-test comparison.

Cumulative Review, page 131.
Assesses skills and concepts in Chapters 1–3.
An alternative form is available in Chapter Support File.

Computer Item Generator for Chapter 3
Customized tests can be generated for each lesson and for mid-chapter and end-of-chapter assessments, and for pre- and post-test comparisons of achievement.

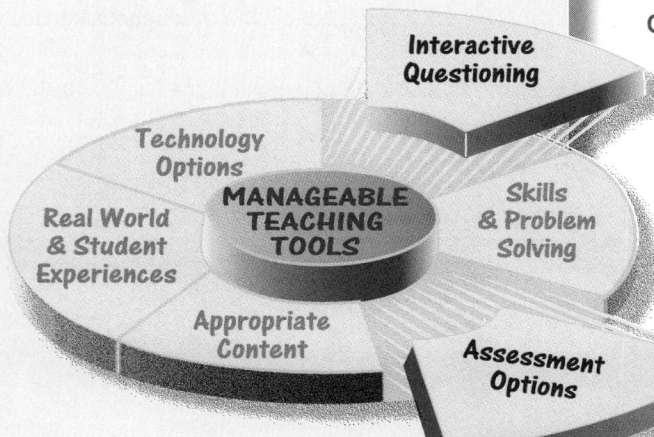

Interactive Questioning

Technology Options

MANAGEABLE TEACHING TOOLS

Skills & Problem Solving

Real World & Student Experiences

Appropriate Content

Assessment Options

CHAPTER PROJECT

The Chapter Project in the student edition provides a real-world connection to the math context of the chapter. The Teacher's Edition contains a scoring rubric.

Another performance-based Chapter Project with a scoring rubric can be found in the Chapter Support File in the Teaching Resources Box.

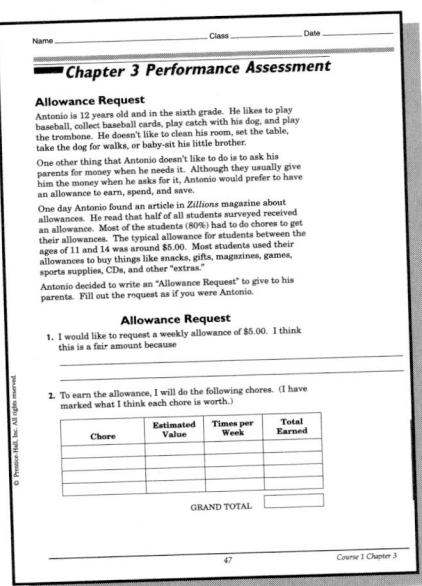

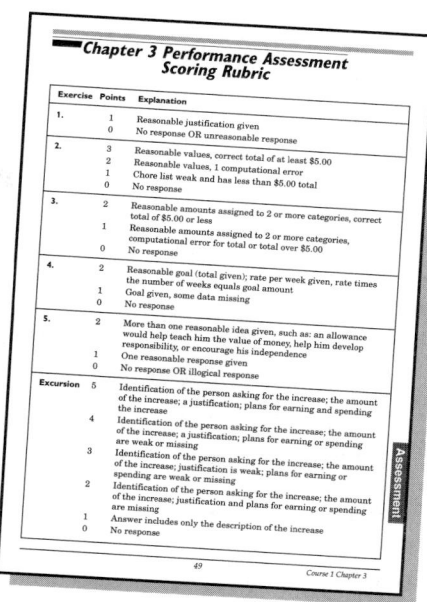

Correlation to Standardized Tests

Lesson		CAT5	CTBS/5 Terra Nova	ITBS	MAT7	SAT9	Your Local Test
			STANDARDIZED TEST ITEMS				
3-1	Geometry: Exploring Decimal Models			■	■		
3-2	Reading and Writing Whole Numbers and Decimals			■	■		
3-3	Comparing and Ordering Decimals	■	■	■	■	■	
3-4	Problem Solving Strategy: Guess and Test			■	■	■	
3-5	Modeling the Addition and Subtraction of Decimals	■	■	■	■	■	
3-6	Data Analysis: Rounding and Estimating Data	■	■	■	■		
3-7	Algebra: Adding and Subtracting Decimals	■	■	■	■	■	
3-8	Measurement: Metric Units of Length	■				■	
3-9	Measurement: Metric Units of Mass and Capacity	■			■		
3-10	Measurement: Measuring Elapsed Time	■	■	■		■	

CAT5 California Achievement Test, 5th Edition
CTBS/5 Comprehensive Test of Basic Skills, 5th Edition

ITBS Iowa Test of Basic Skills, Form B
MAT 7 Metropolitan Achievement Test, 7th Edition

SAT9 Stanford Achievement Test, 9th Edition

82D

MAKING CONNECTIONS

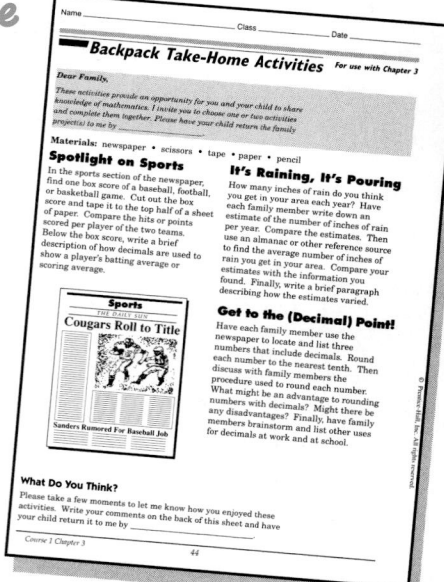

TEAM TEACHING WITH PRENTICE HALL MATERIALS

MIDDLE GRADES MATH INTERDISCIPLINARY UNITS

- **Consumer Awareness:**
  Activities 1 & 10
- **Space Exploration: Activity 4**
- **Travel and Geography: Activity 2**

INTERDISCIPLINARY EXPLORATIONS

- *Sleuth's Supper* **p. 22**

SCIENCE EXPLORER

L Life Science **E** Earth Science **P** Physical Science

E Sec. 4-1 The Earth in Space
(day, night, time)

Lesson	Interdisciplinary Connections	Real World Connections	Math Integration
3-1	Science	Money Accountants	Geometry
3-2	Social Studies Science Biology	Sports Money	Statistics
3-3	Social Studies Earth Science	Geography Astronomy	Data Analysis
3-4	Sports Literature	Jewelry Fundraising Entertainment Money Consumer Issues	Data Analysis
3-5	Economics	Consumer Issues	Data Analysis
3-6	Consumer Issues	Consumer Issues Nutrition	Data Analysis
3-7	Sports	Banking Consumer Issues Transportation Natural Resources	Algebra Data Analysis
3-8	History	World Standard Measure Science Research	Measurement Geometry
3-9	Science	Nutrition Label Information	Measurement
3-10	Consumer Issues	Schedules Entertaining Amusement Parks Studying Party Planning	Measurement Data Analysis

School to Home

MATERIALS:
newspaper
almanac
scissors
tape
paper
pencil

English and Spanish versions are available in the Teacher's Communication Kit, Teacher's Resource box.

USING TECHNOLOGY TO ENHANCE INSTRUCTION

FOR THE STUDENT

Multimedia Math Hot Pages™
This interactive software and video package on CD-ROM integrates solid math content through a variety of media.

- Hot Page™ 7 (3-1)
- Hot Page™ 8 (3-5)
- Hot Page™ 9 (3-10)

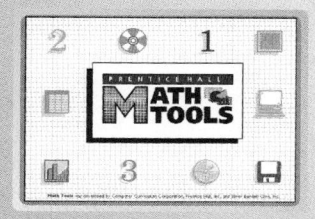

Math Labs
This software, available on both diskette and CD-ROM, includes on-screen Math Lab activities. Students use linkable, interactive tools to explore math concepts.

- Math Lab: Decimals and Measurement (3-8)

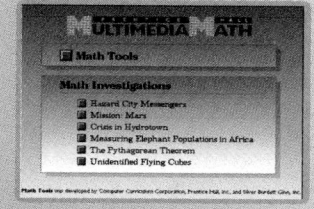

Multimedia Math Investigations
These in-depth interactive activities on CD-ROM develop real-world applications of mathematics. They allow students the opportunity to reinforce key concepts.

- Hazard City Messengers
- Measuring Elephant Population in Africa

Interactive Student Tutorial
Available on CD-ROM, this test preparation program contains self-tests with questions in standardized test format. Software includes electronic versions of the text lessons and the Math Tools and Math Labs.

MathBlaster® Mystery
This award-winning, interactive software program on CD-ROM can be used to maintain skills or to accommodate early finishers.

- Level: Earn 2 coins; Pay 6 coins
- Mission Mode (all lessons)
- Kitchen Comparisons (3-1, 3-3, 3-9)
- Number Guesser (3-4, 3-6)
- Equation Maker (3-5, 3-7, 3-10)
- Word Problems (3-2, 3-8, Problem Solving Practice)

Internet Connection

For Students
Support for the Chapter Project
A career-oriented link for Math at Work feature

www.phschool.com/math

For teachers
Curriculum Support
Product Information
Regional Support Information

FOR THE TEACHER

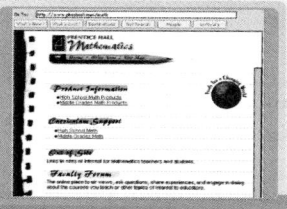

Computer Item Generator
Available on both CD-ROM and diskette, this software generates customized practice sheets, quizzes, and tests. It generates an unlimited supply of questions with varying levels of difficulty.

The Resource Pro™
Available on CD-ROM, this software can be used to customize and plan lessons.

Technology Options

MANAGEABLE TEACHING TOOLS
- Interactive Questioning
- Skills & Problem Solving
- Assessment Options
- Appropriate Content
- Real World & Student Experiences

CONNECTING TO PRIOR LEARNING Ask students: *Where have you seen decimals?* **Answers may vary. Sample: prices, statistics in the newspaper, grade point averages** *What would be useful to know in order to solve problems with these decimals?* **Answers may vary. Sample: how to add and divide them, how to round and compare them**

CULTURAL CONNECTIONS The Inca culture flourished from about A.D. 1400 to 1540 in areas of present-day Peru, Bolivia, Ecuador, Chile, and Argentina. The Incas kept careful social and economic records by using the quipu (pronounced KEE poo), a collection of dyed cords knotted in a base-ten number system.

INTERDISCIPLINARY CONNECTIONS Bring chemistry boks to class. Let groups of students look through the books to see that decimals are used throughout the course.

ABOUT THE PROJECT By completing the Chapter Project, students apply their knowledge of adding and subtracting decimals to evaluate a possible purchase.

Internet • For information and activities related to the Chapter Project, visit the Prentice Hall site at www.phschool.com/mgm1/ch3

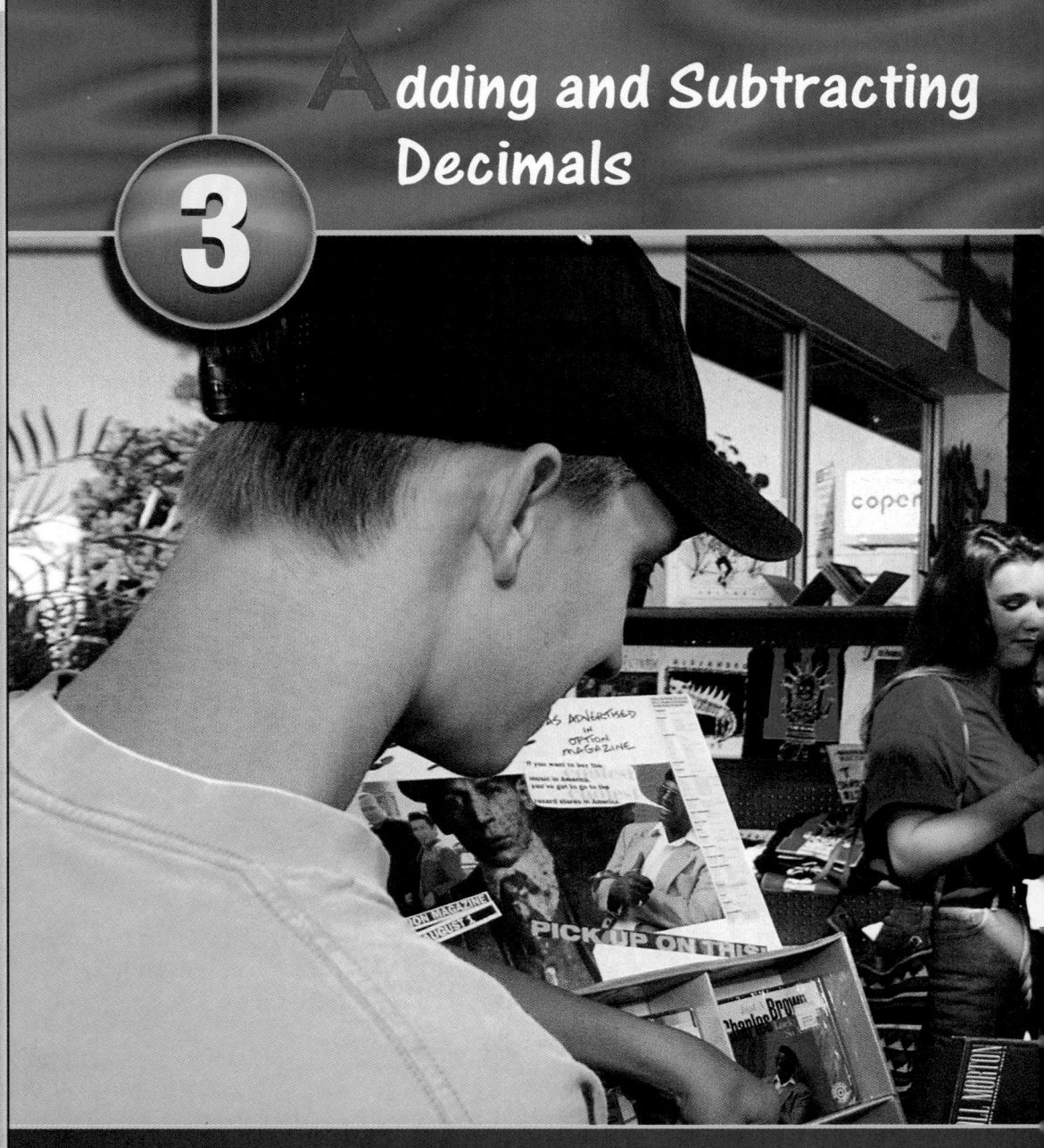

Adding and Subtracting Decimals

3

WHAT YOU WILL LEARN IN THIS CHAPTER	• How to read, write, and compare decimals	• How to add and subtract decimals	• How to use metric units of length, mass, and capacity

LAUNCHING THE CHAPTER PROJECT

PROJECT NOTEBOOK Encourage students to keep all project-related materials in a separate folder or notebook.

Ask students: *Have you ever evaluated a possible purchase? What questions did you have to consider?* **Answers may vary.**

TRACKING THE PROJECT You may wish to have students read Finishing the Chapter Project on page 127 to help them get an overview of the project. Set benchmark deadlines for students to show you their work in progress.

Name that TUNE

CHAPTER PROJECT

THEME: CONSUMER ISSUES

Don't you just love to browse through a music store? But you love bargains, too! You have probably seen magazine ads that promise eight music CDs for only a penny. But is this really a bargain? Suppose that after you get your eight CDs, you must buy eight more CDs at regular club prices ($12.95–$17.95) over the next two years. Also, you must pay a shipping and handling charge per CD, including the eight CDs you got for a penny. Is the club still a good deal?

Compare Prices and Decide Your project will be to compare the costs of buying CDs through a CD club and at a store and to make a decision whether to join the club or not.

Steps to help you complete the project:

p. 95   **Project Link:** *Comparing*
p. 102   **Project Link:** *Estimating*
p. 121   **Project Link:** *Calculating*
p. 127   *Finishing the Chapter Project*

- **How to solve problems using the guess and test method**

PROBLEM SOLVING

SCORING RUBRIC

3 Your calculations were accurate. You considered average CD prices in local stores, the range of club prices (rather than a single value), and shipping costs. Your estimations were listed or displayed in a way that made them easy to follow. You considered other factors that might have influenced your decision to join the club or not.

2 Your calculations were reasonable, based on average CD prices, and took into account shipping costs. Your estimations were listed or displayed in an organized and clear way.

1 Your calculations were inaccurate or were based on a single CD price rather than on an average. You did not consider shipping costs, or your data was not organized or presented neatly enough for others to follow easily.

0 You either didn't make a decision about whether or not to join the club, or your decision was not supported with complete data and calculations.

Teaching Notes

1 Focus

CONNECTING TO PRIOR KNOWLEDGE Ask students: *Where have you seen decimals?* **prices, measurements, calculators** *Why don't we just use whole numbers all the time?* **Answers may vary. Sample: Sometimes we need to talk about parts of a whole.**

Lesson Planning Options

Prerequisite Skills
• understanding decimal place value (precourse)

Vocabulary/Symbols
one tenth, one hundredth, equivalent

Materials/Manipulatives
• graph paper

Resources

 Student Edition

Skills Handbook, p. 535
Extra Practice, p. 524
Glossary/Study Guide

 Teaching Resources

Chapter Support File, Ch. 3
• Lesson Planner 3-1
• Practice 3-1, Reteaching 3-1
• Answer Masters 3-1
Teaching Aids Master 20
Glossary, Spanish Resources

 Transparencies
11, 12, Minds on Math 3-1

Warm Up

Ask students to draw an 8 slice pizza. Have students determine how many slices will be left without a topping if they put only mushrooms on $\frac{1}{2}$ of them, and only sausage on $\frac{5}{8}$ of them. **1 slice**

---

2 Teach

THINK AND DISCUSS

TACTILE LEARNING Have students work with base-ten blocks.

ERROR ALERT! Students may confuse the tenths' and hundredths' places. They may read 0.06 as six tenths instead of six hundredths. **Remediation:** Have students relate decimals to money. They know $.06 is six cents, the same as six pennies or six hundredths of a dollar. They also know $.60 is sixty cents, the same as six dimes or six tenths of a dollar.

ASSESSMENT Question 5 Have students work in pairs. One student shows 0.7 and the other shows 0.70. Make sure the squares are the same size. Have students discuss the similarities and differences in their drawings. **The size of the shaded areas should be the same. The 0.70 model has 70 equal sections. The 0.7 model has 7 equal sections.**

GEOMETRY Connection

 **3-1**

Exploring Decimal Models

What You'll Learn

▼ **1** To model decimals
▼ **2** To explore equivalent decimals

...And Why

You can draw models to represent decimals and use your models to identify equivalent decimals.

Here's How

Look for questions that
⚬ build understanding
✔ check understanding

Tenths' Model

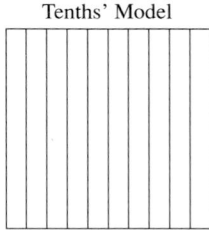

Hundredths' Model

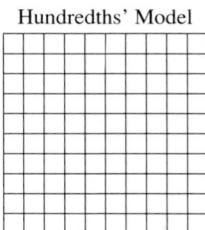

THINK AND DISCUSS

▼ 1 Modeling Decimals

Suppose you are in charge of cutting a huge, square birthday cake. One hundred people must be served. How would you cut the cake so that everyone receives an equal-sized piece?

To model the cake, draw a square with sides 10 centimeters long. **See tenths' model below left for diagram.**

1. ⚬*Modeling* Cut the "cake" vertically into ten equal strips. On your model, draw a line for each cut.

Since there are ten equal strips, one strip is *one tenth* of the cake. You can write one tenth as 0.1. Two strips are two tenths, or 0.2, of the cake.

2. a. How many strips are 0.3 of the cake? **3 strips**
   b. How many tenths are 0.8 of the cake? **8 tenths**
3. **See hundredths' model below left for diagram; 100 pieces.**
3. ⚬*Go a Step Further* Now cut the "cake" horizontally so that each strip is cut into 10 pieces. On your model, draw a line for each cut. How many pieces of cake do you have now?

One piece is *one hundredth* of the cake. You can write one hundredth as 0.01. Two pieces equal two hundredths, or 0.02.

4. a. How many pieces equal 0.07 of the cake? **7 pieces**
   b. How many hundredths equal 0.43 of the cake? **43 hundredths**

■ EXAMPLE 1

Write a decimal for this model.

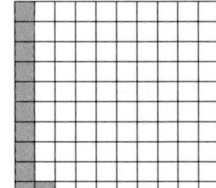

Eleven out of 100 pieces of the model are shaded.

The model represents eleven hundredths, or 0.11.

Now you may assign Exercises 1–24, 32–36.

■ ADDITIONAL EXAMPLES

FOR EXAMPLE 1

Write a decimal for this model. **0.55**

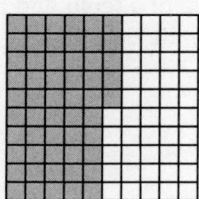

FOR EXAMPLE 2

How many tenths are equivalent to twenty hundredths? **2**

Work Together

TACTILE LEARNING Ask students to bring in pennies. Group students and give each group 100 pennies. Have them represent a penny, nickel, dime, quarter, and dollar using the pennies.

AEP Make sure students know the value of each coin and its name. Show and name a penny, nickel, dime, and quarter before the Work Together activity.

CONNECTING TO THE STUDENTS' WORLD Ask students to find decimals in magazines or newspapers. Have them decide why the publication used decimals.

CONNECTION TO SCIENCE Scientists use the metric system to measure. Ask students for examples of decimal measurements. **Answers may vary. Sample: 2.34 cm**

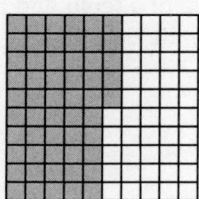

On October 18, 1989, a huge cake in the shape of the state of Alabama was made to celebrate the 100th birthday of the town of Fort Payne. The cake weighed 128,238.5 lb, including 16,209 lb of icing. A 100-year-old resident named Ed Henderson made the first cut.

Source: Guinness Book of Records

9. A dime is 0.1 of a dollar; a penny is 0.01 of a dollar.

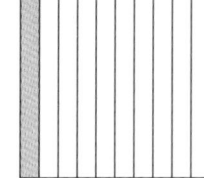

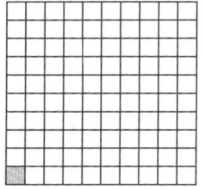

② *Exploring Equivalent Decimals*

5. ⁂ *Modeling* Draw models to represent the decimals 0.7 and 0.70. What do you notice? **See back of book for diagram; the amount shaded is the same.**

Decimals that represent the same amount are **equivalent.**

6. a. How many tenths describe the whole cake? **10**
  b. How many hundredths describe the whole cake? **100**
  c. ⁂ *Explain* Are the decimals 0.1 and 0.10 equivalent? Why or why not? **Yes; they represent the same amount.**

7. What whole number describes the whole cake? **1**

■ **EXAMPLE 2**

How many hundredths are equivalent to five tenths?

Five tenths equals 0.5. Draw a model for 0.5. Five strips are shaded.

Then divide your model into hundredths. Fifty squares are shaded. This represents 0.50.

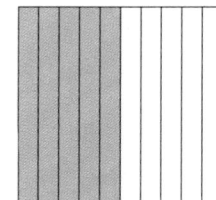

five tenths = 0.5

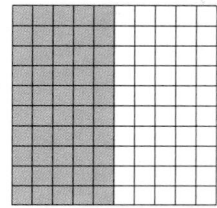

fifty hundredths = 0.50

0.50 = 0.5

8. ✔*Try It Out* How many hundredths are equivalent to nine tenths? **90 hundredths**

Work Together   *Applying Decimal Models to Money*

Suppose you have a dime and a penny.

9. ⁂*Modeling* Describe each coin as a decimal portion of a dollar. Draw models for one dollar, one dime, and one penny. **See left.**

10. Draw models for one nickel and one quarter. Write the decimal representation for each coin. **See back of book.**

Now you may assign Exercises 25–31.

Technology Options

Prentice Hall Technology

  Software for Learners

- Hot Page™ 7*
- Math Blaster® Mystery*
- Interactive Student Tutorial, Chapter 3*

 Teaching Resource Software

- Computer Item Generator 3-1
- Resource Pro™ Chapter 3*

Internet • For related mathematics activities, visit the Prentice Hall site at www.phschool.com/math

*Available on CD-ROM only

Assignment Options for Exercises On Your Own

To provide flexible scheduling, this lesson can be split into parts.

▼**1 Core** 1–24
  Extension 32–36

▼**2 Core** 25–30
  Extension 31

Use Mixed Review to maintain skills.

3 Practice/Assess

WRITING Exercise 31 Before students write, have them debate the views of Miki and Paulo.

ESTIMATION Exercises 34–36 Suggest students first decide whether the shading covers more than or less than half of the region.

OPEN-ENDED Exercise 35 Encourage students to create models to show the value of their coins. Ask: *Why did the United States decide to mint a penny, nickel, dime, quarter, and half-dollar?* **Answers may vary. Sample: The values of these coins are equal parts of 100.**

WRAP UP

IDENTIFYING THE BIG IDEA Ask students to discuss the value of a tenth and a hundredth. Have them write the decimals.

pages 86–87   On Your Own

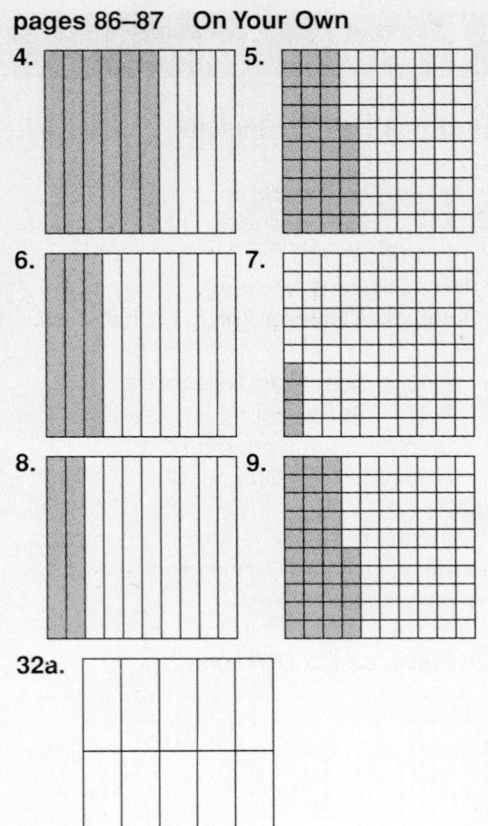

4.
5.
6.
7.
8.
9.
32a.

EXERCISES *On Your Own*

Write a decimal for each model.

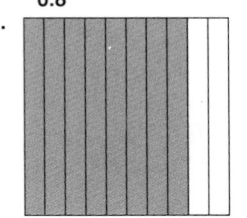
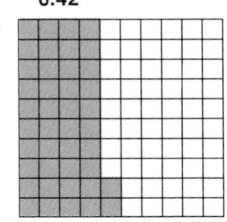
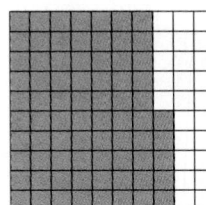

1. 0.8   **2.** 0.42   **3.** 0.75

Draw a model for each decimal.   4–9. See margin.

4. 0.6   **5.** 0.36   **6.** 0.3   **7.** 0.04   **8.** 0.2   **9.** 0.35

Write each decimal in words.

10. 0.08   **11.** 0.2   **12.** 0.56   **13.** 0.40   **14.** 0.65   **15.** 0.30
eight hundredths | two tenths | fifty-six hundredths | forty hundredths | sixty-five hundredths | thirty hundredths

Write a decimal for the given words.

16. seven tenths 0.7
17. forty hundredths 0.40
18. five hundredths 0.05

19. five tenths 0.5
20. twenty-two hundredths 0.22
21. thirty-one hundredths 0.31

22. fifty-four hundredths 0.54
23. twelve hundredths 0.12
24. forty-seven hundredths 0.47

How many hundredths are equivalent to each amount?

25. two tenths 20   **26.** six tenths 60   **27.** eight tenths 80   **28.** ten tenths 100   **29.** four tenths 40

30. How many tenths are equivalent to sixty hundredths? 6

31. *Writing* Miki thinks this model shows 0.4. Paulo thinks it shows 0.40. Do you agree with Miki or with Paulo? Explain. **See right.**

31. Answers may vary. Sample: Both; although the model shows 40 square shaded, 0.40 is equivalent to 0.4.

32. Suppose you want to cut a square birthday cake into 10 equal pieces. A vertical strip will not fit on a party plate, so you decide on a different shape. **See margin.**
  a. Draw a model that shows how you will cut the cake.
  b. Write a decimal number to represent one piece of cake. 0.1

33. *Open-ended* Imagine you are asked to invent a new coin. Describe your coin as a decimal portion of a dollar. **Check students' work.**

Math at Work

If you have block scheduling or extended class periods, have students create a budget for a family of four. Suggest students research monthly expenses for housing, food, clothing, and other necessities. Help students choose a realistic monthly income. Encourage students to use a spreadsheet to create this budget.

PRACTICE

Practice 3-1 *Exploring Decimal Models*

Draw a model for each decimal. Sample answers shown.
1. 0.4   2. 0.72   3. 0.10

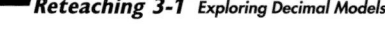
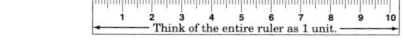

Write each decimal in words.
4. 0.9 — nine tenths
5. 0.1 — one tenth
6. 0.04 — four hundredths
7. 0.07 — seven hundredths
8. 0.29 — twenty-nine hundredths
9. 0.46 — forty-six hundredths
10. 0.80 — eighty hundredths
11. 0.30 — thirty hundredths
12. 0.03 — three hundredths

Write a decimal for each model.
13. 0.56   14. 0.3 or 0.30   15. 0.61

Write a decimal for the given words.
16. three tenths — 0.3
17. fifty-two hundredths — 0.52
18. eight tenths — 0.8
19. two hundredths — 0.02
20. seventy-nine hundredths — 0.79
21. forty hundredths — 0.40

How many hundredths are equivalent to each amount?
22. five tenths — fifty hundredths
23. nine tenths — ninety hundredths
24. one tenth — ten hundredths
25. How many tenths are equivalent to 30 hundredths? — three tenths

In copymaster and workbook formats

Estimation **Each square model represents 1. Write a decimal to estimate the amount shaded.**

34. 0.25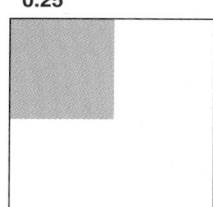

35. about 0.94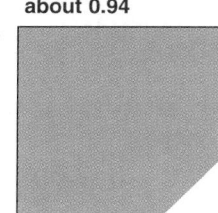

36. 0.25

Mixed Review

37. An ant can lift 50 times its own body weight. Suppose a student weighing 85 lb could do the same. How much could the student lift? *(Previous Course)* **4,250 lb**

Choose **Use tiles, mental math, or a calculator to solve each equation.** *(Lesson 2-7)*

38. $3x = 27$ **9**
39. $17 = y \div 9$ **153**
40. $a \div 10 = 210$ **2,100**
41. $950 = 5b$ **190**
42. $125 = y \div 5$ **625**

Compare using <, >, or =. *(Previous Course)*

43. 13×7 **<** $120 - 27$
44. $237 + 338$ **=** 25×23
45. $450 \div 90$ **=** $4500 \div 900$

RETEACHING

Reteaching 3-1 *Exploring Decimal Models*

Think of the entire ruler as 1 unit.

Tenths
1 centimeter is $\frac{1}{10}$ of the ruler.
There is one zero in 10. Let this remind you that there is one decimal place in a number of tenths.
Write $\frac{1}{10}$ as 0.1.
Both are read as *one tenth*.
Read 0.4 as *four tenths*.

Hundredths
1 millimeter is $\frac{1}{100}$ of the ruler.
There are two zeros in 100. There are two decimal places in a number of hundredths.
Write $\frac{1}{100}$ as 0.01.
Both are read as *one hundredth*.
Read 0.38 as *thirty-eight hundredths*.

The point shown on the ruler marks 0.6 or 0.60 of the ruler. Six tenths and sixty hundredths are **equivalent** decimals.

Write each decimal in words.
1. 0.2 — two tenths
2. 0.15 — fifteen hundredths
3. 0.29 — twenty-nine hundredths
4. 0.11 — eleven hundredths
5. 0.60 — sixty hundredths
6. 0.9 — nine tenths
7. 0.07 — seven hundredths
8. 0.3 — three tenths
9. 0.48 — forty-eight hundredths

How many hundredths are equivalent to each amount?
10. five tenths — fifty hundredths
11. eight tenths — eighty hundredths
12. one tenth — ten hundredths
13. three tenths — thirty hundredths

How many tenths are equivalent to each amount?
14. seventy hundredths — seven tenths
15. fifty hundredths — five tenths
16. twenty hundredths — two tenths
17. ninety hundredths — nine tenths

Math at Work

ACCOUNTANT

Accountants usually work in some area of finance. They must enjoy working with numbers and know how to budget money well. Accountants use mathematics to prepare and analyze financial reports and tax returns, create budgets, and to manage company costs. Accountants' reports help people make good business decisions.

 Visit the Careers in the Field of Accounting Web site: www.beckercpa.com/careers.html

ENRICHMENT

Minds on Math Transparency

3-1

Jeremi, Orin, and Marcia all like yogurt. They all like a different flavor best. Their favorites are vanilla, lemon, and strawberry. Jeremi's favorite is not vanilla. Orin likes strawberry best. What flavor does Marcia like best?

vanilla

See *Solution Key* for worked-out answers.

1 Focus

CONNECTING TO PRIOR KNOWLEDGE Ask students to compare the value of one quarter with four nickels. **The quarter is worth $.25, or twenty-five hundredths of a dollar, more than four nickels.**

Lesson Planning Options

Prerequisite Skills
• modeling decimals (precourse)

Vocabulary/Symbols
standard form, expanded form, mill

Resources

 Student Edition

Skills Handbook, p. 536
Extra Practice, p. 524
Glossary/Study Guide

 Teaching Resources

Chapter Support File, Ch. 3
• Lesson Planner 3-2
• Practice 3-2, Reteaching 3-2
• Alternative Activity 3-2
• Answer Masters 3-2
Teaching Aids Master 20
Glossary, Spanish Resources

 Transparencies
11, 12, 82, Minds on Math 3-2

Warm Up

If 300 cheeseburgers are ordered for lunch on a field trip and one out of every five must have mustard on it, how many will have mustard on them? **60**

---

2 Teach

THINK AND DISCUSS

ERROR ALERT! Some students may say the word *and* when reading whole numbers. For example, "thirty-five thousand *and* one hundred *and* six" for 35,106. **Remediation:** Remind students when reading numbers to say the word *and* only for the decimal point. Discuss why having more than one *and* can be confusing.

2a. fifty-six million, seven hundred eighty-nine thousand, four hundred forty-five

b. six billion, two hundred fifty-three million, seven hundred eighty-eight thousand, five hundred fifty-four

c. forty-five thousand, five hundred sixty-eight

Need Help? For more practice with whole numbers, see Skills Handbook pages 535 and 536.

CONNECTION TO SOCIAL STUDIES Suggest students research the U.S. national debt for the last five years. Ask them to also find debt predictions.

REASONING Question 1 Ask students to examine the place-value names for patterns. This might give them clues to how the values change.

AEP Point out decimal numbers always end in "th." Have students practice identifying and saying: tens and tenths, hundreds and hundredths, thousands and thousandths.

3-2 ## Reading and Writing Whole Numbers and Decimals

What You'll Learn

1 To read and write whole numbers
2 To read and write decimals in expanded and standard forms

...And Why

You can write whole numbers and decimals to solve problems in social studies and sports.

Here's How

Look for questions that
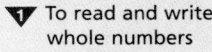 build understanding
✔ check understanding

THINK AND DISCUSS

1 *Reading and Writing Whole Numbers*

Social Studies The national debt is now over five trillion dollars. How large a number is this?

The position of a digit in a number determines the place value of that digit. The digits in a whole number are grouped into periods. A period has 3 digits, and each period has a name.

Trillions Period			Billions Period			Millions Period			Thousands Period			Ones Period		
Hundreds	Tens	Ones	Hundreds	Tens	Ones	Hundreds	Tens	Ones	Hundreds	Tens	Ones	Hundreds	Tens	Ones
	6	1	4	0	2	6	1	7	0	8	0	1	2	5

Read the number in each period followed by its period name.

61 trillion, 402 billion, 617 million, 80 thousand, 125

1. *Reasoning* As you move from left to right in the place value chart, how do the values increase or decrease? **The values decrease by a factor of 10.**
2. Write each number in words.
   a. 56,789,445   **b.** 6,253,788,554   **c.** 45,568

To write a number in **standard form,** use commas to separate the periods. Add zeros if you need to so that each period has 3 digits.

■ EXAMPLE 1

Write 65 million, 3 thousand, 47 in standard form.

65 million + 3 thousand + 47 = 65,000,000 + 3,000 + 47

$$= 65,003,047$$

65 million, 3 thousand, 47 in standard form is 65,003,047.

| ASSESSMENT and KINESTHETIC LEARNING | ■ ADDITIONAL EXAMPLES | # 3 Practice/Assess |

ASSESSMENT and KINESTHETIC LEARNING

Assign digits 0–9 to students. Draw a place-value chart on the board large enough for students to stand under each heading. Make sure the decimal point on the board is clearly visible. Read a decimal number aloud. Have students model the number by standing in front of the board so each digit is in the correct space. Fill the gaps in the chart with zeros. Have each student in the chart say their portion of the number aloud.

■ **ADDITIONAL EXAMPLES**

FOR EXAMPLE 1

Write 20 billion, 45 million, 2 thousand, 45 in standard form. **20,045,002,045**

FOR EXAMPLE 2

The diameter of a quarter is two and forty-three hundredths of a centimeter. Write this number in standard form. **2.43**

3 Practice/Assess

EXERCISES *On Your Own*

AUDITORY LEARNING Exercises 8–17
Have students work in pairs. Ask one student to read a number. Have the partner write the number in standard form. Have them continue for half the problems, then switch roles.

VISUAL LEARNING Exercises 19–28 Have students write numbers on a place-value

---

3a. 232,000,753,000

  b. 65,002,042

3. ✔Try It Out Write each number in standard form.
  a. 232 billion, 753 thousand   **b.** 65 million, 2 thousand, 42

Now you may assign Exercises 1–18.

 **Reading and Writing Decimals**

Two tenths and five hundredths is equivalent to twenty-five hundredths. One is expressed in expanded form, the other in standard form.

Expanded Form	=	Standard Form
0.2 + 0.05	=	0.25

two tenths and five hundredths = twenty-five hundredths

A number in **expanded form** shows the place and value of each digit. Look at 47.2586 in the place value chart below.

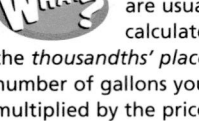

Hundreds	Tens	Ones		Tenths	Hundredths	Thousandths	Ten-Thousandths	Hundred-Thousandths
	4	7	.	2	5	8	6	

4. In the number 47.2586, the digit 2 is in the tenths place. What is the value of the 8? **eight thousandths**

When you read or write a decimal greater than 1, the word "and" tells you where to place the decimal point.

Gasoline prices are usually calculated to the thousandths' *place. The number of gallons you buy is multiplied by the price. Then the total is rounded up to the nearest cent.*

■ **EXAMPLE 2** *Real-World Problem Solving*

Sports A marathon race is about twenty-six and seventy-three thousandths miles long. Write this number in standard form.

26 ←——Write the whole number part.

26.■ ■ ■ ←—— Thousandths is 3 places to the right of the decimal point.

26.■ 73 ←——Place 73 to the far right.

26.073 ←——Insert a zero for tenths.

Twenty-six and seventy-three thousandths in standard form is 26.073.

Technology Options

Prentice Hall Technology

Software for Learners
- Math Blaster® Mystery*
- Interactive Student Tutorial, Chapter 3*

Teaching Resource Software
- Computer Item Generator 3-2
- Resource Pro™ Chapter 3*

Internet • For related mathematics activities, visit the Prentice Hall site at www.phschool.com/math

Available on CD-ROM only

Assignment Options for Exercises On Your Own

To provide flexible scheduling, this lesson can be split into parts.

▼**1** **Core** 1–17
  Extension 18

▼**2** **Core** 19–43, 46–51
  Extension 44, 45

Use Mixed Review to maintain skills.

89

chart to help them see the value of the digit 4 in each number.

OPEN-ENDED **Exercise 34** Have students work with a partner. Ask one student to write the decimal in standard and expanded forms. Have the partner write the decimal in words. Then have students switch roles. Encourage partners to check each other's work.

Exercises 35 and 36 Remind students the word *and* indicates a decimal.

RESEARCH **Exercise 44** Have students find out more about leap years. Ask: *When was the first leap year? Is the year 2000 a leap year? Was 1900 a leap year?* 46 B.C.; yes; no

Exercise 45 Have students find out how much a gallon of gas costs and write the price in mills.

CONNECTION TO BIOLOGY **Exercises 46–51** Have students find another biology fact and write a similar statement.

IDENTIFYING THE BIG IDEA Ask students to explain how to express decimals in standard and expanded forms. Have them also explain how to read and write decimals.

---

pages 90–91 On Your Own

6. two hundred twenty-three million, four hundred fifty-five thousand, seven hundred eighty-four

7. forty-five million, six hundred fifty-four thousand, three hundred thirty-two

44. The extra 0.24 days are combined into a leap day every 4 years. This makes up too many days, so only 1 out of every 4 years that are multiples of 100 is a leap year.

---

5. ✔*Try It Out* Write each number in standard form.
  a. four and one hundred fifty-one thousandths 4.151
  b. two hundred forty-one and three ten-thousandths 241.0003

Now you may assign Exercises 19–51.

EXERCISES *On Your Own*

Complete each statement.

1. 3,460,800 = ▨ million, ▨ thousand, ▨   (3, 460, 800)

2. 56,450,000,000 = ▨ billion, ▨ million   (56, 450)

Write each number in words.
3. two hundred five   5. six thousand, seven hundred forty-five
  3. 205   **4.** 456,785   **5.** 6,745   **6.** 223,455,784   **7.** 45,654,332
4. four hundred fifty-six thousand, seven hundred eighty-five   6–7. See margin.

Write each number in standard form.

8. eight hundred ninety 890   **9.** four thousand, six hundred 4,600   **10.** fourteen million 14,000,000

11. 478 thousand, 27 478,027   **12.** 240 million, 85 thousand, 11 240,085,011   **13.** 213 million, 125 213,000,125

14. 28 billion, 35 thousand, 40 28,000,035,040   **15.** 6 billion, 23 million, 158 thousand 6,023,158,000

16. 7 trillion, 2 million, 13 thousand 7,000,002,013,000   **17.** three hundred thousand, twenty 300,020

18. *Science* Scientists estimate the universe was formed about sixteen billion years ago. Write this number in standard form. 16,000,000,000

What is the value of the digit 4 in each number?
four tenths   thousandths   four hundred-thousandths   four tens   four ones
19. 0.4   **20.** 3.004   **21.** 1.28864   **22.** 42.3926   **23.** 4.0052

24. 530.34   **25.** 17.55643   **26.** 34,567.89   **27.** 433.0005   **28.** 3.40365
four hundredths   four ten-thousandths   four thousands   four hundreds   four tenths

Write each number in words.
  30. six and twenty-five thousandths
29. three hundred fifty-two and three tenths   32. seventy and nine thousandths
29. 352.3   **30.** 6.025   **31.** 11.2859   **32.** 70.009   **33.** 0.00657
31. eleven and two thousand, eight hundred fifty-nine ten-thousandths

34. *Open-ended* Write a decimal with 5 decimal places in standard form and in expanded form.   33. six hundred fifty-seven hundred-thousandths
  Sample: 1.32537; 1 + 0.3 + 0.02 + 0.005 + 0.0003 + 0.00007

Write each number in standard form.
  2.00004   400.075
35. two and four hundred-thousandths   **36.** four hundred and seventy-five thousandths

37. 40 + 2 + 0.3 + 0.07 + 0.009 + 0.0004 42.3794   **38.** 50 + 1 + 0.6 + 0.03 51.63

LESSON QUIZ

1. Write 29 trillion, 305 billion, 28 million, 75 thousand, 105 in standard form.
29,305,028,075,105

2. Write 300.033 in words. **three hundred and thirty-three thousandths**

3. Write one hundred thirty-five thousandths in expanded form. **0.1 + 0.03 + 0.005**

4. Write two hundred twenty-two and two hundred twenty-two thousandths in standard form. **222.222**

Money **Write each amount as a decimal part of $1.00.**

39. 8 dimes **$.8**
40. 6 pennies **$.06**
41. 49 pennies **$.49**
42. 3 quarters **$.75**

43. *Writing* Describe how the value of the digit 2 changes in each place in the number 22.222.
As you move left to right, the value decreases by a factor of 10.

44. *Research* Earth revolves around the sun in 365.24 days. Find out how our calendar deals with the extra 0.24 day.
See margin p. 90.

45. *Money* A mill is a very small unit of money that state governments sometimes use to calculate taxes. One mill is equivalent to one thousandth of a dollar ($.001).
    a. Write each amount as part of a dollar.
       i. 6 mills **ii.** 207 mills **iii.** 53 mills **iv.** 328 mills
    b. About how many cents is each amount worth?
      1 cent   **21 cents**   **5 cents**   **33 cents**

    i. $.006
    ii. $.207
    iii. $.053
    iv. $.328

Biology **Write each measurement in standard form.**

46. Human fingernails grow about two thousandths of an inch a day. **0.002 in./d**

47. A goat produces four and seven tenths pints of milk a day. **4.7 pt/d**

48. A flea can jump six hundred forty-six thousandths of a foot. **0.646 ft**

49. One beat of a housefly's wings takes about one thousandth of a second. **0.001 s**

50. A bee's wing has a mass of five hundred-thousandths of a gram. **0.00005 g**

51. A tortoise moves seventeen hundredths of a mile per hour. **0.17 mi/h**

Mixed Review

52. Ten students took Mr. Yuji's science test. Their scores were 91, 84, 78, 84, 70, 93, 68, 89, 77, and 76. Find the mean, median, and mode of the scores. *(Lesson 1-3)* **81; 81; 84**

53. Order the following numbers from greatest to least: 3,201,455; 2,684,387; 978,897; 2,852,238; 4,527,982; and 3,097,854. *(Previous Course)* **4,527,982; 3,201,455; 3,097,854; 2,852,238; 2,684,387; 978,897**

54. *Choose a Strategy* Evan saves two quarters and three nickels each day. At the end of 30 days, how much has he saved? **$19.50**

Practice 3-2 *Reading and Writing Whole Numbers and Decimals*

Write each number in words.

1. 1,760   one thousand, seven hundred sixty
2. 84,508   eighty-four thousand, five hundred eight
3. 75,398,012   seventy-five million, three hundred ninety-eight thousand, twelve

Write each number in standard form.

4. three thousand forty   3,040
5. eleven billion   11,000,000,000
6. one hundred ten   110
7. 400,000 + 20,000 + 8,000 + 400 + 6   428,406
8. 921 million, 750 thousand, 33   921,750,033
9. eighty-two thousand sixty   82,060

What is the value of the digit 7 in each number?

10. 0.7   7 tenths
11. 4.00712   7 thousandths
12. 2.179   7 hundredths
13. 28,467.089   7 ones
14. 348.92971   7 ten-thousandths
15. 72.14   7 tens

Write each number in words.

16. 12.873   twelve and eight hundred seventy-three thousandths
17. 8.0552   eight and five hundred fifty-two ten-thousandths
18. 0.00065   sixty-five hundred-thousandths

Write each number in standard form.

19. six and five thousandths   6.005
20. nine hundred fifty-four ten thousandths   0.0954
21. 20 + 0.01 + 0.003 + 0.0008   20.0138
22. 30 + 4 + 0.9 + 0.02   34.92
23. forty and eight hundredths   40.08
24. 200 + 10 + 0.04   210.04

In copymaster and workbook formats

Reteaching 3-2 *Reading and Writing Whole Numbers and Decimals*

Millions Period			Thousands Period			Ones Period		
Hundreds	Tens	Ones	Hundreds	Tens	Ones	Hundreds	Tens	Ones
		4	2	0	1	5	7	8

4 million 201 thousand 578

Ones	Tenths	Hundredths	Thousandths
2	3	6	9

2 and 369 thousandths

- *Standard form:* 4,201,578
- To find the value of a digit, multiply the digit by its place value.
  4 stands for 4 × 1,000,000, or 4,000,000
- *Expanded forms:*
  4,201,578 = 4,000,000 + 200,000 + 1,000 + 500 + 70 + 8

- *Standard form:* 2.369
- To find the value of a digit, multiply the digit by its place value.
  9 stands for 9 × 0.001, or 0.009
  2.369 = 2 + 0.3 + 0.06 + 0.009

Write each number in standard form.

1. 2 + 0.7 + 0.02 + 0.006   2.726
2. 45 + 0.08 + 0.003   45.083
3. 0.3 + 0.006   0.306
4. 0.04 + 0.008   0.048
5. six thousand one hundred four   6,104
6. fifteen million twenty-one thousand   15,021,000
7. sixty thousand one hundred twelve   60,112
8. 2 billion, 9 million, 6 thousand, 1   2,009,006,001
9. seventeen thousandths   0.017
10. twenty-nine hundredths   0.29

What is the value of the digit 8 in each number?

11. 58.3   8 ones
12. 40.08   8 hundredths
13. 0.81   8 tenths
14. 5,608.92   8 ones
15. 19.948   8 thousandths
16. 281.44   8 tens
17. 8,913.93   8 thousands
18. 1,690.85   8 tenths

Minds on Math Transparency

3-2

I am a three-digit number. My last digit is three times my first digit. My first digit is twice my middle digit. What number am I?

216

See Solution Key for worked-out answers.

91

1 Focus

CONNECTING TO PRIOR KNOWLEDGE Have students review how they compare and order whole numbers. Ask students: *Which number is greater, 1,786 or 1,900?* **1,900** How do you know? **Answers may vary. Sample: Both numbers have a 1 in the thousands place, but 1,900 has a 9 in the hundreds**

Lesson Planning Options

Prerequisite Skills
- comparing numbers (precourse)
- using graphs and number lines (precourse)

Materials/Manipulatives
- graph paper

Resources

 Student Edition

Skills Handbook, p. 535
Extra Practice, p. 524
Glossary/Study Guide

 Teaching Resources

Chapter Support File, Ch. 3
- Lesson Planner 3-3
- Practice 3-3, Reteaching 3-3
- Alternative Activity 3-3
- Answer Masters 3-3
Teaching Aids Master 20
Glossary, Spanish Resources

 Transparencies

11, 12, 18, Minds on Math 3-3

Warm Up

If a certain number was squared and then multiplied by 3, the result is 48. What was the original number? **4**

---

place and 1,786 has a 7. Since
$9 > 7, 1,900 > 1,786$.

2 Teach

THINK AND DISCUSS

DIVERSITY **Question 1** Have students research the official language of Brazil and Argentina. **Portuguese; Spanish** Have students find out how to say 12.79 in

Portuguese and 12.23 in Spanish. **doze ponto setenta e nove; doce y veintitrés centésimas**

ERROR ALERT! **Question 2** Students may have difficulty comparing two decimal numbers, such as 0.7 and 0.70.
Remediation: Remind students that writing zeros to the right of the decimal number does not change the value. If students need to be convinced, have them draw a decimal model of each number.

3-3 Comparing and Ordering Decimals

What You'll Learn
▼ To compare decimals using models
▼ To order decimals using place value

...And Why
You can order lists of data by comparing decimals.

Here's How
Look for questions that
▪ build understanding
✔ check understanding

QUICKreview
To compare numbers, use these symbols.
< is less than
= is equal to
> is greater than

Need Help? For practice with comparing and ordering whole numbers, see Skills Handbook p. 537.

THINK AND DISCUSS

▼ 1 Comparing Decimals Using Models

Social Studies Buenos Aires, Argentina, has an estimated population of 12.23 million people. About 12.79 million people live in Rio de Janeiro, Brazil. To compare the two populations, look at the whole number parts. They are the same. Now look at the decimal parts, 0.23 and 0.79.

| 0.23 | 0.79 |

$0.23 < 0.79$, so $12.23 < 12.79$. Buenos Aires has an estimated population less than that of Rio de Janeiro.

1. Draw models for 0.7 and 0.72. Which number is greater?
   See back of book for models; p. 72.

You can also graph decimals on a number line to compare them. Numbers on a number line are greater as you move to the right.

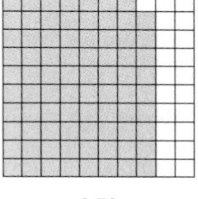

2. Use <, =, or > to complete each statement.
   a. 0.7 ▪ 0.4   b. 0.4 ▪ 0.7   c. 0.7 ▪ 0.70
      >   **<**   **=**
3. a. What decimals are at points *A* and *B*? **1.2; 1.6**
   b. Write two statements to compare the numbers.
   4. 0.13 > 0.08; 5   **1.2 < 1.6; 1.6 > 1.2**
4. ▪*Modeling* Use a number line to compare 0.13 and 0.08. How many hundredths are between the two decimals?
   5. Answers may vary. Sample: an infinite number; 0.81, 0.85, 0.88889
5. ▪*Analyze* How many numbers are between 0.8 and 0.9? Name three.
   Now you may assign Exercises 1–5, 19–21, 26.

VISUAL LEARNING Have students write 0.28 and 0.285 with the decimal points and place values aligned. Then have them compare the digits in each place from left to right. Ask students to highlight the first pair of numbers that are different. Ask students to compare these numbers and write a missing zero, if necessary. Ask: *Since 5 > 0, what does this tell you about 0.285 and 0.280?* **Answers may vary. Sample: 0.285 is greater.**

Questions 3–5 Some students may need to review number lines with decimals before answering the questions.

■ **ADDITIONAL EXAMPLES**

FOR EXAMPLE 1

Look at the table on page 93. Which body of salt water is saltier, the Dead Sea or the ocean? **the Dead Sea**

FOR EXAMPLE 2

Order the numbers 213, 211.987, 213.07, and 211.098 from least to greatest. **211.098, 211.987, 213, 213.07**

ALTERNATIVE METHOD Question 8a Have students use $.32 and $.35 in change to compare which decimal is greater.

ASSESSMENT Write 0.24, 0.42, 0.245, and 0.4 on the board. Ask: *If I asked you to put these numbers in order from least to greatest, which numbers would you compare first?*

2 Ordering Decimals Using Place Value

You can compare decimals using place value. Start at the decimal point and move right, one place at a time.

■ **EXAMPLE 1** *Real-World Problem Solving*

Earth Science Which body of salt water is saltier, the Dead Sea or the Great Salt Lake?

Compare 0.28 and 0.205. Line up decimal points.

0.28	0.28	0.28
0.205	0.205	0.205
↑	↑	↑
same	same	8 > 0

Salt per Liter in Major Bodies of Water

Water	Salt per Liter
Black Sea	0.018 kg
Caspian Sea	0.013 kg
Dead Sea	0.28 kg
Great Salt Lake	0.205 kg
Ocean (average)	0.035 kg

Source: *Natural Wonders of the World*

The Dead Sea is saltier than the Great Salt Lake.

6. ✔*Try It Out* Which body of salt water is saltier, the Caspian Sea or the ocean? Refer to Example 1. **ocean**

7. ⬛*Look Back* How could you use a model or number line to solve Example 1? **See below left.**

8. Use place value to compare each pair of decimals.
   a. 0.32 and 0.35   **b.** 0.14 and 0.041   **c.** 0.760 and 0.76
   0.32 < 0.35   0.14 > 0.041   0.760 = 0.76

You can graph decimals on a number line to place them in order.

■ **EXAMPLE 2** *Real-World Problem Solving*

Order the bodies of water above from least to most salty.

Graph 0.018, 0.013, 0.28, 0.205, and 0.035 on a number line.

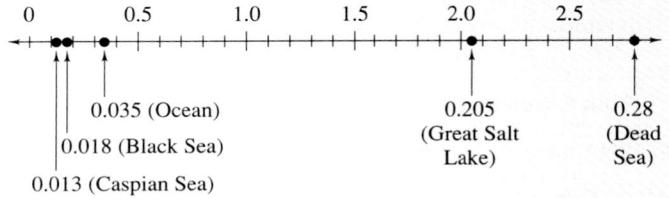

0.035 (Ocean)
0.018 (Black Sea)
0.013 (Caspian Sea)
0.205 (Great Salt Lake)
0.28 (Dead Sea)

The bodies of water from least to most salty are Caspian Sea, Black Sea, the ocean, Great Salt Lake, and Dead Sea.

Now you may assign Exercises 6–18, 22–25.

GEOGRAPHY People float easily in the salty water of the Dead Sea, between the countries of Israel and Jordan.

Israel and Jordan

7. Place the values on a number line. The point for the ocean is to the right of the point for the Caspian Sea, so the ocean is saltier.

Technology Options

Prentice Hall Technology

💾 📀 **Software for Learners**
• Math Blaster® Mystery*
• Interactive Student Tutorial, Chapter 3*

💾 📀 **Teaching Resource Software**
• Computer Item Generator 3-3
• Resource Pro™ Chapter 3*

🔄 **Internet** • For related mathematics activities, visit the Prentice Hall site at www.phschool.com/math

*Available on CD-ROM only

Assignment Options for Exercises On Your Own

To provide flexible scheduling, this lesson can be split into parts.

1 **Core** 1–5, 19, 20, 26
  Extension 21

2 **Core** 6–18
  Extension 22–25

Use Mixed Review to maintain skills.

Why? Answers may vary. Sample: 0.24 and 0.245. These numbers have a 2 in the tenths place. *How would you compare these numbers?* Sample: Rewrite 0.24 as 0.240. Compare each digit, starting at the left, until one is greater. Have students write the numbers in order from least to greatest. 0.24, 0.245, 0.4, 0.42 Compare lists with a partner and discuss any differences.

3 Practice/Assess

EXERCISES *On Your Own*

TACTILE LEARNING Exercises 1–5 These students may find modeling the exercises with coins helpful.

EXTENSION Exercises 22–26 Have students locate these stars on a star chart.

RESEARCH Exercises 22–26 A light-year is a measure of distance, not time. Students can research the origin of the term.

WRAP UP

IDENTIFYING THE BIG IDEA Ask students to explain how to compare and order decimals. Have them also describe how to show decimals on a number line.

CHECKPOINT 1

Name _____ Class _____ Date _____

Checkpoint 1   Lessons 3-1 through 3-3

Write each decimal in words.

1. 0.4   2. 0.49   3. 0.60   4. 0.05
four tenths   forty-nine   sixty   five hundredths
                hundredths   hundredths

Write each number as a decimal in standard form.

5. seven tenths   6. sixteen hundredths   7. 0.3 + 0.09
0.7   0.06   0.39

Write the value of the underlined digit.

8. 4.6̲43   9. 0.6̲91   10. 5̲.701   11. 2.50̲8
6 tenths   9 hundredths   5 ones   8 thousandths

Compare. Use >, <, or =.

12. 0.31 ⊡ 0.3   13. 24.04 ⊡ 24.040   14. 5.07 ⊡ 5.7

---

pages 94–95   On Your Own

1. The shaded area for 0.4 is less than the shaded area for 0.5, so 0.4 < 0.5.

2. The shaded area for 0.35 is less than the shaded area for 0.53, so 0.35 < 0.53.

3. The shaded area for 1.42 is less than the shaded area for 1.44, so 1.42 < 1.44.

4. The shaded area for 0.76 is less than the shaded area for 0.78, so 0.76 < 0.78.

5. The shaded area for 0.2 is greater than the shaded area for 0.02, so 0.2 > 0.02.

19.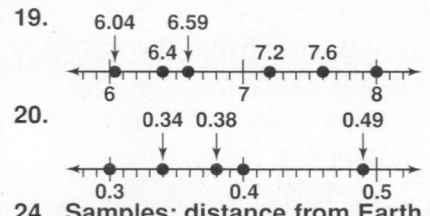

20.

24. Samples: distance from Earth to Proxima Centauri < distance from Earth to Sirius; distance from Earth to Alpha Centauri A = distance from Earth to Alpha Centauri B; distance from Earth to Procyon B > distance from Earth to 61 Cygni B

94

EXERCISES *On Your Own*

Draw models for each pair of decimals. Explain how the models show which number is greater. 1–5. See back of book for models; see margin for reasoning.

1. 0.4 and 0.5   2. 0.35 and 0.53   3. 1.42 and 1.44   4. 0.76 and 0.78   5. 0.2 and 0.02

6. *Writing* Explain how you can use place value to compare 1.679 and 1.697.
The first digit that is different is in the hundredths' place. 7 < 9, so 1.679 < 1.697.

Use <, =, or > to complete each statement.

7. 0.58 $\overset{>}{■}$ 0.578   8. 5.7 $\overset{=}{■}$ 5.70   9. 0.37 $\overset{>}{■}$ 0.3651   10. 0.09 $\overset{>}{■}$ 0.002

11. 8.009 $\overset{<}{■}$ 8.079   12. 6.6 $\overset{>}{■}$ 6.2   13. 49.5 $\overset{>}{■}$ 49.05   14. 0.4389 $\overset{<}{■}$ 0.45

15. 0.06 $\overset{<}{■}$ 0.60   16. 3.968 $\overset{<}{■}$ 4.007   17. 0.05 $\overset{=}{■}$ 0.050   18. 0.2 $\overset{<}{■}$ 0.29

Graph each set of numbers on a number line. 19–20. See margin.

19. 6.4, 6.04, 7.6, 6.59, and 7.2   20. 0.49, 0.34, 0.4, 0.3, and 0.38

21. **Choose A, B, C, or D.** Graph the decimals 0.2, 0.4, and 0.6 on a number line. Which statement is *not* true? C

A. 0.2 < 0.4 and 0.4 < 0.6   B. 0.2 < 0.4 and 0.2 < 0.6
C. 0.2 < 0.6 and 0.6 < 0.4   D. 0.4 < 0.6 and 0.6 > 0.2

Astronomy **Read the article at the right. Use the information for Exercises 22–25.**
Procyon B; Proxima Centauri

22. Which star is farthest from Earth? Which is closest to Earth?

23. Write the distances from Earth to each of the six stars in order from least to greatest.
4.28, 4.37, 8.7, 11.09, and 11.4 light-years

24. Use <, =, and > to write three statements about the distances of any of these stars from Earth. See margin.

25. *Research* Look up the meaning of *light-year*. Why do you think astronomers use this measure? Check students' work.

26. What decimals are at points *A*, *B*, and *C*? 0.4; 0.8; 1.1

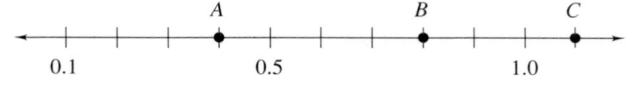

Light-Years Away

The brightest star in the sky is Sirius, which is about 8.7 light-years from Earth. The stars Alpha Centauri A and B are each about 4.37 light-years from Earth. Proxima Centauri is about 4.28 light-years away. Other stars are 6121 CygniB, about 11.09 light-years away, and Procyon B, about 11.4 light years away.

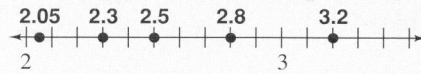

PROJECT LINK Make sure students understand they will use this data to compare the price of a CD through a club to the price of a CD from a store. Have them keep a record of all data, not just the average store price, as a reference.

LESSON QUIZ

1. Which number is greater, 0.702 or 0.710?
   0.710

2. Order these numbers from least to greatest.
   0.710, 1.7, 170, 1.71, 0.017
   0.017, 0.710, 1.7, 1.71, 170

3. Use <, =, or >.
   a. 0.212 ■ 0.221 **<**
   b. 0.891 ■ 0.8910 **=**

4. Graph these numbers on a number line.
   2.05, 2.5, 3.2, 2.3, 2.80

 **Mixed Review**

Find the value of each expression. *(Lesson 2-3)*

27. $4 - (24 \div 8) + 4$ **5**

28. $16 - 3 \times 2 + 5$ **15**

29. $55 \div (5 + 6) + 6$ **11**

Find each answer. *(Previous Course)*

30. 13,789 + 23,653
    37,442

31. 34,567 − 27,488
    7,079

32. 152 × 27
    4,104

33. 585 ÷ 9
    65

34. *Choose a Strategy* A large stone weighs 5 times as much as a small brick. Together they weigh 30 lb. What is the weight of the stone? **25 lb**

CHAPTER PROJECT

PROJECT LINK: RESEARCHING

Research the prices of CDs at different stores in your area. Compare your prices with those of other students. Calculate the average price of a CD based on the prices you have found.

Check students' work.

✓ **CHECKPOINT 1**   *Lessons 3-1 through 3-3*

Write each decimal in words.

1. 0.9 **nine tenths**
2. 0.01 **one hundredth**
3. 0.73 **seventy-three hundredths**
4. 0.60 **sixty hundredths**
5. 0.56 **fifty-six hundredths**
6. 0.99 **ninety-nine hundredths**

Write each number as a decimal in standard form.

7. three tenths **0.3**
8. two hundredths **0.02**
9. 0.9 + 0.02 **0.92**
10. 0.3 + 0.06 **0.36**

Find the value of each underlined digit.

11. 5.68 **6 tenths**
12. 0.870 **7 hundredths**
13. 8.005 **8 ones**
14. 4.203 **3 thousandths**
15. 3.632 **6 tenths**
16. 1.111 **1 hundredth**

Use <, =, or > to complete each statement.

17. 32.07 ■ 32.070 **=**
18. 1.8 ■ 1.08 **>**
19. 72.6 ■ 7.62 **>**
20. 55.05 ■ 55.50 **<**
21. 1.082 ■ 1.28 **<**
22. 3.04 ■ 3.040 **=**
23. 6.402 ■ 6.042 **>**
24. 2.2 ■ 2.22 **<**

25. *Open-ended* Make a list of five 6-digit whole numbers and decimals. Order the numbers from least to greatest. **Check students' work.**

Practice 3-3 Comparing and Ordering Decimals

Use >, <, or = to complete each statement.

1. 0.62 > 0.618
2. 9.8 < 9.80
3. 1.006 < 1.02
4. 41.3 > 41.03
5. 2.01 < 2.011
6. 1.400 = 1.40
7. 5.079 < 5.08
8. 12.96 < 12.967
9. 15.8 = 15.800
10. 7.98 > 7.89
11. 8.02 = 8.020
12. 5.693 > 5.299

Graph each set of numbers on a number line.

13. 0.2, 0.6, 0.5
14. 0.26, 0.3, 0.5, 0.59, 0.7

15. Circle A, B, C, or D. Three points are graphed on the number line below. Read statements A–D. Which statement is true?
    A. 0.3 < 0.5 and 0.7 < 0.5
    B. 0.5 > 0.3 and 0.7 < 0.5
    C. 0.3 < 0.7 and 0.7 > 0.5
    D. 0.7 < 0.5 and 0.3 < 0.5

16. Draw a model to represent 0.67 and a model to represent 0.675. Check students' work.
    a. Which number is greater? 0.675
    b. How do the models show which number is greater? more is shaded

17. Models for three decimals are shown below.
    a. Write the decimal that each model represents.
    0.73; 0.84; 0.12
    b. Order the decimals from least to greatest.
    0.12; 0.73; 0.84

In copymaster and workbook formats

Reteaching 3-3 Comparing and Ordering Decimals

Use >, <, or = to show how 4.092 and 4.089 compare.
① Write the numbers on grid paper with the decimal points lined up.
② Compare digits in the greatest place. Move to the right until you find digits that are not the same.
   4 ones = 4 ones
   0 tenths = 0 tenths
   9 hundredths > 8 hundredths
   So, 4.092 > 4.089.

To order numbers from least to greatest:
① Write the numbers on grid paper (decimal points lined up) and compare.
② Then arrange the numbers from least to greatest.
   4.089, 4.09, 4.092

Use <, >, or = to complete each statement.

1. 0.01 < 0.15
2. 0.25 > 0.21
3. 0.30 > 0.26
4. 0.10 < 0.12
5. 0.35 > 0.34
6. 0.1 < 0.4
7. 34.4 > 34.40
8. 0.207 < 0.27
9. 0.08 < 0.40
10. 0.32 > 0.309
11. 6.12 > 6.099
12. 0.990 = 0.99
13. 2.36 > 2.036
14. 0.05 < 0.15
15. 1.19 < 1.91

Write in order from least to greatest.

16. 3.46, 3.64, 3.59
    3.46, 3.59, 3.64
17. 22.97, 21.79, 22.86
    21.79, 22.86, 22.97
18. 43, 43.22, 43.022
    43, 43.022, 43.22
19. 10.02, 10.2, 1.02
    1.02, 10.02, 10.2
20. 1.09, 1.9, 1.1
    1.09, 1.1, 1.9
21. 7.54, 75.4, 7.4
    7.4, 7.54, 75.4
22. 0.67, 0.7, 0.6
    0.6, 0.67, 0.7
23. 0.03, 0.29, 0.019
    0.019, 0.03, 0.29
24. 8.36, 8.01, 8.1
    8.01, 8.1, 8.36

Minds on Math Transparency

3-3

During a pancake eating contest Team A ate 8 more pancakes than Team B. Team C ate twice as many pancakes as Team B. Together, the three teams ate a total of 72 pancakes. How many pancakes did Team A eat?

24 pancakes

See *Solution Key* for worked-out answers.

3-4 Teaching Notes

1 Focus

CONNECTING TO PRIOR KNOWLEDGE Ask students to think of times they tried to solve problems or obtain answers by making reasonable guesses. **Answers may vary. Sample: solving math multiple choice problems** Have students describe their process for making these guesses. **Answers may vary.**

2 Teach

THINK AND DISCUSS

VISUAL LEARNING   Question 1 Have students copy the problem and highlight the answers.

EXTENSION and WRITING   Question 3d Ask: *What would happen if Marny made one more bracelet and one less ring?* **Answers may vary. Sample: She would use 12 cm more thread.**

ASSESSMENT Tell students Marny made 8 items out of another piece of thread 112 cm long. Ask: *How many bracelets and rings did she make?* **4 bracelets, 4 rings** Before students make their first guess, have them review their answers to Questions 3–5 to help them make a first guess.

Lesson Planning Options

Prerequisite Skills
• multiplying whole numbers (precourse)

Vocabulary/Symbols
guess and test

Resources

 Student Edition

Skills Handbook, p. 540
Extra Practice, p. 524
Glossary/Study Guide

 Teaching Resources

Chapter Support File, Ch. 3
• Lesson Planner 3-4
• Practice 3-4, Reteaching 3-4
• Answer Masters 3-4
Glossary, Spanish Resources

 Transparencies
Minds on Math 3-4

Warm Up

Give students the following recipe for a health yogurt shake and ask them to rewrite the quantities in lowest terms.
$\frac{9}{12}$ c lowfat milk $\frac{3}{4}$
$\frac{7}{14}$ c of lowfat yogurt $\frac{1}{2}$
$\frac{4}{8}$ c of pineapple $\frac{1}{2}$
$\frac{2}{8}$ tsp of cinnamon $\frac{1}{4}$
$\frac{20}{32}$ c of ice $\frac{5}{8}$

96

3-4 Guess and Test

Problem Solving Strategies
  Draw a Diagram
✔ Guess and Test
  Look for a Pattern
  Make a Model
  Make a Table
  Simulate a Problem
  Solve a Simpler Problem
  Too Much or Too Little Information
  Use Logical Reasoning
  Use Multiple Strategies
  Work Backward

THINK AND DISCUSS

A good problem solving strategy is *Guess and Test*. First make a reasonable guess, and then test it against the given information. If your guess is incorrect, change it to make it more reasonable. Keep trying until you find the correct answer.

SAMPLE PROBLEM...

Handmade friendship bracelets use 20 cm of thread. Handmade rings use 8 cm of thread. Marny used a total of 184 cm of thread to make 14 items. How many friendship bracelets did she make?

....

 READ

Read for understanding. Summarize the problem.

Look at the given information. Decide what you are being asked to find.

1. **a.** How much thread is needed for a bracelet? A ring? **20 cm; 8 cm**
   b. How much thread did Marny use in all? **184 cm**
   c. How many items did Marny make? **14 items**

2. What does the problem ask you to find?
   the number of friendship bracelets Marny made

Guess and Test is a good strategy to use.

 PLAN

Decide on a strategy.

a. If there are 14 items and 4 of them are bracelets, the remaining 14 − 4 = 10 items are rings.

b. Multiply the number of items by the length of thread for each item.

c. 4 bracelets and 10 rings use 160 cm of thread, not 184 cm.

d. Each bracelet uses more thread than a ring. So by increasing the number of bracelets, you increase the total length.

3. Suppose you guess that Marny made 4 bracelets.
   a. *Reasoning* Why does this mean she made 10 rings?
   b. How many centimeters of thread are used to make 4 bracelets? 10 rings? Explain how you found each answer.
   c. Is a guess of 4 bracelets correct? Why or why not?
   d. *Writing* Should your next guess be higher or lower? Explain.

EXTENSION Have students work in groups to write a word problem they can solve with Guess and Test.

■ ADDITIONAL PROBLEM

The product of three consecutive numbers is 1,320. What are the numbers? **10, 11, and 12**

3 Practice/Assess

EXERCISES *On Your Own*

ERROR ALERT! **Exercises 1–3** Some students may guess randomly on their second guess without considering the information from their first guess. **Remediation:** Have students organize their guesses and results in a table. Remind them to look not only at their most recent guess, but also the information from any other guesses.

KINESTHETIC LEARNING **Exercise 4** Make four name tags labeled Juan, Maria, Noel, and Della. Give them to four students who would benefit from acting out the situation. Have the students arrange themselves into a line that solves the problem.

CONNECTION TO LITERATURE **Exercise 6** Some students may not be familiar with the book types. Consider discussing with the class examples of mysteries, fantasies, and biographies. Ask: *What kind of book is The Case of the Missing Body?* **mystery**

SOLVE
Try the strategy.

You can organize your guesses in a table like the one below.

Bracelets	Rings	Thread	High/Low
5×20 cm $= 100$ cm	9×8 cm $= 72$ cm	172 cm	low
8×20 cm $= 160$ cm	6×8 cm $= 48$ cm	208 cm	high
■	■	■	■

a. 6 or 7 bracelets

b. Yes; the length with 5 bracelets was closer to 184 cm than the length with 8 bracelets. So 6 is a better guess.

d. 6 bracelets

4. In the table above you can see that 5 bracelets required too little thread and 8 bracelets required too much thread.
   a. What guess would be reasonable to make next?
   b. 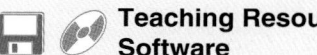*Analyze* Is one of the guesses more reasonable to make than the other? Explain.
   c. Copy and complete the table above to test your next guess. Keep guessing until you find the correct answer.
   d. How many friendship bracelets did Marny make?
   c. 6×20 cm $= 120$ cm; 8×8 cm $= 64$ cm; 184 cm; exact

LOOK BACK
Think about how you solved the problem.

Check your answer with the information given in the problem.

5. Is the total number of bracelets and rings 14? Is the total amount of thread used 184 cm? **yes; yes**

Now you may assign Exercises 1–10.

EXERCISES *On Your Own*

Use *Guess and Test* to solve each problem.

1. *Fund-raising* Parents in Fullerton are raising money for the school by conducting a raffle. You can buy a ticket for a video game for $2 or a ticket for a remote-control car for $3. On Saturday, $203 was raised by selling 80 raffle tickets. How many remote-control car tickets were sold? **43 tickets**

2. Place the digits 2, 3, 4, 6, and 8 in a copy of the figure at the right so the product in both directions is the same. Find the product.
   Answers may vary. See samples at right.

3. *Entertainment* Movie tickets cost $4.00 for children and $7.00 for adults. On Friday the theater collected $720 by selling 120 tickets. How many adult tickets were sold?
   80 adult tickets

Use any strategy to solve. Show your work.

Maria, Juan, Noel, Della

4. *Sports* In a race, Juan was behind Maria, but ahead of Noel. Noel was behind Juan, but ahead of Della. Order the students from fastest to slowest.

product 48

or

4
2–8–6
3
product 96

Technology Options

Prentice Hall Technology

Software for Learners
- Math Blaster® Mystery*
- Interactive Student Tutorial, Chapter 3*

Teaching Resource Software
- Computer Item Generator 3-4
- Resource Pro™ Chapter 3*

Internet • For related mathematics activities, visit the Prentice Hall site at www.phschool.com/math

*Available on CD-ROM only

Assignment Options for Exercises On Your Own

Core 1–4, 6, 8, 9
Extension 5, 7, 10

Use Mixed Review to maintain skills.

PRACTICE

Practice 3-4 *Problem-Solving Strategy: Guess and Test*

Use *guess and test* to solve each problem.

1. A deli sells ham sandwiches for $2 and roast beef sandwiches for $3. A committee organizing a family reunion placed orders for 85 sandwiches. The bill came to $218, before tax. How many ham sandwiches were ordered?
   37 ham sandwiches

2. Tickets for a community dinner cost $4 for adults and $3 for children. A total of 390 tickets was sold, earning $1,380. How many of each type of ticket were sold?
   210 adult, 180 children

3. Place the digits 3, 4, 7, 9, and 12 in the circles at the right so that the product is the same left to right and up and down. What is the product?
   _252_

Use any strategy to solve each problem. Show your work.

4. Two numbers have a sum of 42 and a product of 432. What are the two numbers? _18 and 24_

5. Two numbers have a sum of 70 and a product of 1,189. What are the numbers? _29 and 41_

6. Louise, Bill, and Fran each had a different piece of fruit packed in their lunches. An apple, an orange, and a banana were packed. Louise won't eat apples. Bill is allergic to oranges. Fran eats only bananas. What piece of fruit did each person have?
   Louise: orange; Bill: apple; Fran: banana

7. Paco joins a baseball card club. He brings 2 cards to the first meeting, 3 cards to the second meeting, 5 cards to the third meeting, and 8 cards to the fourth meeting. If he continues this pattern, how many cards will he bring to the fifth meeting?
   12 cards

8. The floor plan of the first floor of a museum is shown at the right. If you enter at A, is it possible to go through each doorway only one time, see each room, and exit at B? If this can be done, show how. You may enter each room more than one time.
   Sample answer shown.

In copymaster and workbook formats

RETEACHING

Reteaching 3-4 *Problem-Solving Strategy: Guess and Test*

Lincoln Middle School needs new smoke alarms. The school has $415 to spend. Alarms with escape lights cost $18, and alarms with a false-alarm silencer cost $11. The school wants 4 times as many escape-light alarms as silencer alarms. How many of each kind can the school purchase?

Read What facts are needed to solve the problem? *You need the costs of the alarms, $18 and $11; the amount to be spent, $415; and the fact that 4 times as many escape-light alarms as silencer alarms will be bought.*

Plan You can guess and test to solve this problem.
Guess: Buy 12 escape-light alarms and 3 silencer alarms.
Test:
   12 × $18 = $216
   3 × $11 = $ 33
   Add: $249

$249 is a lot less than the $415 that the school has to spend. Continue with different guesses until you solve the problem.

Solve Buy 20 escape-light alarms and 5 silencer alarms.
   20 × $18 = $360
   5 × $11 = $ 55
   Add: $415

Look Back Check to see whether your answer agrees with the information in the problem. *Is the total amount spent $415, or slightly less? Are there 4 times as many escape-light alarms as silencer alarms?*

Use *guess and test* to solve each problem.

1. Tina needs batteries. AA batteries cost $3 per pack. D batteries cost $4 per pack. If she has $26 to spend and buys 3 times as many packs of AA batteries as D batteries, how many packs of each does she buy?
   6 packs of AA, 2 packs of D

2. Ian needs cassette tapes for his recorder. One package of 3 tapes sells for $5. Another pack of 2 costs $4. If Ian has $19 and buys 11 cassettes, how many packs of each kind does he buy?
   three $5 packs and one $4 pack

3. Hyugen has $50 to spend on CDs. New ones cost $9 and used cost $7. He wants to buy more new CDs than used. How many of each can he buy?
   4 new CDs and 2 used CDs

4. Frank has $41 to spend on floppy disks. A pack of 10 ES brand costs $13 and a pack of 11 CW brand costs $14. How many packs of each can he buy if he spends all his money?
   1 ES brand and 2 CW brand

ENRICHMENT

Minds on Math Transparency

3-4

At Monroe Middle School there are three sixth-grade history classes. The largest class has 28 students. There are 79 students in the sixth grade. How many students are in the smallest possible class?

24 students

See *Solution Key* for worked-out answers.

98

Exercise 7 Encourage students to make beginning guesses with numbers that are easy to calculate, such as 21 dimes and 20 quarters. Tell them it is more important to learn from each guess than to guess correctly right away.

WRAP UP

IDENTIFYING THE BIG IDEA Ask students to explain how to solve a problem using Guess and Test.

LESSON QUIZ

1. Two numbers have a sum of 34 and a product of 285. What are the two numbers? **15 and 19**

2. Tameka and Greg together have 80 CDs. Tameka has three times as many CDs as Greg. How many CDs does each person have? **Tameka has 60, Greg has 20.**

5. *School Outings* The 182 sixth-graders at the Fannie Lou Hamer Middle School are taking a trip to the museum. The entrance fee is $1.75 per pupil and $3.25 per adult. The bus fee is $189 per bus. Each bus holds 44 people. Find the total cost for the students and 14 adults to visit the museum. **$1,309**

6. *Literature* Millie, Bobbi, and Francesca are reading a mystery, a fantasy, and a biography. Each is reading a book type that does not begin with the same letter as her name. Francesca is reading *The Case of the Howling Wolves*. Who is reading a fantasy? **Bobbi**

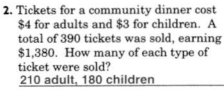

19 quarters
7. *Money* Suppose you save quarters and dimes in a jar. Last night you counted $6.75. The number of dimes is one more than the number of quarters. How many quarters are there?

8. *Consumer Issues* At the sub shop, you ate two slices of pizza and a small salad. You paid for your meal with a ten-dollar bill. Your change was $5.11. What was the price of your meal? **$4.89**

9. *Patterns* A train makes 5 stops. At the first three stops there are 3, 9, and 27 passengers. If the pattern continues, find the number of passengers at the fifth stop. **243 passengers**

10. *M* = 1, *F* = 9, *A* = 0; others will vary
10. *Puzzles* The following is a *cryptarithm*, a puzzle in which each letter represents a different digit. Find a value for each letter. (*Hint:* What is the only possible value for M?)

$$\begin{array}{r} F\ U\ N \\ +\ \ I\ S \\ \hline M\ A\ T\ H \end{array}$$

13. sixteen billion, seven hundred sixty-five million, eight hundred three thousand, five hundred seventy-eight

Mixed Review

12. three million, seven hundred thousand, eight

Write each number in words. *(Lesson 3-2)*

See above.   See below.

11. 973,430,624   12. 3,700,008   13. 16,765,803,578   14. 234,467,345,234,633

11. nine hundred seventy-three million, four hundred thirty-thousand, six hundred twenty-four

Find the value using the order of operations. *(Lesson 2-3)*

15. $5 + 2 \times 8 - 1$ **20**   16. $16 \div 2 \times 3 - 20$ **4**   17. $6 \times (2 + 9) \div 3$ **22**   18. $26 + 2 \times (95 - 5)$ **206**

19. A mountain climber starts at an altitude of 2,830 ft above sea level and climbs 4,920 ft. The next day, she climbs another 3,130 ft. What is her final altitude? *(Previous Course)* **10,880 ft**

14. two hundred thirty-four trillion, four hundred sixty-seven billion, three hundred forty-five million, two hundred thirty-four thousand, six hundred thirty-three

Teaching Notes

1 Focus

CONNECTING TO PRIOR KNOWLEDGE Ask students to describe decimal models they used in the previous lessons. Ask: *How could you use models to add and subtract decimals?* **Answers may vary. Sample: Use base-ten blocks. To add, model the first decimal. Model the second decimal. Put**

the blocks together and count them. To subtract, model the first decimal and model the second decimal from those blocks. Count the blocks left.

2 Teach

Work Together

Suggest students work in pairs.

TACTILE LEARNING Some students may find it easier to use base-ten blocks instead of drawing models.

THINK AND DISCUSS

AUDITORY LEARNING Questions 5–9 Have students work in small groups. Have one student read a question aloud. Have the other students write the problem. Remind students to write a decimal point when they hear the word *and*.

3-5 Modeling the Addition and Subtraction of Decimals

What You'll Learn

▼ To model addition of decimals

▼ To model subtraction of decimals

...And Why

You use decimals to add and subtract money.

Here's How

Look for questions that
🔹 build understanding
✔ check understanding

QUICK review

To find a sum, add. To find a difference, subtract.

Need Help? For practice adding and subtracting whole numbers, see Skills Handbook pages 538 and 539.

Work Together ___ *Investigating Decimal Addition*

1. 🔹*Modeling* Draw a model for 0.63.

2. Write 0.63 in expanded form.
   $$0.6 + 0.03$$

3. Draw models for the sum 0.6 + 0.03.

4. Draw models for the sum 0.3 + 0.06.
   3–4. See back of book.

THINK AND DISCUSS

▼ *Modeling Addition of Decimals*

You can use models to find any sum.

0.4	0.3	0.7
four tenths	three tenths	seven tenths

5. Use models to find each sum.
   a. 0.1 + 0.8 **0.9**   **b.** 0.31 + 0.09 **0.4**   **c.** 0.44 + 0.23 **0.67**

6. **a.** 🔹*Analyze* Use words to describe 0.8 + 0.5. What is the total number of tenths?   **eight tenths plus five tenths; 13**

   b. Thirteen tenths is equivalent to one and ■ tenths.   **3**

   c. You can write the sum as:
   $$\begin{array}{r} 0.8 \\ + 0.5 \\ \hline 1.3 \end{array}$$
   Draw a model showing that 0.8 + 0.5 = 1.3.
   See back of book for models.

7. **a.** Three hundredths + nine hundredths = ■ hundredths.   **twelve**

   b. Use decimals to write the sum described in part (a).   **0.03 + 0.09**

   c. 🔹*Modeling* Draw models to show this addition.
   See margin p. 101 for models.

Lesson Planning Options

Prerequisite Skills
- decimal place value (precourse)

Materials/Manipulatives
- graph paper

Resources

📖 **Student Edition**

Skills Handbook, p. 538, 539
Extra Practice, p. 524
Glossary/Study Guide

📦 **Teaching Resources**

Chapter Support File, Ch. 3
- Lesson Planner 3-5
- Answer Masters 3-5
Teaching Aids Master 20
Glossary, Spanish Resources

💻 **Transparencies**
11, 12, Minds on Math 3-5

Warm Up

Find the pattern and write the next four numbers in the sequence.
$$\frac{1}{9}, \frac{3}{10}, \frac{5}{11}, \frac{7}{12}, \frac{9}{13}, \frac{11}{14}, \frac{13}{15}, \frac{15}{16}$$

ALTERNATIVE METHODS **Questions 5 and 8** Give students play money in dollar bills, dimes, and pennies as models. Have students trade bills and coins to rename places.

ASSESSMENT **Question 10** Ask students how they would rename the decimals to find the difference. 10a. rename 1.2 as 12 tenths; 10b. rename 0.92 as 8 tenths and 12 hundredths; 10c. rename 2.3 as 1 and 13 tenths

Question 11c Discuss with students how renaming decimals is like renaming whole numbers when they subtract.

■ **ADDITIONAL EXAMPLE**

FOR EXAMPLE
Using models, find the difference 2.3 − 0.9.
1.4

3 Practice/Assess

EXERCISES *On Your Own*

Exercises 1–12 Make graph paper and base-ten blocks available for students to use.

OPEN-ENDED **Exercise 17** Challenge students to write a subtraction problem which requires them to rename a decimal.

REASONING **Exercise 18** Encourage students to try subtracting several numbers

Technology Options

Prentice Hall Technology

  Software for Learners

- Hot Page™ 8*
- Math Blaster® Mystery*
- Interactive Student Tutorial, Chapter 3*

  Teaching Resource Software

- Computer Item Generator 3-5
- Resource Pro™ Chapter 3*

Internet • For related mathematics activities, visit the Prentice Hall site at www.phschool.com/math

*Available on CD-ROM only

Assignment Options for Exercises On Your Own

To provide flexible scheduling, this lesson can be split into parts.

▼**1** **Core** 1–4, 9–13, 15, 19–25
Extension 26

▼**2** **Core** 5–8, 14, 16, 18, 27–32
Extension 17, 33

Use Mixed Review to maintain skills.

8. Add. Use models if they help you.

	a.	**b.**	**c.**	**d.**
	0.31	0.06	1.50	0.87
	0.8 + 0.49	0.61 + 0.55	2.42 + 0.92	1.43 + 0.56

9. You need to add the numbers with the same place value.

9. ⬛*Think About It* Why is it important to line up the decimal points?

Now you may assign Exercises 1–4, 9–13, 15, 19–26.

2 *Modeling Subtraction of Decimals*

You can also use models to subtract decimals.

■ **EXAMPLE**

Using models, find the difference 1.4 − 0.6.

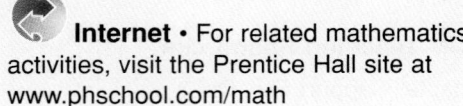

←Remove six tenths from fourteen tenths. Eight tenths remain.

1.4 − 0.6 = 0.8

10. ✔*Try It Out* Use models to find each difference.
a. 1.2 − 0.5 0.7   **b.** 0.92 − 0.75 0.17   **c.** 2.3 − 0.8 1.5

11. Think about the difference 0.52 − 0.07 in two ways.
a. ⬛*Modeling* Draw a model for 0.52. Remove 0.07. What is the answer? **See margin p. 101 for models; 0.45.**
b. Write the difference as:

$$\begin{array}{r} {}^{4\,12} \\ 0.\cancel{5}2 \\ -\ 0.07 \\ \hline 0.45 \end{array}$$

How could you check your answer?

The sum 0.45 + 0.07 must be equal to 0.52.

c. ⬛*Analyze* The number 0.52 is equivalent to four tenths and twelve hundredths. How does the model show this? **0.4 = 0.40; 0.40 + 0.12 = 0.52**

12. Subtract. Use models if they help you.

	a.	**b.**	**c.**
	3.65	5.8	9.92
	− 0.57 **3.08**	− 2.37 **3.43**	− 4.74 **5.18**

Now you may assign Exercises 5–8, 14, 16–18, 27–33.

before they start to answer this problem. Tell them to use the solutions to their problems to support their answer.

Exercises 19–32 To help prepare them for the next lessons, encourage students to visualize models in their head before they do each exercise.

ERROR ALERT! Exercises 29–30 Some students may become confused when problems contain a different number of digits to the right of the decimal point.

Remediation: Have students line up the decimal points to align the same place values. If one number has fewer digits, have students fill in the missing places with zeros. Ask: *When can you write zeros without changing the number's value?* **when the zero is to the right of the decimal point and all other digits**

IDENTIFYING THE BIG IDEA Ask students to explain how to model the addition and subtraction of decimals.

JOURNAL Have groups of students list ways they can compare, order, add, and subtract decimals. Ask them to discuss the advantages and disadvantages of each method.

EXERCISES *On Your Own*

Use models to find each sum.

.9 + .4 =

1. 0.8 + 0.5 **1.3**   2. 0.12 + 0.34 **0.46**   3. 0.67 + 0.33 **1**   4. 0.5 + 0.5 **1**

Use models to find each difference.

5. 1.2 − 0.5 **0.7**   6. 1.7 − 1.5 **0.2**   7. 0.88 − 0.57 **0.31**   8. 0.72 − 0.54 **0.18**

Use models to help you complete each statement.

six   sixteen
9. 1.6 = one and ▧ tenths = ▧ tenths

forty-seven   four   seven
10. 0.47 = ▧ hundredths = ▧ tenths and ▧ hundredths

five   fifteen
11. 2.5 = 2 ones and ▧ tenths = 1 one and ▧ tenths

eleven
12. 3 tenths and 1 hundredth = 2 tenths and ▧ hundredths

Write the sum or difference statement shown by each model.

13.
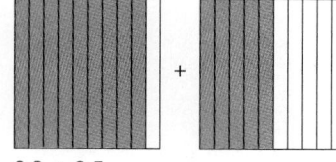
0.9 + 0.5

14.
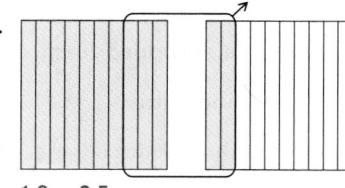
1.2 − 0.5

15.
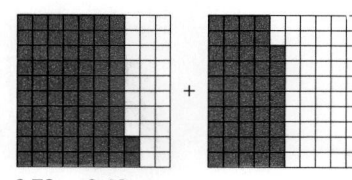
0.72 + 0.48

16.
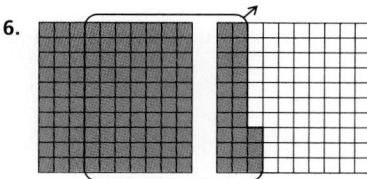
1.23 − 0.93

17. *Open-ended* Write a sum or a difference and find the answer in two different ways. **Check students' work.**

18. *Reasoning* Suppose you subtract hundredths from hundredths. Is an answer in terms of thousandths ever reasonable? Explain.
No; subtracting hundredths from hundredths will produce an answer in terms of hundredths.

pages 99–100   **Think and Discuss**
7c.
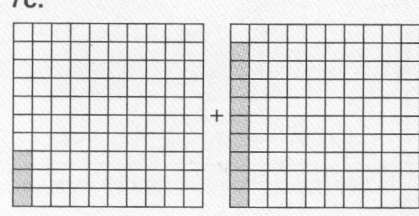
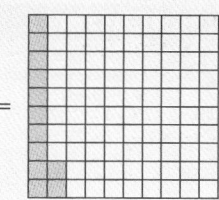

11a.
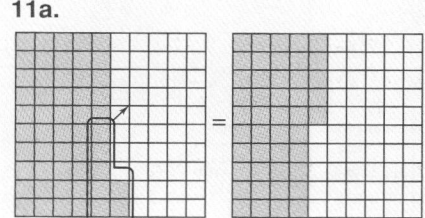

PRACTICE

Name_____ Class_____ Date_____

Practice 3-5 *Modeling the Addition and Subtraction of Decimals*

Write the sum or difference shown by the models.

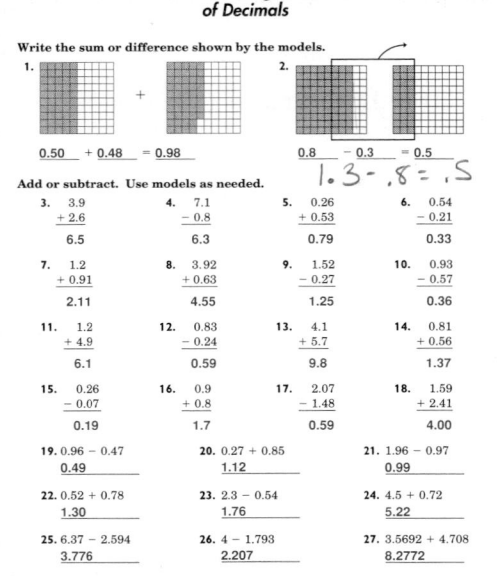

1. 0.50 + 0.48 = 0.98

2. 0.8 − 0.3 = 0.5
    1.3 − .8 = .5

Add or subtract. Use models as needed.

3.	4.	5.	6.
3.9 + 2.6 **6.5**	7.1 − 0.8 **6.3**	0.26 + 0.53 **0.79**	0.54 − 0.21 **0.33**

7.	8.	9.	10.
1.2 + 0.91 **2.11**	3.92 + 0.63 **4.55**	1.52 − 0.27 **1.25**	0.93 − 0.57 **0.36**

11.	12.	13.	14.
1.2 + 4.9 **6.1**	0.83 − 0.24 **0.59**	4.1 + 5.7 **9.8**	0.81 + 0.56 **1.37**

15.	16.	17.	18.
0.26 − 0.07 **0.19**	0.9 + 0.8 **1.7**	2.07 − 1.48 **0.59**	1.59 + 2.41 **4.00**

19. 0.96 − 0.47 **0.49**
20. 0.27 + 0.85 **1.12**
21. 1.96 − 0.97 **0.99**
22. 0.52 + 0.78 **1.30**
23. 2.3 − 0.54 **1.76**
24. 4.5 + 0.72 **5.22**
25. 6.37 − 2.594 **3.776**
26. 4 − 1.793 **2.207**
27. 3.5692 + 4.708 **8.2772**

In copymaster and workbook formats

RETEACHING

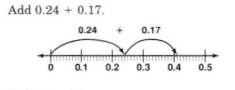

Reteaching 3-5 *Modeling the Addition and Subtraction of Decimals*

Add 0.24 + 0.17.

① Begin at 0.
② Move 0.24 to the right.
③ Move another 0.17 to the right.
0.24 + 0.17 = 0.41

Subtract 0.42 − 0.14.

① Begin at 0.
② Move 0.42 to the right.
③ Move 0.14 to the left.
0.42 − 0.14 = 0.28

Use the number line to find each sum.

1. 0.5 + 0.6 **1.1**
2. 0.8 + 0.7 **1.5**
3. 0.23 + 0.56 **0.79**
4. 0.11 + 0.19 **0.30**
5. 0.36 + 0.19 **0.55**
6. 0.9 + 0.7 **1.6**
7. 0.82 + 0.43 **1.25**
8. 0.65 + 0.35 **1.00**
9. 0.55 + 0.62 **1.17**

Use the number line to find each difference.

10. 0.8 − 0.5 **0.3**
11. 1.4 − 1.1 **0.3**
12. 1.1 − 0.3 **0.8**
13. 1.3 − 0.8 **0.5**
14. 1.2 − 0.4 **0.8**
15. 0.32 − 0.21 **0.11**
16. 0.54 − 0.26 **0.28**
17. 0.73 − 0.36 **0.37**
18. 1.15 − 0.94 **0.21**

Write the sum or difference shown.

19. 0.23 + 0.15 = 0.38

20. 0.4 − 0.2 = 0.2

21. 0.30 − 0.14 = 0.16

ENRICHMENT

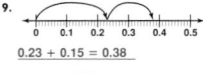inds on Math Transparency

3-5

Write the numbers 0 through 5 in the circles, using each digit only once, so that the numbers in any three circles connected by a straight line total 10.

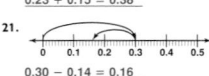

Answers may vary. Sample is shown.

See *Solution Key* for worked-out answers.

PROJECT LINK Have students discuss how they will round the prices and estimate the cost of eight CDs. Have them discuss which price to use. Have them keep in mind that the goal is to decide whether the club is a good deal.

LESSON QUIZ

Find each sum or difference.

1. 9.281 + 0.75 **10.031**
2. 7.421 − 3.951 **3.47**
3. 0.956 + 2.813 **3.769**
4. 3.52 − 0.721 **2.799**

Add.

19. 0.65 + 4.23 **4.88**
20. 0.83 + 0.67 **1.50**
21. 3.93 + 7.14 **11.07**
22. 0.85 + 6.09 **6.94**
23. 0.32 + 0.12 **0.44**
24. 3.46 + 9.17 **12.63**
25. 5.52 + 0.99 **6.51**
26. 7.11 + 5.93 **13.04**

Subtract.

27. 8.63 − 4.39 **4.24**
28. 2.34 − 0.73 **1.61**
29. 8.2 − 1.93 **6.27**
30. 8 − 3.62 **4.38**
31. 6.04 − 2.49 **3.55**
32. 3.74 − 2.81 **0.93**

33. *Writing* Explain why five tenths and eleven hundredths is equivalent to six tenths and one hundredth. Model each sum to support your explanation. **Each number is equivalent to sixty-one hundredths; see back of book for models.**

> **JOURNAL**
> Explain the different ways you can compare, order, add, and subtract decimals. List the advantages and disadvantages of each.

Mixed Review

34. *Data Analysis* Refer to the graph at the right. The total amount of revenue was $1.61 billion. How much money came from merchandising? *(Lesson 1-5)* **$32 million**

Write each number in standard form. *(Lesson 3-2)*

35. five and thirteen hundredths **5.13**
36. nine hundred fifty thousandths **0.950**
37. six hundred-thousandths **0.00006**
38. forty-three and fifteen ten-thousandths **43.015**

Sources of Olympic Revenue
(Millions of dollars)

559.5
90.8
422
505.7

▨ Broadcast rights   ▨ Merchandising
▨ Corporate sponsors   ▨ Other
▨ Ticket sales

Source: Atlanta Committee for the Olympic Games

Use mental math. *(Previous Course)*

39. 0 + 332 **332**
40. 332 ÷ 1 **332**
41. 30 × 20 **600**
42. 2,567 × 1 **2,567**
43. 40 ÷ 2 **20**
44. 200 × 10 **2,000**

CHAPTER PROJECT

PROJECT LINK: ROUNDING AND ESTIMATING

You must buy eight CDs at regular club prices, which range from $12.95 to $17.95. Round these prices and estimate the total cost for the eight CDs. Will you use the higher price listed or the lower price? What number do you think best represents the price you'll usually have to pay? Explain.

Check students' work.

In Lesson 3-6, students will learn to round data in order to estimate sums and differences. This toolbox helps students review rounding whole numbers.

ERROR ALERT! Students may lose track of which digit determines whether a number rounds up or down. **Remediation:** Direct students to copy the number to be rounded and underline the digit in the place they are

rounding to. Students can then circle the digit to the right of the underlined digit. The circled digit determines whether they round the underlined digit up or down.

ASSESSMENT Exercises 1–4 Have pairs of students work together. Write the numbers 123, 549, 898, and 304 on the board. Have one student draw a partial number line to round to the nearest ten. Have the other student round mentally to the nearest ten. Have students switch roles after two problems and compare results. 120, 550, 900, 300

■ **ADDITIONAL PROBLEM**

Round 35,492 to the nearest ten, hundred, and thousand. 35,490; 35,500; 35,000

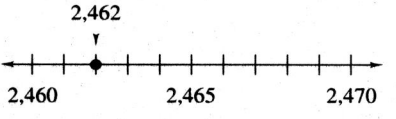 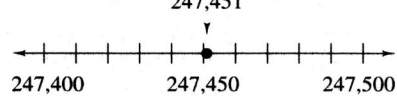

SKILLS REVIEW

Rounding Whole Numbers

Before Lesson 3-6

Number lines can help you round numbers. On a number line, 5 is halfway between 0 and 10, 50 is halfway between 0 and 100, and 500 is halfway between 0 and 1,000. The acceptable method of rounding is to round 5 up to 10, 50 up to 100, and 500 up to 1,000.

■ **EXAMPLE 1**

Round 2,462 to the nearest ten.

2,462

2,460   2,465   2,470

2,462 is closer to 2,460 than to 2,470.

2,462 rounded to the nearest ten is 2,460.

■ **EXAMPLE 2**

Round 247,451 to the nearest hundred.

247,451

247,400   247,450   247,500

247,451 is closer to 247,500 than to 247,400.

247,451 rounded to the nearest hundred is 247,500.

Round each number to the nearest ten.

1. 65 70   **2.** 832 830   **3.** 4,437 4,440   **4.** 21,024 21,020   **5.** 3,545
                                                                                    3,550

Round each number to the nearest hundred.

6. 889 900   **7.** 344 300   **8.** 2,861 2,900   **9.** 1,138 1,100   **10.** 50,549
                                                                                   50,500

11. 6,411 6,400   **12.** 88,894 88,900   **13.** 13,735 13,700   **14.** 17,459 17,500   **15.** 6,059
                                                                                                        6,100

Round each number to the nearest thousand.

16. 2,400 2,000   **17.** 16,218 16,000   **18.** 7,430 7,000   **19.** 89,375 89,000   **20.** 9,821
                                                                                                      10,000

21. 15,631 16,000   **22.** 76,900 77,000   **23.** 163,875   **24.** 38,295 38,000   **25.** 102,359
                                                   164,000   102,000

26. *Writing* Describe a situation in which it is helpful to round data.
Check students' work.

27. Explain how to round each of the numbers in Exercises 1–25 to the nearest ten thousand.

28. Suppose 31 is rounded to the nearest hundred. Is 0 a reasonable response? Why or why not?
Yes; 31 is closer to zero than it is to 100.

27. Label a number line with multiples of 5,000. Locate each number and determine which multiple of 10,000 it is closest to.

1 Focus

CONNECTING TO PRIOR KNOWLEDGE Have students relate experiences when they had to estimate the cost of several items. Ask students to share the strategies they used. Ask students: *Did you try to make the estimate as close as possible? Did you try to make it greater than the exact amount?*

Lesson Planning Options

Prerequisite Skills
- comparing decimals (precourse)
- adding and subtracting whole numbers (precourse)

Vocabulary/Symbols
front end estimation

Material/Manipulatives
- calculator

Resources

 Student Edition

Skills Handbook, p. 535
Extra Practice, p. 524
Glossary/Study Guide

 Teaching Resources

Chapter Support File, Ch. 3
- Lesson Planner 3-6
- Practice 3-6, Reteaching 3-6
- Answer Masters 3-6
Teaching Aids Master 20
Glossary, Spanish Resources

 Transparencies
11, 12, Minds on Math 3-6

Warm Up

A 12-in. submarine sandwich is divided into 6 slices and a second 12-in. sandwich is divided into 8 slices. Which sandwich has the larger slices? **the sandwich with 6 slices**

Answers may vary. Sample: I wanted the estimate to be greater than the exact amount to make sure I had enough money.

2 Teach

THINK AND DISCUSS

AEP **VISUAL LEARNING** Have students underline the digit they are rounding to. Have them circle the digit to its right. Emphasize that the digit in the circle decides whether you round the underlined digit up or down. Suggest that students associate the round circle with the rounded number.

Example 1 Ask students: *Why do you compare the hundredths' digit with the number 5?* **It helps you decide if you need to round up or down.**

DATA ANALYSIS Connection

3-6 Rounding and Estimating Data

What You'll Learn

1 To round data
2 To estimate sums and differences

...And Why

You can check for reasonable answers by rounding and estimating.

Here's How

Look for questions that
- build understanding
- check understanding

THINK AND DISCUSS

1 Rounding Data

Do you ever wonder what is in the food you eat? For example, 0.138 of a kernel of corn is water.

To round 0.138 to the nearest hundredth, think about how you round whole numbers. The rules are similar.

Contents of Whole-Grain Field Corn

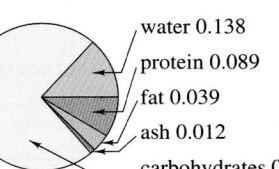

water 0.138
protein 0.089
fat 0.039
ash 0.012
carbohydrates 0.722

Locate the hundredths' place.
↓
0.1<u>3</u>8

Now look at the digit to the right.
0.13⑧
Is it ≥ 5?

You decide. Should you round 0.138 to 0.14 or to 0.13?

■ EXAMPLE 1

Round 0.138 to the nearest tenth.
You can use a number line or mental math.

0.1   0.2

1 is in the tenths' place so 0.138 rounds to 0.1 or 0.2.   0.<u>1</u>38

0.138
0.1   0.15   0.2

3 is the digit to the right of 1.   0.1<u>3</u>

Since 3 < 5, 0.138 is closer to 0.1 than 0.2.
To the nearest tenth, 0.138 rounds to 0.1.

1. a. ✔*Try It Out* Round the other four decimals in the circle graph above to the nearest hundredth. **0.09; 0.04; 0.01; 0.72**
   b. Then round each decimal to the nearest tenth. **0.1, 0.1, 0.0, 0.0, 0.7**

ASSESSMENT Have students work in pairs. Write the decimal 45.2579 on the board. Have one student round it to any place they want. Have the partner decide what place the student rounded to and whether the answer is correct. Write the decimal 3.4598 on the board. Have the pairs switch roles. **Answers may vary. Sample: 45.26; rounded to the hundredths' correctly; 3.460, rounded to the thousandths' place correctly**

■ **ADDITIONAL EXAMPLES**

FOR EXAMPLE 1

Round 0.349 to the nearest tenth. **0.3**

FOR EXAMPLE 2

Use rounding to estimate the total cost of renting a video machine for $12.99 and a video for $3.59. **about $17**

FOR EXAMPLE 3

Use front-end estimation. Estimate the total cost of the following items: pen: $.95, binder: $3.95, book bag: $9.89. **about $15**

3 Practice/Assess

EXERCISES *On Your Own*

CONNECTION TO TECHNOLOGY Exercises 1–12 Students can use the rounding function

ROUNDING DECIMALS

Decide to which place you are rounding.

- **If the digit to the right of that place is greater than or equal to 5, round up.**

- **If the digit to the right of that place is less than 5, round down.**

Now you may assign Exercises 1–19.

▼2 *Estimating Sums and Differences*

You can use rounding to estimate a sum or a difference.

■ **EXAMPLE 2** *Real-World Problem Solving*

To the nearest dollar, estimate the combined cost of the 1-gallon and 2-gallon tins of popcorn shown at the left.

$ 6.45 →	$ 6	←Round $6.45 to the nearest dollar.
+ $11.95 →	+ $12	←Round $11.95 to the nearest dollar.
	$18	

The cost of the two tins is about $18.

2. ✔Try It Out Estimate the total cost of two 2-gallon tins. **$24**

3. ♣Estimation About how much more does the largest tin of popcorn cost than the smallest tin? Use rounding to estimate. **about $14**

To use **front-end estimation,** add the front-end digits, estimate the sum of the remaining digits, and add the results. The symbol ≈ means *is approximately equal to*.

■ **EXAMPLE 3** *Real-World Problem Solving*

Use front-end estimation to estimate the total cost of three books marked $6.99, $7.25, and $15.80.

The books cost $6.99, $7.25, and $15.80.

Add the front-end digits, the dollars.	Estimate the cents.	Add.
$ 6.99	$ 6.99—$1	
$ 7.25	$ 7.25	$28
+ $15.80	+ $15.80—$1	$ 2
$28	$2	$30

The total cost of the three books is about $30.

Popcorn Prices

Size	Cost
1-gallon tin	$6.45
2-gallon tin	$11.95
3-gallon tin	$13.25
6-gallon tin	$19.95

Technology Options

Prentice Hall Technology

 **Software for Learners**
- Math Blaster® Mystery*
- Interactive Student Tutorial, Chapter 3*

 Teaching Resource Software
- Computer Item Generator 3-6
- Resource Pro™ Chapter 3*

Internet • For related mathematics activities, visit the Prentice Hall site at www.phschool.com/math

Available on CD-ROM only

Assignment Options for Exercises On Your Own

To provide flexible scheduling, this lesson can be split into parts.

▼1 **Core** 1–12, 14–19
Extension 13

▼2 **Core** 20–30, 32, 35–40
Extension 31, 33, 34

Use Mixed Review to maintain skills.

on a spreadsheet program to check their answers.

ERROR ALERT Exercise 5 Students may round 23.45 to the nearest tenth instead of going back to the original problem before rounding. **Remediation** Tell students it is important to round a number only once.

ERROR ALERT Exercise 11 Students may want to drop the zero on 491.30 when rounding to hundredths. **Remediation:** Compare 491.30 and 491.3. Ask students: *To which place did we round each number?*

hundredths', tenths' *Why is the zero important?* Answers may vary. Sample: It holds the hundredths' place.

OPEN ENDED EXERCISE 13 Ask: *How many decimals can you write that round to 6.7?* an infinite number

REASONING Exercise 29 Ask students to answer the problem and defend their answer without finding the exact sum.

WRITING Exercise 30 Have students focus on the idea that different situations require different estimation strategies.

RESEARCH Exercise 31 Ask: *How do you know whether the decimals are estimates? Are there situations in which you would not know? Describe them.*

IDENTIFYING THE BIG IDEA Ask students to explain how to round decimals and estimate decimal sums and differences.

---

pages 106–107   On Your Own

29. Higher; each number is rounded up. Yes; the actual answer is 21.112.

30. Samples: Estimate the time it would take to commute to work; check if the door opening is wide enough to move a couch through.

page 107   Mixed Review

41. 26, 37, 50; start with 2, then add 3, then continue by adding a number 2 greater than the one added before it.

42. 21, 25, 29; start with 5, then add 4 repeatedly.

43. 625; 3,125; 15,625; start with 1, then multiply by 5 repeatedly.

44. 10,000; 100,000; 1,000,000; start with 1, then multiply by 10 repeatedly.

---

4. a. *Calculator* Use a calculator to find the exact total cost of the three books in Example 3 on page 105. $30.04

b. *Look Back* How reasonable is the estimate? good

5. a. ✔*Try It Out* Estimate the total cost of the following items: jeans: $29.95; shirt: $12.50; shoes: $22.87; socks: $4.45. about $70

b. How reasonable is your estimate? very good

Now you may assign Exercises 20–40.

EXERCISES *On Your Own*

Round each decimal to the nearest hundredth. Then round your answer to the nearest tenth.

2.64; 2.6	0.58; 0.6	0.74; 0.7	3.47; 3.5	23.45; 23.5	0.09; 0.1
1. 2.64372	**2.** 0.5817	**3.** 0.7352	**4.** 3.4746	**5.** 23.4546	**6.** 0.087

7. 0.6873   **8.** 2.7082   **9.** 4.0625   **10.** 2.0056   **11.** 491.2993   **12.** 1.001
0.69; 0.7   2.71; 2.7   4.06; 4.1   2.01; 2.0   491.30; 491.3   1.00; 1.0

13. *Open-ended* Write five different decimals that round to 6.7.
Sample: 6.65, 6.69, 6.70, 6.71, 6.739

Round each number to the underlined place value.

14. 1.366 1.4   **15.** 0.4018 0.402   **16.** 5.1251   **17.** 0.0062 0.01   **18.** 2.3196   **19.** 0.6087
5.13   2.320   0.6

Use rounding or front-end estimation. Estimate each sum or difference to the nearest dollar.

20. $4.89 + $3.97	21. $8.97 − $2.15	22. $5.19 − $2.79	23. $6.15 + $8.86
$9	$7	$2	$15

24. $14.65 + $ 3.85	25. $9.93 − $3.26	26. $16.81 + $11.49	27. $12.44 − $ 8.25
$19	$7	$28	$4

28. *Consumer Issues* Regular unleaded gasoline costs $1.259/gal. You spend $5 on gasoline. About how many gallons did you buy? 4 gal

29. *Reasoning* Is an estimate of 22 higher or lower than the sum of 6.83, 9.57, and 4.712? How can you tell? Is the estimate reasonable? Explain. See margin.

30. *Writing* Describe a situation in which you might want your estimate to be high. Then describe one in which you might want your estimate to be low.
See margin.

31. *Research* Look through newspapers or magazines to find five decimals. Decide whether each decimal is an estimate. To which places were the decimals rounded? Check students' work.

LESSON QUIZ

1. Round to the place of the underlined digit.
  a. 0.0̲57 **0.1**
  b. 1.70̲93 **1.709**

2. Which pair of numbers has an estimated sum of 10: 8.47 and 1.228, or 3.158 and 6.8? **3.158 and 6.8**

3. Estimate. Is $13 enough to buy both you and your friend a sandwich for $2.95, a garden salad for $1.50, and a juice for $0.95? **yes**

---

32. *Nutrition* Use the chart at the right. Estimate and round to the nearest tenth.
  a. About how much sugar is in a soft drink **1.9 oz;** plus a granola bar? In one of everything?**5.2 oz**
  b. About how much more sugar is in $\frac{1}{2}$ cup of sherbet than in 8 oz of yogurt? **0.2 oz**
  c. About how much sugar is in the last three items combined? **3.7 oz**

33. **Choose A, B, C, or D.** Which sum might give you a low estimate of $19 and a high estimate of $22? **B**
  A. $4.22 + $10.85 + $8.97
  B. $2.50 + $13.75 + $4.50
  C. $6.05 + $7.86 + $9.22
  D. $15.32 + $9.63 + $0.45

34. Is the last statement true or false? Explain your answer.

  Tony has $10. He will have about $1 after buying pencils for $2.79, a notebook for $1.39, a ruler for $.85, and 3 pens for $1.69 each. **False; the total cost is over $10.**

Use front-end estimation to estimate each total cost to the nearest dollar.

$58

35. $1.29 + $3.52 + $8.89 **$14**   **36.** $3.89 + $9.95 + $6.59 **$20**   **37.** $23.56 + $33.33 + $1.50

38. $12.49 + $5.51 + $9.95 **$28**   **39.** $1.29 + $3.52 + $8.89 **$14**   **40.** $3.25 + $7.53 + $12.87
$24

Food	Sugar Content
Orange juice (4 oz)	0.417 oz
Plain granola bar	0.333 oz
Raisins (7 oz)	0.75 oz
Sherbet ($\frac{1}{2}$ cup)	1.166 oz
Soft drink (12 oz)	1.5 oz
Yogurt (8 oz)	1 oz

Mixed Review

Find the next three terms in each number pattern. Write a rule to describe each number pattern. *(Lesson 2-1)* 41–44. See margin p. 106.

41. 2, 5, 10, 17, . . .   **42.** 5, 9, 13, 17, . . .   **43.** 1, 5, 25, 125, . . .   **44.** 1; 10; 100; 1,000; . . .

Solve each equation. *(Lessons 2-6 and 2-7)*

45. $a - 7 = 23$ **46.** $35 = 19 + c$ **47.** $54 = 3t$ **48.** $x \div 8 = 16$ **49.** $10y = 30$
  30   **16**   **18**   **128**   **3**

50. A bookcase has three shelves. You place 20 books on each shelf. What is the total number of books in the bookcase? *(Previous Course)* **60**

PRACTICE

Round to the place of the underlined digit.

1. 1.1̲09   **2.** 2.3̲57   **3.** 4.8̲772   **4.** 5.8̲045
   1.11   2.4   4.877   5.80

Use rounding or front-end estimation. Estimate each sum or difference.

5. $8.92   **6.** $32.18   **7.** $29.99   **8.** $26.49
    + 5.19   − 14.09   + 15.29   − 13.99
   ___   ___   ___   ___
    $14 $18 $45 $12

9. $21.95   **10.** $83.49   **11.** $1.87   **12.** $43.87
    − 7.15   − 56.13   + 5.28   + 26.15
   ___   ___   ___   ___
    $15 $27 $7 $70

13. $15.49   **14.** $23.57   **15.** $49.17   **16.** $19.95
    + 12.86   − 18.99   − 5.88   + 21.36
   ___   ___   ___   ___
    $28 $5 $43 $41

Use front-end estimation to estimate each total cost.

17. $2.59 + $3.76 + $2.41 $9   **18.** $8.19 + $2.46 + $3.57 $14
19. $3.61 + $2.17 + $5.84 $12   **20.** $9.14 + $8.72 + $5.63 $24

Circle A, B, C, or D. Choose the sum that is most appropriate for the given range of low and high estimates.

21. low: 11; high: 14
  Ⓐ 2.89 + 3.51 + 6.62
  B. 1.27 + 1.89 + 2.34
  C. 3.45 + 4.62 + 7.32
  D. 2.01 + 3.22 + 4.56

22. low: 24; high: 25
  A. 9.83 + 8.16 + 7.58
  Ⓑ 7.08 + 8.91 + 9.23
  C. 8.12 + 7.43 + 6.27
  D. 10.06 + 6.94 + 8.58

23. low: 56; high: 58
  A. 14.78 + 23.92 + 16.37
  B. 34.96 + 2.43 + 8.74
  C. 16.88 + 17.12 + 25.94
  Ⓓ 15.78 + 23.41 + 18.49

24. low: 52; high: 54
  A. 14.78 + 21.05 + 14.71
  B. 23.86 + 15.93 + 18.92
  Ⓒ 15.96 + 18.72 + 19.41
  D. 42.56 + 8.32 + 5.64

25. Dom has $13. He wants to buy 2 audio cassette tapes that cost $5.79 each and a notebook that costs $1.89. Does Dom have enough money? Explain.
  No. $5.79 rounded to the nearest dollar twice plus $1.89 rounded to the nearest dollar is more than $13.

In copymaster and workbook formats

RETEACHING

Name _____ Class _____ Date _____

■ *Reteaching 3-6* *Rounding and Estimating Data*

To **round** $76.38 to the nearest dollar:
① Find the rounding place. $7̲6.38
② Look at the digit to the right. $76.3̲8
③ If that digit is less than 5, leave the digit in the rounding place as is. If the digit is 5 or greater, round up.
$76.38 rounds to $76.

You can use rounding to estimate a sum.
  3.76 + 0.85 + 4.09
Round each number to the ones place.
  3.76 → 4
  0.85 → 1
  4.09 → 4
Then add.   9
The sum is about 9.

Round to the nearest hundredth.

1. 1.679 1.68   **2.** 4.981 4.98   **3.** 12.602 12.60

4. 32.9744 32.97   **5.** 0.159 0.16   **6.** 2.008 2.01

7. 4.031 4.03   **8.** 18.8942 18.89   **9.** 1.0983 1.10

Round to the nearest tenth.

10. 6.457 6.5   **11.** 15.0886 15.1   **12.** 0.1235 0.1

13. 1.036 1.0   **14.** 25.671 25.7   **15.** 6.390 6.4

16. 2.909 2.9   **17.** 17.951 18.0   **18.** 312.554 312.6

Estimate each sum or difference.

19. $2.98   **20.** $5.33   **21.** $10.02   **22.** $15.84
    + 7.22   + 2.91   − 6.89   + 37.12
   ___   ___   ___   ___
    $10 $8 $3 $53

23. $45.99   **24.** $11.53   **25.** $4.92   **26.** $9.71
    + 12.87   − 8.99   + 6.88   − 3.13
   ___   ___   ___   ___
    $59 $3 $12 $7

ENRICHMENT

◼inds on Math Transparency

3-6

Danielle thinks of two numbers that are multiples of 9. The product of the two digits of either of her numbers is also a multiple of 9. What are her numbers?

63 and 36

See *Solution Key* for worked-out answers.

3-7 Teaching Notes

1 Focus

CONNECTING TO PRIOR KNOWLEDGE Ask students to estimate $.25 + $.52 and $1.05 − $.48. **$.75; $.50** Then have them model the sum and difference using coins to solve.

2 Teach

THINK AND DISCUSS

Example 1 Ask students to explain how to make the estimate. Review how to use zeros as place holders.

AEP **Example 2** Make sure students understand the words *maximum* and *minimum*. On the board, write *maximum* in large letters and *minimum* in small letters.

Underline *mini* in minimum. Tell students: *Mini* means small, so minimum is the smallest. Maximum is the largest or the most.

KINESTHETIC LEARNING If you have block scheduling or extended class periods, gather a selection of round balls from the gymnasium. Have students drop each type of ball from a height of 1 m and use a metric ruler to measure the height of the first bounce of each ball. Record their measurements in a table. When students finish collecting data, ask them to find the range of values.

Lesson Planning Options

Prerequisite Skills
• rounding decimals (3-6)

Resources

Materials/Manipulatives
• calculator

 Student Edition

Skills Handbook, p. 538, 539
Extra Practice, p. 524
Glossary/Study Guide

 Teaching Resources

Chapter Support File, Ch. 3
• Lesson Planner 3-7
• Practice 3-7, Reteaching 3-7
• Alternative Activity 3-7
• Answer Masters 3-7
Teaching Aids Master 20
Glossary, Spanish Resources

 Transparencies

11, 12, 19, 83, Minds on Math 3-7

Warm Up

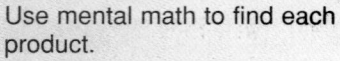

Use mental math to find each product.

$\frac{1}{2} \times 24 = 12$
$\frac{3}{4} \times 24 = 18$
$\frac{1}{4} \times 24 = 6$
$1\frac{1}{2} \times 24 = 36$

ALGEBRA Connection

3-7 Adding and Subtracting Decimals

What You'll Learn

❶ To add decimals
❷ To subtract decimals

...And Why

You can do calculations with weights in decimal form.

Here's How

Look for questions that
▪ build understanding
✔ check understanding

Need Help? For practice adding whole numbers, see Skills Handbook p. 538.

2a. 10; 10.1
b. 6; 6.16
c. 11; 11.123

A properly inflated basketball should bounce between 1.2 m and 1.4 m if you drop it on a hard wooden floor from a height of about 1.8 m.

Source: The Rules of the Game

THINK AND DISCUSS

❶ Adding Decimals

If you estimate the answer before adding, you can tell if your answer is reasonable.

■ EXAMPLE 1

Find the sum $3.026 + 4.7 + 1.38$.

Estimate: $3.026 + 4.7 + 1.38 \approx 3 + 5 + 1 = 9$

Add:
$$\begin{array}{r} 3.026 \\ 4.7 \\ + 1.38 \\ \hline \end{array} \qquad \begin{array}{r} 3.026 \\ 4.700 \\ + 1.380 \\ \hline 9.106 \end{array}$$

← Line up decimal points and write zeros to make the columns even.

Check: 9.106 is reasonable since it is close to 9. ✓

1. ▪*Writing* Explain why you can write 4.7 as 4.700.
7 tenths is equivalent to 700 thousandths, so 4.7 is equivalent to 4.700.
2. ✔*Try It Out* First estimate. Then find each sum.
   a. $6.5 + 0.6 + 3$ b. $0.84 + 2 + 3.32$ c. $9.008 + 2.115$

   Now you may assign Exercises 1–13, 15, 30, 32, 34.

❷ Subtracting Decimals

You may need to regroup decimals when you subtract.

■ EXAMPLE 2 *Real-World Problem Solving*

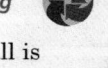

Sports The official maximum weight of a basketball is 22.93 oz. The minimum weight is 21.16 oz. Find the range of weights. (Remember that range = maximum − minimum.)

Estimate: $22.93 - 21.16 \approx 23 - 21 = 2$

$$\begin{array}{r} \overset{8\ 13}{22.9\cancel{3}} \\ - 21.16 \\ \hline 1.77 \end{array}$$

← Regroup 9 tenths and 3 hundredths as 8 tenths and 13 hundredths.
← Subtract.

The range of standard weights for a basketball is 1.77 oz.

108

Example 3 Ask students to discuss the steps they used to solve the equation.

REASONING **Question 5** Have students consider their answers for Question 1 before answering this question.

■ **ADDITIONAL EXAMPLES**

FOR EXAMPLE 1
Find the sum. Estimate to check your answer.
2.49 + 3.011 + 4.8 **10.301**

FOR EXAMPLE 2
You use a $5 bill to pay for a bottle of orange juice that costs $1.29. How much change will you get? Estimate to check your answer. **$3.71**

FOR EXAMPLE 3
Solve $x + 2.85 = 36$. $x = $ **33.15**

 **Work Together**

Question 8 Have students discuss what it takes to make the statement true or false.
Ask: *If the statement is not true for one ball, is the statement untrue?* **yes**

CONNECTING TO THE STUDENTS' WORLD
Bring an example of each type of ball. Work in groups to weigh each ball. Have students compare the weights they measure with the minimum and maximum weights given in their textbook.

DIVERSITY People in Mexico and Brazil call soccer *football*. They call the game of U.S. football *American football*. Ask students if they know of other differences in the sports of other countries.

You can also use a calculator to add or subtract decimals.

■ **EXAMPLE 3**

Algebra Solve the equation $x + 5.22 = 20$.

$$x + 5.22 = 20$$
$$x + 5.22 - 5.22 = 20 - 5.22 \quad \longleftarrow \text{Subtract 5.22 from each side.}$$
$$20 \; \boxminus \; 5.22 \; \boxminus \; 14.78 \quad \longleftarrow \text{Use a calculator.}$$

Check: $14.78 + 5.22 = 20$ ✓

$$x = 14.78$$

3. Estimate the difference in Example 3. How reasonable is your estimate? **15; the estimate is very close to the actual answer.**

4. ✔*Try It Out* Solve each equation.
   a. $x + 2.25 = 5$ **2.75**
   b. $x - 0.468 = 1.8$ **2.268**
   c. $x - 37.63 = 50$ **87.63**

5. ⁂*Reasoning* Suppose you use a calculator to find $7.87 - 1.47$. Why will the display show 6.4 instead of 6.40? **The calculator does not show 0 as the last digit because 6.4 is equivalent to 6.40.**

 **Work Together** *Subtracting Decimals Using Data*

Data Analysis Most sports equipment has standard sizes.

Official Standard Weights

Type	Minimum Weight (oz)	Maximum Weight (oz)
Baseball	5	5.5
Football	14	15
Soccer ball	14	16
Softball	6.25	7
Tennis ball	2	2.06
Volleyball	9.17	9.88

6. List the types of sports balls from heaviest to lightest. **soccer, football, volleyball, softball, baseball, tennis**

7. Find the range of standard weights for each sports ball. **0.5 oz, 1 oz, 2 oz, 0.75 oz, 0.06 oz, 0.71 oz**

8. ⁂*Analyze* Based on the given data, do you think the following statement is true or false: The heavier the ball, the smaller its range of standard weights is. **false**

Now you may assign Exercises 14, 16–29, 31, 33, 35–37.

On September 7, 1997, Venus Williams became the first unseeded woman to play in the final of the U.S. Open Championship tennis tournament.

 **Technology Options**

Prentice Hall Technology

Software for Learners
- Math Blaster® Mystery*
- Interactive Student Tutorial, Chapter 3*

Teaching Resource Software
- Computer Item Generator 3-7
- Resource Pro™ Chapter 3*

Internet • For related mathematics activities, visit the Prentice Hall site at www.phschool.com/math

*Available on CD-ROM only

Assignment Options for Exercises On Your Own

To provide flexible scheduling, this lesson can be split into parts.

1 Core 1–13, 30, 32, 34
Extension 15, 40

2 Core 16–29, 31, 33, 35, 36, 38, 39
Extension 14, 37

Use Mixed Review to maintain skills.

3 Practice/Assess

ERROR ALERT! Exercise 13 Students may include the costs for both 12- and 24- exposure film. **Remediation:** Remind students to read the table carefully. Ask them to list the items you need to buy. **poster, birthday card, film, wrapping paper, bow**

ASSESSMENT Exercise 16 Write decimals on index cards. Give each student a card. Pair students. Have one student estimate the sum of the two cards and find the difference. The partner estimates the difference and finds the sum. The pairs compare answers and decide if they are reasonable.

WRITING Exercise 27b Have students use their answer to 27a to help them with this exercise.

ESTIMATION Exercise 27c Encourage students to round the decimal for each natural resource before answering the question.

MENTAL MATH Exercises 28–30 Have students write the property they used to find the answer beside each exercise.
Commutative; Identity; Associative

WRAP UP

IDENTIFYING THE BIG IDEA Have students explain how to add and subtract decimals.

---

pages 110–111   On Your Own

27a. **1; the total amount of energy produced**

  b. **0.66; yes; 0.5 is half of 1 and 0.66 > 0.5.**

  c. **gas and firewood/charcoal**

  d.
  Nuclear power
  Other
  Hydro power
  Gas
  Oil   Coal
  Firewood/charcoal

110

First estimate each sum. Then find the actual sum.

8. 6; 5.79   12. 4.5; 4.64

21.5; 21.516

1. $0.6 + 3.4$ **4; 4**
2. $6.2 + 0.444$ **6.5; 6.644**
3. $8.001 + 0.77$ **9; 8.771**
4. $7 + 11.436 + 3.08$

5. $4.035 + 8.99$ **13; 13.025**
6. $22.2 + 4.3$ **26; 26.5**
7. $9.76 + 3.45$ **13.5; 13.21**
8. $0.445 + 2.345 + 3$

9. $0.5 + 4.6$ **5; 5.1**
10. $8.7 + 0.368$ **9; 9.068**
11. $9.011 + 0.45$ **9.5; 9.461**
12. $0.33 + 1.11 + 3.2$

13. *Data Analysis* You have a $10 bill and a $5 bill. You wish to buy all the items on the list shown at the right. Can you afford to buy the 24-exposure film?   **yes**

14. Jonah had $340.87 in his checking account. He withdrew $52 and wrote a check for $18.72. Find the new balance. **$270.15**

15. **Choose A, B, C, or D.** Suppose you place the digits 1–6 in the boxes ▨ ▨.▨ + ▨.▨ ▨ to give the greatest possible sum. What is the digit in the third box from the left? **C**
   A. 2   **B.** 3   **C.** 2 or 3   **D.** 4

16. *Consumer Issues* At the movie theater, you order popcorn for $2.75 and two drinks for $1.50 each. You pay with a $10 bill. How much change will you get? **$4.25**

First estimate. Then find the difference.

17. $3.8 - 2.1$ **2; 1.7**
18. $9.1 - 6.05$ **3; 3.05**
19. $3.06 - 1.9$ **1; 1.16**

20. $4.068 - 1.29$ **3; 2.778**
21. $0.8 - 0.126$ **0.7; 0.674**
22. $8.91 - 6.08$ **3; 2.83**

23. $6.08 - 0.93$ **5; 5.11**
24. $18.2 - 9.26$ **9; 8.94**
25. $16.5 - 8.71$ **8; 7.79**

26. *Transportation* The length of the Eurotunnel between England and France is 49.94 km. The Seikan Tunnel in Japan is 53.9 km long. How much longer is the Seikan Tunnel? **3.96 km**

27a–d. See margin.
27. *Data Analysis* Refer to the data at the right.
   a. Add the numbers in the chart. What does this sum mean?
   b. *Writing* What part of all the energy is produced from oil and coal? Is it more than half? Explain.
   c. *Estimation* Which two natural resources produce an amount of energy approximately equal to that of coal?
   d. Make a hundredths' model showing the part of all energy produced by each natural resource.

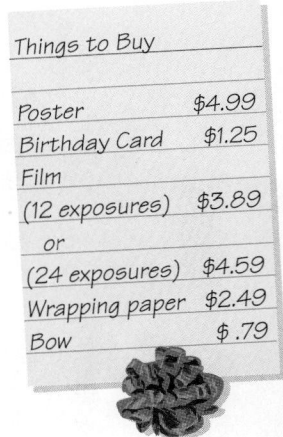

Things to Buy

Poster	$4.99
Birthday Card	$1.25
Film	
(12 exposures)	$3.89
or	
(24 exposures)	$4.59
Wrapping paper	$2.49
Bow	$.79

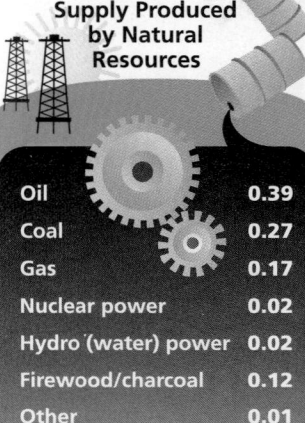

Part of Energy Supply Produced by Natural Resources

Oil	0.39
Coal	0.27
Gas	0.17
Nuclear power	0.02
Hydro (water) power	0.02
Firewood/charcoal	0.12
Other	0.01

1. Find the sum. Estimate to check your answer.
   a. $2.091 + 5.75$ 7.841
   b. $12.34 + 1.68$ 14.02

2. Find the difference. Estimate to check your answer.
   a. $8.7 - 0.368$ 8.332
   b. $22.2 - 4.3$ 17.9

3. Solve the equation.
   $x + 6.54 = 84$ $x = 77.46$

4. Sarah used a $5 bill to pay for a sandwich. She received $3.31 in change. How much did she spend? $1.69

Mental Math **Find each missing number.**

28. $6.4 + 3.1 = \blacksquare + 6.4$ 3.1   **29.** $0.43 + \blacksquare = 0.43$ 0   **30.** $(2.1 + 0.3) + 4 = 2.1 + (\blacksquare + 4)$ 0.3

Algebra **Solve each equation.**

31. $12.45 = 3.44 + k$ 9.01   **32.** $h - 0.455 = 3.44$ 3.895   **33.** $x + 2.033 = 7.899$ 5.866

34. $p - 45.678 = 65.887$ 111.565   **35.** $34.768 = 12.356 + m$ 22.412   **36.** $32.432 + c = 56.986$ 24.554

37. *Data Analysis* When you order by mail, you usually pay for shipping and handling. Suppose the company bases the fee on the cost of the order. Use the information at the right and below.
   a. You order one adult sweatshirt, size XXL, and three children's T-shirts. How much do you pay without shipping and handling? $67.45
   b. Find the charge for shipping and handling your order. b. $6.95
   c. Suppose you order one of each item in size M. What is the total cost, including shipping and handling? $80.90

Shipping and Handling Charges

Order Amount	Charge
Under $15.00	$2.95
$15.00–$24.99	$3.95
$25.00–$39.99	$4.95
$40.00–$49.99	$5.95
$50.00–$74.99	$6.95
$75.00–$99.99	$7.95
$100.00 and over	$8.95

HAPPY BIRTHDAY SHIRTS

#345 Adult Birthday Tee
   (M – XL) $15.00
   (XXL) $17.95

#355 Adult Birthday Sweatshirt
   (M – XL) $29.50
   (XXL) $29.95

#445 Child's Birthday Tee
   $12.50

#455 Child's Birthday Sweatshirt
   $16.95

Mixed Review

Evaluate each expression for $x = 10$. *(Lesson 2-6)*

38. $20 \div x$ 2   **39.** $4x$ 40   **40.** $4 + 2x$ 24   **41.** $3x - 5$ 25

Arrange the numbers in increasing order. *(Lesson 3-3)*

42. 0.05 5.55 0.505 0.55
   0.05, 0.505, 0.55, 5.55

43. 9.04 90.4 900.4 9.004
   9.004, 9.04, 90.4, 900.4

44. 60.92 603.8 68.3 62.9
   60.92, 62.9, 68.3, 603.8

45. Rod earns $10 for mowing one lawn. After mowing seven lawns, how much money has he earned? *(Previous Course)* $70

Practice 3-7 *Adding and Subtracting Decimals*

First estimate. Then find the sum or difference.

1. $0.6 + 5.8$ 7 6.4   **2.** $2.1 + 3.4$ 5 5.5   **3.** $3.4 - 0.972$ 2 2.428   **4.** $3.1 - 2.076$ 1 1.024

5. $8.13 - 2.716$ 5 5.414   **6.** $5.91 + 2.38$ 8 8.29   **7.** $3.086 + 6.152$ 9 9.238   **8.** $4.7 - 1.9$ 3 2.8

9. $9.3 - 3.9$ 5 5.4   **10.** $5.2 - 1.86$ 3 3.34   **11.** $15.98 + 26.37$ 42.35   **12.** $9.27 + 15.006$ 24.276

13. $5.9 - 2.803$ 3.097   **14.** $15.7 - 8.923$ 6.777   **15.** $4.19 - 2.016$ 2.174   **16.** $14.75 - 6.9264$ 7.8236

17. $5.1 + 4.83 + 9.002$ 18.932   **18.** $3 + 4.02 + 8.6$ 15.62   **19.** $4.7 + 5.26 + 8.931$ 18.891

Solve each equation.

20. $x - 0.31 = 6.29$ 6.6   **21.** $b + 16.12 = 18.57$ 2.45   **22.** $28.854 = 3.722 + y$ 25.132

23. $14.56 = 5.51 + s$ 9.05   **24.** $t - 0.785 = 2.49$ 3.275   **25.** $y + 4.027 = 5.954$ 1.927

26. $47.809 = m + 34.731$ 13.078   **27.** $p - 23.509 = 56.84$ 80.349   **28.** $67.357 = n - 43.516$ 110.873

Use the table at the right for Exercises 29–31.

29. Find the sum of the decimals given in the chart. What is the meaning of this sum? 1; it includes all the workers who are paid on an hourly basis.

30. What part of the hourly work force is ages 25–44? 0.53

31. Which three age groups combined represent about one-fourth of the hourly work force? 16–19, 20–24, and 65 & over; or 20–24, 55–64, and 65 & over

Ages of Workers Earning Hourly Pay

Age of Workers	Part of Work Force
16–19	0.08
20–24	0.15
25–34	0.29
35–44	0.24
45–54	0.14
55–64	0.08
65 & over	0.02

Source: Bureau of Labor Statistics, U.S. Dept. of Labor

In copymaster and workbook formats

Reteaching 3-7 *Adding and Subtracting Decimals*

Add $3.25 + 12.6 + 18.93$.

First estimate.
$$\begin{array}{rcl} 3.25 & \to & 3 \\ 12.6 & \to & 13 \\ +18.93 & \to & 19 \\ \hline & & 35 \end{array}$$

Then follow these steps.

Step 1 Line up the decimal points. Write in any needed zeros.
$$\begin{array}{r} 3.25 \\ 12.60 \\ +18.93 \\ \hline \end{array}$$

Step 2 Add as you would add whole numbers. Regroup when needed.
$$\begin{array}{r} {}^{1\,1} \\ 3.25 \\ 12.60 \\ +18.93 \\ \hline 34\,78 \end{array}$$

Step 3 Place the decimal point.
$$\begin{array}{r} 3.25 \\ 12.60 \\ +18.93 \\ \hline 34.78 \end{array}$$ ← Compare to your estimate

To subtract decimals, follow similar steps. Work from right to left and regroup when needed. Place the decimal point to complete the subtraction.

First estimate. Then find the sum.

1. $0.9 + 6.7$
   Estimate 1 + 7 = 8
   Sum 7.6

2. $3.1 + 9.4$
   Estimate 3 + 9 = 12
   Sum 12.5

3. $4.88 + 8.19$
   Estimate 5 + 8 = 13
   Sum 13.07

4. $14.05 + 9.2$ 23; 23.25   **5.** $6.008 + 0.22$ 6; 6.228   **6.** $9.104 + 5.2 + 7.99$ 22; 22.294

First estimate. Then find the difference.

7. $8.5 - 4.2$
   Estimate 9 − 4 = 5
   Difference 4.3

8. $7.2 - 3.05$
   Estimate 7 − 3 = 4
   Difference 4.15

9. $5.07 - 2.8$
   Estimate 5 − 3 = 2
   Difference 2.27

10. $6.347 - 2.986$ 3; 3.361   **11.** $14.2 - 9.86$ 4; 4.34   **12.** $13.45 - 5.001$ 8; 8.449

13. $22.7 - 12.06$ 11; 10.64   **14.** $16.1 - 10.88$ 5; 5.22   **15.** $1.79 - 0.879$ 1; 0.911

Minds on Math Transparency

3-7

Six days after the day before yesterday is Monday. What day is it today?

Thursday

See *Solution Key* for worked-out answers.

In Lesson 3-7, students learned to add and subtract decimals. This toolbox allows students to apply their knowledge to making calculations on spreadsheets and bank statements.

ERROR ALERT! Students may not remember the labeling procedure for a spreadsheet. **Remediation:** Before students begin work on

the exercises, remind students how to use the letter column headings and the number row headings. Ask for volunteers to name the contents of cell A2 and cell E4. **11/3; $1.99**

ASSESSMENT Have students subtract the value in cell F4 from the value in B2. **3.99** Have students write their answers on a piece of paper and hold them up for you to see. Ask: *What does this value represent?* **Answers may vary. Sample: $3.99 is the difference between the end balance and the starting balance.**

■ **ADDITIONAL PROBLEM**

Ask students: *What cell is the $100 in?* **D2** *What does this number mean?* **Answers may vary. Sample: $100 was deposited in the account on 11/3.**

Resources

 Teaching Resources

Teaching Aids Master 1

 Transparencies
1, 13

TECHNOLOGY

MATH TOOLBOX

Spreadsheets and Bank Statements

After Lesson 3-7

Banks usually send you a monthly report, or a *statement*, for your account. The statement shows the money you put into the account (*deposits*), the money you take out of the account (*withdrawals*), and the *interest* you earned on the account. The balance is the amount of money in the account at a given time.

■ **EXAMPLE**

The spreadsheet below shows a portion of a bank statement.

	A	B	C	D	E	F
1	Date	Balance	Withdrawal	Deposit	Interest	End Balance
2	11/3	$73.47		$100.00		$173.47
3	11/14	$173.47	$98.00			$75.47
4	11/30	$75.47			$1.99	$77.46

a. What does the number in cell B2 represent?
   The number in cell B2, $73.47, shows the balance on 11/3.
b. How is the number in cell F2 calculated?
   The number in cell F2, $173.47, is the sum of the balance on 11/3 and the deposit on 11/3.

Refer to the spreadsheet above.

1. How was the amount in cell F3 calculated?

2. How was the amount in cell F4 calculated?

3. Which cells show the same amounts? Why?

4. Suppose you deposit $32.00 to the account in the Example on 12/2, withdraw $15.50 on 12/15, and receive interest of $1.25 on 12/30.
   a. Estimate your account balance on 12/31. about $95
   b. Find the exact balance on 12/31. $95.21

1. The amount in cell F3, $75.47, is the difference between the balance on 11/14, in B3, $173.47, and the withdrawal on 11/14, in C3.

2. The amount in cell F4, $77.46, is the sum of the balance on 11/30 in B4, $75.47, and the interest added on 11/30 in D4, $1.99.

3. F2 and B3, F3 and B4; the ending balance after one transaction is the initial balance for the next transaction.

112

Teaching Notes

1 Focus

CONNECTING TO PRIOR KNOWLEDGE Ask students to list units of measurement. **Answers may vary. Sample: meter, mile, centimeter, inch, foot** Have students estimate the length of a meter, a centimeter, and a millimeter using their hands.

2 Teach

Work Together

Question 5 Encourage students to be creative and use things such as their hand or pencil as measurement units. You may want some objects on hand, such as paper clips, just in case. Then have students use a measuring tape to measure the width of their desk in inches.

THINK AND DISCUSS

DIVERSITY Ask: *What is the standard measurement system in the United States?* **the U.S. customary system** *What do they use in England?* **the metric system** *What other countries use the metric system?* **Answers may vary. Sample: Mexico, Japan, France**

MEASUREMENT Connection

3-8 Metric Units of Length

What You'll Learn

▼ To use metric units of length

▼ To choose appropriate units of measurement

...And Why

You can use metric units to measure common objects.

Here's How

Look for questions that
🔹 build understanding
✔ check understanding

Work Together — *Using Nonstandard Units of Length*

Suppose you invent a new unit of length. How about using the length of the cover of your favorite textbook?

1. Find the width of your desk in terms of your book's length. How many "books" wide is your desk?

2. 🔹*Analyze* Compare your result with those of your classmates. Explain any differences you notice.

3. Is your book a good unit of measurement? Why or why not?

4. 🔹*Reasoning* List some advantages and disadvantages of using your system of measurement.

5. Name two other objects you could use to measure the width of your desk.
1–5. Check students' work.

THINK AND DISCUSS

▼ *Using Metric Units of Length*

A **standard unit** of measurement is one on which everyone agrees. The **metric system** of measurement uses a decimal system. The standard unit of length is the **meter (m)**.

Unit	Relationship to the Meter
kilometer (km)	1 km = 1000 m
meter (m)	
centimeter (cm)	1 cm = 0.01 m
millimeter (mm)	1 mm = 0.001 m

1 cm

10 mm

6. 🔹*Reasoning* How many centimeters are there in one meter? **100 cm**

7. 🔹*What If . . .* Suppose you had a strip of paper 1 m long. How could you model centimeters on the paper? **Divide the strip into 100 equally-wide parts.**

Lesson Planning Options

Prerequisite Skills
• modeling decimals (precourse)
• multiplying by powers of ten (precourse)

Vocabulary/Symbols
standard unit, metric system, meter

Materials/Manipulatives
• metric ruler

Resources

📖 **Student Edition**
Skills Handbook, p. 543
Extra Practice, p. 524
Glossary/Study Guide

📦 **Teaching Resources**
Chapter Support File, Ch. 3
• Lesson Planner 3-8
• Practice 3-8, Reteaching 3-8
• Answer Masters 3-8
Teaching Aids Master 3
Glossary, Spanish Resources

🖥 **Transparencies**
17, Minds on Math 3-8

Warm Up

Write the integers described in each case.
greater than −3 and less than +5 **−2, −1, 0, +1, +2, +3, +4**
between −6 and −1 **−5, −4, −3, −2**

RESEARCH Have students investigate the origins of the metric system. The French determined that a meter was one ten-millionth of the length of an imaginary arc drawn from the equator through Paris to the North Pole.

AEP Have students compare the prefixes *kilo-*, *centi-*, and *milli-* with words in other languages. You can help students remember there are 100 centimeters in a meter just as there are 100 cents in a dollar.

■ **ADDITIONAL EXAMPLES**

FOR EXAMPLE 1

Have students work in pairs to measure the length and width of a math book and a board eraser in both millimeters and centimeters. **Answers may vary.**

FOR EXAMPLE 2

Choose an appropriate metric unit of measure for each.

a. the distance between two classrooms in your school **meters**

b. the distance between two schools in your city **kilometers**

Question 11 Measuring precisely can be difficult, especially with small measures. Measurements usually have a margin of error. Discuss why acceptable measurements might be slightly different. Ask: *How do you report a measurement when the object being measured falls between two marks on the ruler?* **Answers may vary. Sample: Use the next closest mark, keeping the same system of measure.**

Technology Options

Prentice Hall Technology

 **Software for Learners**

- Math Lab: Decimals and Measurement
- Math Blaster® Mystery*
- Interactive Student Tutorial, Chapter 3*

 Teaching Resource Software

- Computer Item Generator 3-8
- Resource Pro™ Chapter 3*

Internet • For related mathematics activities, visit the Prentice Hall site at www.phschool.com/math

*Available on CD-ROM only

Assignment Options for Exercises On Your Own

To provide flexible scheduling, this lesson can be split into parts.

▼1 **Core** 1–5, 9, 11, 26
Extension 6, 7, 8, 10, 12

▼2 **Core** 13–25
Extension 27

Use Mixed Review to maintain skills.

 **HISTORY** Ancient Egyptians based measures of length on the royal cubit, palm, and digit. The cubit (forearm) was the length from the elbow to the fingers. The palm was the width of the palm excluding the thumb. The digit was the width of the finger.

Source: The Macmillan Dictionary of Measurement

8. a. ⸫*Reasoning* One millimeter is one thousandth of a meter. To model millimeters, into how many equal parts would you divide a segment that represents 1 m? **1,000 parts**
b. How many millimeters are there in one centimeter? **10 mm**

9. Complete the following. Use models if they help you.
a. 100 cm = ▦ m **1** **b.** ▦ m = 1 km **1,000**
c. ▦ mm = 1 m **1,000** **d.** ▦ mm = 1 km **1,000,000**
e. ▦ mm = 1 cm **10** **f.** 1 km = ▦ cm **100,000**

When you need to measure short distances, you can use a centimeter ruler.

■ **EXAMPLE 1**

Find the length of the segment below. Use a metric ruler.

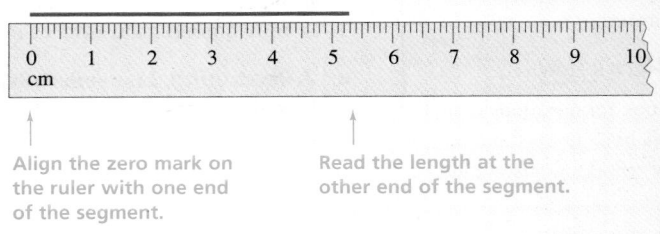

Align the zero mark on the ruler with one end of the segment.

Read the length at the other end of the segment.

The segment is 53 mm, or 5.3 cm, long.

10. a. ⸫*Measurement* What do the smaller marks on the ruler represent? **millimeters**
b. What do the numbers 0, 1, 2, 3, . . . represent? **centimeters**

11. ✔*Try It Out* Find each length in millimeters. Then find each length in centimeters.
a. ▬▬▬ **19 mm; 1.9 cm**
b. ▬▬▬▬▬▬ **51 mm; 5.1 cm**
c. ▬▬▬▬▬▬▬ **73 mm; 7.3 cm**

Now you may assign Exercises 1–12, 26.

❷ Choosing Appropriate Units

Before you measure an object you should first choose an appropriate unit of measure. Longer distances are measured in kilometers. Short distances are measured in millimeters.

ASSESSMENT If you have block scheduling or extended class periods, send students on a metric measurement scavenger hunt around the classroom. Assign pairs of students a measurement such as 20 cm. Have them find objects about that long or wide. Have students share their finds with the class.

3 Practice/Assess

EXERCISES *On Your Own*

ERROR ALERT! Exercises 1–5 Some students may make measurements starting from the end of the ruler instead of the zero mark. **Remediation:** Remind students to line up the rulers carefully with the zero mark.

Exercises 1–4 Ask students how they found both millimeters and centimeters. Have

students discuss the advantages of different methods such as finding one measure and then converting or measuring again.

CONNECTION TO GEOMETRY Exercise 11b
Ask: *What does the question ask you to find?* the perimeter of a triangle

VISUAL LEARNING Exercises 8, 9, and 12 Have students draw figures to help find the answers.

■ **EXAMPLE 2**

Choose an appropriate metric unit of measure for each.

a. length of a pencil

A pencil is a lot shorter than a meter but a lot longer than a millimeter. The appropriate measure is centimeters.

b. height of your classroom

The height of the classroom is shorter than a kilometer but much longer than a centimeter. The appropriate measure is meters.

12. ✔*Try It Out* Choose an appropriate metric unit of measure for each. **a. meter b. cm c. mm d. km**
a. width of a playground   **b.** length of a shirtsleeve
c. width of a nailhead   **d.** distance between towns

14a. postage stamp; pencil lead
b. notebook paper; high jump
c. football field; depth of a lake
d. flight distance; asteroid width

13. ♣*Writing* Explain why it is not convenient to measure long distances in small units or short distances in larger units. **See margin.**

14. ♣*Open-ended* Name two objects or distances you might measure using each unit. **a–d. See left for samples.**
a. millimeter **b.** centimeter **c.** meter **d.** kilometer
Now you may assign Exercises 13–25, 27.

EXERCISES *On Your Own*

Measurement **Find each length in millimeters. Then find each length in centimeters.**

1. ────────── 28 mm; 2.8 cm   2. ─────────── 42 mm; 4.2 cm

3. ──────────────────── 92 mm; 9.2 cm

4. ───────────────────────── 114 mm; 11.4 cm

5. **a.** Draw a segment that is 16 cm long.   **a–b. Check students' work.**
   b. Draw a segment that is 128 mm long.
   c. Which segment is longer? **16 cm**

6. *Reasoning* The height of a table is about one meter. Explain how to estimate the height of your classroom from the floor to the ceiling using the height of that table. Is your estimate reasonable? Explain. **See margin.**

pages 113–115 Think and Discuss
13. When you measure large distances and use a small unit, you get a large number of units, with many digits. When you measure small distances and use a large unit, you get a very small number, with many digits after the decimal point. In each case, the measurement must be written with a large number of digits, which is not convenient.

pages 115–117 On Your Own
6. Try to picture how many tables stacked on top of each other would reach the ceiling. Yes; you can tell roughly how many table heights equal the height of the room.

OPEN-ENDED Exercise 10 Ask students: *What activities do you do around the house, at school, or for fun? When do you use perimeters in these activities?* Answers may vary. Sample: tying string around a package, running around the bases at baseball practice

Exercise 12 Suggest students use the Guess and Test strategy.

EXTENSION Exercises 13–15 Have students give an estimate for each measurement.

ESTIMATION Exercise 26b Have students compare their estimations.

WRITING Exercise 27 To help students think of reasons, have them consider ideas such as the cost of buying new tools for factories. Ask students: *Why do scientists in this country prefer to use metric measurements?*

Answers may vary. Sample: It is easier to convert within the metric system. Scientists using metric in different countries can work together.

WRAP UP

IDENTIFYING THE BIG IDEA Ask students to describe the metric system for measuring lengths. Have students explain how to choose an appropriate unit of measure.

CHECKPOINT 2

Name _____ Class _____ Date _____

■ Checkpoint 2   *Lessons 3-4 through 3-8*

First estimate. Then find the sum or difference. Estimates may vary.

1. 3.24
    + 1.06
    ——————
    4; 4.30

2. 6.09
    − 3.7
    ——————
    2; 2.39

3. 8.45
    + 0.92
    ——————
    9; 9.37

Round to the place of the underlined digit.

4. 1.64$\underline{3}$4   5. 0.$\underline{3}$72   6. 4.8$\underline{2}$5   7. 2.3$\underline{9}$23
    1.643   0.4   4.83   2.39

8. **Circle A, B, C, or D.** You have $6.00. Suppose you want to buy a notebook for $2.19, a pen for $.69, a protractor for $.49, and a ruler for $.49. Estimate the total to be sure you have enough money. Which is the best estimate?

   A. $5.00   **B.** $4.50   **C.** $4.00   **D.** $3.50

Assessment

12. 2.5 m and 1.5 m; the sum of the four lengths is 8 m, so the sum of the width and the length is 4 m. The length is 1 m longer than the width, so twice the width is 1 m less, or 3 m. The width is 1.5 m. The length is 1 m longer, or 2.5 m.

---

7. *Geometry* Find the perimeter of each figure. (*Hint*: The perimeter of a figure is the sum of the lengths of its sides.)

a. 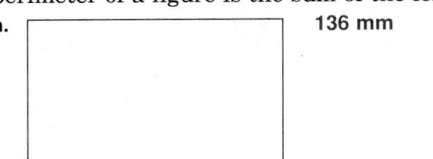 136 mm   b.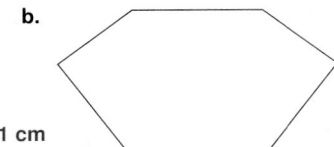

11 cm

8. *Geometry* Draw a figure with a 20-cm perimeter. **Check students' work.**

9. *Geometry* A rectangular dog kennel measures 4 m by 5 m. What length of fence do you need to enclose the kennel? (*Hint:* A rectangle has two pairs of equal sides.) **18 m**

10. *Open-ended* Describe some situations where you might need to know the distance around a figure. **Samples: building a fence, putting wallpaper border around a room, installing gutters on a house**

11. a. *Geometry* Measure each side of the triangle at the right in centimeters. **3.3 cm, 4.8 cm, 6.7 cm**
   b. What is the distance around the triangle? **14.8 cm**

12. *Reasoning* The perimeter of a rectangular table is 8 m. The table is 1 m longer than it is wide. Find the length of each side. Explain how you got your answer. **See margin.**

Choose an appropriate metric unit of measure for each.

13. width of a highway **km**   **14.** length of an eyelash **mm**   **15.** distance between cities **m**

16. your height **m**   **17.** width of your classroom door **cm**   **18.** width of your finger **mm**

19. length of your pen **cm**   **20.** length of your desk **m**   **21.** width of your classroom **m**

Is each measurement reasonable? If not, give a reasonable measurement. 22–25. Numerical answers may vary. Samples are given.

22. The sidewalk is 30 km wide. **no; 1 m**   **23.** Your friend is about 160 cm tall. **yes**

24. Your pencil is 18 mm long. **no; 18 cm**   **25.** A kitchen table is about 123 cm long. **yes**

26. a. *Reasoning* The width of a door is about 1 m. How can you estimate the length of a wall that contains the door? **Estimate how many doors would fit along the wall side by side.**
   b. *Estimation* Estimate the length of your classroom wall using the method you just described. **Check students' work.**

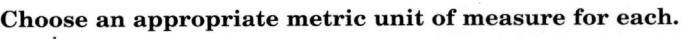

LESSON QUIZ

1. The perimeter of a rectangle is 12 m. Its length is 2 m more than its width. Find the length and width. **4 m; 2 m**

2. How many millimeters are in 2 m? **2,000 mm**

3. What unit would you use to measure the distance for a marathon race? **kilometer**

4. Name something you would measure in millimeters. **Answers may vary. Sample: an insect**

---

27. *Writing* Read the article at the right. List some possible reasons why the metric system is not more widely used in this country. Do you think it should be more widely used? Why or why not? **Check students' work.**

U.S. Still Catching Up

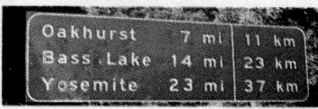

Oakhurst	7 mi	11 km
Bass Lake	14 mi	23 km
Yosemite	23 mi	37 km

THE UNITED STATES OFFICIALLY began to "go metric" in 1973. Since most of the rest of the world's countries were using the metric system, it seemed to be a good idea.

There has been little progress. Still, scientists use the metric system, and there are metric units on some highway signs and on some food and hardware items.

Mixed Review

Compare. Use >, <, or =. *(Lesson 3-3)*

28. 0.39 **<** 0.399 **29.** 1.2 **>** 1.02 **30.** 0.7 **>** 0.0700 **31.** 4.6 **=** 4.60 **32.** 5.5 **<** 5.55

Write a variable expression. *(Lesson 2-5)* **33–34. Variable labels may vary. Samples are given.**

33. 10 less than a number $n - 10$

34. the sum of a number and 5 $n + 5$

35. Paper cups come in packages of 50. There are 576 students and teachers at Memorial Middle School. How many packages of paper cups should be purchased for the school picnic? *(Previous Course)* **12 packages**

✓ CHECKPOINT 2

Lessons 3-4 through 3-8

First estimate. Then find the sum or difference.

1.
  1.25
+ 6.07
  7; 7.32

2.
  9.06
− 0.8
  8; 8.26

3. 5.59 + 12.6 **18; 18.19**

4. 37 − 7.8 **29; 29.2**

5. 789.456 + 564.9 **1,354; 1,354.356**

Round each number to the underlined place value.

6. 12.04<u>1</u> **12.04**

7. <u>2</u>.40 **2**

8. 9.06<u>5</u>5 **9.066**

9. 53.8<u>5</u> **53.9**

10. 0.4<u>4</u>32 **0.44**

11. 23.5<u>6</u>75 **23.57**

12. Choose A, B, or C. Suppose you wish to buy three items priced $2.09, $.59, and $1.46. Which is the best estimate of the total cost? **A**

A. $4.00 **B.** $3.50 **C.** $5.00

13. Find the length of the segment in millimeters and then in centimeters. **105 mm; 10.5 cm**

PRACTICE

Practice 3-8 *Metric Units of Length*

Find each length in millimeters and centimeters.

1. _____ **46** mm, **4.6** cm
2. _____ **21 mm, 2.1 cm**
3. _____ **63 mm, 6.3 cm**
4. _____ **37 mm, 3.7 cm**

Find the perimeter of each figure.

5. **8.3 cm** **6.** **10 cm** **7.** **10.8 cm**

8. Draw a figure that has a perimeter of 14 cm.
Sample: rectangle with length 5 cm and width 2 cm

Is each measurement reasonable? If not, choose a reasonable measurement. Circle A, B, C, or D.

9. Your friend is 1,500 mm tall.
A. 1.5 mm **B.** 1,500 cm
C. 1.5 km **D.** reasonable

10. Your desk is about 50 mm wide.
A. 50 m **B.** 50 cm
C. 5 m **D.** reasonable

11. A tree is about 20 km tall.
A. 20 m **B.** 2 km
C. 20 cm **D.** reasonable

12. An envelope is about 24 cm long.
A. 2.4 cm **B.** 24 mm
C. 2.4 m **D.** reasonable

Circle A, B, C, or D. What unit would you use to measure each item?

13. the height of an office building
A. km **B.** m
C. cm **D.** mm

14. the width of a page of a text
A. km **B.** m
C. cm **D.** mm

15. the length of an ant
A. km **B.** m
C. cm **D.** mm

16. the depth of a lake
A. km **B.** m
C. cm **D.** mm

In copymaster and workbook formats

RETEACHING

Reteaching 3-8 *Metric Units of Length*

The standard unit of length in the metric system is a **meter**.

millimeter (mm)	= 0.001 meter
centimeter (cm)	= 0.01 meter
meter (m)	= 1 meter
kilometer (km)	= 1,000 meters

A length can be named using different metric units. The point marked on the ruler is 2.7 cm.

Since each centimeter is 10 millimeters, the point is also 27 mm.

To measure length, choose a unit that is shorter than the length you want to measure—but not too short!

To measure:	Use:
the length of a staple	millimeters
the length of a book	centimeters
the height of an apartment house	meters
the distance between cities	kilometers

Find each length in millimeters and centimeters.

1. _____ 18 millimeters 1.8 centimeters
2. _____ 25 millimeters 2.5 centimeters
3. _____ 41 millimeters 4.1 centimeters
4. _____ 33 millimeters 3.3 centimeters

Choose an appropriate metric unit of measure for each.

5. distance across the end of a pencil millimeters
6. length of a thumb centimeters
7. distance from your home to Australia kilometers
8. width of a swimming pool meters
9. height of a water tower meters
10. length of a ladybug millimeters

ENRICHMENT

Minds on Math Transparency

3-8

Hayley is 2 in. taller than Vi. Tina is 5 in. shorter than Alli. Alli is 1 in. shorter than Hayley. Who is the shortest?

Tina

See *Solution Key* for worked-out answers.

1 Focus

CONNECTING TO PRIOR KNOWLEDGE
Discuss with students situations in which they measured liquids. Ask students:

• *Which units did you use to measure liquids?* **Answers may vary. Sample: ounces, cups, milliliters**

• *What units of measure have you seen used for liquid products in grocery stores?* **Answers may vary. Sample: ounces, liters**

2 Teach

Work Together

VISUAL / TACTILE LEARNING Questions 3 and 4 Use a balance-beam scale to show mass by comparison. Find two objects of about the same size, but of different mass, such as a rock and a sponge. Put them on either side of the scale so students can see the balance tip. Have students find two more objects of about the same mass, but of different sizes, such as a marble and a polystyrene foam ball. Let students practice balancing the scale.

THINK AND DISCUSS

ASSESSMENT Pair students. Have one student think of an object. Have the partner name the unit they would use to measure the

Lesson Planning Options

Prerequisite Skills
• multiplying by powers of ten (precourse)

Vocabulary/Symbols
mass, gram, capacity, liter

Materials/Manipulatives
• newspaper

Resources

 Student Edition

Skills Handbook, p. 543
Extra Practice, p. 524
Glossary/Study Guide

 Teaching Resources

Chapter Support File, Ch. 3
• Lesson Planner 3-9
• Practice 3-9, Reteaching 3-9
• Answer Masters 3-9
Glossary, Spanish Resources

 Transparencies
17, Minds on Math 3-9

Warm Up

What are the values of 9 in 9.0349? **ones place and ten-thousandths place**

3-9 Metric Units of Mass and Capacity

What You'll Learn

▼ To choose metric units of mass

▼ To choose metric units of capacity

...And Why

You can use metric units of mass and capacity to measure and compare everyday objects.

Here's How

Look for questions that
🔧 build understanding
✔ check understanding

Work Together
Comparing Units of Measure

Look at a flyer or newspaper ad from a local grocery store.

1. Make a list of all the units of measurement shown in the ad.

2. Divide your list into categories according to the units used.

3. Compare two differently sized packages that are labeled with similar units of measurement.

4. 🔧*Reasoning* Explain why differently sized packages may be labeled with the same measurements.
1–4. **Check students' work.**

THINK AND DISCUSS

▼ *Metric Units of Mass*

Solids are sometimes measured in units of mass. **Mass** is a measure of the amount of matter in an object. The standard unit of mass is the **gram (g).** Another commonly used unit of mass is the kilogram (kg).

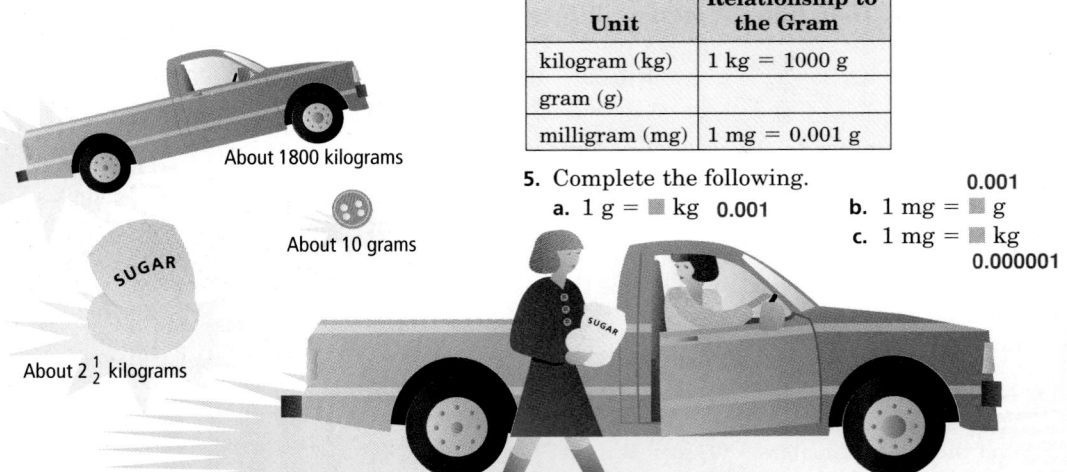

About 1800 kilograms

About 10 grams

About 2 ½ kilograms

SUGAR

Unit	Relationship to the Gram
kilogram (kg)	1 kg = 1000 g
gram (g)	
milligram (mg)	1 mg = 0.001 g

5. Complete the following.
   a. 1 g = ■ kg **0.001**
   b. 1 mg = ■ g **0.001**
   c. 1 mg = ■ kg **0.000001**

object's mass and explain why. Have students switch roles.

ERROR ALERT! **Question 7c** Students may become confused about the operations and steps to convert mL to kL. **Remediation:** Suggest that students first convert mL into L. Then have them convert 0.001 L to kL. When they finish, they can discuss the reasonableness of the result by visualizing a milliliter and a kiloliter.

■ **ADDITIONAL EXAMPLES**

FOR EXAMPLE 1

Choose an appropriate metric unit of mass.

a. three pennies gram

b. a sewing needle milligram

FOR EXAMPLE 2

Choose an appropriate metric unit of capacity.

a. bottle of orange juice liter

b. a raindrop milliliter

CONNECTION TO SCIENCE Explain to students the difference between mass and weight. Make sure students understand the following.

• Mass is a measure of the amount of matter in an object.

• Weight is a measure of how much force gravity puts on an object.

• Mass remains the same despite gravity changes.

Point out that weight changes if the gravity

■ **EXAMPLE 1**

Choose an appropriate metric unit of mass for each.

a. a pea **b.** a baby **c.** a car

a. A pea has about the same mass as a paper clip. It is measured in milligrams.

b. A baby has about the same mass as a few bags of sugar. The mass would be measured in kilograms.

c. A car's mass is a little less than that of a small truck. It is measured in kilograms.

6. ✔*Try It Out* Choose an appropriate metric unit of mass for each. g kg mg

a. a bag of popcorn **b.** a desk **c.** a grain of sand

Now you may assign Exercises 1–9, 31, 33, 35, 37, 39, 41, 42.

2 *Metric Units of Capacity*

Liquids are measured by units of capacity. **Capacity** is a measure of the amount of space an object occupies. The standard unit of capacity is the **liter (L).** Another commonly used unit of capacity is the milliliter (mL).

Unit	Relationship to the Liter
kiloliter (kL)	1 kL = 1000 L
liter (L)	
milliliter (mL)	1 mL = 0.001 L

A dewdrop is about 0.5 mL of water. A bottle of milk is about 1 L. A lake contains hundreds of thousands of kiloliters of water.

7. Complete the following.

a. 1 L = ■ kL
   0.001

b. 1 mL = ■ L
   0.001

c. 1 mL = ■ kL
   0.000001

Technology Options

Prentice Hall Technology

Software for Learners
• Math Blaster® Mystery*
• Interactive Student Tutorial, Chapter 3*

Teaching Resource Software
• Computer Item Generator 3-9
• Resource Pro™ Chapter 3*

Internet • For related mathematics activities, visit the Prentice Hall site at www.phschool.com/math

*Available on CD-ROM only

Assignment Options for Exercises On Your Own

To provide flexible scheduling, this lesson can be split into parts.

1 Core 1–9, 31, 33, 35
Extension 37, 39, 41, 42

2 Core 10–18, 32, 34, 36, 43
Extension 19–30, 38, 40, 44

Use Mixed Review to maintain skills.

force changes. For example, objects on the moon have the same mass as on Earth but weigh less.

CONNECTIONS TO TECHNOLOGY Students can visit the NASA web site at www.osf.hq.nasa.gov/heds to learn more about the affects of weightlessness on living things and the challenge of exercising to maintain muscle mass in space.

3 Practice/Assess

AUDITORY LEARNING Exercises 1–9 Drop a paper clip and a bag of flour on the floor. Have students compare the sounds. Ask them to imagine the sound of a toy truck dropped on the floor, or play a recording of a large crash. The comparison of sounds may help auditory learners choose the correct units.

OPEN-ENDED Exercise 43 Suggest students classify each unit as a mass or capacity measurement before answering the question.

WRAP UP

IDENTIFYING THE BIG IDEA Ask students to describe the units of measurement for mass and capacity and give examples of objects they would measure using each unit.

---

pages 120–121 On Your Own

43a. hot sauce bottle; amount a hedgehog drinks in a day

b. vitamin dose; grain of sand

c. cylinder capacity of a car engine; bottle of liquid detergent

d. loaf of bread; computer monitor

44. Answers may vary. Sample: The metric system makes it easier to compare quantities expressed in different units. Each unit is equivalent to another unit multiplied or divided by a power of 10. People may have trouble visualizing amounts expressed in metric units.

■ **EXAMPLE 2**

Choose an appropriate metric unit of capacity for each.

   a. a raindrop   **b.** carton of milk   **c.** swimming pool

   a. A raindrop has about the same capacity as a dewdrop. It is measured in milliliters.
   b. A carton of milk has about the same capacity as a soda bottle. It is measured in liters.
   c. The capacity of a swimming pool is a little less than that of a small pond. It is measured in kiloliters.

8. ✔*Try It Out* Choose an appropriate metric unit of capacity for each.
   a. a bottle of juice L   **b.** a lake kL   **c.** a test tube mL

Now you may assign Exercises 10–30, 32, 34, 36, 38, 40, 43, 44.

EXERCISES *On Your Own*

Choose an appropriate metric unit of mass for each.

1. a pen g   **2.** a garbage can kg   **3.** a pin mg

4. a chair kg   **5.** a telephone g   **6.** an eyelash mg

7. a potato g   **8.** a shirt button mg   **9.** a mug g

Choose an appropriate metric unit of capacity for each.

10. a flu shot mL   **11.** water used in a shower L **12.** Lake Michigan kL

13. tank of gasoline L   **14.** bottle of sunscreen mL   **15.** a bucket of rainwater L

16. cup of milk mL   **17.** a puddle L   **18.** a drop of water mL

State whether each of the following is best measured in terms of mass or capacity.

19. a bottle of lamp oil   **20.** newspaper   **21.** bread

22. ears of corn   **23.** stick of butter   **24.** flour

25. box of rice   **26.** water in a fish tank   **27.** bricks

28. bag of oranges   **29.** orange juice   **30.** popcorn

19, 26, 29. capacity   20–25, 27–28, 30. mass

120

PROJECT LINK Ask: *What unit would you use to find the mass of a CD?* **gram**

LESSON QUIZ

1. Choose an appropriate metric unit for each.

   a. pocketful of coins **grams**

   b. water in a water cooler **liters**

2. How many milliliters are in 3 L? **3,000**

Is each measurement reasonable? If not, give a reasonable measurement. 31–36. Numerical answers may vary. Samples are given.

31. A car has a mass of 300 kg. **no; 3,000 kg**

32. You drink 2 L of water a day. **yes**

33. Your mass is 20 mg. **no; 50 kg**

34. You use 4 mL of water to wash your hands. **no; 400 mL**

35. A ladybug has a mass of 4 kg. **no; 4g**

36. A cow produces 500 kL of milk a day. **no; 20 L**

True or *False?* If false, explain why.

37. A tennis ball has a mass of about 58 mL. **False; mL is not a unit of mass.**

38. A dime has a capacity of about 2.5 g. **False; g is not a unit of capacity.**

39. 1000 mg = 1 g **true**

40. 10 L = 1000 mL **false; 10 L = 10,000 mL**

41. 100 kg = 100,000 g **true**

42. Your math book has a mass of 3 L. **False; L is not a unit of mass.**

43. *Open-ended* Name two things you might measure using each unit. **a–d. See margin p. 120.**

   a. milliliter   **b.** milligram   **c.** liter   **d.** kilogram

44. *Writing* Describe the advantages and disadvantages of using the metric system. **See margin p. 120.**

> **JOURNAL**
> Describe some parts of your daily life that would be affected if everybody changed to the metric system.

Mixed Review

Estimate using mental math. *(Lesson 3-5)*

45. $54.99 + $3.25 **$58**

46. $5.49 − $2.99 **$2.50**

47. $20.00 − $13.98 **$6**

48. $23.89 + $3.78 **$28**

Write in words. *(Lesson 3-2)* 49. six hundred thirty-eight thousand, nine hundred seventy

50. thirty-five hundredths   52. sixty-seven and eight hundredths

49. 638,970   **50.** 0.35   **51.** 2.43   **52.** 67.08   **53.** 1,003.289   **54.** 0.0082

51. two and forty-three hundredths

53. one thousand, three and two hundred eighty-nine thousandths

54. eighty-two ten-thousandths

55. Randa received $25 for her birthday. Then she baby-sat and earned $13, $8.50, and $9.75. How much money does she have now? *(Lesson 3-7)* **$56.25**

CHAPTER PROJECT

PROJECT LINK: CALCULATING

The shipping and handling charge is $2.15 per CD. Calculate the shipping and handling costs for the total number of CDs you plan to buy. Calculate the average cost per CD. Don't forget to include the penny for the first eight CDs.

Check students' work.

PRACTICE

Practice 3-9 *Metric Units of Mass and Capacity*

Choose an appropriate metric unit of mass for each.

1. a grain of rice **gram**   **2.** a bag of groceries **kilogram**   **3.** a feather **milligram**

4. a cat **kilogram**   **5.** a leaf **milligram**   **6.** an eraser **gram**

Choose an appropriate metric unit of capacity for each.

7. a gasoline tank **liter**   **8.** a coffee mug **milliliter**   **9.** 6 raindrops **milliliter**

10. a pitcher of juice **liter**   **11.** a swimming pool **kiloliter**   **12.** a can of paint **liter**

State whether each of the following is best measured in terms of mass or capacity.

13. a bag of potatoes **mass**   **14.** water in a birdbath **capacity**   **15.** an apple **mass**

16. a box of raisins **mass**   **17.** a cup of hot cider **capacity**   **18.** a refrigerator **capacity**

19. a baby's bottle **capacity**   **20.** a fish tank **capacity**   **21.** a watering can **capacity**

Write *true* or *false*.

22. The mass of the horse is about 500 kg. **true**

23. Jean drank 5.8 L of juice at breakfast. **false**

24. A mug holds 250 mL of hot chocolate. **true**

25. A penny is about 3 kg. **false**

26. A teaspoon holds about 5 L. **false**

27. A textbook is about 1 kg. **true**

In copymaster and workbook formats

RETEACHING

Reteaching 3-9 *Metric Units of Mass and Capacity*

In the metric system solids can be measured in units of **mass**.

| milligram (mg) = 0.001 gram |
| gram (g) = 1 gram |
| kilogram (kg) = 1,000 grams |

The standard unit of mass is a **gram**.
- The mass of a vitamin pill may be measured in milligrams.
- A thumbtack has a mass of about 1 gram.
- A full liter bottle of soda has a mass of about 1 kilogram.

Liquids are measured in units of **capacity**.

| milliliter (mL) = 0.001 liter |
| liter (L) = 1 liter |
| kiloliter (kL) = 1,000 liters |

The standard unit of capacity is a **liter**.
- The capacity of a soup spoon is measured in milliliters.
- A 1-liter soda bottle is enough for about 4 or 5 drinks.
- Water in a river is measured in kiloliters.

Choose an appropriate metric unit of mass for each.

1. a television set **kilograms**   **2.** an envelope **grams**

3. a grapefruit **grams**   **4.** a baseball player **kilograms**

5. a sports car **kilograms**   **6.** a staple **milligrams**

7. a human hair **milligrams**   **8.** a paperback book **grams**

Choose an appropriate metric unit of capacity for each.

9. a bottle of perfume **milliliters**   **10.** a swimming pool **kiloliters**

11. a mug of soup **milliliters**   **12.** a raindrop **milliliters**

13. a barrel of oil **liters**   **14.** the Atlantic Ocean **kiloliters**

State whether each of the following is best measured in terms of mass or capacity.

15. gasoline **capacity**   **16.** peanut butter **mass**

17. air in the lungs **capacity**   **18.** milk **capacity**

19. frozen peas **mass**   **20.** a bag of apples **mass**

ENRICHMENT

Minds on Math Transparency

3-9

I am a two-digit number less than 100. When I am divided by 2, 3, 4, or 5, the remainder is 1. What number am I?

61

See *Solution Key* for worked-out answers.

PROBLEM SOLVING PRACTICE ★★

This page provides problems for students to solve using their knowledge of rounding decimals, reading graphs, estimating, measuring distances, finding patterns, calculating mean, adding, and subtracting. Allow students to use any method they find helpful.

COOPERATIVE GROUPS **Exercise 2** Have groups discuss objects with the lengths listed. Have groups share their objects and compare answers to the problem.

USING MANIPULATIVES **Exercise 3** Students can work with a partner. Pairs of students can model the pattern using blocks or counters.

Exercise 4 Remind students to read the instruction line carefully. The problem calls for the *top* three scores in order from *greatest to least*.

Exercise 7 Encourage students to write a multiplication sentence for each day and then add the products. Have them subtract the expenses as the final step. Dividing the problem into steps will help students find the correct answer.

PROBLEM SOLVING PRACTICE

Choose the best answer.

1. At a concert, the attendance was 782 people. A reporter rounded the attendance to the nearest hundred. Which number is a reasonable estimate? **C**

   A. 700   **B.** 780   **C.** 800   **D.** 1,000

2. Which metric length would be closest to the length of a baseball bat? **J**

   F. 1 mm   **G.** 1 cm   **H.** 1 dm   **J.** 1 m

3. Billie is stacking cubes. The first stack has 4 cubes, the second has 7 cubes, the third has 10 cubes, and the fourth has 13 cubes. If she continues the same pattern, how many more cubes will she need to complete two more stacks? **C**

   A. 16 cubes   **B.** 19 cubes
   C. 35 cubes   **D.** 69 cubes

4. Five contestants received scores of 93.1, 90.9, 93.4, 98.4, and 90.7. Name the top three scores from greatest to least. **H**

   F. 93.1, 90.9, 93.4   **G.** 90.7, 90.9, 93.1
   H. 98.4, 93.4, 93.1   **J.** 93.1, 93.4, 98.4

5. During which 10-year period was there a decrease in the population of Oak City? **D**

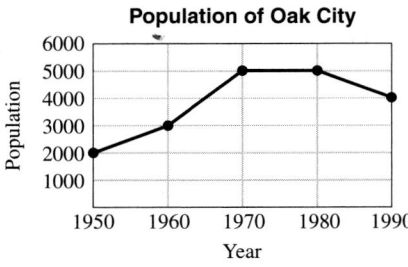

Population of Oak City

   A. 1950 to 1960   **B.** 1960 to 1970
   C. 1970 to 1980   **D.** 1980 to 1990

Please note that items 6 and 7 have *five* answer choices.

6. Mr Majko has only $20 to spend at the grocery store. He finds a steak costing $7.29, a roast costing $12.95, hamburger costing $3.95, and fish costing $6.25. Using estimation, he determines that he cannot buy all the items, but he can buy some of them and have less than $1 left in change. Which items could he buy? **G**

   F. steak, hamburger, and fish
   G. roast and fish
   H. steak and roast
   J. roast and hamburger
   K. roast, hamburger, and fish

7. The number of people entering a garden show each day is shown by the graph. Each person pays $3 to enter, but the promoters have expenses of $580. How much profit will they make for the show? **F**

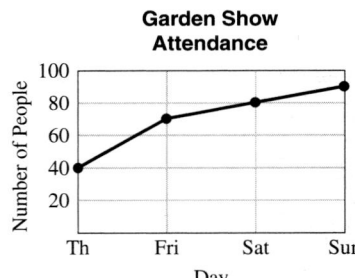

Garden Show Attendance

   F. $260   **G.** $360
   H. $840   **J.** $1,420
   K. Not Here

122

1 Focus

CONNECTING TO PRIOR KNOWLEDGE Ask students: *How do you measure time?* **Answers may vary. Sample: with a watch or calendar** *What units do you use?* **Answers may vary. Sample: minutes, days, seconds, years**

2 Teach

Work Together

Questions 1–5 Some students have learned to tell time on a digital clock and may have difficulty reading the hands of clocks 1 and 2, and drawing clocks 3 and 4. Have students work together in groups to answer these questions. Make sure there is a student in each group who can read the clocks.

AEP **DIVERSITY Questions 1 and 2** Have students who can tell time in other languages read the time on clocks 1 and 2 in their language. Then have a student read the times in English.

TACTILE/AUDITORY LEARNING Questions 1–5 Students can make their own clocks using a clock face, a prong paper fastener, and two strips of paper. Have them model the time on Clock 1. Ask them to move the hands on their clock and count aloud by fives until their clock shows the time on Clock 2.

MEASUREMENT Connection

3-10 Measuring Elapsed Time

What You'll Learn

▼ To add and subtract measures of time

▼ To read, use, and make schedules

...And Why

You will use elapsed time to make and use schedules and to plan events.

Here's How

Look for questions that
⊞ build understanding
✔ check understanding

Work Together _____ *Investigating Elapsed Time*

Look at the clocks at the right.

1. What time does Clock 1 show? **6:30**

2. What time does Clock 2 show? **7:10**

3. ⊞*Analyze* How much time has passed between the time on the first clock and the time on the second? **40 min**

4. Copy and complete Clock 3 so that it shows fifteen minutes after four.

5. Draw a fourth clock showing the time 40 minutes after Clock 3.

4–5. See back of book.

Clock 1

Clock 2
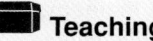

Clock 3

THINK AND DISCUSS

▼ *Adding and Subtracting Measures of Time*

The standard unit of time is the **second (s).**

Units of Time	
second (s)	
minute (min)	1 min = 60 s
hour (h)	1 h = 60 min = 3,600 s
day (d)	1 d = 24 h = 1,440 min
week (wk)	1 wk = 7 d = 168 h
year (yr)	1 yr ≈ 52 wk ≈ 365 d

6. ⊞*Reasoning* 1 h 20 min is equivalent to how many minutes? How many seconds? Explain how you got your answer.
See back of book.

Lesson Planning Options

Prerequisite Skills
• reading a clock (precourse)

Vocabulary/Symbols
second, elapsed time

Resources

📖 **Student Edition**
Skills Handbook, p. 540
Extra Practice, p. 524
Glossary/Study Guide

📦 **Teaching Resources**
Chapter Support File, Ch. 3
• Lesson Planner 3-10
• Practice 3-10, Reteaching 3-10
• Answer Masters 3-10
Glossary, Spanish Resources

📽 **Transparencies**
17, Minds on Math 3-10

Warm Up

In each case, which one of the quantities is the most reasonable estimate?
shoes: 1 mg, 1 g, 1 kg **1 kg**
horse: 500 mg, 500 g, 500 kg **500 kg**
bucket: 10 mL, 10 L, 10 kL **10 L**

ERROR ALERT! Question 6 Some students may say 1 h 20 min is 120 min. **Remediation:** Remind students an hour is 60 min. So, 1 h 20 min is 60 min + 20 min, or 80 min.

Example 1 Help students understand they need to rename 3 h 27 min as 2 h 87 min before they can subtract. Tell them this is similar to borrowing to subtract decimals. Before they can borrow, they must rewrite the hour as minutes.

■ ADDITIONAL EXAMPLES

FOR EXAMPLE 1

Find the elapsed time between 1:52 P.M. and 5:15 P.M. **3 h 23 min**

FOR EXAMPLE 2

Lee wants to visit a store that is a 15-minute walk from Kagy Boulevard. At what time does Lee need to catch the bus to arrive at the store about 8:30 A.M.? **7:50 A.M.**

CONNECTING TO THE STUDENTS' WORLD

Have groups of students research bus, subway, train, or airline schedules. Ask groups to create a table as in Example 2. Have them write story problems using their tables. Then have each group work another group's problem.

Technology Options

Prentice Hall Technology

  Software for Learners

- Hot Page™ 9*
- Math Blaster® Mystery*
- Interactive Student Tutorial, Chapter 3*

  Teaching Resource Software

- Computer Item Generator 3-10
- Resource Pro™ Chapter 3*

Internet • For related mathematics activities, visit the Prentice Hall site at www.phschool.com/math

Available on CD-ROM only

Assignment Options for Exercises On Your Own

To provide flexible scheduling, this lesson can be split into parts.

▼**1 Core** 1–20
Extension 24, 25, 28

▼**2 Core** 21–23
Extension 26, 27

Use Mixed Review to maintain skills.

124

The time between two events is called **elapsed time.** To calculate elapsed time, you can add or subtract hours and minutes. You may need to rewrite the hours and minutes.

■ EXAMPLE 1

Find the elapsed time between 1:45 P.M. and 3:27 P.M. Subtract 1:45 from 3:27.

$$3:27 \longrightarrow 3 \text{ h } 27 \text{ min} \longrightarrow 2 \text{ h } 87 \text{ min} \longleftarrow \text{Rewrite 3 h 27 min as 2 h 87 min.}$$
$$1:45 \longrightarrow 1 \text{ h } 45 \text{ min} \longrightarrow \underline{- 1 \text{ h } 45 \text{ min}}$$
$$1 \text{ h } 42 \text{ min} \longleftarrow \text{Subtract.}$$

The elapsed time is 1 h 42 min.

7. ✔**Try It Out** Find the elapsed time between 7:25 A.M. and 8:12 A.M. Then find the elapsed time between 8:45 P.M. and 10:25 P.M. **47 min; 1 h 40 min**

8. ⬥**Writing** Explain how you would find the elapsed time between 10:00 A.M. and 3:15 P.M. What extra step must you follow? **Find the elapsed time from 10:00 A.M. to noon and from noon to 3:15 P.M. Then add the two times; you need to use noon.**

9. ⬥**Open-ended** What time do you get up in the morning on a school day? What time does school begin? Find the elapsed time. **Check students' work.**

Now you may assign Exercises 1–20, 24, 25, 28.

▼2 Reading, Using, and Making Schedules

You use elapsed time when using schedules.

WK Bus Line

Buses Run Every 30 Minutes
Monday–Friday

| Leave | Arrive |
Willson St.	Kagy Blvd.
7:20 A.M.	7:45 A.M.
7:50 A.M.	8:15 A.M.
...	...
11:20 P.M.	11:45 P.M.
Kagy Blvd.	**Willson St.**
7:50 A.M.	8:15 A.M.
8:20 A.M.	8:45 A.M.
...	...
11:50 P.M.	12:15 A.M.

■ EXAMPLE 2 *Real-World Problem Solving*

Use the bus schedule at the left. Suppose you arrive at the Willson Street bus stop 5 minutes after the 11:50 A.M. bus has left.

a. How long do you have to wait for the next bus?

The buses run every 30 minutes. You will wait 25 minutes.

b. When do you arrive at Kagy Boulevard?

11:50 A.M. + 30 min = 11:80
= 11 h 80 min = 12 h 20 min

The next bus will arrive at 12:20 P.M. The trip takes 25 minutes. You will arrive at 12:45 P.M.

3 Practice/Assess

EXERCISES *On Your Own*

MENTAL MATH Exercise 3 Ask: *How can you use 3 h to find this answer?*
3 h − 1 min = 2 h + 59 min

ASSESSMENT Have students form pairs. Each partner thinks of a time and writes it down. They find the elapsed time between 1:05 A.M. and that time. Then each student finds the difference between their partner's time and 1:05 A.M. Partners compare answers.

DIVERSITY Exercise 23 Some religions and cultures do not celebrate birthdays. Have students share the different holidays they do celebrate.

OPEN-ENDED Exercise 28 Students can write down what they did last Saturday.

WRAP UP

IDENTIFYING THE BIG IDEA Have students explain why we use elapsed time and how to find it.

---

10. ✔Try It Out Lee is going to a party at 6:00 P.M. The party is a 5-minute walk from the bus stop on Kagy Boulevard. In order to be at the party on time, which bus should Lee take from Willson Street? **5:20 P.M. bus**

11. ⚓Reasoning By what time should Lee leave the party to catch a bus and be home by 9:00 P.M.? **8:15 P.M.**

Now you may assign Exercises 21–23, 26, 27.

EXERCISES *On Your Own*

Mental Math **How many minutes are in each amount of time?**

1. 1 h 30 min **90 min**
2. 3 h 35 min **215 min**
3. 2 h 59 min **179 min**
4. 5 h 17 min **317 min**
5. 10 h 15 min **615 min**
6. 4 h 45 min **285 min**
7. 6 h 12 min **372 min**
8. 8 h 2 min **482 min**

Find the elapsed time between each pair of times.

9. 8:25 A.M. and 10:52 A.M. **2 h 27 min**
10. 8:35 P.M. and 9:18 P.M. **43 min**
11. 5:25 P.M. and 11:11 P.M. **5 h 46 min**
12. 6:45 A.M. and 9:02 A.M. **2 h 17 min**
13. 4:25 A.M. and 7:24 A.M. **2 h 59 min**
14. 3:25 A.M. and 4:37 P.M. **13 h 12 min**
15. 3:27 P.M. and 7:32 P.M. **4 h 5 min**
16. 9:25 A.M. and 11:12 P.M. **13 h 47 min**
17. 2:25 P.M. and 2:59 A.M. **12 h 34 min**
18. 1:09 P.M. and 8:12 A.M. **19 h 3 min**
19. 10:25 A.M. and 11:58 P.M. **13 h 33 min**
20. 3:59 P.M. and 5:01 P.M. **1 h 2 min**

21. *Entertaining* Susan is having a party at 4:00 P.M. On the day of the party she needs to do the activities at the right.
   a. If Susan does the activities in the order given, at what time should she begin? **12:15 P.M.**
   b. Look more carefully at the activities. Which activities must be done in order? Could any be done at the same time? What is the latest time Susan could begin? **See margin.**
   c. Susan does not want to shower until she has frosted the cake. Does this change your answer? **yes; 1:15 P.M.**
   d. Susan decides she needs 25 minutes before the party to take care of last minute details. To allow for the extra 25 minutes, when should she begin her activities? **12:50 P.M.**

> decorate room (1 h)
> mix cake (40 min)
> bake cake (35 min)
> cool cake (45 min)
> frost cake (20 min)
> shower and dress (25 min)

22. Bonnie does the activities shown at the right after school but before her 6:00 P.M. dinner. School is out at 3:30 P.M.
   a. How much time does she have to visit neighbors? **25 min**
   b. *Writing* Explain how you solved this problem.
   c. Make a schedule for Bonnie's afternoon. **b–c. See margin.**

Ride bike home	20 min
Feed the dog	10 min
Do homework	1 h
Visit neighbors	■
Help prepare dinner	35 min

---

pages 125–126 On Your Own

21b. Mixing, baking, cooling, and frosting the cake must be done in order; she can decorate the room or shower and dress at the same time as baking or cooling the cake (but she cannot start showering while the cake is baking and finish while it is cooling); 1:35 P.M.

22b. Bonnie has 2 h 30 min until dinner. Subtract the time for going home, feeding the dog, and doing homework. This leaves 1 h or 60 min. Subtract the time to help prepare dinner.

c.

Time	Activity
3:30 P.M.	Leave school
3:50 P.M.	Feed the dog
4:00 P.M.	Start homework
5:00 P.M.	Visit neighbors
5:25 P.M.	Help prepare dinner

23c.

Time	Activity
11:00 A.M.	Friends arrive, play outside
12:00 noon	Clown show
12:45 P.M.	Lunch
1:30 P.M.	Open presents
2:30 P.M.	Friends leave

Practice 3-10 *Measuring Elapsed Time*

Clark is trying to plan his Saturday. He estimates each activity will take the following times.
Make a schedule for Clark's day if he wakes up at 7:00 A.M. Assume all his activities are done in the given order.

	Activity	Amount of Time	Time of Day
1.	Get up, eat breakfast	30 min	7:00 A.M. - 7:30 A.M.
2.	Mow lawn	1 h	7:30 A.M. - 8:30 A.M.
3.	Rake yard	2 h	8:30 A.M. - 10:30 A.M.
4.	Wash, wax car	45 min	10:30 A.M. - 11:15 A.M.
5.	Walk dog	15 min	11:15 A.M. - 11:30 A.M.
6.	Clean room	45 min	11:30 A.M. - 12:15 P.M.
7.	Eat lunch	30 min	12:15 P.M. - 12:45 P.M.
8.	Shop for school clothes	1 h 30 min	12:45 P.M. - 2:15 P.M.
9.	Read book	45 min	2:15 P.M. - 3:00 P.M.
10.	Do homework	1 h 15 min	3:00 P.M. - 4:15 P.M.
11.	Baby-sit brother	2 h	4:15 P.M. - 6:15 P.M.
12.	Eat supper	45 min	6:15 P.M. - 7:00 P.M.
13.	Get ready for party	30 min	7:00 P.M. - 7:30 P.M.
14.	Ride to party	20 min	7:30 P.M. - 7:50 P.M.
15.	Party	2 h	7:50 P.M. - 9:50 P.M.
16.	Ride home	20 min	9:50 P.M. - 10:10 P.M.

Find the elapsed time between each pair of times.

17. 2:12 P.M. and 10:18 P.M.
8 h 6 min

18. 9:35 A.M. and 8:48 P.M.
1 h 13 min

19. 6:45 P.M. and 11:24 A.M.
16 h 39 min

20. 2:55 A.M. and 8:13 A.M.
5 h 18 min

21. 7:00 P.M. and 8:56 P.M.
1 h 56 min

22. 8:22 A.M. and 11:47 A.M.
15 h 25 min

Solve.

23. The movie begins at 7:45 P.M. and lets out at 10:20 P.M. How long is the movie?
2 h 35 min

In copymaster and workbook formats

Practice

Reteaching 3-10 *Measuring Elapsed Time*

Find the **elapsed time** between 6:15 A.M. and 11:10 A.M.

① Set up as subtraction. ② Exchange 1 h for 60 min. ③ Subtract.

```
  11:10          11:10  →  10:70        10:70
 - 6:15         - 6:15  →  - 6:15      - 6:15
                                        4:55
```

The elapsed time is 4 h 55 min.

You can find elapsed time from a schedule.

Leave	Arrive
Boston 7:09 A.M.	New York 11:02 A.M.

For travel time, find the elapsed time between 7:09 A.M. and 11:02 A.M.

11:02 − 7:09 = 3 h 53 min

Convert to minutes.
Example: 4 h 55 min = 4 × 60 + 55 = 295 min

1. 3h 25 min
205 min

2. 2 h 17 min
137 min

3. 2 h 48 min
168 min

4. 5 h 18 min
318 min

5. 6 h 13 min
373 min

6. 5 h 39 min
339 min

Find the elapsed time between each pair of times.

7. 6:45 P.M. and 9:20 P.M.
2 h 35 min

8. 9:36 A.M. and 11:50 A.M.
2 h 14 min

9. 5:45 A.M. and 11:30 A.M.
5 h 45 min

10. 3:11 P.M. and 10:40 P.M.
7 h 29 min

11. 8:15 A.M. and 10:09 A.M.
1 h 54 min

12. 1:00 P.M. and 7:28 P.M.
6 h 28 min

Use the schedule for Exercises 13–14.

13. How much time do you have to get to the game?
1 h 20 min

14. How long is the game?
2 h 45 min

Leave for game	6:15 P.M.
Game begins	7:35 P.M.
Game ends	10:20 P.M.

Reteaching

Minds on Math Transparency

Draw 3 lines without lifting your pencil to divide the square into 4 identical triangles.

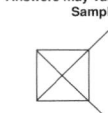

3-10
Answers may vary.
Sample:

See *Solution Key* for worked-out answers.

PORTFOLIO Share with students the criteria you will use to assess their work in portfolios, as well as how you plan to use the results. Students should understand how the rubrics are used to assess their work, how each piece in the portfolio counts, and how the scores they get in their portfolios will affect their overall evaluation.

LESSON QUIZ

1. Find the elapsed time between 6:49 P.M. and 9:30 P.M. **2 h 41 min**

2. A dance starts at 6:00 P.M. and ends at 9:00 P.M. Sean stays for the entire dance. Chris arrives at 6:45 P.M. and leaves at 8:15 P.M. How much more time does Sean spend at the dance than Chris? **1 h 30 min**

---

23. *Party Planning* You plan a birthday party for your younger brother and make the schedule shown at the right.
    a. How long will the party last? **3 h**
    b. How much time did you allow for the clown show? For lunch? For presents? **45 min**
    c. The clown calls at 10:30 A.M. to say that he will not be at the party until noon. Make a new party schedule. **See margin p. 125.**

Party for Joey	
11:00 A.M.	Friends arrive, play outside.
11:30 A.M.	Clown show
12:15 P.M.	Lunch
1:00 P.M.	Open presents
2:00 P.M.	Friends leave

Amusement Parks **Use the data at the right for Exercises 24–26.**

24. Find the total time you would expect to spend for the Vortex ride at Kings Island.
32 min 30 s

25. Which ride has a wait time of 10 times the ride time? **The Beast**

26. Suppose you get to the park at 2:15 P.M. If you ride The Beast, Vortex, and The Racer, when will you be done? **3:55 P.M.**

Kings Island Amusement Park

Ride	Wait Time (min)	Ride Time (min:s)
The Beast	45	4:30
Vortex	30	2:30
The Racer	15	2:15
Beastie (for kids)	10	1:30

27. *Studying* Jackson has 3 h of homework tonight. He likes to take a $\frac{1}{2}$-h break. To finish by 9:30 P.M., what is the latest he can begin studying? **6:00 P.M.**

28. *Open-ended* Name at least five activities you do on Saturdays. Estimate the elapsed time for each activity.
Check students' work.

PORTFOLIO
Select two or three of your favorite lessons from this chapter. Explain why you enjoyed them.

Mixed Review

29. *Choose a Strategy* Mark does his laundry every six days beginning on the second day of the year. At the end of a year, how many times will he have done his laundry? **60 times**

30. A teacher took a poll to see how many class members watched two or more hours of television each evening for a week. The data collected, beginning with Saturday, were 22, 13, 18, 11, 16, 24. Draw an appropriate graph using the data. *(Lesson 1-6)*
See back of book.

What is the value of the digit 9 in each number? *(Lesson 3-2)*

				9 thousandths	9 million
31. 59,872	32. 0.94	33. 982,450	34. 12.0349	35. 6.0098	36. 9,007,321
9 thousand	9 tenths	9 hundred thousand	9 ten-thousandths		

Extra Practice, Lesson 3-10, page 524

FINISHING THE CHAPTER PROJECT

PROJECT DAY You may wish to plan a project day on which students share their completed projects. Encourage students to explain their process as well as their product.

PROJECT NOTEBOOK Ask students to review their project work and bring their notebooks up to date.

Have students review their methods for organizing the data and comparing the prices.

SCORING RUBRIC

3 Your calculations were accurate. You considered average CD prices in local stores, the range of club prices (rather than a single value), and shipping costs. Your estimations were listed or displayed in a way that made them easy to follow. You considered other factors that might have influenced your decision to join the club or not.

2 Your calculations were reasonable, based on average CD prices, and took into account shipping costs. Your estimations were listed or displayed in an organized and clear way.

1 Your calculations were inaccurate or were based on a single CD price rather than on an average. You did not consider shipping costs, or your data was not organized or presented neatly enough for others to follow easily.

0 You either didn't make a decision about whether or not to join the club, or your decision was not supported with complete data and calculations.

FINISHING THE CHAPTER PROJECT

CHAPTER PROJECT

Name that TUNE

Compare Prices and Decide The Project Link questions on pages 95, 102, and 121 will help you to complete your project. Here is a checklist to help you gather the parts of your project together.

- ✔ the average price of CDs in your area
- ✔ estimate of cost of eight CDs from the club
- ✔ cost of shipping and handling per CD

Write a report that summarizes whether you should join the CD club or not. Include any tables, lists, and calculations that helped you to make a decision. Show your work in organized steps. State other factors that helped you make your decision, such as the number of CDs you buy per year now and how much you spend on them. Include any advantages and disadvantages of joining the club.

Reflect and Revise

Share your report with a classmate or family friend. Is your report clear and logical? Are your calculations accurate? Have you included reasons for your decision? If necessary, revise your report.

Web Extension

Prentice Hall's Internet site contains information you might find helpful as you complete your project. Visit www.phschool.com/mgm1/ch3 for some links and ideas related to consumer issues.

STUDENT SELF-ASSESSMENT SURVEY

Chapter 3 Student Self-Assessment Survey

1. Now that you have finished this chapter, think about what you have learned about decimals. Check each topic that you feel confident you understand.
   _____ make models of decimals (3-1)
   _____ read and write whole numbers and decimals (3-2)
   _____ compare and order decimals (3-3)
   _____ solve problems by using *Guess and Test* (3-4)
   _____ make models of adding and subtracting decimals (3-5)
   _____ round data (3-6)
   _____ estimate sums and differences of decimals (3-6)
   _____ add and subtract decimals (3-7)
   _____ use metric units of length (3-8)
   _____ choose appropriate units of measurement (3-8)
   _____ choose metric units of mass and capacity (3-9)
   _____ add and subtract measures of time (3-10)
   _____ read, use, and make schedules (3-10)

2. Before the Chapter Assessment, I need to review _____

3. **a.** Check one. In general, I thought this chapter was

   _____ a snap _____ easy _____ average _____ hard _____ a monster
   b. Why do you feel this way? _____

4. In this chapter, I did my best work on _____

5. In this chapter, I had trouble with _____

6. Check each one that applies. Now that I've spent some time studying metric units, I think they are
   _____ important _____ boring _____ useful _____ fun
   _____ a waste of time _____ confusing _____ tricky _____ interesting

7. Did you use a spreadsheet to work with bank accounts? _____
   If yes, did you find the spreadsheet helpful? _____ Explain. _____

Vocabulary/Symbols

capacity, elapsed time, equivalent, expanded form, front end estimation, gram, guess and test, liter, mass, meter, metric system, mill, one hundredth, one tenth, place value, second, standard form, standard unit

Resources

 Student Edition

Extra Practice, p. 524
Glossary/Study Guide

 Teaching Resources

Chapter Support File, Ch. 3
• Student Self-Assessment Survey
Glossary, Spanish Resources
Tools for Studying Smarter

WRAP UP

Exercise 6 Remind students that the standard form for a decimal is the numerical form, such as 2.187.

Exercises 13–17 Have students use estimation to check whether their answers are reasonable.

ASSESSMENT Exercises 22–24 Have students work in pairs. After students have finished these exercises, have them make a list of objects. Partners can take turns to choose an appropriate metric unit of length to measure each object on the list. For Exercise 26, encourage partners to think of more than one approach to solving the problem.

Remind students that the new mathematical terms in this chapter are defined in the Glossary/Study Guide in the back of the book.

---

3 WRAP UP

Whole Numbers and Decimals   3-1, 3-2

Numbers that represent the same amount are **equivalent**. You can write decimals in **standard form**, **expanded form**, or in words.

How many hundredths are equivalent to each amount?

1. five tenths **50**   2. two **200**   3. 3.1 **310**   4. 0.9 **90**   5. 0.3 + 0.03 **33**

6. **Choose A, B, C, or D.** Which of the following is five hundred twenty-five and five tenths in standard form? **C**
   A. 0.5255   **B.** 5255.5   **C.** 525.5   **D.** 500.255

Comparing and Ordering Decimals   3-3

You can compare and order decimals using place value or using a number line.

Use <, =, or > to complete each statement.

7. 1.839 **>** 1.8380   8. 11.721 **>** 6.731   9. 0.18 **>** 0.081   10. 500.2 **>** 50.02

11. Order 14.02, 14.2, 14.18, 14.1, and 14 from lowest to highest. **14, 14.02, 14.1, 14.18, 14.2**

Problem Solving Strategies   3-4

A good problem solving strategy is *Guess and Test*.

12. Suppose your class is making plastic bird feeders in two sizes. Small bird feeders use 2 rods. Large bird feeders use 3 rods. The class used 103 rods to make 38 feeders. How many small bird feeders did the class make? **11 small feeders**

Addition and Subtraction of Decimals   3-5, 3-7

You can use models to find any sum or difference. You can also line up the decimal point and then add or subtract numbers in the same place value or you can use a calculator. Use estimation to check if answers are reasonable.

128

Add or subtract. Use models if they help you.

13. $0.5 + 0.2$
0.7

14. $0.99 - 0.76$
0.23

15. $1.741 - 0.81$
0.931

16. $62.24 - 8.598$
53.624

17. $337.4 + 20.08$
357.48

Rounding and Estimating Data   3-6

Rounding Decimals

Decide to which place you are rounding.

If the digit to the right of that place is greater than or equal to 5, round up.

If the digit to the right of that place is less than 5, round down.

To use **front-end estimation**, add the front-end digits, estimate the remaining digits, and then add the results.

Use rounding or front-end estimation. Estimate each sum or difference.

18. $\$5.82$
   $+ \$7.93$
   $\$14$

19. 84.97
   $- 26.15$
   59

20. 5.19
   $- 2.79$
   2

21. 615.345
   $+ 8.86$
   624

Metric Units of Length, Mass, and Capacity   3-8, 3-9

The **metric system** of measurement uses a decimal system. The **standard unit** of length is the **meter (m)**. The standard unit of **mass** is the **gram (g)**. The standard unit of **capacity** is the **liter (L)**.

25. Each prefix describes how different units are related to each other. The units of length, mass, and capacity measure different kinds of quantities.

Choose an appropriate unit of measure for each.

22. altitude of an airplane
km

23. mass of a dog
kg

24. capacity of a kitchen sink
L

25. *Writing* Explain how the metric units for length, mass, and capacity are similar. How are they different? **See above right.**

Measuring Elapsed Time   3-10

The time between two events is **elapsed time**. You use elapsed time when using schedules.

26. It's 6:00 P.M. Can Lori do everything on her list and still read for 25 minutes before her 9:30 P.M. bedtime? If she works continuously, at what time will she complete her to-do list?
yes; 8:15 P.M.

Eat dinner	40 min
Homework	55 min
TV program	30 min
Feed dog	10 min

Chapter 3 Assessment • Form A

Answers

1. Write 0.6 in words.   **1.** six-tenths

2. Write a decimal for the given words: twenty-five hundredths.   **2.** 0.25

3. Write the words for the number. 3,405.2   **3.** three thousand four hundred five and two tenths

4. Write 3.14 in expanded form.   **4.** $3 + 0.1 + 0.04$

5. Compare. Use >, <, or =. 10.35 ▇ 10.347   **5.** >

6. Place the numbers in order from least to greatest. 0.34, 0.58, 0.25, 0.20, 0.63   **6.** 0.20, 0.25, 0.34, 0.58, 0.63

7. Find the sum $0.27 + 0.56$. Use models if they help.   **7.** 0.83

8. Find the difference $1.30 - 0.46$. Use models if they help.   **8.** 0.84

9. Round to the place of the underlined digit. 3.4$\underline{5}$64   **9.** 3.46

10. Estimate the cost of the meal by rounding to the nearest dollar.
hamburger $2.33
fries $.89
drink $.78
hot cherry pie $.53   **10.** about $5.00

11. Find the sum $3.5 + 0.679$.   **11.** 4.179

12. Find the difference $8.3 - 3.09$.   **12.** 5.21

13. The school theater sold 55 tickets to the class play. Adult tickets were $5.00 and children's tickets were $3.50. If a total of 55 tickets were sold for $245.00, how many of each kind were sold?   **13.** adult: 35 tickets; children's: 20 tickets

Assessment

Chapter 3 Assessment • Form A (continued)

14. How many tenths are equivalent to seventy hundredths?   **14.** 7 tenths

15. Sean bought some birthday presents for his baby brother that cost $2.98, $3.18, $2.65, and $5.30. Estimate how much Sean spent for all four presents.   **15.** about $14

16. How many centimeters are there in 3.5 m?   **16.** 350 cm

Choose A, B, C, or D

17. Choose an appropriate metric capacity for a pitcher of lemonade.   **17.** A
   A. 2 L   **B.** 2 mL
   C. 2 kL   **D.** 20 L

Choose a Strategy

18. Every 5 min a child gets to sit on Santa's knee and have his or her picture taken. If Santa is available for 10 h, how many children can get their pictures taken?   **18.** In 1 h, 12 children have their picture taken. Therefore, in 10 h, 120 children can have their pictures taken.

Writing

19. You want to meet Karen at the movies at 12:15 P.M. today. It is now 10:20 A.M. You have the following plans. Make a table including the chore, how long each chore takes, and the actual time you will start and finish each chore.

Chore	How long it takes	Time
clean up room	20 min	10:20–10:40
mow lawn	35 min	10:40–11:15
fix and eat lunch	20 min	11:15–11:35
shower and dress	25 min	11:35–12:00
ride bike to theater	10 min	12:00–12:10

Will you make it in time or not? How much time will you have left or how much more time do you need?
on time, with 5 min left

CHAPTER ASSESSMENT • FORM B

Chapter 3 Assessment • Form B

Choose the best answer. Circle A, B, C, or D.

1. What is 0.36 in words?
   - **(A)** thirty-six hundredths
   - **B.** thirty-six tenths
   - **C.** thirty-six thousandths
   - **D.** thirty-six

2. Which decimal represents five tenths?
   - **A.** 0.05
   - **B.** 5
   - **(C)** 0.5
   - **D.** 50

3. Which number represents one hundred five and three hundredths?
   - **A.** 150.30
   - **B.** 150.03
   - **C.** 105.30
   - **(D)** 105.03

4. What is 6.28 in expanded form?
   - **(A)** 6 + 0.2 + 0.08
   - **B.** 60 + 2 + 0.8
   - **C.** 0.6 + 0.02 + 0.008
   - **D.** 600 + 20 + 8

5. Which of the following is *not* true?
   - **A.** 10.4 > 10.2
   - **(B)** 0.37 < 0.30
   - **C.** 0.03 < 0.29
   - **D.** 1.30 > 1.29

6. Which answer shows the decimals in order from least to greatest?
   - **A.** 0.47, 0.24, 0.15
   - **B.** 0.15, 0.47, 0.24
   - **C.** 0.24, 0.15, 0.47
   - **(D)** 0.15, 0.24, 0.47

7. Find the sum 0.36 + 0.45.
   - **A.** 0.71
   - **(B)** 0.81
   - **C.** 0.11
   - **D.** 1.71

8. Find the difference 1.24 − 0.53.
   - **(A)** 0.71
   - **B.** 1.77
   - **C.** 1.293
   - **D.** 1.187

9. Round 10.4<u>7</u>7 to the place of the underlined digit.
   - **A.** 10.5
   - **B.** 10.47
   - **(C)** 10.48
   - **D.** 10.46

10. Estimate the cost of lunch by rounding to the nearest dollar.

    | hot dog | $1.53 | drink | $.89 |
    | onion rings | $1.15 | two cookies | $.75 |

    - **A.** about $4.00
    - **B.** about $6.00
    - **C.** about $4.50
    - **(D)** about $5.00

CHAPTER ASSESSMENT • FORM B

Chapter 3 Assessment • Form B (continued)

11. Tickets for a puppet show cost $3.00 for adults and $2.50 for children. The theater collected $505 by selling 185 tickets. How many of each type of ticket were sold?
    - **A.** adult: 75; children's: 110
    - **(B)** adult: 85; children's: 100
    - **C.** adult: 87; children's: 98
    - **D.** adult: 80; children's: 105

12. Find the sum 10.35 + 1.55.
    - **A.** 8.80
    - **(B)** 11.90
    - **C.** 12.00
    - **D.** 11.80

13. Find the difference 4.44 − 1.32.
    - **A.** 4.76
    - **B.** 5.76
    - **(C)** 3.12
    - **D.** 4.12

14. Kelly decided to run a 5-km race. How many meters did she run?
    - **A.** 0.5 m
    - **B.** 50 m
    - **C.** 500 m
    - **(D)** 5,000 m

15. How many meters are there in 45.6 centimeters?
    - **A.** 456 m
    - **B.** 4.56 m
    - **(C)** 0.456 m
    - **D.** 4,560 m

16. Which metric unit of mass would be appropriate for a school bus?
    - **A.** A liter
    - **B.** gram
    - **(C)** kilogram
    - **D.** milligram

17. You have a birthday party to attend at 2:30 P.M. today. It is now 1:05 P.M. You have the following schedule.

ride bike to store	5 min
look for and buy present	20 min
ride bike home	5 min
wrap present	10 min
shower and dress	35 min
ride bike to party	15 min

    When will you arrive at the party?
    - **A.** 5 minutes early
    - **B.** on time
    - **C.** after the party is over
    - **(D)** 5 minutes late

Choose a Strategy

18. Every 25 minutes there is a car accident on the streets of one particular town. About how many accidents are likely to occur in one day?
    - **A.** about 25 accidents
    - **(B)** about 50 accidents
    - **C.** about 75 accidents
    - **D.** about 100 accidents

 Teaching Resources
- Chapter Support File, Ch. 3, and Spanish Resources

 Teacher's Edition

See pp. 82C–D for Assessment Options.

 Teaching Resource Software
- Computer Item Generator, Ch. 3

130

ASSESSMENT

WRITING QUESTIONS allow students to describe more fully their understanding of the concepts they have learned. **Exercise 1** is a writing question.

WRITING Exercise 1 Suggest students draw a decimal model and use it to support their answer.

ENHANCED MULTIPLE CHOICE QUESTIONS are more complex than traditional multiple choice questions, which assess only one skill. Enhanced multiple choice questions assess the processes that students use, as well as the end results. They are written so that students can use more than one strategy to solve the problem. Using multiple strategies is encouraged by the National Council of Teachers of Mathematics (NCTM). **Exercise 3** is an enhanced multiple choice question. If students select A, ask them to read the question carefully.

ESTIMATION Exercise 8 Have students discuss the methods they used and the

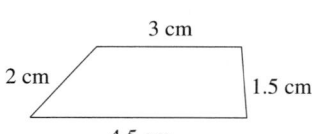

3 ASSESSMENT

1. *Writing* Explain why thirteen hundredths are equivalent to one hundred thirty thousandths. **See back of book.**

2. **Choose A, B, C, or D.** The value of the digit 3 in the number 24.1538 is ■. **D**
   - **A.** three hundreds
   - **B.** three tenths
   - **C.** three hundredths
   - **D.** three thousandths

3. **Choose A, B, C, or D.** Which of the following is *not* true for the number 5.836? **B**
   - **A.** 5.836 rounds to 5.84.
   - **B.** 5.836 > 5.85
   - **C.** The expanded form is 5 + 0.8 + 0.03 + 0.006.
   - **D.** It is read as "five and eight hundred thirty-six thousandths."

4. Compare. Use >, <, or =.
   - **a.** 2.34 ■ 2.4 <
   - **b.** 8.97 ■ 8.970 =
   - **c.** 32.12 ■ 32.42 <
   - **d.** 12.82 ■ 12.81 >

5. Place the digits 1 through 9 in the pattern below so that the sum is the same in both directions. What is the sum? **Answers may vary. Sample:**

   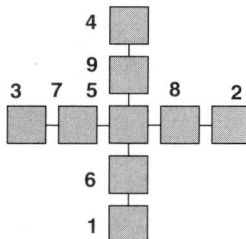

6. Graph 8.1, 8.2, 8.08, 8.15, and 8.03 on a number line. **See back of book.**

7. Find each sum.
   - **a.** 3.89 + 15.638 **19.528**
   - **b.** 8.99 + 6.35 **15.34**
   - **c.** 0.9356 + 0.208 **1.1436**
   - **d.** $4.38 + $2.74 + $1.17 **8.29**

8. *Estimation* Suppose your savings account has a balance of $129.55. You deposit $17.89 and withdraw $83.25. What is the approximate new balance? **$65**

9. Find each difference.
   - **a.** $20 − $15.99 **$4.01**
   - **b.** 8.956 − 6.973 **1.983**
   - **c.** 42.6 − 9.07 **33.53**
   - **d.** 95.03 − 20.875 **74.155**

10. Find the perimeter by adding the lengths. **11 cm**

    3 cm
    2 cm
    1.5 cm
    4.5 cm

11. What unit of metric measure is appropriate for each item?
    - **a.** length of a room **m**
    - **b.** length of a state border **km**
    - **c.** mass of a boat **kg**
    - **d.** capacity of a cup **mL**

12. Jose plans to attend a beach party at 1:00 P.M. He needs to shower and dress (35 min), eat breakfast (25 min), do his chores (1 h 40 min), get his beach supplies (25 min), and bike to the party (20 min). Plan his schedule before he leaves for the beach party. **See back of book.**

Item	Review Topic	Ch		Item	Review Topic	Ch
1	Writing decimals	3		6, 10	Metric length	3
2	Rounding decimals	3		7	Estimation	3
3	Finding range	1		8	Numeration	3
4	Subtracting decimals	3		9	Rates	Precourse
5	Finding mode	1				

3 CUMULATIVE REVIEW

Choose the best answer.

1. Which is the decimal for thirty-four hundredths? **B**

A. 0.034   B. 0.34
C. 3.40   D. 34.00

2. The winning speed of a car in an auto race was listed as 163.89 miles per hour. What is this speed rounded to the nearest mile per hour? **C**

A. 160 miles per hour
B. 163 miles per hour
C. 164 miles per hour
D. 170 miles per hour

3. How would you find the range of five salaries? **B**

A. Add the salaries and divide by 5.
B. Subtract the lowest salary from the highest.
C. Arrange the salaries in order and choose the middle one.
D. Choose the salary that occurs more than once.

4. Alfred bought a notebook costing $2.73 including tax. He gave the clerk $10. How much change should he have received? **A**

A. $7.27   B. $7.73
C. $8.73   D. $12.73

5. All five items in a data set are multiplied by 10. How is the mode changed? **A**

A. It is multiplied by 10.
B. It is multiplied by 50.
C. It is multiplied by 2.
D. The mode does not change.

6. What is a reasonable length for the length of the paper clip below? **B**

A. 5 mm   B. 5 cm
C. 5 m   D. 5 km

7. Unleaded gasoline costs $1.29 per gallon. If you buy 12 gallons, estimate the amount of money you spend. **B**

A. $10   B. $14
C. $20   D. $29

8. If 0.305 is represented by point B, what numbers could be represented by points A and C? **D**

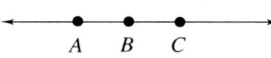

A. A: 0.051, C: 0.7
B. A: 0.03, C: 0.06
C. A: 0.350, C: 0.4
D. A: 0.29, C: 0.32

9. A hot-air balloon is 2,250 ft in the air. It is scheduled to land at 3:30 P.M. It descends 90 ft every minute. When should the balloonist start descending? **B**

A. 3:55 P.M.   B. 3:05 P.M.
C. 2:55 P.M.   D. 2:45 P.M.

10. Without measuring, what is the best estimate for the total distance around the triangle below? **B**

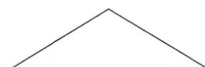

A. 7 mm   B. 7 cm   C. 7 m   D. 7 km

Chapter 3 Cumulative Review

Choose the best answer. Circle A, B, C, or D.

1. Find the median of this set of data.
75, 76, 80, 76, 79, 80, 75, 76
A. 79   (B) 76
C. 75   D. 80

2. How many different ways can you combine dimes, nickels, and pennies to make 13 cents?
(A) 4 ways   B. 2 ways
C. 3 ways   D. 5 ways

3. How many centimeters is 18.56 meters?
A. 185.6 cm   B. 1.856 cm
C. 0.1856 cm   (D) 1,856 cm

4. What is 0.45 in words?
A. forty-five tenths
B. forty-five
(C) forty-five hundredths
D. forty-five thousandths

5. Estimate the cost of the movie and refreshments by rounding to the nearest dollar.
movie $4.60
popcorn $2.79
drink $1.45
snack $1.23
A. $9   (B) $10
C. $11   D. $12

6. Find the difference 35.46 − 22.98.
A. 58.44   B. 12.46
(C) 12.48   D. 13.58

7. Find the next three terms in the number pattern.
0, 4, 6, 10, 12, __, __, __
A. 16, 20, 24   B. 14, 16, 20
C. 18, 24, 30   (D) 16, 18, 22

8. Use mental math to solve $z + 7 = 11$.
(A) 4   B. 6
C. 18   D. 77

9. Use the circle graph below to find the ice cream that is favored the most.

Favorite Ice Cream

(A) chocolate
B. vanilla
C. blueberry cheesecake
D. strawberry

10. Use the circle graph in Exercise 9 to find the ice cream that is favored by the fewest.
A. chocolate
B. vanilla
(C) blueberry cheesecake
D. strawberry

Assessment

Chapter 3 Cumulative Review (continued)

11. Which word phrase does *not* describe the expression $24 - j$?
(A) 24 minus j
B. j less than 24
(C) 24 more than j
D. the difference between 24 and j

12. Find the mean of Jason's test scores.
90, 81, 95, 79, 89, 93, 92, 93
A. 91   (B) 89
C. 93   D. 84

13. A soccer camp ordered equipment for its campers. Soccer balls cost $6 and caps cost $5. The order was for 75 items. The bill came to $410. How many soccer balls were ordered?
A. 30 soccer balls
B. 32 soccer balls
(C) 35 soccer balls
D. 40 soccer balls

14. Evaluate $9 + 6 \div 3 \times 4$.
(A) 17   B. 20
C. 21   D. 72

15. How many hundredths are equivalent to four tenths?
A. 4   (B) 40
C. 400   D. 410

16. Which of the following is *not* true?
A. $1.03 > 1.02$ (B) $0.35 < 0.25$
C. $2.33 < 3.22$ D. $0.04 > 0.03$

17. Find the sum $1.23 + 3.58 + 12.33$.
(A) 17.14   B. 18.14
C. 16.04   D. 17.24

18. Round 12,344.49 to the place of the underlined digit.
A. 12,350   (B) 12,340
C. 12,345   D. 12,300

19. Find the mode of this set of data.
3, 5, 6, 4, 6, 9, 8, 5, 6, 3, 7, 2, 1
A. 5   B. 9
C. 8   (D) 6

20. Aaron opened a savings account with a $25.45 deposit. He then deposited $2.25 weekly for three weeks and then withdrew $6.38. What is his current balance?
A. $25.45   B. $38.58
C. $25.08   (D) $25.82

21. Thirty-three students were polled about their type of transportation. Twenty students had bicycles and fifteen had in-line skates. Five students with bicycles had in-line skates. How many had neither of the two types of transportation?
(A) 3 students   B. 6 students
C. 2 students   D. 15 students

Resources

Teaching Resources

Chapter Support File, Ch. 3
• Cumulative Review

Teacher's Edition

See pp. 82C–D for Assessment Options.

4 Multiplying and Dividing Whole Numbers and Decimals

CHAPTER OVERVIEW

To accommodate flexible scheduling, most lessons are divided into parts. Assignment Options are given in the Teacher's Edition for each lesson.

Pages 134–137	**Lesson 4-1** **Estimating Products and Quotients**	
NCTM 1, 2, 3, 4, 5, 7, 13	Part 1 Estimating Products Part 2 Estimating Quotients **Key term:** compatible numbers **Alternative Activity** 4-1 ▼ **Project Link**	

Pages 139–142	**Lesson 4-2** **Algebra: Exponents**	
NCTM 1, 2, 3, 5, 6, 7, 9	Part 1 Using Exponents Part 2 Simplifying Powers **Key terms:** exponent, base, power **Alternative Activity** 4-2	

Pages 143–147	**Lesson 4-3** **Geometry: The Distributive Property**	
NCTM 1, 2, 3, 4, 5, 7, 12	Part 1 Finding Areas of Rectangles Part 2 Using the Distributive Property **Key terms:** area, distributive property ✓ **Checkpoint 1**	

Pages 160–162	**Lesson 4-7** **Dividing Decimals by Whole Numbers**	
NCTM 1, 2, 3, 4, 5, 6, 7, 13	▼ **Project Link**	

Pages 163–166	**Lesson 4-8** **Dividing Decimals by Decimals**	
NCTM 1, 3, 4, 5, 6, 9, 13	✓ **Checkpoint 2**	

Pages 168–170	**Lesson 4-9** **Problem Solving Strategy**	
NCTM 1, 2, 3, 4, 5, 7, 13	**Too Much or Too Little Information** **Journal**	

Technology Options — Interactive Questioning — **MANAGEABLE TEACHING TOOLS** — Skills & Problem Solving — Real World & Student Experiences — Assessment Options — Appropriate Content

Pacing Options

This chart suggests pacing only for the core lessons and their parts. It is provided merely as a possible guide. It will help you determine how much time you have in your schedule to cover other features, such as the Chapter Project, Math Toolboxes, Wrap Up, and Assessment.

	1 Class Period	1 Class Period	1 Class Period	
Traditional (40–45 min class periods)	4–1 ▼1 4–1 ▼2	4–2 ▼1 4–2 ▼2	4–3 ▼1	
Block Scheduling (90 min class periods)	4–1 ▼1 4–1 ▼2 4–2 ▼1 4–2 ▼2	4–3 ▼1 4–3 ▼2	4–4 ▼1 4–4 ▼2 4–5 ▼1	4–5 ▼2

CHAPTER PROJECT

Celebration!

Goal: Calculate the cost of planning a celebration event and list the supplies needed.

THEME: CONSUMER ISSUES

NCTM STANDARDS

1	Problem Solving	**6**	Number Systems and Number Theory	**10**	Statistics
2	Communication	**7**	Computation and Estimation	**11**	Probability
3	Reasoning	**8**	Patterns and Functions	**12**	Geometry
4	Mathematical Connections	**9**	Algebra	**13**	Measurement
5	Number and Number Relationships				

Pages 148–150

Lesson 4-4
Using Models to Multiply Decimals

NCTM 1, 2, 3, 4, 5, 7

Part 1 Multiply Decimals and Whole Numbers

Part 2 Modeling the Multiplication of Decimals

Journal

Pages 151–155

Lesson 4-5
Algebra: Multiplying Decimals

NCTM 1, 2, 3, 4, 5, 7, 13

Part 1 Multiplying Decimals and Whole Numbers

Part 2 Multiplying Two Decimals

Alternative Activity 4-5

▼ **Project Link**

Pages 157–159

Lesson 4-6
Using Models to Divide Decimals

NCTM 1, 3, 5, 6, 13

Part 1 Modeling Dividing by Tenths

Part 2 Modeling Dividing by Hundredths

Math at Work

Pages 171–174

Lesson 4-10
Measurement: Patterns of Changing Metric Units

NCTM 1, 2, 3, 4, 5, 7, 9, 12, 13

Part 1 Changing Metric Units

Part 2 Using Mental Math to Change Units

Key terms: kilo-, centi-, milli-

Optional Materials and Manipulatives

calculator (4-2, 4-5, 4-6, 4-7, 4-10)
graph paper (4-3)
scissors (4-3)
ruler (4-3)

blank decimal squares (4-4)
colored pencils (red, blue) (4-4)
tenths squares (4-6)
hundredths squares (4-6)

Optional calculator use is integrated throughout the course.

...ss ...d	1 Class Period	1 Class Period	1 Class Period	1 Class Period	1 Class Period	1 Class Period	1 Class Period	1 Class Period	1 Class Period	1 Class Period	1 Class Period

4–4 2 | 4–5 ▼ | 4–5 2 | 4–6 ▼ | 4–6 2 | 4–7 | 4–8 | 4–9 | 4–10 ▼ | 4–10 2 | | |

4–8 | 4–9 4–10 ▼ | 4–10 2 | | | | | | | | | |

132B

MEETING INDIVIDUAL NEEDS

Accommodating Diverse Learning Styles

In your Teacher's Edition, you will find suggestions as to how you can help students complete mathematical tasks in Chapter 4 by meeting individual needs and supporting various learning styles. Here are some examples:

VISUAL LEARNING
shading blank decimal squares with colored pencils *(p. 148)*

TACTILE LEARNING
checking problem answers with play money *(p. 136)*

AUDITORY LEARNING
describing mental math techniques aloud *(p. 136)*

KINESTHETIC LEARNING
arranging students in rows to model problems *(p. 153)*

EARLY FINISHERS
Performance-Based Project, MathBlaster® Mystery, Interdisciplinary Units

GIFTED AND TALENTED
researching meanings of metric prefixes *(p. 173)*

DIVERSITY examining examples of foreign currency *(p. 134)*

ACQUIRING ENGLISH PROFICIENCY (AEP)
elabeling parts of problems with key terms *(p. 163)*

ASSESSING PROGRESS

A broad range of assessment tools are available to reach a variety of learners.

INFORMAL ASSESSMENT

Informal assessments provide day-to-day feedback to help give you a picture of conceptual understanding and skill development.

ONGOING ASSESSMENT is built into lesson instruction and the Teaching Notes of the Teacher's Edition.

In the Teacher's Edition
Lesson Quiz for every lesson

In the Student Edition
On Your Own, Mixed Review, Journal, Portfolio, Project Link, Chapter Wrap Up

Look for **Interactive Questions** within lessons that

- **BUILD UNDERSTANDING** with labels such as Analyze, Reasoning, Estimation, Writing, and Summarize
- ✔ **CHECK UNDERSTANDING** with the Try It Out label.

FORMAL ASSESSMENT

Formal assessment can occur before and after the chapter, as well as at natural breaking points in the chapter.

Checkpoints
Two forms of each self-assessment Checkpoints are available: one in the Student Edition and another in the Chapter Support File in the Teaching Resources box.
- Mid-Chapter Checkpoint 1, page 147
- End-of-Chapter Checkpoint 2, page 166

Chapter 4 Assessment, page 178.
Two alternative forms are available in the Chapter Support File. They may be used after a chapter has been completed, or as a pre-test and post-test comparison.

Cumulative Review, page 179.
Assesses skills and concepts in Chapters 1–4.
An alternative form is available in Chapter Support File.

Computer Item Generator for Chapter 4
Customized tests can be generated for each lesson and for mid-chapter and end-of-chapter assessments, and for pre- and post-test comparisons of achievement.

Interactive Questioning

Technology Options

Real World & Student Experiences

MANAGEABLE TEACHING TOOLS

Skills & Problem Solving

Appropriate Content

Assessment Options

CHAPTER PROJECT

The Chapter Project in the student edition provides a real-world connection to the math context of the chapter. The Teacher's Edition contains a scoring rubric.

Another performance-based Chapter Project with a scoring rubric can be found in the Chapter Support File in the Teaching Resources Box.

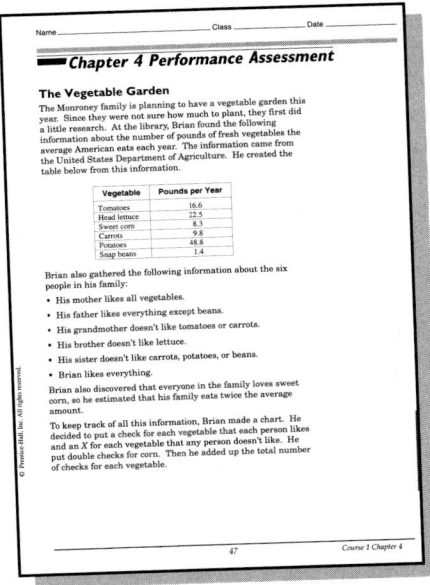

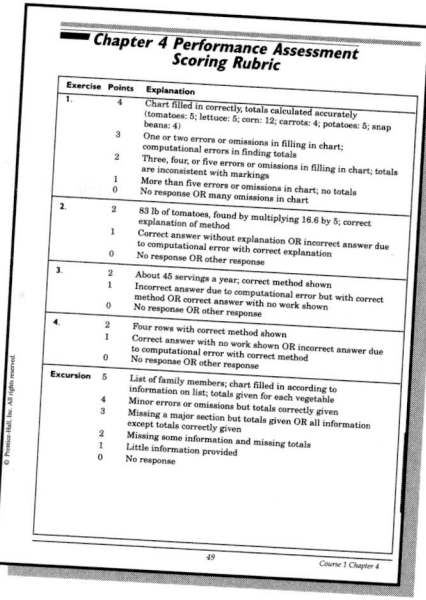

Correlation to Standardized Tests

		STANDARDIZED TEST ITEMS					
Lesson		CAT5	CTBS/5 Terra Nova	ITBS	MAT7	SAT9	Your Local Test
4-1	Estimating Products and Quotients	■	■	■	■	■	
4-2	Algebra: Exponents						
4-3	Geometry: The Distributive Property	■		■	■		
4-4	Using Models to Multiply Decimals	■	■		■	■	
4-5	Algebra: Multiplying Decimals	■	■	■	■	■	
4-6	Using Models to Divide Decimals	■	■	■	■	■	
4-7	Dividing Decimals by Whole Numbers	■	■	■	■	■	
4-8	Dividing Decimals by Decimals	■	■	■	■	■	
4-9	Problem Solving Strategy: Too Much or Too Little Information		■	■	■		■
4-10	Measurement: Patterns of Changing Metric Units		■				■

CAT5 California Achievement Test, 5th Edition
CTBS/5 Comprehensive Test of Basic Skills, 5th Edition
ITBS Iowa Test of Basic Skills, Form B
MAT 7 Metropolitan Achievement Test, 7th Edition
SAT9 Stanford Achievement Test, 9th Edition

MANAGEABLE
TEACHING
TOOLS

Technology
Options

Interactive
Questioning

Real World
& Student
Experiences

Skills
& Problem
Solving

Appropriate
Content

Assessment
Options

MAKING CONNECTIONS

TEAM TEACHING WITH PRENTICE HALL MATERIALS

MIDDLE GRADES MATH INTERDISCIPLINARY UNITS

- **The Great Outdoors: Activity 8**
- **Consumer Awareness: Activities 6 & 8**

INTERDISCIPLINARY EXPLORATIONS

- *The Power of Patterns* pp. 38 & 39
- *Mill Life in the 1840s* p. 18
- *India Beyond the Golden Age* p. 39

Lesson	Interdisciplinary Connections	Real World Connections	Math Integration
4-1	Social Studies Nutrition Library Science Health	Wages Money Jobs	Measurement
4-2	Physics Science	Grocery Shopping Technology	Algebra Geometry
4-3	History Sports	Picnics Advertising	Geometry
4-4	Mythology	Coin Collecting	Data Analysis
4-5	Earth Science Botany Sports	Astronomy Marine Biology	Algebra Measurement
4-6	Nutrition	Postage	Measurement
4-7	Engineering	Travel Weather Hobbies Money	Measurement
4-8	Economics	Fuel Economy Cost of Living	Algebra Measurement
4-9	Crafts	Transportation Interior Decorating Savings	Measurement
4-10	Geography Nutrition Physics	Quality Control	Measurement Algebra

School to Home

MATERIALS:
newspaper
scissors
paper
tape
pencil

English and Spanish versions are available in the Teacher's Communication Kit, Teacher's Resource box.

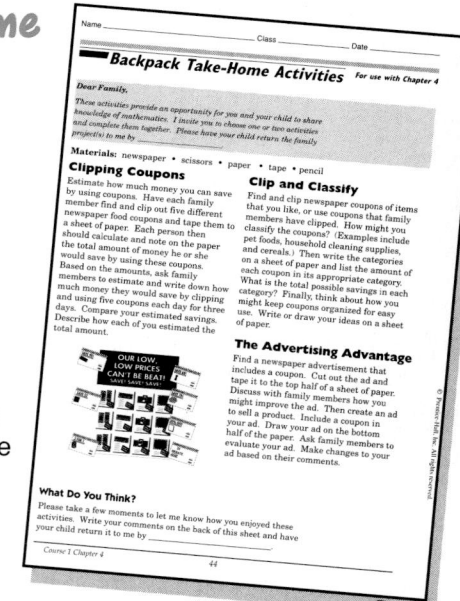

Backpack Take-Home Activities For use with Chapter 4

Dear Family,

These activities provide an opportunity for you and your child to share knowledge of mathematics. I invite you to choose one or two activities and complete them together. Please have your child return the family project(s) to me by _____

Materials: newspaper • scissors • paper • tape • pencil

Clipping Coupons

Estimate how much money you can save by using coupons. Have each family member find and clip out five different newspaper food coupons and tape them to a sheet of paper. Each person then should calculate and note on the paper the total amount of money he or she would save by using these coupons. Based on the amounts, ask family members to estimate and write down how much money they would save by clipping and using five coupons each day for three days. Compare your estimated savings. Describe how each of you estimated the total amount.

Clip and Classify

Find and clip newspaper coupons of items that you like, or use coupons that family members have clipped. How might you classify the coupons? (Examples include pet foods, household cleaning supplies, and cereals.) Then write the categories on a sheet of paper and list the amount of each coupon in its appropriate category. What is the total possible savings in each category? Finally, think about how you might keep coupons organized for easy use. Write or draw your ideas on a sheet of paper.

The Advertising Advantage

Find a newspaper advertisement that includes a coupon. Cut out the ad and tape it to the top half of a sheet of paper. Discuss with family members how you might improve the ad. Then create an ad to sell a product. Include a coupon in your ad. Draw your ad on the bottom half of the paper. Ask family members to evaluate your ad. Make changes to your ad based on their comments.

What Do You Think?

Please take a few moments to let me know how you enjoyed these activities. Write your comments on the back of this sheet and have your child return it to me by _____

Course 1 Chapter 4   44

FOR THE STUDENT

Multimedia Math Hot Pages™
This interactive software and video package on CD-ROM integrates solid math content through a variety of media.

- Hot Page™ 10 (4-3)
- Hot Page™ 11 (4-4)
- Hot Page™ 12 (4-5)

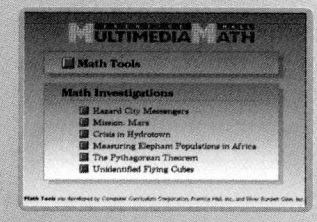
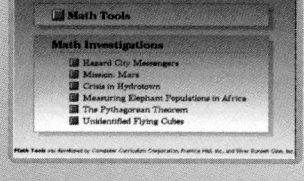

Multimedia Math Investigations
These in-depth interactive activities on CD-ROM develop real-world applications of mathematics. They allow students the opportunity to reinforce key concepts.

- Crisis in Hydrotown
- The Pythagorean Theorem

MathBlaster® Mystery

This award-winning, interactive software program on CD-ROM can be used to maintain skills or to accommodate early finishers.

- Level: Earn 2 coins; Pay 6 coins
- Mission Mode (all lessons)
- Kitchen Comparisons (4-4, 4-6, 4-8)
- Number Guesser (4-1, 4-7, 4-10)
- Equation Maker (4-3, 4-5)
- Word Problems (4-2, 4-9, Problem Solving Practice)

Math Labs
This software, available on both diskette and CD-ROM, includes on-screen Math Lab activities. Students use linkable, interactive tools to explore math concepts.

Interactive Student Tutorial
Available on CD-ROM, this test preparation program contains self-tests with questions in standardized test format. Software includes electronic versions of the text lessons and the Math Tools and Math Labs.

For Students
Support for the Chapter Project
A career-oriented link for Math at Work feature

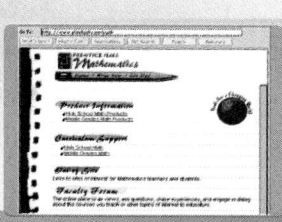

www.phschool.com/math

For teachers
Curriculum Support
Product Information
Regional Support Information

FOR THE TEACHER

Computer Item Generator
Available on both CD-ROM and diskette, this software generates customized practice sheets, quizzes, and tests. It generates an unlimited supply of questions with varying levels of difficulty.

The Resource Pro™
Available on CD-ROM, this software can be used to customize and plan lessons.

Technology Options

MANAGEABLE TEACHING TOOLS

- Interactive Questioning
- Skills & Problem Solving
- Assessment Options
- Appropriate Content
- Real World & Student Experiences

CHAPTER 4 MULTIPLYING AND DIVIDING WHOLE NUMBERS AND DECIMALS

CONNECTING TO PRIOR LEARNING Bring to class several newspaper advertisements. Ask students to identify numbers with decimal points. Then ask students to identify whole numbers. Students can suggest how to use division to find the cost of an individual item sold as a group or multiplication to find the cost of several individual items.

CULTURAL CONNECTIONS Ask students to name a famous person who is a senior citizen. Suggest the names of world leaders, actors, scientists, or artists. Discuss with students how the persons they name disprove many misconceptions about senior citizens.

INTERDISCIPLINARY CONNECTIONS Students can research the life of a senior citizen who has made a positive impact on their community, city, or state. Students can present their findings to the class.

ABOUT THE PROJECT The Chapter Project allows students to apply their knowledge of multiplying and dividing whole numbers and decimals to plan a celebration for a special senior citizen.

Internet • For information and activities related to the Chapter Project, visit the Prentice Hall site at www.phschool.com/mgm1/ch4

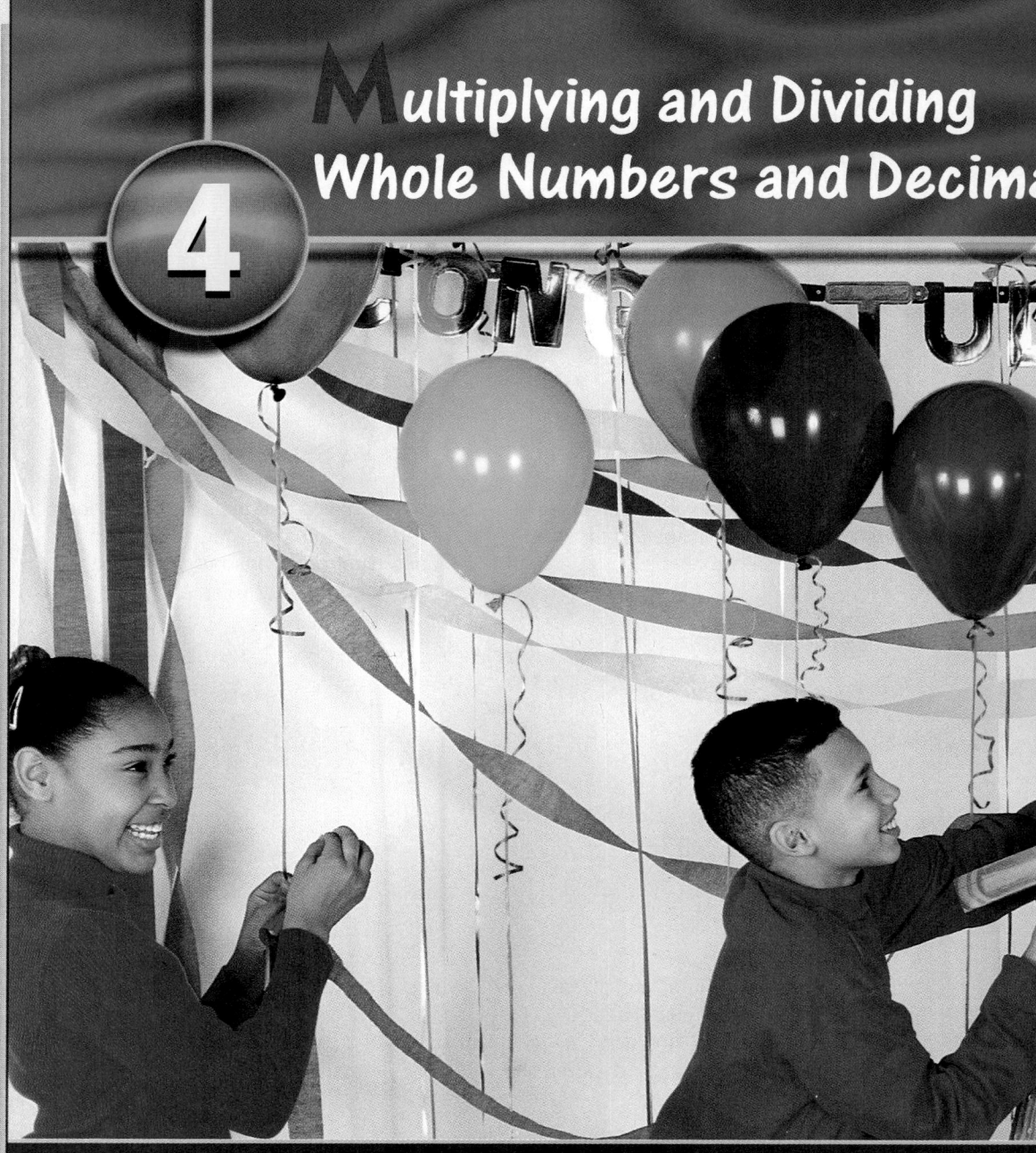

Multiplying and Dividing Whole Numbers and Decimals

WHAT YOU WILL LEARN IN THIS CHAPTER
- How to calculate products and quotients using decimals
- How to estimate decimal products and quotients
- How to explore databases

You may want to wear a party hat to introduce the project. Ask students: *What do you like to do at parties?* **Answers may vary. Sample: play games, eat, dance** Have different students describe parties they have enjoyed.

Tell students to start looking for the items they want to purchase for the party. They will need to research prices for these items.

PROJECT NOTEBOOK Encourage students to keep all project-related materials in a separate folder or notebook.

TRACKING THE PROJECT You may wish to have students read Finishing the Chapter Project on page 175 to help them get an overview of the project. Set benchmark deadlines for students to show you their work in progress.

CHAPTER PROJECT

THEME: PLANNING

CELEBRATION

Suppose your class is planning to honor someone special in the community. Or you want to congratulate a winning team. You need to decide when and where the event will be, the types of decorations, the entertainment, and the refreshments. You may also need to decide how to raise funds for the celebration.

Plan a Celebration Your chapter project is to plan a celebration. You must decide how much it will cost and how much money each member of the class must raise. Your plan will include a list of supplies for the event and their costs.

Steps to help you complete the project:

- **p. 137** Project Link: *Researching*
- **p. 155** Project Link: *Calculating*
- **p. 162** Project Link: *Analyzing*
- **p. 175** *Finishing the Chapter Project*

- How to recognize problems that have too much or too little information

PROBLEM SOLVING

SCORING RUBRIC

3 Your presentation includes an original estimate, a detailed calculation of the actual costs, and the amount that each class member needs to raise. Your data and calculations are very well organized. Your presentation convinces others that your plan should be adopted.

2 Your presentation includes all required data, estimates, and calculations. Almost all of your work is accurate, and you have organized your information into lists, tables, or step-by-step calculations.

1 You left out either the original estimate or the amount that each class member needs to raise. Your calculations of the actual costs are either inaccurate or disorganized.

0 You neglected to gather data for or calculate the actual costs of your proposed celebration.

1 Focus

CONNECTING TO PRIOR KNOWLEDGE
Have students give examples of situations when they estimated a product. **Answers may vary. Sample: estimating how much four CDs will cost** Then have students describe why they estimated instead of calculating the product exactly. **Answers**

Lesson Planning Options

Prerequisite Skills
- multiplying and dividing whole numbers (precourse)

Vocabulary/Symbols
compatible numbers

Resources

 Student Edition

Skills Handbook, p. 535
Extra Practice, p. 525
Glossary/Study Guide

 Teaching Resources

Chapter Support File, Ch. 4
- Lesson Planner 4-1
- Practice 4-1, Reteaching 4-1
- Alternative Activity 4-1
- Answer Masters 4-1
Teaching Aids Master 20
Glossary, Spanish Resources

 Transparencies

11, 12, Minds on Math 4-1

Warm Up

Find the range, mean, median, and mode for the set of numbers 11, 18, 14, 24, 28.
range: 17; mean: 19; median: 18; no mode

---

may vary. Sample: They had no calculator; estimating was faster and easier; didn't need an exact answer.

2 Teach

Work Together

REASONING Question 3 Ask students to predict whether the exact answer will be greater or less than the estimate.

4. **Answers may vary. Sample: 60. Accept any number between 45 and 80.**

THINK AND DISCUSS

Example 1 Ask: *Why do you think the textbook rounds 26.03 to 25 instead of 26?* **Answers may vary. Sample: because 25 × 3 is easy to compute mentally; 25 is easy to work with because it is $\frac{1}{4}$ of 100.**

DIVERSITY Example 2 Ask students to bring in examples of foreign paper money.

4-1 Estimating Products and Quotients

What You'll Learn

▼ To estimate products of numbers containing decimals

▼ To estimate quotients of numbers containing decimals

...And Why

Estimating makes it easier to solve problems that involve money.

Here's How

Look for questions that
- build understanding
- ✔ check understanding

Work Together

Estimating with Decimals

Wages Lisa's time card shows the hours she has worked this week. She gets paid $5.25/h. Let's estimate how much Lisa has earned this week.

1. What two numbers would you multiply to find how much Lisa has earned this week?
11.3 h and $5.25/h
2. Estimate Lisa's earnings by rounding both numbers to the nearest whole number.   **$55**
3. **Reasoning** How does the estimated answer compare to the exact answer? Is the estimate reasonable? Explain. **$4.33 lower; yes; the estimated answer is within $5 of the exact answer, $59.33.**

DH DH DH DH DH		
Downtown Hardware		
Employee		
Lisa M. Smith		
DAY	**DATE**	**HOURS**
MON	5/3	2.1
TUE		
WED	5/5	1.7
THU	5/6	3.5
FRI	5/7	4.0
SAT		
SUN		
TOTAL HOURS		11.3
DH DH DH DH DH		

THINK AND DISCUSS

▼ Estimating Products

You can estimate a product by rounding each factor to the nearest whole number or by using **compatible numbers**. Compatible numbers are numbers that are easy to compute mentally.

■ EXAMPLE 1

Estimate 26.03×3.31.

$$26.03 \Rightarrow 25$$
$$\times 3.31 \Rightarrow \times 3$$
$$\overline{75}$$

Use compatible numbers such as 25 and 3.

The estimated product is 75.

4. ✔ **Try It Out** Estimate the product 3.89×16.03.

Now you may assign Exercises 1–27, 45.

ASSESSMENT Write 445 ÷ 24.5 and 10.85 × 9.8 on the board. Have pairs of students estimate the quotient and product. Have them compare estimates and the compatible numbers they chose. Have students use calculators to determine the actual quotient and product. **18.16; 106.33** Have students discuss whose estimate was closer and why.

■ **ADDITIONAL EXAMPLES**

FOR EXAMPLE 1

Estimate the product of 49.19 × 4.25. Tell how you made your estimate.

49.19	→	50
× 4.25	→	× 4
		200

FOR EXAMPLE 2

Tickets to a baseball game cost $11.75 each. How many tickets at most can you buy with $40? **3**

ERROR ALERT! Students may think there is only one correct answer when they choose compatible numbers. **Remediation:** Review the definition of compatible numbers. Compatible numbers are easy to compute mentally.

Have students share the compatible numbers they might use to estimate the quotient 15.5 ÷ 2.5. **Answers may vary. Sample: 15 ÷ 3; 16 ÷ 2; 15 ÷ 2.5**

2 Estimating Quotients

The largest paper money ever created was the Chinese kwan note of the fourteenth century, shown at the right.

You can also use compatible numbers to estimate quotients.

■ **EXAMPLE 2** *Real-World Problem Solving*

Money The Chinese kwan note was 92.8 cm long. The U.S. dollar bill is 15.6 cm long. About how many times as long as a dollar bill was the kwan note?

92.8 ÷ 15.6 ←——Write the numerical expression.

90 ÷ 15 = 6 ←——Use compatible numbers to divide.

The kwan note was about six times as long as a dollar bill.

5. ✔ Try It Out Use compatible numbers to estimate 37.1 ÷ 3.89.

5. Answers may vary. Sample: 10. Accept any number between 9 and 12.

Now you may assign Exercises 28–44, 46–50.

EXERCISES *On Your Own*

Estimation **Round each factor to the nearest whole number to estimate the product.**

1. 15.3 × 2.6
   45
2. 2.25 × 16.91
   34
3. 3.5 × 2.72
   12
4. 0.95 × 22.8
   23
5. 11.6 × 3.23
   36
6. 15.25 × 3.9
   60
7. 1.79 × 0.12
   2
8. 4.01 × 0.62
   4
9. 31.4 × 3.20
   93
10. 37.1 × 3.89
   148

Write a pair of compatible numbers. Then estimate. **11–22. Answers may vary. Samples are given.**

11. 39.26 × 1.98
   40, 2; 80
12. 18.8 × 4.3
   20, 4; 80
13. 2.18 × 24.19
   2, 24; 48
14. 41.5 × 18.75
   40, 20; 800
15. 1.91 × 15.8
   2, 16; 32
16. 3.5 × 8.9
   4, 9; 36
17. 12.2 × 2.96
   12, 3; 36
18. 5.3 × 7.49
   5, 8; 40
19. 28.5 × 11.1
   30, 11; 330
20. 14.8 × 10.658
   15, 11; 165

21. *Mental Math* Suppose you earn $4.75/h mowing lawns. Estimate how much money you will earn in 3.5 h. **$20**

22. *Mental Math* Suppose you save $6.25 each week. Estimate how much you will save in one year. **$312**

Technology Options

Prentice Hall Technology

 Software for Learners
- Math Blaster® Mystery*
- Interactive Student Tutorial, Chapter 4*

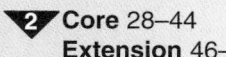 **Teaching Resource Software**
- Computer Item Generator 4-1
- Resource Pro™ Chapter 4*

Internet • For related mathematics activities, visit the Prentice Hall site at www.phschool.com/math

*Available on CD-ROM only

Assignment Options for Exercises On Your Own

To provide flexible scheduling, this lesson can be subdivided into parts.

▼**1** Core 1–23
   Extension 24–27, 45

▼**2** Core 28–44
   Extension 46–50

Use Mixed Review to maintain skills.

3 Practice/Assess

AUDITORY LEARNING and MENTAL MATH Exercises 21 and 22 Ask students with an auditory learning style to describe their mental math process aloud to a partner.

CONNECTION TO SOCIAL STUDIES Exercise 23 If you have block scheduling or extended class periods, students may want to research the lengths of some of the world's longest tunnels. Challenge them to create problems using the information they find.

CONNECTION TO HEALTH Exercises 25–27 Ask students how estimation can be helpful when planning healthy family meals. Have them use nutritional labels at home to make up math problems.

ESTIMATION Exercise 43 Students may wish to use calculators to see how close their estimates come to the actual speed of the car.

TACTILE LEARNING Exercise 49 Ask students to use play bills to check their answers.

WRITING Exercise 50 Encourage students to explain their criteria for choosing the compatible numbers in their examples.

---

page 137   Mixed Review

53.

Q	1	1	1	0	0	0	0	0
D	2	1	0	4	3	2	1	0
N	0	2	4	1	3	5	7	9

(8)

---

23. *Social Studies* The Apennine Railroad Tunnel in Italy is 18.5 km long. The Seikan Tunnel in Japan is 2.9 times as long. Estimate the length of the Seikan Tunnel. **57 km**

24. *Packaging* A volleyball weighs 283.5 g and a shipping crate weighs 595.34 g. Estimate the weight of a shipping crate containing 9 volleyballs. **3,300 g**

23–27. Answers may vary. Samples are given.

Nutrition **Use the chart below to answer Exercises 25–27.**

Food	Serving Size	Protein (grams)
Canned Tuna	3 oz (drained)	24.4
Rye Bread	1 slice	2.3
Cheese Pizza	1 slice (14-in. pie)	7.8

25. About how many grams of protein are in 2 slices of cheese pizza? **16 g**

26. About how many grams of protein are in 8 slices of cheese pizza? **64 g**

27. Estimate how many grams of protein are in a sandwich consisting of 2 slices of rye bread and 2 oz of tuna. **20 g**

Use compatible numbers to estimate each quotient.

28–42. Answers may vary. Samples are given.

28. $46.4 \div 4.75$ **9**

29. $39.3 \div 7.7$ **5**

30. $56.1 \div 6.9$ **8**

31. $17.33 \div 5.49$ **3**

32. $15.76 \div 2.51$ **5**

33. $65 \div 0.8$ **65**

34. $37.2 \div 6.12$ **6**

35. $79.8 \div 2.2$ **40**

36. $32.36 \div 1.87$ **16**

37. $149 \div 14.4$ **10**

38. $11.801 \div 2.9$ **4**

39. $101 \div 9.25$ **10**

40. $65.1 \div 2.89$ **22**

41. $73.09 \div 0.9$ **73**

42. $80.34 \div 7.82$ **10**

THE SOAP BOX DERBY

The Soap Box Derby held in Akron, Ohio, is a downhill race for cars without motors. The cars are built and driven by young people between the ages of 9 and 16. The cars race on a 953.75 ft downhill track.

One year more than 200 girls and boys from 35 states and 6 countries entered the race. Carolyn Fox, an 11-year-old from Salem, Oregon, was the winner of the Kit Car division. Her winning time was 28.27 seconds.

43–44. Answers may vary. Samples are given.

43. *Estimation* To find speed, divide the distance by the time. Estimate Carolyn Fox's average speed. **32 ft/s**

44. Suppose the track is 2.5 times its original length. A racer finishes the race in 52.56 s. Estimate the racer's average speed. **50 ft/s**

WRAP UP

IDENTIFYING THE BIG IDEA Ask students to explain how to estimate decimal products and quotients.

▶ **PROJECT LINK** You may want to bring in grocery flyers and catalogs to help students obtain prices.

LESSON QUIZ

Estimate.

1. 18.3 × 3.2 **Answers may vary. Sample: 20 × 3 = 60**

2. 47.1 ÷ 6.89 **Answers may vary. Sample: 49 ÷ 7 = 7**

3. Material costs $7.83 per yd. Estimate about how much 3.25 yd will cost. **Answers may vary. Sample: $24**

4. The Chan family drove 516 mi in 11 h. Estimate their speed in miles per hour. **Answers may vary. Sample: 50 mph**

---

45. *Number Sense* Estimate 29.26 × 11.62.
   a. First use compatible numbers. **Answers may vary. Sample: 30 × 11 = 330**
   b. Then estimate by rounding. **348**
   c. Which method is closer to the exact answer? Why? **Answers may vary. Sample: The factors used to find a rounded estimate are closer to the exact factors used to find the exact product.**

46. **Choose A, B, C, or D.** Between what two numbers is the quotient 18.7 ÷ 5? **B**

   A. 2 and 3   **B.** 3 and 4   **C.** 4 and 5   **D.** 5 and 6

47–49. Answers may vary. Samples are given.

47. *Jobs* Yvonne earned $33.25 in one week baby-sitting. She earns $3.50 per hour. Estimate the number of hours she worked. **10 hours**

48. *Savings* Suppose you saved $443.75 in one year. Estimate how much you saved each week. **$9.00/wk**

49. *Library Science* The bill for 3 copies of a book is $38.85. Estimate the cost of 1 book. Is your estimate higher or lower than the book's actual cost? **$13; higher, since $38.85 was rounded to $39**

50. *Writing* Suppose two different people estimate a product or quotient using compatible numbers. Will they always get the same result? Use examples to explain. **See below.**

Mixed Review

Use the graph at the right for Exercises 51 and 52.
(Lesson 1-5)

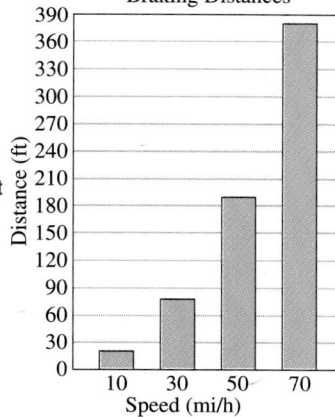

Braking Distances

51. If the braking distance is about 190 ft, how fast was the car traveling? **50 mi/h**

52. Find the braking distance for a car traveling 30 mi/h. **75 ft**

53. *Choose a Strategy* Name the ways you could make $.45 with no pennies. **See margin p. 136.**

54. A bus trip from Austin to San Antonio takes 2 h 57 min. What time will the bus arrive if it leaves Austin at 10:35 A.M.? *(Lesson 3-10)* **1:32 P.M.**

CHAPTER PROJECT

PROJECT LINK: RESEARCHING

Brainstorm a list of all the celebration costs. Note the items you need to purchase and then research a reasonable price for each item. Decide the quantity you will need of each item. Be sure you have enough for every member of your class and the guest(s) of honor. Estimate the total cost of the event.

Check students' work.

50. No; for example, a compatible estimate for 37.5 ÷ 3.89 could be either 36 ÷ 4 or 40 ÷ 4.

PRACTICE

▶ **Practice 4-1** *Estimating Products and Quotients*

Round each factor to the nearest whole number to estimate the product. Estimates may vary.

1. 0.97 × 13.21 **13**
2. 11.9 × 4.76 **60**
3. 14.7 × 2.2 **30**
4. 18.95 × 0.76 **19**
5. 28.02 × 1.94 **56**
6. 11.93 × 1.63 **24**
7. 43.75 × 3.17 **132**
8. 5.02 × 3.16 **15**
9. 9.04 × 8.71 **81**
10. 17.41 × 8.04 **136**
11. 8.59 × 0.81 **9**
12. 21.7 × 2.03 **44**
13. 8.07 × 9.63 **80**
14. 0.96 × 15.41 **15**
15. 5.21 × 6.78 **35**

Use compatible numbers to estimate. Estimates may vary.

16. 38.9 × 19.7 **800**
17. 18.47 ÷ 5.96 **3**
18. 21.19 × 9.4 **200**
19. 38.4 ÷ 3.6 **10**
20. 76.3 ÷ 15.1 **5**
21. 11.9 × 9.8 **120**
22. 49.1 ÷ 15.6 **3**
23. 21.8 × 6.31 **120**
24. 18.6 ÷ 2.8 **6**
25. 18.9 × 4.7 **100**
26. 63.7 ÷ 7.6 **8**
27. 24.6 × 3.8 **100**
28. 19.7 ÷ 4.1 **5**
29. 16.1 × 7.42 **112**
30. 82.3 ÷ 8.76 **9**

Tim went shopping and spent $31.79 at each of 3 stores.

31. Use compatible numbers to estimate how much Tim spent altogether. **about $90**
32. Estimate how much Tim spent by rounding. **about $96**
33. Which estimate is closer to the amount Tim actually spent? **the rounded estimate**

In copymaster and workbook formats

RETEACHING

▶ **Reteaching 4-1** *Estimating Products and Quotients*

You can estimate decimal products and quotients by using **compatible numbers.**

Estimate the product 9.47 × 3.81.

9.47 → 10   Change to compatible
× 3.81 → × 4   numbers—numbers that
_____ 40   are easy to multiply.

The product is about 40.

Estimate the quotient 23.96 ÷ 4.18.

23.96 ÷ 4.18
  ↓   ↓   Change to compatible
  24 ÷ 4 = 6 numbers—numbers that
            are easy to divide.

The quotient is about 6.

Write a pair of compatible numbers. Then estimate the product. Accept reasonable estimates.

1. 3 × 4.1 **3** × **4** Estimate: **12**
2. 4.9 × 9.7 **5** × **10** Estimate: **50**
3. 7.8 × 5.4 **8** × **5** Estimate: **40**
4. 14.7 × 3.1 **about 45**
5. 1.86 × 9.7 **about 20**
6. 4.57 × 2.5 **about 10**
7. 45.79 × 3.76 **about 150**
8. $25.95 × 4 **about $100**
9. $19.90 × 40 **about $800**
10. 3.9 × 4.6 **about 20**
11. 6.157 × 14 **about 90**
12. 9.9 × 2.33 **about 20**

Use compatible numbers to estimate the quotient. Accept reasonable estimates.

13. 7.21 ÷ 3 **about 2**
14. 31.74 ÷ 5 **about 6**
15. 34.06 ÷ 12.7 **about 3**
16. 90.87 ÷ 33.6 **about 3**
17. 51.7 ÷ 9.8 **about 5**
18. 46.81 ÷ 8.7 **about 5**
19. 63.11 ÷ 9.1 **about 7**
20. 16.87 ÷ 7.9 **about 2**
21. 43.01 ÷ 1.97 **about 22**
22. 124.6 ÷ 25 **about 5**
23. 80.02 ÷ 11 **about 8**
24. 32.889 ÷ 6.74 **about 5**

ENRICHMENT

Minds on Math Transparency

4-1

How many different three-digit numbers can be formed using the digits 1, 4, and 9 only once in each number?

6

See *Solution Key* for worked-out answers.

137

In Lesson 4-1, students learned how to estimate the products and quotients of numbers containing decimals. This toolbox shows students how to use a database to order decimals from least to greatest or from greatest to least.

ERROR ALERT! Some students may find the new vocabulary confusing. **Remediation:** Carefully explain the terms *database, field*, and *record* using the sample spreadsheet. Explain that the database is all the information in the spreadsheet, the field is the information in a column, a record is the information in a row.

ASSESSMENT Ask students to choose a field. **Answers may vary. Sample: issue number** Ask: *How could you sort this database using the field you chose?* **Sample: Order the numbers from least to greatest.** Have students sort the database and list the record order. **Sample: Indiana Jones, The Atom, Spiderman, Justice League, Batman**

EXTENSION Ask: *How do you think the database is presently sorted?* **Answers may vary. Sample: alphabetically by title**

Resources

 Teaching Resources

Teaching Aids Master 5

 Transparencies
4, 5

TECHNOLOGY

MATH TOOLBOX

Decimals and Databases

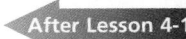 After Lesson 4-1

You can use an electronic spreadsheet to create a *database*. An electronic database is powerful, because once you enter a set of data items, you can organize, reorganize, and recall that information for a variety of purposes.

For example, look at the comic book database screen shown below. You can organize this database to show all comics in the collection alphabetically or by their dollar value.

Here are some common database terms.
A *field* is a category within a database of information.
A *record* is a group of fields relating to one entry.
Sort is the computer command used to organize the fields.

	A	B	C	D
1	Issue Number	Title	Value	
2	270	Batman	8.00	
3	1	Indiana Jones	2.50	
4	99	Justice League	10.00	
5	28	Spiderman	335.00	
6	1	The Atom	750.00	

The **fields** are *Issue Number, Title*, and *Value*.

You could add a **field** to describe each comic's condition.

Each row is a **record**.

Source: *Overstreet Comic Book Price Guide*

Use the database screen above for Exercises 1–3.

1. How many records are shown in the database screen? **5 records**

2. Suppose you sort the comics shown by value from greatest to least. Which comic would be listed first? Last? **The Atom; Indiana Jones**

3. Besides a field for each comic's condition, what other fields could you add? **Answers may vary. Sample: publication date**

4. *Writing* Think of a database you could create. **a–c. Check students' work.**
   a. Tell how the database would be useful to you.
   b. Show what fields would be contained in each record.
   c. Explain at least one way in which you might sort your database.

138

Teaching Notes

1 Focus

CONNECTING TO PRIOR KNOWLEDGE Have students calculate $2 \times 2 \times 2 \times 2$, 6×6, and $4 \times 4 \times 4$ **16; 36; 64**

2 Teach

THINK AND DISCUSS

AEP Help students understand the terms *exponent, base,* and *power.* Write $100{,}000 = 10^5$ on the board. Label the exponent, base, and power. To help students remember, tell them: *The exponent is extra small and extra high. The base holds the exponent. Together, the base and the exponent are the power.*

DIVERSITY Be aware that some students with visual impairment may have trouble distinguishing exponents from bases. For example, they may see 10^5 as 105. Suggest these students use a ruler to help them see the exponents. They can align the straight edge of a ruler with the base of the number and look for the raised exponent.

CONNECTION TO TECHNOLOGY Example 3 You may need to help students locate the y^x and x^2 keys on their calculators.

ALGEBRA Connection

4-2 Exponents

What You'll Learn

▼ To use exponents
▼ To apply the order of operations to simplify powers and expressions

...And Why

Exponents make it easy to use multiple factors.

Here's How

Look for questions that
⚬ build understanding
✔ check understanding

Elis Stenman made the walls of his house by pasting and folding layers of newspaper. He used papers rolled into different sizes to make his furniture, which includes tables, chairs, lamps, and an upright piano.

Source: *The Kids' World Almanac of Records and Facts*

THINK AND DISCUSS

▼ Using Exponents

Would you believe that Elis Stenman built a house and its furniture, including a piano, from about 100,000 newspapers? You can express 100,000 as $10 \times 10 \times 10 \times 10 \times 10$ or you can use an exponent.

$$10 \times 10 \times 10 \times 10 \times 10 = 10^5 \quad \leftarrow \text{exponent}$$
$$\underbrace{\qquad\qquad\qquad\qquad}_{\text{5 factors}} \qquad \uparrow$$
$$\text{base}$$

The **exponent** tells you how many times a number, or **base,** is used as a factor.

■ EXAMPLE 1

Write $5 \times 5 \times 5 \times 5$ using an exponent. Name the base and the exponent.

$$5 \times 5 \times 5 \times 5 = 5^4 \quad \leftarrow \text{The number 5 is used as a factor 4 times.}$$

The base is 5 and the exponent is 4.

1. ✔ *Try It Out* Rewrite each expression using an exponent. Name the base and exponent.
   a. $7 \times 7 \times 7$ 7^3
   b. $2 \times 2 \times 2 \times 2 \times 2 \times 2$ 2^6

You call a number that is expressed using an exponent a **power.** You read 10^5 as "ten to the fifth power."

Lesson Planning Options

Prerequisite Skills
- multiplying whole numbers (precourse)
- using the order of operations (2-3)

Vocabulary/Symbols
exponent, base, power

Materials/Manipulatives
- calculator

Resources

📖 **Student Edition**

Skills Handbook, p. 540
Extra Practice, p. 525
Glossary/Study Guide

📼 **Teaching Resources**

Chapter Support File, Ch. 4
- Lesson Planner 4-2
- Practice 4-2, Reteaching 4-2
- Alternative Activity 4-2
- Answer Masters 4-2

Glossary, Spanish Resources

🖥 **Transparencies**
19, Minds on Math 4-2

Warm Up

Use mental math to choose the smallest fraction in each set.
$$\frac{5}{7}, \frac{1}{3}, \frac{4}{6}, \frac{8}{10} \quad \frac{1}{3}$$
$$\frac{5}{9}, \frac{4}{8}, \frac{11}{15}, \frac{3}{7} \quad \frac{3}{7}$$

AUDITORY LEARNING **Example 4** Have students say aloud "Please excuse my dear Aunt Sally." Then ask individual students what the first letter of each word stands for. Suggest students create their own acronyms to share with the class.

■ **ADDITIONAL EXAMPLES**

FOR EXAMPLE 1
Rewrite the expression using an exponent.
$4 \times 4 \times 4 \times 4 \times 4$ **4^5**

FOR EXAMPLE 2
Simplify 6^3. **216**

FOR EXAMPLE 3
Use a calculator to simply 35^3. **42,875**

FOR EXAMPLE 4
Simplify $3 \times (3^3 + 6)$. **99**

ERROR ALERT! Students may treat an exponent as a factor. For example, they may evaluate 4^3 as 4×3, or 12. **Remediation:** Remind students that the digit 3 tells how many times the base is used as a factor. Have students write $4 \times 4 \times 4$.

CONNECTION TO SCIENCE Tell students scientists use exponents in scientific notation to express large numbers such as the distance between planets. For example, Earth is 9.3×10^7 mi from the Sun.

Technology Options

Prentice Hall Technology

 **Software for Learners**
- Math Blaster® Mystery*
- Interactive Student Tutorial, Chapter 4*

 Teaching Resource Software
- Computer Item Generator 4-2
- Resource Pro™ Chapter 4*

Internet • For related mathematics activities, visit the Prentice Hall site at www.phschool.com/math

*Available on CD-ROM only

Assignment Options for Exercises On Your Own

To provide flexible scheduling, this lesson can be subdivided into parts.

▼**1 Core** 1–12, 22–24
  Extension 25–27

▼**2 Core** 13–21, 29–42
  Extension 28, 43–44

Use Mixed Review to maintain skills.

140

QUICKreview

The length and width of a square are equal. The area of a square is $s \times s$, where s is the length of a side. The length, width, and height of a cube are equal. The volume of a cube is $s \times s \times s$, where s is the length of a side.

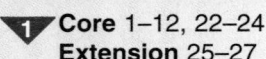 **PROBLEM SOLVING HINT**
The phrase _Please Excuse My Dear Aunt Sally_ can help you to remember the order of operations. The first letter of each word in the phrase stands for an operation.

In geometry, the exponents 2 and 3 have special names.

- The area of the square is 3×3, or 3^2. You read 3^2 as "three squared."

- The volume of the cube is $4 \times 4 \times 4$ or 4^3. You read 4^3 as "four cubed."

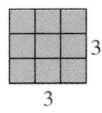 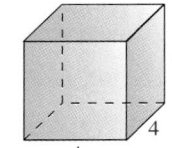

Now you may assign Exercises 1–12, 22–27.

2 Simplifying Powers

You can simplify a power by writing it as a product.

■ **EXAMPLE 2**

a. Simplify 4^3.
$4^3 = 4 \times 4 \times 4 = 64$

b. Simplify 1^2.
$1^2 = 1 \times 1 = 1$

2. ✔ **Try It Out** Simplify.
a. 3^4 **81**   b. 9^2 **81**   c. 5^3 **125**   d. 10^4 **10,000**

A calculator is helpful for exponents. You can use the x^2 key to square a number. Use the y^x key to evaluate _any_ power.

■ **EXAMPLE 3**

Use a calculator.
a. Simplify 26^2.
26 x^2 _676_
$26^2 = 676$

b. Simplify 6^8.
6 y^x 8 = _1679616_
$6^8 = 1,679,616$

3. ✔ **Try It Out** Use a calculator to simplify.
a. 31^2 **961**   b. 22^4 **234,256**   c. 15^5 **759,375**   d. 99^2 **9,801**

THE ORDER OF OPERATIONS

You can extend the order of operations to include powers.

1. Do all operations within parentheses first.
2. **Do all the work which has exponents.**
3. Multiply and divide in order from left to right.
4. Add and subtract in order from left to right.

ASSESSMENT Write $3 \times 4^2 + 5^3$ on the board. Ask students to list the order in which they would perform the operations. **Answers may vary. Sample: Evaluate 4^2 and 5^3, multiply, then add.** Then have students add parentheses that do not change the order. **Answers may vary. Sample: $(3 \times 4^2) + 5^3$** Then add parentheses that do change the order. **Answers may vary. Sample: $3 \times (4^2 + 5^3)$** Have students evaluate both expressions. **Sample: 173; 423**

3 Practice/Assess

EXERCISES *On Your Own*

VISUAL LEARNING and CONNECTION TO GEOMETRY Exercises 22 and 24 Students can model the squares on graph paper and check their answer by counting.

Exercise 25c Have students express 1,000,000 and 10,000,000,000,000 as powers of 10. **10^6; 10^{13}**

Exercise 27 Challenge students to generate their own number pattern using exponents.

WRAP UP

IDENTIFYING THE BIG IDEA Have students use the terms base and exponent to explain how to evaluate a power.

■ EXAMPLE 4

a. Simplify $2 \times (4^2 - 5)$.

$$2 \times (4^2 - 5) = 2 \times (16 - 5) \quad \longleftarrow 4^2 = 4 \times 4 = 16$$
$$= 2 \times 11 \quad \longleftarrow \text{Subtract 5 from 16.}$$
$$= 22 \quad \longleftarrow \text{Multiply 2 and 11.}$$

b. Simplify $2^3 - 9 \div 3$.

$$2^3 - 9 \div 3 = 8 - 9 \div 3 \quad \longleftarrow 2^3 = 2 \times 2 \times 2 = 8$$
$$= 8 - 3 \quad \longleftarrow \text{Divide 9 by 3.}$$
$$= 5 \quad \longleftarrow \text{Subtract 3 from 8.}$$

4. ✔ *Try It Out* Simplify each expression.
  a. $60 \div (6 + 3^2)$ **4**   **b.** $(3 + 7)^2 \div 5^2$ **4**

5. ⬛*Reasoning* How can you use a calculator to simplify each expression in Example 4? **Check students' work.**

Now you may assign Exercises 13–21, 28–44.

EXERCISES *On Your Own*

Name the base and the exponent.

1. 4^5 **4, 5**   **2.** 3^2 **3, 2**   **3.** 6^3 **6, 3**   **4.** 7^9 **7, 9**   **5.** 8^1 **8, 1**   **6.** 10^3 **10, 3**

Write using an exponent. Name the base and the exponent.

7. $6 \times 6 \times 6$ **6^3; 6, 3**   **8.** $3 \times 3 \times 3 \times 3 \times 3$ **3^5; 3, 5**   **9.** $8 \times 8 \times 8 \times 8$ **8^4; 8, 4**

10. $12{,}432 \times 12{,}432$ **11.** $1{,}500 \times 1{,}500 \times 1{,}500$ **12.** $4 \times 4 \times 4 \times 4 \times 4 \times 4$
  $12{,}432^2$; 12,432 , 2   **$1{,}500^3$; 1,500, 3**   **4^6; 4, 6**

Simplify each expression.

13. 5^4 **625**   **14.** 4^5 **1,024**   **15.** 7^3 **343**   **16.** 6^5 **7,776**   **17.** 8^4 **4,096**

18. $(24 - 8) \times 3$ **48**   **19.** $5^3 \div 25$ **5**   **20.** $24^2 - 4^3$ **512**   **21.** $10^3 \div 1{,}000 + 10$
                                                                                                                    11

Geometry **Express each square's area (length × width) or cube's volume (length × width × height) using an exponent.**

22. 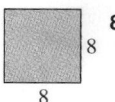 **8^2**

23. 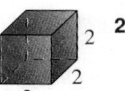 **2^3**

24. 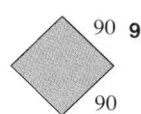 **90^2**

141

PRACTICE

Practice 4-2 *Exponents*

Choose a calculator, mental math, or paper and pencil to simplify.

1. 9^2 **81**
2. 6^4 **1,296**
3. 5^3 **125**
4. 7^3 **343**

5. $156 + (256 \div 8^2)$ **160**
6. $32 + 64 + 2^3$ **104**
7. $53 + 64 \div 2^3$ **61**
8. $1,280 - 5 \times 6^2$ **1,100**

9. $7^3 - 3 \times 6 \div 2$ **334**
10. $17^2 - 8 \times 3$ **265**
11. $167 + (13 - 4)^3$ **896**
12. $(4 + 3)^2 - 17$ **32**

13. $8^3 - 5 \times 18 \div 3$ **482**
14. $5^2 \times 3 - 40$ **35**
15. $(9 + 3)^3$ **1,728**
16. $(24 - 16)^4$ **4,096**

Find each answer to complete the puzzle.

Across
1. $(3 \times 4)^2$
3. $60 \div (8 + 7) + 11$
4. $2^2 \times 5^2 + 106$
5. $4 + 7 \times 2^3$
6. $7^2 + 4$
9. $48 \div 4 \times 5 - 2 \times 5$
10. $(4 + 3) \times (2 + 1)$
12. $12 \times (30 + 37)$
13. $5 \times (9 + 4) + 362 \div 2$
14. $29 \times 18 \div 9$

Down
1. $8 \times (5 + 4) \div 6$
2. $700 \times (2 + 4) \div (17 - 7)$
3. $11 \times (18 - 3)$
5. $60 + (5 \times 4^3) + 2^2 \times 55$
7. $7^2 - 7 \times 2$
8. $(4^2 - 4) \times 10$
9. $2^4 \times 2^5$
11. $(3 + 2) \times (6^2 - 7)$
12. $3^4 + 405 \div 81$

In copymaster and workbook formats

RETEACHING

Reteaching 4-2 *Exponents*

An **exponent** tells how many times a number is used as a factor.
$3 \times 3 \times 3 \times 3$ shows the number 3 is used as a factor 4 times.
$3 \times 3 \times 3 \times 3$ can be written 3^4.
In 3^4, 3 is the **base** and 4 is the exponent.
Read 3^4 as "three to the fourth power."

- To *simplify* a power, first write it as a product.
  $2^5 = 2 \times 2 \times 2 \times 2 \times 2 = 32$
- When you simplify expressions with exponents, do all operations inside parentheses first. Then simplify the powers.
  Example: $30 - (2 + 3)^2 = 30 - 5^2$
  $= 30 - 25$
  $= 5$

Name the base and the exponent.

1. 3^6 base **3** exponent **6**
2. 6^2 base **6** exponent **2**
3. 8^4 base **8** exponent **4**

Write using an exponent. Name the base and the exponent.

4. $9 \times 9 \times 9$ **9^3; 9; 3**
5. $6 \times 6 \times 6 \times 6$ **6^4; 6; 4**
6. $1 \times 1 \times 1 \times 1 \times 1$ **1^5; 1; 5**

Choose a calculator, mental math, or paper and pencil to simplify.

7. 6^2 **36**
8. 3^5 **243**
9. 10^4 **10,000**
10. $4^2 + 5^2$ **41**
11. $2 \times 6 - 2^3$ **4**
12. $6^2 + 4^2$ **52**
13. $5 + 5^2 - 2$ **28**
14. $24 \div 4 + 2^4$ **22**
15. $9 + (40 \div 2^3)$ **14**
16. $(4^2 + 4) \div 5$ **4**
17. $10 \times (30 - 5^2)$ **50**
18. $12 + 18 \div 3^2$ **14**

ENRICHMENT

Minds on Math Transparency

4-2

Andrew, Andrea, and Amy divided four boxes of baseball trading cards evenly. If they each got 48 cards, how many trading cards were in each box?

36 cards

See Solution Key for worked-out answers.

142

LESSON QUIZ

Write using an exponent. Name the base and the exponent.

1. $6 \times 6 \times 6 \times 6$
   6^4; 6 is the base, 4 is the exponent.

2. $4 \times 4 \times 4 \times 4 \times 4 \times 4$
   4^6; 4 is the base, 6 is the exponent.

Use a calculator, mental math, or paper and pencil to simplify each expression.

3. 17^3 **4,913**
4. $75 \div 5^2$ **3**
5. $(14 - 3^2) \times 6$ **30**

---

25. a. *Patterns* Copy and complete the table at the right.
   b. Look at the standard form numbers in the table. Explain how the number of zeros that follow the numeral 1 relate to the exponent. **The number of zeros is the same as the exponent.**
   c. Extend and complete the table for $10^6, 10^7, 10^8$.   **See below.**
   d. Add three rows to the top of the table. Look at the standard form column. Continue the pattern to write the three standard form numbers that precede 10. **1, 0.1, 0.01**
   1,000,000; 10,000,000; 100,000,000

Power	Standard Form
10^1	10
10^2	100
10^3	1,000
10^4	10,000 ▨
10^5	▨ 10,000 ▨

26. *Algebra* How would you write $n \times n \times n$ using exponents? **n^3**

27. Look at the number pattern 1, 8, 27, 64, 125, 216, ... How does this number pattern relate to exponents? **When written using exponents, the sequence is $1^3, 2^3, 3^3, 4^3, 5^3, 6^3, \ldots$**

28. *Entertainment* The size of the image of a motion picture is related to the distance of the projector from the screen. Use the table at the right.
   a. *Writing* Describe how the size of a motion picture is related to the distance from the projector to the screen.
   b. *Reasoning* A projector is 25 ft from the screen. How big will the image of the motion picture be? **625 ft²**
   a. **The size of the image equals the square of the distance from the screen.**

Distance from Screen	Picture Size
1 unit	1 unit²
2 units	4 units²
3 units	9 units²
4 units	16 units²

⊞ *Choose* Use a calculator, mental math, or paper and pencil to simplify each expression.

29. 5^2 **25**
30. 2^3 **8**
31. 3^7 **2,187**
32. 22^3 **10,648**
33. 10^{10} **10,000,000,000**
34. 11^7 **19,487,171**
35. $475 \div 5^2$ **19**
36. $5 \times 3^2 - 10$ **35**
37. 7×2^4 **112**
38. $2 \times 4^2 - 32$ **0**
39. $35 + 7 \times 2^4$ **147**
40. $(56 - 4^2) \times 9$ **360**
41. $3^3 - 2^4 + 30$ **41**
42. $12 \times (60 - 2^5)$ **336**
43. $6^3 \div (2 \times 6) + 64$ **82**
44. $498 + (2^{12} \div 2^4) \div (2^5 \times 2) - 2$ **500**

Mixed Review

Find each sum or difference. *(Lesson 3-7)*

45. $2.365 + 8.36$ **10.725**
46. $10.25 - 7.86$ **2.39**
47. $7.9 + 11.71$ **19.61**
48. $20 - 13.07$ **6.93**
49. $95.21 + 82.96$ **178.17**

Evaluate each expression for $x = 10$. *(Lesson 2-4)*

50. $4(x - 6)$ **16**
51. $6x \div 3$ **20**
52. $x + 27$ **37**
53. $2(x + 10)$ **40**
54. $(x \div 2) - 5$ **0**

55. *Grocery Shopping* Is $4.00 enough money to buy yogurt for $.79, blueberries for $1.59, and bread for $1.49? Explain. *(Lesson 3-6)*
   Yes; the total cost is only $3.87.

Teaching Notes

1 Focus

CONNECTING TO PRIOR KNOWLEDGE
Have students use the order of operations to simplify $4 \times (8 + 2)$ and $4 \times 8 + 4 \times 2$. **40; 40** Ask students to think of similar pairs of problems.
Answers may vary. Sample: $1 \times (3 + 5)$ and $1 \times 3 + 1 \times 5$

2 Teach

Work Together

TACTILE LEARNING Students may benefit from using square tiles to construct the rectangles.

EXTENSION   Questions 1–3 Have students cut out two rectangles. They can be any size, but one dimension in both must be the same. Students answer the questions using these rectangles.

THINK AND DISCUSS

Example 1 Ask: *Why are the 3 and the 4 added together in the parentheses?*
Answers may vary. Sample: 3 and 4 equal the width of the combined tables, so the numbers can be added together to find the area of the tables.

Example 3 Have students share the numbers they selected to help them multiply mentally.

GEOMETRY Connection

4-3   The Distributive Property

What You'll Learn

▼ **1** To find areas of rectangles

▼ **2** To use the distributive property

...And Why

You'll use the distributive property to solve picnic planning problems and to do mental math.

Here's How

Look for questions that
⚏ build understanding
✔ check understanding

Work Together _____ *Creating Area Models*

Geometry On graph paper, draw rectangles with the dimensions shown below. Cut out the rectangles.

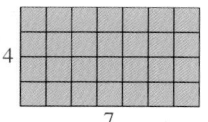   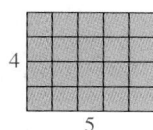

1. Find and record the number of squares in each rectangle.
   28, 20
2. Put the two rectangles end to end so the sides of equal length touch. What is the length and width of the new rectangle?
   12, 4
3. ⚏*Reasoning* Find the number of squares in the new rectangle. How does this number relate to the numbers for the two smaller rectangles? **48; the number of squares in the new rectangle is the sum of the number of squares in the two smaller rectangles.**

THINK AND DISCUSS

▼ **1** Finding Areas of Rectangles

Area is the number of square units in a figure. The area of a rectangle is equal to the product of its length and width. You write units of area in square units (units^2).

Area = length × width
$A = \ell \times w$

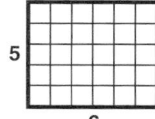

4. ⚏*Geometry* Use graph paper to draw a rectangle that is 5 units wide and 6 units long. **See left.**
   a. Count the number of square units to find its area. **30 units^2**
   b. Multiply the length times the width to find the area of the rectangle. Do you get the same result? **yes**
   c. Which method seems easier? Explain.
      Answers may vary. Sample: Multiplying; it requires less time.
5. ✔*Try It Out* Find the area of a 3 ft-by-6 ft rectangle. **18 ft^2**

Now you may assign Exercises 1–10, 22.

Lesson Planning Options

Prerequisite Skills
• using the order of operations (2-3)

Vocabulary/Symbols
area, distributive property

Materials/Manipulatives
• graph paper   • scissors
• ruler

Resources

📖 **Student Edition**
Skills Handbook, p. 538
Extra Practice, p. 525
Glossary/Study Guide

📁 **Teaching Resources**
Chapter Support File, Ch. 4
• Lesson Planner 4-3
• Practice 4-3, Reteaching 4-3
• Answer Masters 4-3
Teaching Aids Masters 1, 2
Glossary, Spanish Resources

📽 **Transparencies**
1, 84, Minds on Math 4-3

Warm Up ⏱
Jake paid $92.40 for 11 yd of fabric. How much did the fabric cost per yard? **$8.40**

CONNECTION TO GEOMETRY The formula for the area of a rectangle is $l \times w$. The formula for the perimeter of a rectangle is $l + w + l + w$, or $(2 \times l) + (2 \times w)$. Challenge students to use the distributive property to rewrite the formula for the perimeter of a rectangle. $2 \times (l + w)$

■ **ADDITIONAL EXAMPLES**

FOR EXAMPLE 1
Find the area of the combined table top. **50 ft²**

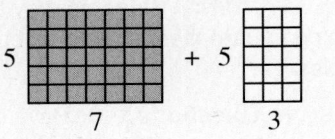

FOR EXAMPLE 2
Use the distributive property to simplify $(9 \times 6) + (9 \times 21)$. **243**

FOR EXAMPLE 3
Use the distributive property to multiply 5×59 mentally. **295**

EXTENSION Write these lines on the board. Have students decide what property—Associative, Communitive, or Distributive—makes each step possible.

$(2 \times 3) \times 4 + 3 \times 5$
$(3 \times 2) \times 4 + 3 \times 5$ **Commutative**
$3 \times (2 \times 4) + 3 \times 5$ **Associative**
$3 \times [(2 \times 4) + 5]$ **Distributive**
Have students find the value of each line. **39**

Prentice Hall Technology

 **Software for Learners**

- Hot Page™ 10*
- Math Blaster® Mystery*
- Interactive Student Tutorial, Chapter 4*

Teaching Resource Software

- Computer Item Generator 4-3
- Resource Pro™ Chapter 4*

Internet • For related mathematics activities, visit the Prentice Hall site at www.phschool.com/math

*Available on CD-ROM only

Assignment Options for Exercises On Your Own

To provide flexible scheduling, this lesson can be subdivided into parts.

1 Core 1–3, 7–10
Extension 4–6, 22

2 Core 11–20, 23–31
Extension 21, 32–36

Use Mixed Review to maintain skills.

144

 Using the Distributive Property

Example 1 shows how you can use the **distributive property** to simplify an expression that has multiplication and addition.

■ **EXAMPLE 1** *Real-World Problem Solving*

Picnics Suppose you want to cover the tops of two picnic tables. One table is 5 ft long and 3 ft wide. The other is 5 ft long and 4 ft wide. Find the minimum amount of paper you will need to cover the table tops.

Method 1
Find the area of each table top. Then add the areas.

Method 2
Place the tables side by side. Find the area of the combined table top.

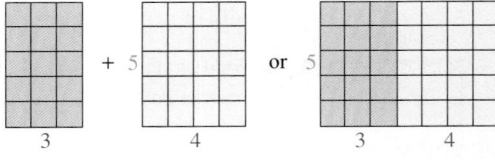

$(5 \text{ ft} \times 3 \text{ ft}) + (5 \text{ ft} \times 4 \text{ ft})$ $5 \text{ ft} \times (3 \text{ ft} + 4 \text{ ft})$
$15 \text{ ft}^2 + 20 \text{ ft}^2$ $5 \text{ ft} \times 7 \text{ ft}$
35 ft^2 ←— Both methods —→ 35 ft^2
give the same total area.

You will need at least 35 ft^2 of paper.

ASSESSMENT Write the symbols (+ §) × ◊ on the board. Ask students to pretend the symbols are numbers and rewrite the expression using the distributive property. × ◊ + § × ◊ Repeat the exercise for (Δ × ∞) − (Δ × ¢). Δ × (∞ − ¢)

WRITING Exercise 3 Ask students to explain when they might use each method.

OPEN-ENDED Exercise 7 Make sure both notebooks have a least one measure in common so students can use the distributive property.

REASONING Exercise 8 Suggest students draw rectangles as one of their examples.

Exercises 15–20 Suggest students compute the value on both sides of the equal sign to check their answers.

DIVERSITY Exercise 22 Tell students the word tennis comes from a French word, *tenetz*. A tennis-like game was played in thirteenth-century France. The French may have learned the game from the Italians and

---

■ **EXAMPLE 2**

Use the distributive property to simplify the expression.
$$(3 \times 4) + (3 \times 7) = 3 \times (4 + 7)$$
$$= 3 \times 11$$
$$= 33$$

6. ✔*Try It Out* Use the distributive property to simplify.
a. $(13 \times 6) + (13 \times 4)$ **130**   **b.** $5 \times (9 + 20)$ **145**

You can use the distributive property to multiply mentally.

■ **EXAMPLE 3**

Mental Math Use the distributive property to find 8×59.
$$8 \times 59 = 8 \times (60 - 1)$$ ◀—Think of 59 as 60 − 1.
$$= (8 \times 60) - (8 \times 1)$$ ◀—Multiply mentally.
$$= 480 - 8$$ ◀— Subtract mentally.
$$= 472$$

7. ✔*Try It Out* Use the distributive property to multiply.
a. 4×59 **236**   **b.** 3×84 **252**   **c.** 6×49 **294**

THE DISTRIBUTIVE PROPERTY

Numbers added or subtracted within a set of parentheses can be multiplied by a number outside the parentheses.

Examples: $8 \times (5 + 3) = (8 \times 5) + (8 \times 3)$
$8 \times (5 - 3) = (8 \times 5) - (8 \times 3)$

HISTORY
Around 300 B.C., Euclid wrote a book called *Elements*. In the book, Euclid shows how the distributive property works for area. He wrote, "If one large rectangle is divided into 3 smaller ones, the area of the one is equal to the areas of the 3 smaller ones added together."

Now you may assign Exercises 11–21, 23–36.

EXERCISES *On Your Own*

1. *Index Cards* Standard index card sizes in the United States are 3 in. by 5 in., 4 in. by 6 in., and 5 in. by 8 in. Find the area of each card. **15 in.², 24 in.², 40 in.²**

2. *Advertising* One side of a regular outdoor billboard is 14 ft by 48 ft. Find the maximum area covered by an advertisement on this billboard. **672 ft²**

3. *Writing* Describe two ways to find the total area of the rectangle at the right. **Answers may vary. Sample: (2 × 1) + (2 × 8); 2 × 9**

---

pages 145–147   On Your Own

11.
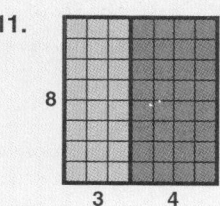

12.
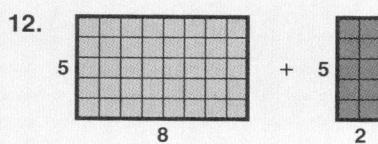

13.
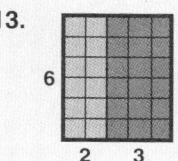

14.
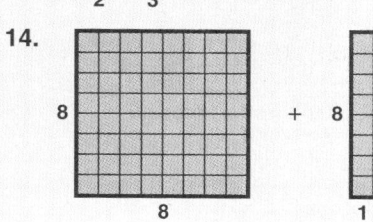

page 147   Mixed Review

41.
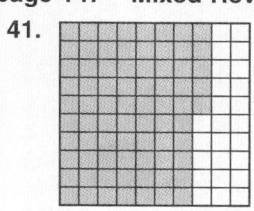

42.
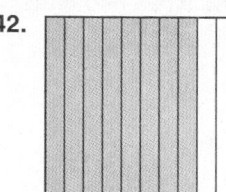

Greeks. The French game was called *jeu de paume*, meaning *game of the palm*, because players used their palms to strike the ball.

ERROR ALERT! Exercises 23–31 Students may forget to distribute to the second addend in problems such as $12 \times (4 + 10)$ and $(25 + 12) \times 4$. **Remediation:** Have students draw arrows to remind them to multiply.

$$12 \times (4 + 10) \qquad (25 + 12) \times 4$$

Have students compute these expressions two ways to check their answers.

Exercises 37–40 Ask students to explain how they found each pattern.

WRAP UP

IDENTIFYING THE BIG IDEA Ask students to explain when and how to use the distributive property.

LESSON QUIZ
Find the missing numbers.
1. $5 \times (3 + 4) = (\blacksquare \times 3) + (5 \times \blacksquare)$
   5; 4
2. $(4 \times 7) - (4 \times 9) = \blacksquare \times (\blacksquare - 9)$
   4; 7

CHECKPOINT 1

Name _____ Class _____ Date _____

Checkpoint 1   *Lessons 4-1 through 4-3*

Use rounding to estimate. Answers may vary. Samples given.
1. 15.8×8.41 2. 6.5×12.3 3. 27.16×53.61
    128   84   1,500

Use compatible numbers to estimate. Answers may vary. Samples given.
4. 49.2×2.98 5. $18.39 \div 3.8$ 6. $37.46 \div 5.17$
    150   5   8

Simplify each expression.
7. 4^3 64   8. $14 + (6 \times 2^2)$ 38   9. $(3^3 - 6) \div 7$ 3

Write the missing numbers.
10. $(7 \times 6) + (7 \times 8) = \blacksquare \times (6 + \blacksquare)$ 7, 8
11. $5 \times (6 - 3) = (5 \times \blacksquare) - (\blacksquare \times \blacksquare)$ 6, 5, 3

Place a decimal point in each product.
12. $6.2 \times 7.1 = 4\,4.0\,2$ 13. $1,000 \times 0.0076 = 7.6$

43.
44.
45.
46.

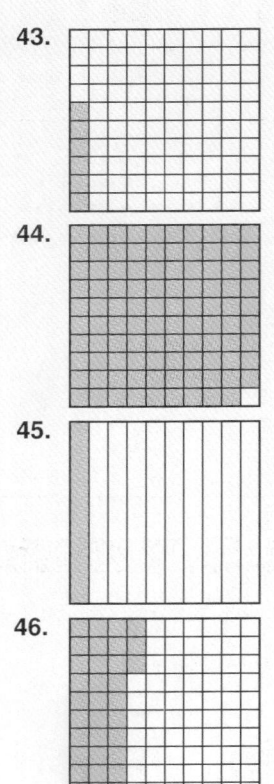

146

Geometry **Write an expression to represent the total area of each figure. Then, find the total area. Show all your work.**   4–6. Expressions may vary.

4.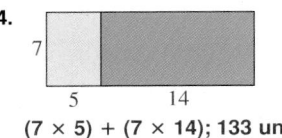
7 |
5   14
$(7 \times 5) + (7 \times 14)$; 133 units²

5.
4 |
5   5
$(4 \times 5) + (4 \times 5)$; 40 units²

6.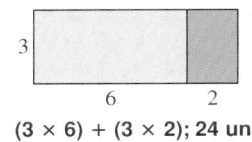
3 |
6   2
$(3 \times 6) + (3 \times 2)$; 24 units²

7. *Open-ended* Measure the length and the width of two different notebook covers. Find the area of each cover. Then find the combined area of both covers. Show two different ways to find the combined area. **Check students' work.**

8. *Reasoning* The formula for the area of a rectangle is *length* × *width*. What happens if you multiply *width* × *length* to find the area? Use an example to support your answer. **You get the same result with either method; for example, $2 \times 3 = 3 \times 2$.**

9. *Frames* The smallest ready-made picture frames measure 4 in. by 5 in. The largest frames measure 24 in. by 36 in.
   a. Find the area of each frame.   **20 in.², 864 in.²**
   b. How much greater area does the largest frame cover than the smallest? **844 in.²**

10. *Washcloths* Typical washcloths range from 12 in. by 12 in. to 14 in. by 14 in.
    a. Find the minimum and maximum areas of washcloths.   **144 in.², 196 in.²**
    b. Find the range of the areas found in part (a). **52 in.²**

Modeling **Draw a rectangular model for each expression.**   11–14. See margin p. 145.

11. $8 \times (3 + 4)$ 12. $(5 \times 8) + (5 \times 2)$ 13. $6 \times (2 + 3)$ 14. $(8 \times 8) + (8 \times 1)$

Find the missing numbers in each equation.

15. $6 \times (12 + 2) = (\overset{6}{\blacksquare} \times 12) + (6 \times \overset{2}{\blacksquare})$

16. $(10 \times \overset{6}{\blacksquare}) - (\overset{10}{\blacksquare} \times \overset{3}{\blacksquare}) = 10 \times (6 - 3)$

17. $(8 \times 3) + (\overset{8}{\blacksquare} \times 4) = 8 \times (\overset{3}{\blacksquare} + 4)$

18. $3 \times (8 - 1) = (\overset{3}{\blacksquare} \times 8) - (3 \times \overset{1}{\blacksquare})$

19. $8 \times (\overset{13}{\blacksquare} - 7) = (\overset{8}{\blacksquare} \times 13) - (8 \times \overset{7}{\blacksquare})$

20. $\overset{20}{\blacksquare} \times (11 + 5) = (20 \times \overset{11}{\blacksquare}) + (\overset{20}{\blacksquare} \times 5)$

21. How can you use the distributive property to find 9×92? **Sample: $9(90 + 2) = 810 + 18 = 828$**

22. *Sports* Look at the regulation-sized tennis court at the right.
    a. Find the rectangular area of the entire tennis court. **2,808 ft²**
    b. Suppose you divided the entire court into four equal-sized sections. Estimate the area of each section. **Estimates may vary. Sample: 700 ft²**

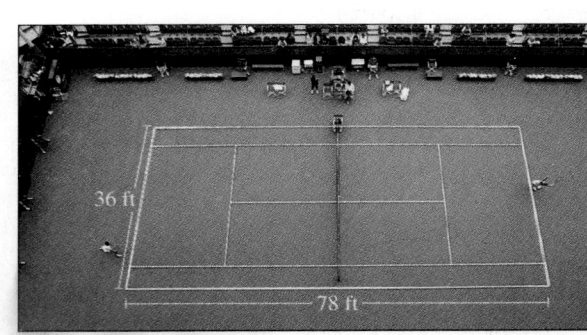
36 ft
78 ft

Use the distributive property to rewrite and
simplify each expression.

3. (3 × 6) + (3 × 10)
  3 × (6 + 10); 48

4. (42 × 6) − (13 × 6) (42 − 13) × 6;
  174

Simplify each expression.

5. (9 + 4) × 3 × 2 **78**

6. 6 × (5 + 5) − 1 **59**

Rewrite and simplify each expression.

23. (4 × 6) + (4 × 3)
  4 × (6 + 3); 36
24. 6 × (20 − 4)
  (6 × 20) − (6 × 4); 96
25. 12 × (4 + 10)
  (12 × 4) + (12 × 10); 168
26. (5 × 3) − (5 × 2)
  5 × (3 − 2); 5
27. (13 × 6) + (13 × 4)
  13 × (6 + 4); 130
28. 15 × (3 + 20)
  (15 × 3) + (15 × 20); 345
29. 11 × (50 − 4)
  (11 × 50) − (11 × 4); 506
30. (25 + 12) × 4
  (25 × 4) + (12 × 4); 148
31. (6 × 22) − (6 × 18)
  6 × (22 − 18); 24

Mental Math **Use the distributive property to simplify.**

32. 4 × 24 **96**   **33.** 2 × 66 **132**   **34.** 3 × 55 **165**   **35.** 6 × 210 **1,260**   **36.** 8 × 109 **872**

Mixed Review

Find the next three terms in each number pattern. *(Lesson 2-1)*

37. 5, 15, 45, 135, . . .
  405; 1,215; 3,645
38. 3, 10, 17, 24, . . .
  31, 38, 45
39. 25, 50, 100, 200, . . .
  400; 800; 1,600
40. 91, 82, 73, 64, . . .
  55, 46, 37

Draw a model for each decimal. *(Lesson 3-1)*   41–46. See margin p. 145–146.

41. 0.75   **42.** 0.8   **43.** 0.06   **44.** 0.99   **45.** 0.1   **46.** 0.33

47. Mr. Garcia began work at 7:37 A.M. and finished at 4:19 P.M.
  He took a 45-minute lunch. How long did he work? *(Lesson 3-10)*   **7 h 57 min**

✓ CHECKPOINT 1

Lessons 4-1 through 4-3

Estimate using rounding.

1. 2.2 × 9.4 **18**   **2.** 26.28 × 1.71 **52**   **3.** 4.9 × 12.2 **60**   **4.** 99.6 × 9.8 **1,000**

Estimate using compatible numbers.   5–8. Answers may vary. Samples are given.

5. 39.4 × 2.34 **80**   **6.** 12.78 × 3.39 **39**   **7.** 28.75 × 51.23 **1,500**   **8.** 210 × 3.6 **840**

Simplify each expression.

9. 2^7 **128**   **10.** $7 \times 3^4 - 99$ **468**   **11.** $(2 \times 4^2) \div 8$ **4**   **12.** $50 \div (5^2 \div 5) + 4$ **14**

13. Choose A, B, C, or D. Find the total area of a rectangle
  that is 3 units long and 4 units wide plus a rectangle that is
  3 units long and 6 units wide.   **C**

  A. 25 square units   **B.** 18 square units   **C.** 30 square units   **D.** 60 square units

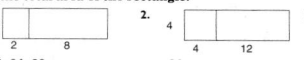

PRACTICE

Practice 4-3 *The Distributive Property*

Find the areas of the two parts of each rectangle. Then find the total area of the rectangle.

1. 3 | 2 8   6; 24; 30
2. 4 | 4 12   64
3. 5 | 6 12   90

Write the missing numbers.

4. 8 × (9 + 4) = (⬚8 × 9) + (8 × ⬚4)
5. (4 × 7) + (4 × 5) = 4 × (⬚7 + 5)
6. 9 × (7 − 1) = (9 × ⬚7) − (⬚9 × 1)
7. (5 × 7) + (5 × 6) = ⬚5 × (7 + 6)
8. 3 × (7 + 9) = (⬚3 × 7) + (3 × ⬚9)
9. 8 × (9 − 6) = (8 × ⬚9) − (⬚8 × 6)

Use the distributive property to rewrite and simplify.

10. 7 × 53
  (7 × 50) + (7 × 3); 371
11. 8 × 97
  (8 × 90) + (8 × 7); 776
12. 5 × 402
  (5 × 400) + (5 × 2); 2,010
13. 8 × 103
  (8 × 100) + (8 × 3); 904
14. 9 × 213
  (9 × 200) + (9 × 10) + (9 × 3); 1,917
15. 7 × 49
  (7 × 40) + (7 × 9); 343

Simplify.

16. 9 × (5 + 3) × 4 − 6   282
17. (8 + 7) × 3 × 2   90
18. 5 × 7 × 3 + (5 − 4)   106
19. 6 × (8 − 3) + 9 × 4   66
20. 7 × (8 − 2) × 4 + 9   177
21. (8 + 6) × 3 × 9   378

Insert parentheses into each equation so that a true statement is formed.

22. 8 + 6 ÷ 2 + 9 − 3 × 2 = 19
  (8 + 6) ÷ 2 + (9 − 3) × 2 = 19
23. 6 × 3 + 4 − 9 + 7 = 26
  6 × (3 + 4) − (9 + 7) = 26
24. 9 − 4 × 6 − 8 + 1 = 21
  (9 − 4) × 6 − (8 + 1) = 21
25. 8 + 7 ÷ 5 + 2 + 7 × 3 = 30
  (8 + 7) ÷ 5 + (2 + 7) × 3 = 30

In copymaster and workbook formats

RETEACHING

Reteaching 4-3 *The Distributive Property*

The **distributive property** allows you to break numbers apart to make mental math easier.

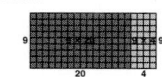

Multiply 9 × 24 mentally.
Think: 9 × 24 = 9 × (20 + 4)
  = (9 × 20) + (9 × 4)
  = 180 + 36
  = 216

The distributive property may also help you to simplify an expression.

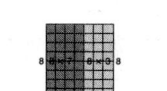

(8 × 7) + (8 × 3) = 8 × (7 + 3)
  = 8 × 10
  = 80

Write the missing numbers.

1. (⬚3 × 4) + (3 × ⬚8) = 3 × (4 + 8)
2. (6 × ⬚5) − (⬚6 × 3) = 6 × (5 − 3)
3. 4 × (⬚9 − 3) = (⬚4 × 9) − (4 × ⬚3)
4. (⬚6 × 7) − (6 × ⬚5) = 6 × (7 − 5)
5. (4 × 5) + (⬚4 × 7) = 4 × (⬚5 + 7)
6. ⬚6 × (12 + 8) = (6 × ⬚12) + (⬚6 × 8)

Use the distributive property to rewrite and simplify each expression.

7. (2 × 7) + (2 × 5)
  2 × (7 + 5); 24
8. 8 × (60 − 5)
  (8 × 60) − (8 × 5); 440
9. (7 × 8) − (7 × 6)
  7 × (8 − 6); 14
10. (12 × 3) + (12 × 4)
  12 × (3 + 4); 84

Use the distributive property and mental math to simplify.

11. 3 × 27 **81**   **12.** 5 × 43 **215**   **13.** 8 × 59 **472**
14. 7 × 61 **427**   **15.** 5 × 84 **420**   **16.** 6 × 53 **318**
17. 8 × 48 **384**   **18.** 4 × 91 **364**   **19.** 9 × 38 **342**

ENRICHMENT

Minds on Math Transparency

4-3

Change two operations in the expression below to make the value of the expression equal to 35.
5 + 5 + 5 + 5 + 5 + 5

Answers may vary.
Sample: 5 + 5 + 5 × 5 − 5 + 5 = 35

See Solution Key for worked-out answers.

147

1 Focus

CONNECTING TO PRIOR KNOWLEDGE
Show students these models.

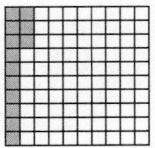

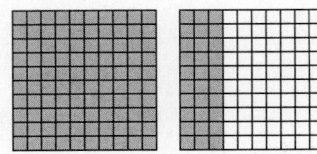

Ask them what decimal each model represents. **0.13; 1.30** Have students draw a model for 3.13. **See students' work.**

2 Teach

Work Together

VISUAL LEARNING Provide each pair of students with blank decimal squares. Suggest students use colored pencils for shading.

THINK AND DISCUSS

AEP Review the terms *tenths* and *hundredths*. Emphasize that the *ths* ending means these measurements are less than 1.

Lesson Planning Options

Prerequisite Skills
• modeling decimals (precourse)

Materials/Manipulatives
• blank decimal squares
• colored pencils (red, blue)

Resources

 Student Edition

Skills Handbook, p. 540
Extra Practice, p. 525
Glossary/Study Guide

 Teaching Resources

Chapter Support File, Ch. 4
• Lesson Planner 4-4
• Practice 4-4, Reteaching 4-4
• Answer Masters 4-4
Teaching Aids Master 20
Glossary, Spanish Resources

 Transparencies
11, 12, Minds on Math 4-4

Warm Up

A box of 20 thank-you cards sells for $9.00. What is the price per card? **$.45**

4-4 Using Models to Multiply Decimals

What You'll Learn

▼ To model the multiplication of a decimal and a whole number

▼ To model the multiplication of two decimals

...And Why

You can use models to find the answers to problems involving hobbies.

Here's How

Look for questions that
⁘ build understanding
✔ check understanding

WHAT? The face on the Mercury dime is Miss Liberty. The wings on her cap represent freedom of thought. Many people mistook the cap and wings to represent the Greek god Mercury, so the coin became known as the "Mercury" dime.

Work Together   *Modeling Decimal Products*

1. Model the sum $0.5 + 0.5 + 0.5 + 0.5$.
   a. How many squares do you need? **4**
   b. How much of each square do you need to shade? $\frac{1}{2}$
   c. How many tenths did you shade altogether? **20 tenths**

2. a. How could you rewrite the addition sentence as a multiplication sentence? $4 \times 0.5 = 2.0$
   b. ⁘ *Think About It* Would the model for the multiplication sentence look any different from the addition model? **no**

THINK AND DISCUSS

▼ *Multiplying Decimals and Whole Numbers*

When you multiply a decimal and a whole number, you can use models to show multiplication as repeated addition.

■ **EXAMPLE 1**   *Real-World Problem Solving*

Coin Collecting A collector buys two 1942 Mercury dimes. Each coin costs $.70. What is the total cost?

Write the cost of the coins as a sum and as a product. $0.7 + 0.7 = 2 \times 0.7$

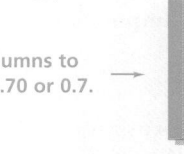

0.7

Shade 7 columns to represent $.70 or 0.7.

Shade two squares to model 2×0.7.

2

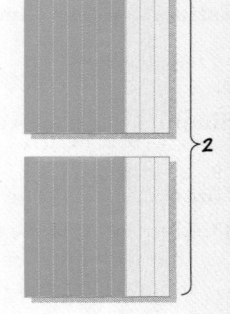

The shaded area is 14 tenths, or 1 whole and 4 tenths (1.4).
$2 \times 0.7 = 1.4$ or $2 \times \$.70 = \$1.40$

Now you may assign Exercises 1–15, 33.

148

EXTENSION **Example 1** Tell students since $2 \times 0.7 = 0.7 \times 2$ it doesn't matter if they stack the decimal models in a column or align them in a row. Have students make a model for 0.7×2 and show they get the same solution.

ASSESSMENT Pair students. Each partner writes a multiplication sentence for a whole number and a decimal. Then each student models their partner's problem and finds the product. Students check their products using addition.

■ **ADDITIONAL EXAMPLES**

FOR EXAMPLE 1

Remi buys 7 stamps. Each stamp costs $.32. What is the total cost? **$2.24**

FOR EXAMPLE 2

Model the product 0.2×1.7.

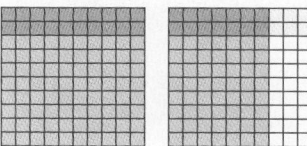

3 Practice/Assess

EXERCISES *On Your Own*

ERROR ALERT! Exercises 1–15 Students may shade grids incorrectly. **Remediation:** Remind them that the side on one small square is one tenth or 0.1. The model for 0.2×3 will be 2 squares across and 30 squares down. Have students review their models by counting the dimensions and matching them with the numbers in the problems.

▼2 *Modeling the Multiplication of Decimals*

You use just one square to model the multiplication of two decimals that are each less than 1.

3. a. ⬛*Modeling* Shade 3 rows blue. What number does this represent? **0.3 or 0.30**

b. 0.8 or 0.80

b. Shade 8 columns red. What number does this represent?

c. The purple (red and blue) area where the shading overlaps shows the product. How many squares are shaded purple? **24**

d. What decimal number does this represent? **0.24**

e. Write a multiplication sentence that describes the model. **Sample: 0.8 × 0.3 = 0.24**

4. ⬛*Number Sense* When you multiply two decimals that are each less than 1, is your answer greater than or less than 1? **less than 1**

5.

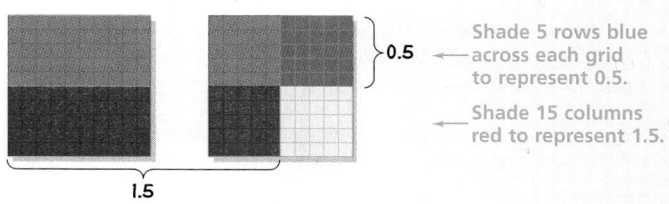

■ **EXAMPLE 2**

Model the product 1.5×0.5.

 0.5 ← Shade 5 rows blue across each grid to represent 0.5.

Shade 15 columns red to represent 1.5.

1.5

The purple area represents 75 hundredths, or 0.75.

5. ✔*Try It Out* Model the product 0.3×2.8.
0.84; see left for model.

Now you may assign Exercises 16–32, 34.

Technology Options

Prentice Hall Technology

💾 ⊙ **Software for Learners**
- Hot Page™ 11*
- Math Blaster® Mystery*
- Interactive Student Tutorial, Chapter 4*

💾 ⊙ **Teaching Resource Software**
- Computer Item Generator 4-4
- Resource Pro™ Chapter 4*

↻ **Internet**
- For related mathematics activities, visit the Prentice Hall site at www.phschool.com/math

*Available on CD-ROM only

Assignment Options for Exercises On Your Own

To provide for flexible scheduling, this lesson can be split into parts.

1 **Core** 1–15
Extension 33

2 **Core** 16–31
Extension 32, 34

Use Mixed Review to maintain skills.

EXERCISES *On Your Own*

Model each product. 1–15. Check students' work for models.

1. 0.2×3 **0.6**   **2.** 6×0.5 **3.0**   **3.** 2×0.3 **0.6**   **4.** 3×0.6 **1.8**   **5.** 0.8×5 **4.0**

6. 4×0.4 **1.6**   **7.** 9×0.1 **0.9**   **8.** 0.3×7 **2.1**   **9.** 2×0.9 **1.8**   **10.** 4×0.8 **3.2**

11. 0.5×8 **4.0**   **12.** 7×0.5 **3.5**   **13.** 6×0.4 **2.4**   **14.** 0.7×6 **4.2**   **15.** 0.2×8 **1.6**

PRACTICE

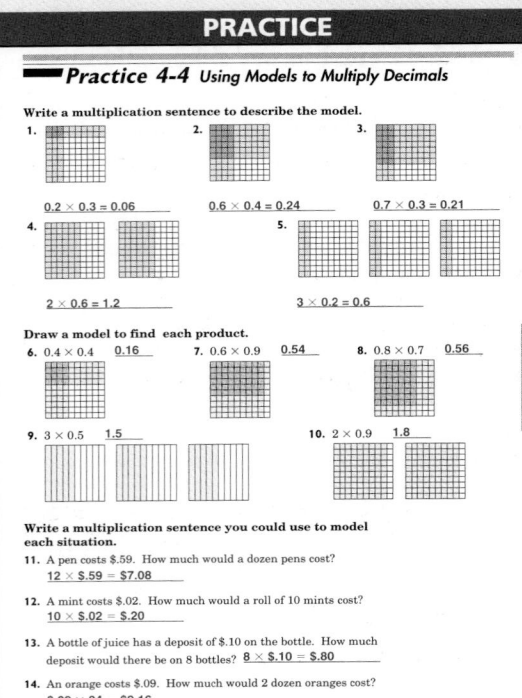

Practice 4-4 *Using Models to Multiply Decimals*

Write a multiplication sentence to describe the model.

1. $0.2 \times 0.3 = 0.06$
2. $0.6 \times 0.4 = 0.24$
3. $0.7 \times 0.3 = 0.21$
4. $2 \times 0.6 = 1.2$
5. $3 \times 0.2 = 0.6$

Draw a model to find each product.

6. 0.4×0.4 **0.16**
7. 0.6×0.9 **0.54**
8. 0.8×0.7 **0.56**
9. 3×0.5 **1.5**
10. 2×0.9 **1.8**

Write a multiplication sentence you could use to model each situation.

11. A pen costs $.59. How much would a dozen pens cost?
$12 \times \$.59 = \$7.08$

12. A mint costs $.02. How much would a roll of 10 mints cost?
$10 \times \$.02 = \$.20$

13. A bottle of juice has a deposit of $.10 on the bottle. How much deposit would there be on 8 bottles? $8 \times \$.10 = \$.80$

14. An orange costs $.09. How much would 2 dozen oranges cost?
$\$.09 \times 24 = \$2.16$

In copymaster and workbook formats

RETEACHING

Reteaching 4-4 *Using Models to Multiply Decimals*

This drawing can help you find 0.3×1.4.

① Shade 3 rows across to represent 0.3.
② Shade 14 columns down to represent 1.4.
③ The area where the shading overlaps is 42 hundredths or 0.42.
$0.3 \times 1.4 = 0.42$

Each small square is 1 hundredth or 0.01.
Each column or row is 10 hundredths or 1 tenth or 0.1.

Write a multiplication sentence to describe each model.

1. $0.5 \times 1.2 = 0.60$
2. $0.3 \times 1.5 = 0.45$
3. $0.4 \times 0.9 = 0.36$
4. $0.5 \times 0.8 = 0.40$
5. $0.7 \times 1.6 = 1.12$
6. $0.2 \times 1.8 = 0.36$

ENRICHMENT

Minds on Math Transparency

4-4

What single-digit numbers do ☐ and △ represent in the equation below?

$(☐ + △) \times (☐ + △ + ☐) = 88$

☐ = 3
△ = 5

See *Solution Key* for worked-out answers.

150

WRAP UP

IDENTIFYING THE BIG IDEA Ask students to explain how to model decimal products using decimal squares.

JOURNAL Suggest students consider factors such as time, accuracy, resources, and understanding.

LESSON QUIZ

Model each product.

1. 0.5×3.1 **1.55; See students' model.**

2. 0.8×0.2 **0.16; See students' model.**

Write a multiplication sentence to describe each model.

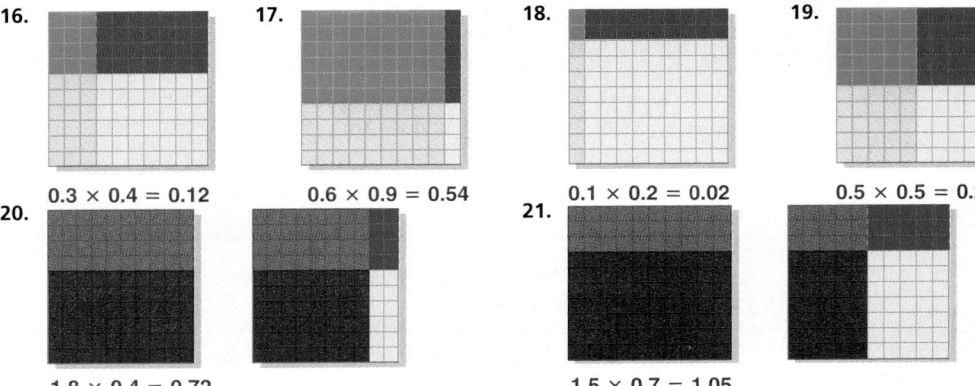

16. $0.3 \times 0.4 = 0.12$
17. $0.6 \times 0.9 = 0.54$
18. $0.1 \times 0.2 = 0.02$
19. $0.5 \times 0.5 = 0.25$
20. $1.8 \times 0.4 = 0.72$
21. $1.5 \times 0.7 = 1.05$

Model each product. **22–31. Check students' work for models.**

22. 2.2×0.4 **0.88** **23.** 0.4×0.1 **0.04** **24.** 0.7×0.2 **0.14** **25.** 1.3×0.2 **0.26** **26.** 1.7×0.5 **0.85**

27. 0.9×1.1 **0.99** **28.** 0.4×0.6 **0.24** **29.** 2.4×0.3 **0.72** **30.** 0.1×0.1 **0.01** **31.** 0.8×1.8 **1.44**

32. *Writing* Explain how to draw a model to find 1.2×0.4. **See back of book.**

33. *Science* The eggs of the Cuban hummingbird are only 0.3 in. long. Draw a model to find the length of four eggs laid end to end. **See back of book.**

34. *Computers* A palmtop computer is usually 3.4 in. deep and 6.3 in. wide. Draw a model to find the area of this computer.

> **JOURNAL**
> What are the advantages of using models? Are there any disadvantages? Explain.

34.
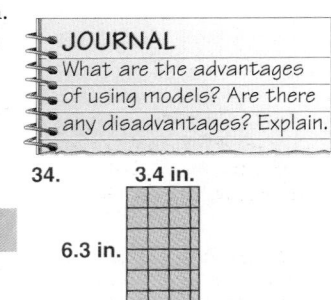
3.4 in.
6.3 in.

Mixed Review

Find the value of each expression. *(Lesson 2-3)*

35. $7 \times (2 + 4) - 4$ **38** **36.** $(3 + 7) \times 5 \div 5$ **10** **37.** $25 + 5 - 4 \times 7$ **2** **38.** $(2 \times 4) \times 3 - 1$ **23**

Find each sum or difference. *(Lesson 3-5)*

39. $0.2 + 0.18$ **0.38** **40.** $2.3 + 1.9$ **4.2** **41.** $3.15 + 0.8$ **3.95** **42.** $1.7 - 0.28$ **1.42** **43.** $0.98 - 0.8$ **0.18**

44. *Choose a Strategy* Suppose the distance to your aunt's apartment is 24 blocks. You walk 3 blocks, and then take the bus 16 blocks. How much farther is it to your aunt's? **5 blocks**

Teaching Notes

1 Focus

CONNECTING TO PRIOR KNOWLEDGE
Have students draw a decimal model to solve
3.1×6.5. 20.15 Ask:

- *How many decimal places are in each of the factors?* 1

- *How many decimal places are there in the problem?* 2

- *How many decimal places are in the solution?* 2

- *Why do you think this happens?* **Answers may vary. Sample: The model is divided into parts horizontally because one factor is in tenths. Each of those parts is divided into parts because the other factor is in tenths.**

2 Teach

Work Together
Have students compare rules when they finish the activity.

THINK AND DISCUSS

CONNECTION TO SCIENCE Example 1
Students may enjoy researching the theory of continental drift. Have students share information.

ALGEBRA Connection

4-5 Multiplying Decimals

What You'll Learn

▼ **1** To multiply decimals and whole numbers

▼ **2** To multiply two decimals

...And Why

You'll multiply decimals to solve problems in earth science and botany.

Here's How

Look for questions that
- ⬛ build understanding
- ✔ check understanding

Work Together *Multiplying Decimals with a Calculator*

 Use a calculator to find each product. Then answer the questions.

31 ✕ 65	31 ✕ 6.5	3.1 ✕ 6.5	3.1 ✕ 0.65
2,015	201.5	20.15	2.015

1. Compare the numbers in each expression. How are they alike? How are they different? **The numbers in all four expressions have the same digits with different place values.**

2. Compare the products. How are they alike and different? **The products have the same digits with different place values.**

3. ⬛*Explain* For each expression, compare the number of decimal places in the original numbers and the number of decimal places in the product. What do you notice? **See below left.**

4. ⬛*Summarize* Write a rule for multiplying decimals. Use examples to test your rule. **Check students' work.**

THINK AND DISCUSS

▼1 *Multiplying Decimals and Whole Numbers*

To multiply a decimal and a whole number, first multiply as if both factors are whole numbers. Then place the decimal point so that there is the same number of decimal places in the product as in the decimal factor.

■ EXAMPLE 1 *Real-World Problem Solving*

Earth Science North America is moving away from Europe at a rate of 0.8 inches per year. About how far will North America move in 5 years?

```
  0.8   ←—1 decimal place
× 5     ←—no decimal places
  4.0   ←—1 decimal place
```

In 5 years, North America will move about 4.0 inches farther away from Europe.

7.2 in.

5. ✔*Try It Out* About how far will North America move in 9 years?

Need Help? For practice multiplying and dividing whole numbers, see the Skills Handbook pages 540–543.

3. The number of decimal places in the product is the sum of the number of decimal places in the original numbers.

Now you may assign Exercises 1–6, 16–24, 37–39, 48–62, 66, 68.

Lesson Planning Options

Prerequisite Skills
- multiplying whole numbers (precourse)

Materials/Manipulatives
- calculator

Resources

📖 **Student Edition**

Skills Handbook, p. 535
Extra Practice, p. 525
Glossary/Study Guide

⬛ **Teaching Resources**

Chapter Support File, Ch. 4
- Lesson Planner 4-5
- Practice 4-5, Reteaching 4-5
- Alternative Activity 4-5
- Answer Masters 4-5
Teaching Aids Master 20
Glossary, Spanish Resources

Transparencies
11, 12, 19, 85, Minds on Math 4-5

Warm Up
If you wrote the integers from 1 to 100, how many times would you write the digit 3? 20

TACTILE LEARNING **Question 5** Students may benefit from using decimal squares and colored pencils.

ASSESSMENT Have pairs of students predict the number of decimal places in the product of 0.16 × 4.3. **Answers may vary. Sample: 3** Then have them find the product. **0.688**

■ **ADDITIONAL EXAMPLES**

FOR EXAMPLE 1

Human hair grows at a rate of about 0.5 in. per month. At this rate, how long will a person's hair grow in 7 mo? **3.5 in.**

FOR EXAMPLE 2

The city of Toronto is sinking at a rate of 8.6 cm per year. If it continues sinking at this rate, how many centimeters will it sink in 5.5 yr? **47.3 cm**

FOR EXAMPLE 3

Solve. $x \div 0.2 = 0.06$ $x = 0.012$

FOR EXAMPLE 4

Multiply 1,000 × 0.013 mentally. **13**

Question 6 Ask students: *How close to the answer do these estimates need to be?* **Answers may vary. Sample: The estimate needs to be close enough to determine the place value of the digits.**

Technology Options

Prentice Hall Technology

  Software for Learners

- Hot Page™ 12*
- Math Blaster® Mystery*
- Interactive Student Tutorial, Chapter 4*

  Teaching Resource Software

- Computer Item Generator 4-5
- Resource Pro™ Chapter 4*

Internet • For related mathematics activities, visit the Prentice Hall site at www.phschool.com/math

Available on CD-ROM only

Assignment Options for Exercises On Your Own

To provide for flexible scheduling, this lesson can be split into parts.

▼**1** **Core** 1–6, 19–24, 37–39, 48–62
Extension 16–18, 66, 68

▼**2** **Core** 7–15, 25–36
Extension 40–47, 63–65, 67

Use Mixed Review to maintain skills.

152

New Guinea

6. Answers may vary.
Sample: The estimated product shows where to place the decimal point in the exact product.

❷ *Multiplying Two Decimals*

When both factors are decimals, you count the decimal places in both factors to find how many places are needed in the product.

■ **EXAMPLE 2** *Real-World Problem Solving*

Botany A eucalyptus tree in New Guinea grew 10.5 m in one year. How much will this tree grow in 2.5 years if it grows at the same rate?

Estimate: $10.5 \times 2.5 \approx 11 \times 3 = 33$

$$
\begin{array}{r}
10.5 \quad \longleftarrow \text{1 decimal place} \\
\times\ 2.5 \quad \longleftarrow \text{1 decimal place} \\
\hline
525 \\
+\ 210 \quad\quad \\
\hline
26.25 \quad \longleftarrow \text{2 decimal places}
\end{array}
$$

The eucalyptus tree will grow about 26.25 m in 2.5 years. Since the estimate was 33 m, 26.25 m is a reasonable answer.

6. ⬩*Number Sense* Explain how an estimated product can help you place the decimal point correctly in the exact product.
See below left.

7. ✔*Try It Out* Find each product.
  a. 0.8×5.2 **b.** 1.3×13.8 **c.** 3.11×2.4 **d.** 0.9×2.26
    4.16   17.94   7.464   2.034

■ **EXAMPLE 3**

Solve $n \div 0.13 = 0.02$. You can rewrite as $n = 0.02 \times 0.13$.

$$
\begin{array}{r}
0.13 \quad \longleftarrow \text{2 decimal places} \\
\times\ 0.02 \quad \longleftarrow \text{2 decimal places} \\
\hline
.0026 \quad \longleftarrow \text{You need 4 decimal places. Insert two zeros and}
\end{array}
$$
place the decimal point so that there are 4 decimal places in the product.

$n = 0.0026$

MULTIPLICATION OF DECIMALS

To multiply with decimals, first multiply as if you are multiplying whole numbers. Count the number of decimal places in the factors. Then place the decimal point in the product so that there is the same number of decimal places.

3 Practice/Assess

KINESTHETIC LEARNING Exercises 1–15
Have students physically model the problems by arranging students in three rows facing the class. Give each person a name tag with a decimal, symbol, or digit to represent their place in the problem. For Exercise 1, there are 5 people in the back row (0, decimal, 4, another 0, and 3), 2 people in the middle row (multiplication sign and 5), and 4 people in the front row (2, 0, 1, and 5). Once students have the problem modeled, ask the students who represent a decimal portion of a number to count off. Then have another student stand where the decimal goes in the front row. You can repeat this activity for each exercise.

WRITING Exercise 18 Point out to students that this is a multi-step problem. Numbering each step can help students organize their answers.

ERROR ALERT! Exercises 19–36 Some students may forget to put a decimal point in their answer. **Remediation:** Encourage students to always check their work by estimating.

---

8. ✔ *Try It Out* Solve.

   a. $x \div 0.1 = 0.1$ **b.** $t \div 0.3 = 0.04$ **c.** $p \div 2.4 = 0.008$
        0.01   0.012   0.0192

9a. 25; 250; 2,500   **9. a.** ▪ *Calculator* Find 2.5×10, 2.5×100, and $2.5 \times 1,000$.
                              b. ▪ *Reasoning* Compare the products. Write a rule for multiplying by 10, 100, or 1,000. **For each zero in the factors 10, 100, or 1,000, move the decimal point one place to the right.**

10a. 0.3, 0.03, 0.003   **10. a.** ▪ *Calculator* Find 3×0.1, 3×0.01, and 3×0.001.
   b. For each decimal   **b.** Write a rule for multiplying by 0.1, 0.01, or 0.001.
   place in the factors
   0.1, 0.01, or 0.001,
   move the decimal   The rules you wrote for multiplying by 10, 100, or 1,000 can help
   point one place to   you multiply mentally.
   the left.

   ■ **EXAMPLE 4**

      Find $1,000 \times 0.26$ mentally.

      $0.260 \Rightarrow 260$ To multiply a decimal by 1,000, move the decimal point 3 places to the right.

      $1,000 \times 0.26 = 260$

   11. ✔ *Try It Out* Find 100×3.42 mentally.   **342**

Now you may assign Exercises 7–15, 25–36, 40–47, 63–65, 67.

EXERCISES *On Your Own*

Place the decimal point in each product.

1. 0.403
  × 5
  2015
  2.015

2. 2.33
  × 8
  1864
  18.64

3. 523
  × 0.5
  2615
  261.5

4. 22.76
  × 3
  6828
  68.28

5. 1842
  × 0.22
  40524
  405.24

6. 0.235
  × 55
  12925
  12.925

7. 3.14
  × 10.1
  3434 31.714
  ~~3.434~~ 31.714

8. 0.15
  × 0.31
  00465
  0.0465

9. 37.3
  × 0.5
  1865
  18.65

10. 8.42
  × 6.7
  56414
  56.414

11. 93.3
  × 1.6
  14928
  149.28

12. 4.222
  × 0.3
  12666
  1.2666

13. $3.2 \times 4.6 = 1472$
  14.72

14. $5.05 \times 3.14 = 158570$
  15.8570

15. $4.50 \times 3.8 = 17100$
  17.100

16. *Astronomy* The circumference of Earth is about 40,200 km at the equator. The circumference of Jupiter is 11.2 times as great. What is the circumference of Jupiter? **about 450,240 km**

17. *Office Supplies* A ream consists of 500 sheets of paper. The thickness of one sheet of paper is 0.01 cm. Calculate the thickness of a ream of paper. **5 cm**

DIVERSITY **Exercises 37 and 38** Some students may have favorite sports or activities not on the list. Have students share any sports popular in other cultures. Suggest they research the calories burned per minute per pound in each of the activities they name. **Answers may vary. Sample: karate; 0.9 calories/min/lb**

CONNECTION TO TECHNOLOGY Have students use spreadsheet software to explore patterns in the multiplication of decimals.

PROJECT LINK Ask: *How many decimal places does the amount of the exact cost have? 2 Could the exact cost ever have more places than that?* **Answers may vary. Sample: Probably not, the factors are price and quantity. Prices rarely have more than two decimal places, and the quantity should be a whole number.**

WRAP UP

IDENTIFYING THE BIG IDEA Ask students to explain how to multiply decimals.

pages 153–155 On Your Own

63. Answers may vary. Sample: Since the last digit of the product is a zero that occurs after the decimal point, the calculator drops it from the display.

18. *Writing* In 1994, the average car traveled about 21.5 miles per gallon of gas. In 1974, the average was 13.4 mils per gallon. How much farther than the average 1974 car could the average 1994 car travel on 12 gallons of gas? **97.2 mi; In 1994, the average car could travel 8.1 mi/gal (21.5 − 13.4) farther than in 1974. 8.1 mi/gal × 12 gal = 97.2 mi.**

Find each product.

19.	20.	21.	22.	23.	24.
1.9	2.065	35.15	5.6	6.108	450
×9	×12	×25	×31	×35	×0.01
17.1	**24.78**	**878.75**	**173.6**	**213.78**	**4.50**

25.	26.	27.	28.	29.	30.
2.065	0.18	3.1	15.35	0.96	7.6
×1.2	×0.06	×0.04	×3.2	×0.12	×0.06
2.478	**0.0108**	**0.124**	**49.12**	**0.1152**	**0.456**

31.	32.	33.	34.	35.	36.
0.7	420	0.56	6.7	0.33	1.04
×1.5	×3.3	×1.1	×10.2	×0.45	×9.5
1.05	**1,386**	**0.616**	**68.34**	**0.1485**	**9.88**

Calorie Counter

The energy in food and the energy you use are measured in calories. Not all foods have the same number of calories, and not all activities use the same number of calories. Your body weight is also a factor in the number of calories you use.

Exercise **Use the expression and the chart for Exercises 37–39.**

Weight × **Number of minutes of activity** × **Calories used per minute per pound**

Activity	Calories/min/lb
Dancing	0.05
Jumping rope	0.07
Roller skating	0.05
Running	0.10
Skateboarding	0.05
Playing soccer	0.05
Playing softball	0.04

37. Jim weighs 100 pounds. He jumps rope for 15 min. How many calories does he use? **105 calories**

38. Tara weighs 80 pounds and dances for 2 h. How many calories does she use? **480 calories**

39. How many calories will you use playing softball for 1 h 10 min? Would you use more calories playing soccer? **Check students' work.**

Algebra **Solve each equation.**

40. $x \div 0.2 = 0.7$
0.14

41. $t \div 0.03 = 0.5$
0.015

42. $p \div 1.6 = 0.04$
0.064

43. $x \div 2.1 = 0.045$
0.0945

44. $y \div 0.01 = 0.1$
0.001

45. $b \div 0.9 = 0.08$
0.072

46. $x \div 0.044 = 0.03$
0.00132

47. $n \div 0.065 = 0.155$
0.010075

154

LESSON QUIZ

Place the decimal point in each product.

1. $0.325 \times 6 = 1{,}950$ **1.95**

2. $714 \times 0.3 = 2{,}142$ **214.2**

3. $48.9 \times 5.2 = 25{,}428$ **254.28**

Find each product.

4. 2.005×1.3 **2.6065**

5. 54.9×0.8 **43.92**

6. 0.09×8.7 **0.783**

Mental Math **Find each product.**

48. 6.2×10
62

49. 7.08×0.1
0.708

50. 3.5×10^3
3,500

51. 26×0.01
0.26

52. 3.25×100
325

53. 0.82×10^3
820

54. 10×25.7
257

55. 100×1.6
160

56. 0.47×10
4.7

57. 4.82×0.001
0.00482

58. 57×0.1
5.7

59. $0.1 \times 1{,}000$
100

60. 10×9.25
92.5

61. $10^2 \times 0.008$
0.8

62. 3.2×0.01
0.032

63. Use a calculator to find 0.05×0.36. You will get 0.018 in the display. Why do you see 3 decimal places instead of 4 places? **See margin p. 154.**

64. *Marine Biology* Dolphins swim about 27.5 mi/h. A person can swim about 0.1 as fast. How fast can a person swim? **2.75 mi/h**

65. *Writing* Explain how multiplying 0.3×0.4 is like multiplying 3×4. How is it different? **Both products involve multiplying the factors 3 and 4, but for 0.3×0.4, you must place a decimal point in the product.**

***True* or *False*? Give an example to support each answer.**

66. The product of any decimal and zero is always zero. **true; $2.3 \times 0 = 0$**

67. If you change the order of two decimal factors, the product will change. **false; $3.5 \times 4.2 = 14.7 = 4.2 \times 3.5$**

68. Any decimal multiplied by 1 is the original decimal. **true; $4.1 \times 1 = 4.1$**

Mixed Review

Solve each equation mentally. *(Lesson 2-6)*

69. $x - 5 = 3$
8

70. $y + 11 = 18$
7

71. $z - 8 = 7$
15

72. $2 + b = 21$
19

73. $a - 4 = 12$
16

Use <, =, or > to complete each statement. *(Lesson 3-3)*

74. $17.34 \overset{>}{\blacksquare} 17.051$

75. $0.1056 \overset{<}{\blacksquare} 0.15$

76. $6.225 \overset{<}{\blacksquare} 6.25$

77. $0.89 \overset{>}{\blacksquare} 0.888$

78. *Choose a Strategy* Karenna has a white blouse, a green blouse, a blue blouse, a plaid skirt, and a pair of striped pants. How many different outfits can she make? **6 outfits**

CHAPTER PROJECT

PROJECT LINK: CALCULATING

Use the list of items and the prices you researched earlier to calculate the exact cost for the celebration event. How much will the event cost? How close to your estimated cost is your exact cost? Was your estimate reasonable? Explain.

Check students' work.

Practice 4-5 *Multiplying Decimals*

Place a decimal point in each product.

1. $4.3 \times 2.9 = 1247$
12.47

2. $0.279 \times 53 = 14787$
14.787

3. $4.09 \times 3.96 = 161964$
16.1964

4. $5.90 \times 6.3 = 3717$
37.17

5. $0.74 \times 83 = 6142$
61.42

6. $2.06 \times 15.9 = 32754$
32.754

Find each product mentally.

7. 8.7×100
870

8. 43.59×0.1
4.359

9. 5.97×10
59.7

10. 246×0.01
2.46

11. 726×0.1
72.6

12. 5.23×100
523

Find each product.

13. $\begin{array}{r} 5.342 \\ \times\ \ 13 \\ \hline 69.446 \end{array}$

14. $\begin{array}{r} 0.19 \\ \times 0.05 \\ \hline 0.0095 \end{array}$

15. $\begin{array}{r} 6.4 \\ \times 0.09 \\ \hline 0.576 \end{array}$

16. $\begin{array}{r} 240 \\ \times 0.02 \\ \hline 4.8 \end{array}$

17. $\begin{array}{r} 43.79 \\ \times\ \ 42 \\ \hline 1{,}839.18 \end{array}$

18. $\begin{array}{r} 0.72 \\ \times 0.43 \\ \hline 0.3096 \end{array}$

19. $\begin{array}{r} 6.72 \\ \times\ \ 83 \\ \hline 557.76 \end{array}$

20. $\begin{array}{r} 0.27 \\ \times\ 8.1 \\ \hline 2.187 \end{array}$

21. $\begin{array}{r} 5.96 \\ \times 0.08 \\ \hline 0.4768 \end{array}$

22. $\begin{array}{r} 421 \\ \times 0.07 \\ \hline 29.47 \end{array}$

23. $\begin{array}{r} 9.87 \\ \times\ 5.6 \\ \hline 55.272 \end{array}$

24. $\begin{array}{r} 1.09 \\ \times 2.14 \\ \hline 2.3326 \end{array}$

25. $\begin{array}{r} 8.76 \\ \times\ \ 29 \\ \hline 254.04 \end{array}$

26. $\begin{array}{r} 42.7 \\ \times\ 8.9 \\ \hline 380.03 \end{array}$

27. $\begin{array}{r} 4.03 \\ \times 0.09 \\ \hline 0.3627 \end{array}$

28. $\begin{array}{r} 0.25 \\ \times 0.78 \\ \hline 0.195 \end{array}$

Write a digit in each space so that a true multiplication problem results. Place a decimal point in each product. No digit may be repeated. Use digits 1 to 9.

29. $\begin{array}{r} \boxed{1}\,\boxed{5}.\boxed{7} \\ \times\ \ \ \boxed{2}.\boxed{8} \\ \hline 4\,\boxed{3}.\boxed{9}\,\boxed{6} \end{array}$

30. $\begin{array}{r} \boxed{1}\,\boxed{8}.\boxed{6} \\ \times\ \ \ \boxed{3}.\boxed{9} \\ \hline \boxed{7}\,\boxed{2}.\boxed{5}\,\boxed{4} \end{array}$

In copymaster and workbook formats

RETEACHING

Reteaching 4-5 *Multiplying Decimals*

Multiply 8.7×2.8.

An estimate can help you check multiplication.   **Estimate:** $9 \times 3 = 27$

Step 1 Multiply the factors as if they are whole numbers.

Step 2 Count the total number of decimal places in the factors.

Step 3 Place the decimal point in the product.

$$\begin{array}{r} 8.7 \leftarrow \text{1 decimal place} \\ \times\ 2.8 \leftarrow \text{1 decimal place} \\ \hline 6\,9\,6 \\ 17\,4 \\ \hline 24.3\,6 \leftarrow \text{2 decimal places} \end{array}$$

Compare the product to your estimate. 24.36 is close to 27.

Write the product with the decimal point in the correct place.

1. $\begin{array}{r} 0.9 \\ \times 2.8 \\ \hline 252 \\ \hline 2.52 \end{array}$

2. $\begin{array}{r} 3.1 \\ \times 77 \\ \hline 2387 \\ \hline 238.7 \end{array}$

3. $\begin{array}{r} 6.22 \\ \times 8 \\ \hline 4976 \\ \hline 49.76 \end{array}$

4. $\begin{array}{r} 19.6 \\ \times 2.03 \\ \hline 39788 \\ \hline 39.788 \end{array}$

Estimate, then find each product.

5. $\begin{array}{r} 1.6 \\ \times 3.7 \\ \hline 5.92 \end{array}$

6. $\begin{array}{r} 8.12 \\ \times\ 59 \\ \hline 479.08 \end{array}$

7. $\begin{array}{r} 12.3 \\ \times 6.1 \\ \hline 75.03 \end{array}$

8. $\begin{array}{r} 5.9 \\ \times 1.2 \\ \hline 7.08 \end{array}$

9. $\begin{array}{r} 23.4 \\ \times 5.2 \\ \hline 121.68 \end{array}$

10. $\begin{array}{r} 4.8 \\ \times 42 \\ \hline 201.6 \end{array}$

11. $\begin{array}{r} 9.2 \\ \times 12.4 \\ \hline 114.08 \end{array}$

12. $\begin{array}{r} 120 \\ \times 7.6 \\ \hline 912 \end{array}$

13. $\begin{array}{r} 3.15 \\ \times 2.3 \\ \hline 7.245 \end{array}$

14. $\begin{array}{r} 0.5 \\ \times 5.8 \\ \hline 2.9 \end{array}$

15. $\begin{array}{r} 4.06 \\ \times 82 \\ \hline 332.92 \end{array}$

16. $\begin{array}{r} 6.2 \\ \times 0.04 \\ \hline 0.248 \end{array}$

17. $\begin{array}{r} 3.9 \\ \times 10 \\ \hline 39 \end{array}$

18. $\begin{array}{r} 5.81 \\ \times 0.1 \\ \hline 0.581 \end{array}$

19. $\begin{array}{r} 8.2 \\ \times 0.001 \\ \hline 0.0082 \end{array}$

20. $\begin{array}{r} 2.84 \\ \times 100 \\ \hline 284 \end{array}$

ENRICHMENT

Minds on Math Transparency

4-5

I am a four-digit number. All of my digits are different. My first digit is twice my fourth digit. My second digit is twice my first digit. My last digit is twice my third digit. The sum of my digits is 15. What number am I?

4,812

See *Solution Key* for worked-out answers.

MATH TOOLBOX

In Lesson 4-5, students learned how to multiply decimals and whole numbers and how to multiply two decimals. This toolbox shows students how to use scientific notation to write large numbers.

ASSESSMENT Arrange students in groups of three. Each student writes a number with at least five digits and a decimal point and tells the number to the student on the right. That student writes the number in scientific notation and passes this number to the right. The student on the right writes the number in standard form. Students then compare numbers with the original.

ERROR ALERT! Exercises 9–12 If the exponent on the ten is larger than the number of digits to the right of the decimal point in the number, students may not be sure how to move the decimal point. **Remediation:** Remind students that writing zeros at the end of a decimal number does not change its value. Students can write as many zeros as they want to the right of the decimal number. They can move the decimal point and rewrite the number in standard form.

■ **ADDITIONAL PROBLEM**

Have students write 129.34 in scientific notation. **1.2934 × 10²**

Resources

 Transparencies
 19

pages 157–158   Think and Discuss

2a.

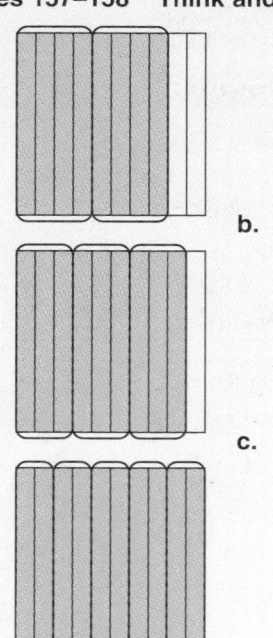

b.

c.

156

Scientific Notation

After Lesson 4-5

The *Mars Pathfinder* went to Mars in 1997. The trip distance was more than 309 million miles. You can write this number in either standard form or *scientific notation*.

Standard form:
309,000,000

To write a number in scientific notation, you write the number as two factors. The first factor is any number between 1 and 10. The second factor is a number which is a power of 10, for example, numbers such as 10^2, 10^5, or 10^{11}.

Scientific notation:
3.09×10^8

■ **EXAMPLE 1**

Biology The average human body contains about 25,000,000,000 blood cells. Write the number in scientific notation.

$$25{,}000{,}000{,}000. = 2.5 \times 10^{10}$$

Move the decimal point to make a factor between 1 and 10. You use 2.5.

The exponent shows that in this example the decimal point moved **10** places to the left.

■ **EXAMPLE 2**

Write 4.99×10^6 in standard form.

$$4.99 \times 10^6 = 4990000. \quad \longleftarrow \text{Move the decimal point 6 places to the right.}$$
$$= 4{,}990{,}000$$

Write each number in scientific notation.

3.4×10^4	1.65×10^{11}	6.54321987×10^8	2.83154734×10^5
1. 34,000	**2.** 165,000,000,000	**3.** 654,321,987	**4.** 283,154.734

5. 800,000	**6.** 93,000,000,000,000	**7.** 9,415,027,392	**8.** 92.3421
8×10^5	9.3×10^{13}	9.415027392×10^9	9.23421×10^1

Write each number in standard form.

9. 1.64×10^5	**10.** 9.0×10^6	**11.** 8.234×10^2	**12.** 9.2×10^{12}
164,000	9,000,000	823.4	9,200,000,000,000

13. *Open-ended* Use an almanac or the Internet to find data with large numbers. Write the data in scientific notation. **Check students' work.**

1 Focus

CONNECTING TO PRIOR KNOWLEDGE Ask students to recall the models used for the products of decimal numbers. Then have students brainstorm ways they could use similar models for quotients of decimal numbers.

2 Teach

THINK AND DISCUSS

TACTILE LEARNING Some students may benefit by using centimeter cubes on centimeter graph paper.

ERROR ALERT! Question 2 Students may confuse the procedure for using a model to find quotients with the procedure for finding products. **Remediation:** Remind students

that division means they must divide the model into parts. Model 0.8×0.4 and $0.8 \div 0.4$ to show them the difference.

REASONING Question 4 Some students may not understand a quotient could be greater than both the dividend and the divisor. Stress that the quotient tells the number of groups.

AEP Help students recognize the dividend. Say: *The dividend is the number you want to divide into groups.*

4-6

Using Models to Divide Decimals

What You'll Learn

▼ To model dividing by tenths

▼ To model dividing by hundredths

...And Why

You can divide decimals to solve problems when preparing food.

Here's How

Look for questions that

⚎ build understanding

✔ check understanding

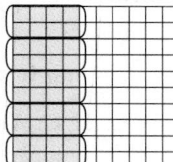

THINK AND DISCUSS

▼ Modeling Dividing by Tenths

Measurement Alika is making fruit smoothies. She has 0.8 lb of strawberries. She uses 0.2 lb in each smoothie. The expression below represents the number of smoothies Alika can make.

$$0.8 \div 0.2$$

You can use a model to divide a decimal number by tenths.

   a. 8 columns   **b. groups of 2 columns**

1. Use the model at the right.
   a. How is 8 tenths, 0.8, shown?
   b. How is 2 tenths, 0.2, shown?
   c. How many groups of 0.2 are there in 0.8? **4**
   d. ⚎ *Calculator* Find the quotient $0.8 \div 0.2$. How many smoothies can Alika make? **4; 4 smoothies**

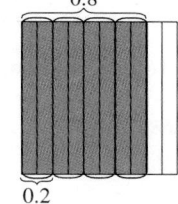

2a–c. See margin p. 156 for models.
2. ✔*Try It Out* Draw a model to find each quotient.
   a. $0.8 \div 0.4$ **2**   b. $0.9 \div 0.3$ **3**   c. $1 \div 0.2$ **5**

Now you may assign Exercises 1–3, 8, 10–19.

▼ Modeling Dividing by Hundredths

You can also use a model to divide a decimal number by hundredths.

■ EXAMPLE

Find the quotient $0.4 \div 0.08$.

Shade 4 columns to represent 0.4. $\longrightarrow$

Circle groups of 0.08. There are 5 groups. $\longrightarrow$

$0.4 \div 0.08 = 5$

Lesson Planning Options

Prerequisite Skills
- modeling decimals (precourse)

Materials/Manipulatives
- calculator
- tenths squares
- hundredths squares

Resources

📖 **Student Edition**

Skills Handbook, p. 541
Extra Practice, p. 525
Glossary/Study Guide

▣ **Teaching Resources**

Chapter Support File, Ch. 4
- Lesson Planner 4-6
- Practice 4-6, Reteaching 4-6
- Answer Masters 4-6
Teaching Aids Master 20
Glossary, Spanish Resources

▦ **Transparencies**

11, 12, Minds on Math 4-6

Warm Up

The average temperature in Mound Vernon for 7 days was 68°F. The temperatures were 72, 67, 63, 71, 75, and 61°F for the first 6 days. What must the temperatures have been on the seventh day? **67°F**

DIVERSITY Students who understand dividing decimals may be impatient with modeling. Pair these students with those who need practice modeling. Encourage them to facilitate their partner's learning.

■ ADDITIONAL EXAMPLE

Use a model to find the quotient. 1.2 ÷ 0.3 4

ASSESSMENT Write 0.8 ÷ 0.05 on the board. Have each student use a model to find the quotient. **16** Ask students to compare models and describe how they arrived at their answers.

3 Practice/Assess

EXERCISES *On Your Own*

Exercises 10–24 Give students graph paper to use for these exercises.

WRAP UP

IDENTIFYING THE BIG IDEA Ask students to describe how to use models to divide decimals.

Math at Work

If you have block scheduling or extended class periods, consider having each member of the class research a different animal. For each animal, have students gather statistical information such as weight, height,

---

Technology Options

Prentice Hall Technology

  Software for Learners
- Math Blaster® Mystery*
- Interactive Student Tutorial, Chapter 4*

  Teaching Resource Software
- Computer Item Generator 4-6
- Resource Pro™ Chapter 4*

Internet • For related mathematics activities, visit the Prentice Hall site at www.phschool.com/math

*Available on CD-ROM only

Assignment Options for Exercises On Your Own

To provide for flexible scheduling, this lesson can be split into parts.

▼**Core** 1–3, 10–19
   Extension 8

▼**Core** 4–7, 20–24
   Extension 9, 25

Use Mixed Review to maintain skills.

QUICKreview

Each number in a division sentence has a special name.

$$24 \div 8 = 3$$

Dividend | Quotient
Divisor

Now you may assign Exercises 4–7, 9, 20–25.

---

3. ✔*Try It Out* Draw a model to find each quotient.
   a. 0.3 ÷ 0.06 5   **b.** 0.9 ÷ 0.18 5   **c.** 0.6 ÷ 0.12 5
   a–c. See back of book for models.

4. ▪*Reasoning* In the sentence 0.8 ÷ 0.2 = 4, the divisor, 0.2, represents the size of each group. What does the quotient, 4, represent?   the number of groups

Work Together _____ *Modeling Decimal Division*

Work with a partner. Draw a model to find each quotient. First decide how many decimal squares you need. Next shade your model to show the dividend. Then circle groups of equal size. In these problems the divisor tells you the size of each group.
5–7. See back of book for models.
   5. 1.8 ÷ 0.3 6   **6.** 1.2 ÷ 0.2 6   **7.** 2 ÷ 0.4 5

EXERCISES *On Your Own*

Complete each sentence.

1.
▦ ÷ 0.4 = 2
0.8

2.
0.9 ÷ 0.3 = ▦
3

3.
▦ ÷ 0.4 = 4
1.6

4.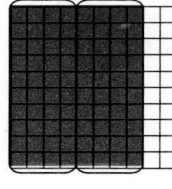
0.3 ÷ 0.03 = ▦
10

5.
0.4 ÷ ▦ = 8
0.05

6.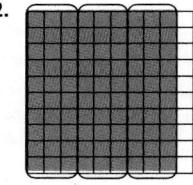
1 ÷ ▦ = 4
0.25

7.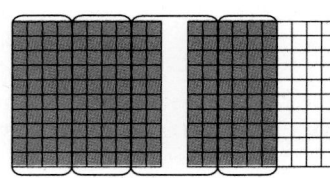
0.3 ÷ ▦ = 5
0.06

8. *Writing* Explain how to model 2.4 ÷ 0.6. Use three squares, each with ten columns; shade 24 columns; circle groups of 6 columns. There are 4 groups, so 2.4 ÷ 0.6 = 4.

9. Choose A, B, C, or D. What is the quotient 1 ÷ 0.25?   A
   A. 4   **B.** 40   **C.** 0.4   **D.** 0.04

158

population, amount of food required for feeding, and anything else that interests them. You may wish to organize students in small groups. Students use the information they found to write word problems containing decimals. Allow groups to exchange their word problems to solve.

3. Complete the sentence.

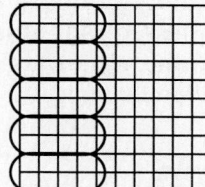

$0.4 \div \blacksquare = 5$ **0.08**

LESSON QUIZ

Draw a model to find each quotient.

1. $1.5 \div 0.3$ **5**

2. $4.2 \div 0.7$ **6**

PRACTICE

Practice 4-6 *Using Models to Divide Decimals*

Complete each sentence.

1. 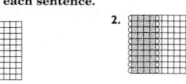
$\boxed{0.6} \div 0.3 = 2$

2.
$0.4 \div 0.04 = \boxed{10}$

3. 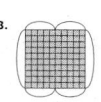
$1 \div \boxed{0.5} = 2$

4.
$\boxed{1.8} \div 0.2 = 9$

5.
$1.5 \div \boxed{0.3} = 5$

Draw a model to find each quotient.

6. $0.4 \div 0.08$ __5__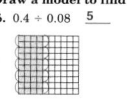

7. $0.8 \div 0.4$ __2__

8. $0.9 \div 0.15$ __6__

9. $1.5 \div 0.75$ __2__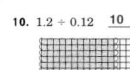

10. $1.2 \div 0.12$ __10__

In copymaster and workbook formats

Draw a model to find each quotient.   **10–24. Check students' work for models.**

10. $0.6 \div 0.2$ **3**   **11.** $1.6 \div 0.8$ **2**   **12.** $2 \div 0.5$ **4**   **13.** $1.2 \div 0.3$ **4**   **14.** $0.2 \div 0.2$ **1**

15. $1.5 \div 0.5$ **3**   **16.** $1.8 \div 0.3$ **6**   **17.** $2.4 \div 0.8$ **3**   **18.** $3 \div 0.6$ **5**   **19.** $2.8 \div 0.4$ **7**

20. $0.8 \div 0.16$ **5**   **21.** $1.35 \div 0.45$ **3**   **22.** $0.3 \div 0.15$ **2**   **23.** $0.9 \div 0.01$ **90**   **24.** $0.36 \div 0.18$ **2**

25. *Postage* Refer to the table at the right.   **Check students' work; 3 times greater.**
  a. Draw a model that shows how many times greater the postage for a 1-oz letter was in 1980 than in 1965.
  b. How many times greater was the postage in 1995 than in 1960? **8 times greater**
  c. The table does not show the price of stamps for the years 1970, 1985, 1990, and 2000. What might be appropriate stamp prices for each of these years? **Answers may vary. Sample: $0.09, $0.21, $0.27, $0.38**

U.S. Postage for a 1-oz Letter

Year	Postage
1960	$.04
1965	$.05
1975	$.13
1980	$.15
1995	$.32

Mixed Review

Solve each equation. *(Lesson 2-7)*

26. $9a = 72$ **8**   **27.** $11x = 33$ **3**   **28.** $5y = 155$ **31**   **29.** $4b = 24$ **6**   **30.** $18c = 18$ **1**

31. *Choose a Strategy* Suppose you cut a piece of string in half and then cut those pieces in half. If you continue this process, how many pieces will you have after the fifth round of cuts? **32 pieces**

Math at Work

VETERINARIAN

If you have a love for animals, then a career as a veterinarian might be right for you. These special doctors use their problem solving skills to diagnose medical problems, interpret laboratory data, perform surgery, and prescribe appropriate medicines for creatures that cannot describe their aches and pains.

If you would like to know more about working with animals as a veterinarian, visit www.avma.org for more information.

RETEACHING

Reteaching 4-6 *Using Models to Divide Decimals*

This drawing can help you find $0.3 \div 0.02$.

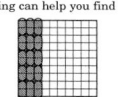

Each small square is 1 hundredth or 0.01.
Each column is 10 hundredths or 1 tenth or 0.1.

① Shade 3 columns to show 0.3 (3 tenths or 30 hundredths).
② Circle groups of shaded 2 hundredths to divide by 0.02.
③ Count how many circled groups of 0.02 there are in 0.3.

There are 15. So, $0.3 \div 0.02 = 15$.

Complete each sentence.

1. 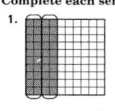
$0.4 \div 0.2 = \underline{2}$

2.
$0.6 \div 0.2 = \underline{3}$

3.
$0.36 \div 0.03 = \underline{12}$

4. 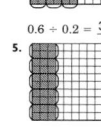
$\underline{0.4} \div 0.04 = 10$

5. 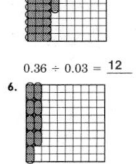
$0.3 \div \underline{0.06} = 5$

6.
$\underline{0.18} \div 0.02 = \underline{9}$

ENRICHMENT

Minds on Math Transparency

4-6

Margaret, Ron, and Eugene each bought a new movie. They each chose a different type of movie: science fiction, musical, or romance. Ron never watches science fiction. Margaret watches only musicals. What type of movie did each person buy?

Margaret: musical
Ron: romance
Eugene: science fiction

See *Solution Key* for worked-out answers.

---

1 Focus

CONNECTING TO PRIOR KNOWLEDGE
Have students model 3.2 ÷ 0.8. **4** Ask: *Does the quotient have to always be a whole number?* **no** Have students try to model 3.2 ÷ 0.7. Discuss the limitations of models. Ask: *When are models useful?* **Answers may vary. Sample: when learning to** divide; to understand what dividing means; when numbers divide evenly *When are they hard to use?* **Answers may vary. Sample: when the divisor does not divide the dividend evenly**

2 Teach

THINK AND DISCUSS

KINESTHETIC LEARNING **Example** Have students measure their walking pace by measuring the length of the classroom in feet and having a partner count how many seconds it takes to walk across the room. Then have students calculate how long it would take for them to walk across the Great Seto Bridge. They may need the fact there are 5,280 feet in 1 mile.

Question 1 Remind students to round to compatible numbers. Point out estimates help to determine if the decimal point is in the correct place.

Lesson Planning Options

Prerequisite Skills
- dividing whole numbers (precourse)

Materials/Manipulatives
- calculator

Resources

 Student Edition
Skills Handbook, p. 543
Extra Practice, p. 525
Glossary/Study Guide

 Teaching Resources
Chapter Support File, Ch. 4
- Lesson Planner 4-7
- Practice 4-7, Reteaching 4-7
- Answer Masters 4-7
Teaching Aids Master 20
Glossary, Spanish Resources

 Transparencies
11, 12, 19, Minds on Math 4-7

Warm Up
Lincoln School District has 196 sixth graders. If the students are grouped 28 to a class, how many classes are there? **7 classes**

4-7 Dividing Decimals by Whole Numbers

What You'll Learn
▼ To divide decimals by whole numbers

...And Why
You can divide decimals by whole numbers to find travel times.

Here's How
Look for questions that
🔹 build understanding
✓ check understanding

 The Great Seto Bridge crosses Japan's Inland Sea. It is the longest road and railway suspension bridge in the world.
Source: *Guinness Book of Records*

THINK AND DISCUSS

Dividing decimals is similar to dividing whole numbers. With decimals, you place a decimal point in the quotient.

■ **EXAMPLE** *Real-World Problem Solving*

Travel Time The Great Seto Bridge is 7.64 mi long. How long would it take to cross the bridge if you were walking at 4 mi/h?

Estimate: 7.64 ÷ 4 ≈ 8 ÷ 4 = 2

```
      1.91
   4)7.64
    −4 ↓
     36
    −36 ↓
      04
     − 4
       0
```
← Divide as with whole numbers. Place the decimal point in the quotient above the decimal point in the dividend. Compare the answer and estimate to determine the reasonableness of the answer.

It would take 1.91 h, or almost 2 h, to walk across the bridge.

Japan

FOR EXAMPLE

Walking at a rate of 3 mi/h, how long would it take to walk 11.25 mi? **3.75 h**

Work Together

ASSESSMENT Write 313.8 ÷ 6 and 0.092 ÷ 4 on the board. Have students find the quotients. **52.3; 0.023** Have them check their answers by multiplying and then comparing their work with classmates.

3 Practice/Assess

EXERCISES *On Your Own*

ERROR ALERT! Exercises 1–16 Students may switch the divisor and the dividend, especially when the problem is written with a ÷ sign. **Remediation:** Remind students the dividend is always the first number in division problems written with a ÷ sign. The dividend is also the number under the division house.

Have students circle the dividend in each form of problem.

OPEN-ENDED Exercise 32 Ask students to use their method to find the thickness of a page in the textbook. Then compare their results with their classmates.

RESEARCH Exercise 35 Have students pick a size and brand of peanut butter they can find easily in several stores.

---

1. ✔*Try It Out* Find each quotient.
   a. 9.12 ÷ 6   b. 385.6 ÷ 8   c. 17.28 ÷ 12   d. 77.35 ÷ 17
      1.52   **48.2**   **1.44**   **4.55**
2. ▪*Go a Step Further* The answer to the Example is 1.91 hours or about 2 hours. Find how many minutes 0.91 h is by multiplying 0.91 × 60 minutes. **54.6 min**

You can use patterns to divide mentally.

Need Help? For more practice dividing, see the Skills Handbook pages 542–543.

3a. 2.9 ÷ 10,000 = 0.00029;
    2.9 ÷ 100,000 = 0.000029;
    2.9 ÷ 1,000,000 = 0.0000029

3. a. ▪*Patterns* Write the next three division equations for the pattern shown.
   b. What happens to the quotient as the divisor increases? **It decreases.**
   c. How is the number of zeros in each divisor related to the number of places the decimal point "moves" left?

Dividend	Divisor	Quotient
2.9 ÷ 10	= 0.29
2.9 ÷ 100	= 0.029
2.9 ÷ 1,000	= 0.0029

   c. They are equal.

   d. ▪*Writing* Find 0.8 ÷ 100 mentally. Explain your method. **0.008; move the decimal two places to the left.**
4. ▪*Draw a Conclusion* Write a rule for dividing a decimal by 10, by 100, or by 1,000. **Answers may vary. Sample: Move the decimal point to the left the same number of places as there are zeros in the divisor.**

Work Together
Exploring Division Patterns

 Work with a partner. Complete each statement.
5. 1.6 ÷ ■ = 0.16 **10**   6. 1.6 ÷ ■ = 0.016 **100**
7. 1.6 ÷ 20 = ■ **0.08**   8. 1.6 ÷ 200 = ■ **0.008**

Now you may assign Exercises 1–35.

EXERCISES *On Your Own*

Find each quotient.

1. 3)‾204‾ **68**   2. 404 ÷ 16 **25.25**   3. 1,022 ÷ 28 **36.5**   4. 11)‾539‾ **49**

5. 7.5 ÷ 3 **2.5**   6. 15.40 ÷ 5 **3.08**   7. 3)‾$19.80‾ **$6.60**   8. 13.4 ÷ 4 **3.35**

9. 82)‾155.8‾ **1.9**   10. 33)‾237.6‾ **7.2**   11. 10.35 ÷ 3 **3.45**   12. 5)‾56.1‾ **11.22**

13. 569.36 ÷ 22 **25.88** 14. 22)‾$1,057.10‾ **$48.05** 15. 4.08 ÷ 3 **1.36** 16. 114.24 ÷ 56 **2.04**

17. **Choose A, B, C, or D.** Which quotient is greatest? **D**
   A. 0.075 ÷ 5   B. 0.75 ÷ 10   C. 0.625 ÷ 25   D. 7.5 ÷ 10

Technology Options

Prentice Hall Technology

 Software for Learners
- Math Blaster® Mystery*
- Interactive Student Tutorial, Chapter 4*

 Teaching Resource Software
- Computer Item Generator 4-7
- Resource Pro™ Chapter 4*

Internet • For related mathematics activities, visit the Prentice Hall site at www.phschool.com/math

*Available on CD-ROM only

Assignment Options for Exercises On Your Own

> **Core** 1–16, 20–31
> **Extension** 17–19, 32–35
>
> Use Mixed Review to maintain skills.

PRACTICE

Practice 4-7 *Dividing Decimals by Whole Numbers*

Find each quotient.

1. $1.8 \div 6$ 0.3	**2.** $16\overline{)3.2}$ 0.2	**3.** $17\overline{)5.1}$ 0.3	**4.** $9\overline{)21.6}$ 2.4
5. $15\overline{)123}$ 8.2	**6.** $108 \div 5$ 21.6	**7.** $50\overline{)17.5}$ 0.35	**8.** $24\overline{)120.60}$ 5.025
9. $19\overline{)11.4}$ 0.6	**10.** $14\overline{)889}$ 63.5	**11.** $5\overline{)316}$ 63.2	**12.** $4.15 \div 5$ 0.83
13. $7.8 \div 10$ 0.78	**14.** $89.1 \div 100$ 0.891	**15.** $10\overline{)46.3}$ 4.63	**16.** $0.6 \div 10$ 0.06
17. $20\overline{)23.4}$ 1.17	**18.** $5\overline{)0.18}$ 0.036	**19.** $26.12 \div 4$ 6.53	**20.** $7.3 \div 5$ 1.46
21. $0.12 \div 8$ 0.015	**22.** $6\overline{)3.39}$ 0.565	**23.** $1.45 \div 10$ 0.145	**24.** $20\overline{)12.6}$ 0.63

Choose a calculator, pencil and paper, or mental math to solve.

25. A package of 25 mechanical pencils costs $5.75. How much does each pencil cost? $.23

26. A sales clerk is placing books side by side on a shelf. She has 12 copies of the same book. If the books cover 27.6 in. of the shelf, how thick is each book? 2.3 in.

27. A car traveled 234.3 mi on 11 gal of gas. How many miles per gallon did the car average? 21.3 mi per gal

28. Mr. Garza spent $80.73 on 9 cassette tapes. If they all cost the same amount, how much did each cassette tape cost? $8.97

In copymaster and workbook formats

RETEACHING

Reteaching 4-7 *Dividing Decimals by Whole Numbers*

Find the quotient $1.52 \div 4$.
First, use compatible numbers to estimate the quotient.
$$1.52 \div 4 \rightarrow 1.60 \div 4$$
The quotient is about 0.40.

Step 1 Divide as with whole numbers.	**Step 2** Place the decimal point in the quotient above its place in the dividend.	**Step 3** Insert zero if necessary. Compare the quotient to the estimate.
38 $4\overline{)1.52}$ -12 32 -32 0	.38 $4\overline{)1.52}$ -12 32 -32 0	0.38 $4\overline{)1.52}$ -12 32 -32 0 0.38 is close to 0.40.

Estimate, then find each quotient.

1. $3\overline{)1.35}$ 0.45	**2.** $4\overline{)2.68}$ 0.67	**3.** $8.4 \div 6$ 1.4
4. $8\overline{)27}$ 3.375	**5.** $12.96 \div 5$ 2.592	**6.** $5\overline{)\$11.30}$ $2.26
7. $0.4 \div 16$ 0.025	**8.** $9\overline{)13.86}$ 1.54	**9.** $20\overline{)47.6}$ 2.38
10. $15\overline{)\$55.20}$ $3.68	**11.** $5\overline{)0.03}$ 0.006	**12.** $3 \div 8$ 0.375

Choose mental math, paper and pencil, or a calculator to divide.

13. $0.4 \div 10$ 0.04	**14.** $2.3 \div 100$ 0.023	**15.** $7 \div 100$ 0.07
16. $87 \div 24$ 3.625	**17.** $52.3 \div 10$ 5.23	**18.** $3 \div 1,000$ 0.003
19. $73.05 \div 15$ 4.87	**20.** $41 \div 100$ 0.41	**21.** $10.62 \div 3$ 3.54

ENRICHMENT

Minds on Math Transparency

4-7

Rebecca's little sister Tina has 48 yellow blocks and 40 green blocks. Tina builds some number of towers using all 88 blocks. What is the greatest number of identical towers that Tina can build?

8 towers each with 6 yellow blocks and 5 green blocks

See *Solution Key* for worked-out answers.

162

WRAP UP

IDENTIFYING THE BIG IDEA Ask students to explain how to divide a decimal by a whole number.

PROJECT LINK After students calculate how much money each person needs to raise, have them determine how many pounds of recycled cans each would need to collect if each pound is worth $.30.

LESSON QUIZ

Find each quotient.

1. $28.86 \div 13$ **2.22**

2. $15.5 \div 100$ **0.155**

3. $3.24 \div 6$ **0.54**

4. $10\overline{)5.5}$ **0.55**

5. $6\overline{)1.56}$ **0.26**

18. *Weather* On Thursday, 1.4 in. of rain fell. On Friday, 2.2 in. of rain fell. What was the mean rainfall for the two days? **1.8 in.**

19. *Hobbies* A pack of 15 baseball cards costs $.75. How can you use the guess and test strategy to find the cost of one card?

Sample: Write a number sentence $15 \times \square$ ¢ = 75¢, then guess numbers that multiply to make 75¢.

Choose Use mental math, paper and pencil, or a calculator to find each quotient.

20. $15\overline{)23.25}$ 1.55

21. $\$20.70 \div 10$ $2.07

22. $82\overline{)155.8}$ 1.9

23. $1.5 \div 100$ 0.015

24. $3 \div 100$ 0.03

25. $12\overline{)\$96.36}$ $8.03

26. $4.8 \div 100$ 0.048

27. $3\overline{)7.32}$ 2.44

28. $122.9 \div 10$ 12.29

29. $8.17 \div 10$ 0.817

30. $22\overline{)78.32}$ 3.56

31. $15\overline{)664.5}$ 44.3

32. *Open-ended* Describe a method for finding the thickness of a page in a book.

33. *Writing* How is dividing decimals different from dividing whole numbers?

32–33. See back of book.

34. *Money* A stack of 300 coins is 23.7 in. high. Find the thickness of one coin. Round to the nearest hundredth inch. **0.08 in.**

35. *Research* Find out the price of a jar of peanut butter at three stores in your town. Research just one size and brand. Find the mean price for that type of peanut butter. **Check students' work.**

Mixed Review

36. *Choose a Strategy* Solve if possible. If not, tell what additional information is needed.

  a. Twelve-year-old Jeron swam the 100-m freestyle in 29.56 s. His best time in 1993 was 29.6 s. What time does he need to swim in order to break the pool record? **Need pool record information.**

  b. In how many ways can you have coins that total 15¢? **6 ways**

D	1	1	0	0	0	0
N	1	0	3	2	1	0
P	0	5	0	5	10	15

Compare. Write <, >, or = . *(Previous Course)*

37. 24×5 ▣ $600 \div 5$ =

38. $1,100 \div 100$ ▣ $110 \div 10$ =

39. 19×17 ▣ $176 + 83$ >

CHAPTER PROJECT

PROJECT LINK: ANALYZING

Suppose you decide to raise money for the celebration event by recycling cans. Using your calculated costs for the event, determine how much money each student in your class needs to raise. **Check students' work.**

1 Focus

CONNECTING TO PRIOR KNOWLEDGE

Write $0.8 \div 0.2 = 4$ on the board. Have students write this problem using a division house.

$$0.2\overline{)0.8}^{\,4}$$

2 Teach

THINK AND DISCUSS

AEP Review the terms *divisor, dividend,* and *quotient*. Have students label these parts on at least three homework division problems.

Question 2 Make sure students understand that they should move the decimal points in the divisor and the dividend the same number of places to the right.

■ **ADDITIONAL EXAMPLES**

FOR EXAMPLE 1

Alayna spent $1.56 on bananas. The bananas cost $.39 per pound. How many pounds did Alayna purchase? **4**

FOR EXAMPLE 2

Find each quotient.

a. $1.44 \div 0.3$ **4.8**

b. $0.72 \div 0.012$ **60**

c. $0.231 \div 0.07$ **3.3**

ALGEBRA Connection

 **4-8**

Dividing Decimals by Decimals

What You'll Learn

▼ To divide decimals by decimals

...And Why

You can find gas mileage by dividing decimals by decimals.

Here's How

Look for questions that
🔧 build understanding
✔ check understanding

THINK AND DISCUSS

To divide by a decimal, rewrite the divisor as a whole number.

■ **EXAMPLE 1**   *Real-World Problem Solving*

Pet Care Eric spent $3.12 on pet food. The food cost $0.06 per cup. How many cups of pet food did Eric purchase?

Find the quotient for $0.06\overline{)3.12}$

Multiply the divisor by a multiple of ten: $0.06 \times 100 = 6$
Multiply the dividend by the same number: $3.12 \times 100 = 312$

$$0.06\overline{)3.12} \quad \Rightarrow \quad 6.\overline{)312.}^{\,52.}$$

$$\begin{array}{r} 52. \\ 6.\overline{)312.} \\ -30 \\ \hline 12 \\ -12 \\ \hline 0 \end{array}$$

Move both decimal points the same number of spaces to the right.

Check: $52 \times 0.06 = 03.12$ ✔

Estimate: Think $6 \times \blacksquare = 300$?
$6 \times 50 = 300$
Use the estimate to help place the first digit in the quotient.

Compare the answer to the estimate. The quotient 52 is close to the estimate 50.

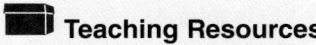

Eric purchased 52 cups of pet food.

1. ✔ *Try It Out* Find each quotient.
   a. $0.04\overline{)0.248}$ **6.2**
   b. $36.6 \div 1.2$ **30.5**
   c. $0.08\overline{)8.64}$ **108**

■ **EXAMPLE 2**

Find the quotient for $0.162 \div 0.54$.

$$0.54\overline{)0.162} \quad \Rightarrow \quad 54.\overline{)16.2}^{\,0.3}$$

$$\begin{array}{r} 0.3 \\ 54.\overline{)16.2} \\ -16.2 \\ \hline 0 \end{array}$$

Move both decimal points.

Estimate: Think $50 \times \blacksquare = 15.0$?
$54 < 16$ so write a zero in the ones place. $50 \times 0.3 = 15.0$
Place the first digit in the tenths place.

Check: $0.3 \times 0.54 = 0.162$ ✔

$0.162 \div 0.54 = 0.3$

Lesson Planning Options

Prerequisite Skills

• dividing whole numbers (precourse)

Resources

📖 **Student Edition**

Skills Handbook, p. 541
Extra Practice, p. 525
Glossary/Study Guide

📦 **Teaching Resources**

Chapter Support File, Ch. 4
• Lesson Planner 4-8
• Practice 4-8, Reteaching 4-8
• Answer Masters 4-8
Glossary, Spanish Resources

💻 **Transparencies**

19, 85, Minds on Math 4-8

Warm Up ⏱

A soccer player is preparing for a tournament by running 3 mi every day for 6 wk. The first week her run took 21 min and 40 s. Each week she trimmed 25 s off her time. How long did the 3 mi run take her during the last week? **19 min 35 s**

FOR EXAMPLE 3
A package of chicken that weighs 3.45 lb costs $5.52. How much does the chicken cost per pound? **$1.60**

VISUAL LEARNING Give students six decimal squares representing tenths and have them model 4.8 ÷ 0.8. **8**

ASSESSMENT Write 0.312 ÷ 0.06 on the board. Ask students to name the number they must multiply the divisor and the dividend by. **100** Then have them solve the problem. **5.2** Have students write a division problem in which they must multiply the divisor and dividend by 1,000 before they divide.
Answers may vary. Sample: 10 ÷ 0.875

3 Practice/Assess

EXERCISES *On Your Own*

ERROR ALERT! Exercises 1–16 Students may not know where to place the decimal point in the quotient. **Remediation:** Have students draw arrows to show the movement

Technology Options

Prentice Hall Technology

  Software for Learners
- Math Blaster® Mystery*
- Interactive Student Tutorial, Chapter 4*

  Teaching Resource Software
- Computer Item Generator 4-8
- Resource Pro™ Chapter 4*

Internet • For related mathematics activities, visit the Prentice Hall site at www.phschool.com/math

*Available on CD-ROM only

Assignment Options for Exercises On Your Own

Core 1–16, 25–40
Extension 17–24, 41, 42

Use Mixed Review to maintain skills.

164

You can divide by decimals in many real-world situations.

■ EXAMPLE 3 *Real-World Problem Solving*

Fuel Economy A family car travels 367.9 miles on 12.5 gallons of gas. To find the gas mileage to the nearest hundredth of a gallon, divide *miles driven* by *gallons of gas*.

Estimate: 367.9 ÷ 12.5 ≈ 360 ÷ 12 = 30
Use the estimate to place the first digit in the quotient.

$$
12.5\overline{)367.9} \Rightarrow 125\overline{)3679.000}
$$

```
              29.432
125)3679.000          ← Add zeros when
   -250↓                 needed.
   1179
  -1125↓               Divide to the
    540                thousandths
   -500↓               place. Then round.
    400
   -375↓
    250
   -250
      0
```

Move both decimal points the same number of spaces to the right.

Round 29.432 to the hundredths place. Since the 2 in the thousandths place is less than 5, write 29.43. The gas mileage is about 29.43 mi/gal.

2. ✔ *Try It Out* Find the gas mileage to the nearest hundredth for a car that travels 335.6 miles on 15.6 gallons of gas.
21.51 mi/gal

3. *Reasoning* Suppose you are given a car's gas mileage to the nearest hundredth and the number of miles the car traveled. How would you find the amount of gas used?
Divide the miles traveled by the gas mileage.

of the decimal points in the dividend and the divisor. Make sure students understand that the decimal point in the quotient aligns with the decimal point in the dividend after the dividend decimal has been moved.

CONNECTION TO ALGEBRA **Exercises 17–21** Ask: *What is the relationship between multiplication and division?* Answers may vary. Sample: They are opposite operations.

Exercise 23 Have students research the price of $\frac{1}{2}$ gal of milk to compare with the values in the exercise.

VISUAL LEARNING **Exercise 24** Use a stack of papers to help students visualize the problem.

CONNECTING TO THE STUDENTS' WORLD Ask students to describe how dividing decimals might be useful at the grocery store. Answers may vary. Sample: finding the unit price to compare the cost of items

WRAP UP

IDENTIFYING THE BIG IDEA Ask students to explain how to divide a decimal by another decimal.

You can use patterns to divide mentally.

a. 5.2; 52; 520; 5,200; 52,000

b. It increases by a factor of 10.

c. Move the decimal point in the dividend the same number of places that are in the divisor.

d. 360; check students' work.

4. a. ⚙*Patterns* Complete the equations at the right.
b. What happens to the quotient as the divisor decreases?
c. ⚙*Reasoning* How can you tell how many places to move the decimal point to the right?
d. Find $3.6 \div 0.01$ mentally. Explain what you did.
e. ⚙*Draw a Conclusion* Write a rule for dividing a decimal by 0.1, 0.01, or 0.001. Check students' work.

Dividend	Divisor	Quotient
0.52 ÷	0.1	= ▪
0.52 ÷	0.01	= ▪
0.52 ÷	0.001	= ▪
0.52 ÷	0.0001	= ▪
0.52 ÷	0.00001	= ▪

Now you may assign Exercises 1–42.

EXERCISES *On Your Own*

Find each quotient. Estimate first.

1. $29 \div 0.4$ 72.5

2. $0.34\overline{)0.204}$ 0.6

3. $51 \div 0.06$ 850

4. $81 \div 5.4$ 15

5. $0.5\overline{)66}$ 132

6. $5.6\overline{)16.24}$ 2.9

7. $0.04 \div 0.8$ 0.05

8. $75.03 \div 6.1$ 12.3

9. $6.497 \div 8.9$ 0.73

10. $0.9\overline{)4.05}$ 4.5

11. $0.1266 \div 0.6$ 0.21

12. $7.1\overline{)39.05}$ 5.5

13. $3.1\overline{)10.261}$ 3.31

14. $91.8 \div 5.4$ 17

15. $0.18\overline{)2.25}$ 12.5

16. $1.048 \div 0.08$ 13.1

Algebra **Solve each equation.**

17. $0.3x = 12.45$ 41.5

18. $6.64y = 1.66$ 0.25

19. $0.05r = 0.695$ 13.9

20. $1.7g = 65.62$ 38.6

21. $12.2x = 109.8$ 9

22. **Choose A, B, or C.** Which expression is equivalent to three and eight-tenths divided by thirty-two thousandths? **B**

A. $0.032 \div 3.8$ B. $3.8 \div 0.032$ C. $3.8 \div 0.32$

23. *Cost of Living* Use the chart at the right.
    a. How many times greater was the price of milk in 1990 than in 1940? **5.56 times greater**
    b. How many times greater was the price of milk in 1980 than in 1950? **2.69 times greater**

24. *School Supplies* A stack of paper measures 0.9 cm thick. Each piece of paper is 0.01 cm thick.
    a. How many pieces of paper are in the stack? **90 pieces**
    b. Could each of 25 students get three pieces? **yes**

Average Milk Prices $\left(\frac{1}{2}\text{ gal}\right)$

Year	Price
1940	$.25
1950	$.39
1960	$.49
1970	$.57
1980	$1.05
1990	$1.39

CHECKPOINT 2

Name _____ Class _____ Date _____

■■■ *Checkpoint 2*   Lessons 4-4 through 4-8

Find each product.
1. 6.8×4.5 30.6
2. 4.07×9.7 39.479
3. 0.164×36 5.904
4. 32.4×0.35 11.34

Find each quotient.
5. $2.5\overline{)63.75}$ 25.5
6. $0.16\overline{)3.728}$ 23.3
7. $7.65 \div 5$ 1.53

Solve each equation.
8. $a \div 0.3 = 0.5$ 0.15
9. $0.4x = 12.48$ 31.2
10. $4.2m = 1.428$ 0.34
11. $y \div 2.4 = 0.03$ 0.072
12. $0.06c = 0.918$ 15.3
13. $b \div 0.6 = 0.07$ 0.042

Assessment

PRACTICE

Practice 4-8 *Dividing Decimals by Decimals*

Find each quotient.

1. 0.4 ÷ 0.02
20

2. 3.9 ÷ 0.05
78

3. 0.2)26
130

4. 2.05 ÷ .05
41

5. 0.4)1.08
2.7

6. 0.68 ÷ 0.2
3.4

7. 0.7)3.57
5.1

8. 0.6)5.88
9.8

9. 0.02)0.06
3

10. 0.09)0.108
1.2

11. 0.04)0.024
0.6

12. 0.07)0.3304
4.72

13. 11.18 ÷ 4.3
2.6

14. 5.7)24.225
4.25

15. 3.6)18.072
5.02

16. 7.1)63.19
8.9

17. 5.2)43.68
8.4

18. 9.3)49.29
5.3

19. 65.026 ÷ 8.2
7.93

20. 14.82 ÷ 5.7
2.6

21. 5.3)2.279
0.43

22. 9.1)6.552
0.72

23. 4.042 ÷ 8.6
0.47

24. 2.9)2.175
0.75

Choose a calculator, paper and pencil, or mental math to divide.

25. 2.4 ÷ 0.08
30

26. 9.6 ÷ 0.6
16

27. 0.21 ÷ 0.003
70

28. 3.2 ÷ 0.04
80

29. 0.49 ÷ 0.7
0.7

30. 3.6 ÷ 0.06
60

31. 0.9 ÷ 0.003
300

32. 5.25 ÷ 0.01
525

33. 0.75 ÷ 0.15
5

34. 4.56 ÷ 0.02
228

35. 7.11 ÷ 0.01
711

36. 1.45 ÷ 0.05
29

In copymaster and workbook formats

RETEACHING

Reteaching 4-8 *Dividing Decimals by Decimals*

Find the quotient 10.8 ÷ 0.25.

Step 1
Move the decimal point to make the divisor a whole number. Move the same in the dividend.

0.25)10.8 → 25)1080.

Then use compatible numbers to estimate the quotient.

1000 ÷ 25 = 40 ← Estimate.

Step 2
Place the decimal point in the quotient above the decimal point in the dividend.

25)1080.

Step 3
Divide. Insert a zero if needed.

```
      43.2
25)1080.0
   -100
     80
    -75
      50
     -50
       0
```

Compare the quotient to the estimate. 43.2 is close to 40.

Estimate, then find each quotient.

1. 3 ÷ 0.12 __25__

2. 1.5)84 __56__

3. 78 ÷ 15.6 __5__

4. 6.4)23.68 __3.7__

5. 7.28 ÷ 9.1 __0.8__

6. 3)4.11 __1.37__

7. 0.9)1.35 __1.5__

8. 0.5)0.935 __1.87__

9. 1.9)19.95 __10.5__

10. 5.84 ÷ 0.8 __7.3__

11. 7.2)0.936 __0.13__

12. 1.01)6.464 __6.4__

13. 0.05)4.10 __82__

14. 5.2)0.832 __0.16__

15. 5.3)15.9 __3__

Choose mental math, paper and pencil, or a calculator to divide.

16. 8.05 ÷ 0.1
__80.5__

17. 0.46 ÷ 0.02
__23__

18. 0.06 ÷ 0.01
__6__

19. 24.43 ÷ 3.49
__7__

20. 5.7 ÷ 0.3
__19__

21. 0.225 ÷ 0.15
__1.5__

ENRICHMENT

Minds on Math Transparency

4-8

Write the numbers 1 through 9 in the circles, using each digit only once, so that the numbers along each side of the triangle have a sum of 20.

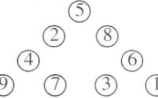

⑤
② ⑧
④ ⑥
⑨ ⑦ ③ ①

Answers may vary. Sample is shown.

See Solution Key for worked-out answers.

Find each quotient.

1. 52.06 ÷ 0.2 **260.3**

2. 0.253 ÷ 4.6 **0.055**

3. 44.7 ÷ 0.15 **298**

4. If 6.5 lb of peaches cost $8.32, what is the cost per pound? **$1.28**

Choose Use mental math or paper and pencil to find each quotient. When necessary, round to the nearest hundredth.

25. 64.97 ÷ 3.2 **20.30**

26. 0.09)4.05 **45**

27. 0.126 ÷ 0.6 **0.21**

28. 26.03 ÷ 0.1 **260.3**

29. 29.37 ÷ 4.45 **6.6**

30. 5.04 ÷ 0.01 **504**

31. 6.3)0.1386 **0.02**

32. 0.004 ÷ 0.01 **0.4**

33. 6.4 ÷ 0.1 **64**

34. 0.05)14.9 **298**

35. 0.99 ÷ 0.01 **99**

36. 0.32 ÷ 0.002 **160**

37. 3.25)26.8125 **8.25**

38. 3.8 ÷ 0.1 **8.25**

39. 10.126 ÷ 2.3 **4.40**

40. 0.85 ÷ 0.1 **8.5**

41. *Fuel Economy* Find the gas mileage of a truck that travels 303.8 mi on 24.5 gal. **12.4 mi/gal**

42. *Writing* Describe how to find the quotient 12.5 ÷ 0.04. **Answers may vary. Sample: Multiply both the divisor and dividend by 100 to get 1,250 ÷ 4. Then divide.**

Mixed Review

Write a variable expression for each word phrase. *(Lesson 2-5)*

43. x more than 14
14 + x

44. 2 times v plus 2
$2v + 2$

45. p divided by q
$\dfrac{p}{q}$

46. 6 less than b
$b - 6$

Write each number in words. *(Lesson 3-2)*

47. forty-five and nine hundred twenty-seven thousandths

48. seven thousand, fifty-six

47. 45.927   48. 7,056   49. 457,258,654   50. 2.00008   51. 0.0054

49. four hundred fifty-seven million, two hundred fifty-eight thousand, six hundred fifty-four

52. *Choose a Strategy* Talisha got off the elevator at the 9th floor. She had already gone down 5, up 6, and down 3 floors. On what floor did she first enter the elevator? **11th floor**

50. two and eight hundred thousandths

51. fifty-four ten thousandths

✓ CHECKPOINT 2

Lessons 4-4 through 4-8

For each, find the product or quotient.

1. 5.2 × 6.3 **32.76**

2. 0.239 × 8.2 **1.9598**

3. 0.13)2.132 **16.4**

4. 3.5154 ÷ 0.7 **5.022**

5. Sam's shampoo costs 0.12 cents per ounce. How many ounces are in a bottle that costs $2.88? **24 oz**

6. Cory has 0.275 L of pond water. If her test tubes are filled with 0.02 L each, how many test tubes can be completely filled? **13 test tubes**

7. *Jobs* Rosa earns $6.50 per hour as a cashier. For any time over 40 hours, she earns $9.75 per hour. Rosa worked 45 hours in a recent week. What were her wages that week? **$308.75**

PROBLEM SOLVING PRACTICE ★★

This page provides problems for students to solve using their knowledge of writing expressions, finding the mean, using equations, using too much or too little information to solve problems, and multiplying and dividing decimals. Allow students to use any method they find helpful.

Exercise 1 Direct students to first write out the factors before working to answer the question.

Exercise 2 Have students read each expression aloud and insert the labels *dollars, boys,* and *girls* after the appropriate number.

Exercise 5 Suggest students sketch the problem to help them understand it.

COOPERATIVE GROUPS **Exercise 9**
Students can work together to determine which data are needed and which are not needed.

USING MANIPULATIVES **Exercise 10** Have students model the problem with pennies.

PROBLEM SOLVING PRACTICE

Choose the best answer.

1. Which expression is equivalent to 100?   **A**

  A. $2^2 \times 5^2$
  B. 10^3
  C. $2^2 \times 2^5$
  D. $5^2 \times 2^3$

2. A group of 11 boys and 9 girls plans to go to a skating rink that charges $5 for each person. Which expression does *not* show the total amount the group will pay?   **H**

  F. $5 \times (11 + 9)$
  G. $(5 \times 11) + (5 \times 9)$
  H. $5 \times 11 \times 9$
  J. 5×20

3. Althea took a trip. On Monday she spent $12.53 for food, on Tuesday she spent $15.25 for food, and on Wednesday she spent $14.46 for food. What was the mean (average) amount Althea spent on food per day?   **A**

  A. $14.08
  B. $14.80
  C. $15.25
  D. $42.24

4. Which equation does *not* have 3 as its solution?   **H**

  F. $x + 2.3 = 5.3$
  G. $3.1x = 9.3$
  H. $x - 2 = 5.3$
  J. $x \div 3 = 1$

5. A ten-foot board is cut five times. Each cut is an equal distance from the previous cut. How many pieces of wood are there?   **C**

  A. 2 ft long   **B.** 5 pieces
  C. 6 pieces   **D.** 1 ft long

6. Which of the following is a solution to $x - 19 = 16 + 4 \times 2$?   **J**

  F. 5
  G. 24
  H. 40
  K. 43

Note that Exercises 7–10 have *five* answer choices.

7. A sheet of metal has a thickness of 0.006 in. What is the total thickness of a stack of 12 sheets?   **D**

  A. 72 in.   **B.** 7.2 in.
  C. 0.72 in.   **D.** 0.072 in.
  E. Not Here

8. A set of 5 videos costs $68.79. Estimate the cost of one video.   **J**

  F. less than $8
  G. less than $10
  H. between $10 and $11
  J. between $12 and $20
  K. more than $20

9. Pizza, salad, cake, and soft drinks are served at a party for 36 people. Each pizza serves 4 people. Each pound of salad and each cake serves 6 people. Each person drinks 2 soft drinks. Which cost is *not* needed to find the total cost of the food?   **C**

  A. cost of each pizza
  B. cost of each soft drink
  C. cost of renting the bowling alley
  D. cost of salad per pound
  E. cost of each cake

10. Cookies cost $.08 each. What is the greatest number you can buy with $2.00?   **J**

  F. 2   **G.** 16   **H.** 20
  J. 25   **K.** 160

1 Focus

CONNECTING TO PRIOR KNOWLEDGE
Have students imagine they want to spend $150 for a new bicycle and helmet. Ask: *What information do you need?* **Answers may vary. Sample: cost of the bicycle and helmet, amount of sales tax**

Lesson Planning Options

Prerequisite Skills

• multiplying and dividing decimals (4-5 and 4-8)
• recognizing patterns (2-1)

Resources

 Student Edition

Skills Handbook, p. 540
Extra Practice, p. 525
Glossary/Study Guide

 Teaching Resources

Chapter Support File, Ch. 4
• Lesson Planner 4-9
• Practice 4-9, Reteaching 4-9
• Answer Masters 4-9
Glossary, Spanish Resources

 Transparencies
Minds on Math 4-9

Warm Up

Round to the nearest hundredth.
23.673 **23.67**
0.798 **0.80**
572.398 **572.40**

2 Teach

THINK AND DISCUSS

AEP **DIVERSITY** Tell students the word perimeter comes from the Greek words for *measure* and *around*. Have them share the word for perimeter in other languages. **Answers may vary. Sample: perimetro (Italian), périmètre (French)**

AUDITORY LEARNING Read the problem aloud. Have students listen for the question and write it down.

ASSESSMENT Give students this problem. *It costs $3.50 to rent a bike for 1 h and $2.50 to rent a paddle boat for $\frac{1}{2}$ h. Jim rents a bike at 8:00 A.M. Cindy rents a paddle boat at 9:00 A.M. Jim returns the bike at noon. For how long did Jim rent the bike?* Have students rewrite the problem so that it has only the information they need to solve the problem. **Answers may vary. Sample: Jim rents a**

PROBLEM SOLVING STRATEGY

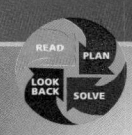

4-9 Too Much or Too Little Information

Problem Solving Strategies

Draw a Diagram
Guess and Test
Look for a Pattern
Make a Model
Make a Table
Simulate a Problem
Solve a Simpler Problem
Use Logical Reasoning
Use Multiple Strategies
✔ Too Much or Too Little Information
Work Backward

THINK AND DISCUSS

Sometimes you do not have enough information to solve a problem. At other times, problems have more information than you need. You have to decide.

SAMPLE PROBLEM...

Pablo is making a box kite out of wooden dowels and paper strips. The top and bottom of the kite are square. The sides of each square are 26.5 cm long. The dowels cost $2.20. Other supplies such as glue, string, and tape cost $4.27 altogether. The paper strips wrap around the kite. Paper strips are 13 cm wide and are sold by length in centimeters. Find the total length of the paper strips he will need. Pablo has $10.00 to spend on supplies and is wondering if he has enough money.

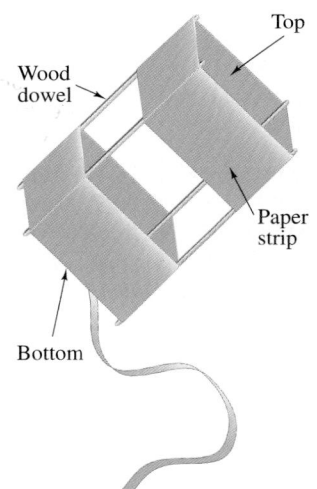

Top
Wood dowel
Paper strip
Bottom

1a. the total length of the paper strips needed for the kite and if Pablo's $10 covers the cost of materials

 READ

Read for understanding. Summarize the problem.

PLAN

Decide on a strategy.

1. Think about the information that is given.
   a. What do you need to find out? **See above left.**
   b. What information do you need to solve the problem?
      1b. the dimensions of the kite   2a. square
2. a. What is the shape of the top and bottom of the kite?
   b. What is the length of each side of the top and bottom squares? **26.5 cm**   **c. See below.**
   c. How can you use this information to solve the problem?
   d. Do you need to know the width of each paper?
      No; the paper strips are sold by length.
3. You have decided what information you need. What unnecessary information is given? **none**

2c. Add the lengths of the sides to find the length needed for each strip.

bike at 8:00 A.M. and returns the bike at noon. For how long did Jim rent the bike? Then have them solve the problem. **4 h**

■ **ADDITIONAL PROBLEM**

Suppose you want to put a fence around a rectangular garden. Plastic fencing costs $.25 per ft. Wood fencing costs more. The garden is 21 ft by 15 ft and has an area of 315 sq. ft. How much will you pay for plastic fencing? **$18** How much more does wood fencing cost? **cannot find; need to know cost of wood fencing**

3 Practice/Assess

EXERCISES *On Your Own*

ERROR ALERT! Exercise 4 Students may not recognize a problem that contains too much or too little information because they do not read the problem carefully. Remediation: Have students read the problem carefully and highlight the question. Have them make a list of the facts they need to answer the question and check to see if that information is given.

WRITING Exercise 12 Encourage students to think of additional information that might seem useful.

WRAP UP

IDENTIFYING THE BIG IDEA Ask students to explain how to tell if a problem has too little or too much information.

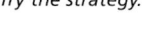 **SOLVE**
Try the strategy.

4. One way to solve the problem is to find the perimeter of the square. Then double the perimeter to find the total length of paper needed for the two paper strips.
   212 cm
   a. What is the length of paper Pablo needs for the two strips?
   b. What is another way to solve the problem?
   Multiply 26.5 × 8.

LOOK BACK
Think about how you solved the problem.

5. Let's find how much it will cost to make the kite.
   a. What information will help you find the total cost?
   b. What information is missing? **cost of paper**
   a. cost of materials

Now you may assign Exercises 1–12.

EXERCISES *On Your Own*

Solve if possible. If not, tell what additional information is needed.

1. *Transportation* Nathon bought two identical bicycle tires for a total of $21.90. The diameter of each tire is 20 in. The combined weight of the two tires is 2.9 lb.
   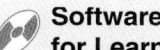 *e — diameter of tire*
   a. How much did each tire cost? **$10.95**
   b. What information did you use to solve part (a)? **cost for two tires**
   c. How much does one tire weigh? **1.45 lb**
   d. What information did you use to solve part (c)? **weight of two tires**

2. *Money* Matt buys some comic books. He hands the clerk $10.00 and receives $1.45 in change. Each comic book has the same price. How much does each comic book cost? **Answers may vary. Sample: If 5 comics purchased each is $1.71, if 3 comics purchased each is $2.85.**

3. *Interior Decorating* A pair of curtains costs $69.99. Each curtain measures 45 in. by 98 in. The pair weighs 1.50 lb.
   a. How much does each curtain weigh? **0.75 lb**
   b. What unnecessary information is given? **curtain cost and measurements**

4. *Savings* When Sasha was 7 years old, her mother started a college fund with $2,000. Every year she deposited the same amount into the account. Suppose she continues the pattern shown in the table. How much money will Sasha's mother have deposited when Sasha is 18 years old? (Note: Ignore interest earned.) **$10,250**

   Sasha's College Fund

Sasha's Age	Total Amount Deposited
7 years old	$2,000
8 years old	$2,750
9 years old	$3,500
10 years old	$4,250

5. *Quilting* A quilt pattern has a 5-by-5 grid of squares. The design of the grid calls for alternating blue and red squares. How many squares of each color does the grid contain?
   either 12 blue and 13 red or 12 red and 13 blue

Technology Options

Prentice Hall Technology

💾 💿 **Software for Learners**
• Math Blaster® Mystery*
• Interactive Student Tutorial, Chapter 4*

💾 💿 **Teaching Resource Software**
• Computer Item Generator 4-9
• Resource Pro™ Chapter 4*

🔄 **Internet** • For related mathematics activities, visit the Prentice Hall site at www.phschool.com/math

*Available on CD-ROM only

Assignment Options for Exercises On Your Own
> **Core** 1–11
> **Extension** 12

Use Mixed Review to maintain skills.

169

Practice 4-9 *Problem-Solving Strategy:*
Too Much or Too Little Information

Solve if possible. If not, tell what information is needed.

1. The electrician charged Audun for a wiring job. The rates were $48 per hour plus $23.56 for parts. What was the total amount Audun was charged?
need to know number of hours worked

2. A horse measured 12.6 hands in height. If a hand is about 4 in., what was the horse's height in inches?
50.4 in.

3. Camilla worked 8 hours a week for 14 weeks. She earns $4.55 per hour. How much did she earn?
$509.60

4. Kosey's school sold 397 tickets for a fun night and collected $893.25. If expenses came to $247.93, how much profit did the school make?
$645.32

5. The Picnic Committee split up posters to be distributed to local merchants. If each committee member took 12 posters, how many merchants can display a poster about the picnic?
need to know number of committee members

6. Rashida bought some boxes of greeting cards. One type cost $5.98 a box. Another type cost $7.29 a box. Rashida bought 15 boxes, and spent $97.56 total. How many boxes of each type did she buy?
9 of the $5.98 boxes, 6 of the $7.29 boxes

7. Herman plans to work for 30 weeks. He will earn $175 per week. He plans to save all except $55 per week so that he can pay back a loan of $1,000. How much will he save in 16 weeks?
$1,920

8. Jodi has some quarters and dimes. How many possible amounts of money could she have?
need to know the numbers of quarters
and dimes

In copymaster and workbook formats

Reteaching 4-9 *Problem-Solving Strategy:*
Too Much or Too Little Information

The first horse on earth is called eohippus or dawn horse. It was 11 inches high. Its fossil was discovered in the South Dakota Badlands in 1903. How long ago was the fossil discovered? How long ago did eohippus live?

Read What does the problem ask you to find? *How long ago was the fossil discovered? How long ago did eohippus live?*

Plan What information do you need to answer each question? Is there information given that is not needed? *The first question can be answered by using the information that the eohippus was discovered in 1903. To answer the second question you would need to know when eohippus lived. You do not need to use the height of the eohippus.*

Solve To find how long ago the fossil was discovered, subtract 1903 from the current year. For example:

1999
−1903
96 years ago

Look Back How can you be sure that you cannot answer the second question? *Reread the problem to be certain that you have not missed the needed information.*

Solve if possible. If not, tell what information is needed.

1. The age of reptiles lasted from 275,000,000 years ago to 65,000,000 years ago. How long did the age of reptiles last?
210,000,000 yr

2. The kronosaurus was a large marine reptile that lived 100 million years ago. It measured 55 ft long with a skull 11.5 ft long. How long was the rest of the body?
43.5 ft

3. The largest prehistoric shark lived 15 million years ago. It was about 43 ft long. A modern hammerhead shark can grow to be 15 ft long and weigh 1,000 lb. How much more did the prehistoric shark weigh than the hammerhead shark?
need to know weight of prehistoric shark

4. The winged reptile pterosaur lived 70 million years ago. It may have had a wingspread as great as 69 ft. How much longer was the wingspread than the body length?
need to know body length

Minds on Math Transparency

4-9

Karl keeps losing buttons. One minute after losing one button, he lost another. He lost another button two minutes later, and then he lost another button four minutes later, and so on. Will Karl lose 25 buttons in one year?

no

See *Solution Key* for worked-out answers.

JOURNAL Have students think of problems they have tried to solve and either they did not know enough to solve the problem and had to do some research or they knew too much and had to sort through the information. If they cannot think of a problem they had to solve, have them think of a problem a friend or a family member had to solve.

LESSON QUIZ

Solve if possible. If not, tell what information is needed.

1. Rob buys red biking shorts for $27.50, black shorts for $19.95, and a helmet for $34.99. How much did he spend on shorts? **$47.45**

2. Rob had $33.55 left after he bought shorts and a helmet. Then he bought biking gloves. How much money did he have left? **cannot solve; need to know cost of gloves**

---

6. *Cost of Living* Use the chart at the right.
   a. How much more did bread cost in 1990 than in 1950? **$0.55**
   b. How many times greater was the price of a loaf of bread in 1970 than in 1940? **3 times greater**

7. *Horses* The record shoulder height for a horse is 78 in. A horse's height is measured in hands. One hand is about 4 in. What is the record shoulder height in hands? **19.5 hands**

8. *Jobs* Paul works for 2 hours each Monday, Wednesday, and Friday. He is saving to buy a bike that costs $245. He earns $6 per hour. How many weeks must he work to be sure he has enough money? **7 wk**

60 Years of Bread Prices (1-lb loaf)	
1930	$.04
1940	$.08
1950	$.14
1960	$.20
1970	$.24
1980	$.51
1990	$.69

Source: Bureau of Labor

9. *Dressmaking* A dressmaker sent 250 dresses to several department stores. The dressmaker sent every store the same number of dresses. How many did each store receive?
You need to know the number of stores.

10. *Telecommunications* The telephone company charged Ron for a phone call. The rates were $2.40 for the first minute and $.60 for each additional minute. For how many additional minutes was Ron charged? **You need to know the total phone bill.**

11. *Hobbies* Mark collected 15 postcards. Some of the cards cost $.79 and some cost $1.19. He spent a total of $14.25. How many postcards of each price did he buy? **nine $.79 cards and six $1.19 cards**

12. a. *Writing* Write a word problem with too much information. **a–b. Check students' work.**
    b. Write a word problem with too little information.

JOURNAL
How can you use the problem solving strategy you studied in this lesson in your daily life? Give an example.

Mixed Review

Use mental math to find each product or quotient.
(Lessons 4-4 and 4-8)

13. 2.3×10
23

14. $0.12 \div 4$
0.03

15. 25.8×100
2,580

16. $1 \div 0.5$
2

17. $579 \times 1,000$
579,000

Round each decimal to the nearest tenth. *(Lesson 3-6)*

18. 44.68
44.7

19. 8.146
8.1

20. 0.0519
0.1

21. 658.444
658.4

22. 8,291.09
8,291.1

23. Marsha has 19 nickels. Jerry has 11 dimes. Who has more money? How much more? *(Previous Course)* **Jerry; $.15 more**

1 Focus

CONNECTING TO PRIOR KNOWLEDGE Ask students to name metric units of length from smallest to largest. **millimeter, centimeter, meter, kilometer** Ask: *How many millimeters are in a centimeter?* **10** *How many centimeters are in a meter?* **100** *How many meters are in a kilometer?* **1,000** *What do all these answers have in common?* **Answers may vary. Sample: They are multiples of 10.**

2 Teach

THINK AND DISCUSS

KINESTHETIC LEARNING If you have extended class periods or block scheduling, give pairs of students a meter stick and a metric ruler. Have them measure their bodies to find parts that measure 1 mm, 1 cm, and 1 m. **Answers may vary. Sample: diameter of ten strands of hair; width of a finger; body length from shoulder to knee** Have students research the history of the metric system. **Answers may vary. Sample: A meter is $\frac{1}{10,000,000}$ of an arc from the equator through Paris to the North Pole. The word *meter* comes from the Greek word *metron*, meaning a *measure*.**

MEASUREMENT Connection

4-10 Patterns of Changing Metric Units

What You'll Learn

▼ To change metric units

▼ To use mental math to change units

...And Why

You often need to change metric units to solve problems in geography and nutrition.

Here's How

Look for questions that
⊹ build understanding
✔ check understanding

THINK AND DISCUSS

▼ Changing Metric Units

Metric units are used in science and technology. They are universally recognized, and changes from one unit to another are easy to do.

You can rewrite one metric unit as another metric unit by multiplying or dividing by a multiple of 10.

Multiply to change from greater units to lesser units.

$$\text{km} \quad \times 1{,}000 \quad \text{m} \quad \times 100 \quad \text{cm} \quad \times 10 \quad \text{mm}$$

$$\text{km} \quad \div 1{,}000 \quad \text{m} \quad \div 100 \quad \text{cm} \quad \div 10 \quad \text{mm}$$

Divide to change from lesser units to greater units.

■ EXAMPLE 1 *Real-World Problem Solving*

The distance from Earth's equator to the North Pole along the Earth's surface is 10,000,000 meters. What is the distance in kilometers?

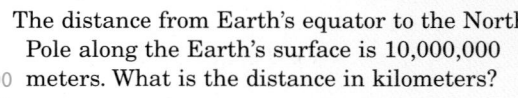

$$\begin{array}{r} 10{,}000 \\ 1{,}000\overline{)10{,}000{,}000} \\ \underline{-1{,}000} \\ 0 \end{array}$$ ◄— Divide by 1,000 to change m to km.

The equator is 10,000 km from the North Pole.

1. ⊹*Look Back* In Example 1, you started with 10,000,000 meters.
   a. Is the meter a larger or smaller unit than the kilometer? **smaller**
   b. Is the answer greater than or less than 10,000,000? **less than**

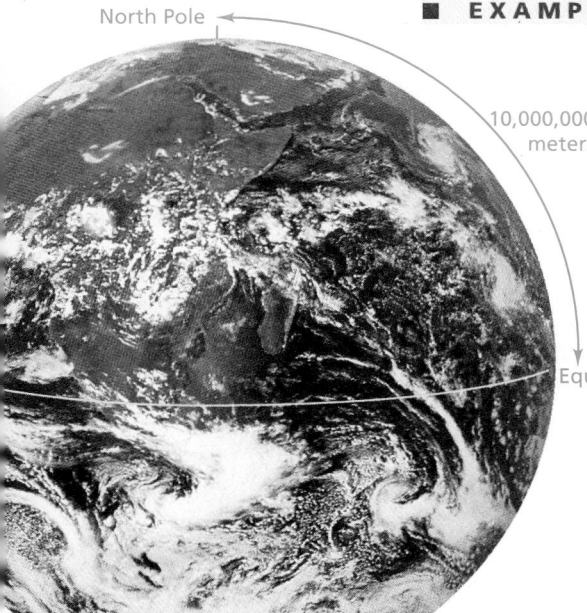

North Pole ◄

10,000,000 meters

Equator

Lesson Planning Options

Prerequisite Skills
- recognizing patterns (2-1)
- multiplying and dividing by multiples of 10 (precourse)

Vocabulary/Symbols
kilo-, centi-, milli-

Materials/Manipulatives
- calculator

Resources

📖 **Student Edition**

Skills Handbook, p. 543
Extra Practice, p. 525
Glossary/Study Guide

📚 **Teaching Resources**

Chapter Support File, Ch. 4
- Lesson Planner 4-10
- Practice 4-10, Reteaching 4-10
- Answer Masters 4-10
Teaching Aids Master 3
Glossary, Spanish Resources

🖥 **Transparencies**
17, 19, Minds on Math 4-10

Warm Up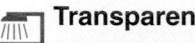

Write five decimal numbers that round to 6. **Answers may vary; any number from 5.5 to 6.4.**

171

Question 3a Ask: *Do you multiply or divide to convert from milliliters to liters?* **divide**

■ **ADDITIONAL EXAMPLES**

FOR EXAMPLE 1
The 10,000-m run is an Olympic event. How many kilometers long is it? **10 km**

FOR EXAMPLE 2
A container of peach yogurt has 18 g of sugar. How many milligrams is that? **18,000 mg**

DIVERSITY Most countries in the world use the metric system. Ask students to discuss the advantages and disadvantages of converting to this system in the United States.

ASSESSMENT Ask pairs of students to write a rule for changing kilograms to grams, centimeters to meters, and milliliters to liters.

3 Practice/Assess

EXERCISES *On Your Own*

Exercises 1–18 Encourage students to use mental math to complete the exercises.

Technology Options

Prentice Hall Technology

  Software for Learners
- Math Blaster® Mystery*
- Interactive Student Tutorial, Chapter 4*

  Teaching Resource Software
- Computer Item Generator 4-10
- Resource Pro™ Chapter 4*

Internet • For related mathematics activities, visit the Prentice Hall site at www.phschool.com/math

Available on CD-ROM only

Assignment Options for Exercises On Your Own

To provide for flexible scheduling, this lesson can be split into parts.

▼ **Core** 1–18
Extension 19, 20, 36

▼ **Core** 21–32
Extension 33–35

Use Mixed Review to maintain skills.

172

---

2. ✔*Try It Out* Complete each statement. Use the diagram on page 171 to help you decide whether to multiply or divide.
   a. One of the world's longest dogs measures 240 cm. How many meters long is this dog?
      240 cm = ■ m **2.4**
   b. A sprinter runs 60,000 m a week to train for the 400-m race event. How many kilometers is this?
      60,000 m = ■ km **60**
   c. The world's largest wave was about 3.36 kilometers tall. How many meters tall is this?
      3.36 km = ■ m **3,360**

The most common metric units use the prefixes *kilo-*, *centi-*, and *milli-*.

Prefix	Meaning	Examples
kilo-	1,000	kilometer (1,000 m), kilogram (1,000 g)
centi-	$\frac{1}{100}$ or 0.01	centimeter (or 0.01 m), centigram (or 0.01 g)
milli-	$\frac{1}{1,000}$ or 0.001	milliliter (or 0.001 L), millimeter (or 0.001 m)

Knowing what the prefixes mean can help you more easily change units. For example, to write 2 kilometers as meters, you multiply 2 by 1,000 to get 2,000 meters.

Greater units   Lesser units

$\times 1,000$ $\times 1,000$

| kL, kg, km | | L, g, m | | mL, mg, mm |

$\div 1,000$ $\div 1,000$

3. Change each measure to either liters, meters, or grams.
   a. 2,000 mL   b. 3.7 kL   c. 830 mL   d. 6,300 mg
   e. 0.5 km   f. 7,525 cm g. 1.56 kg   h. 75 cm

4. ⸬*Reasoning* When you are changing units, how do you decide whether you multiply or divide? Explain.

Now you may assign Exercises 1–20, 36.

▼ 2 *Using Mental Math to Change Units*

You can use mental math to multiply or divide by multiples of 10. The important part of this process is deciding the direction and number of places to move the decimal point.

QUICKreview

Common Metric Units

kL = kiloliter
L = **liter**
mL = milliliter

kg = kilogram
g = **gram**
mg = milligram

km = kilometer
m = **meter**
cm = centimeter
mm = millimeter

3a. 2 L
b. 3,700 L
c. 0.83 L d. 6.3 mg e. 500 m f. 75.25 m g. 1,560 g h. 0.75 m

4. Answers may vary. Sample: Think about how one unit relates to the other.

ERROR ALERT! Exercises 1–18 Some students may be confused about which way to move the decimal point when changing units. **Remediation:** Tell students moving the decimal to the right makes the number larger. Moving the decimal to the left makes the number smaller. When they change units, they must match a smaller unit with a larger number and a larger unit with a smaller number. Have students check their answers using this idea.

CONNECTION TO ALGEBRA Exercise 36 Have students fill in the missing number. x kg = ■ g **1,000x** Suggest they check their formula with their answers to Exercises 13, 15, and 18.

EXTENSION Ask students to research the meaning of metric prefixes *pico, nano, mega,* and *giga.* **one-trillionth; one-billionth; one million, one billion**

WRAP UP

IDENTIFYING THE BIG IDEA Ask students to tell how to change units within the metric system.

PORTFOLIO Share with students the criteria you will use to assess their work in portfolios, as well as how you plan to use the results. Students should understand how the rubrics are used to assess their work, how each piece in the portfolio counts, and how the scores they get in their portfolios will affect their overall evaluation.

MULTIPLYING AND DIVIDING BY MULTIPLES OF 10

To multiply by a multiple of 10, move the decimal point one place to the right for each zero in the multiple of 10.

To divide by a multiple of 10, move the decimal point one place to the left for each zero in the multiple of 10.

When you understand the pattern, you simply move the decimal point.

■ **EXAMPLE 2** *Real-World Problem Solving*

Nutrition A banana contains 950 mg of protein. How many grams of protein does a banana contain?

950 mg ÷ 1,000 = __?__ g ⟵ Divide by 1,000 to change milligrams to grams.

950 ⟹ 0.950 ⟵ Move the decimal point 3 places to the left.

A banana contains 0.95 g of protein.

5. ✔*Try It Out* Complete each statement. Use the charts on pages 171 and 172 when needed.
   a. 102.4 mL = ■ L **0.1024**   **b.** 745.3 cm = ■ m **7.453**
   c. 26.8 kg = ■ g   **26,800**   **d.** 0.5 L = ■ mL **500**

Now you may assign Exercises 21–35.

EXERCISES *On Your Own*

Change each measure to meters.

1. 1.3 km
   1,300 m
2. 500 mm
   0.5 m
3. 20 cm
   0.2 m
4. 6 km
   6,000 m
5. 3700 mm
   3.7 m
6. 40 cm
   0.4 m

Change each measure to liters.

7. 0.005 kL
   5 L
8. 120 mL
   0.12 L
9. 3070 mL
   3.07 L
10. 0.61 kL
    610 L
11. 503 mL
    0.503 L
12. 6.4 kL
    6,400 L

Change each measure to grams.

13. 8 kg
    8,000 g
14. 7,000 mg
    7 g
15. 0.24 kg
    240 g
16. 34,000 mg
    34 g
17. 500 mg
    0.5 g
18. 0.07 kg
    70 g

19. **Choose A, B, C, or D.** Which is *not* equivalent to the others? (*Hint:* Write each measure in meters.) **A**

   A. 355.5 cm   **B.** 35.55 m   **C.** 0.03555 km   **D.** 35,550 mm

Practice 4-10 Patterns of Changing Metric Units

Change each measure to meters.

1. 800 mm	2. 50 cm	3. 2.6 km	4. 7 km	5. 250 mm
0.8 m	0.5 m	2,600 m	7,000 m	0.25 m

6. 35 km	7. 40 mm	8. 300 cm	9. 1.8 km	10. 450 cm
35,000 m	0.04 m	3 m	1,800 m	4.5 m

Change each measure to liters.

11. 160 mL	12. 0.36 kL	13. 0.002 kL	14. 240.9 mL	15. 368.5 mL
0.16 L	360 L	2 L	0.2409 L	0.3685 L

16. 8 kL	17. 80 mL	18. 17.3 mL	19. 0.09 kL	20. 330 mL
8,000 L	0.08 L	0.0173 L	90 L	0.33 L

Change each measure to grams.

21. 4,000 mg	22. 7 kg	23. 56,000 mg	24. 0.19 kg	25. 754.8 mg
4 g	7,000 g	56 g	190 g	0.7548 g

26. 600 mg	27. 90 kg	28. 2,800 mg	29. 0.4 kg	30. 58.1 mg
0.6 g	90,000 g	2.8 g	400 g	0.0581 g

Use mental math to complete each statement.

31. ■ km = 3,400 cm	32. 42,000 mL = ■ kL	33. 3.7 cm = ■ km
0.034	0.042	0.000037

34. 5,100 mL = ■ L	35. 77.8 mm = ■ cm	36. 9.5 kL = ■ mL
5.1	7.78	9,500,000

37. 2.564 mL = ■ kL	38. ■ km = 400,000 mm	39. 948 mm = ■ cm
0.000002564	0.4	94.8

40. ■ mL = 0.648 kL	41. ■ kg = 6,000 mg	42. ■ mL = 0.1678 kL
648,000	0.006	167,800

In copymaster and workbook formats

RETEACHING

Reteaching 4-10 Patterns of Changing Metric Units

Multiply to change from larger units to smaller units.

    1 kL = 1,000 L
    1 L = 1,000 mL

    1 km = 1,000 m
    1 m = 100 cm
    1 cm = 10 mm

    1 kg = 1,000 g
    1 g = 1,000 mg

Divide to change from smaller units to larger units.

    1,000 mL = 1 L
    1,000 L = 1 kL

    10 mm = 1 cm
    100 cm = 1 m
    1,000 m = 1 km

    1,000 mg = 1 g
    1,000 g = 1 kg

Change 4.7 km to meters.
• A kilometer is larger than a meter. Multiply.
• Since 1 km = 1,000 m, multiply by 1,000.
    $4.7 \times 1,000 = 4,700$
    4.7 km = 4,700 m
• Or use mental math. Multiply by 1,000 by moving the decimal point three places to the *right*.
    $4.7 \rightarrow 4,700$

Change 347 mL to liters.
• A milliliter is smaller than a liter. Divide.
• Since 1,000 mL = 1 L, divide by 1,000.
    $347 \div 1,000 = 0.347$
    347 mL = 0.347 L
• Or use mental math. Divide by 1,000 by moving the decimal point three places to the *left*.
    $347 \rightarrow 0.347$

Change each measure to meters.

1. 2.5 km 2,500 m	2. 371 cm 3.71 m	3. 490 mm 0.49 m
4. 48 cm 0.48 m	5. 4 km 4,000 m	6. 1,500 mm 1.5 m

Change each measure to liters.

7. 0.6 kL 600 L	8. 799 mL 0.799 L	9. 0.9 mL 0.0009 L
10. 35.6 mL 0.0356 L	11. 0.06 kL 60 L	12. 1.8 kL 1,800 L

Change each measure to grams.

13. 4 kg 4,000 g	14. 661 mg 0.661 g	15. 1,500 mg 1.5 g
16. 24 mg 0.024 g	17. 1.95 kg 1,950 g	18. 0.23 kg 230 g

Use mental math to complete each statement.

19. 19 mL = 0.019 L	20. 5.5 kg = 5,500 g	21. 4.9 cm = 0.049 m
22. 730 mg = 0.73 g	23. 0.06 kL = 60 L	24. 2,540 mm = 254 cm

ENRICHMENT

Minds on Math Transparency

4-10

Gerri told Paul that if she began with 15, multiplied by 3, divided by some number, and then added 10, the result would be 15. By what number did Gerri divide?

9

See *Solution Key* for worked-out answers.

Complete each statement.

1. 12.6 mm = ■ cm **1.26**

2. 35.6 km = ■ m **35,600**

3. 5,600 mL = ■ L **5.6**

4. 670,000 m = ■ km **670**

5. 54,000 g = ■ kg **54**

6. 4,300 cm = ■ m **43**

---

20. *Quality Control* A bottle is supposed to contain 1 L of juice. The table shows several quality control test measurements.
  a. Write each measurement in milliliters.
  b. Which measurement is furthest away from 1 L? Explain.
  a. 1,002.3 mL; 1,001 mL; 999.7 mL; 996 mL
  b. Test 4; it is 4 mL away from 1 L.

Test #	Measurement
1	1,002.3 mL
2	1.001 L
3	999.7 mL
4	0.996 L

Complete each statement.

21. 8.6 mm = ■ cm **0.86**

22. ■ m = 8,600 cm **86**

23. 10,800 cm = ■ m **108**

24. ■ km = 300,000 cm **0.3**

25. 2.1 km = ■ m **2,100**

26. 356 mm = ■ cm **3.56**

27. 4,500 mL = ■ L **4.5**

28. 35,000 mL = ■ L **35**

29. ■ mL = 1.2 kL **1,200,000**

30. 8.2 L = ■ mL **8,200**

31. ■ mL = 0.5 kL **500,000**

32. ■ L = 6,000 mL **6**

33. Answers may vary. Sample: Mark the bottle into fourths, then cut out and use the bottom fourth.

33. *Writing* Suppose you want to make a bird feeder that holds about 500 mL of birdseed. Explain how you could make it out of an empty 2-L soft drink bottle.

34. *Nutrition* A cup of whole milk has 8.5 g of fat. A cup of skim milk has 400 mg of fat. Find the difference in fat content per cup. **8,100 mg**

35. *Physics* Light travels at 299,792,458 meters per second. How many kilometers does light travel in a second?
  299,792.458 km/s

36. *Algebra* Write an expression for changing kilograms to grams. **Let x = number of kg; 1,000x g.**

PORTFOLIO
For your portfolio, select one or two items from your work for this chapter. For example:
• your best work
• drawings of models
Explain why you have chosen each item.

Mixed Review

Choose an appropriate metric unit of measure for each.

(Lessons 3-8 and 3-9)

37. a tank of gas **L**   **38.** a can of soda **mL**   **39.** a piano **kg**   **40.** a spoonful of honey **mL**

Write a word phrase for each variable expression.

(Lesson 2-5)   **41–45. Answers may vary. Samples are given.**

41. $x \div 5$
  x divided by 5

42. $s + 14$
  14 more than *s*

43. $9a$
  9 times *a*

44. $42 - b$
  42 minus *b*

45. $2c + 42$
  42 more than two times *c*

46. *Choose a Strategy* Your town has 8 soccer teams. They are playing in a tournament. Each team will be out of the tournament after one loss. How many games will be played? **7 games**

PROJECT DAY You may wish to plan a project day on which students share their completed projects. Encourage students to explain their process as well as their product.

PROJECT NOTEBOOK Ask students to review their project work and bring their notebooks up to date.

Have students review their methods for calculating the costs of the items, the total cost for the event, and the amount each class member needs to raise for the project.

SCORING RUBRIC

3 Your presentation includes an original estimate, a detailed calculation of the actual costs, and the amount that each class member needs to raise. Your data and calculations are very well organized. Your presentation convinces others that your plan should be adopted.

2 Your presentation includes all required data, estimates, and calculations. Almost all of your work is accurate, and you have organized your information into lists, tables, or step-by-step calculations.

1 You left out either the original estimate or the amount that each class member needs to raise. Your calculations of the actual costs are either inaccurate or disorganized.

0 You neglected to gather data for or calculate the actual costs of your proposed celebration.

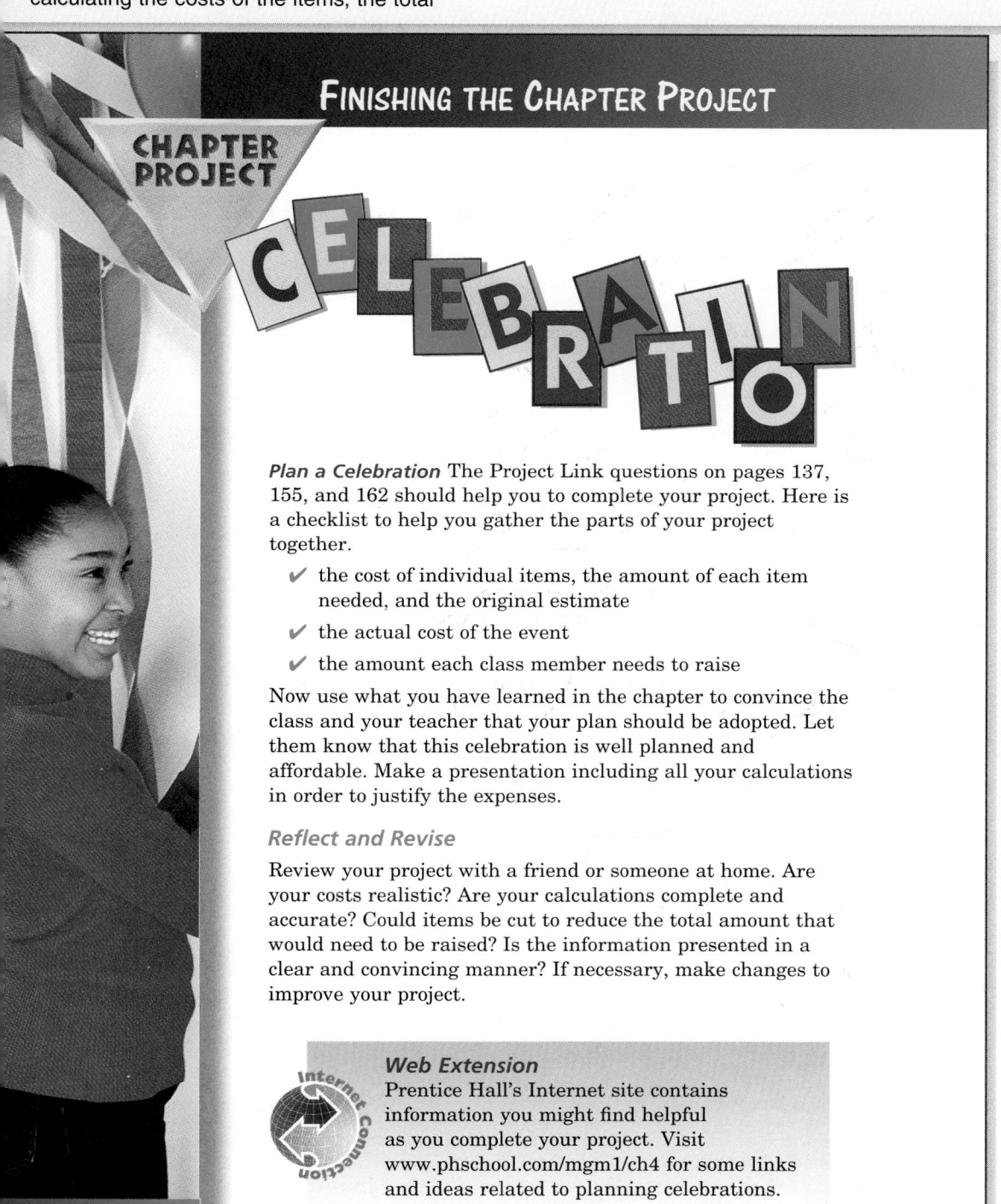

CHAPTER PROJECT

FINISHING THE CHAPTER PROJECT

CELEBRATION

Plan a Celebration The Project Link questions on pages 137, 155, and 162 should help you to complete your project. Here is a checklist to help you gather the parts of your project together.

✔ the cost of individual items, the amount of each item needed, and the original estimate

✔ the actual cost of the event

✔ the amount each class member needs to raise

Now use what you have learned in the chapter to convince the class and your teacher that your plan should be adopted. Let them know that this celebration is well planned and affordable. Make a presentation including all your calculations in order to justify the expenses.

Reflect and Revise

Review your project with a friend or someone at home. Are your costs realistic? Are your calculations complete and accurate? Could items be cut to reduce the total amount that would need to be raised? Is the information presented in a clear and convincing manner? If necessary, make changes to improve your project.

Web Extension
Prentice Hall's Internet site contains information you might find helpful as you complete your project. Visit www.phschool.com/mgm1/ch4 for some links and ideas related to planning celebrations.

STUDENT SELF-ASSESSMENT SURVEY

▪ Chapter 4 Student Self-Assessment Survey

1. Now that you have finished this chapter, think about what you have learned about multiplying and dividing decimals. Check each topic that you feel confident you understand.

_____ estimate decimal products and quotients (4-1)
_____ use exponents and find the values of powers (4-2)
_____ find the areas of rectangles (4-3)
_____ use the distributive property to find products (4-3)
_____ make models of decimal products (4-4)
_____ multiply decimals (4-5)
_____ make models of decimal quotients (4-6)
_____ divide decimals by whole numbers (4-7)
_____ divide decimals by decimals (4-8)
_____ decide what information is needed to solve a problem (4-9)
_____ change metric units (4-10)

2. Before the Chapter Assessment, I need to review _____

_____

3. **a.** Check one. In general, I thought this chapter was

____ a snap ____ easy ____ average ____ hard ____ a monster

   b. Why do you feel this way? _____

_____

4. In this chapter, I did my best work on _____

5. I think the hardest thing about working with decimals is _____

_____

6. List three places outside the classroom where people use decimals in everyday life.

_____

7. Did you use a database on the computer? _____

   If yes, did it help? _____ Explain. _____

_____

Vocabulary/Symbols

area, centi-, compatible numbers, distributive property, exponent, kilo-, milli-, power

Materials/Manipulatives

• blank decimal squares

 Student Edition

Extra Practice, p. 525
Glossary/Study Guide

 Teaching Resources

Chapter Support File, Ch. 4
• Student Self-Assessment Survey
Glossary, Spanish Resources
Tools for Studying Smarter

176

WRAP UP

Exercises 1–4 After students estimate the products and quotients, have them use a calculator to see how accurate their estimates are. Tell students to only change an answer if it is way off. They can then reestimate to change it. The correct answer for an estimation is a quick product or quotient, not necessarily an exact answer.

ASSESSMENT Exercises 13–18 Have students work in pairs. Partners work the problems separately, then compare results. If results differ, partners can work together to figure out why they differ and which result is correct.

Exercises 21–28 Remind students to use estimates to check that their answers are reasonable.

(4) WRAP UP

Estimating Products and Quotients   4-1

You can round to estimate decimal products and quotients. You can use **compatible numbers** to estimate products and quotients.

Estimate using rounding or compatible numbers.   1–4. Answers may vary. Samples are given.

1. 23.78×5.3 125   **2.** $34.1 \div 6.67$ 5   **3.** 4.09×82.3 328   **4.** $84.6 \div 1.94$ 42

Exponents   4-2

You can use an **exponent** to show how many times a number, or **base,** is multiplied. A number expressed using an exponent is called a **power.** The order of operations includes powers.

Simplify each expression.

5. 4^7 16,384   **6.** $500 \div 5^2$ 20   **7.** $100 - 2 \times 6^2$ 28   **8.** $3^2 - 2^3 + 30$ 31   **9.** $(4^2 - 1) \div 5^3$
                                                                                                        0.12

10. *Writing* State the order of operations. Give an example.   Check students' work.

The Distributive Property   4-3

You can use the **distributive property** to simplify expressions involving multiplication and addition or subtraction.

Complete each equation.
                       90   30
11. $5 \times 97 = (5 \times ▨) + (5 \times 7)$ **12.** $8 \times 27 = 8 \times (▨ - 3)$

Simplify using the distributive property.

13. $(11 \times 6) + (9 \times 6)$ 120   **14.** $5 \times (4 + 12)$ 80   **15.** $(8 \times 21) - (8 \times 9)$ 96

16. 4×59 236   **17.** $9 \times (50 - 9) - 27$ 342   **18.** $6 \times 3 + 6 \times 2 - 1$ 29

Multiplying Decimals and Dividing Decimals   4-4, 4-5, 4-6, 4-7, 4-8

You can model multiplication and division of decimals.

Exercises 31–36 Remind students a smaller unit goes with a larger number, and a larger unit goes with a smaller number. Have them check their work with this idea.

Remind students that the new mathematical terms in this chapter are defined in the Glossary/Study Guide in the back of the book.

19. Write a multiplication sentence to describe the model. **0.1 × 0.3 = 0.03**

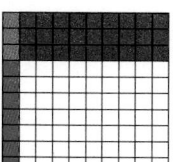

20. Write a division sentence to describe the model. **0.5 ÷ 0.1 = 5**

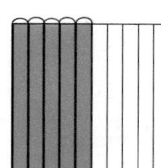

To multiply decimal numbers, count the number of decimal places in both factors to find how many places are needed in the product.

To divide by a decimal, "move" the decimal point in the divisor to make it a whole number. Then "move" the decimal point in the dividend the same number of places.

Find each product or quotient. Use models if they help you.

21. 3.215×0.04
0.1286

22. 1.5×30.72 **46.08**

23. $4.5 \div 6$ **0.75**

24. $3.2\overline{)96}$ **30**

25. $1.25\overline{)8.3}$ **6.64**

26. $0.645 \times 1,000$ **645**

27. $7.2 \div 12$ **0.6**

28. 0.15×0.75 **0.1125**

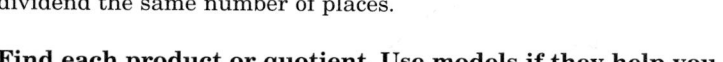

Problem Solving Strategies   4-9

Some problems have too much or too little information.

Solve if possible. If not possible, tell what additional information you need.

29. Mr. Chen's class wants to go to a game. Tickets cost $10. Food costs $7. Students will share evenly the $125 rental fee for a bus. How much will it cost each student?
Not possible; you need to know the number of students in the class.

30. Denika is 152.4 cm tall and weighs 44.5 kg. Her twin sister, Janika, is 1.1 cm taller and weighs 0.9 kg more. How tall is Janika? **153.5 cm**

Patterns of Changing Metric Units   4-10

You can change metric units by moving the decimal point.

Complete each statement.

31. **2,500** ▨ m = 2.5 km

32. 57,000 mL = ▨ L **57**

33. 1,257 mg = ▨ g **1.257**

34. 8,090 L = ▨ kL **8.09**

35. ▨ kg = 300,000 mg **0.3**

36. 150 mm = ▨ cm **15**

▬ Chapter 4 Assessment • Form A

                                                          Answers

1. Round each factor to the nearest whole number to estimate the product of 27.63 × 3.3.   **1.** 84

2. Use compatible numbers to estimate the quotient 49.4 ÷ 9.3.   **2.** 5

3. Simplify 4 + (4 × 3²).   **3.** 40

4. Write using an exponent. Name the base and the exponent. 7 × 7 × 7 × 7 × 7   **4.** 7⁵; base: 7, exponent: 5

5. Use the distributive property to rewrite and evaluate 3 × (5 + 6).   **5.** (3 × 5) + (3 × 6); 33

6. One rectangle is 4 in. long and 6 in. wide and another rectangle is 3 in. long and 6 in. wide. Find the total area of both rectangles.   **6.** 42 in.²

7. Find the product 0.14 × 1.20.   **7.** 0.1680

8. If ten pencils cost $.97, what is the price for one pencil? Round your answer to the nearest cent.   **8.** $.10

9. Write a multiplication sentence to describe the model shown below.   **9.** 0.5 × 0.2 = 0.10

10. Draw a model to find the product 0.4 × 0.3.   **10.** 0.12 0.4 0.3 0.12

11. Draw a model to find the quotient 0.6 ÷ 0.2.   **11.** 3

12. Find the product 0.23 × 4.   **12.** 0.92

Chapter 4 Assessment • Form A (continued)

13. Find the quotient 12.48 ÷ 0.03.   **13.** 416

14. A stack of 500 sheets of paper measures 1.875 in. thick. Find the thickness of one sheet of paper.   **14.** 0.00375 in.

15. Use mental math to find the quotient 3.1 ÷ 100.   **15.** 0.031

16. A six-pack of juice is priced at $1.98. What is the price for one drink?   **16.** $.33

17. Bananas cost $.43 per lb. Find the cost of 2.3 lb. Round your answer to the nearest cent.   **17.** $.99

Choose A, B, C, or D.

18. Which is *not* equivalent to the others?   **18.** B
   A. 3 L   **B.** 0.03 kL   **C.** 3,000 mL   **D.** 0.003 kL

19. Use mental math to complete 484 cm = ■ mm.   **19.** 4,840

20. How many grams are there in 4.5 kg?   **20.** 4,500 g

Choose a Strategy

21. The mayor of Twin Falls decided to take a walk from one end of the town to the other end. His walking shoes cost $85.35. The town is 60 blocks long. He walked 3 mi. How long is the average block in the town?   **21.** 0.05 mi

Writing

22. Explain what a record in a database might look like if the following information were to be included.

Mountain Peak	Range	Location	Height(ft)
Everest	Himalayas	Nepal-Tibet	29,028
Mamaslu	Himalayas	Nepal	26,760
Nanda Devi	Himalayas	India	25,645
Victory Peak	Pamir	Tajikstan	24,406
Veladero	Andes	Argentina	22,244
El Muerto	Andes	Argentina-Chile	21,456
McKinley	Alaska	Alaska	20,320
Nevada	Andes	Argentina	20,023

Source: *The 1993 Information Please Almanac*
a record would contain the following: MOUNTAIN PEAK: RANGE: LOCATION: HEIGHT(ft):

Chapter 4 Assessment • Form B

Choose the best answer. Circle A, B, C, or D.

1. Round each factor to the nearest whole number to estimate 67.6 × 4.23.
   - **(A)** 272
   - **B.** 268
   - **C.** 335
   - **D.** 340

2. Use compatible numbers to estimate 98.4 ÷ 19.2.
   - **A.** 5.1
   - **(B)** 5
   - **C.** 4
   - **D.** 4.75

3. Use mental math to evaluate 4² × (5 − 4).
   - **A.** 0
   - **(B)** 16
   - **C.** 19
   - **D.** 76

4. Simplify 6³.
   - **A.** 18
   - **B.** 36
   - **C.** 63
   - **(D)** 216

5. Simplify 10⁴.
   - **A.** 100
   - **B.** 1,000
   - **(C)** 10,000
   - **D.** 100,000

6. Use the distributive property to rewrite the expression 4 × 5 + 4 × 3.
   - **A.** 4 × (5 × 3)
   - **B.** 5 × (4 + 3)
   - **(C)** 4 × (5 + 3)
   - **D.** 3 × (5 + 4)

7. One rectangle is 3 cm long and 4 cm wide, and another rectangle is 3 cm long and 6 cm wide. Find the total area of both rectangles.
   - **A.** 16 cm²
   - **(B)** 30 cm²
   - **C.** 96 cm²
   - **D.** 72 cm²

8. Find the product 1.34 × 0.06.
   - **(A)** 0.0804
   - **B.** 0.804
   - **C.** 8.04
   - **D.** 0.00804

9. If a case of 24 cans of juice costs $7.20, how much do 6 cans cost?
   - **A.** $2.00
   - **(B)** $1.80
   - **C.** $.99
   - **D.** $1.30

10. Write a multiplication sentence to describe the model at the right.
    - **A.** 0.6 × 0.3 = 0.18
    - **B.** 0.2 × 0.6 = 1.2
    - **(C)** 0.2 × 0.6 = 0.12
    - **D.** 0.6 × 0.2 = 0.012

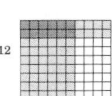

Chapter 4 Assessment • Form B (continued)

11. Find the product 1.25 × 0.05.
    - **A.** 0.00625
    - **B.** 0.625
    - **C.** 6.25
    - **(D)** 0.0625

12. Find the quotient 1.4 ÷ 0.02.
    - **(A)** 70
    - **B.** 7
    - **C.** 0.7
    - **D.** 700

13. Find the product 3.28 × 8.
    - **A.** 2.624
    - **B.** 262.4
    - **(C)** 26.24
    - **D.** 0.2624

14. Find the quotient 0.12 ÷ 0.03.
    - **A.** 0.04
    - **B.** 0.4
    - **(C)** 4
    - **D.** 40

15. A stack of 25 wooden blocks is 37.5 cm tall. How tall is one block?
    - **A.** 2.5 cm
    - **B.** 1.25 cm
    - **(C)** 1.5 cm
    - **D.** 1.15 cm

16. Use mental math to find the quotient 34.5 ÷ 1,000.
    - **A.** 0.345
    - **(B)** 0.0345
    - **C.** 34,500
    - **D.** 3.45

17. A package of 6 bagels costs $.89. What is the price for 2 bagels rounded to the nearest cent?
    - **A.** $.40
    - **B.** $.28
    - **C.** $.15
    - **(D)** $.30

18. Grapes cost $1.95 per lb. Find the cost of 3.2 lb.
    - **A.** $7.30
    - **B.** $5.85
    - **C.** $6.00
    - **(D)** $6.24

19. An object measures 5.7 mm. What is the length in centimeters?
    - **A.** 0.0057 cm
    - **B.** 0.057 cm
    - **(C)** 0.57 cm
    - **D.** 57 cm

20. Change the measure 2,300 g to kilograms.
    - **A.** 0.23 kg
    - **(B)** 2.3 kg
    - **C.** 23 kg
    - **D.** 230 kg

Choose a Strategy

21. Barbara Brown wants to fence her square horse pasture by adding one strand of barbed wire to a wooden fence already around the pasture. The barbed wire costs $25.67 per 1,000 ft. How much would it cost Barbara to fence her pasture with barbed wire if her pasture is 500 ft on each side?
    - **A.** $25.67
    - **B.** $102.68
    - **(C)** $51.34
    - **D.** cannot be solved

 Teaching Resources

Chapter Support File, Ch. 4, and Spanish Resources

 Teacher's Edition

See pp. 132C–D for Assessment Options.

 Teaching Resource Software

• Computer Item Generator, Ch. 4

ASSESSMENT

ENHANCED MULTIPLE CHOICE QUESTIONS are more complex than traditional multiple choice questions, which assess only one skill. Enhanced multiple choice questions assess the processes that students use, as well as the end result. They are written so that students can use more than one strategy to solve the problem. Using multiple strategies is encouraged by the National Council of Teachers of Mathematics (NCTM). **Exercise 5** is an enhanced multiple choice question.

WRITING EXERCISES allow students to describe more fully their thinking and understanding of the concepts they have learned. **Exercise 9** is a writing exercise.

4 ASSESSMENT

1. Estimate using rounding.
   - **a.** 7.3 × 29.7   210
   - **b.** 4.63 × 50.4   250
   - **c.** 75.1 × 2.93   225
   - **d.** 9.4 × 4.03   36

2. Estimate using compatible numbers.
   - **a.** 21.14 × 4.89   100
   - **b.** 17.9 ÷ 3.6   4
   - **c.** 98.13 ÷ 24.27   4
   - **d.** 38.95 × 2.78   120

3. Write a multiplication expression for the model below.   **0.4 × 0.4 = 0.16**

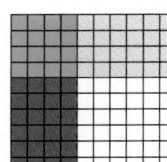

4. Simplify each expression.
   - **a.** 5^4 625
   - **b.** $4^2 \times 2$ 32
   - **c.** $150 \div 5^2$ 6
   - **d.** $11 \times 21 - 4^2$ 215

5. **Choose A, B, C, or D.** Which expression equals 108?   **C**
   - **A.** $3^2 \times 2^2$
   - **B.** $3^2 \times 2^3$
   - **C.** $3^3 \times 2^2$
   - **D.** $3^3 \times 2^3$

6. Complete.   **50**
   - **a.** 8 × 58 = (8 × ■) + (8 × 8)
   - **b.** 6 × 73 = 6 × (■ + 3)   **70**

7. *Mental Math* Use mental math to simplify each expression.
   - **a.** 5 × 102   510
   - **b.** 4 × 58   232

8. Use the distributive property to simplify each expression.
   - **a.** 5 × (6 + 10)   80
   - **b.** (7 × 6) + (7 × 5)   77
   - **c.** 9 × (3 + 10)   117
   - **d.** 4 × 6 + 7 × 10   94

9. *Writing* Explain how to model the quotient 0.6 ÷ 0.12.   Answers may vary. Sample: Divide a square into hundredths and shade 6 columns. Then circle groups of twelve hundredths within the shaded area. Count the number of groups.

10. Find each product.
    - **a.** 9.063 × 24 = 217.512
    - **b.** 0.85 × 0.06 = 0.051
    - **c.** 5.2 × 0.17 = 0.884

11. *Entertainment* Jamal bought three tickets to a matinee movie. The matinee tickets cost $2.00 less than the evening movie tickets. Each matinee ticket cost $4.50. He paid with a $20-dollar bill and two quarters. How much change did Jamal receive?   **$7**

12. Find each quotient.
    - **a.** 3.2)8.832   2.76
    - **b.** 45)$32.85 $0.73
    - **c.** 0.4 ÷ 0.25   1.6
    - **d.** 63.72 ÷ 0.03   2,124

13. *Shopping* Seedless grapes cost $1.79 per pound. Find the cost of a bunch of grapes that weighs 2.2 lb. Round your answer up to the next cent.   **$3.94**

14. Complete each sentence.
    - **a.** 672 mm = ■ cm   67.2
    - **b.** ■ L = 25,040 mL   25.04
    - **c.** 35.1 kg = ■ g   35,100
    - **d.** ■ L = 0.125 kL   125
    - **e.** 514 mg = ■ g   0.514
    - **f.** 42.9 m = ■ cm   4,290

15. *Algebra* Write an expression for changing kilometers to centimeters.
    Let x = number of km; 100,000x cm.

16. Which model represents 0.4 × 0.6?   **a**

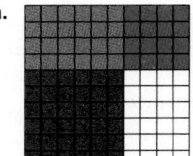   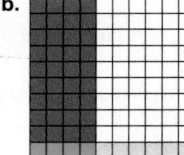

Item	Review Topic	Ch
1	Estimating decimal products	4
2	Metric length	3
3	Finding median	1
4	Problem solving with too much or too little information	4
5	Order of operations	4

Item	Review Topic	Ch
6	Dividing decimals	4
7, 12	Problem solving with patterns	2
8	Writing decimals	3
9	Ordering decimals	3
10	Tables	1
11	Variable equations	2

4 CUMULATIVE REVIEW

Choose the best answer.

1. Which rounded estimate represents the product 34.3×5.98? **A**

A. 34×6 　　B. 35×6
C. 35×5 　　D. 34×5

2. What is the best unit of measurement to use to measure the length of a driveway? **C**

A. millimeters 　　B. centimeters
C. meters 　　D. kilometers

3. Which number represents the median for this set of data? 50, 54, 62, 69, 70, 70, 81 **D**

A. 70 　　B. 455
C. 65 　　D. 69

4. Kevin bought six muffins for $2.39. He paid the cashier with three one-dollar bills and some pennies. He received no pennies in change. How many pennies must he have given the cashier? **D**

A. 1 　　B. 2 　　C. 3 　　D. 4

5. Where would you insert parentheses so that $6 - 2 \times 9 \div 3 + 15$ has the value 5? **D**

A. $(6 - 2) \times 9 \div 3 + 15$
B. $6 - (2 \times 9) \div 3 + 15$
C. $6 - 2 \times (9 \div 3) + 15$
D. $6 - 2 \times 9 \div (3 + 15)$

6. Which has a quotient equal to $0.317 \div 0.08$? **B**

A. $317 \div 8$ 　　B. $31.7 \div 8$
C. $317 \div 0.8$ 　　D. $3.17 \div 8$

7. Kiona has sixty-five cents in quarters, dimes, and nickels. (She has at least one of each of these coins.) What number of nickels can she *not* have? **C**

A. 1 　　B. 2 　　C. 3 　　D. 4

8. Which number is equal to 4.3? **D**

A. four and thirteen hundredths
B. four hundred and three
C. forty-three
D. four and three tenths

9. In which set are the numbers all between 0.5 and 1.95? **C**

A. 0.504, 1.9, 1.951
B. 0.194, 1, 1.94
C. 0.618, 1, 1.009
D. 0.6, 1.04, 2

10. Look at the table below. Which two students have the highest mean (average) scores? **D**

Student	Test 1	Test 2	Mean
Keisha	100	88	▦
Justine	85	95	▦
Greg	77	83	▦
Pritpal	90	92	▦

A. Pritpal and Justine
B. Greg and Justine
C. Justine and Keisha
D. Keisha and Pritpal

11. Which equation is true given $y = 6$? **D**

A. $4y = 28$
B. $88 + y = 92$
C. $42 \div y = 6$
D. $73 - y = 67$

12. Which rule best describes this number pattern? 1, 3, 5, 7, 9, 11, 13, . . . **B**

A. List only prime numbers.
B. Add 2 repeatedly.
C. Subtract 2 repeatedly.
D. Multiply by 2 repeatedly.

CUMULATIVE REVIEW

Chapter 4 Cumulative Review

Choose the best answer. Circle A, B, C, or D.

1. Which variable expression shows eleven less than a number?

A. $11 - j$ 　　B. $\frac{11}{j}$
C. $11j$ 　　**(D)** $j - 11$

2. Use mental math to evaluate $3^3 \times (4 - 2)$.

A. 18 　　B. 44
(C) 54 　　D. 216

3. What are the next three numbers in the number pattern 27, 33, 39, 45?

(A) 51, 57, 63 　　B. 51, 56, 62
C. 51, 55, 61 　　D. 57, 63, 69

4. Which is an appropriate unit of measurement for the capacity of a sink?

A. centimeter 　　B. milliliter
C. meter 　　**(D)** liter

5. Express 2.372 in words.

(A) two and three hundred seventy-two thousandths
B. two and three hundred seventy-two hundredths
C. twenty-three and seventy-two hundredths
D. twenty-three thousand and seventy-two thousandths

6. Find the mode of this data set.
3, 3, 5, 6, 4, 3, 5, 6

(A) 3 　　B. 4
C. 5 　　D. 6

7. Solve the equation $12 = 18 - e$.
(A) 6 　　B. 12
C. 18 　　D. 30

8. Simplify $4 + 7 \times 3$.
A. 14 　　**(B)** 25
C. 33 　　D. 84

9. How many hundredths is equivalent to five tenths?
A. 0.5 　　B. 5
(C) 50 　　D. 500

10. Solve the equation $-6y = 48$.
A. -42 　　**(B)** -8
C. -6 　　D. 8

11. List the decimals in order from least to greatest.
0.49, 0.36, 0.23, 0.25, 0.32, 0.54
A. 0.54, 0.49, 0.36, 0.25, 0.23, 0.32
B. 0.23, 0.25, 0.32, 0.36, 0.54, 0.49
(C) 0.23, 0.25, 0.32, 0.36, 0.49, 0.54
D. 0.54, 0.49, 0.36, 0.32, 0.25, 0.23

CUMULATIVE REVIEW

Chapter 4 Cumulative Review (continued)

12. Find the difference $0.94 - 0.27$.
A. 1.21 　　**(B)** 0.67
C. 0.77 　　D. 0.73

13. Estimate to the nearest dollar the cost of 4 bottles of juice at $1.18 a bottle and 2 large bags of popcorn at $3.58 a bag.
A. about $8 　　B. about $10
C. about $5 　　**(D)** about $12

14. Davis decides to save $2.35 each week from his baby-sitting jobs to buy a present for his father's birthday. If he saves for 5 weeks, how much will he have saved?
A. $10.55 　　B. $15.00
(C) $11.75 　　D. $12.00

15. To raise money for a new school computer, Jan plans to swim 65 lengths of a 50-m pool. She earns $.10 for every meter she swims. How much money will she raise?
(A) $325 　　B. $3,250
C. $32.50 　　D. $5.00

16. Which operation would you perform first? $6 \times (5 - 4) + 6 \div 2$
A. multiplication
B. division
C. addition
(D) subtraction

17. What are the missing numbers?
$3 \times (13 - 4) =$
$(▦ \times 13) - (3 \times ▦)$
A. 3, 13 　　B. 3, -4
C. -4, 3 　　**(D)** 3, 4

18. Evaluate 5.6×0.9.
A. 0.504 　　**(B)** 5.04
C. 56.0 　　D. 50.4

19. Use mental math to find the product $0.034 \times 10,000$.
(A) 340 　　B. 3.40
C. 34.0 　　D. 3,400

20. Find the quotient $8.73 \div 0.3$.
A. 291 　　**(B)** 29.1
C. 2.91 　　D. 0.291

21. Use mental math to find the quotient $0.47 \div 1,000$.
(A) 0.00047 　　B. 0.0047
C. 47.0 　　D. 470.0

22. Issa bought four tickets to the county fair for $4.45 each. He paid for the tickets with a twenty-dollar bill. How much change should he receive?
A. $.20 　　B. $17.80
C. $4.45 　　**(D)** $2.20

23. Reynold decides to earn extra money by walking dogs after school. He walks dogs for one hour each weekday and charges $3.50 per dog. How much money does he make in one week?
(A) too little information
B. $24.00
C. $17.50
D. $35.00

Resources

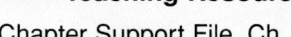

Teaching Resources

Chapter Support File, Ch. 4
• Cumulative Review

Teacher's Edition

See pp. 132C–D for Assessment Options.

5 Investigating Fractions

CHAPTER OVERVIEW

To accommodate flexible scheduling, most lessons are divided into parts. Assignment Options are given in the Teacher's Edition for each lesson.

Pages 182–184	**Lesson 5-1** **Mental Math and Divisibility**
NCTM 2, 3, 5, 7	**Part 1** Divisibility by 1, 2, 5, and 10 **Part 2** Divisibility by 3 and 9 **Key terms:** divisible, divisibility **Alternative Activity** 5-1

Pages 185–188	**Lesson 5-2** **Geometry: Using Models and Factor Trees**
NCTM 1, 2, 3, 5, 6, 7, 12	**Part 1** Prime and Composite Numbers **Part 2** Prime Factorization **Key terms:** factor, prime number, composite number, factor tree, prime factorization **Journal**

Pages 189–191	**Lesson 5-3** **Greatest Common Factor**
NCTM 1, 2, 3, 4, 5, 6	**Part 1** Finding the GCF By Listing Factors **Part 2** Using Prime Factorization to Find the GCF **Key terms:** common factors, greatest common factors **Math at Work**

Pages 206–208	**Lesson 5-7** **Least Common Multiple**
NCTM 1, 3, 4, 5, 6	**Part 1** LCM and Common Multiples **Part 2** Finding the LCM Using Prime Factorizations **Key terms:** multiple, common multiples, least common multiple **Alternative Activity** 5-7 **Journal**

Pages 209–212	**Lesson 5-8** **Comparing and Ordering Fractions**
NCTM 1, 2, 3, 4, 5, 7	**Part 1** Comparing Fractions **Part 2** Ordering Fractions **Key terms:** least common denominator ▽ **Project Link**

Pages 213–217	**Lesson 5-9** **Fractions and Decimals**
NCTM 1, 2, 3, 4, 5, 6, 13	**Part 1** Writing Fractions **Part 2** Writing Decimals **Key terms:** terminating decimal, repeating decimal ▽ **Project Link** ☑ **Checkpoint 2**

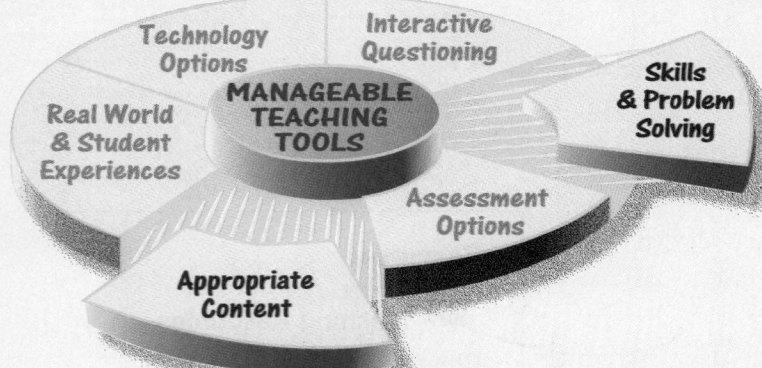

Pacing Options

This chart suggests pacing only for the core lessons and their parts. It is provided merely as a possible guide. It will help you determine how much time you have in your schedule to cover other features, such as the Chapter Project, Math Toolboxes, Wrap Up, and Assessment.

	1 Class Period	1 Class Period	1 Class Period
Traditional (40–45 min class periods)	5-1 5-1 ▽ 2	5-2 5-2 ▽ 2	5-3 5-3 ▽ 2
Block Scheduling (90 min class periods)	5-1 5-1 5-2 ▽ 2 ▽	5-2 5-3 5-3 2 ▽ 2	5-4 5-4 5-5 5-5 5-6 ▽ 2 ▽ 2 ▽

Home-Court Advantage

Goal: Use fractions to compare basketball players.

NCTM STANDARDS

1 Problem Solving	6 Number Systems and Number Theory 10 Statistics
2 Communication	7 Computation and Estimation 11 Probability
3 Reasoning	8 Patterns and Functions 12 Geometry
4 Mathematical Connections	9 Algebra 13 Measurement
5 Number and Number Relationships	

Pages 193–195

Lesson 5-4
Using Fraction Models

NCTM 1, 3, 4, 5, 7, 13

Part 1   Modeling Fractions
Part 2   Rounding Fractions
Key term: fraction model

▼ **Project Link**

Pages 197–200

Lesson 5-5
Equivalent Fractions

NCTM 2, 3, 4, 5, 7, 13

Part 1   Finding Equivalent Fractions
Part 2   Writing Fractions in Simplest Form
Key terms: equivalent fractions, simplest form

Alternative Activity 5-5

☑ **Checkpoint 1**

Pages 202–205

Lesson 5-6   Measurement: Mixed Numbers and Improper Fractions

NCTM 2, 3, 4, 5, 13

Part 1   Writing Improper Fractions
Part 2   Writing Mixed Numbers
Key terms: improper fraction, mixed numbers

Pages 218–220

Lesson 5-10
Problem Solving Strategy

NCTM 1, 2, 3, 13

Work Backward

Key term: working backward

Optional Materials and Manipulatives

calculator (5-1, 5-2, 5-9)

graph paper (5-2, 5-9)

Optional calculator use is integrated throughout the course.

---

	1 Class Period	1 Class Period	1 Class Period	1 Class Period	1 Class Period	1 Class Period	1 Class Period	1 Class Period	1 Class Period	1 Class Period
5	5–6 ▼	5–6 ▼2	5–7 5–7 ▼ ▼2	5–8 5–8 ▼ ▼2	5–9 ▼	5–9 ▼2	5–10			
5–9 ▼	5–9 5–10 ▼2									

MEETING INDIVIDUAL NEEDS

Accommodating Diverse Learning Styles

In your Teacher's Edition, you will find suggestions as to how you can help students complete mathematical tasks in Chapter 5 by meeting individual needs and supporting various learning styles. Here are some examples:

VISUAL LEARNING
highlighting numbers in a grid that are divisible by 2, 3, 5, 9, and 10 *(p. 182)*

EARLY FINISHERS
Performance-Based Project, MathBlaster® Mystery, Interdisciplinary Units

TACTILE LEARNING
modeling problems using straws *(p. 218)*

GIFTED AND TALENTED
deciding if very large numbers are divisible by 9 *(p. 183)*

AUDITORY LEARNING
saying words for the symbols <, >, and = *(p. 210)*

DIVERSITY investigating how Egyptians wrote fractions *(p. 197)*

KINESTHETIC LEARNING
modeling fractions using students *(p. 193)*

ACQUIRING ENGLISH PROFICIENCY (AEP)
pronouncing the th sound in the words of fractions such as tenth *(p. 213)*

ASSESSING PROGRESS

A broad range of assessment tools are available to reach a variety of learners.

INFORMAL ASSESSMENT

Informal assessments provide day-to-day feedback to help give you a picture of conceptual understanding and skill development.

ONGOING ASSESSMENT is built into lesson instruction and the Teaching Notes of the Teacher's Edition.

In the Teacher's Edition
Lesson Quiz for every lesson

In the Student Edition
On Your Own, Mixed Review, Journal, Portfolio, Project Link, Chapter Wrap Up

Look for **Interactive Questions** within lessons that

- **BUILD UNDERSTANDING** with labels such as Analyze, Reasoning, Estimation, Writing, and Summarize
- ✔ **CHECK UNDERSTANDING** with the Try It Out label.

FORMAL ASSESSMENT

Formal assessment can occur before and after the chapter, as well as at natural breaking points in the chapter.

Checkpoints
Two forms of each self-assessment Checkpoints are available: one in the Student Edition and another in the Chapter Support File in the Teaching Resources box.
- Mid-Chapter Checkpoint 1, page 200
- End-of-Chapter Checkpoint 2, page 217

Chapter 5 Assessment, page 224.
Two alternative forms are available in the Chapter Support File. They may be used after a chapter has been completed, or as a pre-test and post-test comparison.

Cumulative Review, page 225.
Assesses skills and concepts in Chapters 1–5. An alternative form is available in Chapter Support File.

Computer Item Generator for Chapter 5
Customized tests can be generated for each lesson and for mid-chapter and end-of-chapter assessments, and for pre- and post-test comparisons of achievement.

Interactive Questioning

Technology Options

Real World & Student Experiences

MANAGEABLE TEACHING TOOLS

Skills & Problem Solving

Appropriate Content

Assessment Options

CHAPTER PROJECT

The Chapter Project in the student edition provides a real-world connection to the math context of the chapter. The Teacher's Edition contains a scoring rubric.

Another performance-based Chapter Project with a scoring rubric can be found in the Chapter Support File in the Teaching Resources Box.

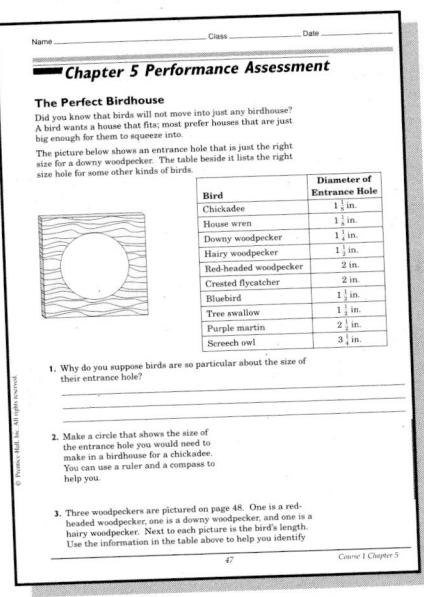

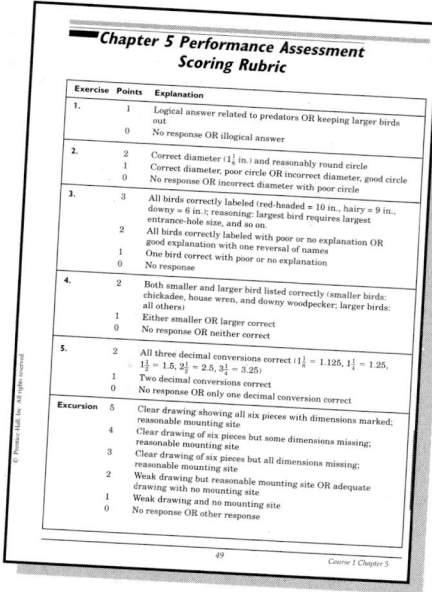

Correlation to Standardized Tests

Lesson		CAT5	CTBS/5 Terra Nova	ITBS	MAT7	SAT9	Your Local Test
5-1	Mental Math and Divisibility	■	■	■	■	■	
5-2	Geometry: Using Models and Factor Trees	■	■	■			
5-3	Greatest Common Factor		■			■	
5-4	Using Fraction Models	■	■	■	■		
5-5	Equivalent Fractions	■	■			■	
5-6	Measurement: Mixed Numbers and Improper Fractions	■	■			■	
5-7	Least Common Multiple		■			■	
5-8	Comparing and Ordering Fractions	■	■	■	■	■	
5-9	Fractions and Decimals	■			■	■	
5-10	Problem Solving Strategy: Work Backward			■	■	■	

CAT5 California Achievement Test, 5th Edition
CTBS/5 Comprehensive Test of Basic Skills, 5th Edition
ITBS Iowa Test of Basic Skills, Form B
MAT 7 Metropolitan Achievement Test, 7th Edition
SAT9 Stanford Achievement Test, 9th Edition

MAKING CONNECTIONS

MANAGEABLE TEACHING TOOLS

Technology Options • Interactive Questioning • Skills & Problem Solving • Assessment Options • Appropriate Content • Real World & Student Experiences

TEAM TEACHING WITH PRENTICE HALL MATERIALS

INTERDISCIPLINARY EXPLORATIONS

● *Riddles of the Pharaohs* p. 15

Lesson	Interdisciplinary Connections	Real World Connections	Math Integration
5-1	History	Money Pledge of Allegiance	Data Analysis
5-2	Geometry	Internet	Geometry
5-3	Chemistry	Collecting	Algebra
5-4	Science	Weather Time Management	Measurement
5-5	History	Traffic Planning	Measurement
5-6	Design Physics	Marine Biology Magazine Subscriptions	Measurement
5-7	History	Scheduling Astronomy	Data Analysis
5-8	Music	Carpentry Shopping Stamp Collecting	Data Analysis
5-9	Economics	Construction Shopping Finance Stock Market Money	Measurement
5-10	Biology Health	Shopping Hobbies Games Entertainment Scheduling Savings Money	Measurement

School to Home

MATERIALS:
12-month calendar paper
colored pencils or pens

English and Spanish versions are available in the Teacher's Communication Kit, Teacher's Resource box.

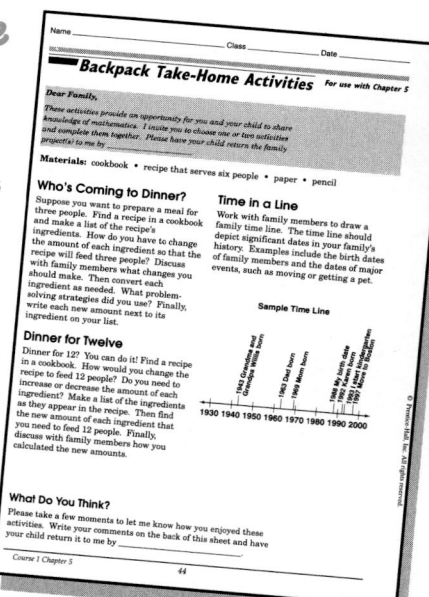

Backpack Take-Home Activities For use with Chapter 5

Dear Family,
These activities provide an opportunity for you and your child to share knowledge of mathematics. I invite you to choose one or two activities and complete them together. Please have your child return the family project(s) to me by _____

Materials: cookbook • recipe that serves six people • paper • pencil

Who's Coming to Dinner?
Suppose you want to prepare a meal for three people. Find a recipe in a cookbook and make a list of the recipe's ingredients. How do you have to change the amount of each ingredient so that the recipe will feed three people? Discuss with family members what changes you should make. Then convert each ingredient as needed. What problem-solving strategies did you use? Finally, write each new amount next to its ingredient on your list.

Time in a Line
Work with family members to draw a family time line. The time line should depict significant dates in your family's history. Examples include the birth dates of family members and the dates of major events, such as moving or getting a pet.

Sample Time Line

1930 1940 1950 1960 1970 1980 1990 2000

Dinner for Twelve
Dinner for 12? You can do it! Find a recipe in a cookbook. How would you change the recipe to feed 12 people? Do you need to increase or decrease the amount of each ingredient? Make a list of the ingredients as they appear in the recipe. Then find the new amount of each ingredient that you need to feed 12 people. Finally, discuss with family members how you calculated the new amounts.

What Do You Think?
Please take a few moments to let me know how you enjoyed these activities. Write your comments on the back of this sheet and have your child return it to me by _____

Course 1 Chapter 5   44

USING TECHNOLOGY TO ENHANCE INSTRUCTION

FOR THE STUDENT

Multimedia Math Hot Pages™

This interactive software and video package on CD-ROM integrates solid math content through a variety of media.

- Hot Page™ 13 (5-4)
- Hot Page™ 14 (5-6)
- Hot Page™ 15 (5-8)

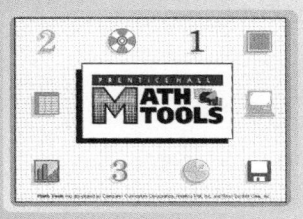

Math Labs

This software, available on both diskette and CD-ROM, includes on-screen Math Lab activities. Students use linkable, interactive tools to explore math concepts.

- Math Lab: Equivalent Fractions (5-5)
- Math Lab: Fractions and Decimals (5-9)

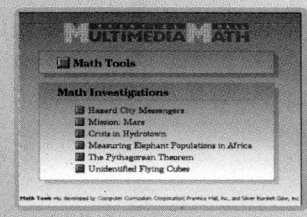

Multimedia Math Investigations

These in-depth interactive activities on CD-ROM develop real-world applications of mathematics. They allow students the opportunity to reinforce key concepts.

- Hazard City Messengers

Interactive Student Tutorial

Available on CD-ROM, this test preparation program contains self-tests with questions in standardized test format. Software includes electronic versions of the text lessons and the Math Tools and Math Labs.

MathBlaster® Mystery

This award-winning, interactive software program on CD-ROM can be used to maintain skills or to accommodate early finishers.

- Level: Earn 2 coins; Pay 6 coins
- Mission Mode (all lessons)
- Kitchen Comparisons (5-5, 5-9)
- Number Guesser (5-1, 5-3, 5-7)
- Equation Maker (5-4, 5-8)
- Word Problems (5-2, 5-6, 5-10, Problem Solving Practice)

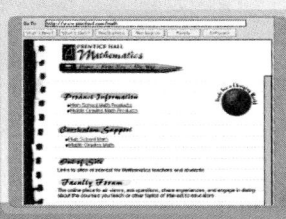

For Students
Support for the Chapter Project
A career-oriented link for Math at Work feature

www.phschool.com/math

For teachers
Curriculum Support
Product Information
Regional Support Information

FOR THE TEACHER

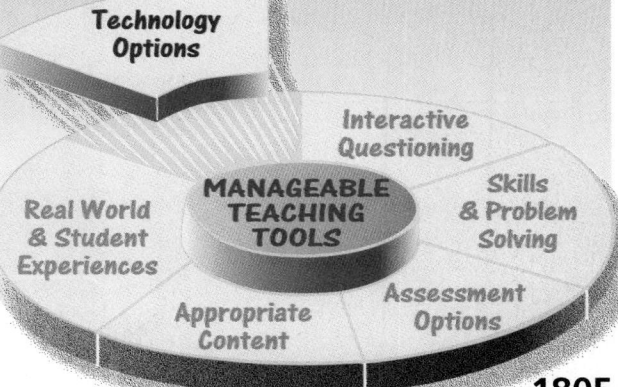

Computer Item Generator

Available on both CD-ROM and diskette, this software generates customized practice sheets, quizzes, and tests. It generates an unlimited supply of questions with varying levels of difficulty.

The Resource Pro™

Available on CD-ROM, this software can be used to customize and plan lessons.

Technology Options

MANAGEABLE TEACHING TOOLS

- Interactive Questioning
- Skills & Problem Solving
- Assessment Options
- Appropriate Content
- Real World & Student Experiences

CONNECTING TO PRIOR LEARNING Ask students: *Where do you see fractions in everyday life?* **Answers may vary.** *How much of a dollar is a quarter or a half dollar?* **A quarter is** $\frac{25}{100}$ **or** $\frac{1}{4}$. **A half dollar is** $\frac{50}{100}$ **or** $\frac{1}{2}$.

CULTURAL CONNECTIONS Sports and games in the United States have players from many countries. Some baseball players are from Japan, Venezuela, or the Dominican Republic. Some basketball players are from Nigeria, Croatia, or China. Many other games, such as chess and mah-jongg, have diverse origins.

INTERDISCIPLINARY CONNECTIONS Keeping long-term records of sports and games involves some knowledge of history. Ask students to choose a favorite sport or game and to report briefly on a specific event in the game's or sport's history.

ABOUT THE PROJECT The Chapter Project gives students an opportunity to apply their knowledge of fractions to designing a game. The Project Link questions help students focus on the appropriate concepts as they develop their board games.

Internet • For information and activities related to the Chapter Project, visit the Prentice Hall site at www.phschool.com/mgm1/ch5

Investigating Fractions

5

WHAT YOU WILL LEARN IN THIS CHAPTER
- How to model and use ratios and proportions
- How to relate fractions, decimals, and percents
- How to estimate percents and find the percent of a number

You may want to bring in games you have at home, including games from other countries. Or find games other students have created. Use the games to inspire creativity and introduce the Chapter Project.

Ask students: *What board games have you played? What made the games enjoyable? Did you use fractions in playing the games? How?*

PROJECT NOTEBOOK Encourage students to keep all project-related materials in a separate folder or notebook.

TRACKING THE PROJECT You may wish to have students read Finishing the Chapter Project on page 221 for an overview of the project. Set benchmark deadlines for students to show you their work in progress.

CHAPTER PROJECT

THEME: SPORTS

HOME COURT ADVANTAGE

In Malcolm's daydream, he is floating in the air on the way to a slam dunk. In reality, he is tossing pieces of paper into a wastebasket. He makes some shots, and he misses others.

Compare Basketball Statistics Your project will be to record and compare attempts and baskets made by the players on your own imaginary basketball team. You can shoot baskets with a real basketball on a real court, or you can toss pieces of paper into a wastebasket.

Steps to help you complete the project:

p. 195 **Project Link:** *Recording*
p. 212 **Project Link:** *Calculating*
p. 217 **Project Link:** *Comparing*
p. 221 *Finishing the Chapter Project*

• How to solve problems by solving a simpler problem

PROBLEM SOLVING

SCORING RUBRIC

3 You've used both fractions and decimals to compare the shooting records of at least seven players. These seven players each made a different number of attempts so that your fractions have different denominators. All your information is accurate and is displayed in an attractive table that lists the players in order from best record to worst record.

2 Most of your comparisons are based on fractions with different denominators. Your fractions and decimals are almost all accurate. The shooting records are listed in order from best to worst in a neat table.

1 You didn't collect data for enough players, you didn't vary the denominator of your fractions, or you incorrectly compared the players' shooting records.

0 You only compared shooting records for a few players, or you left out the fractions, decimals, or table of comparisons.

1 Focus

CONNECTING TO PRIOR KNOWLEDGE Ask students: *Is it difficult to equally share an even number of items among an odd number of people? Answers may vary.* Have students discuss strategies they use to share equally. **Answers may vary. Sample: Divide the items into parts.**

Lesson Planning Options

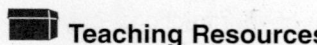

Prerequisite Skills
• dividing whole numbers (precourse)

Vocabulary/Symbols
divisible, divisibility

Materials/Manipulatives
• calculator

Resources

 Student Edition
Skills Handbook, p. 543
Extra Practice, p. 526
Glossary/Study Guide

Teaching Resources
Chapter Support File, Ch. 5
• Lesson Planner 5-1
• Practice 5-1, Reteaching 5-1
• Alternative Activity 5-1
• Answer Masters 5-1
Glossary, Spanish Resources

 Transparencies
19, 86, Minds on Math 5-1

Warm Up

A six pound bag of dog food sells for $2.70. Kay has three dogs. She bought three bags. What is the price per pound for the dog food? **$0.45 per pound**

182

2 Teach

Work Together

ERROR ALERT! Question 1 Students may not understand the divisibility rule for 2.
Remediation: Tell students they only need to look at the last digit of a number to determine if the number is even. If the last digit is divisible by 2, then the number is even. Have students list the even digits. **0, 2, 4, 6, 8**

THINK AND DISCUSS

AEP To explain the word *remainder*, say to students: *Seven friends share 12 cookies equally. Each friend has one cookie. Five remain on the plate. So, 5 is the remainder of 12 divided by 7.*

VISUAL LEARNING Have students write the numbers 1–100 in a 10 × 10 grid. Have them use the divisibility rules to find the numbers divisible by 2, 3, 5, 9, and 10. Have them shade numbers divisible by 2 in yellow, by 3 in pink, by 5 in blue, by 9 in red, and by 10 in green.

5-1 Mental Math and Divisibility

What You'll Learn

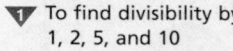

▼ To find divisibility by 1, 2, 5, and 10

▼ To find divisibility by 3 and 9

...And Why
You'll use divisibility to work with and understand fractions.

Here's How
Look for questions that
▪ build understanding
✔ check understanding

Work Together

Discovering Divisibility Rules

The Pledge of Allegiance says our nation is "indivisible, with liberty and justice for all." The United States of America may not be divisible, but numbers are.

1. Look at the numbers in the tables below.

Divisible by 2	Not Divisible by 2
0 14 202 5,756 798 80 120	9 13 467 4,005 99 42,975

a. ▪*Writing* Write a definition of the word *divisible*.
b. Give two more numbers that are divisible by 2. Give two more that are not. **Samples: 2, 24; 3, 101**
c. ▪*Draw a Conclusion* Give a rule for numbers that are divisible by 2.
d. Which of the numbers in the table that are divisible by 2 are also divisible by 5? Divisible by 10? **0, 80, 120; 0, 80, 120**
e. Which of the numbers in the table that are not divisible by 2 are divisible by 5? Divisible by 10? **4,005; 42,975; none**

a, c. Answers may vary. See back of book for samples.

THINK AND DISCUSS

▼ *Divisibility by 1, 2, 5, and 10*

Divisibility is the ability of one whole number to divide into another with no remainder. The chart below gives divisibility rules for 1, 2, 5, and 10.

Divisible By	Rule
1	All numbers are divisible by 1.
2	All even numbers are divisible by 2.
5	Numbers ending in 5 or 0 are divisible by 5.
10	Numbers ending in 0 are divisible by 10.

An *even number* is a whole number that is exactly divisible by 2.

An *odd number* is a whole number that is *not* exactly divisible by 2.

EXTENSION Ask students: *How would you decide if 658,687,967,868,789 is divisible by 9?* Add the digits, find if the sum is divisible by 9. *The sum of the digits is 108. How would you decide if 108 is divisible by 9?* Add the digits and divide by 9. *Is 658,687,967,868,789 divisible by 9?* **yes**

■ ADDITIONAL EXAMPLES

FOR EXAMPLE 1

Is 3,045 divisible by 1? **yes** by 2? **no** by 5? **yes** by 10? **no**

FOR EXAMPLE 2

Is 4,716 divisible by 3? **yes** by 9? **yes**

ASSESSMENT Have students work with a partner to find a number divisible by 2, 5, 10, 3, and 9. **Answers may vary. Sample: 90**

3 Practice/Assess

EXERCISES *On Your Own*

OPEN-ENDED **Exercise 25** Ask students to explain what the one's digit must be. It must be 0 in order to be divisible by 2, 5, and 10.

■ **EXAMPLE 1**

State whether the first number is divisible by the second.

a. 715; 5

Yes, 715 is divisible by 5, since it ends in 5.

b. 1,020; 10

Yes, 1,020 is divisible by 10, since it ends in 0.

2. 27,215 is divisible by 5 but not by 10.

2. ✔*Try It Out* State whether 27,215 is divisible by 5 or 10.

Now you may assign Exercises 1–8, 26–27.

2 *Divisibility by 3 and 9*

You can find whether a number is divisible by 3 by adding up the digits. If their sum is divisible by 3, then the number is, too.

■ **EXAMPLE 2**

Is 2,571 divisible by 3?

$2 + 5 + 7 + 1 = 15$ ← Find the sum of the digits.
$15 \div 3 = 5$ ← Find whether the sum is divisible by 3.

The sum of the digits is divisible by 3, so 2,571 is divisible by 3.

3. ✔*Try It Out* Is 6,319 divisible by 3? **no**

HISTORY
The Greek mathematician Plato (427?–348 B.C.) wrote about the number 5,040 in his work *The Laws*. He stated that 5,040 is divisible by 60 numbers, including 1 through 10.

Source: *Number Theory*

The divisibility rule for 9 is like the divisibility rule for 3.
4e. A number is divisible by 9 if the sum of its digits is divisible by 9.

4. **a.** *Mental Math* Is 99 divisible by 9? **yes**
   b. What is the sum of the digits of the number 99? Is this sum divisible by 9? **18; yes**
   c. Is 66 divisible by 9? **no**
   d. What is the sum of the digits of the number 66? Is this sum divisible by 9? **12; no**
   e. *Reasoning* Give a rule for divisibility by 9. **See above.**

Now you may assign Exercises 9–25, 28–30.

EXERCISES *On Your Own*

Find whether the first number is divisible by the second.

yes	yes	no	yes	no	no
1. 525; 5	**2.** 848,960; 10	**3.** 2,385; 10	**4.** 36,928; 1	**5.** 4,673; 2	**6.** 53,559; 5
7. 99,718; 2	**8.** 202,470; 5	**9.** 60,714; 3	**10.** 22,996; 9	**11.** 757,503; 9	**12.** 333,335; 3
yes	yes	yes	no	yes	no

Technology Options

Prentice Hall Technology

  Software for Learners
• Math Blaster® Mystery*
• Interactive Student Tutorial, Chapter 5*

  Teaching Resource Software
• Computer Item Generator 5-1
• Resource Pro™ Chapter 5*

Internet • For related mathematics activities, visit the Prentice Hall site at www.phschool.com/math

*Available on CD-ROM only

Assignment Options for Exercises On Your Own

To provide flexible scheduling, this lesson can be split into parts.

1 Core 1–8
Extension 26, 27

2 Core 9–25
Extension 28–30

Use Mixed Review to maintain skills.

PRACTICE

Practice 5-1 Mental Math and Divisibility

Use mental math to determine whether the first number is divisible by the second.

1. 475; 5 yes   2. 5,296; 3 no   3. 843; 2 no   4. 76,780; 10 yes

5. 456,790; 5 yes   6. 3,460; 2 yes   7. 4,197; 3 yes   8. 100,005; 10 no

Use mental math to determine whether the number is divisible by 1, 2, 3, 5, 9, or 10.

9. 126   10. 257   11. 430   12. 535
   1, 2, 3, 9   1   1, 2, 5, 10   1, 5

13. 745   14. 896   15. 729   16. 945
   1, 5   1, 2   1, 3, 9   1, 3, 5, 9

17. 4,580   18. 6,331   19. 7,952   20. 8,000
   1, 2, 5, 10   1   1, 2   1, 2, 5, 10

21. 19,450   22. 21,789   23. 43,785   24. 28,751
   1, 2, 5, 10   1, 3, 9   1, 3, 5, 9   1

Find the digit to make each number divisible by 9.

25. 54,78[3]   26. 42,[5]97   27. 83,2[1]4   28. 53[6],904

Circle A, B, C, or D. Which number satisfies the given conditions?

29. divisible by 1, 3, and 5
A. 10   B. 93   (C) 45   D. 54

30. divisible by 1, 2, 3, and 9
(A) 18   B. 9   C. 6   D. 60

31. divisible by 1, 2, 5, and 10
A. 406   (B) 400   C. 205   D. 716

32. divisible by 1, 2, 3, 5, and 10
A. 708   B. 65   C. 200   (D) 600

33. There are 159 students to be grouped into relay teams. Each team is to have the same number of students. Can each team have 3, 5, or 6 students?
3 students

In copymaster and workbook formats

RETEACHING

Reteaching 5-1 Mental Math and Divisibility

A number is **divisible** by a second number if the second number divides into the first with no remainder. Here are some rules.

Last Digit of a Number	The Number Is Divisible by	Examples
Any	1	Any number
0, 2, 4, 6, 8	2	10, 24, 32, 54, 106, 138
0, 5	5	10; 25; 70; 915; 1,250
0	10	10; 20; 90; 500; 4,300

The Sum of the Digits	The Number Is Divisible by	Examples	
is divisible by 3	3	843 → 8 + 4 + 3 = 15 and 15 ÷ 3 = 5	281 R0 / 3)843
is divisible by 9	9	2,898 → 2 + 8 + 9 + 8 = 27 and 27 ÷ 9 = 3	322 R0 / 9)2,898

Circle the numbers that are divisible by the number at the left.

1. 2   (8) 15 (26) (42) 97 105 (218)
2. 5   14 (10) (25) 18 (975) (1,005) (2,340)
3. 10 (100) 75 23 (60) 99 (250) 655
4. 3   (51) (75) (12) 82 (93) (153) 274
5. 9   (27) 32 (36) (108) (126) 245 (387)

Find whether the first number is divisible by the second.

6. 185; 5 yes   7. 76,870; 10 yes   8. 461; 1 yes
9. 456; 3 yes   10. 35,994; 2 yes   11. 6,791; 3 no
12. 12,866; 9 no   13. 151,002; 9 yes   14. 55,340; 5 yes
15. 6,888; 2 yes   16. 31,067; 5 no   17. 901,204; 3 no
18. 2,232; 3 yes   19. 45,812; 9 no   20. 3,090; 10 yes
21. 312; 9 no   22. 1,933; 3 no   23. 28,889; 2 no

ENRICHMENT

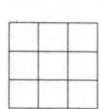 **inds on Math Transparency**

5-1

Which 4 sides of the small squares would you remove to leave 5 small congruent squares?

See Solution Key for worked-out answers.

184

WRITING Exercise 28 Some students may want to design a set of problems to test whether it is easier to use the calculator or mental math.

WRAP UP

IDENTIFYING THE BIG IDEA Ask students to define divisibility. Ask them to tell how to determine divisibility for 2, 3, 5, 9, and 10.

LESSON QUIZ

1. Is 2,121,120 divisible by 2? by 3? by 5? by 9? by 10? **yes**

2. Tell how to find a number that is divisible by 2 and 9. **Select an even number where the sum of the digits is divisible by 9.**

Mental Math **State whether each number is divisible by 1, 2, 3, 5, 9, or 10.**

13. 105   14. 15,345   15. 40,020   16. 70,641   17. 2,021,112   18. 8,516
   1, 3, 5   1, 3, 5, 9   1, 2, 3, 5, 10   1, 3, 9   1, 2, 3, 9   1, 2

Find the digit that makes each number divisible by 9.

19. 9,0[4]5   20. 2,[7]18   21. 34,76[7]   22. [6]7,302   23. 2[4]6,555   24. 19,76[1],228

25. *Open-ended* Find a four-digit number that is divisible by 1, 2, 3, 5, 9, and 10. **Answers may vary. Sample: 9,000**

26. *Reasoning* If a number is divisible by 5, must it also be divisible by 10? Use an example to support your answer.
No; 15 is divisible by 5 but not by 10.

27. **Choose A, B, C, or D.** The five sides of the Pentagon in Washington, D.C., are equal in length. The perimeter of the building is divisible by 5 and 10. Which of the following could be the length of a side? **B**

A. 351 ft   B. 352 ft   C. 353 ft   D. 357 ft

28. *Writing* Describe how you can use a calculator to tell if one number is divisible by another. Do you think it is easier to find divisibility using mental math or a calculator? Explain. **See back of book.**

29. *Money* Elissa and eight friends went to lunch at a restaurant. The check came to $56.61.
   a. Can the group split the check into equal parts? **yes**
   b. Write a possible divisibility rule for dividing a decimal by 9. Use examples to support your answer. **See back of book.**

30a. **78; 8,010; 21,822**   30b. **78; 8,010; 21,822**

30. Use the numbers at the right.
   a. Which numbers are divisible by both 2 and 3?
   b. *Calculator* Which numbers are divisible by 6?
   c. Use your results to write a divisibility rule for 6.
     A number is divisible by 6 if it is divisible by 2 and divisible by 3.

78	154	237
8,010	21,822	

Mixed Review

Round to the place of the underlined digit. *(Lesson 3-6)*

31. 3.9<u>5</u>7   32. 34<u>5</u>.008   33. 32,<u>0</u>19.8   34. 16.9<u>3</u>07   35. 0.<u>5</u>2709   36. 42.0<u>6</u>52
   3.96   345   32,000   16.93   0.5   42.07

37. Efra drinks two juice packs a day. Each pack contains 355 mL. How many liters of juice does she drink in one week? *(Lesson 4-10)* **4.97 L**

5·2 Teaching Notes

1 Focus

CONNECTING TO PRIOR KNOWLEDGE
Have students list the rules for divisibility. Ask students to name numbers divisible by at least five numbers. **Answers may vary. Sample: 24, 16, 32, 50** Ask: *How did you find these numbers?* **Answers may vary. Sample: I multiplied five numbers together.**

2 Teach

Work Together

TACTILE LEARNING Question 3 Have students cut out a 4-by-3 rectangle from graph paper. Suggest they use it to answer the question.

THINK AND DISCUSS

KINESTHETIC LEARNING Start with the number 2 and number the students' desks consecutively. Begin at the desk you numbered 2. Ask this student to remain standing, but ask every second student to sit down. The next student standing is at desk number 3. Have this student remain standing, but ask every third student who is still standing to sit down. Repeat this procedure until the only students who are not sitting down are those you asked to remain standing. Ask: *Why are these students still standing?*

GEOMETRY Connection

5-2 Using Models and Factor Trees

What You'll Learn

▼ To identify prime and composite numbers

▼ To find the prime factorization of a composite number

...And Why

Knowing how to find prime factors will help you simplify fractions.

Here's How

Look for questions that
▪ build understanding
✔ check understanding

A perfect number is a number that is the sum of all its factors except itself. The lowest perfect number is 6, since $6 = 1 + 2 + 3$. The next perfect number is 28.

7. **Answers may vary. Sample: 8 squares; the number of different rectangles is equal to the number of pairs of factors.**

Work Together *Experimenting with Composite Numbers*

1. Use graph paper. How many rectangles with different shapes can you form using exactly 12 squares? **3 rectangles**

2. What are the dimensions of each rectangle? **1 unit by 12 units, 2 units by 6 units, 3 units by 4 units**

3. ▪*Geometry* Does a 4-by-3 rectangle have the same shape as a 3-by-4 rectangle? Explain.
Yes; you can make each rectangle by rotating the other 90°.

THINK AND DISCUSS

▼ Prime and Composite Numbers

The numbers 1, 2, 3, 4, 6, and 12 are factors of 12. One number is a **factor** of another if it divides into that number with no remainder.

4. ▪*Reasoning* Compare the dimensions of the rectangles formed using exactly 12 squares to the factors of 12.
They are the same.

5. Draw rectangles to find all the factors of 17 and of 20.
See margin p. 187.

You call a number that has exactly two factors, 1 and itself, a **prime number.** A number that has more than two factors is called a **composite number.**

6. ▪*Modeling* Use a prime number of squares. How many rectangles with different shapes can you form?
1 rectangle

7. Use a composite number of squares. Describe the number of rectangles with different shapes you can form.

8. ▪*Explain* Why is the number 1 considered to be neither prime nor composite? **1 does not fit either definition.**

Lesson Planning Options

Prerequisite Skills
- multiplying whole numbers (precourse)
- reviewing properties of rectangles (precourse)
- dividing whole numbers (precourse)

Vocabulary/Symbols
factor, prime number, composite number, factor tree, prime factorization

Materials/Manipulatives
- graph paper • calculator

Resources

📖 **Student Edition**
Skills Handbook, p. 541
Extra Practice, p. 526
Glossary/Study Guide

Teaching Resources
Chapter Support File, Ch. 5
- Lesson Planner 5-2
- Practice 5-2, Reteaching 5-2
- Answer Masters 1, 2
Teaching Aids Masters 1, 2
Glossary, Spanish Resources

Transparencies
1, 14, Minds on Math 5-2

Warm Up
Write the next number in the sequence:
0.214, 0.234, 0.254, 0.274, **0.294**

185

Answers may vary. Sample: Their desks have prime numbers.

Question 8 Have students look at the definitions of *composite* and *prime* to answer this question. Ask: *How many factors does 1 have?* one

ASSESSMENT Question 9 Ask students to support their answers. Answers may vary. Sample: 8 is divisible by 2; 23 has only 2 factors; 35 is divisible by 5; 46 is divisible by 2.

■ **ADDITIONAL EXAMPLES**

FOR EXAMPLE 1

Use a rectangular model to tell if 11 is prime or composite. Prime; models show a 1-by-11 rectangle.

FOR EXAMPLE 2

Find the prime factorization of 63.
3 × 3 × 7

Example 2 Ask students: *How can you tell that you can divide 75 by 3 without using a factor tree?* Find the sum of the digits (12); see if it is divisible by 3.

AEP VISUAL LEARNING Help students understand the term *factor tree*. Draw the factor tree for 36 to resemble a tree. Make the 36 the trunk and place the factors above it like branches.

Technology Options

Prentice Hall Technology

 **Software for Learners**
- Math Blaster® Mystery*
- Interactive Student Tutorial, Chapter 5*

 Teaching Resource Software
- Computer Item Generator 5-2
- Resource Pro™ Chapter 5*

Internet • For related mathematics activities, visit the Prentice Hall site at www.phschool.com/math

Available on CD-ROM only

Assignment Options for Exercises On Your Own

To provide flexible scheduling, this lesson can be subdivided into parts.

1 Core 1–25
Extension 26

2 Core 27–42
Extension 43–45

Use Mixed Review to maintain skills.

186

 The greatest prime number found so far has 895,932 digits. It was found in 1997 over the Internet with a team of more than 2,000 partners. You can join the search for greater prime numbers by visiting the following Web site: www.mersenne.org.

■ **EXAMPLE 1**

Tell whether 9 is prime or composite.

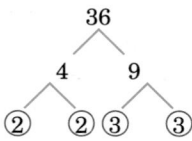

Draw the rectangles that can be made from exactly 9 squares.

The dimensions of the rectangles show that the factors of 9 are 1, 3, and 9. So, 9 is composite.

9. ✔Try It Out Tell whether the number is prime or composite.
a. 8 composite b. 23 prime c. 35 composite d. 46 composite

Now you may assign Exercises 1–26.

2 *Prime Factorization*

A composite number is divisible by its prime factors. You can find these prime factors using a **factor tree**. Two factor trees for the number 36 are shown.

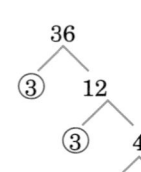

The prime factors in the trees are the same; each tree starts with a different factoring of 36.

10. a. ■*Reasoning* How are the two factor trees alike? How are they different?
b. Name the prime factors of 36. 2, 2, 3, 3

11. ■*Analyze* How can you use divisibility rules to begin a factor tree? If the number has 2, 3, 5, or 9 as a factor, divisibility rules help you find the first factors in your tree.

ERROR ALERT! Question 12 Some students may list composites as factors. **Remediation:** Have students check each factor they list to make sure it has only itself and 1 as factors. Also have students check their list of prime factors by multiplying.

3 Practice/Assess

EXERCISES *On Your Own*

TACTILE LEARNING Exercises 2–7 Suggest students use tiles to make the rectangles.

WRITING Exercise 26 Have students refer to their sketches in their explanations.

WRAP UP

IDENTIFYING THE BIG IDEA Ask students to define prime and composite numbers. Have students explain how to find the prime factorization of a composite number.

JOURNAL Challenge students to use only two examples. Have them find one to illustrate what they know about composites and one to illustrate what they know about primes.

You can write a composite number as a product of its prime factors. This product is the **prime factorization** of the number. If you like, you can use exponents for factors that are repeated.

■ **EXAMPLE 2**

Find the prime factorization of 75 using a factor tree.

PROBLEM SOLVING HINT
Circle each prime factor as soon as it appears in your factor tree.

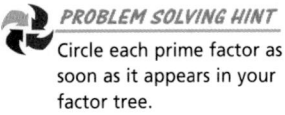

$\qquad$ ← 75 = 3 × 25

$\qquad$ ← 25 = 5 × 5

The prime factorization of 75 is $3 \times 5 \times 5$, or 3×5^2.

12. ✔ *Try It Out* Find the prime factorization of 42. 2 × 3 × 7

Now you may assign Exercises 27–45.

EXERCISES *On Your Own*

1. The rectangles that can be formed using exactly 16 squares are shown below. List all the factors of 16. 1, 2, 4, 8, 16

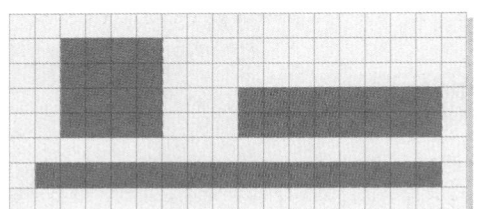

2.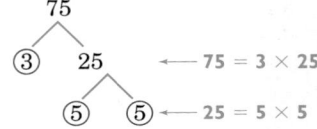
15 × 1

3. 3 × 1

3 × 5

4. 28 × 1

14 × 2

4 × 7

6. 11 × 1

Sketch all the rectangles with different shapes that can be formed using exactly the given number of squares. List all the factors of each number. Tell whether each number is prime or composite. 2–4, 6. See above for diagram. 5, 7. See margin for diagram.

2. 15	**3.** 3	**4.** 28	**5.** 21	**6.** 11	**7.** 18
composite	prime	composite	composite	prime	composite

Tell whether each number is prime or composite.

8. 55	**9.** 51	**10.** 103	**11.** 100	**12.** 59	**13.** 83
composite	composite	prime	composite	prime	prime
14. 43	**15.** 19	**16.** 72	**17.** 90	**18.** 44	**19.** 7
prime	prime	composite	composite	composite	prime
20. 80	**21.** 86	**22.** 93	**23.** 71	**24.** 150	**25.** 56
composite	composite	composite	prime	composite	composite

pages 185–187 Think and Discuss

5.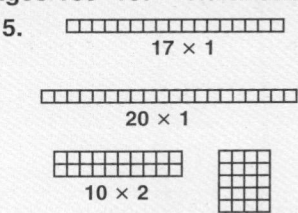

17 × 1

20 × 1

10 × 2

4 × 5

pages 187–188 On Your Own

5.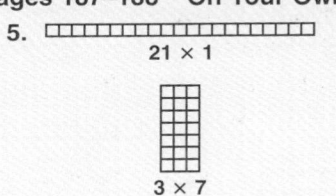

21 × 1

3 × 7

7.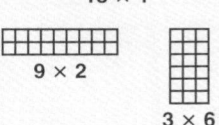
18 × 1

9 × 2

3 × 6

26.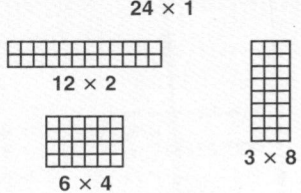

24 × 1

12 × 2

6 × 4

3 × 8

The dimensions of each side of each rectangle represent a factor of the number. The number is prime if there is only 1 rectangle. It is composite if there is more than 1 rectangle.

PRACTICE

Practice 5-2 *Using Models and Factor Trees*

1. The diagram below shows the different rectangles that can be formed using exactly 24 square tiles. Use the diagram to determine all the factors of 24.

1, 2, 3, 4, 6, 8, 12, 24

 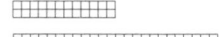

Tell whether each number is prime or composite.

2. 53 prime
3. 86 composite
4. 95 composite
5. 17 prime

6. 24 composite
7. 27 composite
8. 31 prime
9. 51 composite

10. 103 prime
11. 47 prime
12. 93 composite
13. 56 composite

Complete each factor tree. Answers may vary. Samples:

14. 28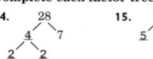
15. 75
16. 84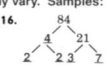
17. 210

Find the prime factorization of each number using a factor tree.

18. 58 2×29
19. 72 $2 \times 2 \times 2 \times 3 \times 3$
20. 40 $2 \times 2 \times 2 \times 5$
21. 30 $2 \times 3 \times 5$

22. 120 $2 \times 2 \times 2 \times 3 \times 5$
23. 100 $2 \times 2 \times 5 \times 5$
24. 144 $2 \times 2 \times 2 \times 2 \times 3 \times 3$
25. 310 $2 \times 5 \times 31$

Find the number with the given prime factorization.

26. $2 \times 2 \times 5 \times 7 \times 11$ 1,540
27. $2 \times 3 \times 5 \times 7 \times 11$ 2,310
28. $2 \times 2 \times 13 \times 17$ 884
29. $7 \times 11 \times 13 \times 17$ 17,017

In copymaster and workbook formats

RETEACHING

Reteaching 5-2 *Using Models and Factor Trees*

A **prime number** has exactly two factors, the number itself and 1.

$5 \times 1 = 5$
5 is a prime number.

A **composite number** has more than two factors. $1 \times 6 = 6$
$2 \times 3 = 6$

1, 2, 3, and 6 are factors of 6.
6 is a composite number.
The number 1 is neither prime nor composite.

Every composite number can be written as a product of prime numbers.

$6 = 2 \times 3$
$8 = 2 \times 2 \times 2$
$12 = 2 \times 2 \times 3$

You can use a **factor tree** to find prime factors. This one shows the prime factors of 50.

$50 = 2 \times 5 \times 5$ is the **prime factorization** of 5.

Tell whether each number is prime or composite.

1. 21 composite
2. 43 prime
3. 53 prime
4. 74 composite

5. 54 composite
6. 101 prime
7. 67 prime
8. 138 composite

9. 83 prime
10. 95 composite
11. 41 prime
12. 57 composite

Complete each factor tree.

13. 60
14. 64
15. 120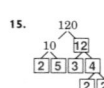

Find the prime factorization using a factor tree.

16. 21 3×7
17. 48 $2 \times 2 \times 2 \times 2 \times 3$
18. 81 $3 \times 3 \times 3 \times 3$
19. 56 3×7

20. 63 $3 \times 3 \times 7$
21. 100 $2 \times 2 \times 5 \times 5$
22. 103 1×103
23. 155 5×31

ENRICHMENT

Minds on Math Transparency

5-2

Norma used a total of 192 digits to number the pages of her book. How many pages are there in Norma's book?

100 pages

See *Solution Key* for worked-out answers.

188

LESSON QUIZ

1. Which of the following numbers are prime? Which are composite?

a. 27 composite

b. 81 composite

c. 107 prime

d. 195 composite

2. Find the prime factorization of 336.
$2 \times 2 \times 2 \times 2 \times 3 \times 7$

3. Is each statement true or false? Explain.

a. The number 19 is a composite number. **False; 19 is prime because it is divisible only by 1 and itself.**

b. Even numbers greater than 2 are composite numbers. **True; all even numbers have 2 as a factor.**

c. All numbers with a last digit of 5 have 5 as one of their prime factors. **True; numbers that end in 5 are divisible by 5.**

26. *Writing* Sketch all the rectangles with different shapes that can be formed using exactly 24 squares. Explain how to use your diagram to find the factors of 24 and to tell if 24 is a prime or composite number. **See margin p. 187.**

Copy and complete each factor tree.

27. 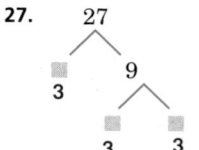 27, 9, 3, 3, 3

28. 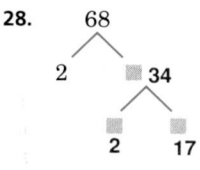 68, 2, 34, 2, 17

29. 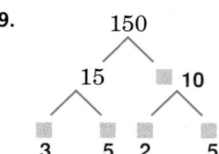 150, 15, 10, 3, 5, 2, 5

Find the prime factorization using a factor tree.

30. 30 $2 \times 3 \times 5$
31. 63 $3^2 \times 7$
32. 120 $2^3 \times 3 \times 5$
33. 275 $5^2 \times 11$
34. 50 2×5^2
35. 32 2^5

36. 45 $3^2 \times 5$
37. 90 $2 \times 3^2 \times 5$
38. 143 11×13
39. 160 $2^5 \times 5$
40. 108 $2^3 \times 3^2$
41. 531 $3^2 \times 59$

42. Use exponents to write the prime factorization $2 \times 2 \times 2 \times 3 \times 3 \times 5$. $2^3 \times 3^2 \times 5$

43. Two prime numbers that differ by 2, such as 3 and 5, are called *twin primes*. Find all twin primes that are less than 100. **3, 5; 5, 7; 11, 13; 17, 19; 29, 31; 41, 43; 59, 61; 71, 73**

Calculator **Find the number with the given prime factorization.**

44. $3 \times 17 \times 17 \times 17 \times 47$ 692,733
45. $7 \times 7 \times 17 \times 23 \times 23$ 440,657

> **JOURNAL**
> Summarize what you have learned about factors. Include examples to support what you write.

Mixed Review

Write a decimal for the given words. *(Lesson 3-1)*

46. forty-five hundredths 0.45
47. nine tenths 0.9
48. six hundredths 0.06

Choose **Use tiles, mental math, or a calculator to solve each equation.** *(Lesson 2-6)*

49. $k + 8 = 14$ 6
50. $m - 2 = 15$ 17
51. $x + 96 = 117$ 21
52. $58 = s - 19$ 77
53. $456 - a = 20$ 436

54. *Choose a Strategy* Guillermo has 20 dimes and nickels altogether. The total value of the coins is $1.35. How many dimes does Guillermo have? **7 dimes**

1 Focus

CONNECTING TO PRIOR KNOWLEDGE
Have students find the prime factorization of
12 and 18. **2 × 2 × 3; 2 × 3 × 3**
What numbers are factors of both 12 and 18?
2, 3, 6 *How can you tell?* **Answers may**
vary. Sample: 2, 3, and 6 all equally divide
both 12 and 18.

2 Teach

Work Together

TACTILE LEARNING Give students colored
tiles to represent the two sets of books—18
tiles of one color and 24 tiles of another color.

THINK AND DISCUSS

AEP Discuss the meanings of *greatest*,
common, and *factor*. Have students decide if

this is a good name for what it is. Some
students may forget what GCF stands for.
Quiz them occasionally throughout the lesson.

VISUAL LEARNING **Example 1** Have
students use a special mark such as a double
circle to distinguish the GCF from other
common factors.

ASSESSMENT Pair students. Have each
student think of a number and find the prime
factorization of their partner's number. Have
one student find the GCF and the other

5-3 Greatest Common Factor

What You'll Learn

▼ To find the greatest
common factor by
listing factors

▼ To find the greatest
common factor using
prime factorization

...And Why

You can use the greatest
common factor to decide
how to share items in a
collection.

Here's How

Look for questions that
▪ build understanding
✔ check understanding

1. No; 18 and 24 cannot
be divided by 5 without
remainders.

2. Yes; each member
would get 6 books from
the first set and 8
books from the second
set.

3. The number of mem-
bers present must be a
factor of 18 and a factor
of 24.

6. Answers may vary.
Sample: List the factors
of each number. The
greatest number that
appears in every list is
the GCF.

Work Together
Investigating Common Factors

One set of classic comic books contains 18
books, and the other contains 24 books. Each
set can be divided equally among the
Collectors Club members present at the club
meeting. **See below left.**

1. ▪ *Number Sense* Is it possible only
five members are present? Explain.

2. Is it possible only three members are
present? Explain.

3. What must be true about the
number of members present?

4. List all the possible numbers of members present. What is
the greatest possible number? **1, 2, 3, 6; 6**

THINK AND DISCUSS

▼ *Finding the GCF By Listing Factors*

Factors that are the same for two or more numbers are
common factors. The **greatest common factor (GCF)** of two or more
numbers is the greatest number that is a factor of every number.

▪ **EXAMPLE 1**

Find the GCF of 18 and 30.

18: (1, 2, 3, 6) 9, 18   ← List the factors for each number.
30: (1, 2, 3) 5, (6) 10, 15, 30   Then circle the common factors.

The GCF is 6, the greatest of the common factors.

5. ✔ *Try It Out* Find the GCF of each set of numbers.
    a. 6, 21 **3**   **b.** 18, 45 **9**   **c.** 28, 42 **14**

6. ▪ *Explain* How can you find the GCF of three numbers?
          Now you may assign Exercises 1–12, 25.

Lesson Planning Options

Prerequisite Skills
• multiplying and dividing whole numbers
(precourse)
• making factor trees (5-2)

Vocabulary/Symbols
common factors, greatest common factors

Resources

📖 **Student Edition**

Skills Handbook, p. 541
Extra Practice, p. 526
Glossary/Study Guide

📦 **Teaching Resources**

Chapter Support File, Ch. 5
• Lesson Planner 5-3
• Practice 5-3, Reteaching 5-3
• Answer Masters 5-3
Glossary, Spanish Resources

📺 **Transparencies**
19, 87, Minds on Math 5-3

Warm Up

The largest crater on the moon
is called Bailly. It covers an area of
about 26,000 square miles. Write
this area in scientific notation.
2.6 × 10⁴ mi²

189

student check the work. Switch roles and repeat.

■ ADDITIONAL EXAMPLES

FOR EXAMPLE 1

Find the GCF of 64 and 48. **16**

FOR EXAMPLE 2

Use prime factorization to find the GCF of 24 and 96. $24 = 2 \times 2 \times 2 \times 3$; $96 = 2 \times 2 \times 2 \times 2 \times 2 \times 3$; GCF $= 2 \times 2 \times 2 \times 3 = 24$

Technology Options

Prentice Hall Technology

   **Software for Learners**

- Math Blaster® Mystery*
- Interactive Student Tutorial, Chapter 5*

   Teaching Resource Software

- Computer Item Generator 5-3
- Resource Pro™ Chapter 5*

Internet • For related mathematics activities, visit the Prentice Hall site at www.phschool.com/math

*Available on CD-ROM only

Assignment Options for Exercises On Your Own

To provide flexible scheduling, this lesson can be split into parts.

▼1 **Core** 1–12
 Extension 25

▼2 **Core** 13–24
 Extension 26

Use Mixed Review to maintain skills.

190

---

3 Practice/Assess

ERROR ALERT! Exercises 1–24 Some students may find the greatest common prime factor instead of the GCF. **Remediation:** Tell students the GCF does not have to be prime and is often not. Remind students to multiply the common prime factors to find the GCF.

LEARNING Exercises 1–24
...nts read the numbers aloud.
...them to read the factors aloud as
...em.

WRAP UP

IDENTIFYING THE BIG IDEA Ask students to explain how to find the GCF of two or more numbers.

❷ Using Prime Factorizations to Find the GCF

You can also use prime factorizations to find the GCF of a set of numbers.

■ EXAMPLE 2

Use prime factorizations to find the GCF of 27 and 36.

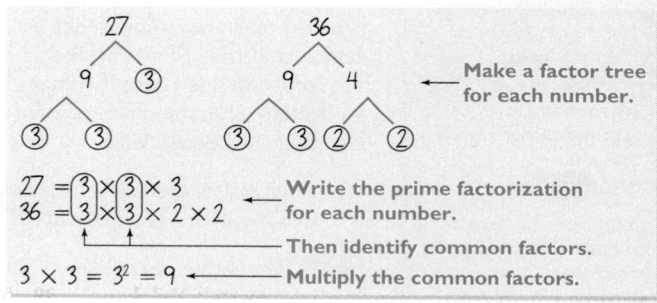

The GCF of 27 and 36 is 9.

8b. $2^2 \times 7, 3 \times 11$; 1; 1 is not a prime factor, so it does not appear in the prime factorization.

c. If the prime factors of each number are not prime factors of the other number, then the GCF is 1.

7. ✔ *Try It Out* Use prime factorizations to find the GCF.
 a. 12, 32 **4** **b.** 42, 90 **6** **c.** 18, 48 **6**

8a. 1, 2, 4, 7; 14, 28; 1, 3, 11, 33; 1

8. a. Make a list to find the GCF of 28 and 33.
 b. Use prime factorizations to find the GCF of 28 and 33. Explain why the GCF is harder to find with this method.
 c. ♣ *Draw a Conclusion* When using prime factorizations, how do you know that the GCF of a set of numbers is 1?

Now you may assign Exercises 13–24, 26.

EXERCISES On Your Own

Make a list to find the GCF of each set of numbers.

1. 14, 35 **7**	**2.** 24, 25 **1**	**3.** 10, 18 **2**	**4.** 15, 19 **1**	**5.** 24, 45 **3**	**6.** 11, 23 **1**
7. 9, 16 **1**	**8.** 25, 32 **1**	**9.** 30, 35 **5**	**10.** 26, 34 **2**	**11.** 12, 15, 21 **3**	**12.** 6, 8, 12 **2**

Use prime factorizations to find the GCF of each set of numbers.

13. 22, 104 **2**	**14.** 64, 125 **1**	**15.** 27, 30 **3**	**16.** 30, 49 **1**	**17.** 48, 54 **6**	**18.** 32, 40 **8**
19. 44, 52 **4**	**20.** 32, 56 **8**	**21.** 13, 120 **1**	**22.** 6, 57, 102 **3**	**23.** 17, 51, 85 **17**	**24.** 45, 90, 150 **15**

If you have block scheduling or extended class periods, have students use a flight simulation computer program. Students can download a program from a web site such as http://www.db.erau.edu/WWW_Virtual_lib/aviiation/flightsim.html. Have students write a short paragraph to explain how you would use math skills to help navigate an airplane.

LESSON QUIZ

1. Use a list to find the GCF of 10, 15, and 20. **5**

2. Find the GCF of 103 and 71. **1** Why is this the GCF? **Both 103 and 71 are prime.**

3. Name two composite numbers greater than 10 with a GCF of 3. **Answers may vary. Sample: 24 and 27**

4. The GCF of 24 and some number is 12. List a possible value for the number. **36**

PRACTICE

Practice 5-3 *Greatest Common Factor*

Make a list to find the GCF of each set of numbers.

1. 8, 12 4	**2.** 18, 27 9	**3.** 15, 23 1	**4.** 17, 34 17
5. 24, 12 12	**6.** 18, 24 6	**7.** 5, 25 5	**8.** 20, 25 5
9. 10, 15 5	**10.** 25, 75 25	**11.** 14, 21 7	**12.** 18, 57 3
13. 32, 24, 40 8	**14.** 25, 60, 75 5	**15.** 12, 35, 15 1	**16.** 15, 35, 20 5

Use prime factorization to find the GCF of each set of numbers.

17. 28, 24 4	**18.** 27, 36 9	**19.** 15, 305 5	**20.** 24, 45 3
21. 57, 27 3	**22.** 24, 48 24	**23.** 56, 35 7	**24.** 29, 87 29
25. 75, 200 25	**26.** 90, 160 10	**27.** 72, 108 36	**28.** 50, 96 2
29. 8, 42, 60 2	**30.** 75, 90, 120 15	**31.** 45, 70, 120 5	**32.** 200, 450, 300 50

Solve.

33. The GCF of two numbers is 850. Neither number is divisible by the other. What is the smallest that these two numbers could be? **1,700 and 2,550**

34. The GCF of two numbers is 479. One number is even and the other number is odd. Neither number is divisible by the other. What is the smallest that these two numbers could be? **958 and 1,437**

35. The GCF of two numbers is 871. Both numbers are even and neither is divisible by the other. What is the smallest that these two numbers could be? **3,484 and 5,226**

In copymaster and workbook formats

---

25. *Writing* What is the GCF of any two prime numbers? Explain.

26. *Open-ended* The GCF of 18 and some number is 6. What are three possible values for the number?
Answers may vary. Sample: 6, 12, 24

25. 1; each number has only two factors. The second factor is the number itself. Since the numbers are different, so are the second factors.

Mixed Review

Find each answer. *(Lessons 2-3 and 4-3)*

27. $8 - 2 \times 3 + 5$ **7**

28. $6 + 2 \times (12 \div 4)$ **12**

29. $(3 + 5) \times 10 - 4$ **76**

30. $7 - 5 \times (3 - 2)$ **2**

Add or subtract. Use models if they help you. *(Lesson 3-5)*

31. $0.8 + 0.5$ **1.3**

32. $1.2 - 0.7$ **0.5**

33. $0.56 + 0.9$ **1.46**

34. $2.59 - 0.83$ **1.76**

35. $1.8 - 0.09$ **1.71**

Find each product. *(Lesson 4-5)*

36. 0.24×7 **1.68**

37. 4.1×0.5 **2.05**

38. 6.2×1.1 **6.82**

39. 5.02×0.09 **0.4518**

40. 6.35×2.6 **16.51**

41. *Choose a Strategy* The houses on Twelfth Avenue are numbered in order from 1 through 85. How many house numbers contain at least one digit 3? **18 numbers**

Math at Work

PILOT

If you like to fly, then a career as a pilot may be right for you. Most pilots are involved in transporting people and cargo. Others have unusual tasks such as crop-dusting, testing aircraft, monitoring traffic, and rescuing injured persons. Pilots use their mathematical skills to choose a route, altitude, and speed that will provide the fastest, safest, and smoothest flight. Pilots must also calculate the speed they must reach in order to take off. To do this, they consider the height of the airport, the outside temperature, the weight of the aircraft, and the speed and direction of the wind.

 Visit the Web site for the National Air and Space Museum at www.nasm.si.edu for more information.

RETEACHING

Reteaching 5-3 *Greatest Common Factor*

You can find the **greatest common factor (GCF)** of 12 and 18 two ways.

① List the factors of 12 and 18.
12: 1, 2, 3, 4, 6, 12
18: 1, 2, 3, 6, 9, 18
② Find the common factors.
12: ①, ②, ③, 4, ⑥, 12
18: ①, ②, ③, ⑥, 9, 18
The common factors are 1, 2, 3, 6.
③ Name the greatest common factor: 6.

① Draw factor trees.
② Write each prime factorization. Identify common factors.
12: ② × 2 × ③
18: ② × ③ × 3
③ Multiply the common factors.
2 × 3 = 6. 6 is the GCF of 12 and 18.

List the factors of each number. Then find the GCF of the two numbers.

1. 10: 1, 2, 5, 10
15: 1, 3, 5, 15
GCF: 5

2. 14: 1, 2, 7, 14
21: 1, 3, 7, 21
GCF: 7

3. 9: 1, 3, 9
21: 1, 3, 7, 21
GCF: 3

4. 12: 1, 2, 3, 4, 6, 12
13: 1, 13
GCF: 1

5. 15: 1, 3, 5, 15
25: 1, 5, 25
GCF: 5

6. 15: 1, 3, 5, 15
18: 1, 2, 3, 6, 9, 18
GCF: 3

7. 36: 1, 2, 3, 4, 6, 9, 12, 18, 36
48: 1, 2, 3, 4, 6, 8, 12, 16, 24, 48
GCF: 12

8. 24: 1, 2, 3, 4, 6, 8, 12, 24
30: 1, 2, 3, 5, 6, 10, 15, 30
GCF: 6

Use prime factorization to find the GCF of each set of numbers.

9. 21, 60 3

10. 15, 45 15

11. 32, 40 8

12. 54, 60 6

13. 20, 50 10

14. 21, 63 21

15. 36, 40 4

16. 48, 72 24

17. 90, 150 30

ENRICHMENT

Minds on Math Transparency

5-3

Suppose you have 2 quarters, 5 dimes, and 10 nickels. How many ways can you make change for 50¢?

10 ways

See Solution Key for worked-out answers.

This page provides problems for students to solve using their knowledge of expressions, patterns, greatest common factor, addition and subtraction of decimals, multiplication and division of decimals, and estimation. Allow students to use any method they find helpful.

VISUAL LEARNING Exercise 2 Have students draw a scale diagram of the stacks of boxes to help them solve the problem.

USING MANIPULATIVES Exercise 3 Students can work with a partner to model the groups using blocks or counters. Have students find all possibilities before narrowing the selection to the group with the greatest number of students.

Exercise 5 Remind students to read the instructions carefully. The exercise asks how to check Mark's answer, not how he found it.

Exercise 8 Caution students to pay attention to the placement of the decimal point in the divisor and dividend.

PROBLEM SOLVING PRACTICE

Choose the best answer.

1. A quiz show contestant was asked to pick the equation having the solution $x = 20$. Which equation should she pick? **C**

   A. $x - 20 = 40$
   B. $2x = 22$
   C. $x + 30 = 50$
   D. $x \div 2 = 40$

2. Boxes 12 inches tall are being stacked next to boxes 18 inches tall. What is the shortest height at which the stacks will be the same height? **G**

   F. 216 inches
   G. 36 inches
   H. 32 inches
   J. 30 inches

3. Natraj has 36 students in his dance class. He plans to divide them into equal groups of 2 or more. What is the greatest number of students that a group can hold? **D**

   A. 2
   B. 4
   C. 9
   D. 18

4. Tyrone has 30 oatmeal cookies and 48 chocolate chip cookies to package in plastic bags. Each bag must contain the same number of cookies. Tyrone wants one type of cookie in each bag. He also wants the greatest possible number in each bag. How many cookies can he put in each bag? **F**

   F. 6
   G. 8
   H. 12
   J. 24

5. Mark subtracted 7.2 from 10. He got 2.8 for an answer. Which number sentence should he use to check his answer? **C**

   A. $10 + 2.8 = 12.8$
   B. $10 \times 2.8 = 28$
   C. $2.8 + 7.2 = 10$
   D. $7.2 \times 10 = 72$

Please note that items 6–8 have *five* answer choices.

6. A family rented a car for 5 days. The cost was $9.95 per day plus $.18 per mile for each mile driven over 500 miles. The family drove 970 miles. Which number sentence could be used to find the total cost of renting the car? **F**

   F. $T = (9.95 \times 5) + (970 - 500) \times 0.18$
   G. $T = (9.95 \times 5) + (970 \times 0.18)$
   H. $T = 9.95 \times 5 \times 970 \times 0.18$
   J. $T = 9.95 \times 5 + (970 + 500) \times 0.18$
   K. Not Here

7. Jolinda earns $5.75 per hour as a lifeguard. She works from 8 to 20 hours per week, depending on the weather. Which is a reasonable estimate of her weekly earnings? **C**

   A. less than $20
   B. less than $40
   C. more than $40 but less than $120
   D. more than $120
   E. Not Here

8. A steak weighing 1.4 pounds cost $4.06. What was the cost per pound? **H**

   F. $.29
   G. $.34
   H. $2.90
   J. $2.66
   K. $5.68

1 Focus

CONNECTING TO PRIOR KNOWLEDGE Ask students: *Where have you seen fractions?* **Answers may vary. Sample: in the hardware store, shopping for shoes, buying buttons** *How are fractions useful?* **Answers may vary. Sample: for measuring things**

3. 1; the numerator and denominator of the modeled fraction are equal.

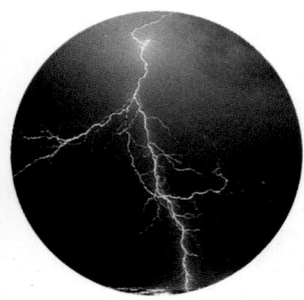

 A flash of lightning lasts for about $\frac{1}{100}$ of a second. That's quicker than the blink of an eye!

2 Teach

THINK AND DISCUSS

KINESTHETIC LEARNING **Question 2** Model the fractions using students. For example, to model $\frac{9}{12}$, ask 12 students to stand at the front of the room. Give 9 of them a piece of paper to hold. You can vary the model by having the 9 students stand with their backs to the class or cross their arms in front.

5-4 Using Fraction Models

What You'll Learn

▼ To model fractions
▼ To round fractions

...And Why

You'll use fractions for measurements in real-world situations, such as data collection.

Here's How

Look for questions that
⚫ build understanding
✔ check understanding

THINK AND DISCUSS

▼ Modeling Fractions

A **fraction model** shows a fraction's numerator and denominator as shaded parts and total parts.

numerator ⟶ $\frac{1}{6}$ ⟵ shaded part
denominator ⟶ ⟵ total parts

■ EXAMPLE 1

Name the fraction modeled.

a. 　　b.

Four of six parts are shaded, so the fraction is $\frac{4}{6}$.

Two of three parts are shaded, so the fraction is $\frac{2}{3}$.

1. ✔ *Try It Out* Name the fraction modeled.

a.  $\frac{1}{4}$　　b.  $\frac{3}{5}$

2. Model the fractions $\frac{2}{6}$, $\frac{3}{4}$, $\frac{6}{10}$, and $\frac{4}{5}$. **See back of book.**

3. ⚫ *Reasoning* What number is represented when *all* the parts in a fraction model are shaded? Explain. **See left.**

Now you may assign Exercises 1–20.

▼ Rounding Fractions

You can round fractions to the nearest half unit.

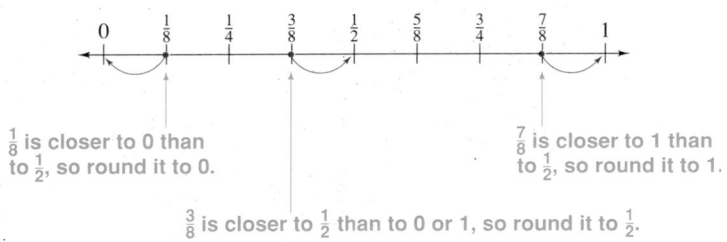

$\frac{1}{8}$ is closer to 0 than to $\frac{1}{2}$, so round it to 0.

$\frac{7}{8}$ is closer to 1 than to $\frac{1}{2}$, so round it to 1.

$\frac{3}{8}$ is closer to $\frac{1}{2}$ than to 0 or 1, so round it to $\frac{1}{2}$.

AEP **AUDITORY LEARNING** We read many fractions with ordinal number pronunciations such as *one sixth* and *two sevenths*. Have students recall the "th" ending on decimal pronunciations. Point out *one half* as an exception. Read the fraction names aloud so students can listen for the "th" endings.

ASSESSMENT Organize students in pairs. Have one student draw a fraction model. Their partner writes the fraction on the model and then rounds it. Students switch roles and check each other's work.

Lesson Planning Options

Prerequisite Skills
• rounding numbers (precourse)
• using fractions (precourse)

Vocabulary/Symbols
fraction model

Resources

📖 **Student Edition**
Skills Handbook, p. 536
Extra Practice, p. 526
Glossary/Study Guide

🗄 **Teaching Resources**
Chapter Support File, Ch. 5
• Lesson Planner 5-4
• Practice 5-4, Reteaching 5-4
• Answer Masters 5-4
Teaching Aids Masters 10, 21–26
Glossary, Spanish Resources

💻 **Transparencies**
22–29, Minds on Math 5-4

Warm Up

What is the value of the 6 in 2.0346? **6 ten-thousandths**

FOR EXAMPLE 1

Ask students to model each fraction.

a. $\frac{3}{8}$

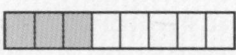

b. $\frac{5}{10}$

FOR EXAMPLE 2

How should the weather team round $\frac{3}{16}$? **0 in.**

3 Practice/Assess

EXERCISES *On Your Own*

ERROR ALERT! Exercises 1–6 Some students may write the shaded parts of the model over the unshaded part. **Remediation:** Remind students the number on the bottom is the total number of parts into which the whole bar is divided. Then examine several examples. For each example, ask: *How many parts are there in this model? What number goes on the bottom?* **Answers may vary.**

TACTILE LEARNING Exercises 7–18 Let students use the fraction bars to model the fractions and then sketch the model.

CONNECTING TO THE STUDENTS' WORLD Exercise 26 Have students record what they do during one day. Have them include the time they spend in school, studying, eating, sleeping, playing sports, and whatever else they do. Have them round the time to the nearest half hour.

Technology Options

Prentice Hall Technology

  Software for Learners
- Hot Page™ 13*
- Math Blaster® Mystery*
- Interactive Student Tutorial, Chapter 5*

Teaching Resource Software
- Computer Item Generator 5-4
- Resource Pro™ Chapter 5*

Internet • For related mathematics activities, visit the Prentice Hall site at www.phschool.com/math

*Available on CD-ROM only

Assignment Options for Exercises On Your Own

To provide flexible scheduling, this lesson can be split into parts.

1 Core 1–18, 20
Extension 19

2 Core 21–25
Extension 26

Use Mixed Review to maintain skills.

194

ROUNDING FRACTIONS

Round a fraction to 0 when the numerator is much less than the denominator. Examples: $\frac{1}{10}$, $\frac{2}{25}$

Round a fraction to $\frac{1}{2}$ when the numerator is about half the denominator. Examples: $\frac{3}{8}$, $\frac{23}{50}$

Round a fraction to 1 when the numerator is about equal to the denominator. Examples: $\frac{5}{6}$, $\frac{99}{100}$

■ **EXAMPLE 2** *Real-World Problem Solving*

♣ *Weather* A science team uses a rain gauge to collect local rainfall data. It decides to round to the nearest half inch. How should the team round $\frac{11}{16}$ inch?

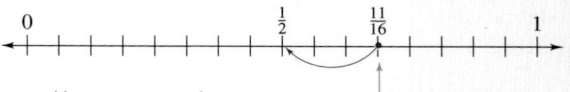

$\frac{11}{16}$ is closer to $\frac{1}{2}$ than to 0 or 1, so round to $\frac{1}{2}$ in.

The team should round $\frac{11}{16}$ inch to $\frac{1}{2}$ inch.

4. ✔ *Try It Out* Round each weight to the nearest half ounce.
a. $\frac{9}{10}$ oz **1 oz** **b.** $\frac{1}{64}$ oz **0 oz** **c.** $\frac{5}{8}$ oz **$\frac{1}{2}$ oz** **d.** $\frac{7}{16}$ oz **$\frac{1}{2}$ oz** **e.** $\frac{30}{32}$ oz **1 oz**

Now you may assign Exercises 21–26.

EXERCISES *On Your Own*

Modeling **Name the fraction modeled.**

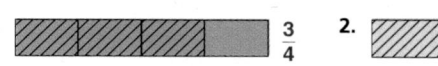

1. $\frac{3}{4}$ **2.** $\frac{1}{3}$ **3.** $\frac{6}{6}$

4. $\frac{5}{10}$ **5.** $\frac{7}{12}$ **6.** $\frac{2}{5}$

Modeling **Model each fraction.** 7–18. See back of book.

7. $\frac{1}{5}$ **8.** $\frac{9}{12}$ **9.** $\frac{3}{3}$ **10.** $\frac{3}{6}$ **11.** $\frac{7}{10}$ **12.** $\frac{8}{12}$

13. $\frac{5}{6}$ **14.** $\frac{4}{4}$ **15.** $\frac{4}{5}$ **16.** $\frac{1}{8}$ **17.** $\frac{4}{12}$ **18.** $\frac{2}{10}$

IDENTIFYING THE BIG IDEA Ask students to explain how to model and round a fraction.

 **PROJECT LINK** Have students write the fraction of shots made for each player. For example, if the first player made 7 out of 10 shots, their fraction is $\frac{7}{10}$. Have students model each of the fractions.

LESSON QUIZ

1. Draw a model to show $\frac{4}{11}$.
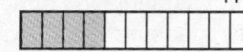

2. Round each fraction to the nearest half unit.

a. $\frac{6}{14}$ $\frac{1}{2}$

b. $\frac{3}{29}$ 0

c. $\frac{34}{38}$ 1

---

19. *Writing* How are the models at the right similar? How are they different? **See right.**

20. Choose A, B, C, or D. Which figure models $\frac{3}{8}$? **C**

A.   B.   C.   D.

19. The models represent the same quantity. The denominators and numerators of the corresponding fractions are different.

Round each fraction to the nearest half unit.

21. (number line: 0, $\frac{1}{2}$, $\frac{7}{8}$, 1 — point at $\frac{7}{8}$) **1**

22. (number line: 0, $\frac{3}{16}$, $\frac{1}{2}$, 1 — point at $\frac{3}{16}$) **0**

23. (number line: 0, $\frac{3}{10}$, $\frac{1}{2}$, 1 — point at $\frac{3}{10}$) $\frac{1}{2}$

24. 0; 1; 0; 1; $\frac{1}{2}$; $\frac{1}{2}$; $\frac{1}{2}$; 0; 1

24. Round each fraction at the right to the nearest half unit.

25. *Open-ended* Write three fractions that are close to 0, three that are close to $\frac{1}{2}$, and three that are close to 1. **See below for sample.**

26. *Time Management* Suppose you keep a record of how you spend your time, to the nearest half hour. How would you round 48 minutes? 20 minutes? **1 h; $\frac{1}{2}$ h**

$\frac{3}{30}$	$\frac{7}{9}$	$\frac{1}{10}$
$\frac{38}{45}$	$\frac{17}{40}$	$\frac{45}{100}$
$\frac{35}{80}$	$\frac{5}{99}$	$\frac{75}{80}$

25. Answers may vary. Sample: $\frac{1}{7}, \frac{1}{12}, \frac{2}{9}; \frac{3}{7}, \frac{4}{7}, \frac{7}{12}; \frac{6}{7}, \frac{7}{9}, \frac{11}{12}$

Mixed Review

First estimate. Then find the sum or difference. *(Lesson 3-7)*

27. 2.2 + 0.4 **2.5; 2.6**

28. 1.05 − 0.95 **0; 0.1**

29. 5.31 + 17.04 **22; 22.35**

30. 10.25 − 6.09 **4; 4.16**

31. 6.09 + 58.7 **65; 64.79**

32. *Choose a Strategy* Yuma drove 1,350 mi. His tank holds 15 gal. His car averaged 25 mi/gal. Gas costs $1.299 per gallon.
  a. How many tanks of gas did he use? **about 4 tanks**
  b. How much did the gas cost? **$70.15**

CHAPTER PROJECT

PROJECT LINK: RECORDING

You'll need five starters and two substitutes for your basketball team. Use the names of real players or make some up. If you use a ball of paper as a basketball, place your "foul line" about 10 ft from the trash can. Your first player should take 10 shots, your second player 9 shots, your third player 8 shots, and so on. Make a table to record the number of shots taken and the number of shots made by each player.

Check students' work.

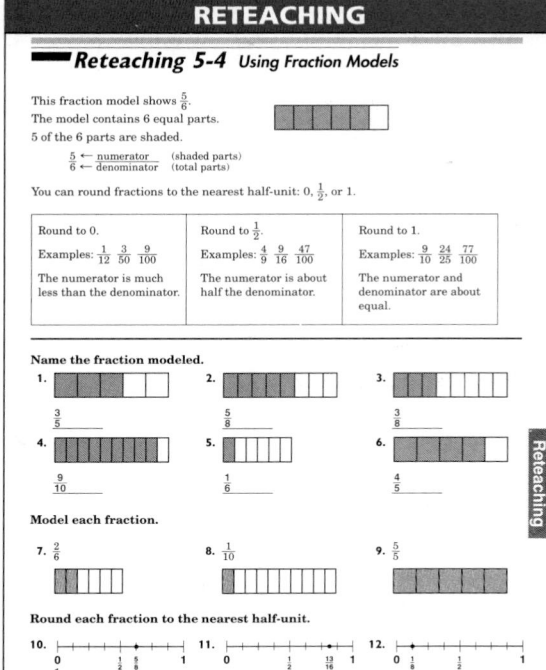

Practice 5-4 *Using Fraction Models*

In copymaster and workbook formats

RETEACHING

Reteaching 5-4 *Using Fraction Models*

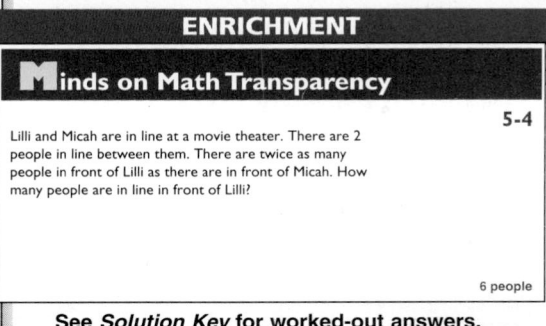

ENRICHMENT

Minds on Math Transparency

5-4

Lilli and Micah are in line at a movie theater. There are 2 people in line between them. There are twice as many people in front of Lilli as there are in front of Micah. How many people are in line in front of Lilli?

6 people

See *Solution Key* for worked-out answers.

195

In Lesson 5-4, students learned to model and round fractions. This toolbox allows students to apply their knowledge of fractions to reading lengths marked on a ruler. It prepares students for writing equivalent fractions in the next lesson.

ERROR ALERT! Students may lose track of the fraction indicated by the mark on the ruler. **Remediation:** Direct students to count the marks aloud as they measure each segment. For a segment $\frac{3}{4}$ in. long, have them count $\frac{1}{4}$, $\frac{2}{4}$, $\frac{3}{4}$. Also point out to students that the mark for $\frac{1}{2}$ is usually longer than the mark for $\frac{1}{4}$ and $\frac{3}{4}$.

ASSESSMENT Exercises 1–3 Have pairs of students work together to complete the exercises. Ask partners to measure the line two different ways and compare their answers.

■ **ADDITIONAL PROBLEM**

Name a length less than 1 in. Draw a line that length and rename it, if possible. **Answers may vary.**

Materials/Manipulatives
• ruler

Resources

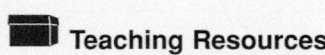 **Teaching Resources**

Teaching Aids Masters 3, 25

pages 197–198 Think and Discuss

1b. Answers may vary. Sample:

2. Answers may vary. Sample:

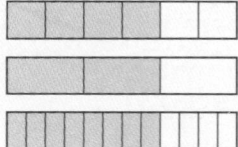

196

SKILLS REVIEW

Fractions and Rulers

After Lesson 5-4

A ruler helps you find the length of a segment.

The ruler below is marked in eighths of an inch.

The ruler below is marked in sixteenths of an inch.

■ **EXAMPLE**

Find the length of each segment.

a.

The ruler is marked in eighths of an inch. The segment is $\frac{7}{8}$ inch long.

b.

The ruler is marked in sixteenths of an inch. The segment is $\frac{10}{16}$ inch long. If you use a ruler that is marked in eighths, you find that the segment is $\frac{5}{8}$ inch long.

Find the length of each segment. Name each length in two ways. 1–3. Answers may vary. Samples are given.

1. 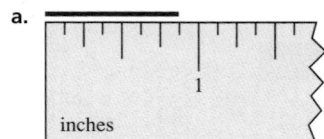 $\frac{6}{8}, \frac{3}{4}$

2. 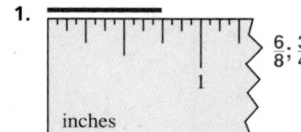 $\frac{4}{16}, \frac{1}{4}$

3. 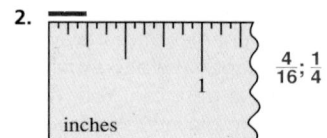 $\frac{6}{16};$

Use a ruler marked in sixteenths of an inch. Find the length of each segment. Name each length in two ways, if possible.

4. ———— $\frac{14}{16}, \frac{7}{8}$

5. ———— $\frac{13}{16}$

6. ———— $\frac{8}{16}, \frac{1}{2}$

1 Focus

CONNECTING TO PRIOR KNOWLEDGE
Have students show models for $\frac{1}{2}$ and $\frac{3}{6}$. Ask students: *How are the models the same?* Answers may vary. Sample: Both models have half of their length shaded. *How are the models different?* Sample: Each model has a different number of parts.

2 Teach

THINK AND DISCUSS

AEP Connect the words *equivalent* and *equal*. Tell students: *Equivalent fractions are equal. They have the same value.*

VISUAL LEARNING Questions 1 and 2
Have students use fraction bars or drawings to answer the questions.

DIVERSITY and RESEARCH Encourage groups of students to investigate how the Egyptians wrote fractions. Have students share their research.

ASSESSMENT Have each student write a fraction and give it to a partner. The partner writes an equivalent fraction. Then partners check each other's work.

5-5 Equivalent Fractions

What You'll Learn

▼ To find equivalent fractions

▼ To write fractions in simplest form

...And Why

You can use equivalent fractions to make measurements and estimates.

Here's How

Look for questions that
 ▪ build understanding
 ✔ check understanding

Egypt

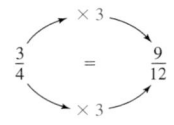

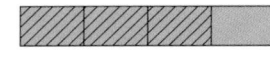

HISTORY The ancient Egyptians wrote fractions by placing an oval above the symbols for their numbers.

Source: *The History of Mathematics*

THINK AND DISCUSS

▼ *Finding Equivalent Fractions*

The fraction models at the right show equivalent fractions.
Equivalent fractions are fractions that represent the same part of a whole.

1. a. ▪ *Modeling* What fraction is shown by the blue fraction model? The green fraction model? $\frac{2}{4}; \frac{1}{2}$
   b. Model two other fractions with the same shaded area as the ones above.   See margin p. 196.
   c. Name three fractions that are equivalent to $\frac{1}{2}$.
      See below.

2. Model the fraction $\frac{4}{6}$. Model two other equivalent fractions.
   See margin p. 196.   1c. Answers may vary. Sample: $\frac{3}{6}, \frac{4}{8}, \frac{6}{12}$

You can form equivalent fractions by multiplying or dividing the numerator and denominator by the same nonzero number.

■ EXAMPLE 1

By what number can you multiply both the numerator and denominator of $\frac{3}{4}$ to get $\frac{9}{12}$?

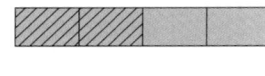

$$\frac{3}{4} = \frac{9}{12}$$

 Multiply the numerator and denominator by 3.

You can check the answer to Example 1 using fraction models.

The model for $\frac{9}{12}$ has 3 times as many shaded parts and 3 times as many total parts as the model for $\frac{3}{4}$.

3a–e. Answers may vary. Samples are given.
3. ✔ *Try It Out* Write two fractions equivalent to each fraction.

   a. $\frac{1}{8}$ b. $\frac{2}{3}$ c. $\frac{4}{7}$ d. $\frac{5}{6}$ e. $\frac{10}{10}$

   $\frac{2}{16}, \frac{3}{24}$ $\frac{4}{6}, \frac{6}{9}$ $\frac{8}{14}, \frac{16}{28}$ $\frac{10}{12}, \frac{25}{30}$ $\frac{2}{2}, \frac{5}{5}$

Lesson Planning Options

Prerequisite Skills
- multiplying and dividing whole numbers (precourse)
- finding the GCF (5-4)

Vocabulary/Symbols
equivalent fractions, simplest form

Resources

📖 **Student Edition**
Skills Handbook, p. 540
Extra Practice, p. 526
Glossary/Study Guide

📦 **Teaching Resources**
Chapter Support File, Ch. 5
- Lesson Planner 5-5
- Practice 5-5, Reteaching 5-5
- Alternative Activity 5-5
- Answer Masters 5-5
Teaching Aids Masters 10, 21–26
Glossary, Spanish Resources

Transparencies
22–29, Minds on Math 5-5

Warm Up

Write the number 8 billion.
8,000,000,000

Example 2 Remind students to divide both the numerator and denominator by the GCF. Ask: *Can you write the fraction in simplest form if you use a common factor other than the GCF?* **Answers may vary. Sample: If you use a common factor other than the GCF, the fraction will not be in simplest form.**

ERROR ALERT! Question 5 Some students may forget to divide the numerator and the denominator by the same number.
Remediation: Have students write all the steps and always check their work.

■ **ADDITIONAL EXAMPLES**

FOR EXAMPLE 1

Have students find five fractions that are equivalent to $\frac{1}{5}$ and explain how they found their answers. **Answers may vary. Sample:** $\frac{2}{10}, \frac{3}{15}, \frac{4}{20}, \frac{5}{25}, \frac{6}{30}$; **multiplied by** $\frac{2}{2}, \frac{3}{3}, \frac{4}{4}, \frac{5}{5}$, **and** $\frac{6}{6}$

FOR EXAMPLE 2

Ask students to write $\frac{16}{40}$ in simplest form. $\frac{2}{5}$

3 Practice/Assess

EXERCISES *On Your Own*

Exercises 1 and 2 Students can use fraction bars or make drawings.

EXTENSION Exercises 3–5 Have students find equivalent fractions for fractions given in the exercises that are not equivalent. Students may want to draw or use models to find equivalent fractions.

Technology Options

Prentice Hall Technology

  Software for Learners

- Math Lab: Equivalent Fractions
- Math Blaster® Mystery*
- Interactive Student Tutorial, Chapter 5*

  Teaching Resource Software

- Computer Item Generator 5-5
- Resource Pro™ Chapter 5*

Internet • For related mathematics activities, visit the Prentice Hall site at www.phschool.com/math

*Available on CD-ROM only

Assignment Options for Exercises On Your Own

To provide flexible scheduling, this lesson can be split into parts.

1 Core 1–27
Extension 28, 29

2 Core 30–42
Extension 43, 44

Use Mixed Review to maintain skills.

198

The fractions $\frac{6}{12}$ and $\frac{2}{4}$ are modeled below.

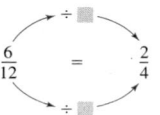 

4b. Each unit in the second model is the same size as 3 units in the first model.

c. $\frac{1}{2}, \frac{3}{6}$

4. a. By what number can you divide both the numerator and denominator of $\frac{6}{12}$ to get $\frac{2}{4}$? **3**
  b. ♣ *Explain* How is division by this number shown by the models?
  c. Use division to find two other fractions equivalent to $\frac{6}{12}$.

Now you may assign Exercises 1–29.

2 Writing Fractions in Simplest Form

You can write a fraction in **simplest form** by dividing both the numerator and denominator by their greatest common factor (GCF).

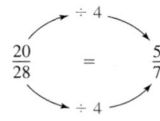

HISTORY
Dick Davis, an inventor and school teacher in Pasadena, California, invented an easy-to-read tape rule that labels fractions of an inch.

6. $\frac{2}{8}$ in.; $\frac{4}{8}$ in.; $\frac{6}{8}$ in.

■ **EXAMPLE 2**

Write $\frac{20}{28}$ in simplest form.

20: ①, ②, ④, 5, 10, 20   List the factors for the numerator and
28: ①, ②, ④, 7, 14, 28   the denominator. Circle the common factors to find the GCF, 4.

$$\frac{20}{28} \xrightarrow[\div 4]{\div 4} \frac{5}{7}$$

Divide both the numerator and denominator by their GCF of 4.

The fraction $\frac{20}{28}$ written in simplest form is $\frac{5}{7}$.

5. ✔ *Try It Out* Write each fraction in simplest form.
  a. $\frac{16}{18}$ $\frac{8}{9}$ **b.** $\frac{12}{16}$ $\frac{3}{4}$ **c.** $\frac{21}{24}$ $\frac{7}{8}$ **d.** $\frac{120}{150}$ $\frac{4}{5}$

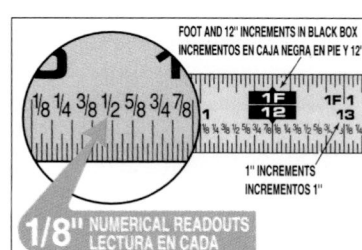

6. ♣ *Measurement*
Refer to the tape rule at the left. Rewrite the labels for $\frac{1}{4}$ in., $\frac{1}{2}$ in., and $\frac{3}{4}$ in. as equivalent fractions in eighths of an inch.
See left.

Now you may assign Exercises 30–44.

VISUAL LEARNING Exercises 6–10 Suggest students rewrite the problems with blanks so they can see what they are looking for. For example: $\frac{2}{5} \times \blacksquare = \frac{8}{20}$.

EXTENSION Exercises 16–27 Ask students to list the equivalent fractions given in the exercises. The fractions in Exercises 23 and 26 are equivalent.

OPEN-ENDED Exercise 28 Students can use the Guess and Check strategy to write equivalent fractions.

ASSESSMENT Exercises 30–41 Ask students: *How do you know when a fraction is in simplest form?* The numerator and denominator do not have a common factor other than 1.

REASONING Exercise 44 Encourage students to use models to explore this exercise.

WRAP UP

IDENTIFYING THE BIG IDEA Ask students to define equivalent fractions and describe how to find them.

EXERCISES *On Your Own*

1. **a.** *Modeling* Model the equivalent fractions $\frac{3}{5}$ and $\frac{6}{10}$.
   b. Model two other fractions equivalent to $\frac{3}{5}$ and $\frac{6}{10}$.
   1a–b. See margin.

2.

2. *Modeling* Model the fractions $\frac{9}{10}$ and $\frac{9}{12}$. Use the models to explain why the fractions are not equivalent.
   See right for models; the shaded parts of the models are not the same size.

Name the fractions modeled. Are they equivalent?

3. $\frac{2}{6}$; $\frac{1}{3}$; yes

3.

4.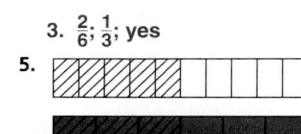

5.

4. $\frac{8}{12}$; $\frac{3}{5}$; no   5. $\frac{5}{10}$; $\frac{3}{6}$; yes

By what number can you multiply the numerator and denominator of the first fraction to get the second fraction?

6. $\frac{2}{5}, \frac{8}{20}$ 4   7. $\frac{6}{7}, \frac{30}{35}$ 5   8. $\frac{3}{4}, \frac{75}{100}$ 25   9. $\frac{3}{8}, \frac{27}{72}$ 9   10. $\frac{4}{9}, \frac{48}{108}$ 12

By what number can you divide the numerator and denominator of the first fraction to get the second fraction?

11. $\frac{8}{48}, \frac{1}{6}$ 8   12. $\frac{40}{50}, \frac{8}{10}$ 5   13. $\frac{10}{32}, \frac{5}{16}$ 2   14. $\frac{28}{49}, \frac{4}{7}$ 7   15. $\frac{60}{150}, \frac{2}{5}$ 30

Write two fractions equivalent to each fraction.   16–27. Samples are given.

16. $\frac{1}{4}$ $\frac{2}{8}, \frac{4}{16}$ 17. $\frac{10}{20}$ $\frac{1}{2}, \frac{5}{10}$ 18. $\frac{4}{5}$ $\frac{12}{15}, \frac{8}{10}$ 19. $\frac{15}{45}$ $\frac{1}{3}, \frac{5}{15}$ 20. $\frac{6}{8}$ $\frac{3}{4}, \frac{9}{12}$ 21. $\frac{1}{7}$ $\frac{2}{14}, \frac{20}{140}$

22. $\frac{12}{18}$ $\frac{2}{3}, \frac{16}{24}$ 23. $\frac{9}{21}$ $\frac{3}{7}, \frac{6}{14}$ 24. $\frac{7}{10}$ $\frac{14}{20}, \frac{49}{70}$ 25. $\frac{3}{18}$ $\frac{1}{6}, \frac{2}{12}$ 26. $\frac{6}{14}$ $\frac{3}{7}, \frac{15}{35}$ 27. $\frac{6}{20}$ $\frac{3}{10}, \frac{36}{120}$

28. *Open-ended* Use some of the numbers 2, 3, 4, 6, 12, 18, and 24 to write three pairs of equivalent fractions.   Sample: $\frac{2}{6}, \frac{4}{12}$; $\frac{2}{4}, \frac{6}{12}$; $\frac{3}{12}, \frac{6}{24}$

29. *Traffic Planning* Two traffic engineers are writing about the average driving time between two towns. One engineer writes the time as 45, but the other writes it as $\frac{3}{4}$. What could explain the difference?
   The first engineer wrote the time in minutes, the second wrote it in hours.

State whether each fraction is in simplest form. If not, write it in simplest form.

30. $\frac{5}{8}$ yes   31. $\frac{4}{6}$ no; $\frac{2}{3}$ 32. $\frac{10}{35}$ no; $\frac{2}{7}$ 33. $\frac{4}{5}$ yes   34. $\frac{24}{56}$ no; $\frac{3}{7}$ 35. $\frac{21}{77}$ no; $\frac{3}{11}$

36. $\frac{25}{150}$ no; $\frac{1}{6}$ 37. $\frac{3}{50}$ yes   38. $\frac{15}{135}$ no; $\frac{1}{3}$ 39. $\frac{17}{51}$ no; $\frac{1}{3}$ 40. $\frac{10}{65}$ no; $\frac{2}{13}$ 41. $\frac{120}{150}$ no; $\frac{4}{5}$

CHECKPOINT 1

■ *Checkpoint 1*   *Lessons 5-1 through 5-5*

State whether each number is divisible by 1, 2, 3, 5, 9, or 10.
1. 135 1, 3, 5, 9   2. 1,006 1, 2   3. 170 1, 2, 5, 10
4. 459 1, 3, 9   5. 2,730 1, 2, 3, 5, 10   6. 2,431 1

7. Use a factor tree to find the prime factorization of 300. Write your answer using exponents. $2^2 \times 3 \times 5^2$

Find the GCF of each pair of numbers using prime factorization.
8. 15, 27 3   9. 125 and 250 125   10. 132 and 156 12

Write each fraction in simplest form.
11. $\frac{13}{39}$ $\frac{1}{3}$ 12. $\frac{48}{64}$ $\frac{3}{4}$ 13. $\frac{36}{72}$ $\frac{1}{2}$ 14. $\frac{40}{48}$ $\frac{5}{6}$

Round each fraction to the nearest half.
15. $\frac{1}{12}$ 0   16. $\frac{3}{8}$ $\frac{1}{2}$ 17. $\frac{14}{16}$ 1

pages 199–200   On Your Own

1a.

b. Answers may vary. Sample:

199

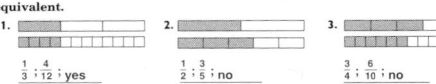

Practice 5-5 Equivalent Fractions

Name the fractions modeled. Tell whether they are equivalent.

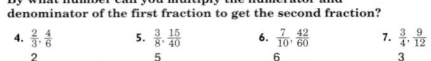

1. $\frac{1}{3}$, $\frac{4}{12}$; yes   2. $\frac{1}{3}$, $\frac{3}{5}$; no   3. $\frac{3}{4}$, $\frac{6}{10}$; no

By what number can you multiply the numerator and denominator of the first fraction to get the second fraction?

4. $\frac{2}{3}$, $\frac{4}{6}$ 5. $\frac{3}{8}$, $\frac{15}{40}$ 6. $\frac{7}{10}$, $\frac{42}{60}$ 7. $\frac{3}{4}$, $\frac{9}{12}$

   2   5   6   3

By what number can you divide the numerator and denominator of the first fraction to get the second fraction?

8. $\frac{6}{8}$, $\frac{3}{4}$ 9. $\frac{70}{80}$, $\frac{7}{8}$ 10. $\frac{15}{60}$, $\frac{1}{4}$ 11. $\frac{75}{100}$, $\frac{3}{4}$

   2   10   15   25

Write two fractions equivalent to each fraction. Samples are given.

12. $\frac{3}{10}$ $\frac{6}{20}$, $\frac{9}{30}$ 13. $\frac{7}{8}$ $\frac{14}{16}$, $\frac{21}{24}$ 14. $\frac{5}{6}$ $\frac{10}{12}$, $\frac{15}{18}$ 15. $\frac{3}{4}$ $\frac{6}{8}$, $\frac{9}{12}$

16. $\frac{15}{20}$ $\frac{3}{4}$, $\frac{6}{8}$ 17. $\frac{8}{12}$ $\frac{2}{3}$, $\frac{4}{6}$ 18. $\frac{15}{45}$ $\frac{1}{3}$, $\frac{3}{9}$ 19. $\frac{8}{32}$ $\frac{1}{4}$, $\frac{2}{8}$

State whether each fraction is in simplest form. If not, write it in simplest form.

20. $\frac{15}{35}$ no; $\frac{3}{7}$ 21. $\frac{22}{55}$ no; $\frac{2}{5}$ 22. $\frac{11}{15}$ yes   23. $\frac{25}{32}$ yes

24. $\frac{34}{36}$ no; $\frac{17}{18}$ 25. $\frac{19}{57}$ no; $\frac{1}{3}$ 26. $\frac{20}{53}$ yes   27. $\frac{125}{200}$ no; $\frac{5}{8}$

28. $\frac{27}{54}$ no; $\frac{1}{2}$ 29. $\frac{30}{41}$ yes   30. $\frac{9}{17}$ yes   31. $\frac{85}{110}$ no; $\frac{17}{22}$

32. Use the numbers 2, 5, 8, and 20 to write two pairs of equivalent fractions.
$\frac{2}{8} = \frac{5}{20}$; $\frac{2}{5} = \frac{8}{20}$

In copymaster and workbook formats

Reteaching 5-5 Equivalent Fractions

The fractions below name the same part of a whole.

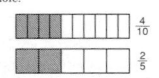 $\frac{4}{10}$

$\frac{2}{5}$

$\frac{4}{10}$ and $\frac{2}{5}$ are **equivalent fractions**.

To find equivalent fractions, multiply or divide the numerator and denominator by the same number.

$\frac{2}{5} \overset{\times 2}{=} \frac{4}{10}$ $\frac{4}{10} \overset{\div 2}{=} \frac{2}{5}$

To write a fraction in **simplest form**, divide the numerator and denominator by their greatest common factor.

Write $\frac{8}{12}$ in simplest form.

① Find the greatest common factor.
   8: 1, 2, **4**, 8
   12: 1, 2, 3, **4**, 6, 12
   The GCF is 4.

② Divide the numerator and denominator by the GCF.
   $\frac{8}{12} = \frac{2}{3}$

$\frac{8}{12}$ in simplest form is $\frac{2}{3}$.

Name the fractions modeled. Tell whether they are equivalent.

1. $\frac{2}{3}$ $\frac{4}{6}$ 2. $\frac{3}{4}$ $\frac{3}{5}$ 3. $\frac{4}{8}$ $\frac{2}{4}$

   yes   no   yes

Write two fractions equivalent to each fraction. Samples are shown.

4. $\frac{5}{6}$ $\frac{10}{12}$, $\frac{15}{18}$ 5. $\frac{3}{7}$ $\frac{6}{14}$, $\frac{9}{21}$ 6. $\frac{7}{8}$ $\frac{14}{16}$, $\frac{21}{24}$

7. $\frac{3}{11}$ $\frac{6}{22}$, $\frac{9}{33}$ 8. $\frac{3}{6}$ $\frac{6}{12}$, $\frac{1}{2}$ 9. $\frac{1}{5}$ $\frac{2}{10}$, $\frac{3}{15}$

State whether each fraction is in simplest form. If not, write it in simplest form.

10. $\frac{12}{15}$ no; $\frac{4}{5}$ 11. $\frac{8}{21}$ yes   12. $\frac{9}{21}$ no; $\frac{3}{7}$

13. $\frac{15}{22}$ yes   14. $\frac{14}{30}$ no; $\frac{7}{15}$ 15. $\frac{25}{70}$ no; $\frac{5}{14}$

Minds on Math Transparency

5-5

How many different triangles can you find in the figure below?

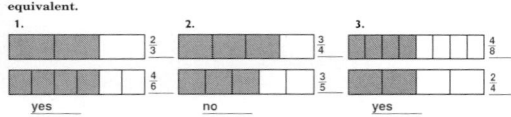

16 triangles

See Solution Key for worked-out answers.

---

1. Write two equivalent fractions for $\frac{6}{16}$.
   Answers may vary. Sample: $\frac{3}{8}$, $\frac{12}{32}$

2. Write each fraction in simplest form.
   a. $\frac{22}{28}$ $\frac{11}{14}$
   b. $\frac{8}{28}$ $\frac{2}{7}$
   c. $\frac{27}{36}$ $\frac{3}{4}$

42. *Analyze* What is the only common factor of the numerator and denominator when a fraction is written in simplest form? 1

43. *Writing* Can you write a fraction in simplest form if you divide the numerator and denominator by a number other than the GCF? Explain.

44. *Reasoning* Can two different fractions that are written in simplest form also be equivalent to each other? Explain.
See margin p. 201.

43. No; every common factor of two numbers is a factor of their GCF. Therefore, the numerator and denominator would still have common factors and the fraction would not be in simplest form.

Mixed Review

Round each fraction to the nearest half. *(Lesson 5-4)*

45. $\frac{23}{25}$ 1   46. $\frac{3}{40}$ 0   47. $\frac{37}{80}$ $\frac{1}{2}$ 48. $\frac{17}{100}$ 0   49. $\frac{101}{196}$ $\frac{1}{2}$ 50. $\frac{350}{400}$ 1

Find each answer. *(Lesson 4-8)*

51. $19.2 \div 6$ 3.2   52. $122 \div 6.25$ 19.52   53. $0.3 \div 0.06$ 5   54. $59.36 \div 7.42$ 8

55. *Choose a Strategy* A flim is worth more than a flam. A flum is worth more than a flom. If a flam is worth less than a flom, which is greater, a flum or a flam? flum

✓ CHECKPOINT 1   *Lessons 5-1 through 5-5*

Mental Math **State whether each number is divisible by 1, 2, 3, 5, 9, or 10.**

1. 960 1, 2, 3, 5, 10   2. 243 1, 3, 9   3. 2,310 1, 2, 3, 5, 10   4. 5,070 1, 2, 3, 5, 10   5. 12,345 1, 3, 5

Find the prime factorization using a factor tree.

6. 40 $2^3 \times 5$ 7. 99 $3^2 \times 11$ 8. 960 $2^6 \times 3 \times 5$ 9. 243 3^5 10. 2,310 $2 \times 3 \times 5 \times 7 \times 11$

Find the GCF of each set of numbers.

11. 48, 56 8   12. 7, 15 1   13. 15, 21 3   14. 24, 42, 72 6   15. 300, 450 150

Write each fraction in simplest form.

16. $\frac{12}{16}$ $\frac{3}{4}$ 17. $\frac{64}{96}$ $\frac{2}{3}$ 18. $\frac{21}{27}$ $\frac{7}{9}$ 19. $\frac{9}{54}$ $\frac{1}{6}$ 20. $\frac{18}{36}$ $\frac{1}{2}$

In Lesson 5-5, students learned how to find equivalent fractions and to write fractions in their simplest form. This toolbox allows students to apply their knowledge by using a fraction calculator to simplify fractions.

ERROR ALERT! **Exercises 1–3** Students may have difficulty following the steps used to simplify a fraction with a fraction calculator. **Remediation:** Draw a flow chart on the board describing the steps. Students follow the flow chart to solve the exercises using the calculator.

ASSESSMENT **Exercise 21** Have small groups of students discuss their answers. Ask: *If the calculator uses the GCF to simplify the fraction, how many times would you need the calculator to rewrite the fraction?* **only once**

■ **ADDITIONAL PROBLEM**

Simplify $\frac{420}{5,250}$ using a fraction calculator. $\frac{2}{25}$

TECHNOLOGY

Simplifying Fractions

After Lesson 5-5

You can use a fraction calculator to simplify a fraction. The fraction calculator divides the numerator and denominator by a common factor and rewrites the fraction. Repeat the process until the fraction is in simplest form.

■ **EXAMPLE**

Use a fraction calculator to simplify $\frac{9}{27}$.

Press	Display	
9 **/** 27	**9/27**	←Enter the fraction.
Simp	SIMP N/D→n/d **9/27**	
=	N/D→n/d **3/9**	←The fraction is simplified once.
Simp	SIMP N/D→n/d **3/9**	
=	**1/3**	←The fraction is in simplest form.

In simplest form, $\frac{9}{27} = \frac{1}{3}$.

The display N/D⟶ n/d can be written $\frac{N}{D}$⟶$\frac{n}{d}$. The symbols N and n represent the numerators. The symbols D and d represent the denominators.

Use a fraction calculator to simplify each fraction.

1. $\frac{18}{51}$ $\frac{6}{17}$
2. $\frac{21}{49}$ $\frac{3}{7}$
3. $\frac{102}{187}$ $\frac{6}{11}$
4. $\frac{35}{56}$ $\frac{5}{8}$
5. $\frac{20}{65}$ $\frac{4}{13}$
6. $\frac{17}{68}$ $\frac{1}{4}$
7. $\frac{12}{15}$ $\frac{4}{5}$
8. $\frac{28}{32}$ $\frac{7}{8}$
9. $\frac{12}{30}$ $\frac{2}{5}$
10. $\frac{45}{75}$ $\frac{3}{5}$
11. $\frac{24}{32}$ $\frac{3}{4}$
12. $\frac{12}{96}$ $\frac{1}{8}$
13. $\frac{35}{45}$ $\frac{7}{9}$
14. $\frac{14}{63}$ $\frac{2}{9}$
15. $\frac{40}{48}$ $\frac{5}{6}$
16. $\frac{105}{180}$ $\frac{7}{12}$
17. $\frac{92}{132}$ $\frac{23}{33}$
18. $\frac{39}{117}$ $\frac{1}{3}$
19. $\frac{126}{324}$ $\frac{7}{18}$
20. $\frac{200}{385}$ $\frac{40}{77}$

21. *Writing* Explain how you know whether the calculator uses the greatest common factor (GCF) when simplifying.
The calculator uses the GCF if the resulting fraction after the first step is the same as the resulting fraction after the second step.

Materials/Manipulatives
• fraction calculator

Resources

 Transparencies
19

pages 199–200   **On Your Own**
44. **No; a fraction in simplest form has only one possible numerator and only one possible denominator. Since two different fractions must have different numerators or different denominators, they cannot be equivalent.**

1 Focus

CONNECTING TO PRIOR KNOWLEDGE Have students give examples of the fractions from the previous lessons. Ask students: *Do these fractions have values of less than 1?* **Answers may vary. Sample: yes** *Are all fractions less than 1?* **no** *Where have you seen fractions that are more than 1?*

2 Teach

Work Together

Question 4 Have students support their rule with examples.

AUDITORY LEARNING Questions 1–4 To help students remember the difference

Answers may vary. Sample: on highway signs such as "construction $1\frac{1}{2}$ mi ahead"

between numerator and denominator, have them say *denominator is down.*

THINK AND DISCUSS

AEP Compare the definitions of proper and improper fractions. A proper fraction is a fraction whose top number is less than its bottom number. An improper fraction is a fraction whose top number is greater than or equal to its bottom number. Tell students: *The word improper suggests people were once*

Lesson Planning Options

Prerequisite Skills
• comparing whole numbers and fractions (precourse)

Vocabulary/Symbols
improper fraction, mixed numbers

Resources

 Student Edition

Skills Handbook, p. 541
Extra Practice, p. 526
Glossary/Study Guide

 Teaching Resources

Chapter Support File, Ch. 5
• Lesson Planner 5-6
• Practice 5-6, Reteaching 5-6
• Answer Masters 5-6
Teaching Aids Master 10
Glossary, Spanish Resources

 Transparencies
19, Minds on Math 5-6

Warm Up

Evaluate $\frac{48}{2 \times 4}$. **6**

5-6 Mixed Numbers and Improper Fractions

What You'll Learn

▼ To write improper fractions
② To write mixed numbers

...And Why

You'll use mixed numbers and improper fractions for drawing and design.

Here's How

Look for questions that
:: build understanding
✔ check understanding

1. $\frac{4}{4}, \frac{3}{3}$; $4 = 4$; $3 = 3$

The next time you're riding in a car, watch for mixed numbers. They are often on signs showing distances.

Work Together *Comparing Numerators and Denominators*

Investigate the fractions modeled below.

 $\frac{4}{4}$ 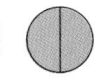 $\frac{5}{2}$ 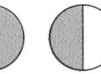 $\frac{1}{6}$

$\frac{1}{2}$  $\frac{11}{8}$ $\frac{3}{3}$

1. :: *Number Sense* Which fractions equal 1? Compare their numerators to their denominators. (*Hint:* Use $>$, $<$, or $=$.) **See left.**

2. Which fractions are less than 1? Compare their numerators to their denominators. $\frac{1}{2}, \frac{1}{6}$; $1 < 2$, $1 < 6$

3. Which fractions are greater than 1? Compare their numerators to their denominators. $\frac{5}{2}, \frac{11}{8}$; $5 > 2$, $11 > 8$

4. :: *Draw a Conclusion* Write a general rule comparing the numerators and denominators of fractions. **See margin p. 204.**

THINK AND DISCUSS

▼ Writing Improper Fractions

An **improper fraction** has a numerator greater than or equal to its denominator. You can write an improper fraction greater than 1 as a **mixed number.** A mixed number shows the sum of a whole number and a fraction. **5a.** $\frac{5}{4}$ **b.** 1 cup **c.** $\frac{1}{4}$ cup

5. **a.** What improper fraction is modeled?
   b. How many whole cups are shaded?
   c. What additional fraction is shaded?
   d. :: *Reasoning* The mixed number $1\frac{1}{4}$ describes the shaded portion. How does this number show the sum of a whole number and a fraction? $1\frac{1}{4}$ means $1 + \frac{1}{4}$.

uncomfortable with fractions greater than 1. Mathematically speaking, there is nothing wrong or improper about them.

REASONING Question 7 Ask students to think how they can determine when an improper fraction is a whole number. **Its numerator is divisible by its denominator.**

■ **ADDITIONAL EXAMPLES**

FOR EXAMPLE 1
Write $2\frac{1}{3}$ as an improper fraction. $\frac{7}{3}$

FOR EXAMPLE 2
Suppose the chart you are designing has columns one forth of an inch wide. The chart has 18 columns. How much space do you need? $4\frac{1}{2}$ **in.**

Question 8 Remind students that the denominator in the improper fraction is the same as the denominator in the mixed number.

Question 9 Point out to students that the method they prefer may reflect their learning style. For example, students with a tactile learning style may prefer modeling.

ERROR ALERT! Question 10d Students may forget to rewrite the fraction in lowest terms. **Remediation:** Remind students to rewrite the fraction. Review the previous lesson.

ASSESSMENT Have students write a mixed number and give it to a partner to write as an improper fraction. Have students check their partner's work by writing the improper fraction

6. $\frac{3}{2}$ in.; $1\frac{1}{2}$ in.

7. The numerator of an improper fraction equivalent to a whole number is the denominator times the whole number.

6. Describe the length shown at the right using both an improper fraction and a mixed number.

7. ⚬ *Reasoning* How would you write a whole number as an improper fraction?

You can use different methods to write a mixed number as an improper fraction.

■ **EXAMPLE 1**

Suppose you have $2\frac{1}{4}$ oranges. Write this quantity as an improper fraction.

Method 1 Use models.

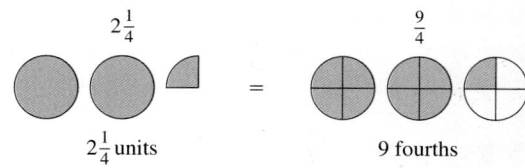

$2\frac{1}{4}$ units   9 fourths

Method 2 Use computation.

Multiply the denominator by the whole number.

Add the numerator.

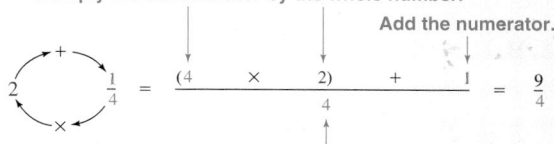

$$2\,\frac{1}{4} = \frac{(4 \times 2) + 1}{4} = \frac{9}{4}$$

Write the result over the denominator, which stays the same.

The mixed number $2\frac{1}{4}$ can be written as $\frac{9}{4}$.

8. ⚬ *Choose* Use modeling or computation to write each mixed number as an improper fraction.
   a. $1\frac{2}{3}$ $\frac{5}{3}$ b. $5\frac{1}{5}$ $\frac{26}{5}$ c. $4\frac{5}{6}$ $\frac{29}{6}$ d. $3\frac{3}{10}$ $\frac{33}{10}$

9. ⚬ *Analyze* Which method do you prefer? Use examples to show what you mean. **Check students' work.**

Now you may assign Exercises 1–17.

Technology Options

Prentice Hall Technology

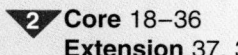 **Software for Learners**
- Hot Page 14*
- Math Blaster® Mystery*
- Interactive Student Tutorial, Chapter 5*

Teaching Resource Software
- Computer Item Generator 5-6
- Resource Pro™ Chapter 5*

Internet • For related mathematics activities, visit the Prentice Hall site at www.phschool.com/math

*Available on CD-ROM only

Assignment Options for Exercises On Your Own

To provide flexible scheduling, this lesson can be subdivided into parts.

1 ▼ **Core** 1–16
   Extension 17

2 ▼ **Core** 18–36
   Extension 37, 38

Use Mixed Review to maintain skills.

as a mixed number. Repeat the exercise using an improper fraction.

3 Practice/Assess

EXERCISES *On Your Own*

Exercise 1 Ask students whether they think they will need more than one model to support their answer. Have students write a short definition of an improper fraction such as: a fraction greater than or equal to 1.

WRITING Exercise 36 Discuss students' answers. Ask them to think of mixed numbers they may have seen but not used.

RESEARCH Exercise 38 Suggest students use a yardstick or measuring tape to measure the heights of at least three people.

DIVERSITY Exercise 38 Many people may be sensitive about their height. Take this opportunity to discuss with students how they might consider people's feelings when doing the research. Discuss asking appropriate questions and being careful what comments they make.

CONNECTING TO THE STUDENTS' WORLD Exercise 44 If you have block scheduling or extended class periods, have students choose a magazine about an interest they have. Ask them to find the store cost and the cost of a yearly subscription. Have them calculate how much they would save by subscribing to the magazine.

---

page 202 Work Together

4. If the numerator of a fraction is less than its denominator, then the fraction is less than 1. If the numerator of a fraction is equal to its denominator, then the value of the fraction is 1. If the numerator of a fraction is greater than its denominator, then the fraction is greater than 1.

---

❷ *Writing Mixed Numbers*

Use division to write an improper fraction as a mixed number.

■ **EXAMPLE 2**   *Real-World Problem Solving*

Design Suppose you are designing a chart for a school report. The chart has 28 rows of type. Each row is one eighth of an inch high. How much space do you need?

$\dfrac{28}{8}$ ◀——Write an improper fraction.

$\begin{array}{r} 3R4 \\ 8\overline{)28} \\ 24 \\ \hline 4 \end{array}$ ◀——Divide 28 by 8.

$3\dfrac{4}{8} = 3\dfrac{1}{2}$ ◀——Express the remainder as a fraction and simplify.

You need $3\dfrac{1}{2}$ in.

10. ✔ *Try It Out* Write each improper fraction as a mixed number.
 a. $\dfrac{15}{4}$ $3\dfrac{3}{4}$ b. $\dfrac{49}{6}$ $8\dfrac{1}{6}$ c. $\dfrac{40}{9}$ $4\dfrac{4}{9}$ d. $\dfrac{27}{12}$ $2\dfrac{1}{4}$

Now you may assign Exercises 18–38.

EXERCISES *On Your Own*

1. *Modeling* Are improper fractions greater than, less than, or equal to one? Use models to support your answer. **Greater than or equal to 1; check students' work for models.**

2. **Choose A, B, C, or D.** What mixed number represents the amount shaded? **B**
 A. $4\dfrac{3}{4}$ B. $3\dfrac{3}{4}$ C. $3\dfrac{15}{16}$ D. $3\dfrac{1}{4}$

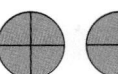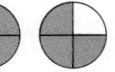

Write each whole or mixed number as an improper fraction.

3. $1\dfrac{2}{5}$ $\dfrac{7}{5}$ 4. $1\dfrac{5}{6}$ $\dfrac{11}{6}$ 5. $2\dfrac{3}{4}$ $\dfrac{11}{4}$ 6. $6\dfrac{3}{5}$ $\dfrac{33}{5}$ 7. $2\dfrac{7}{8}$ $\dfrac{23}{8}$ 8. $4\dfrac{1}{3}$ $\dfrac{13}{3}$

9. 4   10. $3\dfrac{1}{4}$ $\dfrac{13}{4}$ 11. $6\dfrac{7}{10}$ $\dfrac{67}{10}$ 12. $2\dfrac{3}{16}$ $\dfrac{35}{16}$ 13. $8\dfrac{4}{7}$ $\dfrac{60}{7}$ 14. $10\dfrac{2}{5}$ $\dfrac{52}{5}$

Answers may vary. Sample: $\dfrac{8}{2}$

Measurement Describe each length using both an improper fraction and a mixed number.

15. $\dfrac{11}{4}$ in.; $2\dfrac{3}{4}$ in.

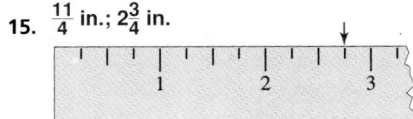

16. $\dfrac{27}{8}$ in.; $3\dfrac{3}{8}$ in.

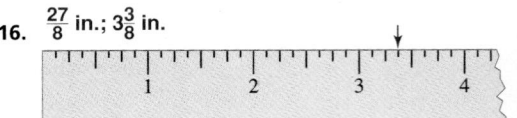

WRAP UP

IDENTIFYING THE BIG IDEA Ask students to define improper fractions and mixed numbers and explain how to change one into the other.

LESSON QUIZ

1. Write each improper fraction as a mixed number.

   a. $\frac{105}{8}$ $13\frac{1}{8}$

   b. $\frac{97}{9}$ $10\frac{7}{9}$

2. You buy three pizzas. You eat $\frac{1}{2}$ of one pizza. Use a mixed number to tell how many pizzas are uneaten. $2\frac{1}{2}$

---

17. *Marine Biology* Find the mixed numbers in the article below. Write each mixed number as an improper fraction.

$9\frac{1}{2}$ in., $5\frac{1}{2}$ in., $14\frac{1}{16}$ lb; $\frac{19}{2}$ in., $\frac{11}{2}$ in., $\frac{225}{16}$ lb

Philippines

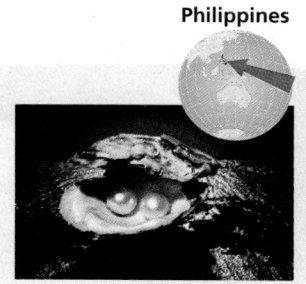

Gifts from the Sea

Pearls are the only gems that come from the sea. They are also the only gems made by living things—mollusks.

The largest pearl was found in the Philippines in 1934. It was $9\frac{1}{2}$ in. long with a diameter of $5\frac{1}{2}$ in. The pearl weighed 14 lb 1 oz.

Write each improper fraction as a mixed number. Write each mixed number as an improper fraction.

18. $\frac{17}{5}$ $3\frac{2}{5}$ **19.** $\frac{13}{7}$ $1\frac{6}{7}$ **20.** $\frac{27}{5}$ $5\frac{2}{5}$ **21.** $\frac{37}{12}$ $3\frac{1}{12}$ **22.** $\frac{21}{4}$ $5\frac{1}{4}$ **23.** $\frac{16}{5}$ $3\frac{1}{5}$

24. $3\frac{5}{6}$ $\frac{23}{6}$ **25.** $\frac{9}{4}$ $2\frac{1}{4}$ **26.** $\frac{17}{7}$ $2\frac{3}{7}$ **27.** $1\frac{2}{9}$ $\frac{11}{9}$ **28.** $4\frac{3}{5}$ $\frac{23}{5}$ **29.** $\frac{19}{8}$ $2\frac{3}{8}$

30. $\frac{23}{7}$ $3\frac{2}{7}$ **31.** $\frac{13}{6}$ $2\frac{1}{6}$ **32.** $1\frac{4}{5}$ $\frac{9}{5}$ **33.** $\frac{53}{23}$ $2\frac{7}{23}$ **34.** $8\frac{2}{11}$ $\frac{90}{11}$ **35.** $\frac{37}{8}$ $4\frac{5}{8}$

36. *Writing* Describe two situations in everyday life in which you have used mixed numbers.   **Answers may vary. Sample: weight of a large fish ($3\frac{1}{2}$ lb); thickness of a board ($1\frac{1}{4}$ in.)**

37. *Physics* The formula to change temperature from degrees Celsius to degrees Fahrenheit is $\frac{9}{5}(°C) + 32 = °F$. Write the improper fraction in the formula as a mixed number. $1\frac{4}{5}$

38. *Research* Find out the heights, to the nearest inch, of several friends or family members. Record the heights in feet using mixed numbers.   **Check students' work.**

Mixed Review

39. Alaina is at a football game. Her piano recital begins at 7:00 P.M. It takes her 15 min to get home, 20 min to eat supper, 25 min to change, and 10 min to get to the recital hall. What time should Alaina leave the game? *(Lesson 3-10)* **5:50 P.M.**

Simplify each answer. *(Lessons 4-2 and 4-3)*

40. $5^2 + 2 \times (6 + 4)$ **45**   **41.** $3^2 + 8^2$ **73**   **42.** $6^2 - 2 \times (8 + 1)$ **18**   **43.** $4 \times (9 - 2) \div 2^2$ **7**

44. An issue of *Teen Monthly* is $2.25. A yearly subscription costs $25.08. How much can you save by subscribing for a year? *(Lessons 3-7 and 4-5)* **$1.92**

Practice 5-6 *Mixed Numbers and Improper Fractions*

Circle A, B, C, or D. Find the mixed number that represents the amount.

1.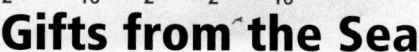

   A. $2\frac{1}{4}$ **B.** $1\frac{3}{4}$ **C.** $2\frac{3}{4}$ **D.** $3\frac{3}{4}$

2. **A.** $4\frac{5}{6}$ **B.** $3\frac{5}{6}$ **C.** $2\frac{5}{6}$ **D.** $3\frac{1}{6}$

3. **A.** $4\frac{5}{8}$ **B.** $4\frac{3}{8}$ **C.** $5\frac{5}{8}$ **D.** $5\frac{3}{8}$

4. **A.** $5\frac{3}{5}$ **B.** $4\frac{2}{5}$ **C.** $2\frac{2}{5}$ **D.** $5\frac{2}{5}$

Write each improper fraction as a mixed number.

5. $\frac{15}{2}$ $7\frac{1}{2}$ **6.** $\frac{8}{3}$ $2\frac{2}{3}$ **7.** $\frac{5}{2}$ $2\frac{1}{2}$ **8.** $\frac{7}{3}$ $2\frac{1}{3}$

9. $\frac{11}{10}$ $1\frac{1}{10}$ **10.** $\frac{7}{6}$ $1\frac{1}{6}$ **11.** $\frac{9}{8}$ $1\frac{1}{8}$ **12.** $\frac{11}{8}$ $1\frac{3}{8}$

13. $\frac{15}{8}$ $1\frac{7}{8}$ **14.** $\frac{21}{4}$ $5\frac{1}{4}$ **15.** $\frac{17}{3}$ $5\frac{2}{3}$ **16.** $\frac{17}{4}$ $4\frac{1}{4}$

17. $\frac{17}{5}$ $3\frac{2}{5}$ **18.** $\frac{17}{6}$ $2\frac{5}{6}$ **19.** $\frac{21}{10}$ $2\frac{1}{10}$ **20.** $\frac{25}{4}$ $6\frac{1}{4}$

Write each whole or mixed number as an improper fraction.

21. $1\frac{7}{8}$ $\frac{15}{8}$ **22.** $2\frac{3}{4}$ $\frac{11}{4}$ **23.** $7\frac{1}{3}$ $\frac{22}{3}$ **24.** 8 sample: $\frac{24}{3}$

25. $3\frac{3}{4}$ $\frac{15}{4}$ **26.** 4 sample: $\frac{16}{4}$ **27.** $5\frac{5}{6}$ $\frac{35}{6}$ **28.** $1\frac{9}{10}$ $\frac{19}{10}$

29. $2\frac{3}{8}$ $\frac{19}{8}$ **30.** $4\frac{7}{8}$ $\frac{39}{8}$ **31.** $2\frac{3}{5}$ $\frac{13}{5}$ **32.** 6 sample: $\frac{12}{2}$

33. $3\frac{11}{12}$ $\frac{47}{12}$ **34.** $2\frac{7}{12}$ $\frac{31}{12}$ **35.** $5\frac{4}{15}$ $\frac{79}{15}$ **36.** $2\frac{7}{15}$ $\frac{37}{15}$

In copymaster and workbook formats

Reteaching 5-6 *Mixed Numbers and Improper Fractions*

To write a mixed number as an improper fraction:

① Multiply the whole number by the denominator.

② Add this product to the numerator.

③ Write this sum over the denominator.

$3\frac{5}{8} = \frac{29}{8}$

An improper fraction has many equivalent forms.

$5 = \frac{5}{1} = \frac{10}{2} = \frac{25}{5} = \frac{50}{10} = \frac{75}{15}$ and so on

To write an improper fraction as a mixed number:

① Divide the numerator by the denominator. $\frac{20}{8} = 2$ remainder 4

② Write the remainder over the denominator. $= 2\frac{4}{8}$

③ Simplify, if possible. $= 2\frac{1}{2}$

$\frac{20}{8} = 2\frac{1}{2}$

Write each mixed number as an improper fraction.

1. $2\frac{2}{7}$ $\frac{16}{7}$ **2.** $5\frac{3}{4}$ $\frac{23}{4}$ **3.** $6\frac{1}{2}$ $\frac{13}{2}$

4. $6\frac{5}{8}$ $\frac{53}{8}$ **5.** $3\frac{4}{10}$ $\frac{34}{10}$ **6.** $4\frac{3}{5}$ $\frac{23}{5}$

7. $9\frac{1}{3}$ $\frac{28}{3}$ **8.** $4\frac{4}{5}$ $\frac{24}{5}$ **9.** $1\frac{7}{8}$ $\frac{15}{8}$

10. $3\frac{3}{8}$ $\frac{27}{8}$ **11.** $2\frac{3}{7}$ $\frac{17}{7}$ **12.** $8\frac{1}{6}$ $\frac{49}{6}$

Write each whole number as an improper fraction.

13. 9 Sample answer: $\frac{18}{2}$ **14.** 1 Sample answer: $\frac{4}{4}$ **15.** 3 Sample answer: $\frac{12}{4}$

Write each improper fraction as a mixed number. Simplify, if possible.

16. $\frac{9}{8}$ $1\frac{1}{8}$ **17.** $\frac{7}{2}$ $3\frac{1}{2}$ **18.** $\frac{12}{5}$ $2\frac{2}{5}$

19. $\frac{8}{3}$ $2\frac{2}{3}$ **20.** $\frac{14}{4}$ $1\frac{3}{4}$ **21.** $\frac{6}{5}$ $1\frac{1}{5}$

22. $\frac{20}{3}$ $6\frac{2}{3}$ **23.** $\frac{17}{5}$ $3\frac{2}{5}$ **24.** $\frac{18}{4}$ $4\frac{1}{4}$

25. $\frac{9}{5}$ $1\frac{4}{5}$ **26.** $\frac{29}{8}$ $3\frac{5}{8}$ **27.** $\frac{24}{9}$ $2\frac{2}{3}$

Minds on Math Transparency

5-6

Use only 5s and plus signs to fill in the ten boxes to get the sum shown. $\square\square\square\square\square\square\square\square\square\square = 1,165$

Answers may vary. Sample:

$\boxed{5}\,\boxed{5} + \boxed{5}\,\boxed{5}\,\boxed{5} + \boxed{5}\,\boxed{5}\,\boxed{5} = 1,165$

See *Solution Key* for worked-out answers.

205

1 Focus

CONNECTING TO PRIOR KNOWLEDGE
Have students imagine they must take two medicines: one every four hours and the other every six hours. Ask: *How often would you take the medicines together?* **every 12 h** Have students share their strategies. **Answers may vary. Sample: Draw a chart.**

Lesson Planning Options

Prerequisite Skills
- finding multiples (precourse)
- using prime factorization (precourse)

Vocabulary/Symbols
multiple, common multiples, least common multiples

Resources

 Student Edition

Skills Handbook, p. 540
Extra Practice, p. 526
Glossary/Study Guide

Teaching Resources

Chapter Support File, Ch. 5
- Lesson Planner 5-7
- Practice 5-7, Reteaching 5-7
- Alternative Activity 5-7
- Answer Masters 5-7

Glossary, Spanish Resources

 **Transparencies**
19, Minds on Math 5-7

Warm Up

The sum of two whole numbers each rounded to the nearest ten is 100. One number rounds to 80. What are the two largest whole numbers that these numbers can be? **84, 24**

2 Teach

Work Together

VISUAL LEARNING Suggest students use calendars and mark the Saturdays on which each girl gets a haircut.

THINK AND DISCUSS

Example 3 Tell students: *If a factor appears in two different prime factorizations the same number of times, circle only one set of factors.*

ASSESSMENT Pair students. Ask them to find the LCM of 6 and 10. **30** Have one student use a list of multiples to find the LCM. The partner uses prime factorization. Students compare answers, then switch roles to find the LCM of 15 and 9. **45**

AUDITORY LEARNING and ERROR ALERT!
Students may confuse LCM with GCF.
Remediation: Review the meanings of the acronyms. LCM stands for the Least Common

---

5-7 Least Common Multiple

What You'll Learn

1 To find the least common multiple by listing multiples
2 To find the least common multiple using prime factorization

...And Why

You'll use the least common multiple to solve problems in astronomy.

Here's How

Look for questions that
 build understanding
✔ check understanding

Work Together

Identifying Common Multiples

Kristen and Dea get their hair cut at The Hair Fair. Kristen gets a haircut every sixth Saturday, and Dea gets one every fourth Saturday. Both look forward to the Saturdays they meet there.

1. Make a table that shows on which Saturdays Kristen and Dea each will be at The Hair Fair.
   See below left.
2. How often will they be there on the same day?
   every 12th Saturday

1. Saturday	Kristen	Tai
1		
2		
3		
4		✓
5		
6	✓	
7		
8		✓
9		
10		
11		
12	✓	✓

THINK AND DISCUSS

▼ LCM and Common Multiples

A **multiple** of a number is the product of that number and a nonzero whole number. For example, 4, 8, and 12 are multiples of 4. Multiples shared by two or more numbers are **common multiples.** For example, 12 is a common multiple of 4 and 6.

3. ✔ *Try It Out* Name two more common multiples of 4 and 6.
   Sample: 24, 36

The lowest common multiple of two or more numbers is their **least common multiple (LCM).**

■ EXAMPLE 1

Find the LCM of 6 and 8.

6: 6, 12, 18, 24, 30, . . .
8: 8, 16, 24, 32, 40, . . .

List the multiples of each number. Then circle the lowest multiple the numbers have in common.

The LCM is 24, the lowest of the common multiples.

206

Multiple. GCF stands for the Greatest Common Factor. Have students say these words to themselves whenever they see either acronym to remind them of what they are looking for.

DIVERSITY Tell students there are other cultures, civilizations, and religions with different calendars. Challenge students to find one and describe the calendar.

■ **ADDITIONAL EXAMPLES**

FOR EXAMPLE 1

Find the LCM of 4 and 10. **20**

FOR EXAMPLE 2

Stacey volunteers at the library every three days. Tomas goes to the library to study once a week. They saw each other at the library today. When will they see each other next? **Answers may vary. Sample: 3 weeks from today**

FOR EXAMPLE 3

Use prime factorization to find the LCM of 3, 10, and 25. **150**

3 Practice/Assess

EXERCISES *On Your Own*

REASONING Exercise 13 Ask students to describe how they reached their solutions.

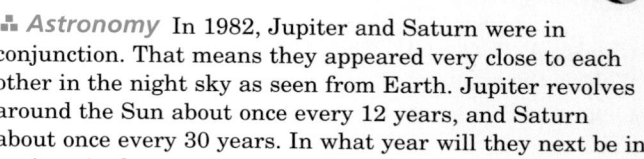

HISTORY The ancient Mayas of Central America used a system of calendars running parallel to each other. One calendar had 365 days, and another had 260 days. The Mayan long-term calendar was based on the LCM of 365 days and 260 days, which is 18,980 days, or 52 years.

Source: *Encyclopædia Britannica*

Central America

5. List the multiples of each number. Then find the least number that appears in all three lists.

4. ✔ *Try It Out* Find the LCM of each set of numbers.
   a. 8, 10 **40**   b. 3, 9 **9**   c. 10, 15 **30**   d. 4, 5 **20**

5. ▴ *Analyze* Explain how to find the LCM of three numbers. **See below left.**

■ **EXAMPLE 2** *Real-World Problem Solving*

▴ *Astronomy* In 1982, Jupiter and Saturn were in conjunction. That means they appeared very close to each other in the night sky as seen from Earth. Jupiter revolves around the Sun about once every 12 years, and Saturn about once every 30 years. In what year will they next be in conjunction?

12: 12, 24, 36, 48, ⟨60⟩, 72, . . .
30: 30, ⟨60⟩, 90, 120, 150, . . .   ← Find the LCM of 12 and 30.
1982 + 60 = 2042   ← Add the LCM to 1982.

The next conjunction of Jupiter and Saturn will be in 2042.

Now you may assign Exercises 1–15.

❷ Finding the LCM Using Prime Factorizations

You can also use prime factorizations to find the LCM.

■ **EXAMPLE 3**

Use prime factorizations to find the LCM of 15, 18, and 20.

$15 = 3 \times ⟨5⟩$
$18 = 2 \times ⟨3⟩ \times ⟨3⟩$
$20 = ⟨2⟩ \times ⟨2⟩ \times 5$

← Write the prime factorizations. Then circle all the different factors where they appear the greatest number of times.

$2 \times 2 \times 3 \times 3 \times 5 = 180$ ← Multiply the circled factors.

The LCM is 180.

6. ✔ *Try It Out* Find the LCM of 5, 8, and 12.   **120**

Now you may assign Exercises 16–29.

EXERCISES *On Your Own*

Find the LCM of each set of numbers by making a list of their multiples.

1. 4, 6 **12**   2. 4, 9 **36**   3. 6, 10 **30**   4. 3, 5 **15**   5. 12, 15 **60**   6. 4, 12 **12**

7. 12, 20 **60**   8. 10, 15 **30**   9. 8, 12 **24**   10. 2, 3, 5 **30**   11. 3, 6, 8 **24**   12. 5, 6, 10 **30**

Technology Options

Prentice Hall Technology

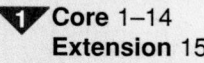
Software for Learners
• Math Blaster® Mystery*
• Interactive Student Tutorial, Chapter 5*

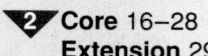
Teaching Resource Software
• Computer Item Generator 5-7
• Resource Pro™ Chapter 5*

Internet • For related mathematics activities, visit the Prentice Hall site at www.phschool.com/math

*Available on CD-ROM only

Assignment Options for Exercises On Your Own

To provide flexible scheduling, this lesson can be subdivided into parts.

▼**1** Core 1–14
   Extension 15

▼**2** Core 16–28
   Extension 29

Use Mixed Review to maintain skills.

207

Practice 5-7 *Least Common Multiple*

Find the LCM of each set of numbers. Use lists of
multiples of each number.

1. 5, 10 10	**2.** 2, 3 6	**3.** 6, 8 24	**4.** 4, 6 12
5. 8, 10 40	**6.** 5, 6 30	**7.** 12, 15 60	**8.** 8, 12 24
9. 9, 15 45	**10.** 6, 15 30	**11.** 6, 9 18	**12.** 6, 18 18
13. 3, 5 15	**14.** 4, 5 20	**15.** 9, 21 63	**16.** 7, 28 28
17. 4, 6, 8 24	**18.** 6, 8, 12 24	**19.** 4, 9, 12 36	**20.** 6, 9, 12 36
21. 6, 12, 15 60	**22.** 8, 12, 15 120		

Find the LCM of each set of numbers. Use prime
factorization.

23. 18, 21 126	**24.** 15, 21 105	**25.** 18, 24 72	**26.** 21, 24 168
27. 15, 30 30	**28.** 24, 30 120	**29.** 24, 72 72	**30.** 18, 72 72
31. 8, 42 168	**32.** 16, 42 336	**33.** 8, 56 56	**34.** 6, 81 162
35. 8, 30 120	**36.** 16, 30 240	**37.** 18, 30 90	**38.** 45, 60 180
39. 12, 24, 16 48	**40.** 8, 16, 20 80	**41.** 12, 16, 20 240	**42.** 15, 20, 25 300

43. At one store hot dogs come in packages of eight. Hot dog
buns come in packages of twelve. What is the least number
of packages of each type that you can buy and have no hot
dogs or buns left over?
3 packages of hot dogs, 2 packages of hot dog buns

In copymaster and workbook formats

Reteaching 5-7 *Least Common Multiple*

Find the **least common multiple (LCM)** of 8 and 12.

① Begin listing multiples of each number.
8: 8, 16, 24, 32, 40
12: 12, 24

② Continue the lists until you find the first multiple that is
common to both lists. That is the LCM.

The least common multiple of 8 and 12 is 24.

List the multiples of each number. Use the list to find the LCM.

1. 4: 4, 8, 12, 16, 20 5: 5, 10, 15, 20 LCM: 20	**2.** 6: 6, 12, 18, 24, 30, 36, 42 7: 7, 14, 21, 28, 35, 42 LCM: 42
3. 9: 9, 18, 27, 36, 45 15: 15, 30, 45 LCM: 45	**4.** 10: 10, 20, 30, 40, 50 25: 25, 50 LCM: 50
5. 8: 8, 16, 24 24: 24 LCM: 24	**6.** 8: 8, 16, 24 12: 12, 24 LCM: 24
7. 4: 4, 8, 12, 16, 20, 24, 28 7: 7, 14, 21, 28 LCM: 28	**8.** 15: 15, 30, 45, 60, 75 25: 25, 50, 75 LCM: 75
9. 15: 15, 30, 45, 60 20: 20, 40, 60 LCM: 60	**10.** 4: 4, 8, 12, 16, 20, 24, 28, 32, 36 9: 9, 18, 27, 36 LCM: 36
11. 6: 4, 12, 18, 24 8: 8, 16, 24 LCM: 24	**12.** 12: 12, 24, 36, 48, 60 15: 15, 30, 45, 60 LCM: 60
13. 18: 18, 36, 54, 72 24: 24, 48, 72 LCM: 72	**14.** 3: 3, 6, 9, 12, 15, 18, 21, 24 8: 8, 16, 24 LCM: 24

Minds on Math Transparency

5-7

Kilta's house number has 4 different digits. The sum of the
last two digits is 6 greater than the sum of the first two
digits. The number is a multiple of 5. The first digit minus the
second digit is 1. The last digit minus the first digit is 4. What
is Kilta's house number?

1,025

See Solution Key for worked-out answers.

WRITING Exercise 29b Have students write
their descriptions as rules.

WRAP UP

IDENTIFYING THE BIG IDEA Have students
explain how to find the LCM of two or more
numbers.

JOURNAL Have students find the LCM
and GCF of two numbers to use as examples.

13. A number has both 8 and 10 as factors. **40**
 a. *Reasoning* What is the lowest the number could be?
 b. Name four other factors of the number.
  Answers may vary. Sample: 1, 2, 4, 5

14. *Fitness* Suppose you jog every third day and swim every
fourth day. You did both this morning. When will you next do
both? **in 12 days**

15. **Choose A, B, C, or D.** The LCM of a number and 15 is 120.
What is the number? **D**

 A. 20 **B.** 12 **C.** 6 **D.** 24

**Use prime factorizations to find the LCM for each set of
numbers.**

16. 16, 24 **48** **17.** 18, 24 **72** **18.** 24, 32 **96** **19.** 3, 4, 5 **60** **20.** 14, 33 **462** **21.** 75, 100
 300

22. 4, 22 **44** **23.** 20, 26 **260** **24.** 3, 4, 9 **36** **25.** 7, 8, 14 **56** **26.** 22, 55, 60
 660 **27.** 12, 18, 108
 108

28. a. List the multiples of each number to find the LCM of 30,
40, and 50. **a–b. 600**
 b. Use prime factorizations to find the LCM of 30, 40,
and 50.
 c. *Writing* Which method is more efficient? Explain.
  See above right.

29. a. For each pair, find the GCF, the LCM, the product of the
two numbers, and the product of the GCF and LCM.
  i. 12 and 18 **ii.** 20 and 25 **iii.** 24 and 28
 b. *Writing* Look over your results. Describe the pattern.
  29a–b. See above right.

Mixed Review

Find each product. *(Lesson 4-5)*

30. 1.9×0.8
 1.52 **31.** 0.95×6
 5.7 **32.** 36.18×4
 144.72 **33.** 517.6×0.01
 5.176 **34.** 4.25×0.32
 1.36

Write a variable expression for each word phrase. *(Lesson 2-5)*

35. 28 less than k
 $k - 28$ **36.** 4 multiplied by h
 $4h$ **37.** y more than 12
 $12 + y$ **38.** 98 times a
 $98a$

39. *Choose a Strategy* A swim team can line up in 6 lanes with
an equal number of swimmers in each lane. If only 5 lanes
are used, two lanes each have an extra person. What is the
least possible number of people on the swim team? **12 people**

---

1. Make a list to find the LCM of 3, 4, and 9.
36

2. Use prime factorization to find the LCM of
21, 24, and 40. **840**

28c. Prime factorization; if the
numbers are large and
have few common
factors, the list may be
very long before a
common multiple
appears.

29a. i. 6; 36; 216; 216;
 ii. 5; 100; 500; 500;
 iii. 4; 168; 672; 672

 b. The product of the GCF
and the LCM is equal to
the product of the
numbers.

JOURNAL
Compare the methods you
use to find the LCM with
those you use to find the
GCF.

1 Focus

CONNECTING TO PRIOR KNOWLEDGE
Have students recall how to determine if a fraction is close to 0, $\frac{1}{2}$, or 1. Discuss with students how they might use this information or other strategies to compare fractions.

2 Teach

THINK AND DISCUSS

MENTAL MATH Ask students why they only compare numerators when the denominators are the same. **Answers may vary. Sample: When the denominators are the same, the parts of the whole are the same size.**

Example 1 Ask students: *How is finding the LCD like finding the LCM?* **The LCD is the**

LCM for the two denominators.

EXTENSION Question 2 Ask students if they can use reasoning to solve part (d). **Answers may vary. Sample: Both fractions are one part short of being a whole. Because tenths are smaller than eighths, $\frac{9}{10}$ is closer to 1 and therefore greater then $\frac{7}{8}$.**

Example 2 Ask students to explain how to change $\frac{3}{4}$ to $\frac{24}{32}$. **Because the LCD of the two fractions is 32, multiply the numerator and denominator by 8.**

5-8 Comparing and Ordering Fractions

What You'll Learn

▼ To compare fractions
▼ To order fractions

...And Why

You'll compare and order fractions to make decisions in activities such as carpentry.

Here's How

Look for questions that
⊞ build understanding
✔ check understanding

Need Help? For practice in comparing and ordering whole numbers, see Skills Handbook p. 537.

QUICKreview

To write equivalent fractions, multiply the numerator and the denominator by the same nonzero factor.

THINK AND DISCUSS

▼ Comparing Fractions

It is easy to compare fractions with the same denominator. The fraction with the larger numerator is greater. For example, as you can see from the model, $\frac{5}{6} > \frac{4}{6}$ because $5 > 4$.

1. ⊞ *Mental Math* Compare each pair using $<$, $>$, or $=$.
   a. $\frac{6}{8}, \frac{7}{8}$ b. $\frac{13}{15}, \frac{9}{15}$ c. $\frac{11}{12}, \frac{10}{12}$ d. $\frac{14}{24}, \frac{16}{24}$
   $<$ $>$ $>$ $<$

You can compare fractions with unlike denominators by using equivalent fractions to find the least common denominator. The **least common denominator (LCD)** is the least common multiple (LCM) of the original denominators.

■ EXAMPLE 1

Compare $\frac{7}{24}$ and $\frac{5}{18}$. Use $<$, $>$, or $=$.

$24 = ②×②×②× 3$
$18 = 2 ×③×③$ ← Find the LCD of the fractions by finding the LCM of 24 and 18.
$2 × 2 × 2 × 3 × 3 = 72$ ← The LCD is 72.

$$\frac{7}{24} \overset{×3}{\underset{×3}{=}} \frac{21}{72} \qquad \frac{5}{18} \overset{×4}{\underset{×4}{=}} \frac{20}{72}$$
← Write equivalent fractions using the LCD.

$21 > 20$ ← Compare the numerators.

Since $\frac{21}{72} > \frac{20}{72}$, then $\frac{7}{24} > \frac{5}{18}$.

2. ✔ *Try It Out* Compare each pair using $<$, $>$, or $=$.
   a. $\frac{4}{6} \blacksquare \frac{5}{8}$ b. $\frac{7}{12} \blacksquare \frac{9}{16}$ c. $\frac{4}{10} \blacksquare \frac{6}{15}$ d. $\frac{7}{8} \blacksquare \frac{9}{10}$
   $>$ $>$ $=$ $<$

Lesson Planning Options

Prerequisite Skills

- using equivalent fractions (5-7)
- using LCM (5-7)

Vocabulary/Symbols

least common denominator

Resources

📖 **Student Edition**

Skills Handbook, p. 537
Extra Practice, p. 526
Glossary/Study Guide

📓 **Teaching Resources**

Chapter Support File, Ch. 5
- Lesson Planner 5-8
- Practice 5-8, Reteaching 5-8
- Answer Masters 5-8
Teaching Aids Masters 21–25
Glossary, Spanish Resources

💻 **Transparencies**
22–29, Minds on Math 5-8

Warm Up

What will be the 23rd position in this pattern?
♥ ♣ ✖ ▲ ♣ ♥ ♣ ✖ ▲ ✖ ✖

ASSESSMENT Have students determine which mixed number in each pair is greater.
a. $2\frac{1}{2}$, $1\frac{1}{2}$ $2\frac{1}{2}$
b. $5\frac{3}{8}$, $5\frac{2}{5}$ $5\frac{2}{5}$

AUDITORY LEARNING **Question 3** Ask students to state the answers. This will help students connect the symbols $<$, $>$, and $=$ with their associated words.

ERROR ALERT! **Question 5b** Students may confuse the identical numerators in this group with the identical denominators in part (a).
Remediation: Remind students that when they compare denominators, the smaller the number, the larger the fraction. Ask them which pizza would yield larger pieces if both were the same size: one divided into fourths, or one divided into twelfths?

Example 3 Review prime factorization with students. Pay special attention to students who had problems with the last lesson.

Discuss with students how ordering fractions and comparing fractions are similar and different. Explain to students that ordering fractions is the same as comparing three or more fractions.

Technology Options

Prentice Hall Technology

  Software for Learners
- Hot Page™ 15*
- Math Blaster® Mystery*
- Interactive Student Tutorial, Chapter 5*

  Teaching Resource Software
- Computer Item Generator 5-8
- Resource Pro™ Chapter 5*

Internet • For related mathematics activities, visit the Prentice Hall site at www.phschool.com/math

Available on CD-ROM only

Assignment Options for Exercises On Your Own

To provide flexible scheduling, this lesson can be split into parts.

1 Core 1–11
Extension 12

2 Core 13–25
Extension 26

Use Mixed Review to maintain skills.

To compare mixed numbers, first compare the whole numbers. If the whole numbers are the same, compare the fraction parts.

■ **EXAMPLE 2**   *Real-World Problem Solving*

Carpentry "Measure twice, cut once" is the carpenter's motto. A carpenter needs a piece of lumber that is at least $6\frac{27}{32}$ inches wide. Is a $6\frac{3}{4}$-inch piece wide enough?

Since the whole numbers are the same, compare $\frac{27}{32}$ and $\frac{3}{4}$.

$\frac{27}{32} = \frac{27}{32}$ $\frac{3}{4} = \frac{24}{32}$ ← Write equivalent fractions.

$6\frac{27}{32} > 6\frac{24}{32}$ ← Compare.

The $6\frac{3}{4}$-inch piece is not wide enough.

3. ✔ *Try It Out* Compare each pair using $<$, $>$, or $=$.
a. $3\frac{2}{5}$ ▨ $2\frac{4}{5}$ $>$ **b.** $1\frac{2}{3}$ ▨ $1\frac{5}{9}$ $>$
c. $5\frac{7}{8}$ ▨ $6\frac{5}{6}$ $<$ **d.** $2\frac{4}{7}$ ▨ $2\frac{12}{21}$ $=$
e. $4\frac{2}{5}$ ▨ $4\frac{3}{7}$ $<$ **f.** $3\frac{8}{12}$ ▨ $3\frac{3}{4}$ $<$

4. *What If . . .* In Example 2, would a $6\frac{7}{8}$-inch piece of lumber be wide enough? Explain. **See left.**

Now you may assign Exercises 1–12.

2 *Ordering Fractions*

You have used fraction models to *compare* fractions. You can also use models to *order* fractions.

5. *Modeling* Use fraction models to order each set of fractions from least to greatest.
a. $\frac{7}{10}$, $\frac{1}{10}$, $\frac{3}{10}$ $\frac{1}{10}$, $\frac{3}{10}$, $\frac{7}{10}$ **b.** $\frac{3}{4}$, $\frac{3}{5}$, $\frac{3}{10}$, $\frac{3}{12}$ $\frac{3}{12}$, $\frac{3}{10}$, $\frac{3}{5}$, $\frac{3}{4}$

6. *Mental Math* How are the fractions in Question 5(a) alike? Without using fraction models, how can you tell which fraction is the greatest? **See left.**

7. *Mental Math* How are the fractions in Question 5(b) alike? Without using fraction models, how can you tell which fraction is the greatest? **See left.**

To order fractions with unlike numerators and denominators, use the LCD to write equivalent fractions. Then order the numerators.

4. yes; $6\frac{7}{8} = 6\frac{28}{32} > 6\frac{27}{32}$

6. The fractions have the same denominator; of fractions with the same denominator, the one with the greatest numerator is the greatest.

7. The fractions have the same numerator; of fractions with the same numerator, the one with the least denominator is the greatest.

FOR EXAMPLE 1
Compare $\frac{3}{4}$ and $\frac{5}{6}$. $\frac{3}{4} < \frac{5}{6}$

FOR EXAMPLE 2
A carpenter needs a piece of lumber that is at least $4\frac{3}{16}$ feet long. Is a $4\frac{1}{4}$-ft piece long enough? **yes**

FOR EXAMPLE 3
Order from least to greatest. $\frac{2}{7}, \frac{3}{10}, \frac{1}{5}$.
$\frac{1}{5} < \frac{2}{7} < \frac{3}{10}$

3 Practice/Assess

EXERCISES *On Your Own*

OPEN-ENDED Exercise 25 Challenge students to write fractions with different numerators and denominators.

CONNECTION TO MUSIC Exercise 26c Ask students who are familiar with music to talk about the relationship between the notes. For example, you hold a half note longer than a quarter note.

■ **EXAMPLE 3**

Order from least to greatest: $\frac{3}{8}, \frac{2}{5}, \frac{7}{20}$.

$8 = ②\times②\times②$
$5 = 5$ ◄—— Find the LCM of 8, 5, and 20.
$20 = 2 \times 2 \times ⑤$
$2 \times 2 \times 2 \times 5 = 40$ ◄—— The LCD is 40.
$\frac{3}{8} = \frac{15}{40} \quad \frac{2}{5} = \frac{16}{40} \quad \frac{7}{20} = \frac{14}{40}$ ◄—— Write equivalent fractions.
$14 < 15 < 16$ ◄—— Arrange the numerators in order.

Since $\frac{14}{40} < \frac{15}{40} < \frac{16}{40}$, then $\frac{7}{20} < \frac{3}{8} < \frac{2}{5}$.

8. ✓**Try It Out** Order from least to greatest: $\frac{2}{6}, \frac{8}{21}, \frac{4}{14}$. $\frac{4}{14}, \frac{2}{6}, \frac{8}{21}$

Now you may assign Exercises 13–26.

EXERCISES *On Your Own*

Compare using <, >, or =.

1. $2\frac{11}{16} \,\overset{>}{\blacksquare}\, 1\frac{13}{16}$

2. $\frac{13}{20} \,\overset{>}{\blacksquare}\, \frac{1}{4}$

3. $\frac{9}{24} \,\overset{=}{\blacksquare}\, \frac{3}{8}$

4. $\frac{15}{16} \,\overset{>}{\blacksquare}\, \frac{9}{10}$

5. $5\frac{4}{7} \,\blacksquare\, 5\frac{5}{7}$ <

6. $\frac{3}{11} \,\blacksquare\, \frac{1}{4}$ >

7. $3\frac{1}{4} \,\blacksquare\, 3\frac{1}{5}$ >

8. $\frac{2}{9} \,\blacksquare\, \frac{4}{15}$ <

9. Timothy ran $1\frac{3}{4}$ mi. Wenona ran $1\frac{7}{10}$ mi. Who ran farther? **Timothy**

10. *Shopping* Two bags of popcorn sell for the same price. One bag contains $1\frac{5}{8}$ oz. The other contains $1\frac{3}{4}$ oz. Which has more? **the bag with $1\frac{3}{4}$ oz**

11. Choose A, B, C, or D. To compare $\frac{9}{24}$ and $\frac{5}{15}$, which would you do first? Explain.

   A. Find the LCM of 24 and 15.
   B. Simplify each fraction.
   C. Find the prime factorization of 24 and 15.
   D. Multiply 24×15 to find a common denominator.

11. B; Reasoning may vary. Sample: It's easier to work with smaller numbers, which you get by simplifying.

12. a. Use models or equivalent fractions to tell whether each fraction is greater than, less than, or equal to $\frac{1}{2}$.

   i. $\frac{3}{5}$ >   **ii.** $\frac{5}{12}$ <   **iii.** $\frac{5}{8}$ >   **iv.** $\frac{2}{3}$ >

   b. *Writing* How can you use your results to compare $\frac{3}{5}$ and $\frac{5}{12}$? Can you use the results above to compare $\frac{3}{5}$ and $\frac{5}{8}$? Explain. $\frac{3}{5} > \frac{5}{12}$, since $\frac{3}{5} > \frac{1}{2}$ and $\frac{5}{12} < \frac{1}{2}$; no; since each fraction is greater than $\frac{1}{2}$, you cannot tell which one is greater.

Practice 5-8 *Comparing and Ordering Fractions*

Compare using <, >, or =.

1. $2\frac{14}{17}$ > $1\frac{16}{17}$ 2. $\frac{15}{21}$ = $\frac{5}{7}$ 3. $2\frac{7}{8}$ > $2\frac{5}{6}$ 4. $1\frac{1}{2}$ < $2\frac{1}{3}$

5. $3\frac{15}{16}$ > $3\frac{21}{32}$ 6. $4\frac{7}{8}$ > $3\frac{9}{10}$ 7. $5\frac{9}{10}$ = $5\frac{18}{20}$ 8. $4\frac{7}{8}$ < $5\frac{1}{8}$

9. $1\frac{19}{20}$ < $2\frac{1}{20}$ 10. $4\frac{5}{6}$ < $5\frac{19}{20}$ 11. $7\frac{3}{10}$ = $7\frac{9}{30}$ 12. $2\frac{7}{15}$ > $1\frac{14}{15}$

13. $4\frac{19}{24}$ > $4\frac{7}{12}$ 14. $5\frac{19}{20}$ < $6\frac{21}{22}$ 15. $4\frac{15}{20}$ = $4\frac{21}{28}$ 16. $1\frac{2}{16}$ < $1\frac{1}{4}$

Order each set of fractions from least to greatest.

17. $\frac{9}{10}, \frac{5}{6}, \frac{14}{15}$
$\frac{5}{6}, \frac{9}{10}, \frac{14}{15}$

18. $1\frac{7}{8}, 1\frac{7}{12}, 1\frac{5}{6}$
$1\frac{7}{12}, 1\frac{5}{6}, 1\frac{7}{8}$

19. $\frac{14}{15}, \frac{9}{10}, \frac{11}{12}$
$\frac{9}{10}, \frac{11}{12}, \frac{14}{15}$

20. $2\frac{1}{4}, 3\frac{7}{8}, 3\frac{5}{6}$
$2\frac{1}{4}, 3\frac{5}{6}, 3\frac{7}{8}$

21. $\frac{2}{3}, \frac{4}{5}, \frac{7}{30}, \frac{11}{15}$
$\frac{7}{30}, \frac{2}{3}, \frac{11}{15}, \frac{4}{5}$

22. $2\frac{1}{6}, 1\frac{3}{4}, 3\frac{7}{8}, 2\frac{1}{10}$
$1\frac{3}{4}, 2\frac{1}{10}, 2\frac{1}{6}, 3\frac{7}{8}$

23. $\frac{5}{12}, \frac{17}{30}, \frac{3}{5}$
$\frac{5}{12}, \frac{17}{30}, \frac{3}{5}$

24. $1\frac{5}{6}, 2\frac{1}{6}, 1\frac{11}{12}, 1\frac{11}{18}$
$1\frac{11}{18}, 1\frac{5}{6}, 1\frac{11}{12}, 2\frac{1}{6}$

25. $\frac{17}{20}, 1\frac{18}{25}, 2\frac{31}{36}$
$\frac{17}{20}, 1\frac{18}{25}, 2\frac{31}{36}$

Circle A, B, C, or D.

26. Which fraction is greater than $\frac{31}{36}$?
A. $\frac{2}{3}$ (B.) $\frac{7}{8}$
C. $\frac{1}{2}$ D. $\frac{13}{24}$

27. Which fraction is less than $\frac{8}{15}$?
A. $\frac{4}{7}$ B. $\frac{3}{5}$
C. $\frac{17}{30}$ (D.) $\frac{4}{9}$

28. Explain how you could answer Exercise 27 without finding common denominators or using a calculator.
$\frac{4}{9}$ is the only choice that is less than $\frac{1}{2}$, so it is the least fraction.

In copymaster and workbook formats

Reteaching 5-8 *Comparing and Ordering Fractions*

To compare and order fractions, use the **least common denominator (LCD)**. The LCD is the least common multiple (LCM) of the original denominators.

Compare Fractions

Compare $\frac{3}{4}$ and $\frac{7}{10}$.

① Find the LCD of the denominators 4 and 10:
$4 = 2 \times 2$
$10 = 2 \times 5$
LCD $= 2 \times 2 \times 5 = 20$

② Write equivalent fractions:
$\frac{3}{4} = \frac{15}{20}$ (×5)
$\frac{7}{10} = \frac{14}{20}$ (×2)

③ Compare: $\frac{15}{20} > \frac{14}{20}$, or
$\frac{3}{4} > \frac{7}{10}$

Order Fractions

Order from least to greatest: $\frac{2}{3}, \frac{5}{8}, \frac{3}{4}$.

① Find the LCD of the denominators 3, 8, and 4:
$3 = 3$
$8 = 2 \times 2 \times 2$
$4 = 2 \times 2$
LCD $= 3 \times 2 \times 2 \times 2 = 24$

② Write equivalent fractions:
$\frac{2}{3} = \frac{16}{24}$ (×8)
$\frac{5}{8} = \frac{15}{24}$ (×3)
$\frac{3}{4} = \frac{18}{24}$ (×6)

③ Order:
$15 < 16 < 18$
$\frac{15}{24} < \frac{16}{24} < \frac{18}{24}$, or $\frac{5}{8} < \frac{2}{3} < \frac{3}{4}$

Compare using <, >, or =.

1. $\frac{2}{9}$ < $\frac{1}{3}$ 2. $\frac{5}{6}$ < $\frac{7}{8}$ 3. $\frac{7}{20}$ > $\frac{3}{10}$
4. $\frac{3}{6}$ > $\frac{4}{11}$ 5. $\frac{2}{3}$ = $\frac{4}{6}$ 6. $\frac{4}{8}$ > $\frac{2}{8}$
7. $\frac{3}{7}$ < $\frac{5}{8}$ 8. $\frac{1}{3}$ = $\frac{3}{9}$ 9. $\frac{1}{2}$ > $\frac{3}{7}$
10. $\frac{4}{5}$ > $\frac{7}{9}$ 11. $\frac{2}{3}$ < $\frac{7}{10}$ 12. $2\frac{5}{9}$ < $2\frac{3}{5}$

Order each set of fractions from least to greatest.

13. $\frac{3}{4}, \frac{5}{8}, \frac{1}{2}, \frac{1}{8}, \frac{3}{4}$ 14. $\frac{5}{8}, \frac{5}{6}, \frac{2}{3}, \frac{3}{8}, \frac{1}{6}$ 15. $\frac{1}{2}, \frac{5}{12}, \frac{2}{3}, \frac{5}{12}, \frac{1}{3}$
16. $\frac{3}{5}, \frac{2}{3}, \frac{7}{12}, \frac{7}{12}, \frac{5}{3}, \frac{1}{3}$ 17. $\frac{1}{2}, \frac{3}{5}, \frac{5}{8}, \frac{3}{2}, \frac{1}{5}, \frac{3}{8}$ 18. $\frac{7}{8}, \frac{3}{4}, \frac{13}{16}, \frac{3}{4}, \frac{13}{16}, \frac{7}{8}$

Minds on Math Transparency

5-8

Fill in the boxes with the numbers 1 through 9 so that the sum of the numbers in each indicated row, column, and diagonal is 15.

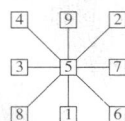

Answers may vary. Sample is shown.

See *Solution Key* for worked-out answers.

WRAP UP

these fractions. Ask: *Do the two lists of fractions give you the same player ranking?*
yes

IDENTIFYING THE BIG IDEA Ask students how to compare and order fractions.

PROJECT LINK If students have already written the fraction of shots each player made, have them check over the work and then order the fractions. Then challenge them to write the shooting record as a different fraction, such as the fraction of shots missed. Have them order

LESSON QUIZ

1. Compare $3\frac{7}{9}$ and $3\frac{6}{7}$.
$$3\frac{6}{7} > 3\frac{7}{9}$$

2. Order from least to greatest: $\frac{3}{7}, \frac{5}{6}, \frac{10}{21}$.
$$\frac{3}{7} < \frac{10}{21} < \frac{5}{6}$$

Order each set from least to greatest. 17. $2\frac{5}{6}, 2\frac{8}{9}, 2\frac{17}{18}$ 20. $1\frac{8}{11}, 1\frac{3}{4}, 2\frac{1}{4}$ 22. $\frac{1}{8}, \frac{7}{40}, \frac{1}{5}, \frac{3}{10}$

13. $\frac{2}{3}, \frac{2}{5}, \frac{2}{7}, \frac{2}{7}, \frac{2}{5}, \frac{2}{3}$ 14. $\frac{4}{8}, \frac{5}{6}, \frac{7}{9}, \frac{4}{9}, \frac{7}{6}, \frac{5}{6}$ 15. $1\frac{2}{3}, 1\frac{3}{4}, 1\frac{5}{6}, 1\frac{2}{3}, 1\frac{3}{4}, 1\frac{5}{6}$ 16. $\frac{3}{5}, \frac{2}{7}, \frac{3}{8}, \frac{2}{7}, \frac{3}{8}, \frac{3}{5}$

17. $2\frac{8}{9}, 2\frac{17}{18}, 2\frac{5}{6}$ 18. $\frac{11}{24}, \frac{5}{8}, \frac{5}{12}, \frac{5}{12}, \frac{11}{24}, \frac{5}{8}$ 19. $\frac{7}{15}, \frac{1}{3}, \frac{7}{12}, \frac{1}{3}, \frac{7}{15}, \frac{7}{12}$ 20. $1\frac{8}{11}, 2\frac{1}{4}, 1\frac{3}{4}$

21. $\frac{5}{7}, \frac{11}{14}, \frac{3}{4}$ 22. $\frac{1}{5}, \frac{1}{8}, \frac{7}{40}, \frac{3}{10}$ 23. $\frac{7}{12}, \frac{23}{40}, \frac{8}{15}, \frac{19}{30}$ 24. $14\frac{7}{9}, 14\frac{3}{4}, 14\frac{13}{18}$
$\frac{5}{7}, \frac{3}{4}, \frac{11}{14}$ $\frac{8}{15}, \frac{23}{40}, \frac{7}{12}, \frac{19}{30}$ $14\frac{13}{18}, 14\frac{3}{4}, 14\frac{7}{9}$

25. *Open-ended* Write three fractions and order them from least to greatest. State the method you used to order them. **Check students' work.**

26. *Music* Musical notes are based on fractions of a whole note.   a. $\frac{1}{16}, \frac{1}{8}, \frac{1}{4}, \frac{1}{2}$
a. Order the fractions shown from greatest to least.
b. Redraw the note symbols so they are in order.
c. *Patterns* Is there a pattern to how the symbols change? Explain. **Answers may vary. Sample: As the fractions decrease, features are added to their symbols.**

$\frac{1}{4}$ $\frac{1}{16}$ $\frac{1}{2}$ $\frac{1}{8}$

Fractions of a Whole Note

b.

Mixed Review

Change to minutes using mental math. *(Lesson 3-10)*

27. 4 h 13 min
253 min
28. 2 h 27 min
147 min
29. 8 h 19 min
499 min
30. 10 h 16 min
616 min
31. 2 h 36 min
156 min

Find each product or quotient. *(Lessons 4-5 and 4-9)*

32. 3.7×83.5
308.95
33. 0.93×34.1
31.713
34. $401.5 \div 5$
80.3
35. $5.34 \div 0.6$
8.9
36. $3.705 \div 3.25$
1.14

37. *Choose a Strategy* A collector buys a stamp for $25, sells it for $30, buys it back for $33, and finally sells it for $35. How much did he make or lose in buying and selling the stamp?
The collector made $7.

CHAPTER PROJECT

PROJECT LINK: CALCULATING

Add a fourth column to your data table and write each player's shooting record as a fraction. Then compare and order the fractions. Rank your players from best to worst at foul shooting. **Check students' work.**

in a grocery store and have to weigh it on a digital scale.

1 Focus

CONNECTING TO PRIOR KNOWLEDGE Ask students: *How much is one quarter of a dollar?* Write this amount in dollars and cents. **$.25** Ask students to name other situations where they would use both a decimal and fraction name. **Answers may vary. Sample: You want to buy a half of a pound of fruit**

2 Teach

Work Together

AEP Remind students to pronounce the the sound at the end of decimal names and fractions. Have students practice pronouncing fractions and decimals with the

following: 0.9 or $\frac{9}{10}$, 0.08 or $\frac{8}{100}$. **nine tenths; eight hundredths**

VISUAL LEARNING Questions 1b and 2b Visual learners may want to write the name of each model. Ask these students how writing and seeing the decimal name helps them write a decimal as a fraction.

5-9 Fractions and Decimals

What You'll Learn

1 To write decimals as fractions

2 To write fractions as decimals

...And Why

You'll use fractions and decimals to solve construction problems.

Here's How

Look for questions that
- build understanding
- ✔ check understanding

QUICKreview

You read 0.225 as "two hundred twenty-five thousandths."

2a.

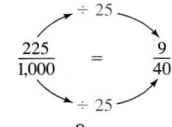

Work Together   *Using Decimal Models to Write Fractions*

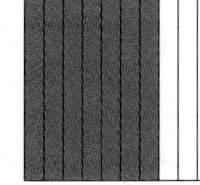

1. a. What decimal does the model represent? **0.7**
   b. Say the decimal in words. **seven tenths**
   c. Write the decimal as a fraction. $\frac{7}{10}$
   d. Complete this statement using the decimal and the fraction: ▧ = ▧. $\frac{7}{10}$
   a. See below left. **0.7**

2. a. Find or draw a decimal square that models 0.05.
   b. Say the decimal in words. **five hundredths**
   c. Write the decimal as a fraction. $\frac{5}{100}$
   d. Simplify the fraction. Complete this statement using the fraction and the decimal: ▧ = ▧. $\frac{5}{100}$
      0.05

3. ⬌ *Reasoning* How does writing the decimal in words help you to write the decimal as a fraction?

The name of the decimal is the same as the name of the fraction before you simplify it.

THINK AND DISCUSS

1 *Writing Fractions*

To write a decimal as a fraction, write the fraction as you would say the decimal. Then simplify it.

■ EXAMPLE 1

Write 0.225 as a fraction in simplest form.

$0.225 = \frac{225}{1,000}$ ◄— Write as a fraction.

$\frac{225}{1,000} = \frac{9}{40}$ ◄— Simplify. The GCF of 225 and 1,000 is 25.

$0.225 = \frac{9}{40}$

4. ✔ *Try It Out* Write each decimal as a fraction in simplest form.
   a. 0.6 $\frac{3}{5}$ b. 0.35 $\frac{7}{20}$ c. 0.130 $\frac{13}{100}$ d. 0.85 $\frac{17}{20}$

Lesson Planning Options

Prerequisite Skills
- writing decimals as fractions (precourse)
- dividing whole numbers and decimals (precourse)
- finding and using the GCF (5-8)

Vocabulary/Symbols
terminating decimal, repeating decimal

Materials/Manipulatives
- calculator
- graph paper

Resources

📖 **Student Edition**

Skills Handbook, p. 541
Extra Practice, p. 526
Glossary/Study Guide

Teaching Resources

Chapter Support File, Ch. 5
- Lesson Planner 5-9
- Practice 5-9, Reteaching 5-9
- Answer Masters 5-9
Teaching Aids Master 20
Glossary, Spanish Resources

Transparencies
11, 12, 19, Minds on Math 5-9

Warm Up

Find three numbers whose sum is 14 and whose product is 54.
2, 3, 9

Example 1 Have students explain how to find the GCF of 225 and 1,000. **List the factors or use a factor tree.**

Question 4 When writing a decimal as a fraction, the unsimplified denominator will always be a multiple of 10. Ask students to name factors they may find when simplifying these denominators. **Answers may vary. Sample: 2, 4, 5, 10, 25**

Example 2 Point out to students that decimals greater than 1 become mixed numbers with the same whole number. Make sure they understand that they need to simplify the fraction part of the mixed number.

ASSESSMENT Challenge one third of the students to write $\frac{11}{27}$ as a decimal. Ask another third to use a calculator to find the decimal. Have them round to the nearest hundredth. The remaining third of the class estimates the fraction as a decimal to check whether the decimal answers are reasonable. Have all students share their answers and strategies with the class. **0.41**

■ **ADDITIONAL EXAMPLES**

FOR EXAMPLE 1

Write 0.55 as a fraction in simplest form. $\frac{11}{20}$

FOR EXAMPLE 2

Write 2.8 as a mixed number in simplest form. $2\frac{4}{5}$

Technology Options

Prentice Hall Technology

  Software for Learners

- Math Lab: Fractions and Decimals
- Math Blaster® Mystery*
- Interactive Student Tutorial, Chapter 5*

  Teaching Resource Software

- Computer Item Generator 5-9
- Resource Pro™ Chapter 5*

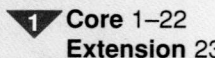 **Internet** • For related mathematics activities, visit the Prentice Hall site at www.phschool.com/math

Available on CD-ROM only

Assignment Options for Exercises On Your Own

To provide flexible scheduling, this lesson can be split into parts.

▼**1** **Core** 1–22
   Extension 23

▼**2** **Core** 24–46
   Extension 47

Use Mixed Review to maintain skills.

If a decimal is greater than 1, it can be written as a mixed number.

■ **EXAMPLE 2**

Write 1.32 as a mixed number in simplest form.

$$1.32 = 1\frac{32}{100} \quad \longleftarrow \text{Keep the whole number 1.}$$

$$\frac{32}{100} = \frac{8}{25} \quad \longleftarrow \text{Simplify the fraction. The GCF is 4.}$$

$$1.32 = 1\frac{8}{25}$$

5. ✔ *Try It Out* Write each decimal as a mixed number in simplest form.

   a. 1.15 $1\frac{3}{20}$ **b.** 3.14 $3\frac{7}{50}$ **c.** 1.034 $1\frac{17}{500}$ **d.** 2.155 $2\frac{31}{200}$

Now you may assign Exercises 1–23.

❷ *Writing Decimals*

You can write a fraction as a decimal by dividing the numerator by the denominator. The fraction symbol itself means division.

$$\frac{3}{4} \longrightarrow \begin{array}{r} 0.75 \\ 4\overline{)3.00} \\ -2\,8\downarrow \\ \hline 20 \\ -20 \\ \hline 0 \end{array}$$

You can also use a calculator.

■ **EXAMPLE 3** *Real-World Problem Solving*

▦ *Construction* A construction worker wants a drill with a diameter of no more than 0.6 inch. Can she use a $\frac{5}{8}$-inch drill?

Use a calculator to divide 5 by 8.

   5 ⊟ 8 ⊟ *0.625*   ⟵ $\frac{5}{8}$ = 0.625

Since 0.625 > 0.6, a $\frac{5}{8}$-inch drill is too big.

FOR EXAMPLE 3

Can the construction worker use a "$\frac{1}{2}$-in." drill bit to drill a hole with a diameter less than 0.75 in.? Explain. **Yes;** $\frac{1}{2}$ = **0.5 and 0.5 < 0.75.**

FOR EXAMPLE 4

Write $\frac{1}{6}$ as a decimal. **0.16**

3 Practice/Assess

EXERCISES *On Your Own*

ERROR ALERT! Students may write incorrect denominators when they change decimals to fractions. **Remediation:** Suggest that students write the decimal name or say it aloud. Remind them to use words such as *tenths, hundredths,* or *thousandths* to help them decide which denominator to write.

Exercise 19 Remind students that they can write 0.0015 on a place-value chart if they have difficulty reading the decimal. Ask students: *What number will you write as the denominator before you simplify the fraction?* **10,000**

WRITING Exercise 22 Suggest students number the steps they use to help the reader follow their thinking process.

If its remainder is zero, the quotient is a **terminating decimal.** A quotient that repeats a digit or a group of digits without end is a **repeating decimal.**

$$0.4444 \ldots = 0.\overline{4}$$ ← The bar over the 4 means that the digit 4 repeats.

■ EXAMPLE 4

Write each fraction as a decimal.

a. $\frac{4}{15}$

Use pencil and paper.

```
    0.266
15 )4.000
   -30
    100
    -90
    100
    -90
     10
```
← The digit 6 repeats.

$\frac{4}{15} = 0.2\overline{6}$

b. $\frac{8}{11}$

Use a calculator.

8 ÷ 11 = 0.72727272

↑ The digits 72 repeat.

$\frac{8}{11} = 0.\overline{72}$

6. ✔ *Try It Out* Write each fraction as a decimal. Use a bar to show repeating decimals.

a. $\frac{9}{20}$ **0.45**　　**b.** $\frac{5}{9}$ **0.$\overline{5}$**　　**c.** $\frac{2}{3}$ **0.$\overline{6}$**　　**d.** $\frac{5}{11}$ **0.$\overline{45}$**

7. a. How would you write $\frac{1}{3}$ as a decimal? **0.$\overline{3}$**
   b. How would you write 2 as a decimal? **2.0**
   c. ⠿*Analyze* How can you use your results from parts (a) and (b) to write $2\frac{1}{3}$ as a decimal? Explain. **Add;** $2.0 + 0.\overline{3} = 2.\overline{3}.$

Now you may assign Exercises 24–47.

EXERCISES *On Your Own*

Write each decimal as a fraction or mixed number in simplest form.

1. 0.3 $\frac{3}{10}$　　**2.** 0.004 $\frac{1}{250}$　　**3.** 2.625 $2\frac{5}{8}$　　**4.** 1.35 $1\frac{7}{20}$　　**5.** 5.500 $5\frac{1}{2}$

6. 0.075 $\frac{3}{40}$　　**7.** 1.62 $1\frac{31}{50}$　　**8.** 0.15 $\frac{3}{20}$　　**9.** 0.07 $\frac{7}{100}$　　**10.** 10.02 $10\frac{1}{50}$

11. 0.064 $\frac{8}{125}$　　**12.** 4.44 $4\frac{11}{25}$　　**13.** 0.008 $\frac{1}{125}$　　**14.** 3.12 $3\frac{3}{25}$　　**15.** 0.145 $\frac{29}{200}$

16. 5.875 $5\frac{7}{8}$　　**17.** 0.565 $\frac{113}{200}$　　**18.** 66.6 $66\frac{3}{5}$　　**19.** 0.0015 $\frac{3}{2,000}$　　**20.** 43.43 $43\frac{43}{100}$

OPEN-ENDED **Exercise 23** Have students work in pairs. Have a partner show one fraction with a fraction model. The other partner shows the same fraction with a decimal model. Students switch roles to show the second fraction with models.

Exercises 24–43 Caution students to check their division or to use estimation to make sure their answers are reasonable. Hint to students that they can write mixed numbers as improper fractions. They can then divide numerators by denominators.

DIVERSITY **Exercise 44** Students from other countries may be more familiar with metric measurements and the use of decimals when buying groceries. Have students share examples.

CONNECTING TO THE STUDENTS' WORLD If you have block scheduling or extended class periods, ask students to look up prices for shares of stock in newspapers or on the Internet. Have them write each fraction price as a decimal. Suggest that students order the prices from least to greatest. Have students share their examples with the class.

WRAP UP

IDENTIFYING THE BIG IDEA Ask students to explain how to write fractions as decimals and decimals as fractions.

PROJECT LINK Have students also find the decimal to represent the fraction of baskets each player missed. Have them compare these decimals to rank the players again. Ask students: *Does this order agree with the other rankings?* **yes**

CHECKPOINT 2

Checkpoint 2   *Lessons 5-6 through 5-9*

Find the LCM of each set of numbers.

1. 6, 12, 18 **36**   2. 15, 20, 30 **60**   3. 24, 48, 16 **48**

Write each decimal as a fraction in simplest form.

4. 0.8 $\frac{4}{5}$ 5. 0.625 $\frac{5}{8}$ 6. 0.06 $\frac{3}{50}$

Write as an improper fraction or a mixed number in simplest form.

7. $\frac{46}{5}$ $9\frac{1}{5}$ 8. $3\frac{3}{8}$ $\frac{27}{8}$ 9. $\frac{34}{4}$ $8\frac{1}{2}$ 10. $5\frac{2}{3}$ $\frac{17}{3}$

Write each set of numbers in order from least to greatest.

11. $\frac{1}{3}$, 0.6, $\frac{5}{6}$, 0.35   12. 2.75, $\frac{4}{2}$, 2.55, 2.1
    $\frac{1}{3}$, 0.35, 0.6, $\frac{5}{6}$ $\frac{4}{2}$, 2.1, 2.55, 2.75

21. *Money* Pervis had $1 to spend. He bought a package of sunflower seeds for $.55. What fraction of his money did he spend? $\frac{11}{20}$

22. *Writing* Explain the steps you would use to write 0.8 as a fraction in simplest form. **Write 0.8 as $\frac{8}{10}$. Divide the numerator and denominator by 2.**

23. *Open-ended* Use decimal models and fraction models to show the decimal equivalents of two fractions. **Check students' work.**

Write each fraction or mixed number as a decimal.

24. $\frac{1}{3}$ $0.\overline{3}$ 25. $\frac{9}{50}$ 0.18   26. $\frac{7}{32}$ 0.21875   27. $\frac{5}{6}$ $0.8\overline{3}$ 28. $\frac{11}{16}$ 0.6875

29. $\frac{7}{8}$ 0.875   30. $2\frac{4}{5}$ 2.8   31. $10\frac{6}{8}$ 10.75   32. $\frac{5}{12}$ $0.41\overline{6}$ 33. $\frac{7}{20}$ 0.35

34. $\frac{11}{8}$ 1.375   35. $\frac{6}{11}$ $0.\overline{54}$ 36. $1\frac{1}{9}$ $1.\overline{1}$ 37. $\frac{14}{25}$ 0.56   38. $\frac{7}{15}$ $0.4\overline{6}$

39. $4\frac{7}{10}$ 4.7   40. $2\frac{7}{12}$ $2.58\overline{3}$ 41. $\frac{5}{24}$ $0.208\overline{3}$ 42. $\frac{7}{16}$ 0.4375   43. $3\frac{4}{11}$ $3.\overline{36}$

44. *Shopping* Suppose you buy a quarter pound ($\frac{1}{4}$ lb) of roasted turkey at the delicatessen. What decimal should you see on the digital scale? **0.25**

45. *Finance* Refer to the article below. A share of stock sold for $10\frac{5}{8}$. What is the equivalent decimal price? **$10.625**

Stock Market Switches from $\frac{1}{8}$ to 0.125!

When it started in 1792, the stock market set the price of stocks in eighths of a dollar.

That's recently changed, and now stock prices are being quoted in decimals.

46a. 0.8, $\frac{9}{11}$, 0.87, $\frac{7}{8}$ b. $1\frac{3}{5}$, 1.65, $1\frac{2}{3}$, 1.7   c. 3.01, $3\frac{2}{29}$, $3\frac{1}{12}$, 3.1, $3\frac{1}{5}$

46. *Number Sense* Order each set of numbers from least to greatest.
    a. $\frac{7}{8}$, 0.8, $\frac{9}{11}$, 0.87   b. 1.65, $1\frac{2}{3}$, $1\frac{3}{5}$, 1.7   c. $3\frac{1}{12}$, 3.1, $3\frac{1}{5}$, $3\frac{2}{29}$, 3.01

47. a. *Calculator* Write each fraction as a decimal: $\frac{17}{50}$, $\frac{1}{3}$, $\frac{8}{25}$, $\frac{26}{75}$. **0.34, $0.\overline{3}$, 0.32, $0.34\overline{6}$**
    b. Arrange the fractions in order from least to greatest. **$\frac{8}{25}$, $\frac{1}{3}$, $\frac{17}{50}$, $\frac{26}{75}$**
    c. Would you prefer to use equivalent fractions with a common denominator to order the numbers in part (a)? Explain. **Check students' work.**

216

What would a greater decimal mean in this case? **more baskets missed**

LESSON QUIZ

1. Write $2\frac{4}{9}$ as a decimal. $2.\overline{4}$

2. Write 0.0252 as a fraction in simplest form.

$$\frac{63}{2,500}$$

Mixed Review

Find each product or quotient. *(Lessons 4-5 and 4-9)*

48. 0.07×4.8 **0.336**

49. $9.8 \div 2.8$ **3.5**

50. 5.03×2.4 **12.072**

51. $12.3 \div 1.5$ **8.2**

52. 0.58×0.6 **0.348**

53. $1.575 \div 0.25$ **6.3**

Data Analysis **Use the table at the right for Exercises 54 and 55.**

54. Copy and complete the chart. *(Lesson 3-7)*

55. *Patterns* Does the last column show a pattern? Why or why not? *(Lesson 2-1)* **No; the numbers in the last column are declining, but not at a constant rate.**

Effect of Aging on Pupil Size

Age (yr)	Diameter of Pupils (mm)		
	daylight	night	difference
20	4.7	8.0	▨ 3.3
30	4.3	7.0	▨ 2.7
40	3.9	6.0	▨ 2.1
50	3.5	5.0	▨ 1.5
60	3.1	4.1	▨ 1.0
70	2.7	3.2	▨ 0.5
80	2.3	2.5	▨ 0.2

Source: *Sizes*

CHAPTER PROJECT

PROJECT LINK: COMPARING

You now have another way to compare the records of your players. Convert the fractions in your table to decimals. Use the decimals to rank your players. Does the order agree with the order you got when you compared fractions?

Check students' work.

✓ CHECKPOINT 2

Lessons 5-6 through 5-9

Find the LCM of each set of numbers.

1. $16, 24, 32$ **96**

2. $28, 56, 63$ **504**

3. $40, 36, 18$ **360**

4. $20, 10, 35$ **140**

Write each fraction as a decimal.

5. $\frac{2}{5}$ **0.4**

6. $\frac{7}{100}$ **0.07**

7. $\frac{3}{8}$ **0.375**

8. $\frac{1}{6}$ **$0.\overline{6}$**

9. $\frac{50}{9}$ **$5.\overline{5}$**

Write each decimal as a fraction in simplest form.

10. 0.52 **$\frac{13}{25}$**

11. 0.04 **$\frac{1}{25}$**

12. 0.75 **$\frac{3}{4}$**

13. 15.025 **$15\frac{1}{40}$**

14. 1.375 **$1\frac{3}{8}$**

15. Choose A, B, C, or D. Which of the following is ordered from greatest to least? **D**

A. $0.56, 0.055, 0.53, 0.52$

B. $1.75, \frac{3}{2}, 1.25, 2.0$

C. $3.47, 3\frac{1}{2}, 3.6, \frac{8}{3}$

D. $\frac{7}{8}, 0.8, 0.75, \frac{8}{11}$

PRACTICE

Practice 5-9 *Fractions and Decimals*

Write the decimal represented by each model. Write this decimal as a fraction in simplest form.

1. 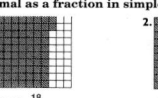 **0.72; $\frac{18}{25}$**

2. 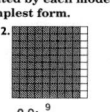 **0.9; $\frac{9}{10}$**

3. 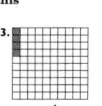 **0.04; $\frac{1}{25}$**

Write each decimal as a fraction or mixed number in simplest form.

4. 0.6 **$\frac{3}{5}$** **5.** 1.25 **$1\frac{1}{4}$** **6.** 0.74 **$\frac{37}{50}$** **7.** 0.29 **$\frac{29}{100}$**

8. 0.635 **$\frac{127}{200}$** **9.** 0.8 **$\frac{4}{5}$** **10.** 6.16 **$6\frac{4}{25}$** **11.** 0.95 **$\frac{19}{20}$**

12. 0.645 **$\frac{129}{200}$** **13.** 0.782 **$\frac{391}{500}$** **14.** 0.493 **$\frac{493}{1,000}$** **15.** 0.758 **$\frac{379}{500}$**

Write each fraction or mixed number as a decimal. Use a bar to show a repeating decimal.

16. $\frac{5}{6}$ **$0.8\overline{3}$** **17.** $\frac{7}{8}$ **0.875** **18.** $\frac{9}{16}$ **0.5625** **19.** $2\frac{4}{25}$ **2.16**

20. $\frac{1}{12}$ **$0.08\overline{3}$** **21.** $1\frac{4}{15}$ **$1.2\overline{6}$** **22.** $\frac{9}{100}$ **0.09** **23.** $\frac{8}{9}$ **$0.\overline{8}$**

24. $\frac{7}{25}$ **0.28** **25.** $\frac{3}{50}$ **0.06** **26.** $\frac{1}{125}$ **0.008** **27.** $\frac{6}{11}$ **$0.\overline{54}$**

Circle A, B, C, or D. Which shows the numbers in order from least to greatest?

28. $\frac{1}{2}, 0.75, \frac{5}{8}, 0.9, \frac{7}{10}$

A. $\frac{1}{2}, \frac{5}{8}, 0.75, \frac{7}{10}, 0.9$

(B.) $\frac{1}{2}, \frac{5}{8}, \frac{7}{10}, 0.75, 0.9$

C. $0.9, 0.75, \frac{7}{10}, \frac{5}{8}, \frac{1}{2}$

D. $\frac{1}{2}, 0.75, \frac{5}{8}, \frac{7}{10}, 0.9$

29. $0.875, \frac{9}{10}, \frac{15}{16}, 0.98$

A. $0.98, \frac{15}{16}, \frac{9}{10}, 0.875$

B. $\frac{15}{16}, \frac{9}{10}, 0.875, 0.98$

C. $\frac{9}{10}, 0.875, \frac{15}{16}, 0.98$

(D.) $0.875, \frac{9}{10}, \frac{15}{16}, 0.98$

In copymaster and workbook formats

RETEACHING

Reteaching 5-9 *Fractions and Decimals*

Write 0.320 as a fraction.
① Read. "320 thousandths"
② Write. $\frac{320}{1,000}$
③ Simplify. $\frac{320}{1000} = \frac{320 \div 40}{1000 \div 40} = \frac{8}{25}$
$0.320 = \frac{8}{25}$

Write 6.95 as a mixed number.
① Read. "6 and 95 hundredths"
② Write. $6\frac{95}{100}$
③ Simplify. $6\frac{95}{100} = 6\frac{19}{20}$
$6.95 = 6\frac{19}{20}$

Write $\frac{1}{5}$ and $\frac{2}{3}$ as decimals.
Divide the numerator by the denominator. Insert zeros if needed.

$\frac{0.2}{5)1.0}$ $\frac{0.666\ldots}{3)2.0000}$ ← The digits repeat because the remainder repeats.
$\frac{-18}{20}$
$\frac{-18}{2}$ ← repeats.

$\frac{1}{5} = 0.2$ $\frac{2}{3} = 0.666\ldots = 0.\overline{6}$

0.2 is a **terminating decimal** because there is no remainder.
0.666 . . . is a repeating decimal because the remainder repeats. Write it as $0.\overline{6}$.

Write each decimal as a fraction or mixed number in simplest form.

1. 0.8 **$\frac{4}{5}$** **2.** 0.55 **$\frac{11}{20}$** **3.** 1.25 **$1\frac{1}{4}$**

4. 1.75 **$1\frac{3}{4}$** **5.** 3.375 **$3\frac{3}{8}$** **6.** 0.125 **$\frac{1}{8}$**

7. 1.32 **$1\frac{8}{25}$** **8.** 0.34 **$\frac{17}{50}$** **9.** 0.084 **$\frac{21}{250}$**

10. 0.006 **$\frac{3}{500}$** **11.** 0.65 **$\frac{13}{20}$** **12.** 4.95 **$4\frac{19}{20}$**

Write each fraction or mixed number as a decimal.

13. $\frac{13}{20}$ **0.65** **14.** $\frac{1}{6}$ **$0.1\overline{6}$** **15.** $\frac{7}{20}$ **0.35**

16. $2\frac{3}{5}$ **2.6** **17.** $\frac{19}{25}$ **0.76** **18.** $\frac{4}{9}$ **$0.\overline{4}$**

19. $\frac{7}{11}$ **$0.\overline{63}$** **20.** $1\frac{5}{8}$ **1.625** **21.** $1\frac{2}{9}$ **$1.\overline{2}$**

22. $2\frac{2}{8}$ **2.25** **23.** $\frac{1}{25}$ **0.04** **24.** $\frac{5}{12}$ **$0.41\overline{6}$**

ENRICHMENT

Minds on Math Transparency

5-9

What single-digit numbers do ☐ and △ each represent in the expressions below?

☐ + ☐ = △ × △

☐ + ☐ + ☐ + ☐ = ☐ × △

☐ = 8

△ = 4

See *Solution Key* for worked-out answers.

217

1 Focus

CONNECTING TO PRIOR KNOWLEDGE Ask students if they have ever retraced their actions to answer a question. For example, after counting their money at the end of the day, they might have thought back to the money they spent to find how much they started with. Discuss this strategy.

2 Teach

THINK AND DISCUSS

TACTILE LEARNING Give students 21 pencils or straws. Have students perform the actions in the sample problem as you discuss each step.

AEP DIVERSITY Pair students who need help with stronger readers. Have students read word problems together.

ERROR ALERT! Students may forget that they need to think of inverse operations when they work backward to solve problems.
Remediation: Help students understand that they need to perform an inverse operation when the problem describes an action involving subtraction or addition. Because they are working backward, ask them to think of the scene or problem being played in reverse. For example, if they were given pencils in the problem, ask students to think about the pencils being taken back.

Lesson Planning Options

Prerequisite Skills
• adding, subtracting, multiplying, and dividing whole numbers (precourse)

Vocabulary/Symbols
working backward

Resources

 Student Edition

Skills Handbook, p. 540
Extra Practice, p. 526
Glossary/Study Guide

 Teaching Resources

Chapter Support File, Ch. 5
• Lesson Planner 5-10
• Practice 5-10, Reteaching 5-10
• Answer Masters 5-10
Glossary, Spanish Resources

 Transparencies
19, Minds on Math 5-10

Warm Up

If you take a number, multiply it by 3 and then subtract 7, you get 11. What was the original number? **6**

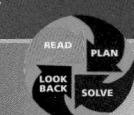

PROBLEM SOLVING STRATEGY

5-10 Work Backward

Problem Solving Strategies
Draw a Diagram
Guess and Test
Look for a Pattern
Make a Model
Make a Table
Simulate a Problem
Solve a Simpler Problem
Too Much or Too Little Information
Use Logical Reasoning
Use Multiple Strategies
✔ Work Backward

THINK AND DISCUSS

Walking backward is dangerous, and talking backward will cause confusion. In math, however, *working backward* can be good for you. Sometimes you can work backward from a known result to find a fact at the beginning.

SAMPLE PROBLEM..

A teacher lends pencils to students. One day she gave out 7 pencils in the morning, collected 5 before lunch, and gave out 3 after lunch. At the end of the day she had 16 pencils. How many pencils did the teacher have at the start of the day?

....

 READ
Read for understanding. Summarize the problem.

3. More; she gave out more pencils than she collected.

 PLAN
Decide on a strategy.

 SOLVE
Try the strategy.

 LOOK BACK
Think about how you solved the problem.

1. How many pencils did the teacher have at the end of the day? **16 pencils**

2. How many times did the teacher give out pencils? Collect pencils? **2 times; 1 time**

3. Do you think she had *more than* or *fewer than* 16 pencils at the start of the day? Explain.

You know that there were 16 pencils at the *end* of the day. Work backward to find out how many pencils the teacher had at the *start* of the day. Add each time she gave out pencils, and subtract each time she collected pencils.

4. What was the teacher's last action with pencils before the end of the day? How many pencils did she have just before that action? **give out 3 pencils; 19 pencils**

5. Continue working backward to find the number of pencils the teacher had at the start of the day. **21 pencils**

6. Check by starting with your answer and working *forward*. Do you have 16 pencils at the end of the day? **yes**

■ **ADDITIONAL PROBLEM**

Cleon and Caitlin baked cookies. They gave a dozen to their neighbor. They gave half the remaining cookies to Cleon's mother, and put the cookies they had left in a jar. The next day, they ate half of those. They saved the remaining eight cookies for their school lunches. How many cookies did Cleon and Caitlin bake? **44**

3 Practice/Assess

EXERCISES *On Your Own*

TACTILE LEARNING Exercises 2, 11, and 13 Give students play bills and coins to help them solve these exercises.

ASSESSMENT After Exercise 3, have students work in groups to write a word problem they can solve by working backward. If they have difficulty, have them use Exercises 1–3 as models. Have groups trade and solve problems. Discuss the problems and the solutions.

CONNECTION TO BIOLOGY Exercise 7 This exercise requires students to calculate how fast bacteria multiply.

WRITING Exercise 8 Have students support their answers with examples.

---

7. Some people may prefer to use *Guess and Test*. Solve the problem using 18 as your guess. Which strategy do you prefer? Explain. **See below.**

Now you may assign Exercises 1–14.

EXERCISES *On Your Own*

Work backward to solve each problem.

1. If you multiply a number by 3, and then add 5, the result is 38. What is the number? **11**

2. *Shopping* Bo spent half her money at a store in the mall. At another store, she spent half her remaining money and $6 more. She had $2 left. How much did Bo have when she arrived at the mall? **$32**

3. *Hobbies* Horace decided to sell all his baseball cards. He sold Juanita half his cards plus 1 card. Next he sold Ethan half the remaining cards. Then he sold Kyoko 13 cards. Finally, he sold the remaining 9 cards to Cleon. How many cards did Horace have at the start? **90 cards**

Use any strategy to solve each problem. Show your work.

4. *Games* A chess player won a chess tournament by winning three games. At each round, the loser was eliminated and the winner advanced to the next round. How many players were in the tournament? **8 players**

5. *Calendar* Suppose March 27 is a Thursday. What day of the week is March 1? **Saturday**

6. *Cooking* Kathy and Bill baked some muffins. They put half away for the next day and divided the remaining muffins among their 3 sisters, each of whom received 3 muffins. How many muffins did Kathy and Bill bake? **18 muffins**

7. 18 − 7 = 11, 11 + 5 = 16, 16 − 3 = 13. 13 is 3 fewer than 16, so guess 18 + 3 = 21, then check again; answers may vary. Sample: working backward, because you get the correct answer the first time.

7. *Biology* A bacterial population doubles in size every 6 minutes. Some bacteria are placed on a microscope slide, and in 2 hours the slide is covered. When was the slide half-covered? **after 1 h 54 min**

8. *Writing* Why is it necessary to use inverse operations when working backward? **Since you are working backward, you may need to "undo" the result of an operation.**

Technology Options

Prentice Hall Technology

  Software for Learners
- Math Blaster® Mystery*
- Interactive Student Tutorial, Chapter 5*

  Teaching Resource Software
- Computer Item Generator 5-10
- Resource Pro™ Chapter 5*

Internet • For related mathematics activities, visit the Prentice Hall site at www.phschool.com/math

Available on CD-ROM only

Assignment Options for Exercises On Your Own

Core 1–13
Extension 14

Use Mixed Review to maintain skills.

PRACTICE

Practice 5-10 Problem-Solving Strategy: Work Backward

Work backward to solve.

1. At the end of a board game, Al had 57 game dollars. During the game he had won $200, lost $150, won $25, lost $10, and lost $35. How much money did Al have at the start?
$27

2. Jan spent half of the money she had on a coat. She spent half of what remained on a dress. Next, she spent half of what remained on a pair of boots. She returned home with $57. How much money did Jan have before shopping?
$456

3. Bill gathered some eggs on Monday. On Tuesday, he gathered half as many eggs, plus an egg, as what he gathered on Monday. On Wednesday, he gathered half the difference of the number of eggs he gathered on Monday and Tuesday, plus an egg. If he gathered 5 eggs on Wednesday, how many eggs did Bill gather on Monday?
18 eggs

4. Carli spent a third of her money, and then spent $4 more. She then spent half of what money remained. It cost her $1 for the bus ride home. She then had $5 left. How much money did she start with?
$24

5. Mick picked a number, doubled it, added 8, divided by 4, and had a result of 12. What number did Mick pick?
20

6. It takes Jenni 50 minutes to get ready for school. The drive to school takes 15 minutes. She needs 8 minutes to get to her locker, then to her first class. If school begins at 8:30 A.M., what is the latest Jenni should get up in the morning?
7:17 A.M.

7. On May 31, Hayden's uncle and grandfather came to visit him. Hayden's grandfather visits every three days, and his uncle visits every twelve days. What is the first day in May that both visited Hayden on the same day?
May 7

In copymaster and workbook formats

RETEACHING

Reteaching 5-10 Problem-Solving Strategy: Work Backward

The store manager recorded 80 greeting cards sold on Friday. The day before she had sold half that number. On Wednesday, she sold 25 more than on Thursday. On Monday and Tuesday she sold a total of twice what she sold on Wednesday. How many cards did she sell during the 5 days?

Read What does the problem ask you to find? *You need to find the total number of cards sold during the 5 days.*

Plan How can you find the number sold on each day? *Use the information given in the problem. Work backward from that information to find the number sold on Thursday, then Wednesday, and finally, the total on Tuesday and Monday.*

Solve Work backward.

Cards sold on Friday	80
One-half that number sold Thursday	40
40 + 25 sold Wednesday	65
2 × 65 sold Monday and Tuesday	+ 130
	315

She sold 315 cards.

Look Back How can you check your answer? *Start with 315 and work forward.*

Work backward to solve each problem about the Star Diner.

1. On Friday, the diner served 56 ears of corn. On Thursday, the diner served one-half as much corn as on Friday. On Wednesday, the diner served two times as much as on Thursday. On Tuesday, the diner served one-half of what it had served on Wednesday. How much corn did the diner serve during the 4 days?
168 ears

2. On Thursday, the diner served 42 lb of green beans. On Wednesday, the diner served one-third that amount. On both Tuesday and Monday, the diner served one-half the amount it had served on Wednesday. How many pounds of beans did the diner serve during the 4 days?
70 lb

3. On Friday, the diner served 60 baked potatoes. On both Tuesday and Thursday, the diner served one-fifth that amount. On both Monday and Wednesday, it served one-sixth of Thursday's amount. How many baked potatoes were served during the 5 days?
104 potatoes

4. The diner served 32 lb of salad on Saturday night. On both Friday and Thursday, one-half that amount was served. On Wednesday, one-eighth that amount was served. How many pounds of salad did the diner serve during the 4 days?
68 lb

ENRICHMENT

Minds on Math Transparency

5-10

Ira has 4 lengths of chain with 3 links each. He wants to join the 4 lengths to form one circular chain with 12 links. How can he do this if he cuts and rejoins only 3 links?

He must separate the 3 links on one length of chain, cut open each of the 3 links, and use the 3 links to join the other 3 lengths into one circular chain.

See *Solution Key* for worked-out answers.

220

WRAP UP

IDENTIFYING THE BIG IDEA Ask students to explain how to solve problems by working backward.

PORTFOLIO Share with students the criteria you will use to assess their work in portfolios, as well as how you plan to use the results. Students should understand how the rubrics are used to assess their work, how each piece in the portfolio counts, and how the scores they get in their portfolios will affect their overall evaluation.

LESSON QUIZ

Work backward to solve each problem.

1. If you add 15 to a number, subtract 4, and then multiply by 7, the result is 259. Find the number. **26**

2. If you multiply a number by 150, and then add 50, the result is 650. Find the number. **4**

---

9. *Entertainment* At the grand opening of the Plex Cinema, every 15th customer got a free ticket. Every 10th customer got a free box of popcorn. Of the 418 ticket buyers, how many received both prizes? **13 people**

10. *Scheduling* Aaron plans to study in the library after school. Then he has a track meet at 4:00 P.M. It takes him 5 min to change his clothes and 10 min to get to the track. Before the start of the race, Aaron needs to meet with his coach for 10 min and stretch for 15 min.
    a. When should Aaron leave the library? **3:20 P.M.**
    b. School lets out at 2:50 P.M. How much time can Aaron spend in the library? **30 min**

11. *Savings* Each time Aretha's grandmother visits, she doubles the amount of money Aretha has saved and gives her $3 extra to spend. After her grandmother's most recent visit, Aretha had a total of $19. How much had Aretha saved? **$8**

12. *Health* Of 25 students, 11 need a dental check-up and 17 need an eye exam. Five students don't need either. How many need both? **8 students**

13. *Money* Taesha has $1.35 in nickels and dimes. She has a total of 15 coins. How many of each coin does she have? **12 dimes and 3 nickels**

14. Box A has 9 green balls and 4 red balls. Box B has 12 green balls and 5 red balls. Suppose you want the fraction of green balls in Box A to equal the fraction of red balls in Box B. How many green balls must you move from Box A to Box B? **8 green balls**

> **PORTFOLIO**
> For your portfolio, select one or two items from your work for this chapter. For example:
> • your best work
> • drawings of models
> • a journal entry
> Explain why you have chosen each item.

Mixed Review

Write a word phrase for each variable expression. *(Lesson 2-4)* **Samples are given.**

15–19. Answers may vary.

15. $a - 13$ — thirteen less than *a*
16. $p \times 11$ — eleven times *p*
17. $x \div 5$ — x divided by five
18. $s + 14$ — the sum of *s* and fourteen
19. $(5 \times c) + 8$ — eight more than five times *c*

Complete. *(Lesson 4-10)*

20. ▨ m = 54 cm **0.54**
21. 18 km = ▨ m **18,000**
22. 400 mm = ▨ cm **40**
23. 850 mL = ▨ L **0.85**

24. *Time Zones* The bus from Montreal to Chicago leaves at 5:43 A.M. and arrives at 4:54 P.M. The bus passes through one time zone, gaining an hour. How long is the trip? *(Lesson 3-10)*
12 h 11 min

PROJECT DAY You may wish to plan a project day on which students share their completed projects. Encourage students to explain their process as well as their product.

After students share their projects, you may want to challenge them to find the best players in all the projects to form an All-Star team.

PROJECT NOTEBOOK Ask students to review their project work and bring their notebooks up to date.

SCORING RUBRIC

3 You've used both fractions and decimals to compare the shooting records of at least seven players. These seven players each made a different number of attempts so that your fractions have different denominators. All your information is accurate and is displayed in an attractive table that lists the players in order from best record to worst record.

2 Most of your comparisons are based on fractions with different denominators. Your fractions and decimals are almost all accurate. The shooting records are listed in order from best to worst in a neat table.

1 You didn't collect data for enough players, you didn't vary the denominator of your fractions, or you incorrectly compared the players' shooting records.

0 You only compared shooting records for a few players, or you left out the fractions, decimals, or table of comparisons.

FINISHING THE CHAPTER PROJECT

CHAPTER PROJECT

HOME COURT ADVANTAGE

Compare Basketball Statistics Project Links on pages 195, 212, and 217 will help you complete your project. Here is a checklist to help you gather together the parts of your project.

- ✔ a table with the foul-shooting records of your basketball players
- ✔ shooting records ranked in order of fractions
- ✔ shooting records ranked in order of decimals

Make a poster to present your table and rankings to your class. You may wish to decorate the poster by adding a team name and logo, home made sports cards for some of your players, or a sketch of a team uniform. You could even make a tape-recorded interview with your top foul shooter!

Reflect and Revise

Review your poster with a classmate, a friend, or a family member. Are your calculations correct? Do your rankings correspond to your calculations? Is your table clearly presented? If necessary, make changes to improve your poster.

Web Extension

Prentice Hall's Internet site contains information you may find helpful as you complete your project. Visit www.phschool.com/mgm1/ch5 for some links and ideas related to sports.

221

STUDENT SELF-ASSESSMENT SURVEY

Chapter 5 Student Self-Assessment Survey

1. Now that you have finished this chapter, think about what you have learned about fractions. Check each topic that you feel confident you understand.

_____ determine whether a number is divisible by 1, 2, 3, 5, 9, or 10 (5-1)
_____ determine whether a number is prime or composite (5-2)
_____ find the prime factorization of a number (5-2)
_____ find the greatest common factor (GCF) of two or three numbers (5-3)
_____ round fractions to the nearest half-unit (5-4)
_____ find equivalent fractions (5-5)
_____ write fractions in simplest form (5-5)
_____ write mixed numbers and improper fractions (5-6)
_____ find the least common multiple (LCM) of two or three numbers (5-7)
_____ compare fractions (5-8)
_____ order fractions (5-8)
_____ write decimals as fractions (5-9)
_____ write fractions as decimals (5-9)
_____ solve problems by working backward (5-10)

2. Before the Chapter Assessment, I need to review _____

3. a. Check one. In general, I thought this chapter was

_____ a snap _____ easy _____ average _____ hard _____ a monster

b. Why do you feel this way? _____

4. In this chapter, I did my best work on _____

5. I think the hardest thing about working with fractions is _____

6. Check each one that applies. Now that I've spent some time studying fractions, I think they are

_____ important _____ boring _____ useful _____ fun
_____ a waste of time _____ confusing _____ tricky _____ interesting

Vocabulary/Symbols

common factors, common multiples, composite number, divisibility, divisible, equivalent fractions, factor, factor tree, fraction model, greatest common factors, improper fraction, least common denominator, least common multiple, mixed numbers, multiple, prime factorization, prime number, repeating decimal, simplest form, terminating decimal, working backward

Resources

 Student Edition

Extra Practice, p. 526
Glossary/Study Guide

 Teaching Resources

Chapter Support File, Ch. 5
• Student Self-Assessment Survey
Glossary, Spanish Resources
Tools for Studying Smarter

WRAP UP

Exercises 1–6 You may want to review the divisibility rules for 3 and 9 before students begin to work.

Exercise 7 Have students review all the divisibility rules. Ask: *Which numbers are not prime? 525, 530, 519 What numbers divide them evenly? 5 divides 525 and 530 evenly, 10 and 2 divide 530 evenly, and 3 divides 519 evenly.*

ASSESSMENT Exercises 8–13 Have each student solve the problems. Then have students compare their answers with a partner and discuss any differences.

Exercises 14–19 You may want to review the difference between GCF and LCM before students begin work.

Exercises 33–38 Remind students that the bar in a fraction means "divided by."

---

5 WRAP UP

Divisibility and Prime Factorization   5-1, 5-2

The rules for divisibility can help you find factors. A **prime number** has exactly two factors, 1 and itself. A **composite number** has more than two factors.

The **prime factorization** of a composite number is written as the product of the prime factors of the composite number.

State whether each number is divisible by 1, 2, 3, 5, 9, or 10.

1. 69 1, 3
2. 146 1, 2
3. 837 1, 3, 9
4. 405 1, 3, 5, 9
5. 628 1, 2
6. 32,870 1, 2, 5, 10

7. **Choose A, B, C, or D.** Which number is a prime number? B
   A. 519   B. 523   C. 525   D. 530

Find the prime factorization using a factor tree.

8. 72 $2^3 \times 3^2$
9. 120 $2^3 \times 3 \times 5$
10. 33 3×11
11. 80 $2^4 \times 5$
12. 234 $2 \times 3^2 \times 13$
13. 345 $3 \times 5 \times 23$

GCF, LCM, and Rounding Fractions   5-3, 5-4, 5-7

The **greatest common factor (GCF)** of two or more numbers is the greatest number that is a factor of every number.

The **least common multiple (LCM)** of two or more numbers is the lowest number that is a multiple of every number.

To round a fraction, compare the numerator to the denominator.

Find the GCF and the LCM of each set of numbers.

14. 40, 140 20; 280
15. 28, 33 1; 924
16. 24, 9 3; 72
17. 15, 25 5; 75
18. 18, 42, 60 6; 1,260
19. 10, 12, 16 2; 240

Round each fraction to the nearest half.

20. $\frac{54}{98}$ $\frac{1}{2}$
21. $\frac{11}{12}$ 1
22. $\frac{1}{6}$ 0
23. $\frac{2}{9}$ 0
24. $\frac{19}{40}$ $\frac{1}{2}$
25. $\frac{5}{11}$ $\frac{1}{2}$

26. *Writing* Explain the value of prime factorization in finding the GCF and the LCM. Include examples. See back of book.

Remind students that the new mathematical terms in this chapter are defined in the Glossary/Study Guide in the back of the book.

Equivalent Fractions and Simplest Form   5-5

You form **equivalent fractions** by multiplying or dividing the numerator and denominator by the same nonzero number.

To write a fraction in simplest form, divide both the numerator and the denominator by their GCF.

If the fraction is in simplest form, write two equivalent fractions. If not, write the fraction in simplest form.

27. $\frac{1}{8}$ 28. $\frac{14}{28}$ $\frac{1}{2}$ 29. $\frac{30}{50}$ $\frac{3}{5}$ 30. $\frac{16}{18}$ $\frac{8}{9}$ 31. $\frac{27}{72}$ $\frac{3}{8}$ 32. $\frac{6}{21}$ $\frac{2}{7}$

27. Answers may vary. Sample: $\frac{3}{24}, \frac{10}{80}$

Comparing and Ordering Fractions and Mixed Numbers   5-6, 5-8

An **improper fraction** has a numerator greater than or equal to its denominator. A **mixed number** shows the sum of a whole number and a fraction. Compare fractions by rewriting them using their **least common denominator (LCD)**.

Write each improper fraction as a mixed number. Write each mixed number as an improper fraction.

33. $4\frac{3}{4}$ $\frac{19}{4}$ 34. $\frac{22}{5}$ $4\frac{2}{5}$ 35. $\frac{57}{7}$ $8\frac{1}{7}$ 36. $2\frac{3}{8}$ $\frac{19}{8}$ 37. $\frac{30}{12}$ $2\frac{1}{2}$ 38. $5\frac{2}{11}$ $\frac{57}{11}$

39. Order from least to greatest: $1\frac{5}{6}, 1\frac{7}{9}, \frac{35}{36}, 1\frac{3}{4}$ $\frac{35}{36}, 1\frac{3}{4}, 1\frac{7}{9}, 1\frac{5}{6}$

Fractions and Decimals; Problem Solving Strategies   5-9, 5-10

To express a decimal as a fraction, write the fraction as you would say the decimal. Then simplify the fraction. To write a fraction as a decimal, divide the numerator by the denominator. Write a bar over the digit or digits that repeat.

Write each decimal as a fraction in simplest form. Write each fraction as a decimal.

40. 0.04 $\frac{1}{25}$ 41. 3.875 $3\frac{7}{8}$ 42. 2.14 $2\frac{7}{50}$ 43. $\frac{17}{40}$ 0.425 44. $\frac{8}{9}$ $0.\overline{8}$ 45. $\frac{6}{11}$ $0.\overline{54}$

46. At the first store, Tina spent $7. At the next store, she spent half of her remaining money. At the last store, she spent half of her remaining money and $3 more. Tina had $5 left. How much money did she have before shopping? **$39**

■ **Chapter 5 Assessment • Form A**

Answers

1. State whether 32,715 is divisible by 1, 2, 3, 5, 9, or 10.   1. __1, 3, 5, 9__

2. Find a digit to make 2 ■ ,402 divisible by 3.   2. __1, 4, or 7__

3. Which of these numbers are prime? 53; 65; 72; 365; 3,411   3. __53__

4. Find the prime factorization of 630 using a factor tree.   4. __$630 = 2 \times 3^2 \times 5 \times 7$__

5. Use prime factorization to find the GCF of 65 and 195.   5. __65: 5×13__
   195: $3 \times 5 \times 13$
   GCF = $5 \times 13 = 65$

6. Construct factor trees to find the GCF of 42 and 63.   6. __GCF = $3 \times 7 = 21$__

7. Name the fraction modeled.   7. __$\frac{5}{9}$__

8. Draw a bar model for $\frac{4}{7}$.   8.

9. Compare $\frac{11}{12}$ ■ $\frac{7}{8}$ using <, >, or =.   9. __>__

10. Write $\frac{36}{60}$ in simplest form.   10. __$\frac{3}{5}$__

11. Use a fraction calculator to simplify $\frac{27}{81}$.   11. __$\frac{1}{3}$__

12. Write $\frac{13}{4}$ as a mixed number.   12. __$3\frac{1}{4}$__

Chapter 5 Assessment • Form A (continued)

13. Write $2\frac{4}{7}$ as an improper fraction.   13. __$\frac{18}{7}$__

14. List the multiples of 15 and 25 to find their LCM.   14. __15: 15, 30, 45, 60, 75__
    25: 25, 50, 75
    LCM = 75

15. Use prime factorization to find the LCM of 12, 18, and 42.   15. __12: $2 \times 2 \times 3$__
    18: $2 \times 3 \times 3$
    42: $2 \times 3 \times 7$
    LCM = $2 \times 2 \times 3 \times 3 \times 7 = 252$

16. Write $\frac{3}{5}$ as a decimal.   16. __0.6__

17. Write 0.048 as a fraction in simplest form.   17. __$\frac{6}{125}$__

Choose A, B, C, or D.

18. Order these fractions from least to greatest. $\frac{2}{5}, \frac{4}{9}, \frac{4}{5}, \frac{7}{15}$ 18. __C__

   A. $\frac{2}{5}, \frac{4}{9}, \frac{4}{5}, \frac{7}{15}$ B. $\frac{4}{5}, \frac{7}{15}, \frac{4}{9}, \frac{2}{5}$

   C. $\frac{2}{5}, \frac{4}{9}, \frac{7}{15}, \frac{4}{5}$ D. $\frac{4}{5}, \frac{4}{9}, \frac{2}{5}, \frac{7}{15}$

Choose a Strategy

19. At the end of the day Carly had $3.02 in change left. She had spent $3.56 for lunch and had given $2.10 to her brother. After school she had bought an ice cream cone for $.58. How much money did she have at the beginning of the day?   19. __$9.26__

Writing

20. How can the GCF be used to write a fraction in simplest form?
    Find the GCF of the numerator and denominator. Divide both the numerator and denominator by this GCF, and the fraction is in simplest form.

223

Chapter 5 Assessment • Form B

Choose the best answer. Circle A, B, C, or D.

1. What set of numbers is 2,745 divisible by?
   A. 1, 2, 5   B. 1, 2, 3, 9   C. 1, 2, 3, 5   **D.** 1, 3, 5, 9

2. Which digit makes 34,▪45 divisible by 1, 3, and 5?
   A. 4   **B.** 5   C. 6   D. 7

3. Which of the following numbers is prime?
   A. 81   B. 58   **C.** 17   D. 18

4. Which factor tree shows the prime factorization of 540?

   A. 540   B. 540   C. 540   D. 540

5. What is the GCF of 78 and 104?
   A. 25   **B.** 26   C. 6   D. 8

6. Use prime factorization to find the GCF of 324 and 90.
   A. 9   **B.** 18   C. 24   D. 45

7. Which fraction model represents $\frac{3}{8}$?
   A. ▪   **B.** ▪   C. ▪   D. ▪

8. Which fraction is represented by this fraction model?
   A. $\frac{13}{7}$ B. $\frac{7}{12}$ C. $\frac{6}{13}$ **D.** $\frac{7}{13}$

9. Which two fractions are equivalent to $\frac{7}{19}$?
   A. $\frac{14}{57}, \frac{21}{38}$ B. $\frac{14}{19}, \frac{21}{19}$ **C.** $\frac{14}{38}, \frac{21}{57}$ D. $\frac{7}{38}, \frac{7}{57}$

10. What is $\frac{65}{195}$ in simplest form?
    A. $\frac{1}{3}$ B. $\frac{13}{39}$ C. $\frac{65}{130}$ D. $\frac{1}{2}$

Chapter 5 Assessment • Form B (continued)

11. Use a fraction calculator to simplify $\frac{114}{456}$.
    A. $\frac{57}{228}$ B. $\frac{1}{3}$ C. $\frac{1}{8}$ **D.** $\frac{1}{4}$

12. What is $\frac{42}{4}$ as a mixed number in simplest form?
    A. $9\frac{6}{4}$ **B.** $10\frac{1}{2}$ C. $11\frac{1}{2}$ D. $10\frac{1}{4}$

13. Write $7\frac{4}{21}$ as an improper fraction.
    A. $\frac{151}{21}$ B. $\frac{11}{21}$ C. $\frac{28}{21}$ D. $\frac{147}{21}$

14. Make a list of multiples to find the LCM of 8 and 10.
    A. 80   **B.** 40   C. 24   D. 30

15. Use prime factorization to find the LCM of 6, 16, and 44.
    A. $2 \times 3 \times 11$ B. $2 \times 2 \times 2 \times 2 \times 2 \times 2 \times 3 \times 11$
    C. $2 \times 2 \times 2 \times 11$ **D.** $2 \times 2 \times 2 \times 2 \times 3 \times 11$

16. Which is $\frac{4}{9}$ as a decimal?
    A. $0.\overline{4}$ B. 2.25   C. 0.04   D. 0.225

17. What is 0.52 as a fraction in simplest form?
    A. $\frac{52}{100}$ **B.** $\frac{13}{25}$ C. $\frac{26}{50}$ D. $\frac{13}{5}$

18. Order these fractions from least to greatest. $\frac{2}{3}, \frac{1}{5}, \frac{4}{7}, \frac{5}{9}$
    A. $\frac{1}{5}, \frac{2}{3}, \frac{4}{7}, \frac{5}{9}$ B. $\frac{1}{5}, \frac{4}{7}, \frac{5}{9}, \frac{2}{3}$
    C. $\frac{1}{5}, \frac{5}{9}, \frac{4}{7}, \frac{2}{3}$ D. $\frac{2}{3}, \frac{4}{7}, \frac{9}{5}, \frac{5}{1}$...

    B. $\frac{1}{5}, \frac{4}{7}, \frac{5}{9}, \frac{2}{3}$
    D. $\frac{2}{3}, \frac{4}{7}, \frac{9}{5}, \frac{1}{5}$

19. What do you know about the numerator and denominator when a fraction is in simplest form?
    A. The GCF is equal to the numerator.
    B. The GCF is equal to the denominator.
    C. The GCF is 1.
    D. The LCM is equal to the numerator.

Choose a Strategy

20. Thomas took his paycheck to the bank and deposited $\frac{2}{3}$ of it. He then spent $7.85 for a movie and refreshments. He loaned $5.45 to his sister for her ticket. He had $36.78 left. How much was his original paycheck?
    A. $50.08   B. $100.16   **C.** $150.24   D. $200.32

 Teaching Resources

Chapter Support File, Ch. 5, and Spanish Resources

Teacher's Edition

See pp. 180C–D for Assessment Options.

 **Teaching Resource Software**

• Computer Item Generator, Ch. 5

ASSESSMENT

WRITING EXERCISES allow students to describe more fully their thinking and understanding of the concepts they have learned. **Exercise 1** is a writing exercise.

ENHANCED MULTIPLE CHOICE QUESTIONS are more complex than traditional multiple choice questions, which assess only one skill. Enhanced multiple choice questions assess the processes that students use as well as the end result. They are written so that students can use more than one strategy to solve the problem. Using multiple strategies is encouraged by the National Council of Teachers of Mathematics (NCTM). **Exercises 2 and 13** are enhanced multiple choice questions.

Exercises 4 and 10 Before students begin work, you may wish to review the difference between a GCF (greatest common factor) and LCM (least common multiple).

5 ASSESSMENT

1. *Writing*
   a. Is 24,357 divisible by 5? Explain your answer. **No; the last digit is not 5 or 0.**
   b. Is 24,357 divisible by 9? Explain your answer. **No; the sum of its digits, 21, is not divisible by 9.**

2. **Choose A, B, C, or D.** Which number is divisible by 2, 3, and 10? **D**
   A. 375   B. 430
   C. 2,328   D. 5,430

3. List all the factors of each number. Tell whether each number is prime or composite. **a. 1, 3, 11, 33; composite**
   a. 33   b. 54 **See below.**
   c. 19   d. 102 **See below.**
   1, 19; prime

4. Find the GCF of each set of numbers.
   a. 24, 36 **12**   b. 20, 25, 30 **5**
   c. 45, 105 **15**   d. 7, 19 **1**

5. Find the prime factorization of each number.
   a. 132 **$2^2 \times 3 \times 11$**   b. 360 **$2^3 \times 3^2 \times 5$**

6. Name the fraction modeled.
   a.  $\frac{1}{3}$
   b.  $\frac{4}{5}$

7. *Estimation* Round each fraction to the nearest half.
   a. $\frac{15}{16}$ **1**   b. $\frac{2}{20}$ **0**
   c. $\frac{24}{50}$ **$\frac{1}{2}$**   d. $\frac{40}{75}$ **$\frac{1}{2}$**

8. Name two fractions that are equivalent to each fraction. **Samples are given.**
   a. $\frac{6}{18}$ **$\frac{1}{3}, \frac{3}{9}$**   b. $\frac{9}{24}$ **$\frac{3}{8}, \frac{18}{48}$**
   c. $\frac{18}{20}$ **$\frac{9}{10}, \frac{90}{100}$**   d. $\frac{60}{100}$ **$\frac{3}{5}, \frac{6}{10}$**

   3b. 1, 2, 3, 6, 9, 18, 27, 54; composite
   d. 1, 2, 3, 6, 17, 34, 51, 102; composite

9. Write each fraction in simplest form.
   a. $\frac{5}{45}$ **$\frac{1}{9}$**   b. $\frac{34}{51}$ **$\frac{2}{3}$**   c. $\frac{56}{128}$ **$\frac{7}{16}$**   d. $\frac{120}{180}$ **$\frac{2}{3}$**

10. Find the LCM of each set of numbers.
    a. 4, 8 **8**   b. 6, 11 **66**
    c. 18, 45 **90**   d. 10, 12, 15 **60**

11. Write each improper fraction as a mixed number. Write each mixed number as an improper fraction. **$4\frac{1}{25}$ $\frac{17}{3}$**
    a. $3\frac{5}{6}$ **$\frac{23}{6}$**   b. $\frac{43}{20}$ **$2\frac{3}{20}$**   c. $\frac{202}{50}$ d. $5\frac{2}{3}$

12. Compare. Fill in the ▪ with <, >, or =.
    a. $1\frac{2}{5}$ ▪ $1\frac{1}{5}$ **>**   b. $\frac{15}{4}$ ▪ $\frac{17}{5}$ **>**
    c. $\frac{7}{14}$ ▪ $\frac{1}{2}$ **=**   d. $2\frac{3}{5}$ ▪ $2\frac{7}{11}$ **<**

13. **Choose A, B, or C.** Lee jogged $\frac{1}{2}$ mi, Orlando jogged $\frac{2}{3}$ mi, and Holden jogged $\frac{3}{8}$ mi. Who jogged the longest distance? **B**
    A. Lee   B. Orlando   C. Holden

14. Order the numbers in each set from least to greatest.
    a. $5\frac{3}{4}, 5\frac{1}{8}, 5\frac{2}{4}, 5\frac{1}{8}, 5\frac{2}{4}, 5\frac{3}{4}$
    b. $4\frac{4}{5}, 3\frac{7}{10}, 3\frac{3}{5}, 3\frac{3}{5}, 3\frac{7}{10}, 4\frac{4}{5}$
    c. $2\frac{1}{4}, 1\frac{3}{4}, 3\frac{2}{4}, 1\frac{3}{4}, 2\frac{1}{4}, 3\frac{2}{4}$
    d. $\frac{2}{9}, \frac{7}{36}, \frac{5}{18}, \frac{1}{2}, \frac{7}{36}, \frac{2}{9}, \frac{5}{18}, \frac{1}{2}$

15. Write each decimal as a fraction in simplest form.
    a. 0.4 **$\frac{2}{5}$**   b. 0.82 **$\frac{41}{50}$**   c. 0.025 **$\frac{1}{40}$**

16. Write each fraction as a decimal. Use a bar to show repeating decimals.
    a. $\frac{5}{8}$ **0.625**   b. $\frac{7}{11}$ **$0.\overline{63}$**   c. $\frac{15}{45}$ **0.3**

17. Solve the following puzzle. When I add 2 to a number, subtract 5, and then multiply by 3, my result is 24. What is my number? **11**

Item	Review topic	Ch
1	Number patterns	2
2	Subtracting decimals	3
3, 6	Evaluating expressions	2
4	Estimating differences	3
5, 9	Fractions and decimals	5

Item	Review topic	Ch
7	Greatest common factor	5
8	Exploring fractions	5
10	Reading graphs and finding averages	1

5 CUMULATIVE REVIEW

Choose the best answer.

1. Which number pattern can be described by the following rule? *Start with the number 12, and subtract 4 repeatedly.* **A**

A. 12, 8, 4, . . .
B. 12, 8, 10, . . .
C. 12, 16, 24, . . .
D. 12, 24, 20, . . .

2. On Venus the length of a day is 243.01 Earth days. On Mercury the length of a day is 58.65 Earth days. How much longer than a Mercury day is a Venus day? **D**

A. 301.66 Earth days
B. 215.64 Earth days
C. 195.46 Earth days
D. 184.36 Earth days

3. Which expression has a value of 13? **C**

A. $3 + (2)^2$
B. $(3 + 2)^2$
C. $3^2 + 2^2$
D. $3^3 + 2^2$

4. A shirt costs $21.95 and a sweater costs $29.75. Which is the best estimate of the difference in costs? **C**

A. $52
C. $8
B. $9
D. $7

5. Which decimal is equivalent to $\frac{3}{8}$? **C**

A. 0.037   B. 0.38   C. 0.375   D. 3.75

6. Which word phrase describes the variable expression $2b - 8$? **D**

A. eight minus two times b
B. two times b
C. two minus eight times b
D. two times b, minus eight

7. Which set of numbers has a GCF of 8? **C**

A. 24, 36, 48
B. 56, 63, 42
C. 64, 24, 56
D. 56, 36, 28

8. Which fraction model does *not* equal $\frac{2}{3}$? **C**

A.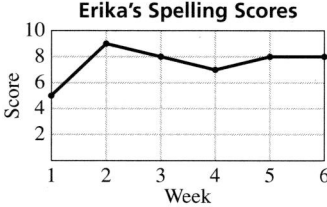

B.

C.

D.

9. Which fraction is *not* equivalent to 0.125? **D**

A. $\frac{5}{40}$
C. $\frac{1}{8}$
B. $\frac{125}{1000}$
D. $\frac{15}{200}$

10. The graph shows Erika's spelling scores for each week during the grading period. At the end of 6 weeks, her teacher drops the lowest score and finds the average of the remaining five scores to determine Erika's final score. What is the final score? **C**

Erika's Spelling Scores

A. 7
C. 8
B. 7.5
D. 40

Chapter 5 Cumulative Review

Choose the best answer. Circle A, B, C, or D.

1. Find the sum 45.23 + 37.08.
A. 8.15   B. 82.21
C. 82.31   D. 83.03

2. What is 0.98 in words?
A. ninety-eight
B. ninety-eight tenths
C. ninety-eight hundredths
D. ninety-eight thousandths

3. Find the mean of this data set. 17, 20, 18, 17, 23
A. 17   B. 19
C. 20   D. 400

4. Round each factor to the nearest whole number to estimate 56.8 × 3.09.
A. 165   B. 168
C. 171   D. 180

5. Find the product 2.54 × 0.07.
A. 0.1758   B. 0.1778
C. 14.78   D. 17.61

6. Estimate to the nearest dollar the cost of going to the basketball game. The ticket is $5.65, a drink is $1.79, and a hot dog is $2.34.
A. about $8   B. about $9
C. about $10   D. about $11

7. Which number pattern can be described by the following rule? *Start with the number 8 and add 3 repeatedly.*
A. 8, 11, 14, . . .   B. 8, 5, 2, . . .
C. 8, 11, 17, . . .   D. 8, 24, 72, . . .

8. A box of eight cookies costs $.99 What is the price for four cookies?
A. $.18   B. $.30
C. $.42   D. $.50

9. Find the quotient 2.4 ÷ 0.04.
A. 0.06   B. 0.6
C. 6   D. 60

10. Write a multiplication sentence to describe the model below.

A. 0.4 × 0.3 = 0.12
B. 0.5 × 0.3 = 0.15
C. 0.4 × 0.3 = 1.2
D. 0.4 × 0.3 = 0.012

11. Complete. 5.3 m = ■ cm
A. 0.053   B. 0.53
C. 53   D. 530

12. Use mental math to evaluate $(4 \times 2)^2 - 12$.
A. 24   B. 36
C. 48   D. 52

Chapter 5 Cumulative Review (continued)

13. Which word phrase describes the expression $3x - 15$?
A. fifteen less than three times a number
B. fifteen times three less than a number
C. three less than fifteen times a number
D. fifteen more than three times a number

14. Solve $12 + n = 21$.
A. 33   B. 12
C. 9   D. 7

15. Solve $24 = m \div 2$.
A. 6   B. 12
C. 36   D. 48

16. Evaluate $3t - s$ for $t = 6$ and $s = 4$.
A. 18   B. 14
C. 6   D. 4

17. Which digit makes 42,■52 divisible by 3 but not divisible by 9?
A. 2   B. 3
C. 5   D. 7

18. Which is the GCF of 54 and 81?
A. 3   B. 6
C. 9   D. 27

19. Which two fractions are equivalent to $\frac{4}{7}$?
A. $\frac{8}{14}, \frac{16}{21}$ B. $\frac{8}{14}, \frac{12}{21}$
C. $\frac{12}{21}, \frac{32}{40}$ D. $\frac{16}{21}, \frac{32}{40}$

20. Write $4\frac{6}{11}$ as an improper fraction.
A. $\frac{24}{11}$ B. $\frac{30}{11}$
C. $\frac{50}{11}$ D. $\frac{10}{11}$

21. The LCM of a number and 14 is 56. Which of the following could be the number?
A. 8   B. 45
C. 7   D. 28

22. Which of the following is *not* true?
A. $\frac{2}{3} < \frac{7}{4}$ B. $1\frac{3}{4} < \frac{13}{8}$
C. $\frac{2}{5} > \frac{2}{7}$ D. $\frac{11}{5} > \frac{13}{7}$

23. Write $\frac{15}{6}$ as a decimal.
A. 0.25   B. 0.5
C. 2.05   D. 2.5

24. You arrived home at 6:30 P.M. one evening after school. You had spent 45 minutes at band practice, 30 minutes at the ice cream shop with friends, 1 hour at the library studying, and 15 minutes riding your bike home. What time did you get out of school?
A. 3:30 P.M.   B. 3:45 P.M.
C. 4:00 P.M.   D. 4:15 P.M.

Resources

Teaching Resources

Chapter Support File, Ch. 5
• Cumulative Review

Teacher's Edition

See pp. 180C–D for Assessment Options.

Mid-Course Skills Assessment

A broad range of assessment tools are available to reach a variety of learners. Options for Formal and Informal Assessment appear on the **Assessing Progress** pages that precede each chapter.

Computer Item Generator

With the Computer Item Generator, you can customize assessment tests and create customized practice worksheets.

Standardized Test Preparation

You may wish to take advantage of the Standardized Test Preparation component that is available on the Computer Item Generator and the Resource Pro™ CD-ROM. With this component, you can generate tests to help students prepare for these standardized tests:

CATS   California Achievement Test, 5th Edition

ITBS   Iowa Test of Basic Skills, Form B

MAT 7   Metropolitan Achievement Test, 7th Edition

SAT9   Stanford Achievement Test, 9th Edition

CTBS/5 (Terra Nova)   Comprehensive Test of Basic Skills, 5th Edition

Mid-Course Assessment

The Mid-Course Assessment is available in the *Cumulative Assessment* booklet in the Teaching Resources.

Structure The Mid-Course Assessment is a two-page, multiple-choice test. The test assesses student progress on the skills and concepts covered in Chapters 1–5 of *Prentice Hall Middle Grades Math* program. The test contains 4–5 test items from each chapter.

Scoring Usually 75% correct should demonstrate that the student has sufficient mastery of the content to be able to succeed in this program. However, you may wish to set your own criteria.

Progress and Remediation Chart To assist you in assessing the skill level of your students, a Progress and Remediation Chart appears with the Mid-Course Assessment. This chart identifies the skills and concepts assessed, student achievement on the assessment test, and suggests where remediation help, if necessary, will be found within the *Prentice Hall Middle Grades Math*.

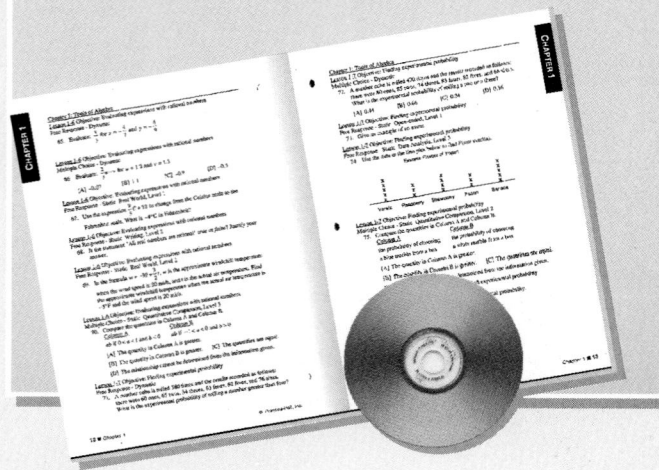

Mid-Course Assessment

To the Teacher:
The Mid-Course Assessment covers Chapters 1–5 and contains 4–5 test items from each chapter. Usually, 75% correct should demonstrate skill; however, you may want to set your own criteria.

Student Name _____

_____ Date _____

Progress and Remediation Chart

Chapter	Test Items	Number of Items Correct	Demonstrates Skill? (yes or no)	Suggested Remediation
1 Using Statistics to Analyze Data	1–4	___/4		Student Edition lessons 1-3, 1-4, 1-5, & 1-6 Reteaching worksheets 1-3, 1-4, 1-5, & 1-6 Computer Item Generator 1-3, 1-4, 1-5, & 1-6
2 Patterns and Algebraic Thinking	5–8	___/4		Student Edition lessons 2-3, 2-4, 2-5, & 2-7 Reteaching worksheets 2-3, 2-4, 2-5, & 2-7 Computer Item Generator 2-3, 2-4, 2-5, & 2-7
3 Adding and Subtracting Decimals	9–13	___/5		Student Edition lessons 3-2, 3-3, 3-6, 3-8, & 3-9 Reteaching worksheets 3-2, 3-3, 3-6, 3-8, & 3-9 Computer Item Generator 3-2, 3-3, 3-6, 3-8, & 3-9
4 Multiplying and Dividing Whole Numbers and Decimals	14–18	___/5		Student Edition lessons 4-2, 4-3, 4-5, 4-7, & 4-8 Reteaching worksheets 4-2, 4-3, 4-5, 4-7, & 4-8 Computer Item Generator 4-2, 4-3, 4-5, 4-7, & 4-8
5 Investigating Fractions	19–22	___/4		Student Edition lessons 5-1, 5-2, 5-3, & 5-7 Reteaching worksheets 5-1, 5-2, 5-3, & 5-7 Computer Item Generator 5-1, 5-2, 5-3, & 5-7

Name _____ Class _____ Date _____

Choose the best answer. Circle A, B, C, or D.

1. Which is the largest for this data?
40, 35, 41, 56, 59, 45, 54, 39, 54

  A. mean   **B.** median

  C. mode   **D.** range

2. Below is part of a spreadsheet from Kallie's savings account. How much money did she have at the end of the day on June 9?

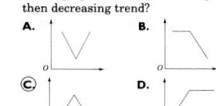

	A	B	C	D	E
1	Date	Balance (start)	Withdrawals	Deposits	Balance (end of day)
2	June 1	$10.00	$ 0.00	$ 5.50	$15.50
3	June 4	$15.50	$ 0.00	$25.00	
4	June 8		$ 6.15		
5	June 9		$15.00		

  A. $25.00   **B.** $34.35

  C. $40.50   **D.** $19.35

3. Which graph shows an increasing then decreasing trend?

  A.   **B.**

  C.   **D.**

4. Suppose you were to graph the given data in a line graph. Which unit should you use for the scale?
$98, $63, $120, $109, $137, $112

  A. 5   **B.** 10

  C. 100   **D.** 1,000

5. Which statement is *not* true?

  A. $10 + 6 \times 3 - 2 \div 2 = 27$

  B. $10 \times 6 + 3 - 2 \div 2 = 62$

  C. $10 - 6 + 3 \times 2 \div 2 = 8$

  D. $10 - 6 \times 3 \div 2 + 2 = 3$

6. Evaluate $3c + 2b + 5$ for $c = 3$ and $b = 6$.

  A. 64   **B.** 47

  C. 26   **D.** 29

7. Write a word phrase for the variable expression $3m - 5$.

  A. five more than three times a number

  B. three less than five times a number

  C. three times five less than a number

  D. five less than three times a number

8. Solve the equation.
$5y = 650$

  A. $y = 655$ **B.** $y = 130$

  C. $y = 645$ **D.** $y = 103$

9. What is 43.632 in expanded form?

  A. $40 + 3 + 0.6 + 0.03 + 0.002$

  B. $4 + 3 + 6 + 3 + 2$

  C. $40 + 3 + 6 + 0.03 + 0.0002$

  D. $0.002 + 0.03 + 0.6 + 40$

10. Order these decimals from least to greatest.
0.035, 0.045, 0.45, 0.02, 0.25

  A. 0.02, 0.035, 0.045, 0.25, 0.45

  B. 0.45, 0.25, 0.045, 0.035, 0.02

  C. 0.02, 0.25, 0.035, 0.045, 0.45

  D. 0.45, 0.045, 0.035, 0.25, 0.02

11. Suppose your savings account has a balance of $148.65. You withdraw $61.20 and deposit $28.89. What is your approximate new balance?

  A. $120   **B.** $180

  C. $240   **D.** $250

12. Which is the same as 360 cm?

  A. 3.6 mm   **B.** 3.6 m

  C. 3600 m   **D.** 3.6 km

13. Choose an appropriate metric unit of mass for an adult.

  A. gram   **B.** kilogram

  C. milligram   **D.** meter

14. Which is *not* the same as 5^4?

  A. $5 \times 5 \times 5 \times 5$

  B. 5×5^3

  C. 54

  D. $5 \times 5 \times 5^2$

15. Which of the following is the same as $(5 \times 6) - (5 \times 3)$?

  A. $5 \times (6 - 3)$

  B. $5 - (6 \times 3)$

  C. $(5 \times 5) - (6 \times 3)$

  D. $5 \times 6 - 3$

16. Micah made $85.50 in wages plus tips for waiting tables for 9.5 h. He makes $3.50 an hour in wages. How much did he make in tips?

  A. $33.35   **B.** $54.00

  C. $52.25   **D.** $42.50

17. Use mental math to evaluate.
$4.54 \div 2$

  A. 0.27   **B.** 227

  C. 22.7   **D.** 2.27

18. Find the quotient.
$4.8 \div 0.6$

  A. 0.08   **B.** 0.8

  C. 8   **D.** 80

19. Which number is divisible by 2, 3, and 10?

  A. 50   **B.** 230

  C. 480   **D.** 1,480

20. Which is the prime factorization of 180?

  A. $4 \times 5 \times 9$ **B.** $2^2 \times 3 \times 5^2$

  C. $2 \times 3^3 \times 5$ **D.** $2^2 \times 3^2 \times 5$

21. What is the GCF of 6, 34, and 114?

  A. 2   **B.** 3

  C. 6   **D.** 114

22. What is the LCM of 8, 12, and 18?

  A. 18   **B.** 72

  C. 216   **D.** 1,728

CHAPTER OVERVIEW

To accommodate flexible scheduling, most lessons are divided into parts. Assignment Options are given in the Teacher's Edition for each lesson.

Pages 228–231	**Lesson 6-1** **Estimating Sums and Differences**
NCTM 1, 2, 3, 4, 5, 7, 12, 13	Part 1 Estimating with Fractions Part 2 Estimating with Mixed Numbers **Key term:** whole number **Alternative Activity** 6-1 ▼ **Project Link**

Pages 232–235	**Lesson 6-2** **Algebra: Modeling Like Denominators**
NCTM 1, 2, 3, 4, 5, 9	Part 1 Adding Fractions with Like Denominators Part 2 Subtracting Fractions

Pages 236–240	**Lesson 6-3** **Algebra: Unlike Denominators**
NCTM 1, 2, 3, 4, 5, 7, 9	Part 1 Using Fraction Models Part 2 Using Equivalent Fractions **Math at Work** ✔ **Checkpoint 1**

Pages 253–256	**Lesson 6-7** **Modeling the Multiplication of Fractions**
NCTM 1, 2, 3, 5	Part 1 Multiplying Fractions by Fractions Part 2 Multiplying Whole Numbers by Fractions **Journal** ▼ **Project Link**

Pages 258–261	**Lesson 6-8** **Geometry: Multiplying Mixed Numbers**
NCTM 1, 2, 3, 4, 5, 7, 12, 13	Part 1 Estimating Products of Mixed Numbers Part 2 Multiplying Mixed Numbers ▼ **Project Link** ✔ **Checkpoint 2**

Pages 262–265	**Lesson 6-9** **Dividing Fractions and Mixed Numbers**
NCTM 1, 2, 3, 5, 7, 9, 13	Part 1 Exploring Division of Fractions Part 2 Division of Mixed Numbers **Key term:** reciprocals **Alternative Activity** 6-9

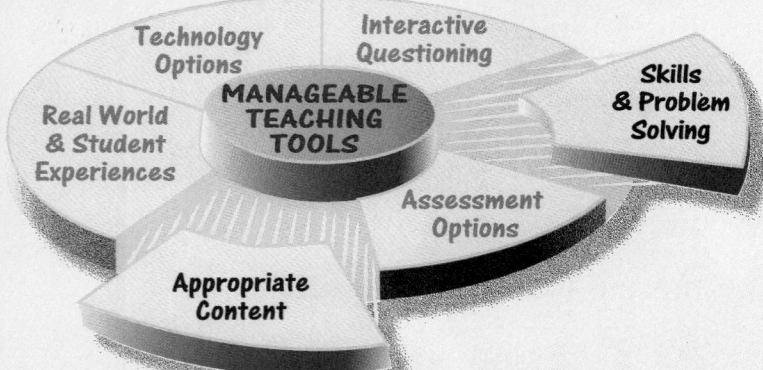

Technology Options

Interactive Questioning

Real World & Student Experiences

MANAGEABLE TEACHING TOOLS

Skills & Problem Solving

Assessment Options

Appropriate Content

Pacing Options

This chart suggests pacing only for the core lessons and their parts. It is provided merely as a possible guide. It will help you determine how much time you have in your schedule to cover other features, such as the Chapter Project, Math Toolboxes, Wrap Up, and Assessment.

	1 Class Period	1 Class Period	1 Class Period
Traditional (40–45 min class periods)	6–1 ▼1 6–1 ▼2	6–2 ▼1 6–2 ▼2	6–3 ▼1
Block Scheduling (90 min class periods)	6–1 ▼1 6–1 ▼2 6–2 ▼1 6–2 ▼2	6–3 ▼1 6–3 ▼2 6–4 ▼1	6–4 ▼2 6–5 ▼1 6–5 ▼2 6–

NCTM STANDARDS

1 Problem Solving
2 Communication
3 Reasoning
4 Mathematical Connections
5 Number and Number Relationships

6 Number Systems and Number Theory
7 Computation and Estimation
8 Patterns and Functions
9 Algebra

10 Statistics
11 Probability
12 Geometry
13 Measurement

Pages 241–244	**Lesson 6-4** **Algebra: Adding Mixed Numbers**
NCTM 1, 2, 3, 4, 5, 7, 9, 13	Part 1 Adding Mixed Numbers Mentally Part 2 Adding Mixed Numbers by Renaming **Journal**

Pages 246–249	**Lesson 6-5** **Algebra: Subtracting Mixed Numbers**
NCTM 1, 2, 3, 4, 5, 6, 7, 9, 13	Part 1 Subtracting Mixed Numbers Mentally Part 2 Subtracting Mixed Numbers by Renaming

Pages 250–252	**Lesson 6-6** **Problem Solving Strategy**
NCTM 1, 3, 4, 5, 6, 13	Draw a Diagram

Pages 267–270	**Lesson 6-10 Measurement: Changing Units in the Customary System**
NCTM 1, 2, 3, 4, 13	Part 1 Changing Units Part 2 Comparing Amounts

---

Optional Materials and Manipulatives

fraction bars (6-1, 6-2, 6-3)
ruler (6-1, 6-4, 6-9)
string (6-4)

graph paper (6-6)
paper (circular) (6-7)
scissors (6-7)

fraction calculator (6-9)
Optional calculator use is integrated
   throughout the course.

---

ss d	1 Class Period	1 Class Period	1 Class Period	1 Class Period	1 Class Period	1 Class Period	1 Class Period	1 Class Period	1 Class Period	1 Class Period
	6-4 ▽	6-5 ▽	6-5 6-6 ▽	6-7 6-7 ▽ ▽	6-8 6-8 ▽ ▽	6-9 ▽	6-9 ▽	6-10 6-10 ▽ ▽		
6-9 ▽	6-9 6-10 6-10 ▽ ▽ ▽									

MEETING INDIVIDUAL NEEDS

Accommodating Diverse Learning Styles

In your Teacher's Edition, you will find suggestions as to how you can help students complete mathematical tasks in Chapter 6 by meeting individual needs and supporting various learning styles. Here are some examples:

VISUAL LEARNING
drawing models *(p. 242)*

TACTILE LEARNING
modeling fractions with fraction bars *(p. 233)*

AUDITORY LEARNING
listening to problems and making notes *(p. 250)*

KINESTHETIC LEARNING
walking a fraction of the way across the classroom *(p. 232)*

EARLY FINISHERS
Performance-Based Project, MathBlaster® Mystery, Interdisciplinary Units

GIFTED AND TALENTED
recording the daily growth of radish sprouts *(p. 228)*

DIVERSITY writing questions about family recipes *(p. 234)*

ACQUIRING ENGLISH PROFICIENCY (AEP)
learning customary units by measuring items in the classroom *(p. 267)*

ASSESSING PROGRESS

A broad range of assessment tools are available to reach a variety of learners.

INFORMAL ASSESSMENT

Informal assessments provide day-to-day feedback to help give you a picture of conceptual understanding and skill development.

ONGOING ASSESSMENT is built into lesson instruction and the Teaching Notes of the Teacher's Edition.

In the Teacher's Edition
Lesson Quiz for every lesson

In the Student Edition
On Your Own, Mixed Review, Journal, Portfolio, Project Link, Chapter Wrap Up

Look for **Interactive Questions** within lessons that

BUILD UNDERSTANDING with labels such as Analyze, Reasoning, Estimation, Writing, and Summarize

✔ **CHECK UNDERSTANDING** with the Try It Out label.

FORMAL ASSESSMENT

Formal assessment can occur before and after the chapter, as well as at natural breaking points in the chapter.

Checkpoints
Two forms of each self-assessment Checkpoints are available: one in the Student Edition and another in the Chapter Support File in the Teaching Resources box.
- Mid-Chapter Checkpoint 1, page 240
- End-of-Chapter Checkpoint 2, page 261

Chapter 6 Assessment, page 274.
Two alternative forms are available in the Chapter Support File. They may be used after a chapter has been completed, or as a pre-test and post-test comparison.

Cumulative Review, page 275.
Assesses skills and concepts in Chapters 1–6. An alternative form is available in Chapter Support File.

Computer Item Generator for Chapter 6
Customized tests can be generated for each lesson and for mid-chapter and end-of-chapter assessments, and for pre- and post-test comparisons of achievement.

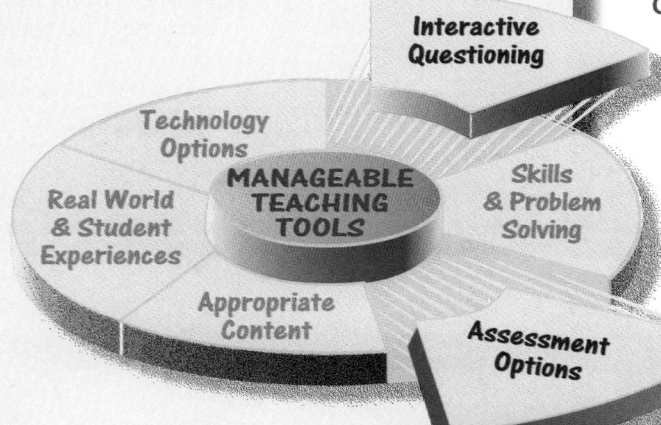

CHAPTER PROJECT

The Chapter Project in the student edition provides a real-world connection to the math context of the chapter. The Teacher's Edition contains a scoring rubric.

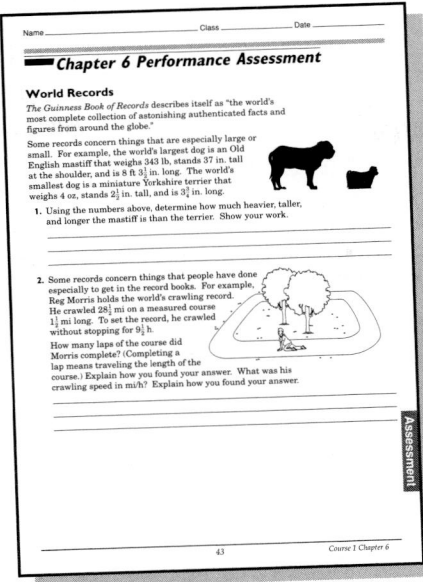

Another performance-based Chapter Project with a scoring rubric can be found in the Chapter Support File in the Teaching Resources Box.

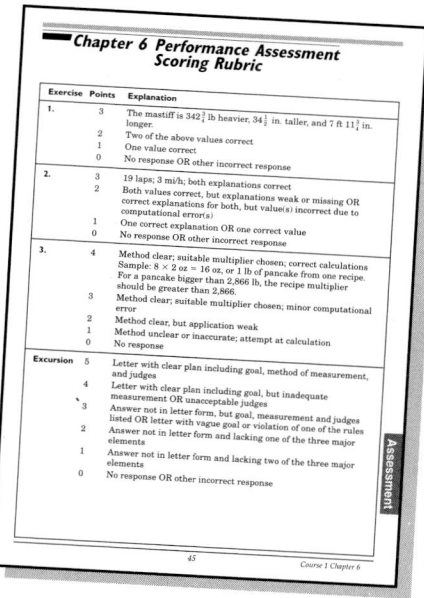

Correlation to Standardized Tests

Lesson	STANDARDIZED TEST ITEMS						
		CAT5	CTBS/5 Terra Nova	ITBS	MAT7	SAT9	Your Local Test
6-1	Estimating Sums and Differences					■	
6-2	Algebra: Modeling Like Denominators	■	■	■	■	■	
6-3	Algebra: Unlike Denominators	■	■	■		■	
6-4	Algebra: Adding Mixed Numbers	■	■	■		■	
6-5	Algebra: Subtracting Mixed Numbers	■	■	■	■	■	
6-6	Problem Solving Strategy: Draw a Diagram			■	■	■	
6-7	Modeling the Multiplication of Fractions	■	■	■	■	■	
6-8	Geometry: Multiplying Mixed Numbers	■	■	■	■	■	
6-9	Dividing Fractions and Mixed Numbers			■	■	■	
6-10	Measurement: Changing Units in the Customary System		■			■	

CAT5 California Achievement Test, 5th Edition
CTBS/5 Comprehensive Test of Basic Skills, 5th Edition

ITBS Iowa Test of Basic Skills, Form B
MAT 7 Metropolitan Achievement Test, 7th Edition

SAT9 Stanford Achievement Test, 9th Edition

MAKING CONNECTIONS

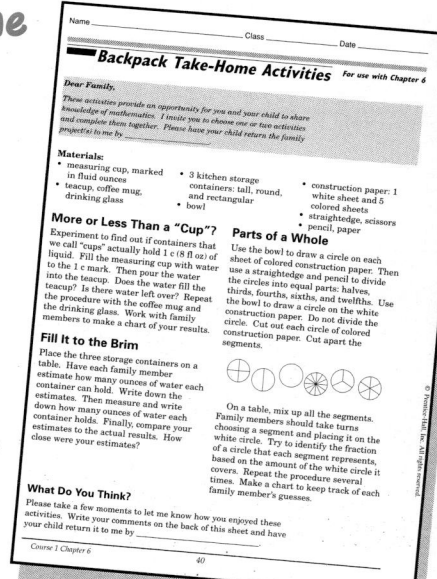

MANAGEABLE TEACHING TOOLS
- Technology Options
- Interactive Questioning
- Skills & Problem Solving
- Assessment Options
- Appropriate Content
- Real World & Student Experiences

TEAM TEACHING WITH PRENTICE HALL MATERIALS

INTERDISCIPLINARY EXPLORATIONS

- *India Beyond the Golden Age* p. 35
- *Wagons West* p. 39

Lesson	Interdisciplinary Connections	Real World Connections	Math Integration
6-1	Earth Science	Money Sewing	Measurement Geometry
6-2	Nutrition	Cooking Archery	Algebra
6-3	Art Social Studies	Geology Cooking	Algebra
6-4	Zoology	Tides Carpentry Cooking World Records	Algebra Geometry
6-5	Biology	Olympics Carpentry	Algebra Data Analysis
6-6	Art Sports Marketing Social Studies	Pets Gardening Rugs Commuting Food Scheduling	Data Analysis
6-7	Drama	Community Planning Landscaping	Data Analysis
6-8	Keyboarding Business	Baking Sewing Carpentry Construction	Geometry
6-9	Nutrition	Sewing Bird Seed	Algebra Measurement
6-10	Nutrition Geography	Wildlife Architecture Energy	Measurement Geometry Data Analysis

School to Home

MATERIALS:
tape measure
utility bill
paper
pencil

English and Spanish versions are available in the Teacher's Communication Kit, Teacher's Resource box.

Backpack Take-Home Activities For use with Chapter 6

Name _____ Class _____ Date _____

Dear Family,

These activities provide an opportunity for you and your child to share knowledge of mathematics. I invite you to choose one or two activities and complete them together. Please have your child return the family project(s) to me by _____

Materials:
- measuring cup, marked in fluid ounces
- teacup, coffee mug, drinking glass
- 3 kitchen storage containers: tall, round, and rectangular
- bowl
- construction paper: 1 white sheet and 5 colored sheets
- straightedge, scissors, pencil, paper

More or Less Than a "Cup"?
Experiment to find out if containers that we call "cups" actually hold 1 c (8 fl oz) of liquid. Fill the measuring cup with water to the 1 c mark. Then pour the water into the teacup. Does the water fill the teacup? Is there water left over? Repeat the procedure with the coffee mug and the drinking glass. Work with family members to make a chart of your results.

Fill It to the Brim
Place the three storage containers on a table. Have each family member estimate how many ounces of water each container can hold. Write down the estimates. Then measure and write down how many ounces of water each container holds. Finally, compare your estimates to the actual results. How close were your estimates?

Parts of a Whole
Use the bowl to draw a circle on each sheet of colored construction paper. Then use a straightedge and pencil to divide the circles into equal parts: halves, thirds, fourths, sixths, and twelfths. Use the bowl to draw a circle on the white construction paper. Do not divide the circle. Cut out each circle of colored construction paper. Cut apart the segments.

On a table, mix up all the segments. Family members should take turns choosing a segment and placing it on the white circle. Try to identify the fraction of a circle that each segment represents, based on the amount of the white circle it covers. Repeat the procedure several times. Make a chart to keep track of each family member's guesses.

What Do You Think?
Please take a few moments to let me know how you enjoyed these activities. Write your comments on the back of this sheet and have your child return it to me by _____

Course 1 Chapter 6   40

FOR THE STUDENT

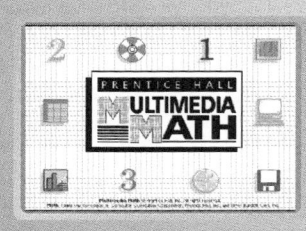

Multimedia Math Hot Pages™
This interactive software and video package on CD-ROM integrates solid math content through a variety of media.

- Hot Page™ 16 (6-3)
- Hot Page™ 17 (6-8)
- Hot Page™ 18 (6-10)

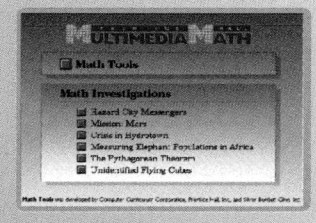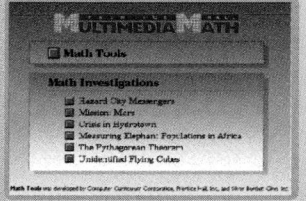

Multimedia Math Investigations
These in-depth interactive activities on CD-ROM develop real-world applications of mathematics. They allow students the opportunity to reinforce key concepts.

- Unidentified Flying Cubes

MathBlaster® Mystery
This award-winning, interactive software program on CD-ROM can be used to maintain skills or to accommodate early finishers.

- Level: Earn 2 coins; Pay 6 coins
- Mission Mode (all lessons)
- Kitchen Comparisons (6-2, 6-5, 6-10)
- Number Guesser (6-3, 6-9)
- Equation Maker (6-1, 6-7, 6-8)
- Word Problems (6-4, 6-6, Problem Solving Practice)

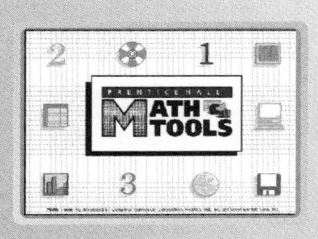

Math Labs
This software, available on both diskette and CD-ROM, includes on-screen Math Lab activities. Students use linkable, interactive tools to explore math concepts.

Interactive Student Tutorial
Available on CD-ROM, this test preparation program contains self-tests with questions in standardized test format. Software includes electronic versions of the text lessons and the Math Tools and Math Labs.

Internet Connection

For Students
Support for the Chapter Project
A career-oriented link for Math at Work feature

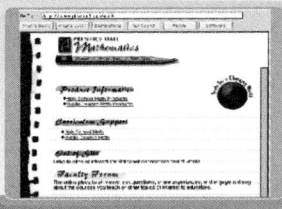

www.phschool.com/math

For teachers
Curriculum Support
Product Information
Regional Support Information

FOR THE TEACHER

Computer Item Generator
Available on both CD-ROM and diskette, this software generates customized practice sheets, quizzes, and tests. It generates an unlimited supply of questions with varying levels of difficulty.

The Resource Pro™
Available on CD-ROM, this software can be used to customize and plan lessons.

Technology Options

MANAGEABLE TEACHING TOOLS
- Interactive Questioning
- Skills & Problem Solving
- Assessment Options
- Appropriate Content
- Real World & Student Experiences

USING FRACTIONS

CONNECTING TO PRIOR LEARNING Ask students what they know about performing experiments. Ask why scientists do experiments. **Answers may vary. Sample: Scientists are trying to solve a problem, prove a hypothesis, or discover a truth.** You may want to discuss with students the scientific method of making a hypothesis and then testing it.

CULTURAL CONNECTIONS The advancements in science over the past few centuries have stemmed from the work of scientists all around the world. Discuss with students the names of famous scientists and, if possible, their contributions to science. **Answers may vary. Sample: Marie Curie, Albert Einstein**

INTERDISCIPLINARY CONNECTIONS *Ask students: What would happen if scientists did not have to test their hypotheses?* **Answers may vary. Sample: Many people would believe scientific facts that are false.**

ABOUT THE PROJECT In the Chapter Project, students use the scientific method of experimenting to find a way to add fractions with different denominators.

Internet • For information and activities related to the Chapter Project, visit the Prentice Hall site at www.phschool.com/mgm1/ch6

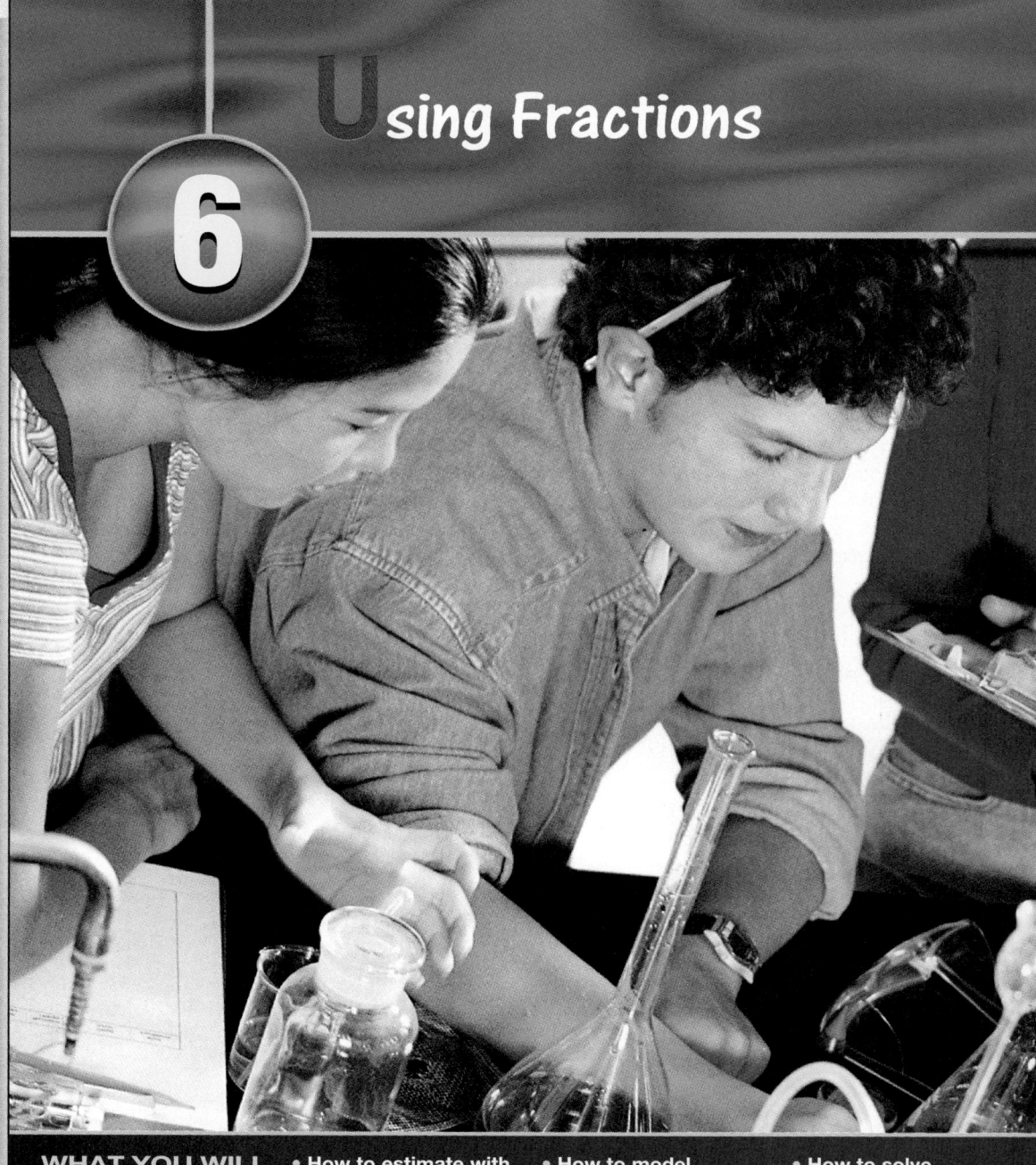

Using Fractions

6

WHAT YOU WILL LEARN IN THIS CHAPTER

• How to estimate with fractions

• How to model fraction concepts and operations

• How to solve equations involving fractions and mixed numbers

Ask students:

- *Have you ever performed an experiment?*
- *How can you design an experiment to make sure the results are reliable?*
- *How might you design an experiment to find out a way to add fractions and mixed numbers with different denominators?*

PROJECT NOTEBOOK Encourage students to keep all project-related materials in a separate folder or notebook.

TRACKING THE PROJECT You may wish to have students read Finishing the Chapter Project on page 271 to help them get an overview of the project. Set benchmark deadlines for students to show you their work in progress.

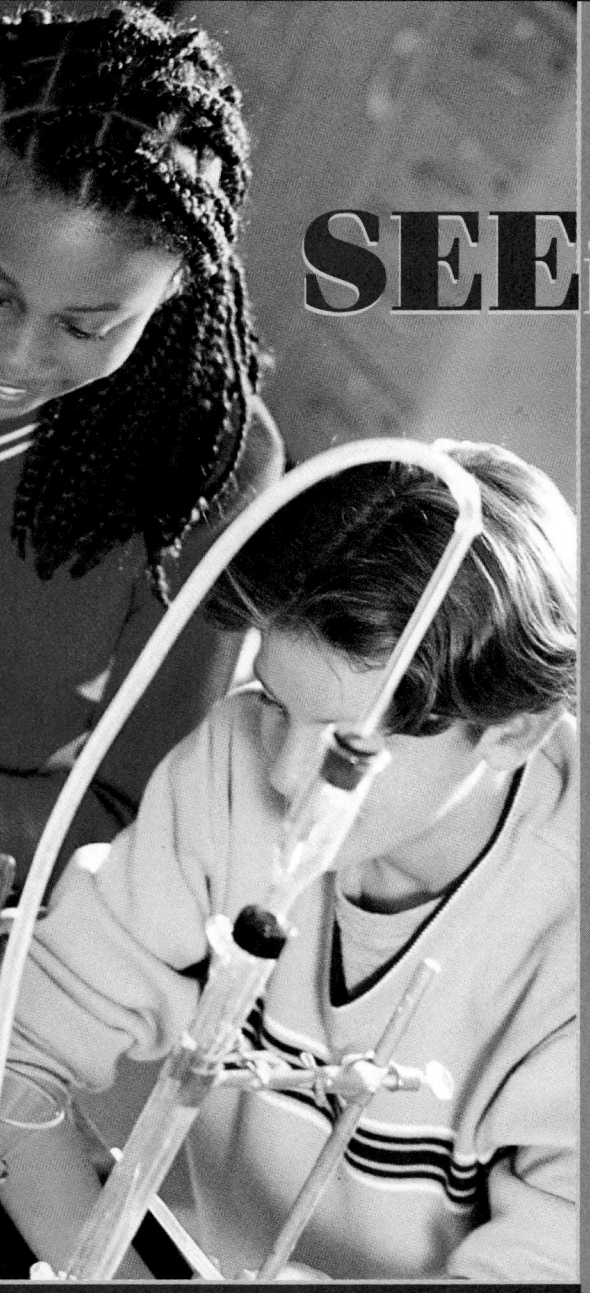

CHAPTER PROJECT

THEME: PROOFS

SEEing is Believing

Have you ever conducted a science experiment to prove that something is true? Scientists do not take someone else's word for something. Instead they plan to prove something is correct or incorrect. You can prove something in math class, too.

Design a Demonstration You will learn ways to add fractions and mixed numbers with unlike denominators, but can you prove these techniques *really* work? Your goal is to prove that they do by giving several demonstrations.

Steps to help you complete the project:

p. 231 **Project Link:** *Researching*
p. 256 **Project Link:** *Demonstrating*
p. 261 **Project Link:** *Modeling*
p. 271 *Finishing the Chapter Project*

- How to solve problems by drawing a diagram

SCORING RUBRIC

3 You provide a step-by-step proof showing that the methods for adding fractions with inlike denominations really work. This proof includes a description of at least two experiments you conducted using itmes you collected. The sums you found by experiment are compared to the results of actual calculations in a table. Your presentation is clear and complete.

2 You provide a proof that includes evidence of only one experiment. The results of the experiment are compared to actual calculations. Your work is neat and easy to follow.

1 You provide the results of one experiment and accompanying calculations, but your work is disorganized or unclear.

0 You failed to conduct any experiments or to prepare a written description of your work.

227

1 Focus

CONNECTING TO PRIOR KNOWLEDGE Ask: *When would you round a fraction to 0?* **when the numerator is much smaller than the denominator** *When would you round a fraction to $\frac{1}{2}$?* **when the numerator is about half of the denominator** *When would you round a fraction to 1?* **when the numerator**

is almost equal to the denominator Have students come up with examples of fractions they would round to 0, $\frac{1}{2}$, and 1. **Answers may vary. Sample: $\frac{2}{9}$, $\frac{6}{11}$, and $\frac{7}{8}$**

2 Teach

THINK AND DISCUSS

TACTILE LEARNING **Questions 1–5** Have students use fraction bars.

REASONING **Question 2** Ask: *Does 15 round to 20 or 10?* **20** *Why?* **Whole numbers ending in 0, 1, 2, 3, or 4 round down; numbers ending in 5, 6, 7, 8, or 9 round up.** *How does knowing this rule help you decide how to round a number half-way between two numbers?* **A number half-way between two numbers rounds up.**

EXTENSION **Example 2** Have students plant radish seeds. When they have sprouted, ask students to measure the seed's daily growth for 5 days. Ask students to estimate the

Lesson Planning Options

Prerequisite Skills
- modeling fractions (precourse)
- rounding fractions (5-4)

Vocabulary/Symbols
whole number

Materials/Manipulatives
- fraction bars   - ruler

Resources

 Student Edition
Skills Handbook, pp. 538, 539
Extra Practice, p. 527
Glossary/Study Guide

 Teaching Resources

Chapter Support File, Ch. 6
- Lesson Planner 6-1
- Practice 6-1, Reteaching 6-1
- Alternative Activity 6-1
- Answer Masters 6-1
Teaching Aids Masters 3, 20–25
Glossary, Spanish Resources

 Transparencies
11, 12, 22–29, Minds on Math 6-1

Warm Up

Daylight Donuts charges $2.00 for 7 doughnuts. How many doughnuts can you buy for $24.00?
84

228

6-1 Estimating Sums and Differences

What You'll Learn

1 To estimate sums and differences by rounding fractions

2 To estimate sums and differences by rounding mixed numbers

...And Why

You can estimate measurements and rates of growth.

Here's How

Look for questions that
- build understanding
- check understanding

THINK AND DISCUSS

1 *Estimating with Fractions*

Look at the ruler at the right.

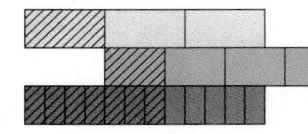

1. **Number Sense** Is each fraction closest to 0, $\frac{1}{2}$, or 1?
   a. $\frac{1}{8}$ **0**   b. $\frac{7}{8}$ **1**   c. $\frac{3}{8}$ **$\frac{1}{2}$**   d. $\frac{15}{16}$ **1**

2. **Reasoning** Does $\frac{1}{4}$ round to 0 or to $\frac{1}{2}$? Explain.
   $\frac{1}{2}$; $\frac{1}{4}$ is halfway between 0 and $\frac{1}{2}$, so round up.

You can estimate sums and differences of fractions by rounding to the nearest half.

■ EXAMPLE 1

Estimate.

a. $\frac{7}{12} + \frac{4}{5}$

$\frac{7}{12} + \frac{4}{5}$

$\approx \frac{1}{2} + 1$ ←── Round each fraction to the nearest $\frac{1}{2}$.

$\approx 1\frac{1}{2}$ ←── Add or subtract the estimates.

b. $\frac{9}{10} - \frac{1}{7}$

$\frac{9}{10} - \frac{1}{7}$

$\approx 1 - 0$

≈ 1

3. **Try It Out** Estimate each sum or difference.
   a. $\frac{6}{7} + \frac{2}{9}$ **1**   b. $\frac{7}{13} - \frac{3}{17}$ **$\frac{1}{2}$**   c. $\frac{21}{44} + \frac{1}{99}$ **$\frac{1}{2}$**   d. $\frac{12}{13} - \frac{1}{12}$ **1**

You can also use models to estimate sums.

4. **Try It Out** Write the fractions shown in the model. What does this model show you?
   $\frac{1}{3} + \frac{1}{4} = \frac{7}{12}$

5. **Modeling** Represent $\frac{7}{8} + \frac{1}{2}$ with a model. Estimate the sum. **See margin p. 230 for diagram; $1\frac{1}{2}$.**

Now you may assign Exercises 1–17.

difference between the daily average growth of the radish plants and kudzu.

Question 8 Suggest some students pretend they never round before adding and subtracting. Have them write their answer from this point of view. Have them discuss any difficulties they would encounter.

■ **ADDITIONAL EXAMPLES**

FOR EXAMPLE 1
Estimate $\frac{13}{16} - \frac{3}{8}$. $\frac{1}{2}$

FOR EXAMPLE 2
Miko bought $1\frac{7}{8}$ yd of fabric to make costumes for the school play. Carlos bought $3\frac{1}{2}$ yd of fabric. They need 6 yd of fabric for all the costumes. Estimate the length of the fabric Miko and Carlos bought. Will they have enough to make the costumes?
$5\frac{1}{2}$ yd; no

Work Together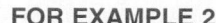

DIVERSITY Some students may feel self conscious about the size of their hands. Help students understand there is no perfect hand size. Differences in characteristics such as hand size, eye color, and height make every person unique.

ESTIMATION Question 11 Ask students to estimate the sum of all the hand-span measurements in their group.

ASSESSMENT Group students in pairs. Have each student think of a mixed number. Both students estimate the sum and difference of the numbers. Then compare answers and discuss differences.

The kudzu plant, from Japan, was introduced to the United States in 1876. It grows fastest during the summer months. Under ideal conditions, a kudzu vine can grow 60 ft in a year.

2 *Estimating with Mixed Numbers*

To estimate the sum or difference of mixed numbers, round each mixed number to the nearest whole number.

■ **EXAMPLE 2** *Real-World Problem Solving*

Life Science The table at the right shows how one kudzu plant grew over five days.

Kudzu Plant Growth

Day	Height (ft)
1	$1\frac{1}{12}$
2	$1\frac{7}{8}$
3	$2\frac{3}{4}$
4	$3\frac{5}{8}$
5	$4\frac{7}{12}$

a. About how much did the kudzu plant grow from Day 1 to Day 2?

Subtract to find the growth in one day.

$$\begin{array}{cc} \text{Height} & \text{Height} \\ \text{on Day 2} & \text{on Day 1} \\ 1\frac{7}{8} & - \quad 1\frac{1}{12} \end{array}$$

$\approx 2 - 1$ ← Round each height to the nearest whole foot.

≈ 1

The kudzu plant grew about 1 ft from Day 1 to Day 2.

b. Estimate the average growth per day for the kudzu plant.

$$\begin{aligned} \text{Average growth} \\ \text{per day} \end{aligned} = \frac{\text{Total growth}}{\text{Number of days}}$$

$= \dfrac{4\frac{7}{12} - 1\frac{1}{12}}{5}$ ← Subtract to find total growth. ← Divide by 5.

$\approx \dfrac{5 - 1}{5}$ ← Round each mixed number to the nearest whole number.

$\approx \frac{4}{5}$

≈ 1

The average growth is about 1 ft per day.

6. ✔*Try It Out* Estimate the height of the kudzu on Day 6 and Day 10. $5\frac{1}{2}$ ft, $9\frac{1}{2}$ ft

7–8. See margin p. 230.

7. Evaluate the reasonableness of your results in Question 6.

8. ■*Think About It* Why does it make sense to round a mixed number to the nearest *whole number* before adding or subtracting? Could you round to the nearest $\frac{1}{2}$ instead?

Technology Options

Prentice Hall Technology

Software for Learners
• Math Blaster® Mystery*
• Interactive Student Tutorial, Chapter 6*

Teaching Resource Software
• Computer Item Generator 6-1
• Resource Pro™ Chapter 6*

  Internet • For related mathematics activities, visit the Prentice Hall site at www.phschool.com/math

Available on CD-ROM only

Assignment Options for Exercises On Your Own

To provide flexible scheduling, this lesson can be subdivided into parts.

▼**1** **Core** 1–15, 17
Extension 16

▼**2** **Core** 18–32, 34–36
Extension 33

Use Mixed Review to maintain skills.

229

3 Practice/Assess

EXERCISES *On Your Own*

VISUAL LEARNING and ESTIMATION
Exercise 17 Have students use real coins. Ask them to estimate visually first, then use the table to check their estimates.

ERROR ALERT! Exercises 18–32 Students may use the rounding rules for fractions when rounding mixed numbers. **Remediation:**

Remind students that when they see a mixed number, they should round to the nearest whole number.

WRITING Exercise 36 Have students expand this question by writing general guidelines. Ask: *When should you calculate the difference exactly? When should you estimate?* **Calculate exactly when the numbers are close or when precision is important. Otherwise, estimate.**

WRAP UP

IDENTIFYING THE BIG IDEA Ask students to explain how to estimate sums and differences of fractions and mixed numbers.

PROJECT LINK Some students may be able to think of items, but not able to gather them. Also, some items may be perishable. Encourage students to draw or find pictures of these items to use with the project.

---

pages 228–229 Think and Discuss

5.

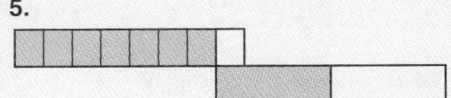

7. The answers show that the kudzu grows at a rate of about 1 ft per day.

8. Whole numbers are easier than fractions to compute with; yes

page 231 Mixed Review

43. **Ages of First Cousins**

Ages	Frequency
5–9	4
10–14	4
15–19	3
20–25	1

Ages of First Cousins

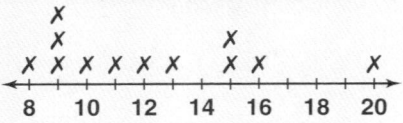

44. **Points Scored by Balance Beam Gymnasts**

Points	Frequency
8.0–8.4	3
8.5–8.9	5
9.0–9.5	2

Points Scored on Balance Beam

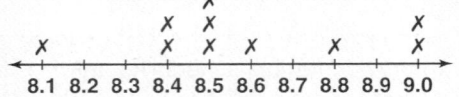

230

hand span

Work Together
Measuring and Estimating

9. **⬦Measurement** Use an inch ruler to measure the hand span of each member of your group.
9–11. Check students' work.
10. Record each measurement to the nearest half inch.

11. **⬦Estimation** Estimate the difference between the greatest and least hand spans within your group.

Now you may assign Exercises 18–36.

EXERCISES *On Your Own*

Estimate each sum or difference to the nearest $\frac{1}{2}$.

1. $\frac{1}{4} + \frac{1}{8}$ $\frac{1}{2}$

2. $\frac{7}{8} - \frac{1}{4}$ $\frac{1}{2}$

3. $\frac{7}{8} + \frac{3}{5}$ $1\frac{1}{2}$

4. $\frac{11}{20} - \frac{2}{15}$ $\frac{1}{2}$

5. $\frac{13}{30} + \frac{19}{25}$ $1\frac{1}{2}$

6. $\frac{9}{16} - \frac{1}{4}$ 0

7. $\frac{15}{16} + \frac{7}{15}$ $1\frac{1}{2}$

8. $\frac{13}{16} - \frac{3}{8}$ $\frac{1}{2}$

9. $\frac{1}{10} + \frac{71}{100}$ 1

10. $\frac{70}{80} - \frac{2}{5}$ $\frac{1}{2}$

11. $\frac{15}{28} + \frac{11}{12}$ $1\frac{1}{2}$

12. $\frac{6}{7} - \frac{43}{80}$ $\frac{1}{2}$

13. $\frac{5}{6} + \frac{4}{9}$ $1\frac{1}{2}$

14. $\frac{11}{12} - \frac{1}{15}$ 1

15. $\frac{47}{50} + \frac{19}{25}$ 2

16. **Number Sense** Will the sum of many different fractions less **yes;** than $\frac{1}{4}$ ever be greater than 1? Support your answer. $\frac{1}{5} + \frac{1}{6} + \frac{1}{7} + \frac{1}{8} + \frac{1}{9} + \frac{1}{10} + \frac{1}{11} + \frac{1}{12} > 1$

17. *Estimation* Use the table at the right. Suppose you place a dime, a penny, a nickel, and a quarter side-by-side as shown below. Estimate the total length of the coins. $3\frac{1}{2}$ in.

U.S. Coins

Coin	Diameter (in.)
Dime	$\frac{11}{16}$
Penny	$\frac{1}{2}$
Nickel	$\frac{13}{16}$
Quarter	$\frac{15}{16}$

Estimate each sum or difference.

18. $7\frac{7}{8} + 8\frac{5}{12}$ 16

19. $12\frac{9}{10} - 4\frac{3}{8}$ 9

20. $3\frac{3}{4} + 1\frac{2}{5}$ 5

21. $25\frac{6}{7} - 13\frac{3}{4}$ 12

22. $2\frac{9}{10} + 43\frac{13}{14}$

23. $11\frac{9}{16} - 10\frac{5}{8}$ 1

24. $7\frac{8}{11} + 4\frac{10}{13}$ 13

25. $4\frac{2}{3} - \frac{5}{6}$ 4

26. $29\frac{1}{8} + 30\frac{8}{11}$ 60

27. $76\frac{6}{23} - 45\frac{2}{5}$

28. $3\frac{9}{10} + 5\frac{3}{8}$ 9

29. $78\frac{3}{4} - 57\frac{17}{23}$ 21

30. $13\frac{7}{43} + 22\frac{1}{8}$ 35

31. $2\frac{5}{7} - \frac{1}{2}$ 2

32. $34\frac{3}{7} + 16\frac{9}{17}$

22. 47   27. 31   32. 51

33. *Sewing* Material costs $4.96 per yard. Suppose you need $1\frac{5}{8}$ yd of a solid-color material and $\frac{3}{4}$ yd of a print material for a quilt. About how much will the material cost?   **$15.00**

Estimate the sum or difference.

1. $4\frac{1}{6} - 1\frac{7}{16}$ 2
2. $\frac{9}{10} - \frac{3}{8}$ $\frac{1}{2}$
3. $1\frac{3}{16} + 2\frac{1}{4}$ 3
4. $\frac{7}{8} + \frac{5}{12}$ $1\frac{1}{2}$

---

34. *Measurement* At the beginning of the summer, Jocelyn, Carlos, and Amanda measured their heights. At the end of the summer, Carlos, Jocelyn, and Amanda measured their heights again. Refer to the table at the right.
  a. About how much did Amanda grow during the summer? **2 in.**
  b. About how much did Carlos and Jocelyn grow during the summer? Which of the three grew the most?
  Carlos: 1 in.; Jocelyn: 0 in.; Amanda

Heights

Person	June	Sept.
Jocelyn	$61\frac{7}{8}$ in.	$62\frac{1}{4}$ in.
Carlos	$60\frac{3}{4}$ in.	$61\frac{5}{8}$ in.
Amanda	$59\frac{1}{8}$ in.	$60\frac{5}{8}$ in.

35. *Geometry* You plan to put a fence around your garden, shown at the right. About how much fencing will you need?
24 ft

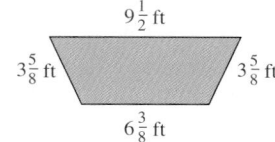

$9\frac{1}{2}$ ft

$3\frac{5}{8}$ ft $3\frac{5}{8}$ ft

$6\frac{3}{8}$ ft

36. *Writing* Finalists in a contest to build the tallest tower of cans build towers $7\frac{7}{8}$ ft, $7\frac{3}{4}$ ft, and $7\frac{15}{16}$ ft high. If you round each height to the nearest foot, is an estimate of the difference in height reasonable? Explain.   **No; all heights round to 8 ft.**

Mixed Review

Write each fraction in simplest form. *(Lesson 5-5)*

37. $\frac{45}{60}$ $\frac{3}{4}$ **38.** $\frac{36}{64}$ $\frac{9}{16}$ **39.** $\frac{75}{350}$ $\frac{3}{14}$ **40.** $\frac{49}{63}$ $\frac{7}{9}$ **41.** $\frac{96}{100}$ $\frac{24}{25}$ **42.** $\frac{112}{400}$ $\frac{7}{25}$

Organize each set of data in a frequency table and in a line plot. *(Lesson 1-1)* **43–44. See margin p. 230.**

43. ages of first cousins at a family reunion: 16 15 9 10 9 13 9 12 15 11 8 20

44. points scored by gymnasts on the balance beam: 8.5 8.8 8.4 8.4 8.5 9 8.6 8.1 8.5 9

45. *Choose a Strategy* Akira spent one third of his money, then spent $6, and then spent half the money he had left, leaving him with exactly $4. How much money did he start with? **$21**

CHAPTER
PROJECT

PROJECT LINK: RESEARCHING

Look around for items that are typically divided into equal parts, or fractions. Some suggestions are rulers, pizzas, and cakes. How are these items usually divided—into halves, thirds, eighths? Make a list of items you could use to demonstrate the proofs you develop. Gather as many of these items as you can.   **Check students' work.**

PRACTICE

Practice 6-1 *Estimating Sums and Differences*

Write the fraction shown by each model. Then round to the nearest $\frac{1}{2}$.

1. $\frac{5}{8}$; $\frac{1}{2}$ 2. $\frac{9}{10}$; 1

Estimate each sum or difference.

3. $\frac{5}{16} + \frac{5}{8}$ 1
4. $\frac{10}{12} + \frac{4}{5}$ 2
5. $\frac{8}{10} - \frac{1}{2}$ $\frac{1}{2}$
6. $4\frac{1}{4} - 1\frac{7}{9}$ 2
7. $8\frac{6}{8} - 2\frac{1}{3}$ 7
8. $2\frac{2}{5} - \frac{5}{6}$ 1
9. $\frac{3}{4} + \frac{3}{8}$ $1\frac{1}{2}$
10. $7\frac{7}{10} - \frac{1}{6}$ $\frac{1}{2}$
11. $5\frac{7}{8} + 3\frac{3}{4}$ 10
12. $8\frac{1}{12} - 3\frac{9}{10}$ 4
13. $6\frac{5}{7} - 2\frac{2}{9}$ 5
14. $3\frac{5}{8} + 2\frac{3}{10}$ 6

15. Name three fractions that round to $\frac{1}{2}$.
   Answers may vary. Sample: $\frac{3}{8}$, $\frac{2}{5}$, $\frac{1}{3}$

16. Name three fractions that round to 1.
   Answers may vary. Sample: $1\frac{9}{8}$, $\frac{9}{10}$, $\frac{11}{12}$

17. The fabric for the play costumes costs $5.95/yd. Patti needs $2\frac{6}{8}$ yd for one costume and $3\frac{5}{8}$ yd for another one. About how much will she spend on these costumes?
   about $39

18. One bag of oranges costs $2.99 and weighs about $3\frac{7}{8}$ lb. Individual oranges are sold at $.89/lb. Which is the better buy? Explain.
   The bag for $2.99 is the better buy because it weighs about 4 lb, and the oranges cost about $.75/lb. It would cost about $3.60 to buy 4 lb at $.90/lb.

In copymaster and workbook formats

RETEACHING

Reteaching 6-1 *Estimating Sums and Differences*

Estimate sums and differences of fractions by rounding to 0, $\frac{1}{2}$, or 1.

Add: $\frac{4}{5} + \frac{3}{8}$

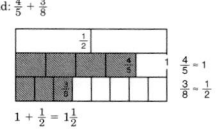

$\frac{4}{5} = 1$
$\frac{3}{8} = \frac{1}{2}$

$1 + \frac{1}{2} = 1\frac{1}{2}$

$\frac{4}{5} + \frac{3}{8} \approx 1\frac{1}{2}$

Estimate sums and differences of mixed numbers by rounding to the nearest whole number.

Subtract: $3\frac{1}{6} - 1\frac{9}{10}$

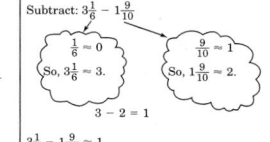

$\frac{1}{6} \approx 0$ So, $3\frac{1}{6} \approx 3$.
$\frac{9}{10} \approx 1$ So, $1\frac{9}{10} \approx 2$.

$3 - 2 = 1$

$3\frac{1}{6} - 1\frac{9}{10} \approx 1$

Estimate each sum or difference.

1. $\frac{7}{8} + \frac{1}{16}$ 1
2. $\frac{9}{10} + \frac{4}{5}$ 2
3. $\frac{15}{16} - \frac{1}{9}$ 1
4. $\frac{5}{8} - \frac{3}{7}$ 0
5. $\frac{21}{25} + \frac{1}{6}$ 1
6. $\frac{1}{2} + \frac{1}{18}$ $\frac{1}{2}$
7. $\frac{4}{10} - \frac{2}{15}$ $\frac{1}{2}$
8. $\frac{6}{7} + \frac{4}{5}$ 2
9. $\frac{7}{10} + \frac{3}{24}$ $\frac{1}{2}$
10. $\frac{5}{9} + \frac{1}{15}$ $\frac{1}{2}$
11. $\frac{1}{10} + \frac{1}{8}$ 0
12. $\frac{7}{18} + \frac{2}{10}$ 0
13. $\frac{6}{7} + \frac{2}{3}$ 2
14. $\frac{11}{12} - \frac{9}{10}$ 0
15. $\frac{13}{14} - \frac{4}{7}$ $\frac{1}{2}$
16. $6\frac{1}{8} + 2\frac{9}{10}$ 9
17. $1\frac{1}{5} - \frac{9}{10}$ 0
18. $3\frac{8}{9} + 4\frac{8}{9}$ 9
19. $8\frac{1}{12} - \frac{8}{10}$ 7
20. $5\frac{8}{9} + 3\frac{2}{13}$ 9
21. $6\frac{9}{11} - 1\frac{1}{8}$ 6
22. $12\frac{7}{8} - \frac{11}{12}$ 12
23. $9\frac{7}{9} - \frac{9}{10}$ 9
24. $15\frac{3}{8} + 1\frac{1}{9}$ $16\frac{1}{2}$
25. $17\frac{2}{7} + \frac{8}{11}$ 18
26. $7\frac{1}{4} - \frac{15}{16}$ 6
27. $5\frac{1}{8} + \frac{13}{16}$ 6

Solve.

28. Katrina has a $7\frac{1}{2}$-ft roll of ribbon. She needs 2 strips of ribbon that measure $3\frac{5}{8}$-ft long each. Does she need more ribbon? **yes**

29. Ricardo jogged $3\frac{3}{4}$ mi on Monday and $2\frac{1}{5}$ on Wednesday. Estimate the total number of miles he jogged.
   6 mi

ENRICHMENT

Minds on Math Transparency

6-1

Fill in each ☐ with one of the digits 4, 5, 6, 7, 8, or 9 to find the least possible difference. Use each digit only once.

☐☐☐
−☐☐☐

745
− 698
47

See Solution Key for worked-out answers.

1 Focus

CONNECTING TO PRIOR KNOWLEDGE Tell students: *Describe the models you might use to find 0.3 − 0.1.* **Answers may vary. Sample: Shade three out of ten spaces in one model and one out of ten in another.** *Could you use the same models to solve $\frac{3}{10} - \frac{1}{10}$?* **yes** Discuss the differences

between decimal and fraction models. We base decimal models on multiples of ten; fractions have any number of parts.

2 Teach

THINK AND DISCUSS

KINESTHETIC LEARNING Ask a volunteer to stand at one end of the classroom and walk $\frac{1}{3}$ of the way across the room. Write $\frac{1}{3}$ on the

board. Now ask the student to walk another $\frac{1}{3}$ of the distance. Next to the $\frac{1}{3}$ on the board, write "+ $\frac{1}{3}$ =." Ask the class: *What fraction of the way across the room has the student walked?* $\frac{2}{3}$ Write $\frac{2}{3}$ on the board. Repeat the activity with other fractions and other volunteers.

Questions 3 and 4 Have students explain why $1\frac{2}{4}$ and $\frac{2}{12}$ are not in lowest terms. **Answers may vary. Sample: You can divide both parts of $1\frac{2}{4}$ and $\frac{2}{12}$ by 2.**

Lesson Planning Options

Prerequisite Skills

• modeling fractions (precourse)

Materials/Manipulatives

• fraction bars

Resources

 Student Edition

Skills Handbook, pp. 538, 539
Extra Practice, p. 527
Glossary/Study Guide

 Teaching Resources

Chapter Support File, Ch. 6
• Lesson Planner 6-2
• Practice 6-2, Reteaching 6-2
• Answer Masters 6-2
Teaching Aids Masters 3, 10, 20–25
Glossary, Spanish Resources

 Transparencies

11, 12, 22–29, 88, Minds on Math 6-2

Warm Up

Erica had a piece of red licorice 15 in. long. If she cut it into 10 equal pieces, how long would each piece be? **$1\frac{1}{2}$ in.**

232

ALGEBRA Connection

6-2 Modeling Like Denominators

What You'll Learn

▼1 To add fractions with like denominators

▼2 To subtract fractions with like denominators

...And Why

You can solve problems involving portions of pizza and apple pie.

Here's How

Look for questions that
⊞ build understanding
✔ check understanding

THINK AND DISCUSS

▼1 *Adding Fractions with Like Denominators*

Food A pizza is cut into eight equal pieces. Suppose you eat two pieces and your friend eats three pieces. What portion of the pizza has been eaten? What portion of the pizza is left? You can model this problem with circles.

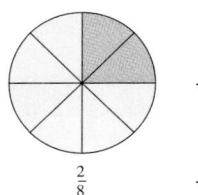 + 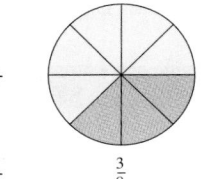 =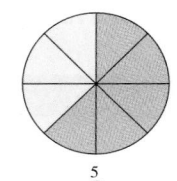

$$\frac{2}{8} \quad + \quad \frac{3}{8} \quad = \quad \frac{5}{8}$$

1. ✔*Try It Out* What fraction represents the amount of pizza you have eaten? What fraction represents the amount of pizza your friend has eaten? What portion of the pizza has been eaten? **$\frac{2}{8}$; $\frac{3}{8}$; $\frac{5}{8}$ of the pizza**

You can use fraction models to show addition problems.

■ EXAMPLE 1

Find $\frac{1}{10} + \frac{5}{10}$. Write the answer in simplest form.

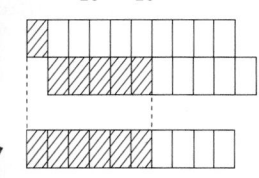

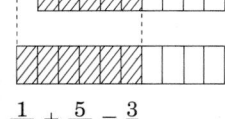

$$\begin{array}{r} \frac{1}{10} \\ + \frac{5}{10} \\ \hline \end{array}$$

Add the numerators. The denominators remain the same.

$$\frac{6}{10} = \frac{3}{5}$$

Simplify. Divide the numerator and denominator by the GCF of 2.

$$\frac{1}{10} + \frac{5}{10} = \frac{3}{5}$$

2. ✔*Try It Out* Add. Write each answer in simplest form.
a. $\frac{2}{5} + \frac{1}{5}$ **$\frac{3}{5}$** **b.** $\frac{1}{6} + \frac{1}{6}$ **$\frac{1}{3}$** **c.** $\frac{3}{10} + \frac{7}{10}$ **1** **d.** $\frac{5}{8} + \frac{1}{8}$ **$\frac{3}{4}$**

TACTILE LEARNING **Question 6** Some students may need to work with fraction bars.

ERROR ALERT! Students may try to subtract or add denominators. **Remediation:** Remind students that the denominator tells the number of equal parts in the whole. Have students use fraction bars to show that the denominator stays the same when they add and subtract fractions. Suggest they write the denominators first before adding or subtracting the numerators.

■ **ADDITIONAL EXAMPLES**

FOR EXAMPLE 1
Add $\frac{1}{12} + \frac{5}{12}$. Write the answer in simplest form. $\frac{1}{2}$

FOR EXAMPLE 2
Subtract $\frac{11}{15} - \frac{8}{15}$. Write the answer in simplest form. $\frac{1}{5}$

CONNECTION TO HOUSEHOLD Ask students to share examples of how they might use addition or subtraction of fractions to change recipes.

ASSESSMENT Pair students. Have each student write a fraction with an 8 in the denominator. One partner adds the fractions, the other checks the answer by estimating. Remind students to simplify their answers. Students switch roles to subtract the fractions.

Technology Options

Prentice Hall Technology

💾 📀 **Software for Learners**
• Math Blaster® Mystery*
• Interactive Student Tutorial, Chapter 6*

💾 📀 **Teaching Resource Software**
• Computer Item Generator 6-2
• Resource Pro™ Chapter 6*

Internet • For related mathematics activities, visit the Prentice Hall site at www.phschool.com/math

*Available on CD-ROM only

QUICKreview

To write an improper fraction as a mixed number, divide the numerator by the denominator.

The sum of fractions is sometimes greater than 1.

3. ▪*Algebra* Write the addition sentence for the model shown below. Write the sum as a mixed number in lowest terms.

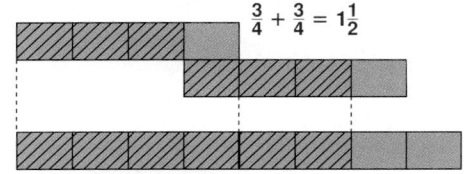

$$\frac{3}{4} + \frac{3}{4} = 1\frac{1}{2}$$

Now you may assign Exercises 1–18, 42, 44–46.

▼2 *Subtracting Fractions with Like Denominators*

Suppose an apple pie was cut into twelve equal pieces. There are three pieces left. You eat one piece. What portion of the pie is left?

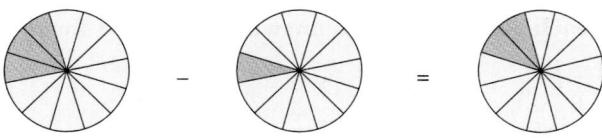

4. ▪*Algebra* Write a subtraction sentence for the problem above. $\frac{3}{12} - \frac{1}{12} = \frac{1}{6}$

You can also use fraction models to subtract.

■ **EXAMPLE 2**

Find $\frac{3}{12} - \frac{1}{12}$. Write the answer in simplest form.

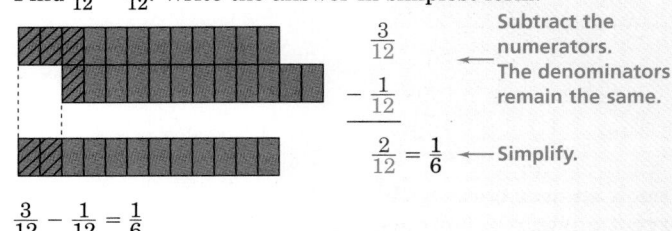

$$\begin{aligned} &\frac{3}{12} \\ -\,&\frac{1}{12} \\ \hline &\frac{2}{12} = \frac{1}{6} \end{aligned}$$

← Subtract the numerators. The denominators remain the same.

← Simplify.

$$\frac{3}{12} - \frac{1}{12} = \frac{1}{6}$$

5. ✔*Try It Out* Subtract. Write each answer in simplest form.
 a. $\frac{3}{5} - \frac{2}{5}$ $\frac{1}{5}$ **b.** $\frac{3}{4} - \frac{1}{4}$ $\frac{1}{2}$ **c.** $\frac{7}{10} - \frac{3}{10}$ $\frac{2}{5}$ **d.** $\frac{5}{12} - \frac{1}{12}$ $\frac{1}{3}$

6. ▪*Algebra* Explain the steps you would follow to solve the equation $\frac{3}{8} + x = \frac{7}{8}$. Subtract $\frac{3}{8}$ from each side. Compute $\frac{7}{8} - \frac{3}{8}$.

Assignment Options for Exercises On Your Own

To provide flexible scheduling, this lesson can be subdivided into parts.

▼1 **Core** 1–17, 42, 44, 46
 Extension 18, 45

▼2 **Core** 19–41
 Extension 43

Use Mixed Review to maintain skills.

3 Practice/Assess

EXERCISES *On Your Own*

VISUAL LEARNING Exercises 4–17 Have students pick three problems and draw models to support their answers.

CONNECTION TO ALGEBRA Exercises 38–42 Have students check their answers by substituting their answer for *x* and adding or subtracting.

DIVERSITY Exercise 43 Have students bring in family recipes. They can exchange recipes and write questions using them.

KINESTHETIC LEARNING and OPEN-ENDED Exercise 45 Have students try to score a basket by tossing a paper ball into the trash can. Ask them to count the number of baskets scored in 12 tries. Ask: *What fraction of tosses did not go in?* **Answers may vary.** Have them draw a model to show their answer.

WRITING Exercise 46 Challenge students to write another statement and describe what it could represent on the flag. Students can use flags from other countries or design their own flag.

WRAP UP

IDENTIFYING THE BIG IDEA Ask students to describe how to add and subtract fractions with like denominators.

pages 232–234 Think and Discuss

7. **Answers may vary. Sample: Two apples weigh a total of $\frac{7}{8}$ lb. One apple weighs $\frac{3}{8}$ lb. How much does the other apple weigh? Answer: $\frac{1}{2}$ lb; Check students' work.**

pages 234–235 On Your Own

18.

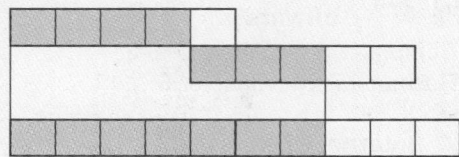

7. ♣ *Open-ended* Write a problem that could be solved using the equation in Question 6. Solve the problem. Justify your solution. **See margin.**

Now you may assign Exercises 19–41, 43.

EXERCISES *On Your Own*

Algebra **Write an addition sentence for each model.**

1.
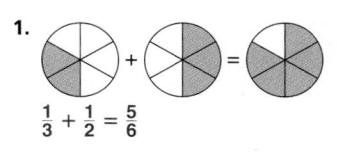
$$\frac{1}{3} + \frac{1}{2} = \frac{5}{6}$$

2.

$$\frac{1}{5} + \frac{3}{5} = \frac{4}{5}$$

3.
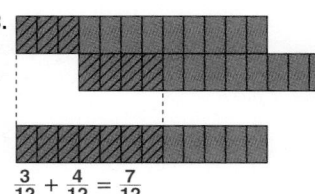
$$\frac{3}{12} + \frac{4}{12} = \frac{7}{12}$$

Find each sum. Write each answer in simplest form.

4. $\frac{3}{5} + \frac{1}{5}$ $\frac{4}{5}$
5. $\frac{7}{12} + \frac{5}{12}$ 1
6. $\frac{2}{6} + \frac{3}{6}$ $\frac{5}{6}$
7. $\frac{3}{10} + \frac{2}{10}$ $\frac{1}{2}$
8. $\frac{1}{3} + \frac{1}{3}$ $\frac{2}{3}$

9. $\frac{5}{12} + \frac{5}{12}$ $\frac{5}{6}$
10. $\frac{3}{4} + \frac{1}{4}$ 1
11. $\frac{1}{2} + \frac{1}{2}$ 1
12. $\frac{1}{4} + \frac{2}{4}$ $\frac{3}{4}$
13. $\frac{9}{16} + \frac{3}{16}$ $\frac{3}{4}$

14. $\frac{1}{20} + \frac{3}{20} + \frac{5}{20}$ $\frac{9}{20}$
15. $\frac{27}{100} + \frac{41}{100} + \frac{3}{100}$ $\frac{71}{100}$
16. $\frac{4}{15} + \frac{1}{15} + \frac{7}{15}$ $\frac{4}{5}$
17. $\frac{19}{50} + \frac{9}{50} + \frac{7}{50}$ $\frac{7}{10}$

18. *Modeling* Draw a model to represent $\frac{4}{5} + \frac{3}{5} = \frac{7}{5}$. Write $\frac{7}{5}$ as a mixed number. Compare the result to your model. **Models may vary. See margin for sample model; $1\frac{2}{5}$.**

Algebra **Write a subtraction sentence for each model.**

19.

$$\frac{9}{10} - \frac{7}{10} = \frac{2}{10}$$

20.
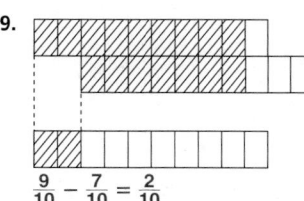
$$\frac{4}{6} - \frac{1}{6} = \frac{1}{2}$$

21.
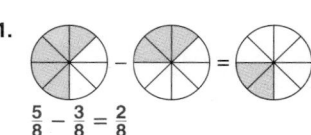
$$\frac{5}{8} - \frac{3}{8} = \frac{2}{8}$$

Is each answer correct? Write *yes* or *no*. If *no*, write the correct answer in simplest form.

22. $\frac{3}{10} + \frac{3}{10} = \frac{4}{5}$ **no; $\frac{3}{5}$**
23. $\frac{7}{12} - \frac{3}{12} = \frac{5}{6}$ **no; $\frac{1}{3}$**
24. $\frac{5}{6} + \frac{4}{6} = 1\frac{1}{2}$ **yes**
25. $\frac{3}{4} - \frac{1}{4} = \frac{1}{2}$ **yes**
26. $\frac{11}{12} - \frac{5}{12} = 2\frac{1}{12}$ **no; $\frac{1}{2}$**

27. *Measurement* A piece of thread is $\frac{9}{16}$ in. long. Another piece of thread is $\frac{7}{16}$ in. long.
   a. To compare their lengths, would you add or subtract? **Subtract.**
   b. Compare their lengths. Justify your solution. $\frac{1}{8}$ in.; check students' work for reasoning.

234

LESSON QUIZ

Find each sum or difference. Write each
answer in simplest form.

1. $\frac{14}{19} - \frac{9}{19}$ $\frac{5}{19}$

2. $\frac{3}{10} + \frac{4}{10}$ $\frac{7}{10}$

Find x.

3. $\frac{4}{9} - x = \frac{2}{9}$ $x = \frac{2}{9}$

4. $x + \frac{4}{5} = \frac{6}{5}$ $x = \frac{2}{5}$

Find each difference. Write each answer in simplest form.

28. $\frac{7}{10} - \frac{4}{10}$ $\frac{3}{10}$

29. $\frac{4}{5} - \frac{2}{5}$ $\frac{2}{5}$

30. $\frac{5}{6} - \frac{1}{6}$ $\frac{2}{3}$

31. $\frac{3}{4} - \frac{2}{4}$ $\frac{1}{4}$

32. $\frac{10}{12} - \frac{5}{12}$ $\frac{5}{12}$

33. $\frac{2}{3} - \frac{1}{3}$ $\frac{1}{3}$

34. $\frac{9}{10} - \frac{3}{10}$ $\frac{3}{5}$

35. $\frac{2}{4} - \frac{1}{4}$ $\frac{1}{4}$

36. $\frac{8}{12} - \frac{5}{12}$ $\frac{1}{4}$

37. $\frac{9}{10} - \frac{7}{10}$ $\frac{1}{5}$

Algebra **Find x.**

38. $\frac{5}{6} - \frac{1}{6} = x$ $\frac{2}{3}$

39. $\frac{3}{10} + x = \frac{8}{10}$ $\frac{1}{2}$

40. $x + \frac{2}{5} = \frac{4}{5}$ $\frac{2}{5}$

41. $x = \frac{2}{8} + \frac{5}{8}$ $\frac{7}{8}$

42. $x - \frac{1}{3} = \frac{1}{3}$ $\frac{2}{3}$

43. *Cooking* Peanut sauce is commonly used as a base for
stews and soups in Nigeria, Ghana, and Sierra Leone.
   a. To make the sauce spicier, you decide to double the $\frac{1}{2}$ tbsp
   amount of cayenne. How much cayenne will you use?
   b. You decide to use equal amounts of apple and apricot
   juices. How much of each type of juice will you use? $\frac{1}{4}$ c

44. *Modeling* In an archery tournament, Zwena hit the target
9 times out of 12. What fraction of Zwena's arrows did not
hit the target? Draw a model to show your solution.
See below right.

45. *Open-ended* Write a problem that could be solved using
one of the equations from Exercises 38–42.
Check students' work.

46. *Writing* The flag of Thailand
is at the right. Describe what
each statement could represent
on the flag.
   a. $\frac{1}{6} + \frac{1}{6} = \frac{1}{3}$ b. $\frac{6}{6} - \frac{4}{6} = \frac{1}{3}$
   Answers may vary. See right for samples.

Peanut Sauce

2 cups chopped onion
1 tablespoon peanut oil
¼ tablespoon cayenne
¼ teaspoon ground ginger
1 ripe banana
1 cup tomato juice
½ cup apple or
   apricot juice
½ cup peanut butter
½ teaspoon salt

44. $\frac{1}{4}$ of the arrows

46a. the portion of the flag that
is white

b. the portion of the flag that
is not red or white

Mixed Review

Write using an exponent. *(Lesson 4-2)*

47. $6 \times 6 \times 6 \times 6$ 6^4

48. $22 \times 22 \times 22$ 22^3

49. $5.8 \times 5.8 \times 5.8 \times 5.8 \times 5.8$ 5.8^5

Find the GCF of each set of numbers. *(Lesson 5-3)*

50. 14, 21 7

51. 10, 15, 20 5

52. 13, 17 1

53. 36, 27 9

54. 24, 60, 72 12

55. *Choose a Strategy* Jan and Leah earn money running
errands for neighbors. Leah earns $1.25 more per hour than
Jan. If together they earned $15.75 for 3 hours of work, how
much did each earn per hour? **Jan: $2.00; Leah: $3.25**

PRACTICE

Practice 6-2 *Modeling Like Denominators*

Write an addition sentence for each model.

1. 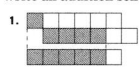   2.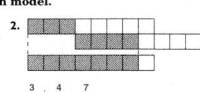

$\frac{1}{6} + \frac{4}{6} = \frac{5}{6}$ $\frac{3}{8} + \frac{4}{8} = \frac{7}{8}$

Write a subtraction sentence for each model.

3. 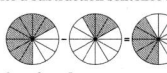   4.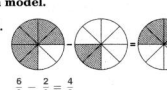

$\frac{8}{12} - \frac{3}{12} = \frac{5}{12}$ $\frac{6}{8} - \frac{2}{8} = \frac{4}{8}$

**Find each sum or difference. Write each answer in
simplest form.**

5. $\frac{1}{4} + \frac{2}{4}$ $\frac{3}{4}$

6. $\frac{7}{10} - \frac{4}{10}$ $\frac{3}{10}$

7. $\frac{5}{8} - \frac{3}{8}$ $\frac{1}{4}$

8. $\frac{1}{8} + \frac{5}{8}$ $\frac{3}{4}$

9. $\frac{5}{8} + \frac{2}{8}$ $\frac{7}{8}$

10. $\frac{3}{10} + \frac{6}{10}$ $\frac{9}{10}$

11. $\frac{11}{12} - \frac{5}{12}$ $\frac{1}{2}$

12. $\frac{11}{16} - \frac{3}{16}$ $\frac{1}{2}$

13. $\frac{3}{6} + \frac{1}{6}$ $\frac{2}{3}$

14. $\frac{7}{9} - \frac{3}{9}$ $\frac{4}{9}$

15. What is the total amount of sugar the
recipe at the right calls for?
$\frac{1}{2}$ c

16. Martha decides to double the recipe.
How much brown sugar will she use?
$\frac{1}{2}$ c

Martha's Cookie Recipe
1 cup shortening
2 eggs
¼ cup white sugar
¼ cup brown sugar
1½ cup flour
1 teaspoon vanilla

In copymaster and workbook formats

RETEACHING

Reteaching 6-2 *Modeling Like Denominators*

Add: $\frac{1}{6} + \frac{3}{6}$ Subtract: $\frac{7}{10} - \frac{2}{10}$

Use models to show the addition.   Use models to show the subtraction.

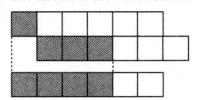   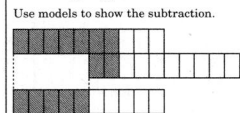

Step 1 Combine
numerators over the
denominator. $\frac{1}{6} + \frac{3}{6} = \frac{1+3}{6}$

Step 2 Add numerators. $= \frac{4}{6}$

Step 3 Simplify, if
possible. $= \frac{2}{3}$

$\frac{1}{6} + \frac{3}{6} = \frac{2}{3}$

Step 1 Combine
numerators over the
denominator. $\frac{7}{10} - \frac{2}{10} = \frac{7-2}{10}$

Step 2 Subtract
numerators. $= \frac{5}{10}$

Step 3 Simplify, if
possible. $= \frac{1}{2}$

$\frac{7}{10} - \frac{2}{10} = \frac{1}{2}$

Find each sum. Write it in simplest form.

1. $\frac{1}{5} + \frac{3}{5}$ $\frac{4}{5}$

2. $\frac{4}{6} + \frac{1}{6}$ $\frac{5}{6}$

3. $\frac{3}{12} + \frac{3}{12}$ $\frac{1}{2}$

4. $\frac{6}{10} + \frac{1}{10}$ $\frac{7}{10}$

5. $\frac{3}{10} + \frac{2}{10}$ $\frac{1}{2}$

6. $\frac{6}{12} + \frac{3}{12}$ $\frac{3}{4}$

7. $\frac{5}{8} + \frac{1}{8}$ $\frac{3}{4}$

8. $\frac{3}{8} + \frac{3}{8}$ $\frac{3}{4}$

9. $\frac{3}{8} + \frac{1}{8}$ $\frac{1}{2}$

Find each difference. Write it in simplest form.

10. $\frac{6}{8} - \frac{3}{8}$ $\frac{3}{8}$

11. $\frac{9}{10} - \frac{3}{10}$ $\frac{3}{5}$

12. $\frac{3}{4} - \frac{1}{4}$ $\frac{1}{2}$

13. $\frac{7}{12} - \frac{1}{12}$ $\frac{1}{2}$

14. $\frac{8}{10} - \frac{6}{10}$ $\frac{1}{5}$

15. $\frac{4}{6} - \frac{2}{6}$ $\frac{1}{3}$

16. $\frac{5}{10} - \frac{1}{10}$ $\frac{2}{5}$

17. $\frac{7}{12} - \frac{6}{12}$ $\frac{1}{12}$

18. $\frac{9}{10} - \frac{4}{10}$ $\frac{1}{2}$

ENRICHMENT

M inds on Math Transparency

6-2

Margaret and Jimmy are playing a game called 99 to 100.
They start with 99 and add or subtract certain numbers until
they reach 100. The object is to be the first player to get to
100. Margaret and Jimmy decided that they would only be
allowed to add 11 or subtract 7 on each move. What is the
fewest number of moves that can be made before someone
wins the game?

5 moves

See *Solution Key* for worked-out answers.

235

1 Focus

CONNECTING TO PRIOR KNOWLEDGE

Write $\frac{2}{5} + \frac{3}{5}$, $\frac{3}{8} - \frac{1}{8}$, $\frac{5}{9} + \frac{2}{9}$, and $3\frac{1}{2} - \frac{1}{2}$ on the board. Ask:

- *What do these problems have in common?* Answers may vary. Sample: The denominators in each statement are the same.
- *What if the denominators were different? How can you add or subtract fractions with different denominators?* Answers may vary. Sample: Estimate the answer; make the denominators the same.

2 Teach

THINK AND DISCUSS

Question 1 Discuss with students how to find the appropriate fraction model to represent the problems. Ask: *How many parts should each model be divided into?* **1a: 10; 1b: 6; 1c: 12; 1d: 12** *How did you choose these numbers?* **Answers may vary. Sample: Each was the LCD for the pair.**

Lesson Planning Options

Prerequisite Skills
- finding the LCD (5-7)
- solving equations using addition and subtraction (2-6)

Materials/Manipulatives
- fraction bars

Resources

 Student Edition

Skills Handbook, p. 540
Extra Practice, p. 527
Glossary/Study Guide

Teaching Resources

Chapter Support File, Ch. 6
- Lesson Planner 6-3
- Practice 6-3, Reteaching 6-3
- Answer Masters 6-3
Teaching Aids Masters 10, 20–25
Glossary, Spanish Resources

Transparencies

11, 12, 19, 22–29, 88, Minds on Math 6-3

Warm Up

In Ms. Nicolay's class of 6 students, each person shakes hands once with each of the other people in the class. How many handshakes are exchanged? **15**

6-3 *Unlike Denominators*

What You'll Learn

▼**1** To use fraction models to add and subtract fractions with unlike denominators

▼**2** To use equivalent fractions to add and subtract fractions with unlike denominators

...And Why

You can add fractions of distances with different denominators.

Here's How

Look for questions that
⠿ build understanding
✔ check understanding

THINK AND DISCUSS

▼**1** *Using Fraction Models*

You can use fraction models when the denominators are different.

■ EXAMPLE 1

Model the sum $\frac{1}{4} + \frac{2}{3}$.

←Use the fraction model for $\frac{1}{4}$.

←Use the fraction model for $\frac{2}{3}$.

Find a fraction model to represent the sum.

$\frac{1}{4} + \frac{2}{3} = \frac{11}{12}$

Sometimes even when the fractions have different denominators, you can use other fraction models to add or subtract.

■ EXAMPLE 2

Model the difference $\frac{1}{2} - \frac{1}{3}$.

←Use the $\frac{3}{6}$ fraction model for $\frac{1}{2}$.

←Use the $\frac{2}{6}$ fraction model for $\frac{1}{3}$.

←Subtract: $\frac{3}{6} - \frac{2}{6}$.

$\frac{1}{2} - \frac{1}{3} = \frac{3}{6} - \frac{2}{6} = \frac{1}{6}$

a–d. See back of book for models.
1. ✔*Try It Out* Model each sum or difference.
   a. $\frac{3}{5} + \frac{1}{10}$ $\frac{7}{10}$ b. $\frac{5}{6} - \frac{2}{3}$ $\frac{1}{6}$ c. $\frac{1}{3} + \frac{1}{4}$ $\frac{7}{12}$ d. $\frac{5}{12} - \frac{1}{4}$ $\frac{1}{6}$

Now you may assign Exercises 1–22.

236

AEP **VISUAL LEARNING** **Question 2**

Some students may need to review the term *least common denominator.* Write on the board:

least	→ smallest
common	→ same
denominator	→ down number

Have students list in increasing order five fractions equivalent to $\frac{1}{2}$ and five fractions equivalent to $\frac{1}{5}$. **Answers may vary. Sample:**
$\frac{2}{4}, \frac{3}{6}, \frac{4}{8}, \frac{5}{10}, \frac{6}{12}; \frac{2}{10}, \frac{3}{15}, \frac{4}{20}, \frac{5}{25}, \frac{6}{30}$ Then ask them

to circle the smallest "down number" that is in both lists. **10** Say: *This is the LCD.*

■ **ADDITIONAL EXAMPLES**

FOR EXAMPLE 1
Model the sum $\frac{1}{5} + \frac{1}{2}$. $\frac{7}{10}$

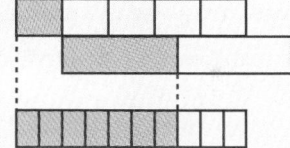

FOR EXAMPLE 2
Model the difference $\frac{5}{6} - \frac{1}{2}$. $\frac{1}{3}$

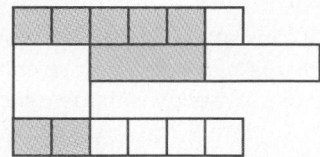

FOR EXAMPLE 3
Find the sum $\frac{3}{7} + \frac{1}{3}$. $\frac{16}{21}$

---

2 *Using Equivalent Fractions*

QUICKreview

The least common denominator (LCD) is the least common multiple (LCM) of the denominators.

To write equivalent fractions, you must first find the least common denominator (LCD) of the fractions.

2. a. ✔*Try It Out* What is the LCD of $\frac{1}{2}$ and $\frac{1}{5}$? **10**

   b. *Go a Step Further* Write equivalent fractions for $\frac{1}{2}$ and $\frac{1}{5}$ using the LCD you found in part (a). $\frac{1}{2} = \frac{5}{10}; \frac{1}{5} = \frac{2}{10}$

■ **EXAMPLE 3**

Find the sum $\frac{7}{8} + \frac{1}{6}$.

Estimate: $\frac{7}{8} + \frac{1}{6} \approx 1 + 0 = 1$

The LCD of $\frac{7}{8}$ and $\frac{1}{6}$ is 24. ←——Find the LCM of 8 and 6.

$$\begin{aligned} \frac{7}{8} &= \frac{7 \times 3}{8 \times 3} = \frac{21}{24} \\ + \frac{1}{6} &= \frac{1 \times 4}{6 \times 4} = \frac{4}{24} \\ \hline &= \frac{25}{24} \\ &= 1\frac{1}{24} \end{aligned}$$

The LCD is 24. Write the fractions with the same denominators.

←——Add the numerators.

←——Write the answer as a mixed number. The answer is close to the estimate.

CALCULATOR HINT

Some calculators can compute with fractions.

3. ✔*Try It Out* Find each sum or difference.

  a. $\frac{2}{9} + \frac{1}{6}$ $\frac{7}{18}$ **b.** $\frac{7}{8} - \frac{1}{2}$ $\frac{3}{8}$ **c.** $\frac{7}{8} + \frac{1}{10}$ $\frac{39}{40}$ **d.** $\frac{4}{5} - \frac{2}{3}$ $\frac{2}{15}$

Sometimes you must add or subtract fractions to solve equations.

■ **EXAMPLE 4**

Algebra Solve the equation $\frac{1}{2} + x = \frac{14}{15}$.

$$\begin{aligned} \frac{1}{2} + x &= \frac{14}{15} \qquad \text{←——Write the equation.} \\ \frac{1}{2} + x - \frac{1}{2} &= \frac{14}{15} - \frac{1}{2} \qquad \text{←——Subtract } \tfrac{1}{2} \text{ from each side.} \\ x &= \frac{14}{15} - \frac{1}{2} \\ x &= \frac{28}{30} - \frac{15}{30} \qquad \text{←——Write equivalent fractions.} \\ x &= \frac{13}{30} \qquad \text{←——Subtract.} \end{aligned}$$

4. ✔*Try It Out* Solve each equation.

  a. $\frac{3}{4} + x = \frac{11}{12}$ $\frac{1}{6}$ **b.** $x - \frac{1}{12} = \frac{5}{6}$ $\frac{11}{12}$ **c.** $\frac{5}{8} + x = \frac{11}{12}$ $\frac{7}{24}$

Now you may assign Exercises 23–58.

Technology Options

Prentice Hall Technology

💾 💿 **Software for Learners**
- Hot Page™ 16*
- Math Blaster® Mystery*
- Interactive Student Tutorial, Chapter 6*

💾 💿 **Teaching Resource Software**
- Computer Item Generator 6-3
- Resource Pro™ Chapter 6*

Internet • For related mathematics activities, visit the Prentice Hall site at www.phschool.com/math

Available on CD-ROM only

Assignment Options for Exercises On Your Own

To provide flexible scheduling, this lesson can be subdivided into parts.

▼**Core** 1–17
   Extension 18–22

▼**Core** 23–53, 55–58
   Extension 54, 59

Use Mixed Review to maintain skills.

FOR EXAMPLE 4
Solve the equation $\frac{3}{15} + x = \frac{11}{30}$.
$x = \frac{5}{30}$ or $\frac{1}{6}$

Example 4 Ask students: *What number do you multiply the numerator and denominator of $\frac{14}{15}$ by to get a fraction with the denominator of 30?* **2**

ASSESSMENT Write $\frac{3}{4} + \frac{1}{6}$ on the board. Have students explain step-by-step how they would solve the problem. Ask:

- *What is the first thing you would do to solve this problem?* **Answers may vary. Sample: Make the denominators the same.**

- *What denominator would you choose?* **12** *Why?* **It is the LCD.**

- *After the fractions have the same denominator, what do you do?* **Add the numerators and write the sum.**

Have students follow the steps to find the sum. $\frac{11}{12}$

3 Practice/Assess

EXERCISES *On Your Own*

AUDITORY LEARNING Exercises 1–3 Have students work in pairs. One student looks at the text and describes a model aloud. Without looking at the text, the partner writes the number sentence and then reads it aloud. Have students switch roles.

Exercises 4–17 Remind students to find the LCD to help them check models.

---

pages 238–239   On Your Own

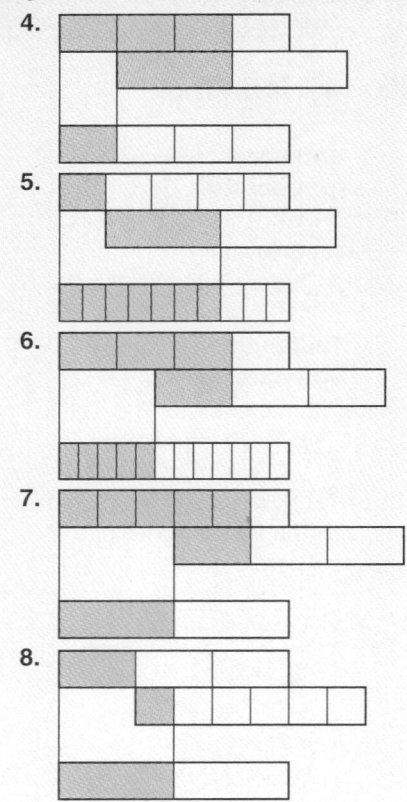

4.
5.
6.
7.
8.

EXERCISES *On Your Own*

Algebra **Write a number sentence for each model shown.**

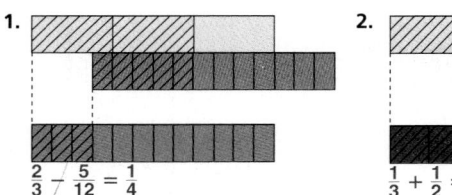

1.
$\frac{2}{3} - \frac{5}{12} = \frac{1}{4}$

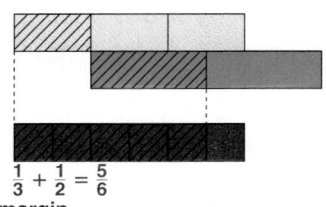

2.
$\frac{1}{3} + \frac{1}{2} = \frac{5}{6}$

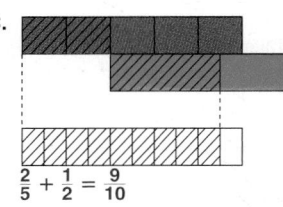

3.
$\frac{2}{5} + \frac{1}{2} = \frac{9}{10}$

Model each statement.   4–7. See margin.

4. $\frac{3}{4} - \frac{1}{2} = \frac{1}{4}$
5. $\frac{1}{5} + \frac{1}{2} = \frac{7}{10}$
6. $\frac{3}{4} - \frac{1}{3} = \frac{5}{12}$
7. $\frac{5}{6} - \frac{1}{3} = \frac{3}{6}$ or $\frac{1}{2}$

Model each sum or difference.   8. See margin for model.

8. $\frac{1}{3} + \frac{1}{6}$ $\frac{1}{2}$
9. $\frac{9}{10} - \frac{3}{5}$ $\frac{3}{10}$
10. $\frac{1}{3} + \frac{1}{2}$ $\frac{5}{6}$
11. $\frac{4}{5} - \frac{1}{10}$ $\frac{7}{10}$
12. $\frac{2}{3} + \frac{1}{12}$ $\frac{3}{4}$

13. $\frac{1}{6} + \frac{1}{3}$ $\frac{1}{2}$
14. $\frac{11}{12} - \frac{3}{4}$ $\frac{1}{6}$
15. $\frac{2}{3} + \frac{1}{4}$ $\frac{11}{12}$
16. $\frac{7}{12} - \frac{1}{4}$ $\frac{1}{3}$
17. $\frac{1}{2} - \frac{3}{10}$ $\frac{1}{5}$

Estimation **Is each answer greater than or less than 1?**

18. $\frac{1}{8} + \frac{1}{4}$
less
19. $\frac{4}{5} - \frac{1}{2}$
less
20. $\frac{1}{2} + \frac{3}{4}$
greater
21. $\frac{6}{7} - \frac{4}{5}$
less
22. $\frac{3}{4} + \frac{5}{12}$
greater

23. *Art* Suppose you use $\frac{3}{4}$ yd of felt on the top of a bulletin board display. Then you use another $\frac{2}{3}$ yd on the bottom of the display. How much felt do you use altogether? $1\frac{5}{12}$ **yd**

24. *Geology* Two students explore a cove along an old road. One student explores $\frac{1}{3}$ mi of the cove. The other explores $\frac{1}{4}$ mi of the cove at the opposite end. How much of the cove do they explore altogether? $\frac{7}{12}$ **mi**

Find each sum or difference. Use equivalent fractions.

25. $\frac{1}{3} + \frac{2}{5}$ $\frac{11}{15}$
26. $\frac{13}{16} - \frac{1}{4}$ $\frac{9}{16}$
27. $\frac{4}{5} - \frac{1}{2}$ $\frac{3}{10}$
28. $\frac{3}{4} + \frac{1}{3}$ $1\frac{1}{12}$
29. $\frac{4}{5} + \frac{1}{6}$ $\frac{29}{30}$

30. $\frac{7}{10} - \frac{1}{4}$ $\frac{9}{20}$
31. $\frac{3}{8} + \frac{4}{5}$ $1\frac{7}{40}$
32. $\frac{5}{6} + \frac{1}{4}$ $1\frac{1}{12}$
33. $\frac{5}{6} - \frac{1}{2}$ $\frac{1}{3}$
34. $\frac{7}{8} - \frac{1}{3}$ $\frac{13}{24}$

35. $\frac{7}{12} + \frac{2}{3}$ $1\frac{1}{4}$
36. $\frac{8}{9} + \frac{5}{6}$ $1\frac{13}{18}$
37. $\frac{7}{12} - \frac{1}{3}$ $\frac{1}{4}$
38. $\frac{2}{3} - \frac{1}{5}$ $\frac{7}{15}$
39. $\frac{5}{12} + \frac{7}{9}$ $1\frac{7}{36}$

40. $\frac{11}{20} + \frac{3}{4}$ $1\frac{3}{10}$
41. $\frac{17}{20} - \frac{2}{5}$ $\frac{9}{20}$
42. $\frac{3}{4} - \frac{1}{5}$ $\frac{11}{20}$
43. $\frac{9}{10} - \frac{7}{8}$ $\frac{1}{40}$
44. $\frac{11}{12} + \frac{9}{10}$ $1\frac{49}{60}$

ERROR ALERT! Students may use a common denominator other than the LCD to find equivalent fractions. **Remediation:** Suggest students list multiples of both denominators. Have students circle the least common denominator. Make sure students understand that if they use a denominator other than the LCD, they must simplify the answer.

EXTENSION Exercises 45–47 If you have extended class periods or block scheduling, have students work in groups to create their own population chart for a region of the world, a country, or a state. Suggest they find a fun

fact about each place and share their findings with the class.

CONNECTION TO ALGEBRA Exercises 48–53 Have students check answers by substituting their value for x into the equation.

CONNECTION TO NUMBER SENSE Exercise 59 Challenge students to solve all or part of the problem mentally. Let students work with a partner to try different strategies. Suggest rounding.

WRAP UP

IDENTIFYING THE BIG IDEA Ask students to describe how to find the sum or difference of fractions with unlike denominators.

Math at Work

If you have block scheduling or extended class periods, suggest that students work in small groups to plan and prepare a meal for the entire

Social Studies **Use the data at the right for Exercises 45–47.**

45. List the countries in order from least to greatest population. **Belize, Panama, Costa Rica, Nicaragua, Honduras, El Salvador, Guatemala**

46. Are the populations of Costa Rica and Nicaragua together greater than or less than the population of Honduras? **greater than**

47. Which country has a population almost equal to the populations of Belize and Honduras combined? **El Salvador**

Algebra **Find x. Write the answer in simplest form.**

48. $x - \frac{1}{2} = \frac{1}{6}$ **$\frac{2}{3}$**   49. $\frac{2}{5} + x = \frac{7}{10}$ **$\frac{3}{10}$**   50. $x + \frac{2}{5} = \frac{5}{12}$ **$\frac{1}{60}$**

51. $x - \frac{2}{3} = \frac{3}{4}$ **$1\frac{5}{12}$**   52. $\frac{1}{10} + x = \frac{7}{12}$ **$\frac{29}{60}$**   53. $x - \frac{2}{3} = \frac{7}{12}$ **$1\frac{1}{4}$**

54. *Writing* Describe two different ways to find the sum of $\frac{1}{6}$ and $\frac{3}{4}$. **You can use fraction models or you can use the LCD to rewrite the fractions.**

Choose **Use any method to add or subtract.**

55. $\frac{5}{8} + \frac{9}{12}$ **$1\frac{3}{8}$**   56. $\frac{11}{30} - \frac{1}{5}$ **$\frac{1}{6}$**   57. $\frac{2}{5} + \frac{1}{2}$ **$\frac{9}{10}$**   58. $\frac{3}{4} - \frac{1}{3}$ **$\frac{5}{12}$**

59. *Number Sense* A package of sliced ham weighs $\frac{1}{2}$ lb. Another package of sliced ham weighs $\frac{3}{4}$ lb. You buy both packages. Do you have enough ham to serve $\frac{1}{3}$ lb to each of four persons? **no**

Mixed Review

Name the type of graph (bar, line, or circle graph) most appropriate for each situation below. Support your answer. (Lesson 1-5)

60. average cost of lunch at six restaurants **bar graph**

61. change in taxes paid from 1950 to 2000 **line graph**

62. number of senior citizens', adults', and children's tickets sold at an art museum in one day **circle graph**

63. *Choose a Strategy* The last Friday of a certain month is the 28th day of the month. On what day of the week is the first day of that month? **Saturday**

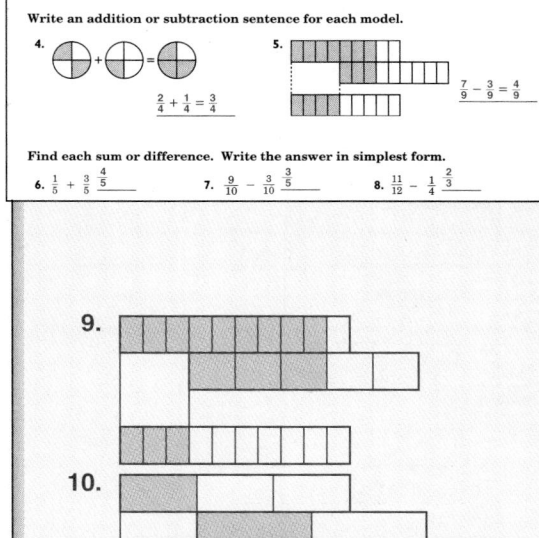

Population of Central America

Country	Portion of Population
Belize	$\frac{1}{125}$
Costa Rica	$\frac{11}{100}$
El Salvador	$\frac{9}{50}$
Guatemala	$\frac{8}{25}$
Honduras	$\frac{17}{100}$
Nicaragua	$\frac{3}{25}$
Panama	$\frac{2}{25}$

CHECKPOINT 1

▬▬ *Checkpoint 1*   Lessons 6-1 through 6-3

Estimate each sum or difference.

1. $2\frac{1}{3} + 3\frac{1}{6}$ **5**   2. $\frac{27}{28} - \frac{14}{17}$ **0**   3. $6\frac{3}{4} + 1\frac{2}{5}$ **8**

Write an addition or subtraction sentence for each model.

4. $\frac{2}{4} + \frac{1}{4} = \frac{3}{4}$

5. $\frac{7}{9} - \frac{3}{9} = \frac{4}{9}$

Find each sum or difference. Write the answer in simplest form.

6. $\frac{1}{5} + \frac{3}{5}$ **$\frac{4}{5}$**   7. $\frac{9}{10} - \frac{3}{10}$ **$\frac{3}{5}$**   8. $\frac{11}{12} - \frac{1}{4}$ **$\frac{2}{3}$**

9.

10.

11.

PRACTICE

Practice 6-3 Unlike Denominators

Write a number sentence for each model.

1.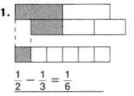

$\frac{1}{2} - \frac{1}{3} = \frac{1}{6}$

2.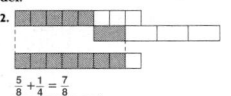

$\frac{5}{8} + \frac{1}{4} = \frac{7}{8}$

Find each sum or difference. Use equivalent fractions.

3. $\frac{1}{4} + \frac{2}{3}$ $\frac{11}{12}$

4. $\frac{2}{5} - \frac{1}{10}$ $\frac{3}{10}$

5. $\frac{1}{6} + \frac{1}{4}$ $\frac{5}{12}$

6. $\frac{5}{8} + \frac{1}{4}$ $\frac{7}{8}$

7. $\frac{7}{8} - \frac{1}{2}$ $\frac{3}{8}$

8. $\frac{3}{8} + \frac{4}{5}$ $1\frac{1}{10}$

9. $\frac{5}{6} - \frac{2}{5}$ $\frac{13}{30}$

10. $\frac{5}{12} - \frac{1}{4}$ $\frac{1}{6}$

11. $\frac{7}{16} + \frac{1}{8}$ $\frac{9}{16}$

12. $\frac{11}{16} + \frac{5}{8}$ $1\frac{5}{16}$

Use estimation to decide if the answer is greater or less than 1. Write > or <. Then add or subtract.

13. $\frac{2}{7} + \frac{1}{2}$ $<; \frac{11}{14}$

14. $\frac{4}{5} - \frac{3}{4}$ $<; \frac{1}{20}$

15. $\frac{2}{3} - \frac{1}{6}$ $<; \frac{1}{2}$

16. $\frac{5}{8} + \frac{2}{3}$ $>; 1\frac{7}{24}$

17. $\frac{5}{7} - \frac{1}{5}$ $<; \frac{18}{35}$

18. $\frac{3}{5} + \frac{7}{10}$ $>; 1\frac{3}{10}$

Find x. Write the answer in simplest form.

19. $x + \frac{1}{3} = \frac{5}{6}$ $\frac{1}{2}$

20. $x + \frac{1}{3} = \frac{4}{5}$ $\frac{7}{15}$

21. $x + \frac{2}{5} = \frac{11}{12}$ $\frac{31}{60}$

22. $x + \frac{5}{8} = \frac{11}{12}$ $\frac{7}{24}$

23. Jeanie has a $\frac{3}{4}$-yd piece of ribbon. She needs one $\frac{3}{8}$-yd piece and one $\frac{1}{2}$-yd piece. Can she cut the piece of ribbon into the two smaller pieces? Explain. Draw a model for the problem. No, she needs $\frac{3}{8} + \frac{1}{2} = \frac{7}{8}$; she has $\frac{3}{4} = \frac{6}{8}; \frac{7}{8} > \frac{6}{8}$. Check students' model.

In copymaster and workbook formats

RETEACHING

Reteaching 6-3 Unlike Denominators

To add or subtract fractions with unlike denominators, you can use equivalent fractions.

Add: $\frac{5}{6} + \frac{1}{2}$

Step 1 Find the least common denominator of 6 and 2.

The LCD is 6.

Step 2 Write equivalent fractions using the LCD.

$\frac{5}{6} = \frac{5}{6}$ $\frac{1}{2} = \frac{1 \times 3}{2 \times 3} = \frac{3}{6}$

Step 3 Add. Write the sum in simplest form.

$\frac{5}{6} + \frac{1}{2} = \frac{5}{6} + \frac{3}{6}$
$= \frac{5+3}{6}$
$= \frac{8}{6}$
$= \frac{4}{3}$
$= 1\frac{1}{3}$

$\frac{5}{6} + \frac{1}{2} = 1\frac{1}{3}$

Subtract: $\frac{4}{5} - \frac{1}{3}$

Step 1 Find the least common denominator of 5 and 3.

The LCD is 15.

Step 2 Write equivalent fractions using the LCD.

$\frac{4}{5} = \frac{4 \times 3}{5 \times 3} = \frac{12}{15}$ $\frac{1}{3} = \frac{1 \times 5}{3 \times 5} = \frac{5}{15}$

Step 3 Subtract. Write the difference in simplest form.

$\frac{4}{5} - \frac{1}{3} = \frac{12}{15} - \frac{5}{15}$
$= \frac{12-5}{15}$
$= \frac{7}{15}$

$\frac{4}{5} - \frac{1}{3} = \frac{7}{15}$

Find each sum or difference. Write it in simplest form.

1. $\frac{1}{2} + \frac{3}{4}$ $1\frac{1}{4}$

2. $\frac{11}{16} - \frac{5}{16}$ $\frac{3}{8}$

3. $\frac{1}{6} + \frac{1}{3}$ $\frac{1}{2}$

4. $\frac{7}{8} - \frac{1}{2}$ $\frac{3}{8}$

5. $\frac{9}{10} + \frac{1}{2}$ $1\frac{2}{5}$

6. $\frac{2}{3} + \frac{5}{9}$ $1\frac{2}{9}$

7. $\frac{1}{2} + \frac{7}{10}$ $1\frac{1}{5}$

8. $\frac{3}{4} - \frac{5}{12}$ $\frac{1}{3}$

9. $\frac{5}{8} + \frac{1}{4}$ $\frac{7}{8}$

10. $\frac{15}{16} - \frac{1}{4}$ $\frac{11}{16}$

11. $\frac{7}{12} - \frac{1}{3}$ $\frac{1}{4}$

12. $\frac{5}{6} + \frac{1}{3}$ $1\frac{1}{6}$

13. $\frac{7}{8} - \frac{1}{4}$ $\frac{5}{8}$

14. $\frac{3}{5} + \frac{1}{6}$ $\frac{23}{30}$

15. $\frac{1}{12} + \frac{1}{10}$ $\frac{11}{60}$

16. $\frac{7}{8} - \frac{3}{10}$ $\frac{23}{40}$

17. $\frac{2}{6} + \frac{3}{4}$ $1\frac{1}{12}$

18. $\frac{3}{8} - \frac{1}{3}$ $\frac{1}{24}$

19. $\frac{5}{8} + \frac{2}{3}$ $1\frac{7}{24}$

20. $\frac{3}{5} - \frac{1}{2}$ $\frac{1}{10}$

21. $\frac{1}{8} + \frac{1}{5}$ $\frac{13}{40}$

22. $\frac{7}{10} - \frac{3}{5}$ $\frac{1}{10}$

23. $\frac{9}{10} - \frac{1}{2}$ $\frac{2}{5}$

24. $\frac{1}{8} + \frac{4}{5}$ $\frac{9}{10}$

ENRICHMENT

Minds on Math Transparency

6-3

How can you cut a board with dimensions 8 ft by 3 ft to cover a hole with dimensions 12 ft by 2 ft if you can only make one cut in the board?

Answers may vary. Sample is shown.

See Solution Key for worked-out answers.

240

class. Have groups select a recipe and adjust the number of servings to fit the class. Ask students to estimate the cost of ingredients and the time required for preparation and cooking.

LESSON QUIZ

Use any method to add or subtract. Write answers in simplest form.

1. $\frac{1}{3} + \frac{3}{4}$ $1\frac{1}{12}$

2. $\frac{4}{9} - \frac{1}{3}$ $\frac{1}{9}$

3. $\frac{3}{4} + \frac{5}{8}$ $1\frac{3}{8}$

4. $\frac{7}{11} - \frac{1}{2}$ $\frac{3}{22}$

✓ CHECKPOINT 1

Lessons 6-1 through 6-3

Estimate each sum or difference.

1. $\frac{1}{4} + \frac{5}{8}$ 1

2. $\frac{46}{47} - \frac{19}{23}$ 0

3. $5\frac{3}{4} + 3\frac{3}{5}$ 10

4. $12\frac{67}{68} + 5\frac{1}{62}$ 18

5. $2\frac{1}{2} - \frac{11}{12}$ 2

Write an addition or subtraction sentence for each model.

6.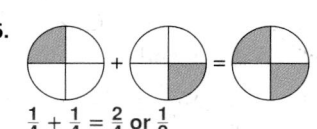

$\frac{1}{4} + \frac{1}{4} = \frac{2}{4}$ or $\frac{1}{2}$

7.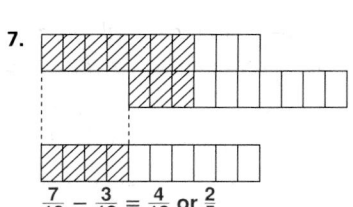

$\frac{7}{10} - \frac{3}{10} = \frac{4}{10}$ or $\frac{2}{5}$

8.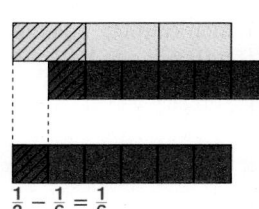

$\frac{1}{3} - \frac{1}{6} = \frac{1}{6}$

Find each sum or difference. Write the answer in simplest form.

9. $\frac{2}{5} + \frac{1}{5}$ $\frac{3}{5}$

10. $\frac{7}{9} - \frac{4}{9}$ $\frac{1}{3}$

11. $\frac{7}{8} - \frac{3}{8}$ $\frac{1}{2}$

12. $\frac{1}{8} + \frac{1}{4}$ $\frac{3}{8}$

13. $\frac{5}{6} - \frac{1}{3}$ $\frac{1}{2}$

14. $\frac{1}{5} - \frac{1}{10}$ $\frac{1}{10}$

15. *Open-ended* Write and solve an equation requiring the addition or subtraction of fractions. **Check students' work.**

Math at Work

CHEF

Generally, there are two types of chefs—institutional chefs and restaurant chefs. No matter where a chef works, he or she will measure, mix, and cook meals according to given recipes.

The art of cooking requires skill in many areas of mathematics. Knowing how to weigh and measure with both metric and customary measures is essential to following a recipe. A knowledge of estimation, ratio, and proportion will help a chef determine quantities and serving sizes.

 Check out the Chef Links Web site: http://www.isle.net/~chez/cheflinks.htm where you'll find the Food Net and the USDA's Nutrient Data Lab.

1 Focus

CONNECTING TO PRIOR KNOWLEDGE

Have students find the sum of $\frac{7}{2}$ and $\frac{9}{4}$ and write the answer as a mixed number. $5\frac{3}{4}$ Ask students to rewrite the problem using mixed numbers. $3\frac{1}{2} + 2\frac{1}{4}$

2 Teach

Work Together

EXTENSION Questions 1–3 Without measuring, have students cut a piece of string into four different lengths. Then ask students to measure each piece to the nearest $\frac{1}{8}$ in. Ask students to answer the same questions about these new lengths.

THINK AND DISCUSS

AEP Review the terms *whole number*, *fraction*, and *mixed number*. Make a table with these terms as headings. Write 3 under Whole Number, $\frac{3}{7}$ under Fraction, and $3\frac{3}{7}$ under Mixed Number. Have students make up more examples.

ALGEBRA Connection

6-4 Adding Mixed Numbers

What You'll Learn

▼ **1** To add mixed numbers mentally

▼ **2** To add mixed numbers by renaming

...And Why

Adding measurements sometimes involves adding mixed numbers.

Here's How

Look for questions that
🔹 build understanding
✔ check understanding

The giant tortoise is one of the slowest-moving animals. The slowest giant tortoise ever recorded crawled only 15 feet in 43.5 seconds.

Source: *Guinness Book of World Records*

Work Together

Using Mixed Numbers

Cut some string into each of the following lengths: $1\frac{3}{8}$ in., $2\frac{1}{4}$ in., $1\frac{7}{8}$ in., $3\frac{1}{8}$ in., and $5\frac{3}{4}$ in. Place two of the pieces end to end.

1. 🔹*Algebra* Estimate the sum of the length of the two pieces and then add. Write an addition sentence for the sum.

2. Repeat Question 1 for several different pairs of string pieces.

3. 🔹*Measurement* Check each addition sentence by measuring the total length of each pair of pieces. **Check students' work.**

1–2. Answers may vary. Sample: $1\frac{3}{8} + 2\frac{1}{4} \approx 4$; $1\frac{3}{8} + 2\frac{1}{4} = 3\frac{5}{8}$

THINK AND DISCUSS

▼ **1 Adding Mixed Numbers Mentally**

One way to add mixed numbers is to compute the whole number and fraction parts separately.

■ **EXAMPLE 1** *Real-World Problem Solving*

Zoology Suppose a giant tortoise traveled $8\frac{1}{4}$ yd in one minute and $7\frac{1}{2}$ yd in the next minute. What total distance did it travel during these two minutes?

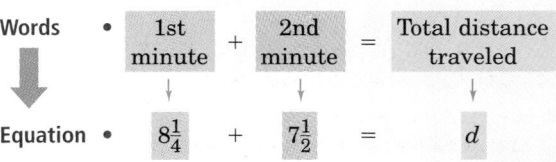

| Words | • | 1st minute | + | 2nd minute | = | Total distance traveled |

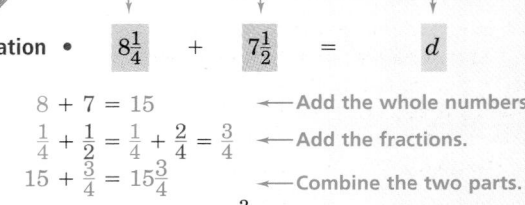

| Equation | • | $8\frac{1}{4}$ | + | $7\frac{1}{2}$ | = | d |

$8 + 7 = 15$ ⟵ Add the whole numbers.
$\frac{1}{4} + \frac{1}{2} = \frac{1}{4} + \frac{2}{4} = \frac{3}{4}$ ⟵ Add the fractions.
$15 + \frac{3}{4} = 15\frac{3}{4}$ ⟵ Combine the two parts.

The giant tortoise traveled $15\frac{3}{4}$ yd.

4. ✔*Try It Out* Find the sum $10\frac{1}{8} + 6\frac{3}{16}$. $16\frac{5}{16}$

Now you may assign Exercises 1–21.

Lesson Planning Options

Prerequisite Skills
- finding the LCD (5-7)
- solving equations with addition and subtraction (2-6)

Materials/Manipulatives
- string
- ruler

Resources

📖 **Student Edition**
Skills Handbook, p. 538
Extra Practice, p. 527
Glossary/Study Guide

📦 **Teaching Resources**
Chapter Support File, Ch. 6
- Lesson Planner 6-4
- Practice 6-4, Reteaching 6-4
- Answer Masters 6-4
Teaching Aids Masters 3, 10, 25
Glossary, Spanish Resources

🖥 **Transparencies**
19, 88, Minds on Math 6-4

Warm Up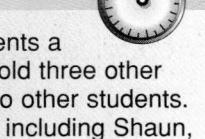

Shaun told two students a number. They each told three other students who told two other students. How many students, including Shaun, know Shaun's number? 21

VISUAL LEARNING Have students draw models for each example.

ERROR ALERT! Students may forget to rewrite an answer that is a mixed number containing an improper fraction.
Remediation: Remind students to look for fractions with numerators that are greater than their denominators. Suggest students model the numbers with fraction bars to help them rewrite the numbers.

CONNECTION TO ALGEBRA Question 7
Have students estimate to see if their solutions are reasonable.

■ ADDITIONAL EXAMPLES

FOR EXAMPLE 1
Suppose a giant tortoise crawled $6\frac{1}{3}$ yd to get a drink of water, then crawled $2\frac{1}{6}$ yd to a shady place. How far did the tortoise travel?
$8\frac{1}{2}$ yd

FOR EXAMPLE 2
Find the sum of $1\frac{1}{3} + 2\frac{3}{4}$. **$4\frac{1}{12}$**

FOR EXAMPLE 3
Solve the equation $x - 1\frac{2}{3} = 4\frac{1}{4}$.
$x = 5\frac{11}{12}$

Technology Options

Prentice Hall Technology

 **Software for Learners**
• Math Blaster® Mystery*
• Interactive Student Tutorial, Chapter 6*

 Teaching Resource Software
• Computer Item Generator 6-4
• Resource Pro™ Chapter 6*

Internet • For related mathematics activities, visit the Prentice Hall site at www.phschool.com/math

*Available on CD-ROM only

Assignment Options for Exercises On Your Own

To provide flexible scheduling, this lesson can be subdivided into parts.

▼**1 Core** 1–20
  Extension 21

▼**2 Core** 22–43, 45–63
  Extension 44, 64, 65

Use Mixed Review to maintain skills.

242

CALCULATOR HINT
You can also use a fraction calculator to add mixed numbers.

✌ *Adding Mixed Numbers by Renaming*

Sometimes the sum of the fraction part is an improper fraction. If so, rename it as a mixed number.

■ EXAMPLE 2

Find the sum $15\frac{3}{4} + 3\frac{1}{2}$.

Estimate: $15\frac{3}{4} + 3\frac{1}{2} \approx 16 + 4 = 20$

$$15\frac{3}{4} \qquad\qquad = 15\frac{3}{4}$$
$$+ \ 3\frac{1}{2} = 3\frac{1 \times 2}{2 \times 2} = 3\frac{2}{4}$$
←The LCD is 4. Write the fractions with the same denominators.
$$= 18\frac{5}{4}$$
←Add whole numbers. Add fractions.
$$= 18 + 1\frac{1}{4}$$
←Rename $\frac{5}{4}$: $\frac{5}{4} = \frac{4}{4} + \frac{1}{4} = 1\frac{1}{4}$
Add the whole numbers.
$$= 19\frac{1}{4}$$
←The answer is close to the estimate.

5. ✔Try It Out Find each sum.
 a. $3\frac{5}{6} + 5\frac{11}{12}$ **$9\frac{3}{4}$** **b.** $12\frac{3}{8} + 6\frac{3}{4}$ **$19\frac{1}{8}$** **c.** $7\frac{3}{5} + 13\frac{2}{3}$ **$21\frac{4}{15}$**

6. ⚬Open-ended Write two mixed numbers whose sum is a whole number. **Answers may vary. Sample: $3\frac{1}{8}$, $1\frac{7}{8}$**

To solve some equations, you may need to add mixed numbers.

■ EXAMPLE 3

Algebra Solve the equation $x - 8\frac{11}{16} = 5\frac{3}{8}$.

$$x - 8\frac{11}{16} = 5\frac{3}{8}$$
$$x - 8\frac{11}{16} + 8\frac{11}{16} = 5\frac{3}{8} + 8\frac{11}{16}$$
←Add $8\frac{11}{16}$ to each side.
$$= (5 + 8) + (\frac{3}{8} + \frac{11}{16})$$
←Separate whole numbers from fractions.
$$= 13 + (\frac{6}{16} + \frac{11}{16})$$
←Add the whole numbers. Then add the fractions.
$$= 13 + \frac{17}{16}$$
$$= 13 + 1\frac{1}{16}$$
←Rename the improper fraction.
$$= 14\frac{1}{16}$$
←Add.

The solution is $14\frac{1}{16}$.

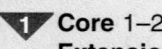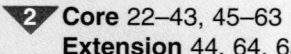

3 Practice/Assess

EXERCISES On Your Own

ASSESSMENT Pair students. Have each student write an addition problem with mixed numbers and estimate the sum. Partners exchange problems and find sums. Then partners switch back to check their original estimate.

WRITING Exercise 21 Have students list fractions they think are easy to add. Answers may vary. Sample: $\frac{1}{2} + \frac{1}{2}$, $\frac{1}{3} + \frac{2}{3}$ Ask: *Why did you choose these numbers?* Answers may vary. Sample: They have the same denominator; their sum is one; they are familiar fractions.

OPEN-ENDED Exercise 27 Suggest students give their mixed number to a partner and have them rename it again.

CONNECTION TO NUMBER SENSE Exercise 64 Challenge students to try different strategies and reasoning for estimating. For example, they can combine the $\frac{1}{2}$ and $\frac{1}{4}$ from $5\frac{1}{2}$ in. and $2\frac{1}{4}$ in. and round to 1. This is similar to front-end estimation with an adjustment for accuracy.

CONNECTION TO GEOMETRY Exercise 65 Suggest students diagram the flower garden to help them decide how to solve this problem.

7. ✔ *Try It Out* Solve each equation.

a. $x - 3\frac{5}{8} = 12\frac{3}{4}$ **b.** $4\frac{1}{12} = x - 11\frac{2}{3}$ **c.** $x - 7\frac{1}{5} = 2\frac{3}{10}$

$16\frac{3}{8}$ $15\frac{3}{4}$ $9\frac{1}{2}$

Now you may assign Exercises 22–65.

EXERCISES On Your Own

Mental Math **Add.**

1. $1 + \frac{1}{6}$ $1\frac{1}{6}$ **2.** $3 + 1\frac{2}{3}$ $4\frac{2}{3}$ **3.** $9\frac{2}{3} + 5\frac{2}{3}$ $15\frac{1}{3}$ **4.** $4\frac{1}{2} + 4\frac{1}{2}$ 9   **5.** $5\frac{3}{5} + 3\frac{2}{5}$ 9

Find each sum.

                                                      $17\frac{5}{6}$

6. $8 + 1\frac{2}{3}$ $9\frac{2}{3}$ **7.** $3\frac{1}{6} + 2$ $5\frac{1}{6}$ **8.** $8\frac{1}{5} + 3\frac{3}{4}$ $11\frac{19}{20}$ **9.** $11\frac{3}{8} + 2\frac{1}{16}$ $13\frac{7}{16}$ **10.** $9\frac{1}{12} + 8\frac{3}{4}$

11. $1\frac{1}{4} + 6\frac{1}{2}$ $7\frac{3}{4}$ **12.** $3\frac{1}{3} + 1\frac{1}{6}$ $4\frac{1}{2}$ **13.** $9\frac{1}{16} + 4\frac{7}{8}$ $13\frac{15}{16}$ **14.** $7\frac{3}{5} + 21\frac{1}{10}$ $28\frac{7}{10}$ **15.** $33\frac{1}{3} + 23\frac{2}{5}$

16. $7\frac{1}{10} + 3\frac{2}{5}$ $10\frac{1}{2}$ **17.** $6\frac{1}{4} + 2\frac{3}{5}$ $8\frac{17}{20}$ **18.** $2\frac{5}{16} + 1\frac{1}{4}$ $3\frac{9}{16}$ **19.** $10\frac{1}{4} + 3\frac{1}{3}$ $13\frac{7}{12}$ **20.** $27\frac{5}{8} + 23\frac{1}{4}$

                                         15. $56\frac{11}{15}$ **20.** $50\frac{7}{8}$

21. *Writing* Explain how you can mentally find the sum below. Add fractions with like denominators: $\frac{1}{3} + \frac{2}{3} = 1$ and $\frac{4}{5} + \frac{1}{5} = 1$.
$5\frac{1}{3} + 3\frac{4}{5} + 2\frac{2}{3} + 6\frac{1}{5}$ Then add whole numbers: $1 + 1 + 5 + 3 + 2 + 6 = 18$.

Complete to rename each mixed number.

       1   5   1   13   11

22. $2\frac{11}{10} = 3\frac{\blacksquare}{10}$ **23.** $4\frac{11}{6} = 5\frac{\blacksquare}{6}$ **24.** $\frac{9}{4} = 2\frac{\blacksquare}{4}$ **25.** $5\frac{\blacksquare}{12} = 6\frac{1}{12}$ **26.** $7\frac{4}{7} = 6\frac{\blacksquare}{7}$

27. *Open-ended* Write a mixed number containing an improper fraction. Rename your mixed number.   Answers may vary. Sample: $3\frac{8}{5} = 4\frac{3}{5}$

Find each sum.

                                              $6\frac{4}{15}$

28. $2\frac{3}{4} + 1\frac{5}{8}$ $4\frac{3}{8}$ **29.** $4\frac{5}{8} + 1\frac{1}{4}$ $5\frac{7}{8}$ **30.** $3\frac{1}{3} + 2\frac{5}{6}$ $6\frac{1}{6}$ **31.** $1\frac{2}{3} + 3\frac{5}{6}$ $5\frac{1}{2}$ **32.** $4\frac{3}{5} + 1\frac{2}{3}$

33. $1\frac{7}{8} + 1\frac{1}{4}$ $3\frac{1}{8}$ **34.** $4\frac{5}{12} + 1\frac{1}{2}$ $5\frac{11}{12}$ **35.** $6\frac{4}{5} + 2\frac{1}{3}$ $9\frac{2}{15}$ **36.** $5\frac{8}{9} + 7\frac{1}{6}$ $13\frac{1}{18}$ **37.** $17\frac{3}{5} + 12\frac{7}{10}$

38. $33\frac{3}{4} + 33\frac{5}{6}$ $67\frac{7}{12}$ **39.** $41\frac{9}{10} + 2\frac{3}{4}$ $44\frac{13}{20}$ **40.** $13\frac{2}{3} + 2\frac{1}{24}$ $15\frac{17}{24}$ **41.** $10\frac{3}{5} + 1\frac{7}{10}$ $12\frac{3}{10}$ **42.** $4 + 13\frac{5}{6}$ $17\frac{5}{6}$

                                            37. $30\frac{3}{10}$

43. *Tides* A mark on the side of a pier shows that the water is $4\frac{7}{8}$ ft deep. When the tide is high, the depth increases by $2\frac{3}{4}$ ft.
  a. What is the depth of the water when the tide is high? $7\frac{5}{8}$ ft
  b. Did you add or subtract to find the answer to part (a)? Justify your solution.   Add; check students' work for reasoning.

44. *Number Sense* Explain why the sum of two mixed numbers is not always a mixed number.   When the sum of the fraction parts is a whole number, then the sum of the mixed numbers is a whole number.

243

Practice 6-4 *Adding Mixed Numbers*

Complete to rename each mixed number.

1. $3\frac{9}{8} = 4\frac{\square}{8}$ **1**
2. $5\frac{7}{4} = 6\frac{\square}{4}$ **3**
3. $2\frac{17}{12} = 3\frac{\square}{12}$ **5**

Find each sum.

4. $4\frac{3}{10} + 5\frac{2}{5}$ $9\frac{7}{10}$
5. $3\frac{7}{8} + 2\frac{1}{8}$ $6\frac{3}{8}$
6. $5\frac{2}{3} + 3\frac{1}{4}$ $8\frac{11}{12}$

7. $6\frac{3}{4} + 2\frac{1}{2}$ $9\frac{1}{4}$
8. $1\frac{1}{12} + 3\frac{1}{6}$ $4\frac{1}{4}$
9. $9\frac{2}{5} + 10\frac{3}{10}$ $19\frac{7}{10}$

10. $7\frac{1}{3} + 5\frac{11}{12}$ $13\frac{1}{4}$
11. $11\frac{7}{10} + 4$ $15\frac{7}{10}$
12. $2\frac{2}{3} + 4\frac{3}{4}$ $7\frac{5}{12}$

13. $7\frac{3}{4} + 2\frac{7}{8}$ $10\frac{5}{8}$
14. $4\frac{1}{2} + 3\frac{5}{8}$ $8\frac{1}{8}$
15. $7\frac{2}{3} + 1\frac{5}{6}$ $9\frac{1}{2}$

16. $2\frac{1}{4} + 4\frac{3}{5}$ $6\frac{17}{20}$
17. $5\frac{3}{8} + 7\frac{1}{4}$ $12\frac{5}{8}$
18. $14\frac{5}{16} + 8\frac{3}{8}$ $22\frac{11}{16}$

Solve each equation for *x*.

19. $x - \frac{11}{12} = 4\frac{5}{12}$ $5\frac{1}{3}$
20. $27\frac{2}{5} = x - 3\frac{4}{5}$ $31\frac{1}{5}$
21. $x - 7\frac{1}{6} = 9\frac{7}{12}$ $16\frac{3}{4}$

22. $22\frac{1}{4} = x - 3\frac{3}{5}$ $25\frac{17}{20}$
23. $x - 39\frac{1}{8} = 6\frac{3}{4}$ $45\frac{7}{8}$
24. $x - 14\frac{1}{16} = 3\frac{7}{8}$ $17\frac{15}{16}$

25. $18\frac{1}{2} = x - 12\frac{1}{6}$ $30\frac{2}{3}$
26. $80\frac{1}{10} = x - 5\frac{3}{5}$ $85\frac{7}{10}$
27. $x - 9\frac{3}{8} = 2\frac{1}{4}$ $11\frac{5}{8}$

28. Estimate the length of rope needed to go around a triangle with sides $6\frac{1}{2}$ ft, $7\frac{1}{4}$ ft, and $10\frac{1}{4}$ ft. about 25 ft

In copymaster and workbook formats

Reteaching 6-4 *Adding Mixed Numbers*

Some mixed numbers can be added mentally.

Add: $5\frac{1}{4} + 2\frac{1}{8}$

Step 1
Add the whole numbers.
$5 + 2 = 7$

Step 2
Add the fractions.
$\frac{1}{4} + \frac{1}{8} = \frac{2}{8} + \frac{1}{8} = \frac{3}{8}$

Step 3
Combine the two parts.
$7 + \frac{3}{8} = 7\frac{3}{8}$

$5\frac{1}{4} + 2\frac{1}{8} = 7\frac{3}{8}$

Otherwise, you can follow these steps.

Add: $4\frac{4}{5} + 2\frac{9}{10}$

Step 1
Write with a common denominator.
$4\frac{4}{5} + 2\frac{9}{10} = 4\frac{8}{10} + 2\frac{9}{10}$

Step 2
Add the whole numbers. Add the fractions.
$= 6\frac{17}{10}$

Step 3
Simplify.
$= 7\frac{7}{10}$

$4\frac{4}{5} + 2\frac{9}{10} = 7\frac{7}{10}$

Find each sum. Write it in simplest form.

1. $4\frac{4}{7} + 1\frac{1}{7}$ $5\frac{5}{7}$
2. $1\frac{1}{3} + 3\frac{1}{3}$ $4\frac{2}{3}$
3. $2\frac{1}{2} + 4$ $6\frac{1}{2}$

4. $8\frac{2}{5} + 4\frac{1}{10}$ $12\frac{1}{2}$
5. $7\frac{3}{4} + 2\frac{1}{2}$ $9\frac{7}{8}$ (?)
6. $2\frac{7}{10} + 3\frac{1}{5}$ $5\frac{9}{10}$

7. $7\frac{2}{9} + 1\frac{4}{9}$ $8\frac{2}{3}$
8. $8\frac{3}{14} + 2\frac{1}{7}$ $10\frac{5}{14}$
9. $9\frac{3}{8} + 2\frac{1}{2}$ $11\frac{7}{8}$

10. $1\frac{3}{4} + 4\frac{7}{8}$ $6\frac{5}{8}$
11. $7\frac{5}{8} + 8\frac{5}{8}$ $16\frac{1}{2}$
12. $1\frac{5}{6} + 9\frac{2}{5}$ $11\frac{7}{15}$

13. $6\frac{3}{4} + 8\frac{4}{5}$ $15\frac{11}{20}$
14. $3\frac{3}{5} + 5\frac{9}{10}$ $9\frac{1}{2}$
15. $4\frac{3}{5} + 6\frac{7}{10}$ $11\frac{3}{10}$

16. $6 + 3\frac{2}{5}$ $9\frac{2}{5}$
17. $9\frac{1}{6} + 1\frac{1}{3}$ $10\frac{1}{2}$
18. $8\frac{1}{16} + 4\frac{5}{16}$ $12\frac{11}{16}$

Minds on Math Transparency

6-4

One of 27 marbles weighs less than the other 26 marbles which are of equal weight. What is the least number of weighings on a balance scale needed to determine the odd marble?

Three weighings are needed. Place 9 marbles on each balance pan. The light marble will be on one of the pans or in the other group of 9. From the light group, place 3 marbles on each pan to find which group of 3 is light. From this group, place 1 marble on each pan.

See *Solution Key* for worked-out answers.

244

IDENTIFYING THE BIG IDEA Ask students to explain how to add mixed numbers.

JOURNAL Have the class discuss strategies they can use to add mixed numbers. **Answers may vary. Sample: using models; adding the parts of the mixed numbers; converting to improper fractions, adding and then converting back** Have students use the ideas from the discussion in their journal.

Find each sum or difference. Write answers in simplest form.

1. $24\frac{1}{2} + 30\frac{1}{6}$ $54\frac{2}{3}$
2. $3\frac{7}{8} + 16\frac{3}{4}$ $20\frac{5}{8}$
3. $9\frac{3}{10} + 2\frac{3}{5}$ $11\frac{9}{10}$
4. $15\frac{2}{3} + 22\frac{5}{6}$ $38\frac{1}{2}$

Algebra **Solve each equation for *x*.**

45. $x - \frac{9}{10} = 23\frac{3}{10}$ $24\frac{1}{5}$
46. $32\frac{4}{5} = x - 1\frac{3}{5}$ $34\frac{2}{5}$
47. $12\frac{1}{2} = x - 15\frac{1}{6}$ $27\frac{2}{3}$
48. $17\frac{11}{12} = x - 6\frac{5}{6}$ $24\frac{3}{4}$

49. $x - \frac{5}{6} = 3\frac{1}{2}$ $4\frac{1}{3}$
50. $x - 11\frac{1}{12} = 11\frac{1}{12}$ $22\frac{1}{6}$
51. $x - 17\frac{2}{3} = 14\frac{1}{4}$ $31\frac{11}{12}$
52. $x - 10\frac{1}{6} = \frac{5}{12}$ $10\frac{7}{12}$

53. $x - 23\frac{1}{2} = \frac{5}{6}$ $24\frac{1}{3}$
54. $12\frac{7}{12} = x - \frac{3}{4}$ $13\frac{1}{3}$
55. $x - 3\frac{1}{2} = 6\frac{3}{4}$ $10\frac{1}{4}$
56. $34\frac{3}{8} = x - \frac{5}{8}$ 35

57. $x - 70\frac{5}{6} = 100\frac{1}{2}$ $171\frac{1}{3}$
58. $x - \frac{4}{5} = 3\frac{1}{2}$ $4\frac{3}{10}$
59. $23\frac{5}{6} = x - 12\frac{7}{8}$ $36\frac{17}{24}$
60. $x - 40\frac{1}{6} = 3\frac{9}{10}$ $44\frac{1}{15}$

61. *Carpentry* A nail is driven through a $3\frac{1}{2}$-in. wooden board. The nail extends beyond the board by $1\frac{5}{8}$ in. How long is the nail? $5\frac{1}{8}$ in.

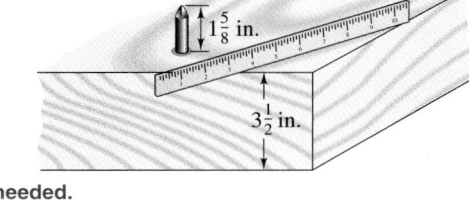

62. *Cooking* One recipe uses $1\frac{3}{4}$ c milk, and another uses $1\frac{1}{2}$ c milk. You have about 3 c milk at home. Do you have enough milk for both recipes? Explain. No; $3\frac{1}{4}$ c is needed.

63. **Choose A, B, C, or D.** Which two mixed numbers have a sum of $6\frac{3}{5}$? **D**

   A. $3\frac{1}{10}$ and $2\frac{6}{5}$
   B. $3\frac{2}{10}$ and $2\frac{6}{5}$
   C. $3\frac{2}{10}$ and $3\frac{6}{5}$
   D. $3\frac{3}{5}$ and $2\frac{5}{5}$

64. *Number Sense* The sides of a triangle have lengths $5\frac{1}{2}$ in., $3\frac{7}{8}$ in., and $2\frac{1}{4}$ in. Is a 12-in. piece of string long enough to fit around the triangle? Explain. **Yes; $11\frac{5}{8}$ in. is the length needed.**

65. *Geometry* Fencing costs $5 per foot. How much will the fence cost for a $4\frac{1}{2}$ ft-by-$3\frac{1}{4}$ ft rectangular flower garden? $77.50

JOURNAL
Summarize the different methods you can use to add mixed numbers. Write a mini-lesson you might use to teach a friend about adding mixed numbers.

Mixed Review

Use the distributive property to find each product. *(Lesson 4-3)*

66. 24×5 120
67. 99×26 2,574
68. 68×8 544
69. 95×4 380
70. 53×7 371
71. 41×9 369

Find the next three terms in each number pattern. *(Lesson 2-1)*

72. $2, 4, 6, 8, \blacksquare, \blacksquare, \blacksquare$ 10, 12, 14
73. $12, 36, 108, 324, \blacksquare, \blacksquare, \blacksquare$ 972; 2,916; 8,748
74. $6, 12, 18, 24, \blacksquare, \blacksquare, \blacksquare$ 30, 36, 42

75. *Choose a Strategy* Kyle counted 12 wheels on the cycles in the Homecoming Parade. His friend Leilani counted 7 cycles in all. The only cycles allowed were unicycles, bicycles, and tricycles. How many cycles of each type were in the parade?

75. **Possible answers:**
2 tricycles, 1 bicycle, 4 unicycles; 1 tricycle, 3 bicycles, 3 unicycles; 0 tricycles, 5 bicycles, 2 unicycles

Extra Practice, Lesson 6-4, page 527

In Lesson 6-4, students learned to add mixed numbers mentally and with paper and pencil. This toolbox shows students how to add and subtract fractions using a fraction calculator.

ERROR ALERT! Students may incorrectly enter some problems. **Remediation:** Remind students to always estimate the answer. Encourage them to take their time when entering the numbers. Have them check their answers with a friend.

ASSESSMENT Write $2\frac{3}{4}$ + $1\frac{1}{5}$ on the board. Have students draw the calculator buttons they would press to solve the problem.

$\boxed{2}$ $\boxed{\text{UNIT}}$ $\boxed{3}$ $\boxed{/}$ $\boxed{4}$ $\boxed{+}$ $\boxed{1}$
$\boxed{\text{UNIT}}$ $\boxed{1}$ $\boxed{/}$ $\boxed{5}$ $\boxed{=}$ Have students enter the problem to find the sum. $3\frac{19}{20}$

■ ADDITIONAL PROBLEMS

Find each sum or difference using a fraction calculator.
1. $1\frac{6}{7}$ + $\frac{1}{2}$ $2\frac{5}{14}$
2. $3\frac{2}{5}$ − $\frac{3}{7}$ $2\frac{34}{35}$

TECHNOLOGY

Using a Fraction Calculator to Compute

 After Lesson 6-4

You can use a fraction calculator to add and subtract fractions.

■ **EXAMPLE 1**

Find the difference: $\frac{5}{6} - \frac{3}{8}$

Estimate: $\frac{5}{6} - \frac{3}{8} \approx 1 - \frac{1}{2} \approx \frac{1}{2}$

Enter 5 $\boxed{/}$ 6 $\boxed{-}$ 3 $\boxed{/}$ 8 $\boxed{=}$ *11/24*

$\frac{5}{6} - \frac{3}{8} = \frac{11}{24}$

You can also use a fraction calculator to add mixed numbers and to simplify the answer when necessary.

■ **EXAMPLE 2**

Find the sum: $1\frac{3}{4} + 3\frac{1}{2}$

Estimate: $1\frac{3}{4} + 3\frac{1}{2} \approx 2 + 3\frac{1}{2} \approx 5\frac{1}{2}$

Enter 1 $\boxed{\text{UNIT}}$ 3 $\boxed{/}$ 4 $\boxed{+}$ 3 $\boxed{\text{UNIT}}$ 1 $\boxed{/}$ 2 $\boxed{=}$ *4u5/4*

To rename this number, press $\boxed{\text{Ab/c}}$ $\boxed{=}$ *5u1/4*

$1\frac{3}{4} + 3\frac{1}{2} = 5\frac{1}{4}$

Find each sum or difference.

1. $\frac{3}{4} - \frac{2}{5}$ $\frac{7}{20}$
2. $\frac{5}{8} + \frac{1}{4}$ $\frac{7}{8}$
3. $\frac{9}{10} - \frac{1}{5}$ $\frac{7}{10}$
4. $\frac{8}{9} + \frac{1}{12}$ $\frac{35}{36}$

5. $\frac{11}{12} - \frac{3}{8}$ $\frac{13}{24}$
6. $\frac{4}{5} + \frac{1}{20}$ $\frac{17}{20}$
7. $\frac{3}{10} - \frac{2}{9}$ $\frac{7}{90}$
8. $\frac{22}{25} + \frac{9}{100}$ $\frac{97}{100}$

9. $\frac{5}{9} - \frac{2}{5}$ $\frac{7}{45}$
10. $\frac{2}{3} + \frac{4}{5}$ $1\frac{7}{15}$
11. $9\frac{3}{4} + 3\frac{3}{4}$ $13\frac{1}{2}$
12. $5\frac{3}{8} + 8\frac{1}{8}$ $13\frac{1}{2}$

13. $11\frac{8}{9} - 7\frac{1}{2}$ $4\frac{7}{18}$
14. $6\frac{9}{10} + 2\frac{1}{12}$ $8\frac{59}{60}$
15. $18\frac{5}{12} - 9\frac{1}{2}$ $8\frac{11}{12}$
16. $1\frac{1}{10} + 8\frac{1}{12}$ $9\frac{11}{60}$

17. $13\frac{5}{12} - 5\frac{1}{3}$ $8\frac{1}{12}$
18. $4\frac{1}{4} + 2\frac{1}{3}$ $6\frac{7}{12}$
19. $14\frac{3}{10} - 3\frac{1}{2}$ $10\frac{4}{5}$
20. $7\frac{8}{9} - 3\frac{1}{6}$ $4\frac{13}{18}$

21. *Writing* How can you use a fraction calculator to simplify an improper fraction? Enter the numerator and denominator as a fraction. Then press $\boxed{\text{Ab/c}}$ $\boxed{=}$.

Materials/Manipulatives
• calculator

Resources

Transparencies
19

1 Focus

CONNECTING TO PRIOR KNOWLEDGE Ask students to add $\frac{4}{5} + \frac{2}{3}$. $1\frac{7}{15}$ Have students write a related subtraction problem. $1\frac{7}{15} - \frac{2}{3} = \frac{4}{5}$; or $1\frac{7}{15} - \frac{4}{5} = \frac{2}{3}$ Ask: *If you want to subtract one mixed number from another, what method would you use?* **Answers may vary.**

Lesson Planning Options

Prerequisite Skills
• renaming mixed numbers (5-6)

Resources

 Student Edition

Skills Handbook, p. 539
Extra Practice, p. 527
Glossary/Study Guide

 Teaching Resources

Chapter Support File, Ch. 6
• Lesson Planner 6-5
• Practice 6-5, Reteaching 6-5
• Answer Masters 6-5
Teaching Aids Masters 3, 10, 25
Glossary, Spanish Resources

 Transparencies
19, 88, Minds on Math 6-5

Warm Up

Leah's scores on her math tests were 84, 64, 72, 86, 69, 85, and 87. Her teacher says that Leah's average score on the tests is about 78. Leah calculated an 84 average. What did each person mean? Whose interpretation of the data describes it most accurately? Why? **Her teacher gave the mean; Leah gave the median. The teacher's interpretation was more accurate because the scores dropped quite far below the median.**

2 Teach

THINK AND DISCUSS

AEP **DIVERSITY** **Questions 1–3** Students from other countries may not be familiar with these animals. You may wish to show students pictures of a coyote, a gray wolf, and a red fox. Encourage students to share the names for these animals from other languages.

Questions 1 and 2 Have students explain how subtracting mixed numbers is like adding mixed numbers. **Answers may vary. Sample: You add and subtract whole numbers separately. You find equivalent fractions. Then you add or subtract fractions.**

ERROR ALERT! **Example 2** Students may say $63\frac{1}{4} - 43\frac{1}{2} = 20\frac{1}{4}$ because $63 - 43 = 20$ and $\frac{1}{2} - \frac{1}{4} = \frac{1}{4}$.
Remediation: Tell students it is important to keep the mixed numbers together. Suggest students write the problem vertically if it helps them.

ALGEBRA Connection

6-5 *Subtracting Mixed Numbers*

What You'll Learn

▼ To subtract mixed numbers mentally

▼ To subtract mixed numbers by renaming

...And Why

To find differences in length and width, you often must subtract mixed numbers.

Here's How

Look for questions that
• build understanding
✔ check understanding

THINK AND DISCUSS

▼ 1 *Subtracting Mixed Numbers Mentally*

Use the scale drawings of animal tracks below.

1. Which is wider, the coyote's track or the red fox's track? **red fox's track**
2. Which is longer, the coyote's track or the gray wolf's track? **gray wolf's track**
3. Is the length or the width of the gray wolf's track greater? **length**

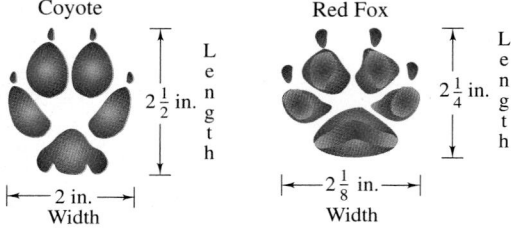

Coyote — $2\frac{1}{2}$ in. Length, 2 in. Width

Red Fox — $2\frac{1}{4}$ in. Length, $2\frac{1}{8}$ in. Width

Gray Wolf — $4\frac{1}{8}$ in. Length, $3\frac{3}{4}$ in. Width

To find the difference between two measurements, you subtract.

■ EXAMPLE 1   *Real-World Problem Solving*

Biology How much wider is the gray wolf's track than the red fox's?

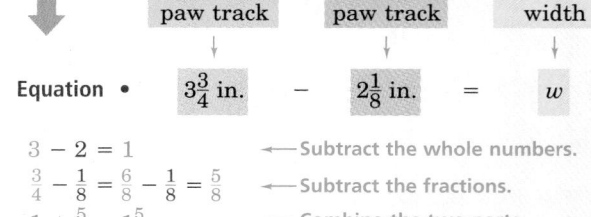

Words •	Width of gray wolf's paw track	−	Width of red fox's paw track	=	Difference in width

Equation •	$3\frac{3}{4}$ in.	−	$2\frac{1}{8}$ in.	=	w

$3 - 2 = 1$ ⟵ Subtract the whole numbers.
$\frac{3}{4} - \frac{1}{8} = \frac{6}{8} - \frac{1}{8} = \frac{5}{8}$ ⟵ Subtract the fractions.
$1 + \frac{5}{8} = 1\frac{5}{8}$ ⟵ Combine the two parts.

The gray wolf's track is $1\frac{5}{8}$ in. wider than the red fox's track.

FOR EXAMPLE 1

What is the difference between the length and width of the red fox's paw track? $\frac{1}{8}$ in.

FOR EXAMPLE 2

A cheetah ran $42\frac{2}{3}$ yd. A coyote ran $36\frac{5}{6}$ yd. How much farther did the cheetah run? $5\frac{5}{6}$ yd

FOR EXAMPLE 3

Solve the equation $3\frac{3}{4} + x = 6\frac{3}{8}$.
$x = 2\frac{5}{8}$

3 Practice/Assess

EXERCISES *On Your Own*

MENTAL MATH Exercise 2 Ask students to explain how they could use the Work Backward strategy to solve this problem.

4. ✔*Try It Out* How much longer is the coyote's track than the red fox's track? $\frac{1}{4}$ in.

Now you may assign Exercises 1–5, 31.

❷ *Subtracting Mixed Numbers by Renaming*

Sometimes you need to rename before you can subtract.

■ **EXAMPLE 2** *Real-World Problem Solving*

Suppose an antelope ran $43\frac{1}{2}$ yd while a cheetah ran $63\frac{1}{4}$ yd. How much farther did the cheetah run than the antelope?

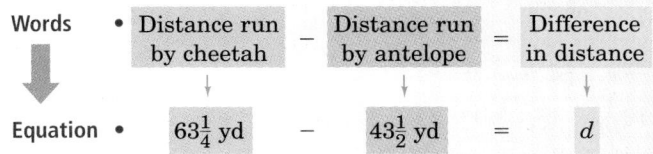

Words	• Distance run by cheetah	−	Distance run by antelope	=	Difference in distance
Equation	• $63\frac{1}{4}$ yd	−	$43\frac{1}{2}$ yd	=	d

Estimate: $63\frac{1}{4} - 43\frac{1}{2} \approx 63 - 44 = 19$

Since $\frac{1}{4}$ is less than $\frac{1}{2}$, you must rename $63\frac{1}{4}$ before you can subtract.

$$63\frac{1}{4} = 62 + 1\frac{1}{4} = 62\frac{5}{4}$$ ◄— Rename $63\frac{1}{4}$ as $62\frac{5}{4}$.
$$- 43\frac{1}{2} = 43\frac{1 \times 2}{2 \times 2} = 43\frac{2}{4}$$ ◄— Write an equivalent fraction for $\frac{1}{2}$.
$$= 19\frac{3}{4}$$ Subtract the whole numbers and fractions. The answer is close to the estimate.

The cheetah ran $19\frac{3}{4}$ yd farther than the antelope.

5. ⬛*Look Back* Check your answer to Example 2 by adding. You can also use equations to solve problems. $63\frac{1}{4}$ yd

■ **EXAMPLE 3**

Algebra Solve the equation $4\frac{1}{2} + x = 6\frac{1}{3}$

$$4\frac{1}{2} + x = 6\frac{1}{3}$$
$$4\frac{1}{2} + x - 4\frac{1}{2} = 6\frac{1}{3} - 4\frac{1}{2}$$ ◄— Subtract $4\frac{1}{2}$ from both sides.
$$x = 6\frac{2}{6} - 4\frac{3}{6}$$ ◄— Write equivalent fractions.
$$= 5\frac{8}{6} - 4\frac{3}{6}$$ ◄— Rename. $6\frac{2}{6} = 5 + 1\frac{2}{6} = 5\frac{8}{6}$.
$$= 1\frac{5}{6}$$ ◄— Subtract whole numbers and then fractions.

The cheetah is the fastest animal on land for distances up to 350 yd. The pronghorn antelope is faster than the cheetah after 350 yd.

Technology Options

Prentice Hall Technology

💾 📀 **Software for Learners**
• Math Blaster® Mystery*
• Interactive Student Tutorial, Chapter 6*

💾 📀 **Teaching Resource Software**
• Computer Item Generator 6-5
• Resource Pro™ Chapter 6*

🔄 **Internet** • For related mathematics activities, visit the Prentice Hall site at www.phschool.com/math

*Available on CD-ROM only

Assignment Options for Exercises On Your Own

To provide flexible scheduling, this lesson can be subdivided into parts.

❶ **Core** 1–5
Extension 31

❷ **Core** 6–30, 32, 34–52
Extension 33, 53

Use Mixed Review to maintain skills.

Exercises 6–30 Encourage students to use addition to check their answers.

ASSESSMENT Exercises 28–30 Ask students to list the problems that need renaming. **29 and 30** Have students rename the problems and share them with a partner. $10\frac{10}{6} - 3\frac{5}{6}$; $9\frac{94}{60} - 3\frac{55}{60}$

ESTIMATION Exercise 37 Ask students: *Is there more than one answer?* **yes** *Give an example.* **the Black and the Red, and the White and Red** *Is one answer better than the other?* **no**

KINESTHETIC LEARNING Exercises 38–40 Have students measure the length of their own long jump in feet and inches to the nearest $\frac{1}{4}$ in. Then ask them to find the difference in length between their jump and one of the Olympic winners from the list.

CONNECTION TO BUSINESS Have students use data from a newspaper or the Internet to find the difference between a high and low stock price.

WRAP UP

IDENTIFYING THE BIG IDEA Ask students to explain how to subtract mixed numbers.

pages 248–249 On Your Own

31. Answers may vary. Sample: Add $\frac{1}{4}$ to each number. Then subtract $12\frac{1}{2} - 11$ to get $1\frac{1}{2}$.

35. **Spruce Tree   Length of Cone (in.)**

Spruce Tree	Length of Cone (in.)
Black	$\frac{7}{8}$
Red	$1\frac{1}{4}$
White	$1\frac{5}{8}$
Norway	$5\frac{1}{2}$

6. ✓*Try It Out* Solve each equation.

a. $x + 1\frac{3}{4} = 3\frac{1}{4}$ 5   b. $5\frac{1}{2} + x = 7\frac{5}{8}$ $2\frac{1}{8}$

Now you may assign Exercises 6–30, 32–53.

EXERCISES *On Your Own*

Mental Math **Subtract.**

1. $9\frac{2}{3} - 5\frac{2}{3}$ 4   2. $1 - \frac{1}{6}$ $\frac{5}{6}$ 3. $3 - 1\frac{2}{3}$ $1\frac{1}{3}$ 4. $4\frac{1}{2} - 4\frac{1}{2}$ 0   5. $12\frac{3}{4} - 10\frac{1}{4}$ $2\frac{1}{2}$

Find each difference.

6. $7\frac{3}{4} - 3\frac{3}{8}$ $4\frac{3}{8}$ 7. $2\frac{5}{16} - 1\frac{1}{4}$ $1\frac{1}{16}$ 8. $9\frac{4}{5} - 4\frac{3}{5}$ $5\frac{1}{5}$ 9. $21\frac{1}{8} - 11\frac{1}{16}$ $10\frac{1}{16}$ 10. $15\frac{11}{12} - 11\frac{1}{2}$ $4\frac{5}{12}$

11. $12\frac{1}{4} - 4\frac{1}{8}$ $8\frac{1}{8}$ 12. $3\frac{2}{3} - 1\frac{1}{6}$ $2\frac{1}{2}$ 13. $6\frac{4}{5} - 2\frac{1}{4}$ $4\frac{11}{20}$ 14. $41\frac{11}{12} - 27\frac{5}{6}$ $14\frac{1}{12}$ 15. $70\frac{9}{10} - 45\frac{4}{5}$ $25\frac{1}{10}$

16. $10\frac{1}{10} - 3\frac{2}{5}$ $6\frac{7}{10}$ 17. $3\frac{3}{8} - 1\frac{3}{4}$ $1\frac{5}{8}$ 18. $4\frac{5}{12} - 1\frac{1}{2}$ $2\frac{11}{12}$ 19. $6\frac{1}{5} - 2\frac{2}{3}$ $3\frac{8}{15}$ 20. $3\frac{2}{3} - 1\frac{3}{4}$ $1\frac{11}{12}$

21. $18\frac{1}{2} - 1\frac{2}{3}$ $16\frac{5}{6}$ 22. $4\frac{3}{8} - 1\frac{7}{16}$ $2\frac{15}{16}$ 23. $3\frac{1}{16} - 2\frac{1}{2}$ $\frac{9}{16}$ 24. $4\frac{1}{4} - 1\frac{2}{3}$ $2\frac{7}{12}$ 25. $25\frac{5}{8} - 17\frac{15}{16}$ $7\frac{11}{16}$

26. $2\frac{1}{4} - 1\frac{7}{8}$ $\frac{3}{8}$ 27. $4\frac{1}{12} - 1\frac{11}{12}$ $2\frac{1}{6}$ 28. $5\frac{5}{8} - 2\frac{7}{16}$ $3\frac{3}{16}$ 29. $11\frac{2}{3} - 3\frac{5}{6}$ $7\frac{5}{6}$ 30. $10\frac{9}{10} - 3\frac{11}{12}$ $6\frac{59}{60}$

31. *Writing* Explain how you can mentally find the difference $12\frac{1}{4} - 10\frac{3}{4}$. **See margin.**

32. **Choose A, B, C, or D.** Which two mixed numbers have a difference of $4\frac{2}{5}$? **C**

    A. $12\frac{7}{10}$ and $8\frac{4}{5}$ B. $16\frac{3}{10}$ and $12\frac{1}{2}$ C. $7\frac{1}{10}$ and $2\frac{7}{10}$ D. $13\frac{1}{5}$ and $9\frac{2}{5}$

33. *Patterns* Write the next two numbers in the pattern below.

    $9\frac{1}{3}$, $8\frac{1}{6}$, 7, $5\frac{5}{6}$, $4\frac{2}{3}$, ▧, ▧. $3\frac{1}{2}$, $2\frac{1}{3}$

34. Explain how you could have used subtraction to answer Exercise 33. **Answers may vary. Sample: Subtract each number from the one before it. The answer is the same each time. Then subtract this amount from $4\frac{2}{3}$ to get the next term.**

Biology **Use the data at the right for Exercises 35–37.**

35. Rewrite the table showing the lengths of the cones from shortest to longest. **See margin.**

36. Find the difference in length between the shortest cone and the longest cone. $4\frac{5}{8}$ in.

37. *Estimation* Which two cones differ in length by about $\frac{1}{2}$ in.? **black and red, red and white**

Spruce Tree	Length of Cone (in.)
White	$1\frac{5}{8}$
Norway	$5\frac{1}{2}$
Black	$\frac{7}{8}$
Red	$1\frac{1}{4}$

248

Find each difference.

1. $4\frac{1}{4} - 1\frac{2}{3}$ $2\frac{7}{12}$

2. $6\frac{1}{3} - 2\frac{4}{5}$ $3\frac{8}{15}$

3. $4\frac{5}{8} - 1\frac{3}{8}$ $3\frac{1}{4}$

Solve the equation for x.

4. $x + 3\frac{1}{3} = 5\frac{1}{6}$ $x = 1\frac{5}{6}$

Data Analysis **Use the table at the right for Exercises 38–40.**

38. How much farther did Heike Drechsler jump than Chioma Ajunwa? $\frac{3}{4}$ in.

39. What is the difference in length between the 1960 and 1996 winning long jumps? 2 ft $5\frac{3}{4}$ in.

40. Find the difference between the longest winning jump and the shortest winning jump shown. 3 ft $4\frac{3}{4}$ in.

Algebra **Solve each equation for x.**

41. $x + 7\frac{1}{2} = 16\frac{3}{4}$ $9\frac{1}{4}$ **42.** $18\frac{5}{6} = x + 12\frac{7}{8}$ $5\frac{23}{24}$ **43.** $23\frac{9}{16} = x + 12\frac{7}{8}$ $10\frac{11}{16}$ **44.** $x + 24\frac{3}{4} = 56\frac{1}{8}$

45. $31\frac{1}{5} + x = 40\frac{1}{2}$ $9\frac{3}{10}$ **46.** $34\frac{1}{3} - x = 11\frac{7}{12}$ $22\frac{3}{4}$ **47.** $x + 8\frac{1}{2} = 12\frac{3}{4}$ $4\frac{1}{4}$ **48.** $5\frac{7}{8} + x = 10\frac{5}{16}$

49. $27\frac{3}{4} = x + 12\frac{7}{8}$ $14\frac{7}{8}$ **50.** $x + 9\frac{1}{3} = 16\frac{3}{4}$ $7\frac{5}{12}$ **51.** $33\frac{1}{4} + x = 45\frac{1}{2}$ $12\frac{1}{4}$ **52.** $18\frac{1}{9} = x + 13\frac{7}{18}$

44, 48, 52.See below.

53. *Carpentry* A $3\frac{5}{8}$-in. nail is driven through a wooden door. The nail extends beyond the door by $\frac{7}{8}$ in.
  a. How thick is the door? $2\frac{3}{4}$ in.
  b. What operation did you use in part (a)? Why? Subtraction; check students' work for reasoning.

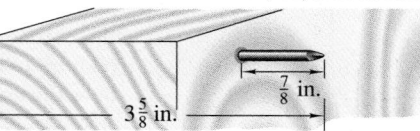

44. $31\frac{3}{8}$

48. $4\frac{7}{16}$

52. $4\frac{13}{18}$

Women's Olympic Long Jump Winners

Year	Winner	Distance
1960	Vera Krepkina, U.S.S.R.	20 ft $10\frac{3}{4}$ in.
1964	Mary Rand, Great Britain	22 ft 2 in.
1968	Viorica Viscopoleanu, Romania	22 ft $4\frac{1}{2}$ in.
1972	Heidemarie Rosendahl, West Germany	22 ft 3 in.
1976	Angela Volgt, East Germany	22 ft $\frac{1}{2}$ in.
1980	Tatiana Kolpakova, U.S.S.R.	23 ft 2 in.
1984	Anisoara Scanclu, Romania	22 ft 10 in.
1988	Jackie Joyner-Kersee, U.S.	24 ft $3\frac{1}{2}$ in.
1992	Helke Drechsler, Germany	23 ft $5\frac{1}{4}$ in.
1996	Chioma Ajunwa, Nigeria	23 ft $4\frac{1}{2}$ in.

Mixed Review

Write each fraction as a decimal. Write each decimal as a fraction in simplest form. *(Lesson 5-9)*

54. $\frac{17}{20}$ 0.85   **55.** 0.48 $\frac{12}{25}$ **56.** 0.06 $\frac{3}{50}$ **57.** $\frac{3}{25}$ 0.12   **58.** 0.152 $\frac{19}{125}$ **59.** $\frac{21}{25}$ 0.84

Round to the place of the underlined digit. *(Lesson 3-6)*

60. 2<u>0</u>,567 21,000   **61.** 9,<u>3</u>48,120 9,300,000   **62.** 0.0<u>9</u>3 0.1   **63.** 5.6<u>1</u>84 5.62   **64.** 6,4<u>5</u>6 6,460   **65.** 0.13<u>2</u>9 0.133

66. *Choose a Strategy* The Rotary Club has $140 in savings. The dues from 8 new members raised the amount to $198. Find the dues collected from each new member. $7.25

PRACTICE

Practice 6-5 *Subtracting Mixed Numbers*

Find the difference.

1. $10\frac{11}{16} - 3\frac{7}{8}$ $6\frac{13}{16}$ 2. $8\frac{1}{3} - 2\frac{3}{8}$ $5\frac{23}{24}$ 3. $9 - 3\frac{2}{5}$ $5\frac{3}{5}$

4. $5\frac{3}{16} - 2\frac{3}{8}$ $2\frac{13}{16}$ 5. $8\frac{1}{6} - 3\frac{2}{5}$ $4\frac{23}{30}$ 6. $7\frac{1}{2} - 3$ $4\frac{1}{2}$

7. $2\frac{3}{4} - 1\frac{1}{8}$ $1\frac{5}{8}$ 8. $4\frac{1}{8} - 2\frac{1}{16}$ $2\frac{1}{16}$ 9. $9\frac{2}{3} - 3\frac{5}{6}$ $5\frac{5}{6}$

10. $2\frac{1}{10} - 1\frac{2}{5}$ $\frac{7}{10}$ 11. $15\frac{7}{12} - 8\frac{1}{4}$ $7\frac{1}{3}$ 12. $6\frac{7}{16} - 2\frac{7}{8}$ $3\frac{9}{16}$

13. $27\frac{1}{4} - 13\frac{11}{12}$ $13\frac{1}{3}$ 14. $5\frac{2}{5} - 1\frac{1}{4}$ $4\frac{3}{20}$ 15. $10\frac{2}{3} - 7\frac{3}{4}$ $2\frac{11}{12}$

Solve each equation for x.

16. $x + 2\frac{1}{2} = 5\frac{3}{4}$ 17. $10\frac{1}{3} + x = 16\frac{5}{12}$ 18. $x + 9\frac{1}{16} = 23\frac{7}{8}$
  $3\frac{1}{4}$ $6\frac{1}{12}$ $14\frac{13}{16}$

19. $32\frac{1}{5} + x = 35\frac{1}{2}$ 20. $x + 17\frac{3}{4} = 25\frac{1}{3}$ 21. $27\frac{1}{10} + x = 33\frac{1}{2}$
  $3\frac{3}{10}$ $7\frac{7}{12}$ $6\frac{2}{5}$

22. $18\frac{5}{6} + x = 24\frac{3}{8}$ 23. $x + 8\frac{3}{16} = 12\frac{3}{8}$ 24. $5\frac{1}{2} + x = 9\frac{1}{4}$
  $5\frac{13}{24}$ $4\frac{3}{16}$ $3\frac{3}{4}$

Solve.

25. Robbie needs to buy fencing for his square vegetable garden that measures $16\frac{3}{4}$ ft on a side. One side borders the back of the garage. The fencing costs $4/ft. Estimate how much the fencing for the vegetable garden will cost. about $204

26. Paula has 2 yd of elastic. One project needs a piece $\frac{3}{4}$ yd. Does she have enough for another project that needs $1\frac{1}{3}$ yd? Explain. No. Answers may vary. Sample: She will have only $1\frac{1}{4}$ yd left after the first project and $1\frac{1}{4} < 1\frac{1}{3}$.

27. Use a ruler or measuring tape to find the perimeter of your desk. Measure to the nearest half inch. Answers may vary.
width:_____   length:_____   perimeter:_____

In copymaster and workbook formats

RETEACHING

Reteaching 6-5 *Subtracting Mixed Numbers*

Some mixed numbers can be subtracted mentally.

Subtract: $5\frac{2}{3} - 2\frac{1}{6}$

Step 1
Subtract the whole numbers.
$5 - 2 = 3$

Step 2
Subtract the fractions.
$\frac{2}{3} - \frac{1}{6} = \frac{4}{6} - \frac{1}{6} = \frac{3}{6} = \frac{1}{2}$

Step 3
Combine the two parts.
$3 + \frac{1}{2} = 3\frac{1}{2}$

$5\frac{2}{3} - 2\frac{1}{6} = 3\frac{1}{2}$

Sometimes you must rename the first fraction before subtracting.

Subtract: $6\frac{1}{2} - 2\frac{3}{4}$ (Cannot subtract $\frac{1}{2} - \frac{3}{4}$)

Step 1
Write with a common denominator.
$6\frac{1}{2} - 2\frac{3}{4} = 6\frac{2}{4} - 2\frac{3}{4}$

Step 2
Rename $6\frac{2}{4}$.
$= 5\frac{6}{4} - 2\frac{3}{4}$

Step 3
Subtract the whole numbers. Subtract the fractions. Simplify, if necessary.
$6\frac{1}{2} - 2\frac{3}{4} = 3\frac{3}{4}$

Find each difference. Write it in simplest form.

1. $7\frac{7}{10} - 2\frac{3}{10}$ $5\frac{2}{5}$ 2. $3\frac{3}{4} - 1\frac{1}{2}$ $2\frac{1}{4}$ 3. $6\frac{2}{3} - 2\frac{1}{6}$ $4\frac{1}{2}$

4. $9\frac{7}{8} - 7\frac{3}{4}$ $2\frac{1}{8}$ 5. $8\frac{1}{2} - 3\frac{1}{4}$ $5\frac{1}{4}$ 6. $14\frac{1}{3} - 8\frac{1}{4}$ $6\frac{1}{12}$

7. $12\frac{1}{3} - 9\frac{2}{3}$ $2\frac{2}{3}$ 8. $6\frac{5}{8} - 2\frac{3}{4}$ $3\frac{7}{8}$ 9. $7\frac{5}{7} - 4\frac{13}{14}$ $2\frac{11}{14}$

10. $10\frac{2}{3} - 7\frac{5}{6}$ $2\frac{5}{6}$ 11. $5\frac{7}{16} - 1\frac{1}{2}$ $3\frac{15}{16}$ 12. $8\frac{5}{7} - 3\frac{2}{5}$ $4\frac{11}{15}$

13. $6\frac{1}{8} - 3\frac{1}{16}$ $3\frac{1}{16}$ 14. $9\frac{1}{12} - 5\frac{3}{4}$ $3\frac{3}{3}$ 15. $12\frac{3}{4} - 6\frac{1}{8}$ $6\frac{5}{8}$

16. $7\frac{2}{5} - 2\frac{1}{4}$ $5\frac{3}{20}$ 17. $15\frac{5}{12} - 8\frac{1}{3}$ $7\frac{1}{12}$ 18. $4\frac{1}{10} - 2\frac{4}{5}$ $1\frac{3}{10}$

ENRICHMENT

Minds on Math Transparency

6-5

A group of 32 students was sitting in a row of chairs. They began with 1 and counted off by 1s. Each student who counted a multiple of 2 stood up. Then only the students who were still sitting counted off by 1s. Again, each student who counted a multiple of 2 stood up. They kept repeating this procedure. How many times will they need to do this before only one student is sitting?

5 times

See *Solution Key* for worked-out answers.

249

1 Focus

CONNECTING TO PRIOR KNOWLEDGE Ask: *When people give you directions to their house, do you prefer a map, written directions, or verbal directions?* **Answers may vary.** Have students discuss the benefits of a map. **Answers may vary. Sample: A map is good because you can just turn it around in order to get home.**

Lesson Planning Options

Prerequisite Skills
- understanding customary measurements (precourse)

Materials/Manipulatives
- graph paper

Resources

 Student Edition

Skills Handbook, p. 536
Extra Practice, p. 527
Glossary/Study Guide

 Teaching Resources

Chapter Support File, Ch. 6
- Lesson Planner 6-6
- Practice 6-6, Reteaching 6-6
- Answer Masters 6-6

Glossary, Spanish Resources

 Transparencies
89, Minds on Math 6-6

Warm Up

What kind of graph represents a whole broken into its parts? **circle graph**

2 Teach

THINK AND DISCUSS

DIVERSITY You may wish to have pictures of Native American art work on display. Encourage students with Native American heritage to share examples or insight about art work. Suggest students research the symbols represented in Native American art.

TACTILE LEARNING Have students use algebra tiles to model the border. Remind students that the side of each square represents $\frac{1}{2}$ ft.

AUDITORY LEARNING Read the sample problem aloud. Have students write down the important information and begin to sketch the tiles as you read.

PROBLEM SOLVING STRATEGY

6-6 Draw a Diagram

Problem Solving Strategies

✔ Draw a Diagram
  Guess and Test
  Look for a Pattern
  Make a Model
  Make a Table
  Simulate a Problem
  Solve a Simpler Problem
  Too Much or Too Little
    Information
  Use Logical Reasoning
  Use Multiple Strategies
  Work Backward

THINK AND DISCUSS

Drawing a diagram is a strategy you can use to solve many problems. A diagram helps you to see a problem and its solution more clearly.

SAMPLE PROBLEM....................

An artist is creating a tiled wall for the Native American wing of a museum. The border will be made of tiles containing Native American designs. Each tile is a square that measures $\frac{1}{2}$ ft on a side. The tiled wall, including the border, will be 6 ft high by 10 ft wide. How many border tiles does the artist need to make?

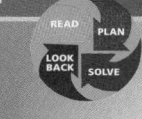

 READ

Read for understanding. Summarize the problem.

Identify the information you need to use to solve the problem.

1. What size and shape are the border tiles? **$\frac{1}{2}$ ft-by-$\frac{1}{2}$ ft squares**

2. What size and shape is the tiled wall? Do the dimensions include the border? **6 ft-by-10 ft rectangle; yes**

3. Is the problem asking you to find the total number of tiles the artist needs to make for the tiled wall? Explain.
   No; the problem asks for only the number of border tiles.

 PLAN

Decide on a strategy.

If you draw a diagram of the tiled wall, you can then draw in the border. If you use graph paper, you can count the number of border tiles needed.

4. What measurement will each unit on the graph paper represent? **$\frac{1}{2}$ ft**

5. How many units high and wide will your diagram be?
   12 units high and 20 units wide

250

CONNECTIONS TO SOCIAL STUDIES Have students research what historical maps and drawings can tell us about people of that time. **Answers may vary. Sample: Maps made in the fourteenth century show that the map makers did not know about all the areas of the world.**

ASSESSMENT Ask: *What are the dimensions of the tiled wall within the border?* **9 ft by 5 ft**

■ ADDITIONAL PROBLEM

A museum gives an artist 60 square tiles to create a mural. The mural must be rectangular and have the smallest perimeter possible. What dimensions will the mural have? **6 tiles by 10 tiles**

3 Practice/Assess

EXERCISES *On Your Own*

ERROR ALERT! **Exercise 1** Students may incorrectly think a rectangle must have two long sides and two short sides. **Remediation:** Remind students that squares are also rectangles. Make sure they understand that not all rectangles are squares.

➤ **SOLVE**
Try the strategy.

Draw a diagram to "see" the problem and its solution.

6. If one unit on the graph paper represents $\frac{1}{2}$ ft, how many feet in height will your diagram represent? How many feet in width? **6 ft high; 10 ft wide**

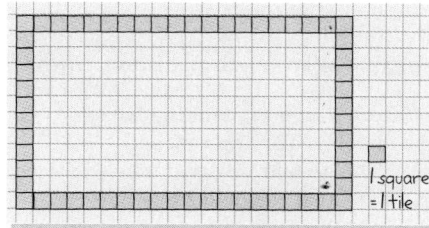

1 square = 1 tile

7. Use the diagram to find the number of border tiles the artist needs to make. **60 border tiles**

➤ **LOOK BACK**
Think about how you solved the problem.

9. **Answers may vary. Sample: Yes; since the corner tiles have two sides on the perimeter, you could have mistakenly counted each corner tile twice.**

8. How did the diagram help you solve this problem? Evaluate your solution for reasonableness. **Border tiles could be counted from the diagram; check students' work.**

9. Do you think this problem would be difficult to solve without drawing a diagram? Explain.

10. Instead of drawing a diagram, one student followed the steps below. Find the number of border tiles needed for each side of the wall: top, 20; bottom, 20; left side, 12; right side, 12. Then add: 20 + 20 + 12 + 12 = 64 border tiles. What is wrong with this solution? **The 4 corner tiles were each counted twice.**

Now you may assign Exercises 1–10.

EXERCISES *On Your Own*

Draw a diagram to solve each problem.

1. *Pets* Suppose you have 24 ft of fence for a rectangular dog kennel. Each side will be a whole number of feet (no fractions). List all possible dimensions for the kennel. Which will give your dog the greatest area? **1 ft by 11 ft, 2 ft by 10 ft, 3 ft by 9 ft, 4 ft by 8 ft, 5 ft by 7 ft, 6 ft by 6 ft; 6 ft by 6 ft**

2. *Gardening* Your brother is planting flowers along the edge of a rectangular flower bed. He will place the plants 6 inches apart. The perimeter of the garden measures 7 feet. How many plants will your brother need? **14 plants**

Technology Options

Prentice Hall Technology

💾 💿 **Software for Learners**
• Math Blaster® Mystery*
• Interactive Student Tutorial, Chapter 6*

💾 💿 **Teaching Resource Software**
• Computer Item Generator 6-6
• Resource Pro™ Chapter 6*

🔗 **Internet**
• For related mathematics activities, visit the Prentice Hall site at www.phschool.com/math

Available on CD-ROM only

Assignment Options for Exercises On Your Own

Core 1–9
Extension 10

Use Mixed Review to maintain skills.

Practice 6-6 Problem-Solving Strategy:
Draw a Diagram

Frank is laying square tiles on a rectangular floor. He wants the perimeter tiles to be a different color for two rows around the edges of the room. The dimensions of the room are 20 ft by 10 ft. Each tile is 1 ft on a side.

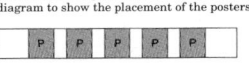

1. Draw a diagram to show how Frank could tile the floor. Use two colors.

2. How many border tiles does he need? **104 tiles**

3. How many inside tiles does he need? **96 tiles**

Draw a diagram to solve.

4. Jessica is hanging five posters on a 19-ft wall. Each poster is 2 ft wide, and she wants to have 1 ft of space between the posters and an equal amount of space at both ends. Draw a diagram to show the placement of the posters.

| P | P | P | P | P |

5. Suppose you are hanging posters along a 35-ft wall in the hallway. Each poster is 2 ft wide.

 a. What is the greatest number of posters that you could fit along the wall without overlap? **17 posters**

 b. What is the greatest number of posters that you could fit along the wall if you kept 2 ft between them? Draw a diagram to show your answer.

| 1 | 2 | 3 | 4 | 5 | 6 | 7 | 8 | 9 |

Choose any strategy to solve.

6. Matthew earns $.10 for each local newspaper he delivers twice a week. His brother earns $.25 for delivering each Sunday newspaper. They deliver papers to the same number of houses and together they earn $13.95/wk. How many papers does each boy deliver each week?
Matthew: 62 papers; brother: 31 papers

7. Megan's car averaged 336 mi on 12 gal of gas. How many gallons of gas did Megan use to drive 1,344 mi on vacation?
48 gal

In copymaster and workbook formats

Reteaching 6-6 Problem-Solving Strategy:
Draw a Diagram

Yori found that each time a ball bounces, it returns to one half its previous height. If she drops the ball from 40 ft, how many feet will it have traveled when it hits the ground the fourth time?

Read What does the problem ask ? *Find the total distance the ball will travel up and down by the time it hits the ground the fourth time.*

Plan You can draw a diagram. How many feet will the first segment represent? *The first segment will represent 40 ft.*

Solve Draw a diagram to represent the problem.

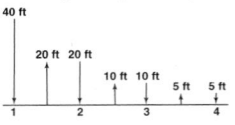

Add to solve. 40 + 20 + 20 + 10 + 10 + 5 + 5 = 110 ft

Look Back How can you be sure that the solution solves the problem? *Count the number of times the ball hits the ground; check that each bounce is one half the height of the previous bounce.*

Draw a diagram to solve each problem.

1. Yori drops a ball from 64 ft. How far will it travel until it hits the ground the fourth time if it also returns to one-half the height of its previous bounce?
176 ft

2. Yori drops a ball from the same height in Exercise 1. She allows it to bounce 4 times before stopping it. If it returns to $\frac{1}{3}$ its dropped height, how much less will it travel than the ball in Exercise 1?
70 ft less; 176 ft − 106 ft

3. A ball returns to one-half its dropped height. By the time it hits the ground the fourth time, it has traveled 66 ft. From what height was it dropped?
24 ft

4. When a ball bounces, it returns to a height $\frac{3}{4}$ its previous height. After it hits the ground the second time, it bounces up 9 ft. From what height was it dropped?
16 ft

Minds on Math Transparency

6-6

Turn the triangle of circles "upside down" by sliding one circle at a time to a new location so that it touches 2 other circles. The minimum number of moves is 3.

See Solution Key for worked-out answers.

WRAP UP

IDENTIFYING THE BIG IDEA Ask students to explain when to and how to draw a diagram to solve a problem.

Draw a diagram to solve each problem.

1. Erica's garden patch is 4 ft by 6 ft. She will plant herbs just inside the garden's perimeter. The plants will be 6 in. apart and 6 in. from the edge of the garden. How many herb plants will she need? **32**

2. You have a rectangular mural made from tiles $2\frac{1}{2}$ ft square. The length of each side of the mural is a whole number of feet, and the perimeter is 40 ft. What are the dimensions of the mural? **10 ft by 10 ft**

3. *Carpentry* Jo is making a bookcase with wood that is $\frac{3}{4}$ in. thick. The bookcase has four shelves. One shelf is used for the top of the bookcase, and one is used for the bottom. The space between shelves is 12 in. Find the total height of the bookcase. **39 in.**

4. *Rugs* Elisha has a rug in her living room that is 12 ft by 18 ft. She wants to cut it into two smaller rectangular rugs that can be placed in other rooms. Show how she can make one cut and end up with two rugs the same size and shape.
Answers may vary. See back of book for sample.

Use any strategy to solve each problem. Show your work.

5. *Patterns* A store owner is stacking boxes for a window display. The top row will have one box. The second row will have three boxes. The third row will have five boxes. If this pattern continues, how many boxes will the tenth row have?
19 boxes

6. *Commuting* William drives about 24 mi total to and from work each day. He works five days each week and takes two weeks of vacation each year. About how many miles does William drive to and from work in one year? **6,000 mi**

7. *Food* Juan is making sandwiches for a party. Each sandwich has one type of bread, one type of cheese, and one type of meat. There are two choices each for bread, cheese, and meat. How many different sandwiches can Juan make?
8 different sandwiches

8. *Marketing* To celebrate its opening day, a store is offering a free gift to every 15th customer. The store manager expects about 100 customers each hour. About how many gifts will the store offer by the end of its 12-h opening day? **80 gifts**

9. *Scheduling* Britta needs to get to work by 9:30 A.M. She must drive her son to school, which takes 12 min. She will also drop off some dry cleaning. From school to the dry cleaners takes about 15 min. From the dry cleaners to work takes about 18 min. When should Britta leave home? **8:45 A.M.**

10. *Sports* A basketball team sold 496 raffle tickets and collected $396.80. Expenses totaled $75.98. How much did each ticket sell for? **$.80**

Mixed Review

11. *Data Analysis* Draw a bar graph of the information found in the table at the right. *(Lesson 1-6)* **See back of book.**

12. What metric unit would you use to measure the height of your school? The amount of juice in a glass? *(Lessons 3-8 and 3-9)* **meter; milliliter**

13. Give the information needed to solve the following problem. Suppose you bought 3 boxes of juice. How much did you pay for them? *(Lesson 4-9)* **price for one box of juice**

Number of Known Species	
Beetles	290,000
Bees/wasps	103,000
Butterflies/moths	112,000
Seed plants	248,400

Source: *The Diversity of Life*

1 Focus

CONNECTING TO PRIOR KNOWLEDGE Ask students to multiply 0.2 by 0.9 **0.18** Have students describe models they can use to multiply decimals. Ask: *Do you think you could use the same models to multiply $\frac{2}{10}$ by $\frac{9}{10}$?* **yes**

2 Teach

Work Together

TACTILE LEARNING **Questions 1–3** Give groups of students an apple and a plastic knife to perform the activity, then answer questions.

Ask students to write the multiplication problem that represents the steps in the activity. $\frac{1}{2} \times \frac{1}{2} = \frac{1}{4}$

THINK AND DISCUSS

AEP **AUDITORY LEARNING** Give examples to show when the word *of* means multiplication. Say: *One third of six is two.* Have students write the number statement. $\frac{1}{3} \times 6 = 2$ Repeat, saying *one half of eight is 4.* $\frac{1}{2} \times 8 = 4$

ERROR ALERT! Students may try to find equivalent fractions for problems such as $\frac{2}{3} \times \frac{1}{6}$ before they multiply. **Remediation:** Have students work the problem with area

---

GEOMETRY Connection

 **6-7**

Modeling the Multiplication of Fractions

What You'll Learn

▼ To multiply fractions by fractions

▼ To multiply whole numbers by fractions

...And Why

Sometimes you will need to find a fraction of a fraction.

Here's How

Look for questions that
⊞ build understanding
✔ check understanding

Work Together
Finding a Fraction of a Fraction

Let's pretend you are sharing an apple with a friend.

1. Use a circular piece of paper to represent the apple. Cut the "apple" into two equal pieces. What portion of the apple does each piece of paper represent? Take one piece. $\frac{1}{2}$

2. Now cut your piece of "apple" into two equal pieces. Give one piece to your friend. What portion of your piece of "apple" does your friend have? $\frac{1}{2}$

3. ⊞*Number Sense* What portion of the whole "apple" does each of you have? $\frac{1}{4}$

THINK AND DISCUSS

▼ Multiplying Fractions by Fractions

You can use area models to multiply fractions by fractions. The word "of" means multiplication when used mathematically.

■ **EXAMPLE 1** *Real-World Problem Solving*

Community Planning A town plans to use one half of a square park for a picnic area. One third of the picnic area will be a playground. What portion of the park will be a playground?

Picnic area = $\frac{1}{2}$ of the park; shade half of a rectangle.

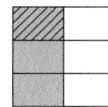
Divide the picnic area into thirds. Draw diagonal lines for $\frac{1}{3}$ of the shaded area.

One sixth of the park will be a playground.

Lesson Planning Options

Prerequisite Skills

- modeling fractions (precourse)
- rewriting improper fractions as mixed numbers (5-6)

Materials/Manipulatives

- paper (circular)
- scissors

Resources

📖 **Student Edition**

Skills Handbook, p. 540
Extra Practice, p. 527
Glossary/Study Guide

🗂 **Teaching Resources**

Chapter Support File, Ch. 6
- Lesson Planner 6-7
- Practice 6-7, Reteaching 6-7
- Answer Masters 6-7
Teaching Aids Masters 21–25
Glossary, Spanish Resources

🖥 **Transparencies**
22–29, Minds on Math 6-7

Warm Up

Find the least common denominator (LCD) of $\frac{3}{4}$ and $\frac{5}{16}$. **16**

models. Point out they do not need to find equivalent fractions to multiply fractions.

VISUAL LEARNING Example 3 Help students see that $\frac{5}{1}$ is equivalent to 5. Have students draw fraction bars for $\frac{5}{1}$. Ask: *Is this different from 5?* **no**

ASSESSMENT Pair students. Have each student think of a fraction. They work together to model the product. Then multiply the fractions to check their work.

■ **ADDITIONAL EXAMPLES**

FOR EXAMPLE 1
One fourth of a square park will be a garden center. Gardeners will plant $\frac{1}{8}$ of the garden center with roses. What portion of the park will they plant with roses? $\frac{1}{32}$

FOR EXAMPLE 2
Find $\frac{5}{7} \times \frac{3}{5}$. Simplify. $\frac{3}{7}$

FOR EXAMPLE 3
Find the product $\frac{2}{9} \times 6$. Simplify. $1\frac{1}{3}$

FOR EXAMPLE 4
Three fifths of Shari's class helped to build a playscape. If Shari's class has 25 students, how many people in her class helped build the playscape? **15**

Technology Options

Prentice Hall Technology

 **Software for Learners**
- Math Blaster® Mystery*
- Interactive Student Tutorial, Chapter 6*

  Teaching Resource Software
- Computer Item Generator 6-7
- Resource Pro™ Chapter 6*

Internet • For related mathematics activities, visit the Prentice Hall site at www.phschool.com/math

*Available on CD-ROM only

Assignment Options for Exercises On Your Own

To provide flexible scheduling, this lesson can be subdivided into parts.

1 Core 1–10, 34
Extension 11, 32

2 Core 12–31
Extension 33

Use Mixed Review to maintain skills.

254

---

4. ✔ *Try It Out* Suppose one fourth of the playground is for baseball. What portion of the park is for baseball? $\frac{1}{24}$

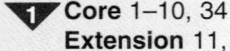 **5.** ▲ *Modeling* Draw an area model to show $\frac{2}{3}$ of $\frac{3}{4}$.

You can also multiply to find a fraction of a fraction.

■ **EXAMPLE 2**

Find $\frac{2}{3}$ of $\frac{1}{2}$.

$\frac{2}{3}$ of $\frac{1}{2}$ ⟶ $\frac{2}{3} \times \frac{1}{2}$ ⟵ Multiply the fractions.

$= \dfrac{2 \times 1}{3 \times 2}$ ⟵ Multiply the numerators. Multiply the denominators.

$= \frac{2}{6} = \frac{1}{3}$ ⟵ Simplify.

So, $\frac{2}{3}$ of $\frac{1}{2} = \frac{1}{3}$.

6. ✔ *Try It Out* Find each product.
a. $\frac{2}{3}$ of $\frac{3}{4}$ $\frac{1}{2}$ b. $\frac{1}{4}$ of $\frac{2}{5}$ $\frac{1}{10}$ c. $\frac{3}{4}$ of $\frac{1}{8}$ $\frac{3}{32}$ d. $\frac{1}{2}$ of $\frac{2}{3}$ $\frac{1}{3}$

Now you may assign Exercises 1–11, 32, 34.

2 *Multiplying Whole Numbers by Fractions*

To solve some problems, you will need to multiply a fraction and a whole number. The model below shows how you can do this.

$4 \times \frac{2}{3} = \frac{2}{3} + \frac{2}{3} + \frac{2}{3} + \frac{2}{3}$

$= \frac{8}{3}$

$= 2\frac{2}{3}$

You can change a whole number to an improper fraction with a denominator of 1 and then multiply two fractions.

■ **EXAMPLE 3**

Find the product $\frac{3}{4} \times 5$.

$\frac{3}{4} \times 5 = \frac{3}{4} \times \frac{5}{1}$ ⟵ Write 5 as $\frac{5}{1}$.

$= \dfrac{3 \times 5}{4 \times 1}$ ⟵ Multiply the numerators and denominators.

$= \frac{15}{4} = 3\frac{3}{4}$ ⟵ Rewrite as a mixed number.

EXERCISES *On Your Own*

OPEN-ENDED Exercise 10 Have students work in pairs. One partner models the product of two like fractions. The other partner models the product of two unlike fractions. Students compare models. Ask: *Would you rather multiply like fractions or unlike fractions?* **Answers may vary. Sample: It does not matter. Both have the same number of steps.**

CONNECTING TO THE STUDENTS' WORLD and RESEARCH Exercise 11 Suggest that students call the local Chamber of Commerce or search the Internet to find the population data for their city or town. They can ask the local school district for student population data. Ask students to find the portion of the population in their grade.

EXTENSION Exercise 33 If you have block scheduling or extended class periods, have students compile a survey of all the members of their families and the age of each member.

Have students determine the percent of females 17 years of age or younger in the United States and compare this with the percent of females 17 years of age or younger in their class' families as a whole.

WRITING Exercise 34 Suggest students include drawings of models to compare multiplying fractions and decimals.

7. ✔ *Try It Out* Find each product.

a. $\frac{1}{9} \times 10$ $1\frac{1}{9}$ b. $\frac{4}{5} \times 12$ $9\frac{3}{5}$ c. $\frac{2}{3} \times 11$ $7\frac{1}{3}$ d. $\frac{3}{8} \times 7$ $2\frac{5}{8}$

If the denominator of one fraction and the numerator of the other have a common factor, you can simplify before multiplying.

■ **EXAMPLE 4** *Real-World Problem Solving*

School Play Suppose 12 students tried out for speaking parts in the school play. Two thirds of the students will get speaking parts. How many students will speak in the play?

$\frac{2}{3}$ of $12 = \frac{2}{3} \times \frac{12}{1}$ ←— Write 12 as $\frac{12}{1}$.

$= \frac{2}{3} \times \frac{\overset{4}{\cancel{12}}}{1}$ ←— Divide both 12 and 3 by their GCF of 3.

$= \frac{2 \times 4}{1 \times 1} = \frac{8}{1} = 8$ ←— Multiply and simplify.

8. ✔ *Try It Out* Find each product.

a. $\frac{1}{2}$ of 16 8   b. $\frac{2}{5}$ of 25 10   c. $\frac{3}{8}$ of 24 9   d. $\frac{5}{6}$ of 30 25

Now you may assign Exercises 12–31, 33.

EXERCISES *On Your Own*

Modeling **What number sentence is represented by each model?**

1. 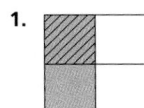 $\frac{1}{2} \times \frac{1}{2} = \frac{1}{4}$

2. 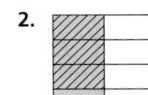 $\frac{3}{4} \times \frac{1}{2} = \frac{3}{8}$

3. 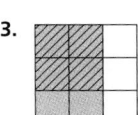 $\frac{2}{3} \times \frac{2}{3} = \frac{4}{9}$

Modeling **Draw a model to represent each product.** **4–8. See margin.**

4. $\frac{1}{4}$ of $\frac{1}{3}$ **5.** $\frac{1}{2}$ of $\frac{3}{4}$ **6.** $\frac{3}{4}$ of $\frac{1}{4}$ **7.** $\frac{1}{5}$ of $\frac{5}{8}$ **8.** $\frac{4}{5}$ of $\frac{5}{16}$

9. Choose A, B, C, or D. Which product does the model at the right represent? **C**

A. $\frac{3}{4} \times \frac{2}{3}$ B. $\frac{1}{3} \times \frac{1}{3}$ C. $\frac{3}{4} \times \frac{1}{3}$ D. $\frac{1}{3} \times \frac{2}{3}$

10. *Open-ended* Choose two fractions. Model their product.
  Answers may vary. Sample: $\frac{1}{2} \times \frac{2}{3}$; See margin for model.
11. *Research* Find out what fraction of your town's population is of school age. What portion of those are in first grade?
  Check students' work.

---

pages 255–256   On Your Own

4.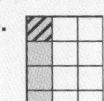

5.

6.

7.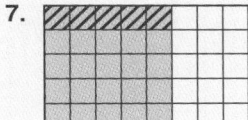

8.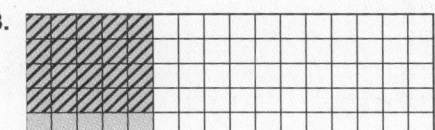

10.

page 256   Mixed Review

47.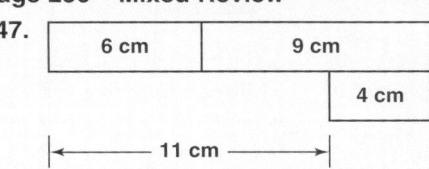

PRACTICE

Practice 6-7 *Modeling the Multiplication of Fractions*

Draw a model to represent each product.

1. $\frac{1}{6}$ of $\frac{3}{4}$ 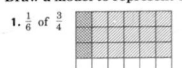   2. $\frac{2}{5}$ of $\frac{1}{2}$

Find each product.

3. $\frac{3}{5}$ of 10 6
4. $\frac{1}{4}$ of 12 3
5. $\frac{2}{3}$ of 6 4
6. $\frac{4}{5}$ of $5\frac{1}{2}$
7. $\frac{5}{6}$ of $3\frac{5}{8}$ $\frac{5}{16}$
8. $\frac{3}{5}$ of $\frac{1}{2}$ $\frac{3}{10}$
9. $\frac{3}{4}$ of 12 9
10. $\frac{2}{5}$ of 15 6
11. $\frac{3}{16}$ of 8 $1\frac{1}{2}$
12. $\frac{1}{2} \times \frac{5}{6}$ $\frac{5}{12}$
13. $\frac{3}{4} \times \frac{7}{8}$ $\frac{21}{32}$
14. $\frac{1}{3}$ of $2\frac{2}{5}$ $\frac{2}{15}$
15. $\frac{3}{5}$ of $\frac{3}{4}$ $\frac{9}{20}$
16. $\frac{1}{2} \times \frac{1}{3}$ $\frac{1}{6}$
17. $\frac{1}{8} \times \frac{3}{4}$ $\frac{3}{32}$
18. $\frac{2}{5} \times \frac{7}{11}$ $\frac{14}{55}$
19. $\frac{2}{3}$ of $\frac{1}{4}$ $\frac{1}{6}$
20. $\frac{2}{5} \times \frac{1}{4}$ $\frac{1}{6}$
21. $\frac{1}{4} \times \frac{4}{5}$ $\frac{1}{5}$
22. $\frac{5}{6} \times \frac{2}{5}$ $\frac{1}{3}$
23. $\frac{2}{7} \times \frac{3}{5}$ $\frac{6}{35}$
24. $\frac{1}{3}$ of $\frac{9}{10}$ $\frac{3}{10}$
25. $\frac{1}{12} \times \frac{3}{4}$ $\frac{1}{16}$
26. $\frac{3}{10} \times \frac{3}{5}$ $\frac{9}{50}$

27. Circle A, B, C, or D. Which product does the model represent?
   A. $\frac{1}{4} \times \frac{2}{3}$
   B. $\frac{3}{4} \times \frac{1}{12}$
   C. $\frac{2}{3} \times \frac{1}{2}$
   D. $\frac{1}{4} \times \frac{1}{2}$

In copymaster and workbook formats

RETEACHING

Reteaching 6-7 *Modeling the Multiplication of Fractions*

You can model $\frac{2}{3}$ of $\frac{1}{4}$.

① Show $\frac{1}{4}$.

② Divide into thirds.

③ Shade $\frac{2}{3}$ of the $\frac{1}{4}$.

$\frac{2}{3}$ of $\frac{1}{4} = \frac{2}{12} = \frac{1}{6}$

Or you can use multiplication.

$\frac{2}{3}$ of $\frac{1}{4} = \frac{2}{3} \times \frac{1}{4} = \frac{2 \times 1}{3 \times 4} = \frac{2}{12} = \frac{1}{6}$

Model $\frac{1}{2}$ of 5.

① Show 5.
☐ ☐ ☐ ☐ ☐

② Find $\frac{1}{2}$ of each.

③ Combine the 5 halves.
$\frac{1}{2}$ of $5 = \frac{1}{2} + \frac{1}{2} + \frac{1}{2} + \frac{1}{2} + \frac{1}{2}$
$= \frac{5}{2} = 2\frac{1}{2}$

Using multiplication:
$\frac{1}{2}$ of $5 = \frac{1}{2} \times 5 = \frac{1}{2} \times \frac{5}{1} = \frac{1 \times 5}{2 \times 1} = \frac{5}{2} = 2\frac{1}{2}$

What product is represented by each model?

1. 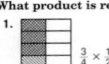 $\frac{3}{4} \times \frac{1}{2}$
2. 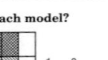 $\frac{1}{2} \times \frac{2}{3}$
3. $\frac{2}{3} \times 2$

Find each product.

4. $\frac{1}{9}$ of $\frac{2}{3}$ $\frac{2}{27}$
5. $\frac{2}{7} \times \frac{1}{2}$ $\frac{1}{7}$
6. $\frac{5}{8} \times 6$ $3\frac{3}{4}$
7. $\frac{3}{4}$ of $4\frac{1}{7}$ $\frac{3}{7}$
8. $\frac{7}{10}$ of $1\frac{1}{7}$ $\frac{7}{30}$
9. $\frac{5}{8} \times 3\frac{1}{5}$ $\frac{5}{8}$
10. $\frac{3}{8}$ of $\frac{7}{10}$ $\frac{21}{80}$
11. $\frac{3}{4} \times \frac{1}{9}$ $\frac{1}{12}$
12. $\frac{2}{9}$ of 8 $1\frac{7}{9}$
13. $\frac{1}{3}$ of 2 $\frac{2}{3}$
14. $\frac{5}{9}$ of 4 $2\frac{2}{9}$
15. $\frac{3}{4}$ of $\frac{2}{5}$ $\frac{3}{10}$

ENRICHMENT

Minds on Math Transparency

6-7

Rio's grandfather is 2 times as old as Rio's dad. Twenty years ago the ratio of their ages was 3 to 1. How old is Rio's grandfather now?

80 years old

See *Solution Key* for worked-out answers.

256

WRAP UP

IDENTIFYING THE BIG IDEA Ask students to explain how to multiply fractions and multiply whole numbers and fractions.

▽ **PROJECT LINK** You may want to perform a sample demonstration for the students.

JOURNAL Have students draw area models in their journal to support their answers.

LESSON QUIZ

Find each product. Simplify.

1. $\frac{4}{5} \times \frac{3}{10}$ $\frac{6}{25}$
2. $25 \times \frac{2}{9}$ $5\frac{5}{9}$
3. $\frac{3}{8}$ of $\frac{6}{10}$ $\frac{9}{40}$

Find each product.

12. $\frac{1}{2}$ of $\frac{1}{4}$ $\frac{1}{8}$
13. $\frac{3}{5} \times \frac{2}{3}$ $\frac{2}{5}$
14. $\frac{5}{8} \times \frac{2}{7}$ $\frac{5}{28}$
15. $\frac{5}{6}$ of $\frac{3}{10}$ $\frac{1}{4}$
16. $\frac{2}{5} \times \frac{7}{8}$ $\frac{7}{20}$
17. $\frac{1}{5}$ of $\frac{1}{2}$ $\frac{1}{10}$
18. $\frac{1}{2}$ of $\frac{1}{5}$ $\frac{1}{10}$
19. $\frac{2}{5} \times \frac{1}{8}$ $\frac{1}{20}$
20. $\frac{1}{2}$ of $\frac{1}{3}$ $\frac{1}{6}$
21. $\frac{3}{5} \times \frac{3}{4}$ $\frac{9}{20}$
22. $\frac{2}{5}$ of 7 $2\frac{4}{5}$
23. $\frac{5}{6} \times 13$ $10\frac{5}{6}$
24. $\frac{3}{8} \times 11$ $4\frac{1}{8}$
25. $\frac{9}{10}$ of 31 $27\frac{9}{10}$
26. $\frac{5}{8} \times 3$ $1\frac{7}{8}$
27. $\frac{2}{3}$ of 16 $10\frac{2}{3}$
28. $\frac{7}{10} \times 80$ 56
29. $\frac{3}{4}$ of 23 $17\frac{1}{4}$
30. $\frac{6}{11} \times 77$ 42
31. $\frac{1}{2}$ of 55 $27\frac{1}{2}$

32. *Landscaping* Suppose two thirds of your yard will be grass. The rest will be plants. Three fourths of the plant area will have flowers. What portion of the yard will have flowers? $\frac{1}{4}$

33. *Population* The U.S. population is about 265 million. About one fourth of the population is 17 years of age or under. About half of this group is female. About how many people in the United States are females 17 years of age or younger?
33 million people

34. *Writing* Explain how multiplying $\frac{3}{10}$ and $\frac{2}{10}$ is similar to multiplying 0.3 and 0.2. **In each case, you find the product of 3 and 2.**

> **JOURNAL**
> Explain what happens when you multiply a fraction by a fraction. Does the value of the first fraction increase or decrease? Why?

Mixed Review

Is each number prime or composite? *(Lesson 5-2)*

35. 61 prime
36. 51 composite
37. 78 composite
38. 79 prime
39. 113 prime
40. 129 composite

Find the value of the digit 3 in each number. *(Lesson 3-2)*

41. 108.39 3 tenths
42. 38.22 3 tens or thirty
43. 0.523 3 thousandths
44. 345,650 3 hundred thousand
45. 0.0293 3 ten-thousandths
46. 3,589,192 3 million

47. *Choose a Strategy* The lengths of three rods are 4 cm, 6 cm, and 9 cm. Arrange these rods to measure 11 cm. See margin p. 255.

△ **CHAPTER PROJECT**
PROJECT LINK: DEMONSTRATING

Using some of the items you have gathered, create a demonstration showing the addition of fractions that have the same denominator. You could use a ruler to add eighths of an inch, a measuring cup to add thirds of a cup of water, or a clock to add sixths of an hour. Make sure you prove that the two fractions add up to the expected sum.

Check students' work.

PROBLEM SOLVING PRACTICE ★★

This page provides problems for students to solve using their knowledge of adding and subtracting mixed numbers, measuring length, finding GCF, and recognizing prime numbers. Allow students to use any method they find helpful.

Exercise 1 Suggest students draw a calendar to solve the problem.

USING MANIPULATIVES Exercises 1 and 3 Students can use fraction bars to help them solve these problems.

COOPERATIVE GROUPS Exercise 6 Have students model the problem with measuring cups and water. Give each student in the group a different size measuring cup. Have them work together to solve the problem.

Exercise 7 Have students sketch a board and label the measurements in the problem.

Exercise 8 Have students list all possible combinations of books she could buy.

PROBLEM SOLVING PRACTICE ★★★★★

Choose the best answer.

1. Bryan walked $1\frac{3}{4}$ mi, $2\frac{3}{4}$ mi, 3 mi, and $3\frac{1}{2}$ mi on consecutive days. Find the mean number of miles he walked for the four days. **B**

   A. $1\frac{3}{4}$ mi   **B.** $2\frac{3}{4}$ mi

   C. $2\frac{7}{8}$ mi   **D.** 11 mi

2. What is the length of the nail below in inches? **G**

   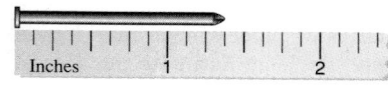

   F. $1\frac{1}{4}$ **G.** $1\frac{3}{8}$

   H. $1\frac{1}{2}$ **J.** $1\frac{3}{4}$

3. Three paint brushes have widths of $\frac{1}{2}$ in., $\frac{3}{8}$ in., and $\frac{3}{4}$ in. Order the widths from least to greatest. **B**

   A. $\frac{1}{2}$ in., $\frac{3}{4}$ in., $\frac{3}{8}$ in.

   B. $\frac{3}{8}$ in., $\frac{1}{2}$ in., $\frac{3}{4}$ in.

   C. $\frac{3}{4}$ in., $\frac{1}{2}$ in., $\frac{3}{8}$ in.

   D. $\frac{1}{2}$ in., $\frac{3}{8}$ in., $\frac{3}{4}$ in.

4. Today two neighbors water their lawns. After today the first will water her lawn every 4 days. The other will water hers every 5 days. How many days will pass before they water their lawns on the same day again? **K**

   F. 8 days   **G.** 9 days

   H. 10 days   **K.** 19 days

5. Alice needed $4\frac{5}{6}$ yd of ribbon for a project. She bought 5 yd of ribbon. How many extra inches of ribbon did Alice buy? **B**

   A. 3   **B.** 6   **C.** 9   **D.** 12

Please note that items 6–9 each have *five* answer choices.

6. A cookie recipe calls for $1\frac{1}{2}$ cups of molasses, $\frac{3}{4}$ cup of water, and $\frac{1}{2}$ cup of milk. How many cups of liquid does the recipe call for in all? **J**

   F. $1\frac{5}{8}$ cups   **G.** $1\frac{3}{4}$ cups

   H. 2 cups   **J.** $2\frac{3}{4}$ cups

   K. Not Here

7. A picket fence is made of pickets that are $4\frac{1}{2}$ ft long. Pierre is using boards for each picket that are $5\frac{1}{4}$ ft long. How much must he trim from each board to make a picket? **B**

   A. $\frac{1}{4}$ ft   **B.** $\frac{3}{4}$ ft

   C. $1\frac{1}{4}$ ft   **D.** $9\frac{3}{4}$ ft

   E. Not Here

8. At a book fair, paperbacks sell at 3 for $2 and hardbacks sell at 3 for $5. Sheila has $10 to spend on books. If she spends all of her money, which of the following could she buy? **H**

   F. 3 paperbacks and 6 hardbacks

   G. 12 hardbacks

   H. 15 paperbacks

   J. 6 paperbacks and 6 hardbacks

   K. 20 paperbacks

9. Suppose you earn $4.75 per hour and work $3\frac{1}{2}$ hours, 4 days per week. What is your weekly salary? **D**

   A. $8.25   **B.** $12.25   **C.** $16.63

   D. $66.50   **E.** Not Here

1 Focus

CONNECTING TO PRIOR KNOWLEDGE
Write $\frac{7}{2} \times \frac{5}{3}$ on the board. Have students explain how to multiply fractions. Ask: *Does it matter that the fractions are improper?* **no** Have them find the product. $\frac{35}{6}$ **or** $5\frac{5}{6}$ Write $3\frac{1}{2} \times 1\frac{2}{3}$. Ask: *How would you find this product?* **Answers may vary. Sample:**

Estimate the answer, change the mixed numbers to improper fractions and multiply.

2 Teach

THINK AND DISCUSS

DIVERSITY Encourage students from other countries to share examples of metric measurements they would use to find the length and width of a newspaper page.

Example 1 You may wish to review rounding mixed numbers. Ask students: *Why do you round $2\frac{3}{4}$ to 3?* **Answers may vary. Sample: $2\frac{3}{4}$ is closer to 3 than to 2.**

Example 2 Review how they found the area of each section of the rectangle.

Lesson Planning Options

Prerequisite Skills
- rounding fractions (5-4)
- renaming mixed numbers (5-6)

Resources

 Student Edition

Skills Handbook, p. 540
Extra Practice, p. 527
Glossary/Study Guide

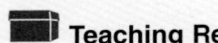 **Teaching Resources**

Chapter Support File, Ch. 6
- Lesson Planner 6-8
- Practice 6-8, Reteaching 6-8
- Answer Masters 6-8
Teaching Aids Masters 21–25
Glossary, Spanish Resources

 Transparencies
19, 22–29, Minds on Math 6-8

Warm Up

At the park Lou watched a group of ducks and squirrels. Lou counted 19 heads and 54 legs. How many ducks and how many squirrels were there? **11 ducks and 8 squirrels**

258

GEOMETRY Connection

6-8 Multiplying Mixed Numbers

What You'll Learn

▼ To estimate products of mixed numbers

▼ To multiply mixed numbers

...And Why

You can find the areas of rectangular shapes.

Here's How

Look for questions that
- build understanding
- ✔ check understanding

WHEN? The smallest newspaper was dated September 5, 1885. It was called "Tid Bits from all the Most Interesting Books, Periodicals and Newspapers in the World." The newspaper was owned by Mark Sundquist of Shoreline, Washington.

Source: *Guinness Book of Records*

THINK AND DISCUSS

▼1 Estimating Products of Mixed Numbers

You can estimate area by estimating the length and width and multiplying. Often you must estimate products of mixed numbers.

■ **EXAMPLE 1** *Real-World Problem Solving*

Newspapers The smallest newspaper ever printed had a page size of $2\frac{1}{8}$ in. wide by $2\frac{3}{4}$ in. long. Estimate the area of the page.

$$\text{area} = \text{width} \times \text{length}$$
$$= 2\frac{1}{8} \times 2\frac{3}{4}$$
$$\approx 2 \times 3 \qquad \leftarrow \text{Round each mixed number to the nearest whole number.}$$
$$\approx 6 \qquad \leftarrow \text{Multiply.}$$

The area of the page is about 6 square inches (in.²).

1. ✔**Try It Out** The largest page size ever used for a newspaper measured $55\frac{3}{4}$ in. long by $39\frac{1}{6}$ in. wide. Estimate the area of the page. **2,240 in.²**

2. **Estimation** Estimate each product.
   a. $12\frac{1}{2} \times 10\frac{2}{3}$ **143**   b. $2\frac{5}{6} \times 4\frac{1}{7}$ **12**   c. $7\frac{7}{12} \times 2\frac{1}{5}$ **16**

Now you may assign Exercises 1–9.

▼2 Multiplying Mixed Numbers

You can use area models to multiply mixed numbers.

The area of a rectangle $1\frac{1}{2}$ in. wide by $2\frac{1}{4}$ in. long is shown below.

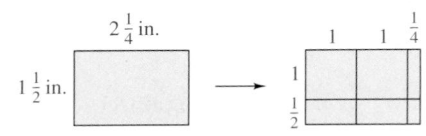

$$1\frac{1}{2} \times 2\frac{1}{4} = 1 + 1 + \frac{1}{4} + \frac{1}{2} + \frac{1}{2} + \frac{1}{8} = 3\frac{3}{8} \text{ in.}^2$$

WRITING Question 4 Have students note why they perform each step.

CONNECTION TO THE STUDENTS' WORLD
Example 3 Ask students to time themselves while they type one page of handwritten text. Ask: *How long would it take you to type a $2\frac{1}{2}$ page paper? A $3\frac{1}{2}$ page paper?* **Answers may vary.**

■ **ADDITIONAL EXAMPLES**

FOR EXAMPLE 1
The pages in a book are $5\frac{1}{9}$ in. wide and $8\frac{3}{4}$ in. long. Estimate the area of each page. **45 in.²**

FOR EXAMPLE 2
Find the product $3\frac{3}{8} \times 9\frac{2}{7}$. Simplify. **$31\frac{19}{56}$**

FOR EXAMPLE 3
Suppose you type one page in $\frac{1}{2}$ h. How long will it take you to type $8\frac{1}{3}$ pages? Simplify your answer. **$4\frac{1}{6}$ h or 4 h 10 min**

ASSESSMENT Students work in pairs. Each partner writes a mixed number. Then partners find the product of both numbers and compare answers. Have pairs trade problems and estimate the products.

To multiply mixed numbers, write each mixed number as an improper fraction.

■ **EXAMPLE 2**

Find the product $2\frac{2}{3} \times 3\frac{1}{4}$.

Estimate: $2\frac{2}{3} \times 3\frac{1}{4} \approx 3 \times 3 \approx 9$

$2\frac{2}{3} \times 3\frac{1}{4} = \frac{8}{3} \times \frac{13}{4}$ ← Write each mixed number as an improper fraction.

$= \frac{{}^2\cancel{8}}{3} \times \frac{13}{\cancel{4}_1}$ ← Simplify by dividing both 8 and 4 by the GCF, 4.

$= \frac{2 \times 13}{3 \times 1}$ ← Multiply.

$= \frac{26}{3} = 8\frac{2}{3}$ ← Simplify.

Check: $8\frac{2}{3} \approx 9 \checkmark$

$2\frac{2}{3} \times 3\frac{1}{4} = 8\frac{2}{3}$

3. ✔ *Try It Out* Find each product.
a. $3\frac{1}{8} \times 3\frac{1}{5}$ **10** **b.** $7\frac{1}{3} \times 3\frac{3}{4}$ **$27\frac{1}{2}$** **c.** $10\frac{4}{5} \times 1\frac{2}{3}$ **18**

4. ⬚ *Explain* List the steps for finding $6\frac{2}{3} \times 1\frac{1}{5}$. Then multiply. Evaluate the reasonableness of the result.

Sometimes you need to know how much work you can do in a given amount of time.

■ **EXAMPLE 3** *Real-World Problem Solving*

Typing Suppose you can type one page in $\frac{1}{3}$ h. How long will it take you to type a $2\frac{1}{2}$-page research paper?

Total time = time per page × number of pages

$= \frac{1}{3} \times 2\frac{1}{2}$

$= \frac{1}{3} \times \frac{5}{2}$ ← Write $2\frac{1}{2}$ as $\frac{5}{2}$.

$= \frac{1 \times 5}{3 \times 2} = \frac{5}{6}$ ← Multiply.

It will take $\frac{5}{6}$ h, or 50 min, to type a $2\frac{1}{2}$-page paper.

5. ⬚ *Look Back* Evaluate the reasonableness of your answer to Example 3. **Check students' work.**

6. ✔ *Try It Out* If your friend can type one page in $\frac{1}{4}$ h, how long will it take him to type a $3\frac{1}{2}$-page paper? **$\frac{7}{8}$ h or $52\frac{1}{2}$ min**

Now you may assign Exercises 10–31.

CALCULATOR HINT
You can use a fraction calculator to find products of mixed numbers.

4. Write $6\frac{2}{3}$ and $1\frac{1}{5}$ as improper fractions. Simplify $\frac{20}{3} \times \frac{6}{5}$ to $\frac{4}{1} \times \frac{2}{1}$ and again to 4×2. Multiply. The result is 8. $6\frac{2}{3}$ is about 7. $1\frac{1}{5}$ is about 1. The product is reasonably close to 8.

Technology Options

Prentice Hall Technology

Software for Learners
• Hot Page™ 17*
• Math Blaster® Mystery*
• Interactive Student Tutorial, Chapter 6*

Teaching Resource Software
• Computer Item Generator 6-8
• Resource Pro™ Chapter 6*

Internet • For related mathematics activities, visit the Prentice Hall site at www.phschool.com/math

*Available on CD-ROM only

Assignment Options for Exercises On Your Own

To provide flexible scheduling, this lesson can be subdivided into parts.

▼ ① **Core** 1–8
 Extension 9

▼ ② **Core** 10–29
 Extension 30, 31

Use Mixed Review to maintain skills.

EXERCISES *On Your Own*

ESTIMATION Exercises 1–8 If students need more practice, have them compute the products after they estimate.

WRITING Exercise 10 Have students write and solve a problem using one of their examples.

ERROR ALERT! Exercises 11–26 Some students may attempt to multiply without rewriting the mixed numbers as improper fractions. **Remediation:** Show students that $4\frac{1}{2} \times 7\frac{1}{2}$ is not the same as $(4 \times 7) + \left(\frac{1}{2} \times \frac{1}{2}\right)$. Have them compute both to see.

$$4\frac{1}{2} \times 7\frac{1}{2} = \frac{9}{2} \times \frac{15}{2} = \frac{135}{4} = 33\frac{3}{4}$$
$$(4 \times 7) + \left(\frac{1}{2} \times \frac{1}{2}\right) = 28\frac{1}{4}$$

Suggest that students draw area models to help reinforce this.

EXTENSION Exercise 28 Calculate the area of a standard sheet of paper that is $8\frac{1}{2}$ in. by 11 in. Then calculate the difference in the areas of the folder and the paper. $16\frac{21}{32}$ in.²

Exercise 29 Have students design and color their own quilt pattern on graph paper. Ask: *If each square on your quilt has $3\frac{3}{4}$ in. sides, what is the area of the quilt?* **Answers may vary.**

CHECKPOINT 2

Checkpoint 2 *Lessons 6-4 through 6-8*

Find each sum or difference.

1. $3\frac{2}{3} + 4\frac{5}{9}$ $8\frac{2}{9}$
2. $7\frac{1}{8} - 2\frac{1}{2}$ $4\frac{5}{8}$
3. $4\frac{3}{4} + 2\frac{2}{5}$ $7\frac{3}{20}$

Solve each equation.

4. $y - 5\frac{1}{3} = 7\frac{5}{6}$ $13\frac{1}{6}$
5. $2\frac{5}{16} = y + 1\frac{1}{4}$ $1\frac{1}{16}$
6. $y + 4\frac{1}{2} = 9\frac{3}{8}$ $4\frac{7}{8}$

7. **Circle A, B, C, or D.** Suppose $\frac{5}{6}$ of the area of a garden is vegetables and $\frac{4}{10}$ of the vegetable area is tomatoes. What portion of the garden is tomatoes?

Ⓐ $\frac{1}{3}$ B. $\frac{2}{15}$ C. $\frac{9}{16}$ D. $\frac{37}{30}$

Find each product or quotient. Write the answer in simplest form.

8. $\frac{1}{2} \times \frac{4}{5}$ $\frac{4}{10}; \frac{2}{5}$
9. $\frac{3}{8}$ of 32 12
10. $2\frac{2}{3} \times 1\frac{1}{11}$ $2\frac{10}{11}$

Assessment

EXERCISES *On Your Own* ·

Estimate each product.

1. $3\frac{1}{2} \times 1\frac{1}{4}$ 4
2. $14\frac{2}{3} \times 5\frac{1}{3}$ 75
3. $7\frac{3}{4} \times 9\frac{1}{2}$ 80
4. $15\frac{9}{10} \times 3\frac{1}{5}$ 48
5. $2\frac{3}{4} \times 6\frac{1}{8}$ 18
6. $5\frac{1}{2} \times 10\frac{3}{10}$ 60
7. $9\frac{1}{5} \times 5\frac{7}{12}$ 54
8. $9\frac{5}{7} \times 10\frac{1}{3}$ 100

9. *Baking* Estimate the area of the cookie sheet shown at the right. **about 150 in.²**

10. *Writing* Describe some items that have an area you can find by multiplying mixed numbers.
Answers may vary. Samples: photographs, walls, floors

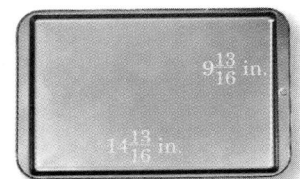

$9\frac{13}{16}$ in.

$14\frac{13}{16}$ in.

Find each product.

11. $4\frac{1}{2} \times 7\frac{1}{2}$ $33\frac{3}{4}$
12. $3\frac{2}{3} \times 6\frac{9}{10}$ $25\frac{3}{10}$
13. $6\frac{1}{2} \times 7\frac{2}{3}$ $49\frac{5}{6}$
14. $8\frac{1}{2} \times 8\frac{1}{2}$ $72\frac{1}{4}$

15. $4\frac{1}{9} \times 3\frac{3}{8}$ $13\frac{7}{8}$
16. $2\frac{1}{5} \times 10\frac{1}{2}$ $23\frac{1}{10}$
17. $2\frac{2}{5} \times 1\frac{1}{6}$ $2\frac{4}{5}$
18. $2\frac{1}{2} \times 10\frac{1}{2}$ $24\frac{1}{2}$

19. $3\frac{1}{5} \times 1\frac{7}{8}$ 6
20. $7\frac{5}{6} \times 4\frac{1}{2}$ $35\frac{1}{4}$
21. $1\frac{2}{3} \times 5\frac{9}{10}$ $9\frac{5}{6}$
22. $1\frac{5}{8} \times 2\frac{2}{3}$ $4\frac{1}{3}$

23. $3\frac{3}{4} \times 5\frac{1}{3}$ 20
24. $1\frac{1}{12} \times 6\frac{1}{2}$ $7\frac{1}{24}$
25. $4\frac{1}{2} \times 3\frac{5}{6}$ $17\frac{1}{4}$
26. $1\frac{2}{3} \times 3\frac{9}{16}$ $5\frac{15}{16}$

27. *Geometry* Find the area of the rectangle at the right. $4\frac{3}{8}$ in.²

28. *Business* Letter-size hanging folders measure $9\frac{3}{8}$ in. $\times$ $11\frac{3}{4}$ in. Find the area of one side of a hanging folder.
$110\frac{5}{32}$ in.²

$3\frac{1}{2}$ in.

$1\frac{1}{4}$ in.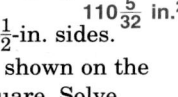

29. *Sewing* A quilt pattern shows a square with $4\frac{1}{2}$-in. sides. Patty wants to reduce each side to $\frac{2}{3}$ the length shown on the pattern. Find the dimensions of the reduced square. Solve the problem two different ways. **3 in. by 3 in.**

Data Analysis **Use the information at the right for Exercises 30 and 31.**

30. *Carpentry* Davar is building the floor of a deck. He will place 32 "2-by-4" boards side by side with $\frac{1}{4}$ in. space between each pair of boards. How wide will the floor of the deck be? $119\frac{3}{4}$ in.

31. *Construction* Simon loaded his truck with a single stack of boards. The stack had three "2-by-6" boards and six "2-by-2" boards. How high is the stack? $13\frac{1}{2}$ in.

Standard Lumber Sizes

Lumber Name	Thickness (in.)	Width (in.)
"1-by-4"	$\frac{3}{4}$	$3\frac{1}{2}$
"2-by-2"	$1\frac{1}{2}$	$1\frac{1}{2}$
"2-by-4"	$1\frac{1}{2}$	$3\frac{1}{2}$
"2-by-6"	$1\frac{1}{2}$	$5\frac{1}{2}$

VISUAL LEARNING **Exercise 30–31**
Suggest students draw a diagram.

WRAP UP

IDENTIFYING THE BIG IDEA Have students explain how to multiply mixed numbers.

▽ **PROJECT LINK** If the items students chose are difficult to bring to class, have them display each step on a poster or make a video of the demonstration at home.

LESSON QUIZ

Find each product. Simplify.

1. $3\frac{3}{4} \times 5\frac{2}{5}$ $20\frac{1}{4}$

2. $5\frac{3}{5} \times 4\frac{2}{7}$ 24

3. $6\frac{1}{9} \times 5\frac{1}{4}$ $32\frac{1}{12}$

Mixed Review

Find the LCM of each set of numbers. *(Lesson 5-7)*

32. 8, 12, 6
24

33. 5, 6, 15
30

34. 9, 15, 18
90

35. 36, 40
360

36. 10, 20, 50
100

37. 35, 36, 180
1,260

Mental Math **Find each answer.** *(Lesson 4-7)*

38. $3.9 \div 10$
0.39

39. $19.1 \div 100$
0.191

40. $0.82 \div 1,000$
0.00082

41. $0.367 \div 10$
0.0367

42. $307.9 \div 1,000$
0.3079

43. *Choose a Strategy* Linda bought 4 movie tickets with a $20 bill. Each ticket cost $4.25. How much change did she get? $3.00

CHAPTER PROJECT

PROJECT LINK: MODELING

Now create a demonstration to calculate the sum of fractions with unlike denominators. See whether or not the sum agrees with the measured results. Again, use items you have gathered, visual models, or other methods. Expand your demonstration to illustrate the addition of mixed numbers.

Check students' work.

✓ CHECKPOINT 2

Lessons 6-4 through 6-8

Find each sum or difference.

1. $6\frac{3}{4} + 4\frac{1}{8}$ $10\frac{7}{8}$

2. $8\frac{7}{16} - 3\frac{1}{4}$ $5\frac{3}{16}$

3. $13\frac{1}{3} + 15\frac{1}{6}$ $28\frac{1}{2}$

4. $8\frac{3}{10} - 3\frac{2}{5}$ $4\frac{9}{10}$

5. $5\frac{3}{5} + 2\frac{2}{3}$ $8\frac{4}{15}$

Solve each equation.

6. $x - 3\frac{1}{2} = 6\frac{3}{4}$ $10\frac{1}{4}$

7. $x + 14\frac{3}{4} = 38\frac{3}{8}$ $23\frac{5}{8}$

8. $3\frac{7}{16} = x + 2\frac{7}{8}$ $\frac{9}{16}$

9. $8\frac{5}{6} = x - 4\frac{7}{8}$ $13\frac{17}{24}$

10. **Choose A, B, C, or D.** Suppose $\frac{7}{8}$ of the area of a geometric drawing is red. A circle makes up $\frac{3}{10}$ of the red part. What portion of the geometric drawing is a red circle? **C**

A. $\frac{20}{21}$

B. $\frac{10}{18}$

C. $\frac{21}{80}$

D. $\frac{24}{70}$

Find each product.

11. $\frac{4}{5} \times \frac{1}{8}$ $\frac{1}{10}$

12. $\frac{5}{12}$ of 36 15

13. $3 \times \frac{3}{4}$ $2\frac{1}{4}$

14. $\frac{3}{8}$ of 27 $10\frac{1}{8}$

15. $3\frac{2}{3} \times 3\frac{1}{11}$ $11\frac{1}{3}$

PRACTICE

Practice 6-8 *Multiplying Mixed Numbers*

Estimate each product. Estimates may vary. Samples are shown.

1. $2\frac{5}{6} \times 1\frac{1}{4}$ 6
2. $3\frac{3}{8} \times 7\frac{1}{4}$ 21
3. $5\frac{3}{8} \times 2\frac{7}{8}$ 15
4. $2\frac{3}{8} \times 4\frac{4}{5}$ 10
5. $6\frac{7}{12} \times 5\frac{9}{10}$ 42
6. $7\frac{1}{3} \times 10\frac{11}{12}$ 77
7. $12\frac{1}{4} \times 3\frac{3}{4}$ 48
8. $8\frac{1}{6} \times 2\frac{1}{4}$ 16
9. $15\frac{2}{3} \times 5\frac{5}{7}$ 96

Find each product.

10. $2\frac{5}{6} \times 1\frac{1}{4}$ $4\frac{23}{24}$
11. $3\frac{3}{8} \times 7\frac{1}{4}$ $24\frac{15}{32}$
12. $5\frac{3}{8} \times 2\frac{7}{8}$ $15\frac{29}{64}$
13. $2\frac{3}{8} \times 4\frac{4}{5}$ $11\frac{2}{5}$
14. $6\frac{7}{12} \times 5\frac{9}{10}$ $38\frac{101}{120}$
15. $7\frac{1}{3} \times 10\frac{11}{12}$ $80\frac{1}{18}$
16. $12\frac{1}{4} \times 3\frac{3}{4}$ $45\frac{15}{16}$
17. $8\frac{1}{6} \times 2\frac{1}{4}$ $18\frac{3}{8}$
18. $15\frac{2}{3} \times 5\frac{5}{7}$ $89\frac{11}{21}$
19. $\frac{1}{4} \times 5\frac{5}{8}$ $1\frac{7}{20}$
20. $2\frac{3}{8} \times \frac{4}{5}$ $1\frac{9}{10}$
21. $1\frac{1}{2} \times 5\frac{1}{8}$ 8
22. $3\frac{3}{8} \times 6$ $20\frac{1}{4}$
23. $\frac{3}{4} \times 1\frac{3}{5}$ $1\frac{1}{5}$
24. $9\frac{3}{5} \times \frac{1}{3}$ $3\frac{1}{5}$
25. $1\frac{1}{4} \times 2\frac{2}{3}$ $3\frac{1}{3}$
26. $1\frac{3}{8} \times \frac{1}{4}$ $\frac{1}{5}$
27. $6\frac{1}{4} \times 1\frac{3}{5}$ $8\frac{3}{4}$
28. $\frac{7}{8} \times 3\frac{1}{2}$ $2\frac{4}{5}$
29. $5\frac{1}{3} \times 2\frac{1}{4}$ 12
30. $\frac{3}{5} \times 4\frac{1}{2}$ $2\frac{7}{10}$
31. $\frac{5}{8} \times 7\frac{3}{5}$ $4\frac{3}{4}$
32. $5\frac{1}{3} \times \frac{5}{8}$ $3\frac{1}{3}$
33. $2\frac{4}{5} \times \frac{3}{7}$ $1\frac{1}{5}$
34. $3\frac{1}{3} \times 3\frac{3}{10}$ 11
35. $5\frac{1}{2} \times \frac{2}{5}$ $2\frac{1}{5}$
36. $1\frac{2}{3} \times 3\frac{3}{4}$ $6\frac{1}{4}$

37. Ken used a piece of lumber to build a bookshelf. If he made three shelves that are each $2\frac{1}{2}$ ft long, how long was the piece of lumber? $7\frac{1}{2}$ ft

38. Deanna's cake recipe needs to be doubled for a party. How much of each ingredient should Deanna use?

Delicious Cake	
flour	$2\frac{1}{4}$ c	$4\frac{1}{2}$ c
sugar	$1\frac{3}{4}$ c	$3\frac{1}{2}$ c
butter	$1\frac{1}{2}$ c	3 c
milk	$\frac{3}{4}$ c	$1\frac{1}{2}$ c

In copymaster and workbook formats

RETEACHING

Reteaching 6-8 *Multiplying Mixed Numbers*

Multiply: $2\frac{1}{7} \times 2\frac{2}{5}$

Multiply: $\frac{2}{3} \times 5\frac{1}{4}$

Step 1 Change to improper fractions.
$\frac{15}{7} \times \frac{12}{5}$
$\frac{2}{3} \times \frac{21}{4}$

Step 2 Simplify.
$\frac{3}{\cancel{15}}{7} \times \frac{12}{\cancel{5}_1}$
$\frac{1}{\cancel{2}}{3} \times \frac{7}{\cancel{21}_4}$

Step 3 Multiply.
$\frac{36}{7} \leftarrow \frac{3 \times 12}{7 \times 1}$
$\frac{7}{2} \leftarrow \frac{1 \times 7}{1 \times 2}$

Step 4 Simplify.
$5\frac{1}{7}$
$3\frac{1}{2}$

$2\frac{1}{7} \times 2\frac{2}{5} = 5\frac{1}{7}$
$\frac{2}{3} \times 5\frac{1}{4} = 3\frac{1}{2}$

Find each product.

1. $1\frac{1}{4} \times 2\frac{2}{3}$ $3\frac{1}{3}$
2. $2\frac{2}{5} \times 4\frac{1}{2}$ $10\frac{4}{5}$
3. $3\frac{1}{7} \times 2\frac{4}{5}$ $8\frac{4}{5}$
4. $\frac{1}{5} \times 2\frac{7}{9}$ $\frac{5}{9}$
5. $12\frac{1}{2} \times 2\frac{2}{5}$ 30
6. $2\frac{1}{8} \times 2\frac{2}{3}$ $5\frac{2}{3}$
7. $5\frac{1}{3} \times 1\frac{7}{8}$ 10
8. $\frac{1}{2} \times 3\frac{3}{8}$ $1\frac{4}{5}$
9. $2\frac{1}{7} \times 4\frac{2}{3}$ 10
10. $1\frac{1}{2} \times 2\frac{6}{7}$ $4\frac{2}{7}$
11. $1\frac{5}{6} \times 2\frac{1}{4}$ $4\frac{1}{8}$
12. $5\frac{1}{4} \times 2\frac{2}{7}$ 12
13. $\frac{1}{4} \times 1\frac{3}{5}$ $\frac{2}{5}$
14. $\frac{4}{7} \times 1\frac{3}{4}$ 1
15. $\frac{2}{9} \times 2\frac{1}{4}$ $\frac{1}{2}$
16. $3\frac{1}{3} \times 3\frac{3}{10}$ 11
17. $1\frac{2}{5} \times 3\frac{1}{2}$ $5\frac{5}{6}$
18. $1\frac{2}{5} \times 4\frac{1}{3}$ $6\frac{1}{15}$
19. $\frac{1}{7} \times 1\frac{3}{5}$ $\frac{8}{35}$
20. $\frac{3}{5} \times 8\frac{1}{2}$ $5\frac{1}{10}$
21. $3\frac{5}{6} \times 2\frac{1}{7}$ $8\frac{1}{2}$

37

ENRICHMENT

Minds on Math Transparency

6-8

Suppose that every 15 min a cell divides into 2 cells. If there were 4,000 cells at 12:00 P.M., at what time were there 500 cells?

11:15 A.M.

See *Solution Key* for worked-out answers.

1 Focus

CONNECTING TO PRIOR KNOWLEDGE Ask:
How many 2-c servings are in 4 c of juice? **2**
How many 1-c servings are in 4 c ? **4** *How
many $\frac{1}{2}$-c servings are in 4 c?* **8** *How did you
find the answers to these questions?* **Answers
may vary. Sample: I divided the number of
cups of juice by the number of servings.**

Lesson Planning Options

Prerequisite Skills
• renaming mixed numbers (5-6)
• multiplying fractions (6-8)

Vocabulary/Symbols
reciprocals

Materials/Manipulatives
• fraction calculator   • ruler

Resources

 Student Edition

Skills Handbook, p. 540
Extra Practice, p. 527
Glossary/Study Guide

 Teaching Resources

Chapter Support File, Ch. 6
• Lesson Planner 6-9
• Practice 6-9, Reteaching 6-9
• Alternative Activity 6-9
• Answer Masters 6-9
Teaching Aids Masters 21–25
Glossary, Spanish Resources

 Transparencies
19, 22–29, Minds on Math 6-9

Warm Up

Write $\frac{3}{8}$ as a decimal.
0.375

262

2 Teach

Work Together

ALTERNATIVE METHOD If you do not have
fraction calculators, students can change
fractions to decimals and then divide.

KINESTHETIC LEARNING Separate students
into equal groups containing an even number
of people. Write the number of groups on the
board. Then divide all the groups in half. Write
"■ ÷ $\frac{1}{2}$ =" on the board. Ask: *How many
groups are there now?* **Answers may vary.**
Write this number on the board next to the
equal sign.

THINK AND DISCUSS

REASONING **Question 6** Have students
write another pair of equivalent expressions.

AEP Help students see that *reciprocal*
comes from the word *reciprocate*, which
means to inerchange.

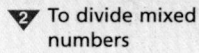 **6-9**

Dividing Fractions and Mixed Numbers

What You'll Learn

❶ To divide fractions

❷ To divide mixed numbers

...And Why

You can calculate how
many items you can make
from a given amount of
material.

Here's How

Look for questions that
▪ build understanding
✔ check understanding

Work Together _____ *Investigating Fraction Division*

What happens when you divide a number by $\frac{1}{2}$? Use a fraction
calculator or a ruler model.

1. Divide several different
   numbers by $\frac{1}{2}$. Copy and
   complete the table
   at the right.

2. ▪ *Number Sense* When
   you divide a number by
   $\frac{1}{2}$, is the quotient
   greater than or less
   than the number? Explain.
   Greater than; it is twice the number.

Number	Fraction	Quotient
10	$\frac{1}{2}$	■ 20
5	$\frac{1}{2}$	■ 10
3.8	$\frac{1}{2}$	■ 7.6
$9\frac{1}{4}$	$\frac{1}{2}$	■ $18\frac{1}{2}$
■	$\frac{1}{2}$	■

Check students' work for last row.

THINK AND DISCUSS

❶ *Exploring Division of Fractions*

You and three friends equally share $\frac{1}{2}$ of a cantaloupe. What
portion of the whole cantaloupe does each friend eat?

3. ▪ *Modeling* Use the circle at the right to
   represent the cantaloupe. Four of you will
   share $\frac{1}{2}$ of the cantaloupe. So divide $\frac{1}{2}$ of
   the circle into four equal pieces. What
   portion of the cantaloupe does each of
   you eat? $\frac{1}{8}$

4. ▪ *Algebra* Write a division sentence to describe the
   situation in Question 3. Explain its meaning. See margin p. 264.

5. You can also think of this as a multiplication problem. Each
   friend gets $\frac{1}{4}$ of $\frac{1}{2}$ of the cantaloupe. Find the product $\frac{1}{4} \times \frac{1}{2}$. $\frac{1}{8}$

6. ▪ *Reasoning* You used both multiplication and division to
   solve the cantaloupe problem. What did you notice about the
   two expressions $\frac{1}{2} \times \frac{1}{4}$ and $\frac{1}{2} \div 4$? **The results are the same.**

Question 9 Have students write a rule to describe the product of a number and its reciprocal. Have students use their rule to check their answers for Exercise 8.

EXTENSION *What number is equal to its reciprocal?* **1**

■ **ADDITIONAL EXAMPLES**

FOR EXAMPLE 1

Tanya has 2 gal of snow cone syrup. It takes $\frac{1}{32}$ gal to make one snow cone. How many snow cones can she make using all her syrup? **64**

FOR EXAMPLE 2

Roberto has 22 yd of string. How many pieces of string can he cut that are $2\frac{3}{4}$ yd long? **8**

ASSESSMENT Question 10 Ask: *What do you do to write a division problem as a multiplication problem?* **Answers may vary. Sample: Replace the second fraction with its reciprocal and the division sign with a** multiplication sign. Have students write each division problem in Question 10 as a multiplication problem. **10a: 4 × 3; 10b: $\frac{6}{7} \times \frac{4}{3}$; 10c: 5 × $\frac{7}{5}$; 10d: $\frac{4}{5} \times \frac{8}{3}$**

Question 11 Remind students to change improper fractions in answers to mixed numbers.

The numbers 4 and $\frac{1}{4}$ are **reciprocals.** The numerators and denominators have been switched.

7. ⚎*Reasoning* Find each product. What do you notice?

a. $4 \times \frac{1}{4}$ **1**   b. $\frac{2}{3} \times \frac{3}{2}$ **1**   c. $\frac{1}{2} \times \frac{2}{1}$ **1**   d. $8 \times \frac{1}{8}$ **1**   e. $\frac{9}{2} \times \frac{2}{9}$ **1**

Each product is 1.

8. ✔*Try It Out* Write the reciprocal of each number.

a. $\frac{2}{3}$ **$\frac{3}{2}$**   b. $\frac{1}{9}$ **9**   c. 5 **$\frac{1}{5}$**   d. 1 **1**   e. $\frac{7}{4}$ **$\frac{4}{7}$**

9. ⚎*Draw a Conclusion* What do you know about a number and its reciprocal? **Their product is 1.**

You will use reciprocals to divide with fractions.

■ **EXAMPLE 1** *Real-World Problem Solving*

Nancy has 3 yd of ribbon. It takes $\frac{3}{8}$ yd to make one bow. How many bows can Nancy make if she uses all the ribbon?

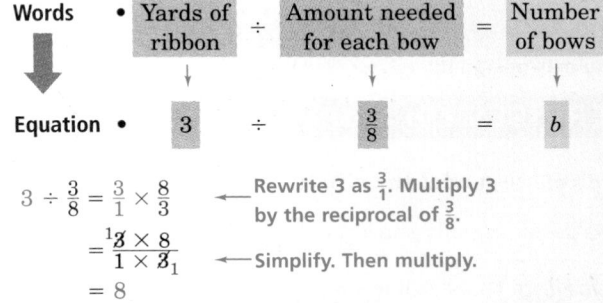

Words	•	Yards of ribbon	÷	Amount needed for each bow	=	Number of bows
Equation	•	3	÷	$\frac{3}{8}$	=	b

$3 \div \frac{3}{8} = \frac{3}{1} \times \frac{8}{3}$ ⟵ Rewrite 3 as $\frac{3}{1}$. Multiply 3 by the reciprocal of $\frac{3}{8}$.

$= \frac{{}^1\cancel{3} \times 8}{1 \times \cancel{3}_1}$ ⟵ Simplify. Then multiply.

$= 8$

Nancy can make 8 bows with 3 yd of ribbon.

10. ✔*Try It Out* Find each quotient.

a. $4 \div \frac{1}{3}$ **12**   b. $\frac{6}{7} \div \frac{3}{4}$ **$1\frac{1}{7}$**   c. $5 \div \frac{5}{7}$ **7**   d. $\frac{4}{5} \div \frac{3}{8}$ **$2\frac{2}{15}$**

You can also use a model to solve Example 1.

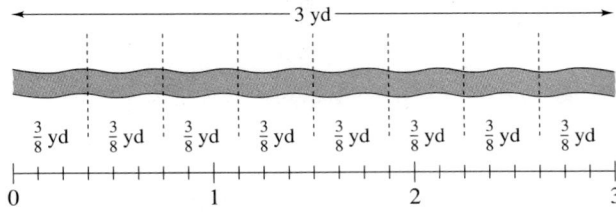

Now you may assign Exercises 1–17.

Technology Options

Prentice Hall Technology

💾 💿 **Software for Learners**
• Math Blaster® Mystery*
• Interactive Student Tutorial, Chapter 6*

💾 💿 **Teaching Resource Software**
• Computer Item Generator 6-9
• Resource Pro™ Chapter 6*

🔁 **Internet**
• For related mathematics activities, visit the Prentice Hall site at www.phschool.com/math

*Available on CD-ROM only

Assignment Options for Exercises On Your Own

To provide flexible scheduling, this lesson can be subdivided into parts.

▼**1** Core 1–15, 17
   Extension 16

▼**2** Core 18–42
   Extension 43, 44

Use Mixed Review to maintain skills.

3 Practice/Assess

TACTILE LEARNING Exercises 1 and 2
Suggest students use paper circles to model the solutions.

Exercise 3 Give groups of students $3\frac{1}{3}$ ft of string, a ruler, and scissors. Have them cut pieces $\frac{1}{3}$ ft long.

ERROR ALERT! Exercises 18–37 Some students may change the division sign to a multiplication sign but forget to replace the second fraction with its reciprocal.
Remediation: Remind students that changing the sign means they must change the fraction. Write $5 \div \frac{3}{8}$ on the board. Write $5 \times \frac{8}{3}$ underneath it. Circle the division sign and draw an arrow to the multiplication sign.
Circle $\frac{3}{8}$ and draw an arrow to its reciprocal.

EXTENSION Exercise 16 Ask students to find how many $\frac{1}{4}$ in. there are in $\frac{1}{2}$ yd. **72**

Exercises 18–37 Have students multiply to check their answers.

WRITING Exercise 38 Suggest students draw models to solve the problem.

CONNECTION TO MEASUREMENT
Exercise 39 Give some students 8 c of water and a $\frac{1}{2}$-c container to use to solve the problem. Ask: *How many $\frac{1}{4}$ c of water are in 8 c?* **32**

---

pages 262–264   Think and Discuss

4. $\frac{1}{2} \div 4 = \frac{1}{8}$; the division sentence shows that $\frac{1}{2}$ of the cantaloupe is divided into 4 pieces and that each piece is $\frac{1}{8}$ of the cantaloupe.

pages 264–265   On Your Own

38. Answers may vary. Sample: The area of a rectangle is 10 ft². The width is $\frac{1}{3}$ ft. What is the length?
Solution 1: $10 \div \frac{1}{3} = 30$ ft.
Solution 2: $10 \times 3 = 30$ ft.

1.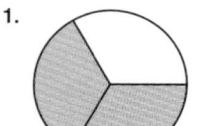

2.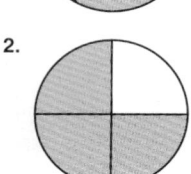

2 *Division of Mixed Numbers*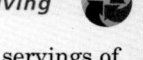

To divide mixed numbers, first write each mixed number as an improper fraction.

■ **EXAMPLE 2**   *Real-World Problem Solving*

Food Leroy made 30 c of soup. How many $1\frac{1}{4}$-c servings of soup does he have?

Divide: $30 \div 1\frac{1}{4}$

$30 \div 1\frac{1}{4} = 30 \div \frac{5}{4}$ ⟵ Write $1\frac{1}{4}$ as $\frac{5}{4}$.

$= \frac{30}{1} \times \frac{4}{5}$ ⟵ Multiply by the reciprocal of $\frac{5}{4}$.

$= \frac{\overset{6}{30} \times 4}{1 \times \underset{1}{5}}$ ⟵ Simplify. Then multiply.

$= 24$

Leroy has 24 $1\frac{1}{4}$-c servings of soup.

11. ✔ *Try It Out* Find the quotient $25 \div 3\frac{3}{4}$. $6\frac{2}{3}$

Now you may assign Exercises 18–44.

EXERCISES *On Your Own*

Use a circle to model the situations of Exercises 1 and 2. **1–2. See above left.**

1. Two people equally share $\frac{2}{3}$ of a pizza.   2. Three people equally share $\frac{3}{4}$ of a cheese wheel.

3. *Modeling* Draw a diagram. Show how many pieces of string $\frac{1}{3}$ ft long you can cut from a $3\frac{1}{3}$-ft piece. **10 pieces**

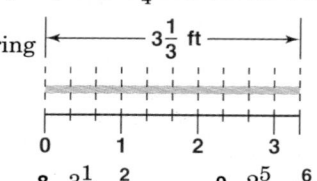

Write the reciprocal of each number.

4. $\frac{4}{5}$ $\frac{5}{4}$ 5. 3 $\frac{1}{3}$ 6. $\frac{2}{10}$ $\frac{10}{2}$ 7. $\frac{1}{5}$ 5 8. $3\frac{1}{2}$ $\frac{2}{7}$ 9. $2\frac{5}{6}$ $\frac{6}{17}$

Mental Math **Find each quotient mentally.**

10. $6 \div \frac{1}{2}$ **12**   11. $5 \div \frac{1}{3}$ **15**   12. $3 \div \frac{1}{8}$ **24**   13. $7 \div \frac{1}{5}$ **35**   14. $8 \div \frac{1}{4}$ **32**   15. $12 \div \frac{1}{3}$ **36**

16. *Measurement* How many $\frac{1}{4}$ in. are in $\frac{1}{2}$ ft? Draw a diagram that shows the problem and your solution.
24 quarter in.; check students' work for diagram.

17. Suppose you cut canvas into pieces. The canvas is $\frac{3}{4}$ yd long. How many pieces $\frac{1}{8}$ yd long can you cut?
6 pieces

WRAP UP

IDENTIFYING THE BIG IDEA Ask students to describe how to divide fractions and mixed numbers.

LESSON QUIZ

Find each quotient.

1. $3 \div \frac{4}{9}$ $6\frac{3}{4}$
2. $6\frac{1}{2} \div 3\frac{1}{4}$ 2
3. $25 \div 3\frac{2}{3}$ $6\frac{9}{11}$
4. $\frac{8}{12} \div \frac{1}{4}$ $2\frac{2}{3}$

Find each quotient.

18. $5 \div \frac{3}{8}$ $13\frac{1}{3}$
19. $15 \div \frac{3}{4}$ 20
20. $\frac{4}{9} \div \frac{3}{5}$ $\frac{20}{27}$
21. $12 \div \frac{1}{3}$ 36
22. $15 \div \frac{5}{8}$ 24

23. $42 \div \frac{6}{7}$ 49
24. $75 \div \frac{1}{2}$ 150
25. $\frac{5}{8} \div \frac{3}{4}$ $\frac{5}{6}$
26. $\frac{1}{5} \div \frac{1}{3}$ $\frac{3}{5}$
27. $\frac{8}{9} \div \frac{2}{3}$ $1\frac{1}{3}$

28. $45 \div 2\frac{1}{2}$ 18
29. $15\frac{1}{2} \div 2$ $7\frac{3}{4}$
30. $52 \div 3\frac{1}{4}$ 16
31. $12 \div 3\frac{1}{3}$ $3\frac{3}{5}$
32. $32 \div 5\frac{1}{3}$ 6

33. $2\frac{1}{5} \div 2\frac{1}{2}$ $\frac{22}{25}$
34. $6\frac{1}{2} \div \frac{1}{4}$ 26
35. $1\frac{3}{4} \div 4\frac{3}{8}$ $\frac{2}{5}$
36. $2\frac{2}{5} \div 7\frac{1}{5}$ $\frac{1}{3}$
37. $7\frac{2}{3} \div \frac{2}{9}$ $34\frac{1}{2}$

38. *Writing* Write a problem that can be solved by dividing 10 by $\frac{1}{3}$. Solve your problem at least two different ways.   **See margin p. 264.**

39. *Measurement* How many $\frac{1}{2}$-c servings are in an 8-c pitcher of juice? Evaluate the reasonableness of your solution.   **16 servings; check students' work for reasoning.**

40. **Choose A, B, C, or D.** Which quotient is greater than 1?   **D**

   A. $\frac{3}{5} \div \frac{3}{5}$
   B. $\frac{1}{4} \div \frac{3}{4}$
   C. $\frac{1}{3} \div 4$
   D. $2 \div \frac{1}{4}$

41. *Apples* Suppose you cut 3 apples into eighths. How many pieces of apple would you have?   **24 pieces**

42. *Baking* How many $\frac{1}{2}$-in. thick cookies can you slice from a roll of cookie dough 1 ft long?   **24 cookies**

43. *Bird Seed* You have a 15-lb bag of bird seed.
   a. If the birds you feed eat $1\frac{1}{2}$ lb of seed each day, how many days will your seed last?   **10 d**
   b. Did you multiply or divide to find your answer to part (a)? Why?   **divide; to find how many $1\frac{1}{2}$-lb measures are in 15 lb**

44. *Measurement* Alex decides to use a $\frac{1}{4}$-gal jug to fill a 5-gal jar. How many times must Alex pour liquid from the jug into the jar to fill it?   **20 times**

Mixed Review

Find each quotient. *(Lesson 4-8)*

45. $25 \div 0.5$ **50**
46. $3.2 \div 0.8$ **4**
47. $0.75 \div 0.25$ **3**
48. $0.144 \div 1.2$ **0.12**
49. $14.4 \div 0.006$ **2,400**

50. Find a three-digit number divisible by 1, 2, 3, and 5. *(Lesson 5-1)*
   Answers may vary. Sample: 300

51. *Choose a Strategy* Taro, Alma, and Wanell are a pharmacist, a teacher, and a stockbroker. Taro met the teacher and the stockbroker at a fund-raiser. The teacher knows Alma. Match each person with the correct occupation.
   Taro is the pharmacist, Alma is the stock broker, and Wanell is the teacher.

Practice 6-9 *Dividing Fractions and Mixed Numbers*

Write the reciprocal of each number.

1. $\frac{7}{10}$ $\frac{10}{7}$
2. $4\frac{1}{4}$
3. $5\frac{3}{16}$ $\frac{3}{16}$
4. $\frac{1}{12}$ 12

5. Draw a diagram to show how many $\frac{3}{4}$-ft pieces of string can be cut from a piece of string $4\frac{1}{2}$ ft long.

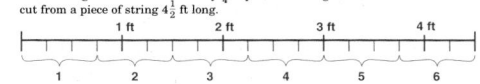

Divide. Write each answer in simplest form.

6. $\frac{3}{10} \div \frac{4}{5}$ $\frac{3}{8}$
7. $\frac{3}{8} \div 3\frac{1}{8}$
8. $3 \div 1\frac{4}{5}$ $1\frac{2}{3}$
9. $2\frac{1}{5} \div 1\frac{5}{6}$ $1\frac{1}{5}$
10. $1\frac{1}{2} \div \frac{3}{16}$ 8
11. $\frac{1}{4} \div \frac{1}{8}$ 2
12. $1\frac{7}{8} \div \frac{5}{8}$ 3
13. $1\frac{3}{4} \div \frac{1}{16}$ 28
14. $3 \div \frac{3}{8}$ 8

15. How many $\frac{3}{4}$-c servings are there in a 6-c package of rice?   **8 servings**

16. George cut 5 oranges into quarters. How many pieces of orange did he have?   **20 pieces**

Anna bought a package of ribbon 10 yd long. She needs $1\frac{1}{3}$-yd pieces for a bulletin board.

17. How many pieces can Anna cut from the ribbon?   **7 pieces**

18. Anna decides to use $\frac{2}{3}$-yd pieces. How many pieces can she cut?   **15 pieces**

19. A bulletin board is 56 in. wide and 36 in. high. How many $3\frac{1}{2}$-in. columns can be created?   **16 columns**

20. Study the tangram pieces at the right. If the entire square is 1, find the fractional value of each piece. You can cut the tangram pieces to compare them.

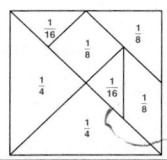

In copymaster and workbook formats

Reteaching 6-9 *Dividing Fractions and Mixed Numbers*

Divide: $8 \div \frac{4}{5}$

Step 1
Find the **reciprocal** of the divisor by switching the numerator and denominator.
$$\frac{4}{5} \rightarrow \frac{5}{4}$$

Step 2
Multiply 8 by the reciprocal.
$$8 \div \frac{4}{5} = 8 \times \frac{5}{4} = \frac{8}{1} \times \frac{5}{4} = \frac{2 \times 5}{1 \times 1} = 10$$
$$8 \div \frac{4}{5} = 10$$

Divide: $5\frac{1}{3} \div 2\frac{2}{5}$

Step 1
Write each mixed number as an improper fraction.
$$5\frac{1}{3} \div 2\frac{2}{5} = \frac{16}{3} \div \frac{12}{5}$$

Step 2
Find the reciprocal of the divisor.
$$\frac{12}{5} \rightarrow \frac{5}{12}$$

Step 3
Multiply $\frac{16}{3}$ by the reciprocal.
$$\frac{16}{3} \div \frac{12}{5} = \frac{16}{3} \times \frac{5}{12} = \frac{4 \times 5}{3 \times 3} = \frac{20}{9} = 2\frac{2}{9}$$
$$5\frac{1}{3} \div 2\frac{2}{5} = 2\frac{2}{9}$$

Find each quotient.

1. $2 \div \frac{2}{3}$ 3
2. $7 \div \frac{7}{8}$ 8
3. $9 \div \frac{3}{4}$ 12
4. $6 \div \frac{2}{5}$ 15
5. $5 \div \frac{2}{3}$ $7\frac{1}{2}$
6. $14 \div \frac{5}{6}$ $16\frac{4}{5}$
7. $\frac{4}{5} \div \frac{4}{7}$ $1\frac{2}{5}$
8. $\frac{7}{8} \div \frac{7}{9}$ $1\frac{1}{8}$
9. $6\frac{1}{2} \div 2\frac{1}{6}$ 3
10. $5\frac{1}{3} \div 2\frac{2}{3}$ 2
11. $6\frac{1}{4} \div 2\frac{1}{2}$ $2\frac{1}{2}$
12. $10 \div 3\frac{1}{3}$ 3
13. $8 \div 6\frac{1}{2}$ $1\frac{3}{13}$
14. $5 \div 1\frac{5}{6}$ $3\frac{4}{7}$
15. $2\frac{7}{10} \div 4\frac{4}{5}$ $\frac{9}{16}$
16. $3 \div \frac{3}{4}$ 4
17. $4\frac{2}{3} \div 1\frac{3}{4}$ $2\frac{2}{3}$
18. $5\frac{1}{8} \div 2\frac{1}{2}$ $2\frac{1}{20}$

Minds on Math Transparency

6-9

I am a proper fraction in simplest form. My numerator is a two-digit prime number. My denominator is 4 more than my numerator. Three of my digits are the same and are also a prime number. What fraction am I?

$\frac{73}{77}$

See *Solution Key* **for worked-out answers.**

265

In Lesson 6-10, students will learn how to change and compare units of measurement. This toolbox allows students to review the Customary System of measurement.

ERROR ALERT! Students may forget equivalent units of measurement.
Remediation: Have students make a conversion chart to refer to as they work on the exercises.

ASSESSMENT Pair students. Have each student think of an object and write it down. Their partner lists the units they would use to measure the object's height, weight, or capacity.

OPEN-ENDED Exercises 7–12 Write each unit on a different area of the board. Have students write their objects around each unit. Discuss each cluster of objects and what they have in common.

■ ADDITIONAL PROBLEMS

Choose an appropriate unit of measurement.
1. length of a fence around a small park **yards**
2. weight of gravel in a railroad car **tons**

Resources

 Teaching Resources
Teaching Aids Masters 3

 Transparencies
17, 19

pages 266   Math Toolbox
 7. **distance between school and home**
 8. **length of a piece of material**
 9. **weight of a truck**
10. **weight of a sack of oranges**
11. **amount of water used in a recipe**
12. **amount of milk left in a gallon**

SKILLS REVIEW

MATH TOOLBOX

The Customary System

 Before Lesson 6-10

The customary system of measurement was established for the British Empire in 1824. The most commonly used units for length, weight, and capacity are shown below.

Length
12 inches (in.) = 1 foot (ft)
3 feet = 1 yard (yd)
5,280 feet = 1 mile (mi)

Weight
16 ounces (oz) = 1 pound (lb)
2,000 pounds = 1 ton (T)

Capacity
8 fluid ounces (fl oz) = 1 cup   2 pints = 1 quart (qt)
2 cups (c) = 1 pint (pt)   4 quarts = 1 gallon (gal)

■ **EXAMPLE**

Choose an appropriate unit of measure for each.
a. the height of a tall building

You usually measure the height of a building in feet.

b. weight of a pencil

The weight of a pencil is measured in ounces.

c. amount of lemonade in a glass

The amount of lemonade in a glass is usually measured in fluid ounces.

Choose an appropriate unit of measure for each.

1. weight of a car **pounds**
2. length of a backyard **feet**
3. amount of water in a tub **gallons**
4. height of a tall tree **feet**
5. amount of water in a mug **ounces or cups**
6. weight of a bag of sugar **pounds**

Open-ended **For each unit, think of something you would measure with that unit. Give examples from your daily life.** 7–12. Answers may vary. See margin for samples.

7. mile   8. yard   9. ton   10. pound   11. cup   12. quart

13. *Writing* Why is it important to choose appropriate units of measure? **Appropriate units of measure help you to understand the size of the quantity measured.**

1 Focus

CONNECTING TO PRIOR KNOWLEDGE Ask students:

• *What units do you use to measure things?*
Answers may vary. Sample: inches, gallons, miles, centimeters, meters

• *How many inches are in one foot?* **12**

• *What other facts do you know that would help you change units of measurement?*
Answers may vary. Sample: There are 4 c in 1 qt.

2 Teach

THINK AND DISCUSS

 DIVERSITY and TACTILE LEARNING
Students from other countries may not be familiar with customary measurements. Give students a ruler, a yardstick, a measuring cup, a gallon jug, and a scale that measures in pounds. Let students measure objects around the classroom to get an idea of how long, how much, and how heavy each unit of measurement is.

KINESTHETIC LEARNING Example 1
Groups students in pairs. Give each pair a ruler and a yardstick. Have one student measure a distance of $8\frac{1}{2}$ ft on the floor. The partner determines how many yards fit into $8\frac{1}{2}$ ft by counting how many times a full yardstick fits and then estimating the fraction left over.

MEASUREMENT Connection

6-10 Changing Units in the Customary System

What You'll Learn

1 To change units of length, weight, and capacity

2 To compare amounts by expressing them in the same units

...And Why

You can compare lengths, weights, and capacity.

Here's How

Look for questions that
▪ build understanding
✓ check understanding

THINK AND DISCUSS

1 *Changing Units*

Fractions and mixed numbers are commonly used with the customary system of measurement. For example, you may buy $1\frac{1}{2}$ gal of milk for your family. Or you may need $1\frac{1}{4}$ c of flour for a recipe.

You can multiply or divide to change units of measurement.

1. **a.** ✓*Try It Out* How many inches are in 2 ft? **24 in.**
   b. How many tons are in 10,000 lb? **5 T**

2. ▪*Number Sense* How do you know when to multiply and when to divide? **If changing to a smaller unit, multiply. If changing to a larger unit, divide.**

To solve many problems, you change units of measurement. To do this, you need to know how the units are related.

■ EXAMPLE 1 *Real-World Problem Solving*

Sewing Suppose you need $8\frac{1}{2}$ ft of fabric for a sewing project. Fabric is sold in yards. About how many yards of fabric should you buy?

Ask yourself how many yards equal $8\frac{1}{2}$ ft.

$$3 \text{ ft} = 1 \text{ yd} \quad \longleftarrow \text{Write the relationship between feet and yards.}$$

$$8\frac{1}{2} \text{ ft} \div 3 = \blacksquare \quad \longleftarrow \text{Divide } 8\frac{1}{2} \text{ by 3.}$$

$$= 8\frac{1}{2} \times \frac{1}{3}$$

$$= \frac{17}{2} \times \frac{1}{3}$$

$$= \frac{17}{6} = 2\frac{5}{6}$$

You need $2\frac{5}{6}$ yd of fabric, or about 3 yd.

3. *Try It Out* How many yards are equivalent to $14\frac{3}{4}$ ft?
   $4\frac{11}{12}$, or about 5 yd

Lesson Planning Options

Prerequisite Skills

• multiplying and dividing fractions and mixed numbers (6-8 and 6-9)

Resources

📖 Student Edition

Skills Handbook, p. 540
Extra Practice, p. 527
Glossary/Study Guide

📕 Teaching Resources

Chapter Support File, Ch. 6
• Lesson Planner 6-10
• Practice 6-10, Reteaching 6-10
• Answer Masters 6-10
Teaching Aids Master 3
Glossary, Spanish Resources

▱ Transparencies
17, 19, Minds on Math 6-10

Warm Up

Eighteen days is what fraction of eight weeks? $\frac{9}{28}$

ASSESSMENT Ask pairs of students to discuss and answer these questions:

- *Which is longer: $2\frac{3}{4}$ ft or $\frac{5}{6}$ yd?* **$2\frac{3}{4}$ ft**
- *Which is more: $2\frac{1}{2}$ gal or 9 qt?* **$2\frac{1}{2}$ gal**
- *Which is heavier: $\frac{1}{4}$ t or 426 lb?* **$\frac{1}{4}$ t**

■ **ADDITIONAL EXAMPLES**

FOR EXAMPLE 1
A restaurant cook needs 84 c of soup for his customers. How many pints of soup should he make? **42**

FOR EXAMPLE 2
Subtract 5 yd 1 ft − 3 yd 2 ft. **1 yd 2 ft**

FOR EXAMPLE 3
Andreas wants to serve frozen yogurt to 50 people at a party. Each serving is $1\frac{1}{2}$ c. He has $4\frac{3}{4}$ gal of yogurt. Will Andre have enough to serve 50 people? **yes**

Technology Options

Prentice Hall Technology

  Software for Learners
- Hot Page™ 18*
- Math Blaster® Mystery*
- Interactive Student Tutorial, Chapter 6*

  Teaching Resource Software
- Computer Item Generator 6-10
- Resource Pro™ Chapter 6*

Internet • For related mathematics activities, visit the Prentice Hall site at www.phschool.com/math

*Available on CD-ROM only

Assignment Options for Exercises On Your Own

To provide flexible scheduling, this lesson can be subdivided into parts.

▼**1** **Core** 1–23, 25–30
   Extension 24, 31–35

▼**2** **Core** 36–47
   Extension

Use Mixed Review to maintain skills.

268

You may need to change units when you add or subtract measurements in the customary system.

■ **EXAMPLE 2**

Find 8 lb 3 oz − 4 lb 7 oz.

$$8 \text{ lb } 3 \text{ oz} \longrightarrow 7 \text{ lb } 19 \text{ oz}$$ ← You cannot subtract 7 from 3.
$$\underline{-\,4 \text{ lb } 7 \text{ oz}} \qquad \underline{-\,4 \text{ lb}\ \ 7 \text{ oz}}$$ ← Since 1 lb = 16 oz, rename 8 lb 3 oz as 7 lb 19 oz.
$$\qquad\qquad\qquad\quad 3 \text{ lb } 12 \text{ oz}$$ ← Subtract.

8 lb 3 oz − 4 lb 7 oz = 3 lb 12 oz

4. ✓*Try It Out* Add or subtract.

    2 ft 11 in.
a.   7 ft 10 in.   **b.**   5 lb 4 oz   **c.**   6 gal 2 qt
      − 4 ft 11 in.   + 3 lb 14 oz   − 2 gal 3 qt
                  9 lb 2 oz   **3 gal 3 qt**

Now you may assign Exercises 1–35.

2 *Comparing Amounts*

It is easy to compare amounts when they are expressed in the same units.

■ **EXAMPLE 3**   *Real-World Problem Solving*

Entertaining Suppose you are planning a party. You invite 24 guests. You want to serve at least 2 c of fruit punch to each guest. You plan to fill a $3\frac{1}{2}$-gal punchbowl. Will you have enough punch?

$$\underset{\text{guests}}{24} \times \underset{\text{per guest}}{2 \text{ c}} = 24 \times 2 = 48 \text{ c}$$ ← Calculate the amount of punch you need.

You will need 48 c of punch.

$$3\tfrac{1}{2} \text{ gal} = (3\tfrac{1}{2} \times 4) \text{ qt} = \tfrac{7}{2} \times 4 = 14 \text{ qt}$$ ← Change gallons to quarts.

$$14 \text{ qt} = (14 \times 2) \text{ pt} = 28 \text{ pt}$$ ← Change quarts to pints.

$$28 \text{ pt} = (28 \times 2) \text{ c} = 56 \text{ c}$$ ← Change pints to cups.

There are 56 c in $3\frac{1}{2}$ gal. You need only 48 c, so you have enough punch.

5. ■*Look Back* Solve the problem in Example 3 by asking yourself "How many gallons are equivalent to 48 c?"

    48 c = 3 gal, so $3\frac{1}{2}$ gal is enough punch.

Now you may assign Exercises 36–47.

EXERCISES *On Your Own*

ERROR ALERT! Exercises 1–20 Students may multiply instead of dividing or divide instead of multiplying when they change the units. **Remediation:** Point out to students that they need more of a smaller unit to equal a bigger unit. Write *3 ft = 1 yd* on the board. Circle *ft* and write *smaller* underneath it. Circle *yd* and write *bigger* underneath it. Circle the *3*

and write *greater* over it. Circle the *1* and write *lesser* over it. Tell students the lesser number must go with the bigger unit, and the greater number must go with the smaller unit in order for the amounts to be the same. Remind students that to go from a lesser number to a greater number, they multiply. To go from a greater number to a lesser number, they divide. Draw an arrow from 1 to 3 and label the arrow *multiply*. Draw an arrow from 3 to 1 and label it *divide*.

EXTENSION Exercise 20 Before Britain began using the metric system, their *Imperial*

ton was equal to 2,240 lb. Americans use a customary ton that equals 2,000 lb. Have students solve the problem for Imperial tons.

RESEARCH Have students investigate why *lb* is the abbreviation for pound. **Lb is short for *libra pondo*, Latin for a *pound by weight*.**

WRITING Exercise 24 Have students write a problem and find the solution for their situation.

CONNECTION TO GEOMETRY Exercise 30 Have students write an equation for the perimeter of the square. **P = 4s**

EXERCISES *On Your Own*

Complete each statement.

1. 9 ft = ▧ yd **27**   2. 32 oz = ▧ lb **2**   3. 16 qt = ▧ gal **4**   4. 6,000 lb = ▧ T **3**

5. 6 lb = ▧ oz **96**   6. ▧ ft = 48 in. **4**   7. 32 c = ▧ pt **16**   8. 3 mi = ▧ ft **15,840**

9. $6\frac{1}{4}$ ft = ▧ yd **$2\frac{1}{12}$**   10. $1\frac{3}{4}$ mi = ▧ ft **9,240**   11. $2\frac{1}{2}$ qt = ▧ pt **5**   12. $1\frac{1}{2}$ gal = ▧ qt **6**

13. 24 oz = ▧ lb **$1\frac{1}{2}$**   14. $4\frac{1}{2}$ T = ▧ lb **9,000**   15. $4\frac{1}{4}$ c = ▧ fl oz **34**   16. $\frac{1}{2}$ lb = ▧ oz **8**

17. $3\frac{1}{2}$ yd = ▧ ft **$10\frac{1}{2}$**   18. 880 yd = ▧ mi **$\frac{1}{2}$**   19. $5\frac{1}{2}$ ft = ▧ in. **66**   20. 7,000 lb = ▧ T **$3\frac{1}{2}$**

21. *Reasoning* What operation do you use to change–
    a. inches to feet?   b. yards to feet?   c. gallons to cups?
       division   **multiplication**   **multiplication**

22. *Wildlife* In some parts of Alaska, moose actually cause traffic jams. An adult moose weighs about 1,000 lb. How many tons does an adult moose weigh? **$\frac{1}{2}$ T**

23. *Architecture* The Washington Monument in Washington, D.C., is 555 ft $5\frac{1}{8}$ in. tall. How many inches tall is it? **$6,665\frac{1}{8}$ in.**

24. *Writing* Describe a situation from daily life in which you need to change from one unit of measure to another. **See margin.**

25. *Cooking* Cranberry mousse requires 32 fl oz nonfat plain yogurt. How many cups is this? **4 c**

Add or subtract. Rename when necessary.

26. $\begin{array}{r} 4 \text{ ft } 10 \text{ in.} \\ + 1 \text{ ft } 9 \text{ in.} \\ \hline \textbf{6 ft 7 in.} \end{array}$ 27. $\begin{array}{r} 5 \text{ yd } 1 \text{ ft} \\ - 1 \text{ yd } 2 \text{ ft} \\ \hline \textbf{3 yd 2 ft} \end{array}$ 28. $\begin{array}{r} 3 \text{ gal } 3 \text{ qt} \\ + 3 \text{ gal } 1 \text{ qt} \\ \hline \textbf{7 gal} \end{array}$ 29. $\begin{array}{r} 17 \text{ lb } 12 \text{ oz} \\ - 9 \text{ lb } 13 \text{ oz} \\ \hline \textbf{7 lb 15 oz} \end{array}$

30. *Geometry* Find the distance in feet around the square at the right. **2 ft**

6 in.
6 in.

31. *Nutrition* Read the article below. Suppose six adults are served a $2\frac{1}{2}$-lb roast beef for dinner. Each adult will eat about the same amount. Should they eat the whole roast? Explain. **See margin.**

LATEST NEWS *from the* AMERICAN HEART ASSOCIATION

THE American Heart Association recommends that an adult eat no more than 6 oz (2–3 servings) of cooked poultry, fish, or lean red meat each day. Meat, fish, and poultry are the major contributors of iron, zinc, and B vitamins in most American diets.

pages 269–270   On Your Own

24. **Answers may vary. Sample: Measurements in a soup recipe serving 4 must be changed to larger units of measure to make soup for a crowd.**

31. **No; if each person eats 3 oz per serving, together they should eat 18 oz, or $1\frac{1}{8}$ lb.**

Practice 6-10 *Changing Units in the Customary System*

Complete each statement.

1. $7\frac{1}{2}$ ft = $2\frac{1}{2}$ yd

2. 45 in. = $3\frac{3}{4}$ ft

3. $1\frac{1}{4}$ mi = 6,600 ft

4. $2\frac{1}{2}$ lb = 40 oz

5. 28 fl oz = $3\frac{1}{2}$ c

6. $2\frac{3}{4}$ t = 5,500 lb

7. 3 lb = 48 oz

8. 10 pt = 5 qt

Compare using <, >, or =.

9. $4\frac{1}{5}$ ft > 50 in.

10. 136 oz = $8\frac{1}{2}$ lb

11. 26 fl oz > 3 c

12. 5 qt = $1\frac{1}{4}$ gal

13. 8 yd > 21 ft

14. 4,500 lb < $3\frac{1}{2}$ t

Solve.

15. The odometer of an automobile shows tenths of a mile. How many feet are in $\frac{1}{10}$ mi? 528 ft

16. How many inches are in one mile? 63,360 in.

17. Jarel bought 3 containers of cottage cheese, each weighing 24 oz. How many pounds did she buy? $4\frac{1}{2}$ lb

18. Katie poured 12 oz of juice from a full 6-qt container. How many cups were left in the container? $22\frac{1}{2}$ c

19. The food committee for the end-of-the-year class picnic plans to serve 4-oz hamburger patties. How many pounds of meat should be bought to make 125 hamburgers? $31\frac{1}{4}$ lb

Add or subtract. Rename when necessary.

20. 8 ft 3 in. − 3 ft 5 in. = 4 ft 10 in.

21. 12 qt 1 pt + 11 qt 1 pt = 24 qt

22. 9 yd 15 in. + 7 yd 28 in. = 17 yd 7 in.

23. 105 lb 8 oz − 98 lb 12 oz = 6 lb 12 oz

24. 4 c 6 fl oz + 4 c 6 fl oz = 8 c 5 fl oz

25. 13 yd 2 ft − 6 yd 1 ft = 7 yd 1 ft

In copymaster and workbook formats

Reteaching 6-10 *Changing Units in the Customary System*

Complete the statement: $5\frac{5}{8}$ c = ■ fl oz

① Find the relationship between cups and ounces: 1 c = 8 fl oz.

② Since there are 8 fl oz. in each cup, multiply the number of cups by 8.

$5\frac{5}{8} \times 8 = \frac{45}{8} \times 8$

$= \frac{45}{\cancel{8}} \times \frac{\cancel{8}}{1}$

$= 45$

$5\frac{5}{8}$ c = 45 fl oz

Subtract: 9 ft 8 in. − 2 ft 11 in.

① Find the relationship between feet and inches: 1 ft = 12 in.

② Use the relationship to rename 9 ft 8 in. as 8 ft 20 in.

③ Subtract.

9 ft 8 in. → 8 ft 20 in.
− 2 ft 11 in. → − 2 ft 11 in.
= 6 ft 9 in.

9 ft 8 in. − 2 ft 11 in. = 6 ft 9 in.

To compare amounts, first change them to the same unit.

Compare: 25 fl oz ? 3 c → 25 fl oz ? 24 fl oz
25 fl oz > 24 fl oz
25 fl oz > 3 c

Complete each statement.

1. 12 ft = ■ yd 4

2. 32 qt = ■ gal 8

3. $1\frac{1}{2}$ mi = ■ ft 7,920

4. 15 pt = ■ qt $7\frac{1}{2}$

5. 440 yd = ■ mi $\frac{1}{4}$

6. $2\frac{1}{2}$ t = ■ lb 5,000

7. $9\frac{1}{4}$ c = ■ fl oz 74

8. 40 oz = ■ lb $2\frac{1}{2}$

9. $8\frac{1}{4}$ ft = ■ in 99

Add or subtract. Rename when necessary.

10. 3 pt 1 c + 4 pt 1 c = 8 pt

11. 4 yd 1 ft − 1 yd 2 ft = 2 yd 2 ft

12. 5 lb 20 oz + 8 lb 12 oz = 15 lb

Compare using <, >, or =.

13. 43 in. < 4 ft

14. $8\frac{1}{2}$ gal = 136 c

15. 108 in. < $3\frac{1}{2}$ yd

16. $2\frac{1}{2}$ lb = 40 oz

17. 7,000 lb > $3\frac{1}{4}$ t

18. $5\frac{1}{2}$ pt < 3 qt

Minds on Math Transparency

6-10

How many different rectangles can you find in the figure below?

18 rectangles

See *Solution Key* for worked-out answers.

WRAP UP

IDENTIFYING THE BIG IDEA Ask students to explain how to change units of measurement.

PORTFOLIO Share with students the criteria you will use to assess their work in portfolios, as well as how you plan to use the results. Students should understand how the rubrics are used to assess their work, how each piece in the portfolio counts, and how the scores they get in their portfolios will affect their overall evaluation.

LESSON QUIZ

1. Subtract 4 gal 1 qt − 2 gal 3 qt.
   1 gal 2 qt

2. $5\frac{1}{4}$ ft = ■ yd $1\frac{3}{4}$

---

32. *Data Analysis* Use the recipe at the right. Odetta bought a 6-fl oz container of nonfat plain yogurt. Did Odetta buy enough yogurt to make Avocado Cream? Explain.
    Yes: only 4 oz are needed.

33. *Number Sense* You have a set of 20 encyclopedias. Each book is $1\frac{7}{8}$ in. thick. Your shelf is 3 ft wide. Will the set of books fit on one shelf? Explain. **No; $3\frac{1}{8}$ ft are needed.**

34. *Geography* The Mont Blanc Tunnel goes through a mountain and connects Italy and France. Its length is 7.2 mi.
    a. What is the length of the tunnel in feet? **38,016 ft**
    b. Did you multiply or divide to find the answer to part (a)? Why? **Multiply; feet are smaller units than miles.**

35. *Energy* La Grande Complexe is a hydroelectric power facility in Canada. One of its dams, LG2, has a channel that allows 750,000 gal of water to pass through per second.
    a. How many gallons pass through LG2 in 1 min? **45,000,000 gal**
    b. A gallon of water weighs about 8 lb. About how many tons of water pass through the dam's channel in 1 s? **about 3,000 T**

Avocado Cream
a sauce for quesadillas, salads, and tortilla chips

1 ripe avocado

juice of 1 lime

$\frac{1}{2}$ cup nonfat plain yogurt

Compare using <, >, or =.

36. 85 in. < 8 ft

37. $3\frac{1}{2}$ lb = 56 oz

38. $2\frac{1}{2}$ gal < 25 pt

39. $1\frac{1}{2}$ T < 4,000 lb

40. $6\frac{1}{2}$ pt > 2 qt

41. 24 fl oz = 3 c

42. 6,750 lb < $3\frac{3}{4}$ T

43. $1\frac{1}{2}$ lb > 10 oz

44. $5\frac{1}{2}$ yd > 180 in.

45. 252 in. < 25 ft

46. 16 yd < 50 ft

47. 3 qt = 96 oz

PORTFOLIO Summarize the different methods you have used to add, subtract, multiply, and divide fractions. List some real-world uses of these procedures.

Mixed Review

Place a decimal point in each product. *(Lesson 4-5)*

48. $5.9 \times 0.46 = 2714$
    2.714

49. $0.08 \times 0.09 = 00072$
    0.0072

50. $0.3 \times 0.2 = 0006$
    0.06

Write each improper fraction as a mixed number. Write each mixed number as an improper fraction. *(Lesson 5-6)*

51. $\frac{49}{5}$ $9\frac{4}{5}$

52. $5\frac{2}{3}$ $\frac{17}{3}$

53. $\frac{49}{6}$ $8\frac{1}{6}$

54. $12\frac{3}{4}$ $\frac{51}{4}$

55. $8\frac{5}{6}$ $\frac{53}{6}$

56. $\frac{21}{8}$ $2\frac{5}{8}$

57. *Choose a Strategy* You have five coins with a total value $.75. Two of the coins are quarters. What are the other coins?
    2 dimes and 1 nickel

PROJECT DAY You may wish to plan a project day on which students share their completed projects. Encourage students to explain their process as well as their product.

PROJECT NOTEBOOK Ask students to review their project work and bring their notebooks up to date.

Have students review their methods for performing their experiments, making their calculations, and preparing their tables for the project.

SCORING RUBRIC

3 You provide a step-by-step proof showing that the methods for adding fractions with inlike denominations really work. This proof includes a description of at least two experiments you conducted using itmes you collected. The sums you found by experiment are compared to the results of actual calculations in a table. Your presentation is clear and complete.

2 You provide a proof that includes evidence of only one experiment. The results of the experiment are compared to actual calculations. Your work is neat and easy to follow.

1 You provide the results of one experiment and accompanying calculations, but your work is disorganized or unclear.

0 You failed to conduct any experiments or to prepare a written description of your work.

FINISHING THE CHAPTER PROJECT

CHAPTER PROJECT

SEEing is Believing

Design a Demonstration The Project Link questions on pages 231, 256, and 261 should help you complete your project. Here is a checklist to help you gather the parts of your project together.

- ✔ list of materials used for your experiment
- ✔ step-by-step descriptions of the procedures you followed
- ✔ calculations of the sums
- ✔ a summary table comparing your calculated and measured sums

Present your demonstration of fractions to your class. Your proofs should convince any nonbelievers.

Reflect and Revise

Show your proofs to some of your classmates. Discuss whether or not these same techniques would work to show subtraction of fractions and mixed numbers. Work together to devise a method for proving that fraction multiplication techniques work. Are your proofs logical and correct? Are your calculations accurate? Revise your demonstration or proofs as necessary.

Web Extension

Prentice Hall's Internet site contains information you might find helpful as you complete your project. Visit www.phschool.com/mgm/c1/ch6 for some links and ideas related to proofs.

STUDENT SELF-ASSESSMENT SURVEY

Chapter 6 Student Self-Assessment Survey

1. Now that you have finished this chapter, think about what you have learned about fractions. Check each topic that you feel confident you understand.
   _____ estimate sums and differences of fractions and mixed numbers (6-1)
   _____ add and subtract fractions with like denominators (6-2)
   _____ add and subtract fractions with unlike denominators (6-3)
   _____ add mixed numbers (6-4)
   _____ subtract mixed numbers (6-5)
   _____ solve a problem by drawing a diagram (6-6)
   _____ multiply fractions (6-7)
   _____ multiply mixed numbers (6-8)
   _____ divide fractions and mixed numbers (6-9)
   _____ change customary units of length, weight, and capacity (6-10)

2. Before the Chapter Assessment, I need to review _____

3. a. Check one. In general, I thought this chapter was
   _____ a snap _____ easy _____ average _____ hard _____ a monster
   b. Why do you feel this way? _____

4. In this chapter, I did my best work on _____

5. In this chapter, I had trouble with _____

6. Check each one that applies. Now that I've spent some time working with fractions, I think they are
   _____ important _____ boring _____ useful _____ fun
   _____ a waste of time _____ confusing _____ tricky _____ interesting

7. List three situations outside the classroom in which you could use fractions in your daily life. _____

8. Do you like using the fraction calculator? _____ Explain. _____

Vocabulary/Symbols

reciprocals, whole number

Materials/Manipulatives

- calculator
- dot paper

Resources

 Student Edition

Extra Practice, p. 527
Glossary/Study Guide

 Teaching Resources

Chapter Support File, Ch. 6
- Student Self-Assessment Survey
Glossary, Spanish Resources
Tools for Studying Smarter

WRAP UP

Exercises 1–4 Remind students to round each fraction to the nearest half or whole number.

Exercises 5–6 Students should go back and compare their sentences to the models.

Exercises 12–16 Have students estimate to see if their answers are reasonable.

Exercise 17 Students may want to use dot paper or graph paper for their diagrams.

Exercises 22–25 Have students write the conversion equation they need for each problem. 1 pt = 2 c; 12 in. = 1 ft; 1 gal = 32 c; 2,000 lb = 1 T

Remind students that the new mathematical terms in this chapter are defined in the Glossary/Study Guide in the back of the book.

---

(6) WRAP UP

Estimating Sums and Differences   6-1

You can estimate the sum or difference of fractions by rounding each fraction to the nearest half. To estimate the sum or difference of mixed numbers, round each mixed number to the nearest whole number.

Estimate each sum or difference.

1. $\frac{15}{16} - \frac{7}{12}$ $\frac{1}{2}$
2. $\frac{6}{11} + \frac{7}{8}$ $1\frac{1}{2}$
3. $7\frac{3}{5} - 3\frac{1}{6}$ 5
4. $4\frac{4}{9} + 1\frac{8}{15}$ 6

Adding and Subtracting Fractions   6-2, 6-3

You can use models to add or subtract fractions.

To add or subtract fractions with unlike denominators, first find a common denominator. Use equivalent fractions.

Write an addition or subtraction sentence to describe each model.

5.
$\frac{1}{5} + \frac{1}{2} = \frac{7}{10}$

6.
$\frac{5}{6} - \frac{1}{3} = \frac{1}{2}$

Find each sum or difference.

7. $\frac{2}{9} + \frac{5}{9}$ $\frac{7}{9}$
8. $\frac{5}{6} - \frac{2}{6}$ $\frac{1}{2}$
9. $\frac{1}{3} + \frac{3}{4}$ $1\frac{1}{12}$
10. $\frac{5}{6} - \frac{4}{5}$ $\frac{1}{30}$
11. $\frac{5}{8} - \frac{3}{10}$ $\frac{13}{40}$

Adding and Subtracting Mixed Numbers   6-4, 6-5

To add or subtract mixed numbers, compute the whole number and fraction parts separately. When subtracting, start with the fractions first.

Find each sum or difference.

12. $2\frac{3}{5} + 3\frac{2}{5}$ 6
13. $6\frac{2}{5} - 2\frac{3}{4}$ $3\frac{13}{20}$
14. $3\frac{7}{8} + 1\frac{2}{12}$ $5\frac{1}{24}$
15. $4\frac{9}{10} - \frac{5}{6}$ $4\frac{1}{15}$
16. $15\frac{5}{12} - 10\frac{7}{9}$ 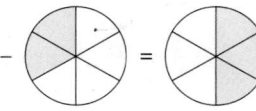 $4\frac{23}{36}$

Problem Solving Strategies 6-6

Sometimes it's helpful to draw a diagram when solving a problem.

17. Mrs. Cruz bought a rectangular piece of carpet that is 12 ft wide and 18 ft long. She will carpet her rectangular bathroom, square office, and a hallway measuring 4 ft wide and 18 ft long.

8 ft × 8 ft	8 ft × 10 ft
4 ft × 18 ft	

12 ft
18 ft

 a. Draw a diagram to show how she can make the three carpets with two cuts.
 b. Find the dimensions of the bathroom and office. **bathroom: 8 ft by 10 ft; office: 8 ft by 8 ft**
 c. Find the area of each room and the combined area of all three rooms. **bathroom: 80 ft²; office; 64 ft²; hallway: 72²; total area: 216 ft²**

Multiplying and Dividing Fractions and Mixed Numbers 6-7, 6-8, 6-9

To multiply fractions, multiply the numerators and then multiply the denominators. To divide fractions, multiply by the reciprocal of the divisor. To find $\frac{2}{3} \div \frac{5}{6}$, multiply $\frac{2}{3} \times \frac{6}{5}$.

Simplify before multiplying when possible. Divide numerators and denominators by any common factors.

Write mixed numbers as improper fractions.

Find each product or quotient.

18. $\frac{3}{5} \times \frac{5}{6}$ $\frac{1}{2}$ 19. $\frac{2}{3} \div 8$ $\frac{1}{12}$ 20. $2\frac{1}{6} \times 3\frac{3}{4}$ $8\frac{1}{8}$ 21. $2\frac{3}{8} \div 2\frac{1}{2}$ $\frac{19}{20}$

Changing Units in the Customary System 6-10

You can multiply or divide to change units of measurement.

To compare amounts, express them in the same units.

Complete each statement.

22. $5\frac{1}{2}$ pt = ■ c   **11**   23. 880 in. = ■ ft   **$73\frac{1}{3}$**   24. $2\frac{1}{2}$ gal = ■ c   **40**   25. 12,000 lb = ■ T   **6**

26. In baseball, the distance from the pitcher to the batter is 60 ft 6 in. How far is this in yards? **$20\frac{1}{6}$ yd**

27. *Writing* Explain why it is useful to be able to change units of measurement. **Comparing quantities and computing with measurements sometimes require changing units of measurement.**

Chapter 6 Assessment • Form A

Answers

1. Estimate the difference $6\frac{2}{5} - 4\frac{1}{8}$.
 1. 2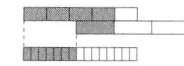

2. Kisha plans to double a recipe for cookies. The single recipe needs $1\frac{3}{8}$ c of flour. How much does she need for the doubled recipe? Write as a mixed number in lowest terms.
 2. $2\frac{3}{4}$ c

3. Subtract. Write the answer in simplest form. $\frac{4}{15} - \frac{1}{15}$
 3. $\frac{1}{5}$

4. Write an addition sentence for the model.
 4. $\frac{3}{8} + \frac{3}{8} = \frac{6}{8}$ or $\frac{3}{4}$

5. Write a subtraction sentence for the model.
 5. $\frac{4}{5} - \frac{1}{3} = \frac{7}{15}$

6. Use equivalent fractions to find the difference. Write the answer in simplest form. $\frac{1}{5} - \frac{1}{6}$
 6. $\frac{1}{30}$

7. Estimate the sum $12\frac{1}{8} + 9\frac{11}{13}$.
 7. 22

8. Divide $\frac{5}{9} \div \frac{5}{6}$.
 8. $\frac{2}{3}$

9. Arman wants to buy enough fabric to make a shirt and a pair of pants. The shirt requires $2\frac{3}{8}$ yd. The pants need $3\frac{1}{4}$ yd. How many total yards does he require? Write the answer as a mixed number in simplest form.
 9. $5\frac{5}{8}$ yd

10. Find the difference. Write the answer as a mixed number in simplest form. $5\frac{1}{3} - 3\frac{1}{4}$
 10. $2\frac{1}{12}$

11. Find $\frac{2}{5}$ of 35.
 11. 14

Assessment

Chapter 6 Assessment • Form A (continued)

12. Find the area of the rectangle.
 12. $\frac{3}{8}$ in.²

 $\frac{1}{2}$ in. $\frac{3}{4}$ in.

13. Find the area of this garden plot. Write the answer as a mixed number in simplest form. $2\frac{2}{5}$ yd $1\frac{1}{3}$ yd
 13. $2\frac{14}{15}$ yd²

14. Sammy wants to make a half portion of a recipe that calls for $1\frac{1}{3}$ c of milk. How much milk does she need for the half portion?
 14. $\frac{2}{3}$ c

15. You want to cut a 10-ft board into $2\frac{1}{2}$ ft lengths. How many pieces will you have?
 15. 4 pieces

16. Divide. Write the answer in simplest form. $1\frac{9}{11} \div \frac{1}{3}$
 16. $5\frac{2}{11}$

17. Complete. 48 pt = ■ gal
 17. 6

Choose A, B, C, or D.

18. Find the sum in simplest form: $3\frac{3}{3}$ pt + $1\frac{1}{2}$ pt
 A. $4\frac{3}{6}$ pt   **B.** $4\frac{3}{5}$ pt   **C.** 5 pt   **D.** $5\frac{1}{6}$ pt
 18. D

Choose a Strategy

19. Keenan is making a trophy rack with wood that is $1\frac{1}{4}$ in. thick. The trophy rack has four shelves. One shelf is the top of the trophy rack, and one is the bottom. The space between shelves is 14 in. Find the height of the trophy rack.
 19. 47 in.

Writing

20. You enter a frog in a leaping contest. The frog is supposed to hop the length of a football field. Your frog starts at one end and jumps half the length of the field the first hop. Then it jumps half of that. It continues to jump half the distance of its last jump each time. Will it ever reach the other end of the field and if so, in how many jumps? **The frog will never reach the other end of the field.**

Chapter 6 Assessment • Form B

Choose the best answer. Circle A, B, C, or D.

1. Estimate the difference $4\frac{5}{6} - 2\frac{1}{9}$.
   A. 2   B. $2\frac{1}{4}$ C. $2\frac{1}{2}$ Ⓓ 3

2. Joshua plans to double a recipe for making muffins. The single recipe calls for $2\frac{1}{4}$ c of milk. How much will he need in the doubled recipe? Write as a mixed number in simplest form.
   A. $2\frac{2}{4}$ c   Ⓑ $4\frac{1}{2}$ c   C. $4\frac{1}{4}$ c   D. 5 c

3. Find the difference in simplest form $\frac{7}{15} - \frac{2}{15}$.
   A. $\frac{2}{3}$ B. $\frac{1}{2}$ C. $\frac{9}{15}$ Ⓓ $\frac{1}{3}$

4. Write an addition sentence for the model.
   Ⓐ $\frac{1}{6} + \frac{2}{6} = \frac{3}{2}$ B. $\frac{1}{6} + \frac{2}{6} = \frac{2}{3}$
   C. $\frac{1}{6} + \frac{2}{6} = \frac{3}{3}$ D. $\frac{5}{6} + \frac{4}{6} = 1\frac{3}{6}$
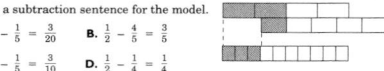

5. Write a subtraction sentence for the model.
   A. $\frac{2}{4} - \frac{1}{5} = \frac{3}{20}$ B. $\frac{1}{2} - \frac{4}{5} = \frac{3}{5}$
   Ⓒ $\frac{2}{4} - \frac{1}{5} = \frac{3}{10}$ D. $\frac{1}{2} - \frac{1}{4} = \frac{1}{4}$
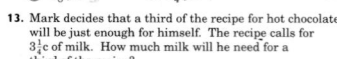

6. Use equivalent fractions to find the difference and write the answer in simplest form. $\frac{1}{3} - \frac{1}{8}$
   A. $\frac{1}{3} - \frac{1}{8} = \frac{1}{5}$ B. $\frac{4}{12} - \frac{2}{12} = \frac{1}{6}$ C. $\frac{3}{18} - \frac{2}{18} = \frac{1}{18}$ Ⓓ $\frac{8}{24} - \frac{3}{24} = \frac{5}{24}$

7. What is the sum of $5\frac{1}{8}$ and $2\frac{1}{4}$?
   Ⓐ $7\frac{3}{8}$ B. $7\frac{3}{4}$ C. $10\frac{1}{32}$ D. $10\frac{3}{8}$

8. Find the sum in simplest form $3\frac{2}{3} + 4\frac{1}{4}$.
   A. $7\frac{2}{7}$ B. $7\frac{3}{7}$ C. 8   Ⓓ $7\frac{11}{12}$

9. Find the difference in simplest form $6\frac{1}{3} - 3\frac{2}{3}$.
   A. $1\frac{4}{3}$ Ⓑ $2\frac{2}{3}$ C. $1\frac{2}{3}$ D. $3\frac{2}{3}$

Chapter 6 Assessment • Form B (continued)

10. What is $\frac{3}{10}$ of 50?
    A. 5   B. 10   Ⓒ 15   D. 20

11. Find the area of the rectangle.
    Ⓐ $\frac{1}{12}$ ft²   B. $\frac{7}{12}$ ft²
    C. $\frac{2}{7}$ ft²   D. $\frac{1}{6}$ ft²

12. Find the area of the rectangular fish pond shown.
    A. $2\frac{5}{4}$ yd²   B. $2\frac{3}{8}$ yd²
    Ⓒ $4\frac{1}{8}$ yd²   D. $3\frac{1}{4}$ yd²

13. Mark decides that a third of the recipe for hot chocolate will be just enough for himself. The recipe calls for $3\frac{1}{2}$ c of milk. How much milk will he need for a third of the recipe?
    Ⓐ $1\frac{1}{2}$ c   B. $9\frac{1}{12}$ c   C. $9\frac{3}{4}$ c   D. $1\frac{1}{3}$ c

14. Ray has a 15-ft piece of lumber and he wants to cut it into $2\frac{1}{2}$-ft lengths. How many $2\frac{1}{2}$-ft pieces can he make from the original lumber?
    A. 7 pieces   B. 37 pieces   Ⓒ 6 pieces   D. 4 pieces

15. Divide. Write the answer in simplest form: $3\frac{1}{2} \div \frac{1}{8}$
    A. $24\frac{1}{16}$ Ⓑ 28   C. $\frac{7}{16}$ D. $3\frac{1}{16}$

16. Complete. 32 c = ▇ qt
    A. 2 qt   B. 4 qt   Ⓒ 8 qt   D. 16 qt

17. Complete. $3\frac{1}{4}$ ft = ▇ in.
    A. 36 in.   Ⓑ 39 in.   C. 48 in.   D. 52 in.

Choose a Strategy

18. Karen is making a spice rack with wood that is $\frac{1}{2}$ in. thick. The spice rack has three shelves. One shelf is used for the top of the spice rack, and one is used for the bottom. The space between the shelves is 3 in. Find the total height of the spice rack.
    A. 6 in.   B. $6\frac{3}{6}$ in.   Ⓒ $7\frac{1}{2}$ in.   D. $7\frac{3}{4}$ in.

 Teaching Resources

Chapter Support File, Ch. 6, and Spanish Resources

 Teacher's Edition

See pp. 226C–D for Assessment Options.

 Teaching Resource Software
- Computer Item Generator, Ch. 6

274

ASSESSMENT

TACTILE LEARNING Exercise 2 Suggest students use fraction bars to help them solve the problem.

WRITING EXERCISES allow students to describe more fully their thinking and understanding of the concepts they've learned. **Exercise 6** is a writing exercise.

CONNECTION TO ALGEBRA Have students check their answer by replacing x in the problem with their value for x and adding.

ENHANCED MULTIPLE CHOICE QUESTIONS

are more complex than traditional multiple choice questions, which assess only one skill. Enhanced multiple choice questions assess the processes that students use, as well as the end result. They are written so that students can use more than one strategy to solve the problem. Using multiple strategies is encouraged by the National Council of Teachers of Mathematics (NCTM). **Exercise 14** is an enhanced multiple choice question.

6 ASSESSMENT

1. Estimate each sum or difference.
   a. $\frac{3}{4} + \frac{1}{9}$ 1   b. $\frac{11}{12} - \frac{1}{10}$ 1
   c. $14\frac{7}{8} + 10\frac{3}{8}$ 25   d. $34\frac{65}{66} - 12\frac{1}{16}$ 23

2. *Modeling* Draw a model to find each sum or difference. **See back of book for models.**
   a. $\frac{1}{4} + \frac{1}{4}$ $\frac{1}{2}$ b. $\frac{11}{12} - \frac{5}{12}$ $\frac{1}{2}$

3. Find each sum. Write the answer in simplest form.
   a. $\frac{1}{5} + \frac{11}{15}$ $\frac{14}{15}$ b. $\frac{7}{12} + \frac{3}{8}$ $\frac{23}{24}$
   c. $4\frac{1}{2} + 6\frac{2}{15}$ $10\frac{19}{30}$ d. $5\frac{4}{5} + 3\frac{1}{2}$ $9\frac{3}{10}$

4. Find each difference. Write the answer in simplest form.
   a. $\frac{3}{4} - \frac{2}{5}$ $\frac{7}{20}$ b. $\frac{5}{6} - \frac{4}{15}$ $\frac{17}{30}$
   c. $7\frac{7}{8} - 5\frac{17}{32}$ $2\frac{11}{32}$ d. $12\frac{9}{10} - 4\frac{3}{5}$ $8\frac{3}{10}$

5. Kelsey tutored for $3\frac{3}{4}$ h on Tuesday and $7\frac{1}{3}$ h on Saturday.
   a. About how many more hours did Kelsey tutor on Saturday than on Tuesday? **about 3 h**
   b. About how much time did Kelsey tutor altogether? **about 11 h**
   6. See back of book.
6. *Writing* Explain how you can mentally find the sum $3\frac{1}{4} + 2\frac{2}{3} + 5\frac{3}{4} + 1\frac{1}{3}$.

7. Roscoe grew $4\frac{1}{4}$ in. over a two-year period. If he grew $2\frac{1}{2}$ in. the first year, how many inches did Roscoe grow during the second year? **$1\frac{3}{4}$ in.**

8. Four students are waiting in line. Joe is behind Sarah, Noton is in front of Max, and Sarah is behind Max. In which order are the students standing?
   Noton, Max, Sarah, Joe

9. *Mental Math* Solve for x.
   a. $\frac{3}{10} + x = \frac{8}{10}$ $\frac{1}{2}$ b. $x + \frac{2}{5} = \frac{4}{5}$ $\frac{2}{5}$

10. *Algebra* Solve for x. $3\frac{1}{2}$
    $3\frac{5}{8} + x = 7\frac{1}{8}$

11. Find each product.
    a. $\frac{3}{8}$ of 64   24   b. $\frac{2}{5} \times 45$ 18
    c. $3\frac{1}{3} \times 2\frac{3}{4}$ $9\frac{1}{6}$ d. $4\frac{3}{10} \times 2\frac{1}{2}$ $10\frac{3}{4}$

12. Estimate each product.
    a. $10\frac{9}{10} \times 5\frac{1}{5}$ 55   b. $9\frac{5}{12} \times 6\frac{11}{12}$ 63

13. Find each product or quotient.
    a. $2\frac{1}{5} \times 2\frac{3}{4}$ $6\frac{1}{20}$ b. $3\frac{3}{8} \times 4\frac{4}{5}$ $16\frac{1}{5}$
    c. $10\frac{1}{2} \div \frac{1}{2}$ 21   d. $6\frac{3}{4} \div 4\frac{1}{2}$ $1\frac{1}{2}$

14. **Choose A, B, C, or D.** A sales representative completed $\frac{4}{7}$ of a 1,394-mi business trip. About how many miles of the trip remain? **B**
    A. about 400   B. about 600
    C. about 800   D. about 1,000

15. A doll maker uses $1\frac{7}{8}$ yd of material to make one doll. How many dolls can be made from a piece of material that is 45 yd long? **24 dolls**

16. Tung has an income of $2,640 each month. He spends $\frac{1}{5}$ of his income on rent. How much does Tung spend on rent? **$528**

Complete each statement.   20. $1\frac{11}{12}$

17. 30 yd = ▇ ft   **90**   18. $14\frac{1}{2}$ gal = ▇ c   **232**

19. 108 fl oz = ▇ pt $6\frac{3}{4}$ 20. $5\frac{3}{4}$ ft = ▇ yd

21. ▇ ft = 86 in. $7\frac{1}{6}$ 22. 150 lb = ▇ oz   **2,400**

Item	Review Topic	Ch
1, 4	Comparing fractions and decimals	5
2	Multiplying fractions	6
3	Ordering decimals and fractions	4
5	Adding decimals	3
6	GCF	5

Item	Review Topic	Ch
7, 8	Solving equations	2
9	Finding mean	1
10	Making graphs	1
11	Solving expressions	2
12	Dividing fractions and mixed numbers	6

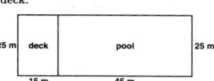

6 CUMULATIVE REVIEW

Choose the best answer.

1. Which is *not* equivalent to five tenths? **A**
A. 0.05
B. $\frac{5}{10}$
C. 0.5
D. fifty hundredths

2. Summer vacation is 68 days long. If $\frac{3}{4}$ of vacation has gone by, how many days are left? **D**
A. 12 days
B. 51 days
C. 23 days
D. 17 days

3. Which set of numbers is ordered from least to greatest? **C**
A. $0.67, \frac{2}{3}, \frac{7}{10}, \frac{3}{4}$
B. $\frac{1}{4}, \frac{6}{25}, 0.23, \frac{2}{9}$
C. $1\frac{1}{4}, 1\frac{2}{7}, 1.3, 1\frac{1}{3}$
D. $0.37, \frac{3}{8}, \frac{1}{3}, 0.4$

4. Which is *not* a true statement? **B**
A. $0.04 > 0.01$
B. $0.48 < 0.4798$
C. $0.014 < 0.02$
D. $29.6 > 29.06$

5. A calculator sells for $18.64. Sales tax is $1.49. How much money do you need to buy the calculator? **D**
A. $19.03
B. $17.15
C. $33.54
D. $20.13

6. Which set of numbers has a GCF of 3? **C**
A. 15, 30, 45
B. 6, 30, 24
C. 24, 36, 9
D. 36, 27, 18

7. Describe how to find $1\frac{3}{4}$ divided by $\frac{1}{2}$.
A. Multiply $1\frac{3}{4}$ and $\frac{1}{2}$. **D**
B. Find $\frac{7}{4} \div 2$.
C. Multiply $\frac{1}{2}$ and $\frac{4}{7}$.
D. Multiply $\frac{7}{4}$ and 2.

8. Which of the following is *not* a solution to the given equation? **C**
A. $4a = 20$; 5
B. $x + 9.5 = 10$; 0.5
C. $y \div 5 = 35$; 7
D. $b + 53.7 = 100$; 46.3

9. Your bowling scores one day were 125, 137, and 92. How would you find the mean score? **C**
A. Subtract 92 from 137.
B. Choose the middle score.
C. Find the total and divide by 3.
D. Add all three scores.

10. A table is shown below. What type of graph should be made from the information? **B**

Sizes of Eggs

Size	Ounces per Dozen
Jumbo	30
Extra large	27
Large	24
Medium	21
Small	18
Peewee	15

A. a line plot
B. a bar graph
C. a line graph
D. a circle graph

11. What is the value of the expression $5 + 7(6 - 1) \div 2$? **B**
A. 18
B. 20
C. 22.5
D. 30

12. Estimate the solution to the equation $x - 17.16 = 33.4$. **B**
A. about 16
B. about 50
C. about 2
D. about 0.5

CUMULATIVE REVIEW

Chapter 6 Cumulative Review

Choose the best answer. Circle A, B, C, or D.

1. What is the decimal for twenty-three hundredths?
A. 23
B. 2.3
C. 0.23
D. 0.023

2. List the decimals 0.25, 0.35, 0.23, 0.04, 0.02 from greatest to least.
A. 0.35, 0.25, 0.23, 0.04, 0.02
B. 0.04, 0.35, 0.25, 0.23, 0.02
C. 0.02, 0.04, 0.23, 0.25, 0.35
D. 0.02, 0.23, 0.04, 0.25, 0.35

3. Find the sum $0.46 + 0.58 + 0.05$.
A. 0.89
B. 1.19
C. 1.09
D. 0.99

4. You have a $10 bill and want to go to the movies for $5.50, buy popcorn for $2.45, and a drink for $1.95. How much change will you get?
A. none
B. $.10
C. $.25
D. $10 is not enough

5. The thread on a spool is 30 m long. Which is *not* an equivalent length?
A. 0.03 km
B. 3,000 cm
C. 30,000 mm
D. 0.3 km

6. Find the total area of the pool and deck.

25 m deck | pool | 25 m
15 m | 45 m

A. 1,500 m²
B. 1,125 m²
C. 675 m²
D. 170 m²

7. Find the product 2.32×0.5.
A. 0.0116
B. 0.116
C. 1.16
D. 11.16

8. Four oranges cost $.99. What is the price for three oranges?
A. $.25
B. $.33
C. $.45
D. $.75

9. Solve $81 \div x = 9$.
A. 9
B. 72
C. 90
D. 729

10. A baker sent 200 loaves of bread to several grocery stores. The baker sent every grocery store the same number of loaves. How many loaves did each store receive?
A. 20 loaves
B. 25 loaves
C. 50 loaves
D. too little information

Assessment

CUMULATIVE REVIEW

Chapter 6 Cumulative Review (continued)

11. Which is the prime factorization tree of 81?
A. 81 / 9 9
B. 81 / 3 27
C. 81 / 3 27 / 3 9
D. 81 / 3 27 / 3 9 / 3 3

12. What is the GCF of 255 and 170?
A. 5
B. 17
C. 10
D. 85

13. Write $\frac{35}{60}$ in simplest form.
A. $\frac{35}{60}$
B. $\frac{5}{12}$
C. $\frac{7}{12}$
D. $\frac{7}{60}$

14. Write $\frac{3}{4}, \frac{15}{8}, 1\frac{2}{3}, \frac{13}{7}, \frac{2}{5}, 1\frac{1}{5}$ in order from least to greatest.
A. $\frac{2}{3}, \frac{3}{4}, 1\frac{1}{5}, 1\frac{2}{3}, \frac{13}{7}, \frac{15}{8}$
B. $\frac{2}{3}, \frac{3}{4}, 1\frac{1}{5}, \frac{13}{7}, 1\frac{2}{3}, \frac{15}{8}$
C. $\frac{2}{3}, \frac{3}{4}, \frac{13}{7}, 1\frac{1}{5}, 1\frac{2}{3}, \frac{15}{8}$
D. $\frac{2}{3}, \frac{3}{4}, 1\frac{1}{5}, \frac{15}{8}, \frac{13}{7}, 1\frac{2}{3}$

15. Write 0.375 as a fraction in simplest form.
A. $\frac{2}{5}$
B. $\frac{37}{100}$
C. $\frac{3}{8}$
D. $\frac{15}{200}$

16. Add $\frac{2}{3} + \frac{1}{8}$. Write in simplest form.
A. $\frac{1}{12}$
B. $\frac{2}{24}$
C. $\frac{3}{11}$
D. $\frac{19}{24}$

17. Your mom says you and your 3 friends can have half the pie on the counter. What portion of the pie will each of you get if the portions are all equal?
A. $\frac{1}{3}$ pie
B. $\frac{1}{8}$ pie
C. $\frac{1}{6}$ pie
D. $\frac{1}{4}$ pie

18. Divide $4\frac{3}{4} \div \frac{1}{4}$. Write in simplest form.
A. $\frac{19}{16}$
B. $16\frac{3}{16}$
C. $4\frac{1}{4}$
D. 19

19. Subtract. 6 lb 4 oz − 2 lb 10 oz
A. 4 lb 4 oz
B. 3 lb 4 oz
C. 3 lb 10 oz
D. 3 lb 6 oz

20. Ramone is making a bookcase with wood that is $\frac{3}{4}$ in. thick. The bookcase has three shelves. One shelf is used for the top of the bookcase, and one is used for the bottom. The space between shelves is 11 in. Find the total height of the bookcase.
A. $23\frac{1}{2}$ in.
B. $24\frac{1}{4}$ in.
C. $24\frac{3}{4}$ in.
D. $30\frac{1}{4}$ in.

Resources

Teaching Resources

Chapter Support File, Ch. 6
• Cumulative Review

Teacher's Edition

See pp. 226C–D for Assessment Options.

CHAPTER OVERVIEW

To accommodate flexible scheduling, most lessons are divided into parts. Assignment Options are given in the Teacher's Edition for each lesson.

Lesson 7-1
Data Analysis: Exploring Ratios

Pages 278–280

NCTM 1, 2, 3, 5

Key term: ratio
Math at Work

Lesson 7-2
Equal Ratios and Unit Rates

Pages 281–284

NCTM 1, 3, 4, 5, 13

Part 1   Writing Equal Ratios
Part 2   Finding Unit Rates
Key terms: equal ratios, rate, unit rate
▼ Project Link

Lesson 7-3
Algebra: Solving Proportions

Pages 285–288

NCTM 1, 2, 3, 4, 5, 7

Part 1   Recognizing Proportions
Part 2   Solving Proportions
Key terms: proportion, cross products

Alternative Activity 7-3
▼ Project Link

Lesson 7-7
Percents, Fractions, and Decimals

Pages 300–303

NCTM 1, 2, 3, 4, 5

Part 1   Writing Percents as Fractions and Decimals
Part 2   Writing Decimals and Fractions as Percents

Lesson 7-8
Estimating with Percents

Pages 305–308

NCTM 1, 2, 3, 4, 7, 13

Part 1   Estimating Percents Using Models
Part 2   Estimating Percents Using Mental Math

Alternative Activity 7-8

Lesson 7-9
Algebra: Finding a Percent of a Number

Pages 309–313

NCTM 1, 2, 3, 4, 5, 13

Part 1   Using Modeling or a Calculator
Part 2   Using Proportions

Journal

Math at Work

☑ Checkpoint 2

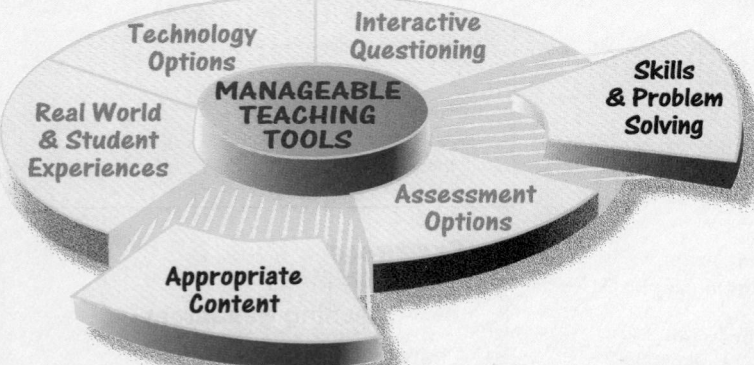

Technology Options
Interactive Questioning
MANAGEABLE TEACHING TOOLS
Real World & Student Experiences
Skills & Problem Solving
Assessment Options
Appropriate Content

Pacing Options

This chart suggests pacing only for the core lessons and their parts. It is provided merely as a possible guide. It will help you determine how much time you have in your schedule to cover other features, such as the Chapter Project, Math Toolboxes, Wrap Up, and Assessment.

	1 Class Period	1 Class Period	1 Class Period
Traditional (40–45 min class periods)	7–1	7–2 ▼ 7–2 ②	7–3 ▼
Block Scheduling (90 min class periods)	7–1 7–2 ▼ 7–2 ②	7–3 ▼ 7–3 ②	7–4 ▼ 7–5 ▼ 7–5 ②	7–

NCTM STANDARDS

1 Problem Solving		6 Number Systems and Number Theory	10 Statistics
2 Communication		7 Computation and Estimation	11 Probability
3 Reasoning		8 Patterns and Functions	12 Geometry
4 Mathematical Connections		9 Algebra	13 Measurement
5 Number and Number Relationships			

Pages 289–291

Lesson 7-4
Problem Solving Strategy

NCTM 1, 3, 4, 6

Solve a Simpler Problem

Pages 292–295

Lesson 7-5
Geometry: Scale Drawings

NCTM 1, 2, 3, 4, 6, 12, 13

Part 1 Enlarging or Reducing Designs
Part 2 Finding the Actual Size of an Object

Key term: scale

▼ **Project Link**

Pages 297–299

Lesson 7-6
Percent Sense Using Models

NCTM 1, 2, 3, 4, 5, 6, 7, 13

Key term: percent

Pages 314–317

Lesson 7-10
Data Analysis: Data and Circle Graphs

NCTM 1, 2, 3, 4, 5, 7, 13

Key term: circle graphs

Optional Materials and Manipulatives

calculator (7-3, 7-7, 7-9, 7-10)
centimeter ruler (7-5)
graph paper (7-5), (7-6), (7-7)
centimeter tape measure (7-6)

scissors (7-10)
tape (7-10)
compass (7-10)

metric ruler (7-10)
Optional calculator use is integrated throughout the course.

---

1 Class Period	1 Class Period	1 Class Period	1 Class Period	1 Class Period	1 Class Period	1 Class Period	1 Class Period	1 Class Period	1 Class Period	1 Class Period
7-5 ▼1 7-5 ▼2	7-6	7-7 ▼1	7-7 ▼2	7-8 ▼1 7-8 ▼2	7-9 ▼1	7-9 ▼2	7-10	7-10		

| 7-8 ▼2 | 7-9 ▼1 7-9 ▼2 | 7-10 | | | | | | | | |

MEETING INDIVIDUAL NEEDS

Accommodating Diverse Learning Styles

In your Teacher's Edition, you will find suggestions as to how you can help students complete mathematical tasks in Chapter 7 by meeting individual needs and supporting various learning styles. Here are some examples:

VISUAL LEARNING
studying photocopier enlargements and reductions
(p. 292)

TACTILE LEARNING
modeling numbers with counters to solve problems
(p. 289)

AUDITORY LEARNING
reading ratios out loud
(p. 278)

KINESTHETIC LEARNING
having students form groups to model equivalent ratios
(p. 282)

EARLY FINISHERS
Performance-Based Project, MathBlaster® Mystery, Interdisciplinary Units

GIFTED AND TALENTED
investigating exchange rates between countries *(p. 281)*

DIVERSITY using manipulatives to represent ratios *(p. 286)*

ACQUIRING ENGLISH PROFICIENCY (AEP)
explaining the meaning of proportion *(p. 286)*

ASSESSING PROGRESS

A broad range of assessment tools are available to reach a variety of learners.

INFORMAL ASSESSMENT

Informal assessments provide day-to-day feedback to help give you a picture of conceptual understanding and skill development.

ONGOING ASSESSMENT is built into lesson instruction and the Teaching Notes of the Teacher's Edition.

In the Teacher's Edition
Lesson Quiz for every lesson

In the Student Edition
On Your Own, Mixed Review, Journal, Portfolio, Project Link, Chapter Wrap Up

Look for **Interactive Questions** within lessons that

BUILD UNDERSTANDING with labels such as Analyze, Reasoning, Estimation, Writing, and Summarize

✔ **CHECK UNDERSTANDING** with the Try It Out label.

FORMAL ASSESSMENT

Formal assessment can occur before and after the chapter, as well as at natural breaking points in the chapter.

Checkpoints
Two forms of each self-assessment Checkpoints are available: one in the Student Edition and another in the Chapter Support File in the Teaching Resources box.

- Mid-Chapter Checkpoint 1, page 288
- End-of-Chapter Checkpoint 2, page 313

Chapter 7 Assessment, page 322.
Two alternative forms are available in the Chapter Support File. They may be used after a chapter has been completed, or as a pre-test and post-test comparison.

Cumulative Review, page 323.
Assesses skills and concepts in Chapters 1–7. An alternative form is available in Chapter Support File.

Computer Item Generator for Chapter 7
Customized tests can be generated for each lesson and for mid-chapter and end-of-chapter assessments, and for pre- and post-test comparisons of achievement.

Interactive Questioning

Technology Options

Real World & Student Experiences

MANAGEABLE TEACHING TOOLS

Skills & Problem Solving

Appropriate Content

Assessment Options

CHAPTER PROJECT

The Chapter Project in the student edition provides a real-world connection to the math context of the chapter. The Teacher's Edition contains a scoring rubric.

Another performance-based Chapter Project with a scoring rubric can be found in the Chapter Support File in the Teaching Resources Box.

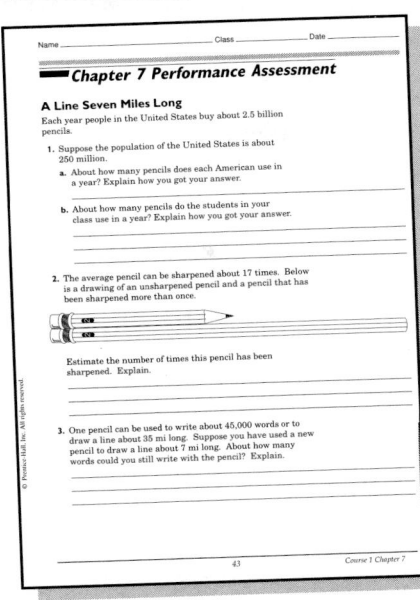

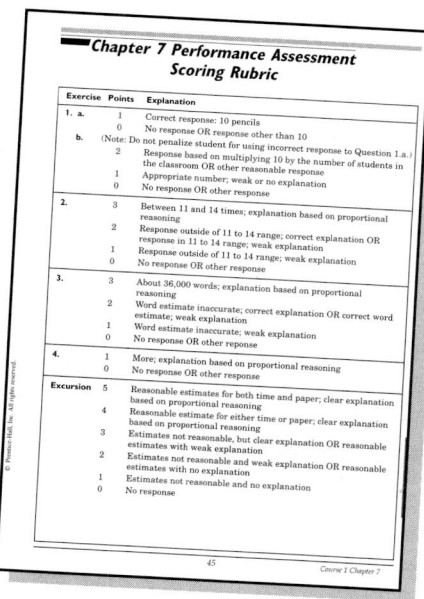

Correlation to Standardized Tests

Lesson	STANDARDIZED TEST ITEMS	CAT5	CTBS/5 Terra Nova	ITBS	MAT7	SAT9	Your Local Test
7-1	Data Analysis: Exploring Ratios	■		■	■	■	
7-2	Equal Ratios and Unit Rates	■		■	■	■	
7-3	Algebra: Solving Proportions	■	■			■	
7-4	Problem Solving Strategy: Solve a Simpler Problem			■	■	■	
7-5	Geometry: Scale Drawings		■		■	■	
7-6	Percent Sense Using Models		■	■			
7-7	Percents, Fractions, and Decimals	■	■			■	
7-8	Estimating with Percents	■	■			■	
7-9	Algebra: Finding a Percent of a Number						
7-10	Data Analysis: Data and Circle Graphs					■	

CAT5 California Achievement Test, 5th Edition
CTBS/5 Comprehensive Test of Basic Skills, 5th Edition

ITBS Iowa Test of Basic Skills, Form B
MAT 7 Metropolitan Achievement Test, 7th Edition

SAT9 Stanford Achievement Test, 9th Edition

MAKING CONNECTIONS

MANAGEABLE TEACHING TOOLS

Technology Options · Interactive Questioning · Skills & Problem Solving · Assessment Options · Appropriate Content · Real World & Student Experiences

TEAM TEACHING WITH PRENTICE HALL MATERIALS

MIDDLE GRADES MATH INTERDISCIPLINARY UNITS	INTERDISCIPLINARY EXPLORATIONS	SCIENCE EXPLORER
		L Life Science **E** Earth Science **P** Physical Science
• The Great Outdoors: Activities 1–3, 5, 7, 9–11 • Consumer Awareness: Activities 3, 5, 7, & 11 • Space Exploration: Activities 1, 9, & 11	• *Mill Life in the 1840s* pp. 12, 13, 40, & 41 • *Wagons West* pp. 24 & 25 • *Where River Meets Sea* p. 36	**E** Lab: Constructing a Telescope p. 42 **P** Sec. 12-2 Measuring Motion

Lesson	Interdisciplinary Connections	Real World Connections	Math Integration
	Drama	Camp	Statistics
	Earth Science Sports Swimming	Food Mileage Jobs	Measurement
	Science Music Sports	Crafts School Supplies Food Photography	Data Analysis
	Biology	Traffic Consumer Issues Savings	Data Analysis
	Architecture Geography	Maps Scale Models	Geometry Measurement
	Sports	Entertainment	Measurement
	Earth Science Physical Science	Graduation Rates Technology	Data Analysis
	Sports	Sales Tax Shopping Pediatrics Recreation	Measurement
	Science Sports Language Statistics	Fitness Savings Entertainment Internet	Measurement
	Science	Environment Fundraising	Measurement Data Analysis

School to Home

MATERIALS:

cookbook
recipe that serves six people
paper
pencil

English and Spanish versions are available in the Teacher's Communication Kit, Teacher's Resource box.

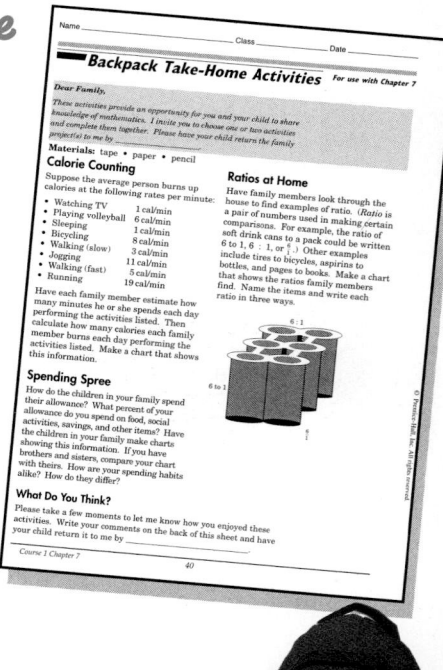

Backpack Take-Home Activities For use with Chapter 7

Dear Family,

These activities provide an opportunity for you and your child to share knowledge of mathematics. I invite you to choose one or two activities and complete them together. Please have your child return the family project(s) to me by

Materials: tape • paper • pencil

Calorie Counting
Suppose the average person burns up calories at the following rates per minute:

* Watching TV — 1 cal/min
* Playing volleyball — 6 cal/min
* Sleeping — 1 cal/min
* Bicycling — 8 cal/min
* Walking (slow) — 3 cal/min
* Jogging — 11 cal/min
* Walking (fast) — 5 cal/min
* Running — 19 cal/min

Have each family member estimate how many minutes he or she spends each day performing the activities listed. Then calculate how many calories each family member burns each day performing the activities listed. Make a chart that shows this information.

Ratios at Home
Have family members look through the house to find examples of ratio. (Ratio is a pair of numbers used in making certain comparisons. For example, the ratio of soft drink cans to a pack could be written 6 to 1, 6 : 1, or $\frac{6}{1}$.) Other examples include tires to bicycles, aspirins to bottles, and pages to books. Make a chart that shows the ratios family members find. Name the items and write each ratio in three ways.

Spending Spree
How do the children in your family spend their allowance? What percent of your allowance do you spend on food, social activities, savings, and other items? Have the children in your family make charts showing this information. If you have brothers and sisters, compare your chart with theirs. How are your spending habits alike? How do they differ?

What Do You Think?
Please take a few moments to let me know how you enjoyed these activities. Write your comments on the back of this sheet and have your child return it to me by

Course 1 Chapter 7   40

USING TECHNOLOGY TO ENHANCE INSTRUCTION

FOR THE STUDENT

Multimedia Math Hot Pages™
This interactive software and video package on CD-ROM integrates solid math content through a variety of media.

- Hot Page™ 19 (7-2)
- Hot Page™ 20 (7-5)
- Hot Page™ 21 (7-7)

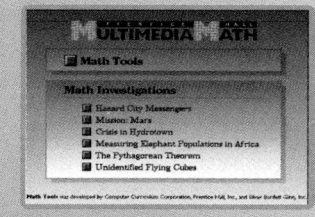

Multimedia Math Investigations
These in-depth interactive activities on CD-ROM develop real-world applications of mathematics. They allow students the opportunity to reinforce key concepts.

- Hazard City Messengers
- Mission: Mars

MathBlaster® Mystery
This award-winning, interactive software program on CD-ROM can be used to maintain skills or to accommodate early finishers.

- Level: Earn 2 coins; Pay 6 coins
- Mission Mode (all lessons)
- Kitchen Comparisons (7-1, 7-7)
- Number Guesser (7-4, 7-8)
- Equation Maker (7-3, 7-6, 7-9)
- Word Problems (7-2, 7-5, 7-10, Problem Solving Practice)

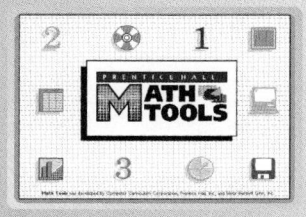

Math Labs
This software, available on both diskette and CD-ROM, includes on-screen Math Lab activities. Students use linkable, interactive tools to explore math concepts.

Interactive Student Tutorial
Available on CD-ROM, this test preparation program contains self-tests with questions in standardized test format. Software includes electronic versions of the text lessons and the Math Tools and Math Labs.

Internet Connection

For Students
Support for the Chapter Project
A career-oriented link for Math at Work feature

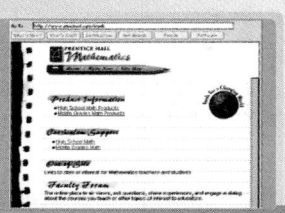

www.phschool.com/math

For teachers
Curriculum Support
Product Information
Regional Support Information

FOR THE TEACHER

Computer Item Generator
Available on both CD-ROM and diskette, this software generates customized practice sheets, quizzes, and tests. It generates an unlimited supply of questions with varying levels of difficulty.

The Resource Pro™
Available on CD-ROM, this software can be used to customize and plan lessons.

Technology Options

MANAGEABLE TEACHING TOOLS

- Interactive Questioning
- Skills & Problem Solving
- Assessment Options
- Appropriate Content
- Real World & Student Experiences

RATIOS, PROPORTIONS, AND PERCENTS

CONNECTING TO PRIOR LEARNING Ask: *Have you ever used or built a scale model? What does the term* scale model *mean?* **Answers may vary. Sample: A scale model shows the design of what it represents, but is proportionally smaller.** Discuss with students their experiences building model cars or airplanes, creating dioramas, or drawing pictures or maps.

CULTURAL CONNECTIONS Point out that many monuments in the United States are made by artists who are the winners of design competitions. One example is the memorial in Washington, D.C., honoring the U.S. soldiers who died in Vietnam. To participate in the competition, artists often submit a plan and a scale model of their ideas.

INTERDISCIPLINARY CONNECTIONS Ask students: *How does a scale model help an architect decide what plan to use?* **Answers may vary. Sample: A scale model shows how a building looks before it is actually built.**

ABOUT THE PROJECT The Chapter Project allows students to apply their knowledge of ratios, proportions, and percents.

Internet • For information and activities related to the Chapter Project, visit the Prentice Hall site at www.phschool.com/mgm1/ch7

Ratios, Proportions, and Percents

WHAT YOU WILL LEARN IN THIS CHAPTER

• How to model and use ratios and proportions

• How to relate fractions, decimals, and percents

• How to estimate percents and find the percent of a number

Ask students:

- *Have you ever made a scale model without using a kit? If so, of what?*

- *What did you do to plan out your scale model?*

- *How can you make sure your scale model will look like the real object?*

PROJECT NOTEBOOK Encourage students to keep all project-related materials in a separate folder or notebook.

TRACKING THE PROJECT You may wish to have students read Finishing the Chapter Project on page 319 to help them get an overview of the project. Set benchmark deadlines for students to show you their work in progress.

CHAPTER PROJECT

THEME: ASTRONOMY

Planet *of the* Stars

When you look up at the stars in the sky, you don't think about how far away they are. Stars appear a lot closer than they really are, and the same is true of planets. The huge distances between planets make it impossible for books to show how vast our solar system really is.

Make a Scale Model In this chapter, you will make scale models of two planets. You will compare sizes and distances for each planet and calculate the ratios involved in your scale model.

Steps to help you complete the project:

p. 284   **Project Link:** *Writing Ratios*
p. 288   **Project Link:** *Calculating*
p. 295   **Project Link:** *Analyzing Data*
p. 319   *Finishing the Chapter Project*

- How to solve problems by solving a simpler problem

PROBLEM SOLVING

SCORING RUBRIC

3 You correctly write ratios for planet diameters and distances to the sun. All scaled dimensions are accurate. You neatly show your calculations and draw your two assigned planets to scale. You use distances familiar to your classmates to describe where in your model your planets would be relative to the sun.

2 You correctly write all ratios, and most of your calculations are correct. You draw your two assigned planets to scale, and you calculate the distances from the sun to these planets. Your work is neat and easy to follow.

1 Your ratios are not correctly written, many of your calculations are inaccurate, or your drawings or explanations are incomplete or not organized.

0 You do not complete the project, or you leave out a large part of the required work.

Teaching Notes

1 Focus

CONNECTING TO PRIOR KNOWLEDGE
Write the fraction $\frac{2}{5}$ for the class. Review the meaning of numerator and denominator. Ask: *What does the denominator stand for?* **5 parts in the whole** *What does the numerator stand for?* **2 parts out of the whole**

Lesson Planning Options

Prerequisite Skills
• using fraction models (5-4)

Vocabulary/Symbols
ratio

Resources

 Student Edition

Skills Handbook, p. 536
Extra Practice, p. 528
Glossary/Study Guide

 Teaching Resources

Chapter Support File, Ch. 7
• Lesson Planner 7-1
• Practice 7-1, Reteaching 7-1
• Answer Masters 7-1
Teaching Aids Masters 8, 9
Glossary, Spanish Resources

 Transparencies
18, MInds on Math 7-1

Warm Up

Ask each student to use graph paper to find $\frac{1}{2} \times \frac{4}{7}$ and $\frac{3}{4} \times \frac{2}{3}$. $\frac{4}{14}$ or $\frac{2}{7}$; $\frac{6}{12}$ or $\frac{1}{2}$

2 Teach

THINK AND DISCUSS

AEP **AUDITORY LEARNING** Tell students you can read ratios in different ways and still be correct. Have students practice reading ratios out loud. For example, 2 : 1 is also "2 to 1," "2 is to 1," "2 divided by 1," "2 per 1," and "2 for each 1."

ERROR ALERT! and **VISUAL LEARNING**
Some students may have difficulty understanding fractions as ratios.
Remediation: Ask students to draw circles and divide the circles into halves, fourths, and sixths. Then have them shade different parts of the circle. Ask students to write what fraction of the circle they shaded. Explain to students that the fraction expresses a ratio of parts to a whole.

DATA ANALYSIS Connection

7-1 Exploring Ratios

What You'll Learn

▼ To explore the meaning of ratio

...And Why

Ratios help you relate numbers to other numbers.

Here's How

Look for questions that
 build understanding
✔ check understanding

THINK AND DISCUSS

Can you sit boy, girl, boy, girl, . . . in your class?

1. **Data Collection**
   Collect data from your class to complete the table at the right.
   1–2. Check students' work.

   Students in Your Class

Total Number of Students	▪
Number of Girls	▪
Number of Boys	▪

2. Use the data in the table to write each fraction.
   a. $\dfrac{\text{number of boys}}{\text{total number of students}}$
   b. $\dfrac{\text{number of girls}}{\text{total number of students}}$

The fractions you wrote in Question 2 are called *ratios*. A **ratio** compares two numbers by division. You can compare a part to its whole, a part to another part, or the whole to one of its parts. For example, suppose you made 3 cups of party mix (whole) using 2 cups of cereal (part A) and 1 cup of pretzels (part B).

Type of Ratio	Statement	Ways to Write Ratio
part A to whole	2 c cereal to 3 c mix	2 to 3, 2 : 3, or $\frac{2}{3}$
whole to part B	3 c mix to 1 c pretzels	3 to 1, 3 : 1, or $\frac{3}{1}$
part A to part B	2 c cereal to 1 c pretzels	2 to 1, 2 : 1, or $\frac{2}{1}$

■ **EXAMPLE** *Real-World Problem Solving*

Camp Suppose you are at camp. There are 3 counselors and 7 campers in every cabin. Write each ratio below in three ways.

a. counselors to people in the cabin

   $\dfrac{3}{10}$ ← counselors
       ← people in the cabin   3 to 10   3 : 10

b. campers to counselors

   $\dfrac{7}{3}$ ← campers
      ← counselors   7 to 3   7 : 3

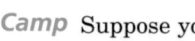

■ ADDITIONAL EXAMPLE

FOR EXAMPLE

Suppose you are going on a school trip. There are 3 teachers and 25 students on every bus. Write each ratio in three ways.

a. teachers to students 3 to 25; 3 : 25, $\frac{3}{25}$

b. students to teachers 25 to 3; 25 : 3; $\frac{25}{3}$

ASSESSMENT and TACTILE LEARNING

Provide students with triangles and trapezoids from a set of pattern blocks. Have students write the ratios of triangles to trapezoids for:

a. 5 triangles to 20 trapezoids 5 to 20 or 1 to 4

b. 8 triangles to 14 trapezoids 8 to 14 or 4 to 7

RESEARCH Exercise 21 Not all students may have access to a newspaper. Provide a classroom newspaper for students to look through.

. **Answers may vary. Samples:** number of free throws made to number of free throws taken in basketball; number of cups of sugar to number of pounds of fruit when making jam

3. ✓*Try It Out* There are 3 times as many peanuts as almonds in a mixture of nuts. Write each ratio in three ways.

a. peanuts to almonds 3 to 1, 3 : 1, $\frac{3}{1}$

b. almonds to peanuts 1 to 3, 1 : 3, $\frac{1}{3}$

4. ⬛*Open-ended* Name two situations where you might use ratios.

Now you may assign Exercises 1–32.

EXERCISES *On Your Own*

Write a ratio in three ways for each comparison.

1. plates to bowls
  3 : 1

2. cups to bowls
  2 : 1

3. bowls to cups
  1 : 2

4. plates to cups
  3 : 2

Draw a picture to represent each ratio.   5–10. See back of book.

5. 4 stars to 8 moons

6. $\frac{2 \text{ apples}}{6 \text{ bananas}}$

7. $\frac{1 \text{ c rhubarb}}{2 \text{ c strawberries}}$

8. 3 big tiles : 7 small tiles   **9.** 3 shirts to 5 shorts   **10.** 1 red tile : 3 white tiles

Write a ratio in three ways for each statement.

11. Combine 1 part ginger ale to 2 parts fruit juice. 1 to 2, 1 : 2, $\frac{1}{2}$

12. There are 120 students for every 5 teachers. 120 to 5, 120 : 5, $\frac{120}{5}$

13. There are 14 girls to 12 boys in your class. 14 to 12, 14 : 12, $\frac{14}{12}$

14. Add 2 parts cream for every 1 part powder. 2 to 1, 2 : 1, $\frac{2}{1}$

A drama club sold 35 student tickets, 24 adult tickets, and 11 discount tickets. Write each ratio in three ways.

15. student tickets to adult tickets 35 to 24, 35 : 24, $\frac{35}{24}$

16. adult tickets to student tickets 24 to 35, 24 : 35, $\frac{24}{35}$

17. adult tickets to discount tickets 24 to 11, 24 : 11, $\frac{24}{11}$

18. student tickets to total tickets 35 to 70, 35 : 70, $\frac{35}{70}$

19. adult tickets to total tickets 24 to 70, 24 : 70, $\frac{24}{70}$

20. discount tickets to total tickets 11 to 70, 11 : 70, $\frac{11}{70}$

21. *Research* Find two examples of ratios in a newspaper. You might try the sports pages or look in a supermarket ad. **Check students' work.**

Technology Options

Prentice Hall Technology

Software for Learners
- Math Blaster® Mystery*
- Interactive Student Tutorial, Chapter 7*

Teaching Resource Software
- Computer Item Generator 7-1
- Resource Pro™ Chapter 7*

Internet • For related mathematics activities, visit the Prentice Hall site at www.phschool.com/math

*Available on CD-ROM only

Assignment Options for Exercises On Your Own

> **Core** 1–20, 22–31
> **Extension** 21, 32

Use Mixed Review to maintain skills.

PRACTICE

Practice 7-1 *Exploring Ratios*

Write a ratio in three ways to compare each.

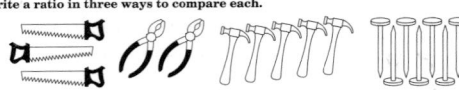

1. saws to pliers
   $3:2; \frac{3}{2}; 3 \text{ to } 2$
2. hammers to nails
   $5:7; \frac{5}{7}; 5 \text{ to } 7$
3. saws to nails
   $3:7; \frac{3}{7}; 3 \text{ to } 7$
4. nails to saws
   $7:3; \frac{7}{3}; 7 \text{ to } 3$
5. hammers to pliers
   $5:2; \frac{5}{2}; 5 \text{ to } 2$
6. pliers to saws
   $2:3; \frac{2}{3}; 2 \text{ to } 3$
7. pliers to nails
   $2:7; \frac{2}{7}; 2 \text{ to } 7$
8. saws to hammers
   $3:5; \frac{3}{5}; 3 \text{ to } 5$
9. nails to hammers
   $7:5; \frac{7}{5}; 7 \text{ to } 5$

Draw a picture to represent each ratio. Sample drawings shown.

10. 7 baseballs : 1 bat
11. 3 CDs to 8 books
12. $\frac{2 \text{ c blueberries}}{3 \text{ c cream}}$

13. In Tanya's family, 6 out of 15 people have blue eyes. What is the ratio of those who have blue eyes to those who do not? $6:9$

14. In Fred's class, 8 of the 21 students earned a grade of B or better. What is the ratio of students who did not earn at least a B to those who did? $13:8$

15. In Todd's class, 14 of the students own cats and 9 of the students own dogs. What is the ratio of dog owners to cat owners? $9:14$

16. In Markita's class, there are 15 boys and 12 girls. Write the ratio that represents the number of girls to the number of boys. $12:15$

In copymaster and workbook formats

RETEACHING

Reteaching 7-1 *Exploring Ratios*

A **ratio** compares two numbers by division.

The ratio of 10 pints of blueberries to 4 blueberry pies can be written as "10 to 4" in three ways: 10 to 4   10:4 $\frac{10}{4}$

The ratio of 2 bushels of apples to 20 jars of applesauce can be written in three ways: 2 to 20   2:20 $\frac{2}{20}$

Use the picture. Write a ratio in three ways to compare each.

1. apples to oranges $5:7; 5 \text{ to } 7; \frac{5}{7}$
2. apples to bananas $5:3; 5 \text{ to } 3; \frac{5}{3}$
3. oranges to apples $7:5; 7 \text{ to } 5; \frac{7}{5}$
4. bananas to oranges $3:7; 3 \text{ to } 7; \frac{3}{7}$
5. oranges to bananas $7:3; 7 \text{ to } 3; \frac{7}{3}$
6. bananas to apples $3:5; 3 \text{ to } 5; \frac{3}{5}$

Write a ratio in three ways for each statement.

7. There are 60 tires for every 15 cars. $60:15; 60 \text{ to } 15; \frac{60}{15}$
8. Use 5 teaspoons butter for every 3 teaspoons flour. $5:3; 5 \text{ to } 3; \frac{5}{3}$
9. There are 21 girls and 28 boys in the class. $21:28; 21 \text{ to } 28; \frac{21}{28}$
10. Make 24 tacos for every 8 plates. $24:8; 24 \text{ to } 8; \frac{24}{8}$
11. There are 4 adults for every 19 children on the bus. $4:19; 4 \text{ to } 19; \frac{4}{19}$

ENRICHMENT

Minds on Math Transparency

7-1

How can you cut a bagel into eight equal pieces with just 3 cuts?

Slice it in half from the side. Then make 2 cuts from the top to slice those halves into quarters.

See *Solution Key* for worked-out answers.

280

WRAP UP

IDENTIFYING THE BIG IDEA Ask students what a ratio is. Have students explain how to model a ratio and give examples.

LESSON QUIZ

1. Write a ratio in three ways for the comparison. There are 5 lab tables for every 20 science students. 5 to 20; 5 : 20; $\frac{5}{20}$

2. There are 14 children, 21 adults under 65, and 35 senior citizens at an afternoon matinee. Write a ratio in three ways for adults to senior citizens. 21 to 35; 21 : 35; $\frac{21}{35}$

Open-ended **Describe a situation with the following ratio.** 22–27. See back of book for samples.

22. $1:2$ 23. $\frac{6}{1}$ 24. 2 to 3   25. $\frac{3}{1}$ 26. 10 to 1   27. $3:5$

Write a ratio to represent each comparison.

28. sunglasses to caps
    $4:6$

29. bats to balls
    $5:7$

30. the number of vowels (not counting *y*) to consonants in the alphabet $5:21$

31. the number of vowels (not counting *y*) to consonants in your first name   **Check students' work.**

32. *Writing* Is 2 : 1 the same ratio as 1: 2? Explain your reasoning. **See above right.**

32. **Reasoning may vary. Sample:** No; a 2 : 1 ratio of boys to girls means that for every 2 boys there is 1 girl. A 1 : 2 ratio means that for every 1 boy there are 2 girls.

Mixed Review

Find each sum or difference. Use models if they help you. (*Lesson 3-5*)

33. $37.5 + 68.7$
    106.2
34. $13.3 - 5.68$
    7.62
35. $18.62 - 0.84$
    17.78
36. $9.99 + 3.7$
    6.29

Write two fractions equivalent to each fraction. (*Lesson 5-5*) 37–42. Answers may vary. Samples are given.

37. $\frac{21}{30}$ $\frac{7}{10}$, $\frac{42}{60}$
38. $\frac{7}{8}$ $\frac{14}{16}$, $\frac{28}{32}$
39. $\frac{25}{525}$ $\frac{1}{21}$, $\frac{2}{42}$
40. $\frac{6}{15}$ $\frac{2}{5}$, $\frac{12}{30}$
41. $\frac{16}{24}$ $\frac{2}{3}$, $\frac{80}{120}$
42. $\frac{5}{8}$ $\frac{10}{16}$, $\frac{625}{1,000}$

43. *Choose a Strategy* The number of homes rented by a real estate agent for each of the first five months of the year has been 11, 9, 13, 8, and 20. Find the monthly average. Use it to estimate the number of rentals for the entire year. about 12.2 homes; about 146 homes

Teaching Notes

1 Focus

CONNECTING TO PRIOR KNOWLEDGE Ask students to give examples of ratios they see around them. **Answers may vary. Sample: miles per hour, batting averages (number of hits to the number of times at bat)**

2 Teach

THINK AND DISCUSS

TACTILE LEARNING Question 5 Some students may benefit by checking their answers with fraction bars or using objects.

DIVERSITY and EXTENSION Have students investigate monetary rates for currency exchange between the United States and other countries. Ask students to write their findings as unit rates to the U.S. dollar. Have them report the country, type of currency, and exchange rate.

CONNECTION TO ART Have students research the history of the golden ratio in painting, design, and architecture.

7-2 Equal Ratios and Unit Rates

What You'll Learn

▼ To write equal ratios
▼ To find unit rates

...And Why

You use equal ratios and unit rates to compare quantities and prices.

Here's How

Look for questions that
▪ build understanding
✔ check understanding

THINK AND DISCUSS

▼ Writing Equal Ratios

You can write a ratio in simplest form the same way you write a fraction in simplest form.

1. Write each ratio in simplest form.
   a. 25 : 75   **b.** 50 : 150   **c.** 4 : 12   **d.** 13 : 39
      1 : 3   1 : 3   1 : 3   1 : 3

2. What do you notice about the answers to Question 1?
   Each ratio is 1 : 3 in simplest form.

Like equivalent fractions, **equal ratios** are names for the same number. You can find equal ratios by multiplying or dividing each term in a ratio by the same nonzero number.

■ **EXAMPLE 1**   *Real-World Problem Solving*

Write three ratios equal to the ratio $\frac{3 \text{ c of unpopped corn}}{24 \text{ qt of popcorn}}$.

$$\overset{\times 2}{\underset{\times 2}{\frac{3}{24} = \frac{6}{48}}} \quad \overset{\div 3}{\underset{\div 3}{\frac{3}{24} = \frac{1}{8}}} \quad \overset{\times 4}{\underset{\times 4}{\frac{3}{24} = \frac{12}{96}}}$$

Cups of unpopped corn
Quarts of popcorn

Three ratios equal to $\frac{3}{24}$ are $\frac{6}{48}$, $\frac{1}{8}$, and $\frac{12}{96}$.

3. ▪*Look Back* Refer to Example 1. How much popcorn can you expect from 9 c of unpopped corn? **48 c**

4. **Answers may vary. Sample: You are multiplying the ratio by 1.**

4. ▪*Reasoning* When you multiply or divide the numerator and the denominator by the same number, you get an equal ratio. Justify this statement. Give an example.

5a–d. Answers may vary. Samples are given.

5. ✔*Try It Out* Write three ratios equal to the ratio given.
   a. 6 : 8   **b.** 10 to 35   **c.** $\frac{21}{42}$ **d.** 12 : 18

a. 3 : 4, 9 : 12, 12 : 16
b. 2 to 7, 4 to 14, 20 : 70
c. 1 : 2, 42 : 84, 105 : 210
d. 2 : 3, 20 : 30, 24 : 36

The ratios in Question 1 are equal because the simplest form of each ratio is the same. Equal ratios have the same simplest form.

Lesson Planning Options

Prerequisite Skills
• equivalent fractions (5-5)

Vocabulary/Symbols
equal ratios, rate, unit rate

Resources

📖 **Student Edition**
Skills Handbook, p. 537
Extra Practice, p. 528
Glossary/Study Guide

📁 **Teaching Resources**
Chapter Support File, Ch. 7
• Lesson Planner 7-2
• Practice 7-2, Reteaching 7-2
• Answer Masters 7-2
Teaching Aids Masters 8, 9
Glossary, Spanish Resources

📽 **Transparencies**
18, Minds on Math 7-2

Warm Up

Ask each student to write $<$, $>$, or $=$ to make each statement true.

$\frac{3}{4} \times 4$ ■ $\frac{3}{7} \times 7$ $=$

$3 - \frac{3}{4}$ ■ $3 \times \frac{3}{4}$ $=$

$\frac{1}{3} \times \frac{1}{3}$ ■ $\frac{1}{3}$ $<$

$\frac{7}{5} \times \frac{4}{4}$ ■ $\frac{5}{7} \times \frac{3}{4}$ $>$

■ ADDITIONAL EXAMPLES

FOR EXAMPLE 1
Write three ratios equal to the ratio $\frac{2c \text{ of rice}}{4c \text{ of water}}$.
$\frac{1}{2}, \frac{8}{16}, \frac{4}{8}$

FOR EXAMPLE 2
Are the given ratios equal?
a. 3 : 7 and 9 : 14 **no**
b. 3 to 13 and 9 to 39 **yes**

FOR EXAMPLE 3
On Saturday, Leslie biked 45 mi in 5 h. Find the unit rate in miles per hour. **9 mi/h**

ERROR ALERT! Example 2 Students may have difficulty finding the simplest forms for ratios. **Remediation:** Encourage students to simplify a ratio until they are sure there is no number that will divide evenly into both the denominator and the numerator.

KINESTHETIC LEARNING Example 2a If you have block scheduling or extended class periods, have students model the ratio 2 : 3 by asking two students to stand together beside a group of three students. Write "2 : 3" on the board. Have two more students join the group of two as you have three more join the group of three. Write "= 4 : 6" next to the 2 : 3 on the board. Continue having students join the groups in this way. Write each ratio they model. Stop when the first group has 10 students and the second group has 15 students. Have students discuss how this exercise relates to Example 2a.

Technology Options

Prentice Hall Technology

 **Software for Learners**
- Hot Page™ 19*
- Math Blaster® Mystery*
- Interactive Student Tutorial, Chapter 7*

  Teaching Resource Software
Computer Item Generator 7-2
- Resource Pro™ Chapter 7*

Internet • For related mathematics activities, visit the Prentice Hall site at www.phschool.com/math

*Available on CD-ROM only

Assignment Options for Exercises On Your Own

To provide flexible scheduling, this lesson can be subdivided into parts.

1 Core 1–27, 29–31
Extension 32–35

2 Core 28, 36–41, 43
Extension 42, 44

Use Mixed Review to maintain skills.

282

WHAT? Did you know that you can use the digits 1 through 9 to write the ratio 4 : 5?
9,876 : 12,345 = 4 : 5

Source: Curious and Interesting Numbers

■ **EXAMPLE 2**

Are the given ratios equal?
a. 8 c sugar : 12 c flour and 10 c sugar : 15 c flour

$$\frac{8}{12} = \frac{2}{3} \qquad \frac{10}{15} = \frac{2}{3}$$
←— Write each ratio in simplest form.

2 : 3 = 2 : 3 ←— Compare ratios.
The ratios 8 : 12 and 10 : 15 are equal.

b. $\frac{25 \text{ A's and B's}}{75 \text{ grades}}$ and $\frac{50 \text{ A's and B's}}{125 \text{ grades}}$

$$\frac{25}{75} = \frac{1}{3} \qquad \frac{50}{125} = \frac{2}{5}$$
←— Write each ratio in simplest form.

$\frac{1}{3} \neq \frac{2}{5}$ ←— Compare ratios.

The ratios $\frac{25}{75}$ and $\frac{50}{125}$ are *not* equal.

6. ✓*Try It Out* Are the given ratios equal?
a. 9 : 45 and 6 : 30 **yes** **b.** 15 to 12 and 5 to 4 **yes** **c.** $\frac{20}{4}$ and $\frac{1}{5}$ **no**

Now you may assign Exercises 1–27, 29–35.

▶ Finding Unit Rates

A **rate** is a ratio that compares two quantities measured in different units. The rate $\frac{46 \text{ mi}}{2 \text{ h}}$ compares miles traveled to hours of travel. A **unit rate** compares a quantity to a unit of one.

■ **EXAMPLE 3**   *Real-World Problem Solving*

A car traveled 300 miles on 12 gallons of gas. Find the unit rate in miles per gallon (mi/gal).

miles —→ $\frac{300}{12}$ ←— Write the comparison as a ratio.
gallons —→

$$\frac{300}{12} = \frac{25}{1}$$
←— Divide the numerator and the denominator by the denominator.

The unit rate is $\frac{25 \text{ mi}}{1 \text{ gal}}$, or 25 mi/gal.

7. ✓*Try It Out* Find the unit rate for each situation.
a. 144 players on 12 teams **b.** $19.50 for 3 shirts
12 players per team   **$6.50 per shirt**

Now you may assign Exercises 28, 36–44.

Example 3 Ask: *Why do you divide both terms in the ratio by 12 rather than by another number?* In order to have a unit rate, the comparison must be equal to 1. For the denominator to be 1, you must divide by 12.

ASSESSMENT Have students set up a ratio involving something in the classroom. For example, they might compare the number of students who wear tennis shoes to the total number of students in the class. Have them give the ratio and explain the relationship.

3 Practice/Assess

EXERCISES *On Your Own*

REASONING Exercise 26 Remind students that it is easier to compare fractions if they are in the same form.

WRITING Exercise 44 Have students bring in examples of unit rates from their local stores to compare prices.

WRAP UP

IDENTIFYING THE BIG IDEA Ask students to explain what ratios are. Have them describe unit rates and how to find them.

PROJECT LINK Allow students to use calculators to find the equal ratios. Have students create a table similar to the one in the text to record their data.

EXERCISES *On Your Own*

Write three ratios equal to the given ratio.

1–12. Answers may vary. See margin for samples.

1. $6 : 18$ 2. $\frac{4}{24}$ 3. 8 to 10 4. $30 : 40$ 5. $3 : 8$ 6. $\frac{32}{36}$

7. $\frac{50}{100}$ 8. 9 to 81 9. $8 : 14$ 10. $\frac{14}{42}$ 11. 20 to 25 12. $\frac{1}{10}$

Write each ratio in simplest form.

13. $\frac{6}{15}$ $\frac{2}{5}$ 14. $75 : 15$ $5 : 1$ 15. $\frac{42}{50}$ $\frac{21}{25}$ 16. $8 : 36$ $2 : 9$ 17. $\frac{18}{12}$ $\frac{3}{2}$ 18. $32 : 90$ $16 : 45$

19. $\frac{18}{3}$ $\frac{6}{1}$ 20. $50 : 150$ $1 : 3$ 21. $\frac{24}{30}$ $\frac{4}{5}$ 22. $64 : 96$ $2 : 3$ 23. $\frac{45}{25}$ $\frac{9}{5}$ 24. $72 : 24$ $3 : 1$

25. *Earth Science* Earth's ratio of water to land is $7 : 3$. Write three ratios equal to this ratio.
Answers may vary. Sample: $14 : 6$, $49 : 21$, $28,000 : 12,000$

26. *Reasoning* Carlos tells you he ate $\frac{1}{3}$ of a pizza. Raylene says she ate $\frac{9}{27}$, and Maggie says she ate $\frac{2}{6}$. You want to know who ate the most pizza. Which of these ratios do you find easier to use? Why?

The simplest form of $\frac{1}{3}$, $\frac{9}{27}$, and $\frac{2}{6}$ is $\frac{1}{3}$, so they all ate equal amounts of pizza. $\frac{1}{3}$ is easiest to use because it has the smallest numerator and denominator.

27. *Sports* A team won 8 of the 12 games it played. Write the ratio of games won to games played in simplest form. $2 : 3$

28. *Jobs* You earn $135 for working 20 hours. Find your unit rate in dollars per hour. $\$6.75/h$

Use the article below for Exercises 29–31.

Sign on the Dotted Line

Autographs from famous people are sometimes worth big money.

Clark Gable's autograph is worth $100. Lucille Ball's autograph is worth $75. President Harry Truman's autograph is worth $40 and Hillary Clinton's autograph is worth $100.

Button Gwinnett signed the Declaration of Independence, and his autograph recently sold for $100,000.

Write each ratio in simplest form.

29. the price of President Truman's autograph to Clark Gable's $2 : 5$

30. the price of Lucille Ball's autograph to Button Gwinnett's $3 : 4,000$

31. the price of Lucille Ball's autograph to Hillary Clinton's $3 : 4$

---

pages 283–284   On Your Own

1. $1 : 3$, $12 : 36$, $60 : 180$
2. $\frac{1}{6}$, $\frac{5}{30}$, $\frac{20}{120}$
3. 4 to 5, 12 to 15, 16 to 20
4. $3 : 4$, $15 : 20$, $60 : 80$
5. $6 : 16$, $9 : 24$, $12 : 32$
6. $\frac{8}{9}$, $\frac{16}{18}$, $\frac{64}{72}$
7. $\frac{1}{2}$, $\frac{5}{10}$, $\frac{100}{200}$
8. 1 to 9, 3 to 27, 81 to 729
9. $4 : 7$, $20 : 35$, $12 : 21$
10. $\frac{1}{3}$, $\frac{2}{6}$, $\frac{3}{9}$
11. 4 to 5, 8 to 10, 40 to 50
12. $\frac{2}{20}$, $\frac{3}{30}$, $\frac{10}{100}$

44. Answers may vary. Sample: You can tell which package is a better buy. For example, a 6-oz package of stuffing costs $.99 and an 18-oz package costs $3.59. The unit cost of the smaller package is $.165/oz. The unit cost of the larger package is about $.20/oz. The 6-oz package is a better buy.

PRACTICE

Practice 7-2 *Equal Ratios and Unit Rates*

Write three ratios equal to the given ratio.
Answers may vary. **Samples:**

1. 8 : 24
   1 : 3; 2 : 6; 4 : 12

2. 15 to 25
   3 to 5; 6 to 10;
   12 to 20

3. 18 : 36
   1 : 2; 2 : 4; 3 : 6

4. $\frac{12}{15}$
   $\frac{4}{5}$, $\frac{24}{30}$; $\frac{8}{10}$

Find the value that makes the ratios equal.

5. $\frac{7}{8} = \frac{\blacksquare}{32}$
   28

6. $\frac{5}{4} = \frac{15}{\blacksquare}$
   12

7. 8 to 12 = $\blacksquare$ to 6
   4

8. 9 : 12 = 3 : $\blacksquare$
   4

Write each ratio as a fraction in simplest form.

9. pencils : squares
   $\frac{6}{1}$

10. flowers : pencils
    $\frac{2}{3}$

11. pencils : flowers
    $\frac{3}{2}$

12. pencils : circles
    $\frac{3}{2}$

13. squares : flowers
    $\frac{1}{4}$

14. flowers : squares
    $\frac{4}{1}$

15. squares : pencils
    $\frac{1}{6}$

16. circles : flowers
    $\frac{1}{2}$

Find the unit rate for each situation.

17. 20 mi in 2 h
    10 mi/h

18. 20 dogs in 10 kennels
    2 dogs/kennel

19. 450 mi in 5 d
    90 mi/d

20. $60 for 5 books
    $12/book

21. 315 grapes for 15 children
    21 grapes/child

22. 20 dimes for 4 children
    5 dimes/child

Circle A, B, or C. For each exercise, choose the expression that represents the greatest number.

23. A. $\frac{9}{27}$ B. $\frac{8}{12}$ C. $\frac{2}{2}$
24. A. $\frac{4}{6}$ B. $\frac{7}{14}$ C. $\frac{5}{15}$
25. A. $\frac{10}{16}$ B. $\frac{28}{32}$ C. $\frac{15}{40}$
26. A. $\frac{24}{32}$ B. $\frac{12}{18}$ C. $\frac{14}{16}$
27. A. $\frac{30}{45}$ B. $\frac{20}{32}$ C. $\frac{27}{30}$
28. A. $\frac{14}{42}$ B. $\frac{15}{20}$ C. $\frac{16}{24}$

In copymaster and workbook formats

RETEACHING

Reteaching 7-2 *Equal Ratios and Unit Rates*

Equal ratios name the same number. They have the same *simplest form*.

• To find equal ratios, multiply *or* divide both the numerator and denominator of a ratio by the same number.

Find a ratio equal to $\frac{4}{7}$.

$\frac{4}{7} = \frac{4 \times 2}{7 \times 2} = \frac{8}{14}$

$\frac{8}{14}$ is equal to $\frac{4}{7}$.

Find the simplest form for the ratio $\frac{16}{20}$.

$\frac{16}{20} = \frac{16 \div 4}{20 \div 4} = \frac{4}{5}$

$\frac{4}{5}$ is the simplest form for $\frac{16}{20}$.

A **rate** is a ratio that compares quantities that are measured in different units. Suppose a sprinter runs 100 yd in 10 s.

• $\frac{100 \text{ yd}}{10 \text{ s}}$ compares yards to seconds.

A **unit rate** compares a quantity to one unit of another quantity.

• You can find the unit rate by dividing by the denominator.

$\frac{100 \text{ yd} \div 10}{10 \text{ s} \div 10} = \frac{10 \text{ yd}}{1 \text{ s}}$

10yd/s is the sprinter's unit rate.

Write three ratios equal to the ratio given. Sample answers are given.

1. $\frac{2}{5}$
   $\frac{4}{10}$, $\frac{6}{15}$, $\frac{8}{20}$

2. 1 : 3
   $\frac{2}{6}$, $\frac{3}{9}$, $\frac{4}{12}$

3. 3 to 4
   $\frac{6}{8}$, $\frac{9}{12}$, $\frac{15}{20}$

4. 5 : 8
   $\frac{10}{16}$, $\frac{15}{24}$, $\frac{20}{32}$

5. 2 to 7
   $\frac{4}{14}$, $\frac{6}{21}$, $\frac{8}{28}$

6. $\frac{1}{5}$
   $\frac{2}{10}$, $\frac{3}{15}$, $\frac{4}{20}$

7. 12 to 20
   $\frac{24}{40}$, $\frac{36}{60}$, $\frac{48}{80}$

8. 6 : 16
   $\frac{12}{32}$, $\frac{18}{48}$, $\frac{24}{64}$

Write each ratio as a fraction in simplest form.

9. 32 : 16 $\frac{2}{1}$
10. $\frac{14}{24}$ $\frac{7}{12}$
11. $\frac{36}{50}$ $\frac{18}{25}$
12. 60 : 25 $\frac{12}{5}$
13. $\frac{25}{40}$ $\frac{5}{8}$
14. 60 : 180 $\frac{1}{3}$
15. $\frac{75}{120}$ $\frac{5}{8}$
16. 80 : 20 $\frac{4}{1}$

Find the unit rate for each situation.

17. walk 36 blocks in 3 h
    12 blocks/h

18. run 12 mi in 2 h
    6 mi/h

19. 20 toys for 5 friends
    4 toys/friend

20. $120 for 6 shirts
    $20/shirt

21. 45 pencils in 5 boxes
    9 pencils/box

22. 132 pages in 3 books
    44 pages/book

23. 100 students for 5 teachers
    20 students/teacher

24. $56 for 7 hours
    $8/h

25. $1.98 for 6 cans
    $.33/can

ENRICHMENT

Minds on Math Transparency

7-2

Damian and Heather ran home from school. Damian ran half the distance and then walked the rest of the way. Heather ran half the time and then walked the rest of the time. If they both ran at the same speed and walked at the same speed, who got home first? Explain your answer.

Heather, because she ran more of the distance than Damian.

See *Solution Key* for worked-out answers.

284

LESSON QUIZ

Write three ratios equal to the given ratio.

1. $\frac{3}{27}$ **$\frac{1}{9}$; $\frac{6}{54}$; $\frac{9}{81}$**

2. 20 to 80 **1 to 4; 4 to 16; 5 to 20**

Write each ratio in simplest form.

3. 10 : 90 **1 : 9**

4. $\frac{28}{40}$ **$\frac{7}{10}$**

5. 119 : 14 **17 : 2**

Find the unit rate for each situation.

6. 6 mi in 2 h **3 mi/h**

7. 87 apples in 3 bushels **29 apples per bushel**

8. $42 in 7 h **$6 per hour**

Find the value that makes the ratios equal.

32. $\frac{5}{10}$, $\frac{\blacksquare}{20}$ **10**

33. 25 : 75, 1 : $\blacksquare$ **3**

34. 6 to 9, $\blacksquare$ to 3 **2**

35. $\frac{\blacksquare}{15}$, $\frac{25}{75}$ **5**

Find the unit rate for each situation.

36. 336 mi in 12 h **28 mi/h**

37. read 66 pages in 2 h **33 pages/h**

38. type 110 words in 5 min **22 words/min**

39. 16 mi in 4 h **4 mi/h**

40. 30 min for 5 customers **6 min/customer**

41. $24 for 8 toys **$3 per toy**

42. *Swimming* Crystal will pay $126 for 28 swimming lessons. Bill will pay $30 for 6 lessons. Who is paying more per lesson? How much more is the person paying?
    Bill; $.50 per lesson

43. *Sports* In the last three softball practices, Julie ran a total of 7.5 miles. Find her unit rate for miles run per practice.
    2.5 mi/practice

44. *Writing* How does a unit rate help you compare prices in a grocery store? Give an example.
    See margin p. 283.

> JOURNAL
> Define in your own words ratio and rate. Provide an example of each.

Mixed Review

Solve each equation. *(Lesson 2-6 and 2-7)*

45. $x - 58 = 107$ **165**
46. $3y = 51$ **17**
47. $a + 39 = 87$ **48**
48. $b \div 6 = 36$ **216**
49. $15c = 105$ **7**

50. At the copy center it costs $33.75 to print every 1,000 copies. What is the cost of printing 5,000 copies? *(Lesson 4-5)* **$168.75**

CHAPTER PROJECT

PROJECT LINK: WRITING RATIOS

Your class's solar system model will be based on a 2-mm diameter for Pluto. For each of your two assigned planets, write the ratio of the planet's real diameter to the real diameter of Pluto. (Use the data at the right.) How many times bigger than Pluto is each of your assigned planets? **Check students' work.**

Body	Diameter (mi)	Mean Distance from Sun (millions of miles)
Sun	865,120	0
Mercury	3,030	36.0
Venus	7,520	67.2
Earth	7,926	93.0
Mars	4,216	141.7
Jupiter	88,724	483.9
Saturn	74,560	885.0
Uranus	31,600	1,781.6
Neptune	30,600	2,790.2
Pluto	1,860	3,670.7

Teaching Notes

1 Focus

CONNECTING TO PRIOR KNOWLEDGE Have students make a list of ratios that are equal to $\frac{1}{2}$. Answers may vary. Sample: $\frac{2}{4}$, $\frac{3}{6}$, $\frac{50}{100}$ Ask students what math symbol could be used between any two ratios on the list. **an equal sign**

2 Teach

THINK AND DISCUSS

Example 1 Ask: *Why do you think 4 × 50 and 10 × 20 are called cross products?* **Answers may vary. Sample: because you can use crossed lines over the equal sign to join the numbers being multiplied**

ERROR ALERT! Example 1 Some students may have difficulty setting up the proportion

correctly. **Remediation:** Have students first write *what* is being compared. Then have them form the proportion.

VISUAL LEARNING Example 2 When showing students how to find the cross products, draw an × across the proportions before writing the equation. Encourage students to draw the × when they work the exercises.

ALGEBRA Connection

7-3 Solving Proportions

What You'll Learn

▼ To recognize proportions
▼ To solve proportions

...And Why

You can solve proportions related to crafts, school supplies, science, and music.

Here's How

Look for questions that
▪ build understanding
✔ check understanding

THINK AND DISCUSS

▼ Recognizing Proportions

A **proportion** is an equation that states two ratios are equal.

$$\frac{1}{2} = \frac{4}{8}$$

A proportion is true only if the ratios are equal.

1. Use the statements below for parts (a), (b), (c), and (d).

   I. $\frac{180}{42} \stackrel{?}{=} \frac{30}{7}$ **II.** $\frac{7}{8} \stackrel{?}{=} \frac{21}{24}$ **III.** $\frac{3}{15} \stackrel{?}{=} \frac{8}{20}$ **IV.** $\frac{16}{30} \stackrel{?}{=} \frac{8}{15}$

   a. Rewrite each statement so the ratios are in simplest form.
   b. Is each statement a proportion? How do you know?
   c. Multiply the blue numbers for each statement. Then multiply the red numbers. **a–c. See margin p. 287.**
   d. ▪*Draw a Conclusion* What do you notice about the products?
   If a statement is a proportion, the products are equal.

You can use **cross products** to tell if two ratios form a proportion. The cross products of a proportion are *always* equal. In the equation $\frac{1}{2} = \frac{4}{8}$, 1×8 and 2×4 are the cross products.

■ EXAMPLE 1   *Real-World Problem Solving*

Crafts In 4 hours, one weaver made 10 baskets. In 20 hours, another weaver made 50 baskets. Are the two weavers working at the same pace?

$$\frac{hours}{baskets} \longrightarrow \quad \frac{4}{10} \stackrel{?}{=} \frac{20}{50} \quad \longleftarrow \text{Write a possible proportion.}$$

$$4 \times 50 \stackrel{?}{=} 10 \times 20 \quad \longleftarrow \text{Write the cross products.}$$

$$200 = 200 \quad \longleftarrow \text{Multiply.}$$

The ratios are proportional. So both weavers are working at the same pace.

2. ✔*Try It Out* Does each pair of ratios form a proportion?

   a. $\frac{3}{9}, \frac{6}{18}$ **yes**   **b.** $\frac{9}{10}, \frac{18}{30}$ **no**   **c.** $\frac{33}{39}, \frac{55}{65}$ **yes**   **d.** $\frac{9}{27}, \frac{7}{21}$ **yes**

Now you may assign Exercises 1–14.

Lesson Planning Options

Prerequisite Skills
• modeling equations that use multiplication or division (2-7)

Vocabulary/Symbols
proportion, cross products

Materials/Manipulatives
• calculator

Resources

▤ **Student Edition**

Skills Handbook, p. 540
Extra Practice, p. 528
Glossary/Study Guide

🗄 **Teaching Resources**

Chapter Support File, Ch. 7
• Lesson Planner 7-3
• Practice 7-3, Reteaching 7-3
• Alternative Activity 7-3
• Answer Masters 7-3
Glossary, Spanish Resources

Transparencies
19, Minds on Math 7-3

Warm Up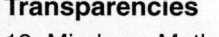

Jeff went to the store with $25.00. If he spent $10.00, what fraction of his money does he have left? $\frac{3}{5}$

285

■ **ADDITIONAL EXAMPLES**

FOR EXAMPLE 1
In 6 hours, one weaver made 16 baskets. In 40 hours another weaver made 96 baskets. Are the two weavers working at the same pace? **no**

FOR EXAMPLE 2
Find the value of n in $\frac{14}{26} = \frac{21}{n}$. **39**

FOR EXAMPLE 3
Paper at the student store is 10 sheets for $.25. Find the cost of 24 sheets. **$.60**

AEP Write the word *proportion* on the board. Cover up the prefix *pro*. Tell students that *portion* can mean "amount." Explain that in a proportion, the amounts are equal.

DIVERSITY Some students may have difficulty visualizing equal ratios. Allow students to use manipulatives or draw diagrams to represent equal ratios.

CONNECTION TO PHOTOGRAPHY Ask students interested in photography to research how they use proportions to enlarge or reduce photos.

Technology Options

Prentice Hall Technology

  Software for Learners
- Math Blaster® Mystery*
- Interactive Student Tutorial, Chapter 7*

  Teaching Resource Software
- Computer Item Generator 7-3
- Resource Pro™ Chapter 7*

Internet • For related mathematics activities, visit the Prentice Hall site at www.phschool.com/math

Available on CD-ROM only

Assignment Options for Exercises On Your Own

To provide flexible scheduling, this lesson can be subdivided into parts.

▼ **Core** 1–12
Extension 13, 14

▼ **Core** 15–33, 35
Extension 34

Use Mixed Review to maintain skills.

286

---

2 *Solving Proportions*

Sometimes you can use mental math to find the missing term in a proportion.

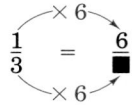 Use the same operation on the numerator and the denominator.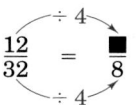

$$\frac{1}{3} = \frac{6}{\blacksquare} \qquad \frac{12}{32} = \frac{\blacksquare}{8}$$

3. ▲*Mental Math* Find the missing term in each proportion above. **18; 4**

You can also use cross products to solve proportions.

■ **EXAMPLE 2**

Find the value of n in $\frac{n}{312} = \frac{5}{24}$.

$$\frac{n}{312} = \frac{5}{24}$$

$n \times 24 = 312 \times 5$ ⟵ Write the cross products.

$24n = 1{,}560$ ⟵ Multiply.

$\frac{24n}{24} = \frac{1{,}560}{24}$ ⟵ Divide both sides by 24.

$n = 65$

Proportions can help you solve problems involving rates.

■ **EXAMPLE 3**   *Real-World Problem Solving*

School Supplies Pencils at the school store are 2 for $.15. Find the cost of 21 pencils.

$$\frac{\text{pencils}}{\text{cost (\$)}} \longrightarrow \frac{2}{0.15} = \frac{21}{c}$$ ⟵ Let c represent the cost.

$2 \times c = 0.15 \times 21$ ⟵ Write the cross products.

.15 ☒ 21 ⊞ 2 ▣ *1.575* ⟵ Use a calculator to solve.

$c = 1.575$

Round to the next cent. So 21 pencils cost $1.58.

4. ✓*Try It Out* Use a calculator, paper and pencil, or mental math. Find the value of each variable.

a. $\frac{9}{39} = \frac{3}{y}$ **13**   b. $\frac{k}{17} = \frac{20}{34}$ **10**   c. $\frac{2}{9} = \frac{25}{x}$ **112.5**   d. $\frac{96}{144} = \frac{n}{12}$ **8**

5. ▲*Reasoning* How could you use a pattern to find the cost of the pencils in Example 3?

QUICKreview

Multiplying or dividing the numerator and the denominator by the same number is the same as multiplying or dividing by 1.

$\frac{1}{3} \times \frac{6}{6} = \frac{1}{3} \times 1$

$\frac{12}{32} \div \frac{4}{4} = \frac{12}{32} \div 1$

 The familiar eraser on the end of a pencil wasn't introduced until about 1860. Some teachers objected because they felt that students would make more errors if they could correct them easily.

5. Start with $.08 and add alternately $.07 and $.08 repeatedly to find the cost of any number of pencils.

Now you may assign Exercises 15–35.

EXERCISES *On Your Own*

MENTAL MATH Exercises 15–19 Encourage students to share their mental math strategies with the class.

ASSESSMENT Exercises 20–29 Have students solve for the variables. Ask them to show their work. Check to see that they used cross products to solve.

CONNECTION TO SPORTS Exercise 32
Have students pick a school sport and find the ratio of players to coaches. Ask if this ratio is larger or smaller than the ratios for Hopkinton's soccer teams?

EXTENSION Challenge students to use proportions to enlarge a drawing to two or three times its original size.

WRAP UP

IDENTIFYING THE BIG IDEA Ask students to explain how to recognize and solve proportions.

PROJECT LINK Have students set up their proportions first using words. Then have them put the numbers in and use calculators to solve.

EXERCISES *On Your Own*

Does each pair of ratios form a proportion?

1. $\frac{1}{2}, \frac{50}{100}$ yes

2. $\frac{10}{20}, \frac{30}{40}$ no

3. $\frac{4}{12}, \frac{6}{8}$ no

4. $\frac{42}{6}, \frac{504}{72}$ yes

5. $\frac{9}{11}, \frac{63}{77}$ yes

6. $\frac{93}{60}, \frac{62}{40}$ yes

7. $\frac{18}{9}, \frac{6}{3}$ yes

8. $\frac{4}{9}, \frac{3}{5}$ no

9. $\frac{10}{16}, \frac{6}{14}$ no

10. $\frac{24}{54}, \frac{8}{18}$ yes

11. Write the cross products of the proportion $\frac{3}{4} = \frac{9}{12}$. 36 = 36

12. **a.** Do the ratios $\frac{45}{50}$ and $\frac{18}{20}$ form a proportion? How do you know? **Yes; write each ratio in simple form. The ratios are equal.**

    b. *Reasoning* How else could you decide whether the ratios in part (a) form a proportion? **Find the cross products. The cross products are equal.**

13. Use the numbers 2, 5, 6, and 15. Write as many proportions as possible. $\frac{2}{5} = \frac{6}{15}, \frac{5}{2} = \frac{15}{6}, \frac{2}{6} = \frac{5}{15}, \frac{6}{2} = \frac{15}{5}$

14. *Open-ended* Describe a situation using a proportion.
    Check students' work.

Mental Math **Find the missing term in each proportion.**

15. $\frac{48}{\blacksquare} = \frac{4}{7}$ 84

16. $\frac{9}{32} = \frac{\blacksquare}{48}$ 13.5

17. $\frac{4}{18} = \frac{6}{\blacksquare}$ 27

18. $\frac{\blacksquare}{55} = \frac{18}{22}$ 45

19. $\frac{\blacksquare}{42} = \frac{5}{6}$ 35

Choose **Use a calculator, paper and pencil, or mental math. Find the value of each variable.**

20. $\frac{10}{3} = \frac{x}{12}$ 40

21. $\frac{12}{n} = \frac{4}{21}$ 63

22. $\frac{3}{11} = \frac{15}{a}$ 55

23. $\frac{42}{g} = \frac{7}{10}$ 60

24. $\frac{25}{6} = \frac{d}{30}$ 125

25. $\frac{b}{9} = \frac{3}{27}$ 1

26. $\frac{7}{2} = \frac{77}{w}$ 22

27. $\frac{72}{c} = \frac{8}{3}$ 27

28. $\frac{16}{27} = \frac{4}{m}$ 6.75

29. $\frac{h}{2} = \frac{3}{16}$ 0.375

30. *Food* A flavor of frozen yogurt has 65 calories in 2 oz. How many calories are in 10 oz of that frozen yogurt? **325 calories**

31. *Science* A glacier moves about 12 in. every 8 h. About how far does the glacier move in 72 h? **108 in.**

32. *Sports* Youth soccer teams in Hopkinton have 22 players and 3 coaches. How many coaches are needed for 196 players?
    27 coaches

33. Suppose you get paid $7 for 2 h of baby-sitting, and you were paid $17.50 last night. How long did you baby-sit? $2\frac{1}{2}$ h

34. *Music* A piano has 88 keys. The ratio of white keys to black keys is 52 to 36. A piano maker has 676 white keys.
    a. How many black keys does the piano maker need to have the correct ratio of white keys to black keys? **468 black keys**
    b. How many pianos can be built? Explain. **13 pianos**

35. *Writing* Describe two different ways to solve a proportion.
    See margin.

CHECKPOINT 1

Checkpoint 1 — *Lessons 7-1 through 7-3*

1. **Circle A, B, C, or D.** There are 3 alligators, 16 turtles, and 12 snakes in the reptile exhibit at the zoo. What is the ratio of turtles to snakes?
   A. $3:4$ **B.** 3 to 16   **C.** $\frac{4}{3}$ **D.** $4:1$

Write two equal ratios for each. Answers will vary. Samples are given.

2. $\frac{12}{48}$ $\frac{1}{4}, \frac{24}{96}$

3. $14:21$ **2:3, 28:42**

4. $64:80$ **4:5, 16:20**

Find the unit rate for each situation.

5. A package of 3 notebooks costs $3.39. **$1.13 /notebook**

6. Fabric costs $12.76 for 4 yd. **$3.19 /yd**

Find the value of *n*.

7. $\frac{2}{7} = \frac{n}{21}$ 6

8. $\frac{n}{4} = \frac{18}{36}$ 2

9. $\frac{12}{18} = \frac{6}{n}$ 9

pages 285–286   Think and Discuss

1a. I. $\frac{30}{7} = \frac{30}{7}$; II. $\frac{7}{8} = \frac{7}{8}$; III. $\frac{1}{5} \neq \frac{2}{5}$; IV. $\frac{8}{15} = \frac{8}{15}$

   b. I, II, and IV are proportions; III is not; a statement is a proportion if the ratios are equal.

   c. I. 1,260; 1,260; II. 168; 168; III. 60; 120; IV. 240; 240

pages 287–288   On Your Own

35. Decide what operation is used on the numerator and denominator. Then use mental math to find the missing term. Write the cross products equal to each other. Solve the equation.

287

Practice 7-3 Solving Proportions

Does each pair of ratios form a proportion?

1. $\frac{8}{9}, \frac{4}{3}$ no

2. $\frac{20}{16}, \frac{18}{15}$ no

3. $\frac{18}{12}, \frac{21}{14}$ yes

4. $\frac{21}{27}, \frac{35}{45}$ yes

5. $\frac{18}{22}, \frac{45}{55}$ yes

6. $\frac{38}{52}, \frac{57}{80}$ no

7. $\frac{10}{65}, \frac{18}{87}$ no

8. $\frac{51}{48}, \frac{68}{64}$ yes

Choose a calculator, paper and pencil, or mental math. Find the value of each variable.

9. $\frac{4}{5} = \frac{x}{15}$ 12

10. $\frac{8}{m} = \frac{4}{15}$ 30

11. $\frac{39}{27} = \frac{26}{m}$ 18

12. $\frac{y}{5} = \frac{32}{20}$ 8

13. $\frac{14}{b} = \frac{8}{12}$ 21

14. $\frac{a}{18} = \frac{16}{24}$ 12

15. $\frac{d}{25} = \frac{12}{15}$ 20

16. $\frac{28}{42} = \frac{26}{x}$ 39

17. $\frac{16}{24} = \frac{y}{27}$ 18

18. $\frac{50}{8} = \frac{x}{25}$ 156.25

19. $\frac{9}{10} = \frac{c}{45}$ 40.5

20. $\frac{x}{90} = \frac{45}{50}$ 81

Solve each problem.

21. In the 1991–92 National Basketball Association Championship games, the Chicago Bulls won 2 games for each game that the Portland Trailblazers won. If Portland won 2 games, how many did Chicago win? __4 games__
Source: World Almanac and Book of Facts

22. In 1915, there was one divorce for every 1,000 people in the United States. If a certain town had a population of 56,000 people, how many divorces would you have expected in that town? __56 divorces__
Source: World Almanac and Book of Facts

23. For every 100 families with TV sets, about 12 families like Star Trek, the Next Generation. In a town of 23,400 families who all have TV sets, how many families would you expect to like Star Trek, the Next Generation? __2,808 families__
Source: World Almanac and Book of Facts

24. In 1800, there were only about 6 people per square mile of land in the U.S. What was the approximate population in 1800 if there were about 364,700 square miles in the U.S.?
Source: World Almanac and Book of Facts
__Answers may vary. Accept answers near 2,100,000 people.__

In copymaster and workbook formats

Reteaching 7-3 Solving Proportions

If two ratios are equal, they form a **proportion**.

$\frac{1}{5} = \frac{2}{10}$

Equal ratios have equal cross products.

$\frac{1}{5} < \frac{2}{10}$ 5 × 2 = 10, 1 × 10 = 10

Equal cross products also show that a proportion is true.

$\frac{3}{6} < \frac{8}{18}$ 6 × 3 = 18, 1 × 18 = 18

The cross products are equal, so the ratios are equal and form a proportion.

You can find the missing term in a proportion by using cross products.

Solve $\frac{4}{7} = \frac{12}{n}$.

① Write the cross products. 4 × n = 7 × 12
② Simplify. 4n = 84
③ Divide by 4. $\frac{4n}{4} = \frac{84}{4}$
④ Simplify. n = 21

Does each pair of ratios form a proportion? Write yes or no.

1. $\frac{6}{7}, \frac{8}{14}$ yes

2. $\frac{5}{2}, \frac{10}{4}$ yes

3. $\frac{6}{8}, \frac{3}{5}$ no

4. $\frac{15}{3}, \frac{10}{2}$ yes

5. $\frac{15}{45}, \frac{25}{60}$ no

6. $\frac{12}{16}, \frac{15}{20}$ yes

7. $\frac{9}{10}, \frac{19}{20}$ no

8. $\frac{32}{12}, \frac{8}{3}$ yes

9. $\frac{56}{8}, \frac{1}{7}$ no

10. $\frac{4}{7}, \frac{14}{21}$ no

11. $\frac{40}{50}, \frac{8}{10}$ yes

12. $\frac{5}{15}, \frac{9}{27}$ yes

Choose a calculator, paper and pencil, or mental math. Find the value of each variable.

13. $\frac{n}{5} = \frac{2}{10}$ n = 1

14. $\frac{9}{n} = \frac{27}{3}$ n = 1

15. $\frac{30}{6} = \frac{a}{9}$ a = 45

16. $\frac{42}{12} = \frac{x}{4}$ x = 14

17. $\frac{t}{24} = \frac{3}{8}$ t = 9

18. $\frac{16}{12} = \frac{r}{18}$ r = 24

19. $\frac{18}{32} = \frac{27}{m}$ m = 48

20. $\frac{48}{30} = \frac{32}{e}$ e = 20

21. $\frac{5}{6} = \frac{h}{36}$ h = 30

22. $\frac{60}{24} = \frac{w}{12}$ w = 30

23. $\frac{11}{14} = \frac{33}{y}$ y = 42

24. $\frac{90}{25} = \frac{x}{5}$ x = 18

25. $\frac{10}{5} = \frac{6}{t}$ t = 3

26. $\frac{9}{a} = \frac{3}{5}$ a = 15

27. $\frac{b}{2} = \frac{16}{4}$ b = 8

28. $\frac{12}{16} = \frac{n}{4}$ n = 3

Minds on Math Transparency

7-3

Mr. Addis makes some shelves with 3 pegs and some with 4 pegs. Yesterday he used 24 pegs to make some shelves of each type. How many of each type of shelf did he make?

4 shelves with 3 pegs and 3 shelves with 4 pegs

See Solution Key for worked-out answers.

LESSON QUIZ

Does each pair of ratios form a proportion?

1. $\frac{6}{10}, \frac{60}{100}$ yes

2. $\frac{16}{3}, \frac{32}{9}$ no

Find the missing term in each proportion.

3. $\frac{14}{72} = \frac{42}{\blacksquare}$ 216

4. $\frac{8}{54} = \frac{4}{\blacksquare}$ 27

5. $\frac{15}{40} = \frac{3}{x}$ 8

Mixed Review

Find each difference. (Lesson 6-3)

36. $\frac{8}{9} - \frac{2}{3}$ $\frac{2}{9}$

37. $\frac{7}{8} - \frac{3}{4}$ $\frac{1}{8}$

38. $\frac{1}{2} - \frac{3}{16}$ $\frac{5}{16}$

39. $\frac{27}{32} - \frac{1}{2}$ $\frac{11}{32}$

40. $\frac{13}{15} - \frac{2}{3}$ $\frac{1}{5}$

41. $\frac{9}{10} - \frac{3}{4}$ $\frac{3}{20}$

Use compatible numbers to estimate. (Lesson 4-1)

42. $9.36 \div 5.1$ 2

43. 17.56×9.31 180

44. 24.83×3.07 75

45. $16.31 \div 4.07$ 4

46. 39.2×3.201 120

47. Abraham Lincoln, who was 1.93 m tall, was the tallest U.S. president. Would he have fit through an 80 cm-by-200 cm doorway? By how many centimeters would the doorway have been taller or shorter than Lincoln? (Lesson 4-10)
yes; 7 cm taller

CHAPTER PROJECT

PROJECT LINK: CALCULATING

You know three pieces of data: the diameter of Pluto, the diameters of your assigned planets, and the scale diameter of Pluto. Use proportions to find the scale-model diameters of your planets. Then make two-dimensional drawings of the planets. **Check students' work.**

✓ CHECKPOINT 1
Lessons 7-1 through 7-3

1–6. Answers may vary. Samples are given.

Write two ratios equal to the given ratio.

1. $\frac{10}{15}$ $\frac{2}{3}, \frac{40}{60}$

2. 20 to 34 10 to 17, 40 to 64

3. 18 : 40 9 : 20, 36 : 80

4. $\frac{23}{44}$ $\frac{46}{88}, \frac{230}{440}$

5. 4 to 7 8 to 14, 16 to 28

6. $\frac{10}{30}$ $\frac{1}{3}, \frac{2}{6}$

Find the unit rate for each situation.

7. You can buy 3 tacos for $2.67.
$.89 per taco

8. A package of 6 batteries costs $2.10.
$.35 per battery

Find the value of each variable.

9. $\frac{21}{36} = \frac{7}{n}$ 12

10. $\frac{x}{42} = \frac{3}{7}$ 18

11. $\frac{m}{12} = \frac{6}{9}$ 8

12. $\frac{6}{45} = \frac{2}{n}$ 15

13. $\frac{54}{c} = \frac{9}{13}$ 78

14. **Choose A, B, C, or D.** A bookstore sold 24 paperbacks, 6 hardcovers, 38 magazines, and 5 calendars. What was the ratio of magazines sold to paperbacks sold? C

A. 24 : 38

B. 19 to 31

C. $\frac{19}{12}$

D. 12 : 24

1 Focus

CONNECTING TO PRIOR KNOWLEDGE Ask: *How would you plan a big party? What steps would you take to make planning the party easier?* **Answers may vary. Sample: Write a list of what you need to do; order the list by what you must do first.** Tell students they can solve problems by first solving simpler problems.

2 Teach

THINK AND DISCUSS

DIVERSITY Some students may not have experience playing computer and video games. Consider explaining the Treacherous Tunnel game as though it were a board game.

Question 1 Video games often offer several choices or paths. A player must decide which path to take. Ask volunteers to explain that their decisions change as they become more proficient at the game. Then ask them to explain how they made their decisions.

TACTILE LEARNING Question 4 Provide students with counters. Have them arrange the counters in groups of 2, 4, 6, and so on, to 20. Students can model pairs of numbers.

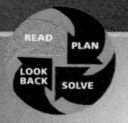

PROBLEM SOLVING STRATEGY

7-4 Solve a Simpler Problem

Problem Solving Strategies

Draw a Diagram
Guess and Test
Look for a Pattern
Make a Model
Make a Table
Simulate a Problem
✔ Solve a Simpler Problem
Too Much or Too Little
  Information
Using Logical Reasoning
Use Multiple Strategies
Work Backward
Write an Equation

THINK AND DISCUSS

When solving a problem, you may find it helpful to solve a similar, simpler problem first.

SAMPLE PROBLEM...
Imagine you are playing the video game Treacherous Tunnel. You have two choices for entering the next level of the game. You don't want to use Choice 1 because it takes too long. Your goal is to use Choice 2 and follow the correct path within the time limit.

Treacherous Tunnel

Choose a path. Travel Time: 1 min

Choice 1 This path has diamonds in bunches of 2, 3, 4, and so on, to 100. You must collect all the even-numbered bunches. If you miss any, or if you collect odd-numbered bunches, the game ends.

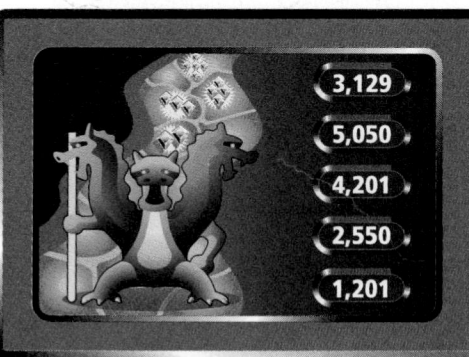

3,129
5,050
4,201
2,550
1,201

Choice 2 A three-headed creature guards the path. One of the numbers at the left is the total number of diamonds you could collect in Choice 1. If you select the wrong number, the creature will not let you pass, and the game ends.

....

Think about the information you have and what you need to find.

READ
Read for understanding. Summarize the problem.

1. Read Choices 1 and 2 carefully. What is your goal?
   Find the total number of diamonds you can collect.

2. What numbers will you add to find the number you should select in Choice 2? **Even numbers from 2 to 100.**

3. The odd numbers: 3,129; 4,201; and 1,201. The sum of even numbers is an even number.

3. What numbers in Choice 2 can you eliminate? Why?

Prerequisite Skills

• looking for a pattern (2-2)

Resources

Student Edition

Skills Handbook, p. 538
Extra Practice, p. 528
Glossary/Study Guide

Teaching Resources

Chapter Support File, Ch. 7
• Lesson Planner 7-4
• Practice 7-4, Reteaching 7-4
• Answer Masters 7-4
Glossary, Spanish Resources

Transparencies
Minds on Math 7-4

Warm Up

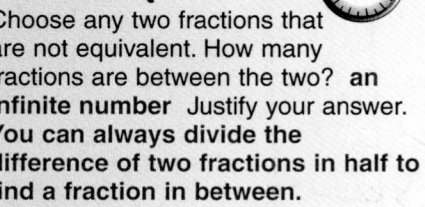

Choose any two fractions that are not equivalent. How many fractions are between the two? **an infinite number** Justify your answer. **You can always divide the difference of two fractions in half to find a fraction in between.**

289

A line of 1,500 people is waiting to see a museum exhibit. Every 20 min, a guard allows 55 people to enter. The exhibit is open for 8 h. Will all 1,500 people get in? **No, 1,320 people will get in.**

ERROR ALERT! Exercise 2 Students may find an incorrect number of pairs of whole numbers. **Remediation:** Ask students to list all the whole numbers from 1 to 100. Then have students cross out numbers as they make their pairs.

3 Practice/Assess

EXERCISES *On Your Own*

ASSESSMENT Exercise 1 Have students write a paragraph explaining how they would solve this problem if the light had changed every 15 s rather than every 30 s. **Answers may vary. Sample: First find out how many** times the traffic light changes in 1 min, then in 1 h, and then in 1 da. It changes 4 times in 1 min and 240 times in 1 h. In 365 da, it would change 2,102,400 times.

Exercises 3–8 Ask volunteers to explain the strategies they used to solve each problem. If strategies differ, ask them to compare the advantages and disadvantages of using a particular strategy.

Technology Options

Prentice Hall Technology

 **Software for Learners**
- Math Blaster® Mystery*
- Interactive Student Tutorial, Chapter 7*

 Teaching Resource Software
- Computer Item Generator 7-4
- Resource Pro™ Chapter 7*

 **Internet** • For related mathematics activities, visit the Prentice Hall site at www.phschool.com/math

Available on CD-ROM only

Assignment Options for Exercises On Your Own

Core 1–7
Extension 8

Use Mixed Review to maintain skills.

PLAN
Decide on a strategy.

One strategy for finding the sum of all even numbers from 2 through 100 is to solve a simpler problem first. Start with all even numbers from 2 through 20: 2, 4, 6, 8, 10, 12, 14, 16, 18, 20. Look for shortcuts to find this sum.

SOLVE
Try the strategy.

4. 2 4 6 8 10 12 14 16 18 20
        $2 + 20$

6a. Answers may vary. Sample: You can see the pattern faster when you work with smaller numbers.

a. Continue to add pairs. What sum do you get each time? **22**
b. How many even numbers did you start with? **10 numbers**
c. How many pairs do you have? **5 pairs**
d. How can you use the number of pairs to find the sum? **5 × 22 = 110**

5. Look at the original problem and use the same method.
a. What are the first and last numbers you will add? What is the sum of these two numbers? **2 and 100; 102**
b. There are 50 even numbers from 2 to 100. How many pairs can you make? **25 pairs**

5c. Sample: 4 + 98 = 102, 6 + 96 = 102; for each pair you increase the first number by 2 and decrease the second number by 2, so the sum does not change.

c. Show with examples that each pair has the same sum.
d. What is the sum of all the even numbers from 2 to 100? This is the number you will select in the video game. **2,550**

LOOK BACK
Think about how you solved the problem.

6. a. Explain how solving a simpler problem helped you find the answer to the original problem. **See above left.**
b. Why is this strategy better than finding the sum by hand or with a calculator? **This strategy is faster and requires fewer calculations.**

Now you may assign Exercises 1–8.

EXERCISES *On Your Own*

Solve by using a simpler problem.
    a. 2 times; 120 times
1. *Traffic* A traffic light was installed exactly 1 year ago. The traffic light changes every 30 seconds. How many times has the traffic light changed since it was installed?
    a. Break the problem into simpler problems. How many times does the light change in 1 minute? In 1 hour?
    b. Solve the problem. Explain your solution. **1,051,200 times; find the number of hours in 1 yr. Then multiply it by 120.**
2. Find the sum of all whole numbers from 1 to 100.
    a. What smaller set of numbers could you start with? **Check students' work.**
    b. How will you make pairs? **Pair the first and last number. Then move in 1 number**
    c. Solve the problem and explain your solution. **at a time from each end.**
    5,050; you have 50 pairs. The sum in each pair is 101, so the sum of all the numbers is 50 × 101.

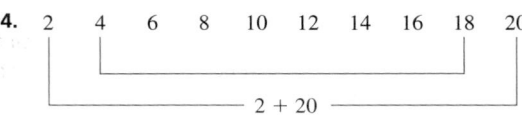

IDENTIFYING THE BIG IDEA Ask students to explain how to solve a complicated problem by solving a simpler problem.

LESSON QUIZ

Solve.

1. Martin works $7\frac{1}{2}$ h per day for 5 days at the auto factory. If he makes $13.90 per h, how much did he earn last week? **$521.25**

2. Factory workers on an assembly line produce 70 vehicles in 1 h. About how many vehicles do they produce each year if they work 52 weeks a year and 40 h each week? **145,600**

Use any strategy to solve each problem. Show your work.

3. *Biology* A baby's heart beats about 120 times per minute. How many times does a baby's heart beat in a year?
63,072,000 times

4. *Consumer Issues* A 3-pack of flowering plants costs $1.59. A flat of these plants costs $11.59. There are 24 plants in a flat. Suppose you want to buy 30 plants. What is the least amount of money you could spend? **$14.77**

5. *Savings* Suppose you save a quarter every day. How much will you have saved in 1 year? In 10 years? **$91.25; $912.50**

6. *Biology* In every quart of blood in your body, you have about 19 fluid ounces of plasma. An average adult has about 5 quarts of blood. About how many quarts are plasma? **3 qt**

7. A line of 1,500 people is waiting to see a museum exhibit. Every 20 min, a guard allows 55 people to enter. The exhibit is open for 8 h. Will all 1,500 people get in? **no**

8. *Consumer Issues* Tickets to the circus are $6.50 per person. The cost of a ticket decreases to $5.00 per person for groups of ten or more people.
   a. How much do you save over the regular ticket price if you buy 18 tickets? **$27**
   b. How much would your class save on a trip to the circus? **Check students' work.**

Mixed Review

Simplify each expression. *(Lesson 2-2)*

9. $7 \times 8 + 4$ **60**
10. $2.2 + 3.1 \times 7$ **23.9**
11. $9.8 \div 2 \times 4.2$ **20.58**
12. $7.7 - 2.3 \div 4$ **7.125**

Complete. *(Lesson 6-10)*

13. $17 \text{ qt} = \blacksquare \text{ pt}$ **34**
14. $7\frac{1}{2} \text{ yd} = \blacksquare \text{ ft}$ **$22\frac{1}{2}$**
15. $8,000 \text{ lb} = \blacksquare \text{ T}$ **4**
16. $3.75 \text{ gal} = \blacksquare \text{ pt}$ **30**

Draw a model to find each product. *(Lesson 4-4)*

17. 0.9×0.2 **0.18**
18. 1.6×0.7 **1.12**
19. 1.2×0.4 **0.48**
20. 2.1×0.6 **1.26**
21. 1.5×1.1 **1.65**
22. 0.3×1.9 **0.57**

23. *Choose a Strategy* Eight birds and some squirrels are at the backyard feeder. You count 24 legs. How many birds and how many squirrels are there? **8 birds; 2 squirrels**

PRACTICE

Practice 7-4 *Problem-Solving Strategy: Solve a Simpler Problem*

Solve by using a simpler problem.

1. At 8:00 P.M., there are 243 people in line for a ride at an amusement park. Every 12 minutes starting at 8 P.M., 42 people are able to enter the ride. A boy gets in line at 8:00. Will he get to ride before the ride shuts down at 9:00 P.M.? Explain.
No, if the last ride ends at 9 P.M.;
yes, if the last ride leaves at 9 P.M.

2. The astronauts who landed on the moon brought back about 842 pounds of moon rocks. Dividing the cost of these moon flights by the weight of the rocks, it is estimated that the rocks cost $3,000,000 per ounce. What was the approximate cost of these moon flights? **$40,416,000,000**

3. While an adult is asleep, his or her heart can pump about 80 gal of blood per hour. About how many gallons of blood will the heart pump during a week of sleep if an adult sleeps 7 h each night? **3,920 gal**

Use any strategy to solve each problem. Show all your work.

4. The Language Club includes students who are enrolled in Latin, German, Spanish, or French. Each person, including John, is enrolled in only one foreign language. Christine does not speak French. Judy is enrolled in German or Latin. Pepe is enrolled in Latin or Spanish. Christine and the person taking Spanish often walk to school together. Christine and the person who is taking German are best friends. Who is enrolled in which course?
Christine: Latin; Judy: German;
Pepe: Spanish; John: French

5. What is the sum of all odd numbers from 101 to 200? **7,500**

6. A small hummingbird beats its wings 70 times/s. How many times will it beat its wings in 8 h? **about 2,016,000 times**

7. It takes the sound of thunder five seconds to travel one mile. How far away is the thunder if it takes 45 s to reach you? **about 9 mi**

8. A company with 628 employees is taking all the employees to see a baseball game. The company will hire buses. If each bus holds 34 passengers, will 15 buses be enough? **no**

In copymaster and workbook formats

RETEACHING

Reteaching 7-4 *Problem-Solving Strategy: Solve a Simpler Problem*

A mystery game has 3 rooms. Each room has 3 desks. Each desk has 3 drawers, and each drawer has 3 dollars. The object of the game is to be the first to collect all the dollars. How many dollars would this be?

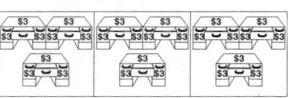

Read	What is the object of the game? *The object is to collect all the money.* What does the problem ask you to find? *Find how much money is hidden in all 3 rooms.*
Plan	If you cannot solve the entire problem at once, how can you break it down into simpler problems? *Find the amount of money in one room. Then multiply by 3.*
Solve	For one room multiply: 3 (desks) × 3 (drawers) × 3 (dollars). There is $27 in one room. 3 × $27 = $81. There is $81 in all three rooms.
Look Back	How does solving a simpler problem help find the solution to the original problem? *The strategy allows you to work with easier numbers.*

Solve by using a simpler problem.

1. Another game has 7 rooms, each with 7 paintings. Behind each painting are 7 safes. Inside each safe are 7 security boxes, each with $70. How much money is hidden in the house? **$168,070**

2. If someone enters one of the 7 rooms while you are there collecting the money, you must give that person the contents of 1 safe. Suppose this happens to you in all 7 rooms. How much would you have at the end of the game? **$164,640**

3. Six students are playing a game. Each student plays the game once with each of the other students. How many games are played? **15 games**

4. Twelve students each have 2 bookbags. Each bookbag contains 4 books. Each book costs $10.95. How much do the books cost altogether? **$1,051.20**

ENRICHMENT

Minds on Math Transparency

7-4

I am a two-digit prime number. The number formed by reversing my digits is also prime. My ones digit is 4 less than my tens digit. What number am I?

73

See *Solution Key* for worked-out answers.

291

Teaching Notes

1 Focus

CONNECTING TO PRIOR KNOWLEDGE Ask students to describe scale models they have seen. Have them explain why we use the term *scale model.* **Answers may vary. Sample: doll houses, model cars, rockets. Scale models model the actual object exactly, but scale it to a smaller size.**

Lesson Planning Options

Prerequisite Skills
• measuring in metric units (precourse)
• using fractions and decimals (5-9)

Vocabulary/Symbols
scale

Materials/Manipulatives
• centimeter ruler   • graph paper

Resources

 Student Edition
Skills Handbook, p. 540
Extra Practice, p. 528
Glossary/Study Guide

 **Teaching Resources**
Chapter Support File, Ch. 7
• Lesson Planner 7-5
• Practice 7-5, Reteaching 7-5
• Answer Masters 7-5
Teaching Aids Master 3
Glossary, Spanish Resources

 Transparencies
16, 90, Minds on Math 7-5

Warm Up
Write an expression that represents this situation. Aretha sang for a number of minutes, then she sang for 8 more minutes. *n* + 8

292

2 Teach

THINK AND DISCUSS

AEP The word scale may confuse students. Explain that scale is a ratio, or a fraction, of the size of the original object. Tell students that for a ratio of 1 to 8, 1 in. may represent 8 in.

2a.

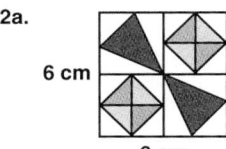
6 cm
6 cm

b. Make every cm in the original design equal 3 cm in the drawing.

1 cm : 30 cm

VISUAL LEARNING Question 2 Use a photocopier to enlarge the original drawing by 200%. Show students the enlargement. Discuss with students how photocopiers can change the size of an image. If possible, allow students to make reduced or enlarged copies on their own.

Question 5 Make sure students record the measurements of the scales. In part (a), centimeters are related to meters. In part (b), centimeters are related to centimeters.

GEOMETRY Connection

7-5 Scale Drawings

What You'll Learn
❶ To enlarge or reduce designs by making a scale drawing
❷ To find the actual size of an object

...And Why
Architects use proportions to make scale drawings called blueprints.

Here's How
Look for questions that
⚏ build understanding
✔ check understanding

THINK AND DISCUSS
❶ *Enlarging or Reducing Designs*

Architects, advertisers, and fashion designers all make drawings *to scale.* You can use graph paper to reduce or enlarge designs. The designs below were created on centimeter graph paper.

Original Design   *Enlarged Design*

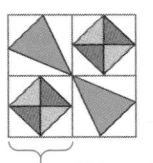 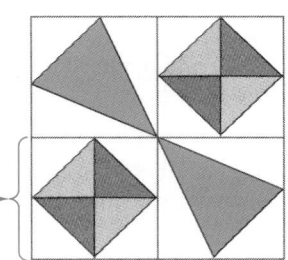

This smaller square corresponds to this larger square.

1. a. ⚏*Measurement* Find the length of the squares in each design.   **1 cm by 1 cm; 2 cm by 2 cm**
   b. What is the ratio of the enlarged design to the original design?   **2 : 1**

2. a. Make a drawing of the original design using a ratio of 3 cm to 1 cm (original design).
   b. Explain the steps you used to make your drawing.
   c. ⚏*Reasoning* Suppose your ratio is 0.5 cm to 1 cm (original design). How would your method be different?
   Make every cm in the original design equal 0.5 cm instead of 3 cm.

A **scale** is a ratio that compares a length on a model (usually listed first) to the actual length of the real object (second).

3. Use the drawing at the left. Write the scale as a ratio in fraction form. $\frac{1}{30}$

4. ⚏*Explain* Why should a scale drawing show the scale?
   You can find the size of the original object using the scale.

ADDITIONAL EXAMPLE

FOR EXAMPLE

Use the scale drawing to find the actual length of the fish. **14 cm**

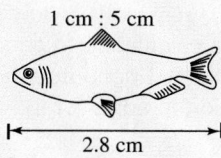

1 cm : 5 cm

2.8 cm

ASSESSMENT Have pairs of students complete the following activity:

- One student measures a math textbook with a ruler.
- The partner constructs a scale drawing that is smaller using the scale 1 in. : 5 in.
- The first student measures the drawing to verify that it is accurately drawn to scale.

DIVERSITY Exercises 5–8 Pair students who are familiar with scale drawings with those who are not. Have pairs work together to make the scale drawings.

▼2 *Finding the Actual Size of an Object*

A scale drawing should be proportional to the actual size of the object so the scale can be used to calculate its actual size.

■ EXAMPLE

Architecture Use the scale drawing at the left to find the actual height of the skyscraper.

$$\frac{\text{drawing (mm)}}{\text{actual (m)}} \longrightarrow \frac{1}{10}$$ ←Write the scale as a ratio.

The building is 34 mm high. ←Measure the height of the model.

$$\frac{\text{drawing (mm)}}{\text{actual (m)}} \longrightarrow \frac{1}{10} = \frac{34}{h}$$ ←Write a proportion. Let h represent the actual height.

$$1 \times h = 10 \times 34$$ ←Write the cross products.

$$h = 340$$

The actual height of the skyscraper is about 340 m.

1 mm : 10 m

5. ✓Try It Out Use each scale drawing to find the actual size.

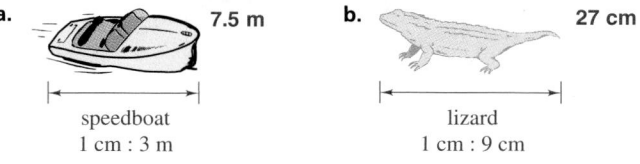

a. 7.5 m

speedboat
1 cm : 3 m

b. 27 cm

lizard
1 cm : 9 cm

Now you may assign Exercises 11–36.

Write the scale used for each scale drawing.

1. a 10-in. drawing of a 40-ft boat
1 in. to 4 ft

2. a 2-in. model of a 8-ft car
1 in. to 4 ft

3. a 4-ft model of a 100-ft building
1 ft to 25 ft

4. a 15-in. drawing of a 300-ft fence
1 in. to 20 ft

Make a scale drawing of each design. Use a scale of 3 cm to 1 cm (original design). 5–8. Check students work for diagrams. Dimensions of scale drawings are given.

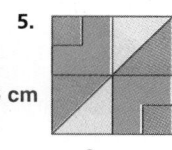
5.
6 cm
6 cm

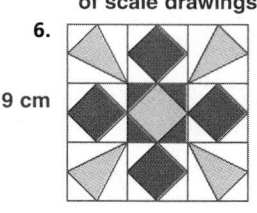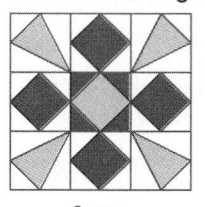
6.
9 cm
9 cm

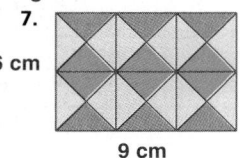
7.
6 cm
9 cm

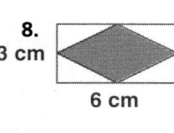
8.
3 cm
6 cm

Technology Options

Prentice Hall Technology

Software for Learners
- Hot Page™ 20*
- Math Blaster® Mystery*
- Interactive Student Tutorial, Chapter 7*

Teaching Resource Software
- Computer Item Generator 7-5
- Resource Pro™ Chapter 7*

Internet • For related mathematics activities, visit the Prentice Hall site at www.phschool.com/math

*Available on CD-ROM only

Assignment Options for Exercises On Your Own

To provide flexible scheduling, this lesson can be subdivided into parts.

▼1 **Core** 1–8, 10
Extension 9, 37

▼2 **Core** 11–26, 32–36
Extension 27–31

Use Mixed Review to maintain skills.

CONNECTING TO THE STUDENTS' WORLD
Exercise 9 Provide students with examples of actual maps. Have them calculate distances from one point to another using the scale on the map.

ERROR ALERT! Exercises 19–26 Students may enlarge when they should reduce and reduce when they should enlarge.
Remediation: Remind students the first number in the scale goes with the model and the second number goes with the actual measurement of the object. If the second number is larger than the first, then the

answer is an enlargement. If the second number is smaller than the first, then the answer is a reduction. Have students check their dimensions with the scales using this reasoning.

OPEN-ENDED Exercise 27 Students may want to select objects that have flat planes and edges to make their scale drawings.

REASONING Exercise 37 Ask: *How is the new design different from the old design?*
Answers may vary. Sample: The length changed but the height did not. The figure appears stretched.

WRAP UP

IDENTIFYING THE BIG IDEA Ask students to explain what scale drawings are and how to make them.

PROJECT LINK Allow students to use calculators to check their proportions. Encourage them to first write an equation to solve for the unknown scale distance.

---

9. *Geography* Shrink the map at the right. Use a scale of 0.5 cm to 1 cm (actual length).
   Check students' work for diagrams. Dimensions are given.
10. *Architecture* The height of a wall in a blueprint is 3 in. The actual wall is 96 in. high. Find the scale of the blueprint.
    1 in. to 32 in.

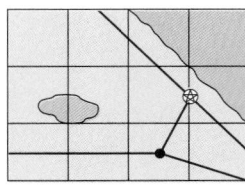

Use a map scale of 1 cm : 100 km. How many kilometers equal each of these lengths on the map?

11. 4 cm	12. 2.5 cm	13. 0.7 cm	14. 12 cm
400 km	250 km	70 km	1,200 km

Use a map scale of 1 cm : 100 km. How many centimeters equal each distance?

15. 125 km	16. 80 km	17. 4,000 km	18. 450 km
1.25 cm	0.8 cm	40 cm	4.5 cm

A scale model measures 2 cm × 7 cm. Find the dimensions of the actual object with the given scale.

19. 1 cm : 5 m	20. 1 cm : 2 km	21. 1 cm : 1 m	22. 1 cm : 80 m
10 m × 35 m	4 km × 14 km	2 m × 7 m	160 m × 560 m
23. 2 cm : 6 m	24. 1 cm : 0.5 m	25. 1 mm : 1 km	26. 1 cm : 2.5 m
12 m × 42 m	1 m × 3.5 m	20 km × 70 km	5 m × 17.5 m

27. *Open-ended* Create a scale drawing of an object.
    Check students' work.

Use the article below for Exercises 28–31. Copy and complete the table.

SCALING

DOWN Have you ever noticed the detail in a toy car? Designers try to make toy cars look real. A designer chooses a car to model and then selects a size for the toy. Next each piece on the real car is scaled down. To determine the scale, the designer uses the ratio $\dfrac{\text{size of toy car}}{\text{size of real car.}}$

	Part	Toy Size	Actual Size	
	Car	3 in.	100 in.	
28.	Door handle	▦	5 in.	0.15 in.
29.	Headlight	▦	8 in.	0.24 in.
30.	Front bumper	▦	6 ft	0.18 in.
31.	Rear window	▦	4.5 ft	0.135 in.

294

1. Make a scale drawing of the design. Use a scale of 4 cm to 1 cm (original design).

Check students' work; drawings should be 16 cm by 16 cm.

2. Use the scale drawing to find the actual length. **42 cm**

1 mm : 1.5 cm

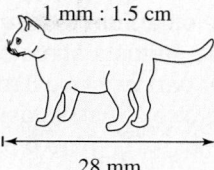

28 mm

Use each scale drawing to find the actual size.

32.

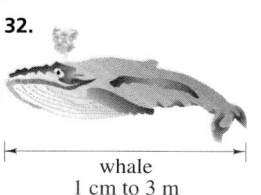

whale
1 cm to 3 m
12 m

33.

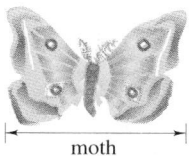

moth
1 cm to 2 cm
6 cm

34.

goat
1 mm to 6 cm
114 cm

35.

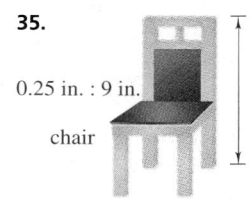

0.25 in. : 9 in.

chair

36 in.

36. *Writing* Why would you want to see the blueprint of a house before construction starts? **Answers may vary. Sample: You want to check that all dimensions have been scaled correctly.**

37. Use the designs at the right.

  a. The original design is on a 4×6 grid. What are the dimensions of the new *distorted* design? **4×12**

  b. *Reasoning* Why is it not in scale with the original? **The height remained the same, but the length doubled.**

Original Design   *Distorted Design*

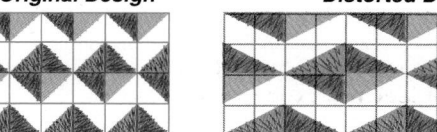

Mixed Review

Find each quotient. Round to the nearest hundredth.
(Lesson 4-9)

38. $36.45 \div 2.1$
17.36

39. $6.4 \div 0.56$
11.43

40. $7.12 \div 4.4$
1.62

41. $4.8 \div 3.2$
1.5

42. $11.22 \div 1.1$
10.2

Find a number that satisfies the given conditions.
(Lesson 5-1) **43–44. Answers may vary. Samples are given.**

43. a four-digit number divisible by 2, 3, 5, and 10 **1,200**

44. a four-digit number divisible by 2, 3, 5, and 9 **1,080**

45. Hank gets ready for school in 45 min. He can walk to school in 22 min. What time should he get up if school starts at 8:05 A.M.? *(Lesson 3-10)* **6:58 A.M.**

CHAPTER PROJECT

PROJECT LINK: ANALYZING DATA

Use ratios, proportions, and the data on page 284 to find the scale distances from the sun to your two assigned planets.

Check students' work.

PRACTICE

Practice 7-5 *Scale Drawings*

For Exercises 1–6, use a ruler and the scale to find the actual length indicated.

1. 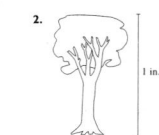 1 cm to 2 m — **8 m**

2. 1 in. to 15 ft — **24 ft**

3. 1 in. to 6 ft — **12 ft**

4. 1 cm to 5 mm — **22.5 mm**

5. 1 mm to 2 cm — **100 cm**

6. 1 mm to 1.5 cm — **52.5 cm**

7. Find the measure in cm of your thumb from the tip of your fingernail to where it meets your wrist. If you drew a $\frac{3}{4}$-size picture of yourself, how long would your thumb be in the drawing? **Measures will vary.**

8. The length of a wall in a floor plan is $6\frac{1}{2}$ in. The actual wall is 78 ft long. Find the scale of the floor plan. **1 in. : 12 ft**

9. The height of a building is $3\frac{3}{8}$ in. on a scale drawing. Find the actual height of the building if the scale used is $\frac{3}{4}$ in. : 2 ft. **9 ft**

In copymaster and workbook formats

RETEACHING

Reteaching 7-5 *Scale Drawings*

The *scale drawing* at the right shows the game field at Weld Middle School. The **scale** is a ratio that compares length on the drawing to the actual length. Here, every inch equals 36 yards on the actual field.

You can write the scale as a ratio in fraction form:
$$\frac{\text{drawing (in.)}}{\text{actual (yd)}} = \frac{1}{36}$$

To find the actual length of the field:
① Measure the scale drawing.   3 in.
② Write the scale as a ratio. $\frac{1}{36}$
③ Use the scale ratio in a proportion. $\frac{1}{36} = \frac{3}{n}$
④ Write cross products. $1 \times n = 3 \times 36$
⑤ Solve for n. $n = 108$
The actual length is 108 yd.

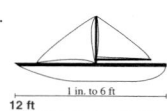

scale: 1 In. : 36 yd

Use the scale drawing to find the actual size.

1. Find the width of the field. **72 yd**

2. Find the perimeter of the field. **360 yd**

3. Find the width of the penalty area. **18 yd**

4. Find the distance from the center spot to the corner marked Z. **63 yd**

5. Brian kicks the ball all the way from the penalty kick line to the opposite goal area. About how far does he kick the ball? **about 90 yd**

6. Kaitlin makes a direct kick from the spot marked X. She scores by getting the ball into the goal nearest her. About how far does she kick the ball? **about 36 yd**

Write the scale used for each scale drawing.

7. a 12-in. model of a 60-ft boat **1 in. to 5 ft**

8. a 6-in. drawing of an 18-in. TV **1 in. to 3 in.**

9. a 4-cm model of a 28-cm hammer **1 cm to 7 cm**

10. a 9-in. drawing of a 54-ft garden **1 in. to 6 ft**

ENRICHMENT

Minds on Math Transparency

7-5

Replace 5 of the digits with zeroes in the problem below so the remaining numbers will have a sum of 1,111.

```
  111
  333
  777
+ 999
```

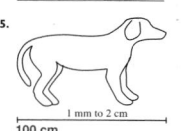

101	011	111
033	303	003
077	707	007
+ 900	+ 090	+ 990

See *Solution Key* for worked-out answers.

In Lesson 7-5, students learn to use a ratio to find the actual size of an object from a scale model. This toolbox shows students how to use indirect measurement.

ERROR ALERT! Students may not always choose the similar sides of triangles.
Remediation: Point out to students that the distance from the top of the person's head to the end of the shadow would not help find the height of the tree. Emphasize that to use indirect measurement, the sides being compared must be similar.

ASSESSMENT Exercises 1 and 2 Have students work with a partner. One partner explains to the other how to complete Exercise 1. The partners agree on the answer. Then the other partner gives directions on how to do Exercise 2. Ask students to share their methods for solving the problems.

Resources

 Teaching Resources

Teaching Aids Master 3

■ **ADDITIONAL PROBLEM**

Have students write a problem and draw a diagram for Exercise 5. The diagrams should show how they used indirect measurement. Ask students to label the measurements used.

EXPLORATION

MATH TOOLBOX

Indirect Measurement

▶ After Lesson 7-5

You can use *similar figures* to find measurements that cannot be found directly, like the height of a tree on a sunny day.

■ **EXAMPLE**

Look at the triangles formed by the person and her shadow and then those formed by the tree and its shadow. The triangles are similar. Write and solve a proportion to find the height of the tree.

$$\frac{\text{person's height}}{\text{length of her shadow}} \longrightarrow \frac{5 \text{ ft}}{3 \text{ ft}} = \frac{x \text{ ft}}{15 \text{ ft}} \longleftarrow \frac{\text{tree's height}}{\text{length of tree's shadow}}$$

$$5 \times 15 = 3x \longleftarrow \text{Solve the proportion.}$$

$$\frac{75}{3} = x$$

$$25 = x$$

The tree is 25 feet tall.

Find the missing length in each drawing.

1. 12 ft
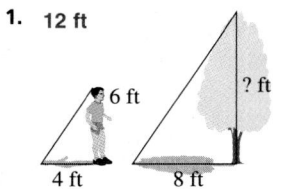
6 ft
? ft
4 ft   8 ft

2.
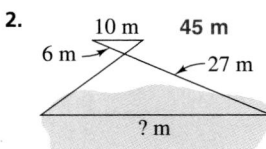
10 m   45 m
6 m   27 m
? m

3. $7\frac{1}{2}$ ft
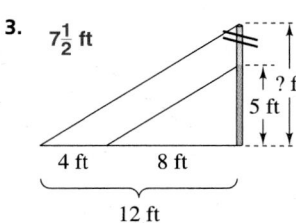
? ft
5 ft
4 ft   8 ft
12 ft

4.
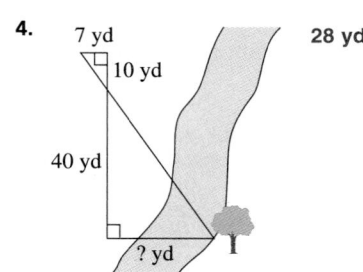
7 yd   28 yd
10 yd
40 yd
? yd

5. *Writing* Think of a situation when you have had to use indirect measurements to estimate the size or height of something. How did you make your estimate? **Check students' work.**

1 Focus

CONNECTING TO PRIOR KNOWLEDGE Ask students if they know the type of information asked for in a poll or survey. Have them give examples. **Answers may vary. Sample: opinions or data; voting choices, television preferences**

2 Teach

THINK AND DISCUSS

DIVERSITY In the United States, you use percents to show who is winning in a political election. Ask students if they know how other countries use percents in their political processes.

ERROR ALERT! Question 4 When students see that a portion of a grid is shaded, some may think the relationship is shaded squares to unshaded squares. **Remediation:** Help students see that you compare shaded squares to the *total number of squares*. Remind students that a percent compares a number to 100. Have students practice reading percent as "out of one hundred." For example, 5% is 5 out of 100.

VISUAL LEARNING Question 5 Help students visualize percents by drawing what the glass looks like when it is 100% full, or what the pizza looks like when it is 100% uneaten.

7-6 Percent Sense Using Models

What You'll Learn

▼ To model percents

...And Why

You can use models to help you understand the meaning of percents.

Here's How

Look for questions that
⊞ build understanding
✔ check understanding

THINK AND DISCUSS

When you compare a number to 100 you are finding a **percent**. You can write the ratio $\frac{75}{100}$ as 75%.

Words	Ratio	Percent
75 out of 100	$\frac{75}{100}$	75%

1. Check students' work.

1. ⊞ *Open-ended* Where have you seen percents used?

2a. 9% of the flashlights are defective.

2. Write each statement as a percent.
   a. 9 flashlights out of every 100 flashlights are defective.
   b. 45 cables of the 100 cables are not working.
   45% of the cables are not working.

You can model percents with 10 × 10 square grids.

■ EXAMPLE

Modeling What percent of the grid is shaded?

$$\frac{\text{amount shaded}}{\text{the whole}} = \frac{15 \text{ squares}}{100 \text{ squares}}$$

Write the ratio as a percent.

$$\frac{15}{100} \longrightarrow 15\%$$

So 15% of the grid is shaded.

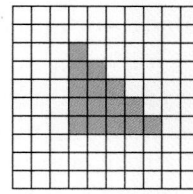

3. a. What percent of the grid in the Example is *not* shaded? 85%
   b. ⊞ *Reasoning* How could you find the answer to part (a) without counting squares? **Subtract 15% from 100%.**

4. ✔ *Try It Out* What percent of each grid is shaded?

   a.
   50%
   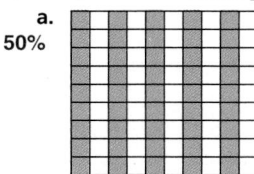

   b.
   28%
   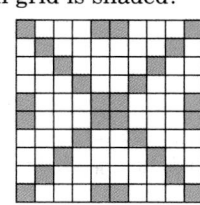

Lesson Planning Options

Prerequisite Skills
- using ratios (7-1)
- working with metric units (precourse)

Vocabulary/Symbols
percent

Materials/Manipulatives
- graph paper
- centimeter tape measure

Resources

📖 **Student Edition**

Skills Handbook, p. 541
Extra Practice, p. 528
Glossary/Study Guide

📼 **Teaching Resources**

Chapter Support File, Ch. 7
- Lesson Planner 7-6
- Practice 7-6, Reteaching 7-6
- Answer Masters 7-6
- Teaching Aids Masters 3, 10, 20–25
Glossary, Spanish Resources

📽 **Transparencies**
11, 12, 18, 22–29, Minds on Math 7-6

Warm Up

What is the prime factorization of 320.
2 × 2 × 2 × 2 × 2 × 2 × 5

297

■ ADDITIONAL EXAMPLE

FOR EXAMPLE
What percent of the grid is shaded? **36%**

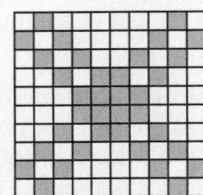

ASSESSMENT Provide students with meter

sticks and ask them to find objects that measure 1% of a meter and 99% of a meter.
Answers may vary. Sample: width of a finger; height of a doorknob

Work Together

Ask students: *How many millimeters are in a centimeter?* **10** *How many centimeters are in a meter?* **100**

3 Practice/Assess

EXERCISES *On Your Own*

TACTILE LEARNING Exercises 17–20 If you have block scheduling or extended class periods, provide students with grids labeled 1–100. Have students place a counter over each number in the problem that is also a solution to the problem. The number of counters on the grid is equal to the percent.

Technology Options

Prentice Hall Technology

  Software for Learners
• Math Blaster® Mystery*
• Interactive Student Tutorial, Chapter 7*

  Teaching Resource Software
• Computer Item Generator 7-6
• Resource Pro™ Chapter 7*

Internet • For related mathematics activities, visit the Prentice Hall site at www.phschool.com/math

*Available on CD-ROM only

Assignment Options for Exercises On Your Own

   Core 1–15, 17–20
   Extension 16

Use Mixed Review to maintain skills.

298

5. ♣*Estimation* Estimate each percent. Choose 25%, 50%, or 75%.
   a. About what percent of the fish tank is full? **75%**
   b. About what percent of the pizza is eaten? **25%**

Work Together
Writing Percents Using Data

6. ♣*Measurement* Use a centimeter tape measure to find each measure.
   a. length of your arm
   b. circumference of your head
   c. width of your smile
   d. length of your thumb

   6–7. Check students' work.

QUICK review

100 cm = 1 m

7. What percent of a meter is each measurement in Question 6?

8. ♣*Analyze* Why is it easier to use metric units than it is to use customary units in this activity?
   1 m is 100 cm, so 1 cm is 1% of 1 m.

Now you may assign Exercises 1–20.

EXERCISES *On Your Own*

Modeling Model each percent using a 10 × 10 square grid.

   1. 5%   **2.** 100%   **3.** 75%   **4.** 37%   **5.** 90%   **6.** 18%
1–6. See back of book.

7. *Entertainment* Use the table at the right.   **46%; 32%**
   a. What percent of those surveyed watch more than 21 hours of TV per week? What percent watched less than 15 hours?
   b. *Writing* How can you use your results from part (a) to find the missing percent in the table? **Subtract both results from 100%.**
   c. Find the missing percent. **22%**

Write each statement as a percent.

8. 11 students out of 100 students are left handed.
   11% of the students are left handed.
9. 97 days out of 100 days last summer were sunny.
   97% of the days last summer were sunny.
10. 4 radios out of every 100 radios arrive damaged.
    4% of the radios arrive damaged.
11. 85 answers out of 100 answers are correct.
    85% of the answers are correct.

How Much TV Do We Watch?

Hours Per Week	Percent
Less than 7	17
7 to 14	29
15 to 21	■
22 to 28	12
29 to 35	9
36 to 42	4
43 to 49	2
50 to 70	3
71 or more	1
No response	1
	100

Source: *TV Guide*

IDENTIFYING THE BIG IDEA Ask students to describe how to model percents.

LESSON QUIZ

1. Model 60% using a 10 × 10 grid.

Answers may vary. Sample:

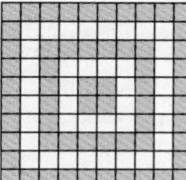

2. What percent of the grid is *not* shaded?
40%

Use the design at the right for Exercises 12 and 13.

12. a. What percent of the design is made up of each pattern?

i. ■ 20%   ii. ▦ 20%   iii. □ 38%   iv. ▨ 18%   v. ▧ 4%

b. Find the sum of the percents in part (a). **100%**

13. *Open-ended* Draw your own design. Use at least three patterns. How many squares should you start with? **Check students' work.**

Modeling **What percent of each grid is shaded? What percent is *not* shaded?**

14. **52%**

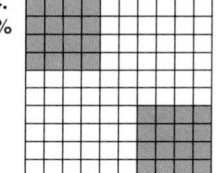

15. **48%**

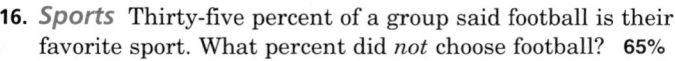

16. *Sports* Thirty-five percent of a group said football is their favorite sport. What percent did *not* choose football? **65%**

Number Sense **Use the numbers 1 through 100.**

17. What percent are multiples of 3? **33%**

18. What percent are odd? **50%**

19. What percent are prime? **25%**

20. What percent have at least one 7? **18%**

Mixed Review

Find each sum or difference. *(Lessons 6-4 and 6-5)*

21. $3\frac{2}{5} - 2\frac{1}{6}$ $1\frac{7}{30}$ **22.** $7\frac{9}{10} + 7\frac{5}{6}$ $15\frac{11}{15}$ **23.** $4\frac{1}{3} - 2\frac{5}{6}$ $1\frac{1}{2}$ **24.** $3\frac{1}{3} + \frac{3}{4}$ $4\frac{1}{12}$ **25.** $1\frac{4}{5} + 4\frac{3}{4}$ $6\frac{11}{20}$

Write each decimal as a fraction or mixed number in simplest form. *(Lesson 5-9)*

26. 0.84 $\frac{21}{25}$ **27.** 5.25 $5\frac{1}{4}$ **28.** 5.6 $5\frac{3}{5}$ **29.** 28.825 $28\frac{33}{40}$ **30.** 6.1 $6\frac{1}{10}$ **31.** 7.9 $7\frac{9}{10}$

32. *Choose a Strategy* There are 30 students in a math class. Twelve belong to the computer club, 8 to the hiking club, and 3 to both. How many belong to neither? **13 students**

Practice 7-6 *Percent Sense Using Models*

Use the 10 × 10 square grid to model each percent.

1. 72%   **2.** 14%   **3.** 34%

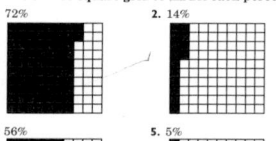

4. 56%   **5.** 5%   **6.** 11%

Write each amount as a percent.

7. 37 students out of 100 students have blue eyes. **37%**

8. 3 lightbulbs per every 100 lightbulbs were found to be defective. **3%**

9. 92 votes out of 100 votes were "yes." **92%**

10. 29 students out of 100 students live in an apartment. **29%**

For Exercises 11–13, use the whole numbers 1 through 100.

11. What percent of the numbers are even numbers? **50%**

12. What percent of the numbers are multiples of 6? **16%**

13. What percent of the numbers are multiples of 8? **12%**

14. A human's brain makes up about 2% of his or her body weight. What is the approximate weight of the brain of a person who weighs 100 lb? **2 lb**

15. Approximately 65% of a person's body weight is water. Merga's aunt weighs 100 lb. How many pounds are water? **approximately 65 lb**

16. Sixteen percent of the seventh-graders at East Side School chose art as an after-school interest. What percent of the students did not choose art? **84%**

In copymaster and workbook formats

Reteaching 7-6 *Percent Sense Using Models*

Percent shows "how many" out of 100. You can use a 10 × 10 square grid to model percent.

• The grid contains 100 squares.
• 65 of the squares are shaded.
• 65 percent (65%) of the squares are shaded.

You can write 65% as a ratio.

$65\% = \frac{65}{100}$

65% of the grid is shaded.

What percent of the grid is *not* shaded?
100 − 65 = 35
35% of the grid is not shaded.

Model each percent using the 10 × 10 square grid.

1. 9%   **2.** 35%   **3.** 78%

What percent of each grid is shaded? What percent is *not* shaded?

4.   **5.**   **6.**

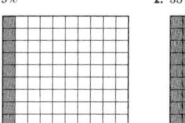 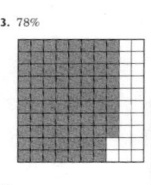 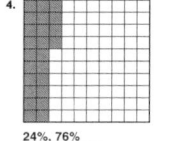 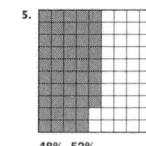 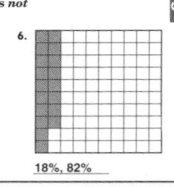

24%, 76%   **48%, 52%**   **18%, 82%**

Minds on Math Transparency

7-6

Jason is cutting 50-ft coils of wire into 6-ft pieces. Each of his 5 workers needs 6 of these pieces. How many full coils does Jason need?

4 full coils

See *Solution Key* for worked-out answers.

299

1 Focus

CONNECTING TO PRIOR KNOWLEDGE Ask students how they can write values as percents, fractions, and decimals. Ask students: *How do you express one half as a percent, as a fraction, and as a decimal?* **50%, $\frac{1}{2}$, 0.5**

Lesson Planning Options

Prerequisite Skills
• simplifying fractions (precourse)
• using fractions and decimals (5-9)

Materials/Manipulatives
• graph paper   • calculator

Resources

 Student Edition

Skills Handbook, p. 541
Extra Practice, p. 528
Glossary/Study Guide

 Teaching Resources

Chapter Support File, Ch. 7
• Lesson Planner 7-7
• Practice 7-7, Reteaching 7-7
• Answer Masters 7-7
Teaching Aids Masters 3, 10, 20–25
Glossary, Spanish Resources

 Transparencies
11, 12, 18, 19, 22–29, Minds on Math 7-7

Warm Up

Find the prime common factors of 52 and 78. **2, 13**

2 Teach

Work Together

Question 2 Have students discuss how to determine which percents, fractions, and decimals are equivalent.

THINK AND DISCUSS

Example 1 Ask students to explain why they can write 36% as $\frac{36}{100}$. **Answers may vary. Sample: Percent is a comparison to 100, so 36% is 36 : 100, or $\frac{36}{100}$.**

ERROR ALERT! Example 3 Some students may not use the correct keys on their calculators. **Remediation:** Have students review the steps. Encourage them to use estimation to check if their answers are reasonable.

7-7 Percents, Fractions, and Decimals

What You'll Learn
▼ To write percents as fractions and decimals
▼ To write decimals and fractions as percents

...And Why
You will better understand numbers in real-world situations, such as those related to animals or earth science.

Here's How
Look for questions that
⁘ build understanding
✔ check understanding

Work Together
Modeling Percents

Work in groups. Use a 10×10 grid for each model.

1. **a.** Model the percents 30%, 75%, 20%, and 50%.
    b. Model the fractions $\frac{3}{4}$, $\frac{1}{2}$, $\frac{3}{10}$, and $\frac{1}{5}$.
    c. Model the decimals 0.2, 0.5, 0.75, and 0.3.
    d. ⁘*Reasoning* Match each percent model with an equivalent fraction model and an equivalent decimal model. **a–d. See back of book.**

2. Express each shaded area as a percent, as a fraction in simplest form, and as a decimal.

   a. 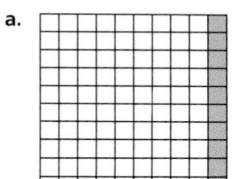   b.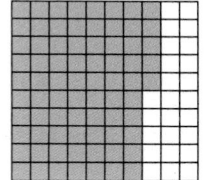

   10%; $\frac{1}{10}$; 0.1   75%; $\frac{3}{4}$; 0.75

THINK AND DISCUSS

▼ Writing Percents as Fractions and Decimals

You can use what you know about percents to write a percent as a fraction and then as a decimal.

■ EXAMPLE 1

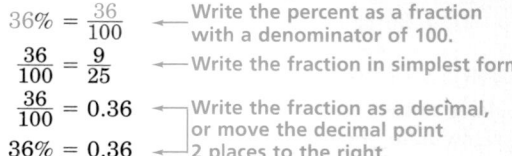
CALCULATOR HINT

You can use the 🔲 **%** key to write a percent as a decimal.

Write 36% as a fraction in simplest form and as a decimal.

$36\% = \frac{36}{100}$ ← Write the percent as a fraction with a denominator of 100.

$\frac{36}{100} = \frac{9}{25}$ ← Write the fraction in simplest form.

$\frac{36}{100} = 0.36$ ← Write the fraction as a decimal,
or move the decimal point
$36\% = 0.36$ ← 2 places to the right.

■ ADDITIONAL EXAMPLES

FOR EXAMPLE 1

Write 2% as a fraction in simplest form and as a decimal. $\frac{1}{50}$; 0.02

FOR EXAMPLE 2

Write $\frac{17}{25}$ as a decimal and then as a percent. 0.68, 68%

FOR EXAMPLE 3

Use a calculator to write the fraction $\frac{4}{9}$ as a percent. about 44.4%

AEP Help students who have difficulty converting fractions, decimals, and percents by asking them to complete a table like the one shown. Tell students to look for number patterns.

Percent	Decimal	Fraction
10%	0.1	$\frac{1}{10}$
20%	0.2	$\frac{2}{10}$
30%	0.3	$\frac{3}{10}$
40%	0.4	$\frac{4}{10}$
50%	0.5	$\frac{5}{10}$

AUDITORY LEARNING Have students work in groups. One student in each group explains how to write a percent as a fraction and as a decimal. The other group members follow the instructions. Students may wish to read their examples aloud to check their work.

ASSESSMENT Have pairs of students write instructions for writing a percent as a fraction and a decimal. Then have them write instructions for writing fractions as percents. Ask students to give examples.

3. ✓Try It Out Write each percent as a fraction in simplest form and as a decimal.

a. 25% $\frac{1}{4}$; 0.25   **b.** 66% $\frac{33}{50}$; 0.66   **c.** 4% $\frac{1}{25}$; 0.04

4. ✓Try It Out Ninety-nine percent of all kinds of plants and animals that have ever lived are now extinct. Write 99% as a fraction and then as a decimal. $\frac{99}{100}$; 0.99

Now you may assign Exercises 1–29.

2 *Writing Decimals and Fractions as Percents*

Sometimes you need to write a fraction as a decimal first, before writing the equivalent percent.

■ EXAMPLE 2

Earth Science About $\frac{7}{10}$ of Earth's surface is covered by water. Write $\frac{7}{10}$ as a decimal and as a percent.

$7 \div 10 = 0.7$ ⟵ Divide or simply write as a decimal.

$\frac{7}{10} = \frac{70}{100} = 70\%$ ⟵ Write as a fraction with a denominator of 100 or move the decimal point
$0.7 = 70\%$ ⟵ 2 places to the right.

5. ✓Try It Out Write each fraction as a decimal and then as a percent.

a. $\frac{4}{5}$ 0.8; 80%   **b.** $\frac{14}{25}$ 0.56; 56%   **c.** $\frac{5}{8}$ 0.625; 62.5%   **d.** $\frac{7}{20}$ 0.35; 35%

6. How would you write 0.285 as a percent? 28.5%

You can use a calculator to write a fraction as a percent.

■ EXAMPLE 3

▦ *Calculator* Use a calculator to write the fraction $\frac{2}{3}$ as a percent.

2  3 ▤ *0.6666666* ☒ 100 ▤ *66.666666* ≈ 66.7%

The fraction $\frac{2}{3}$ is about 66.7%.

7. ▦ *Calculator* Write each fraction as a percent. Then round the percents to the nearest tenth.

a. $\frac{1}{3}$ 33.3%   **b.** $\frac{7}{8}$ 87.5%   **c.** $\frac{8}{11}$ 72.7%   **d.** $\frac{2}{9}$ 22.2%

Now you may assign Exercises 30–63.

Technology Options

Prentice Hall Technology

Software for Learners
- Hot Page™ 21*
- Math Blaster® Mystery*
- Interactive Student Tutorial, Chapter 7*

Teaching Resource Software
- Computer Item Generator 7-7
- Resource Pro™ Chapter 7*

Internet • For related mathematics activities, visit the Prentice Hall site at www.phschool.com/math

*Available on CD-ROM only

Assignment Options for Exercises On Your Own

To provide flexible scheduling, this lesson can be subdivided into parts.

▼**1** Core 1–27
Extension 28, 29

▼**2** Core 30–49, 52–63
Extension 50, 51

Use Mixed Review to maintain skills.

3 Practice/Assess

EXERCISES *On Your Own*

ERROR ALERT! Exercises 7–24 Students may move the decimal point two places to the right instead of two places to the left when changing the percent to a decimal.
Remediation: Suggest students say the problem aloud and write it as a fraction first. Tell students: *Fifteen percent means fifteen per 100 or $\frac{15}{100}$.* Then have them use a calculator to find the decimal the fraction represents. Have them compare the decimal to the percent to see which way to move the decimal point.

CONNECTION TO TECHNOLOGY Exercises 31–48 Allow students to use a spreadsheet program to show each number as a fraction, decimal, and percent to check their work.

CONNECTION TO BUSINESS Ask students if there is a sales tax in your state. Have students figure out how much tax they pay for each dollar spent.

---

pages 302–303 On Your Own

50. Fractions, decimals, and percents each represent some number of parts of a whole. Percents represent the number of hundredth parts. Decimals represent tenths, hundredths, thousandths, or any other parts that are equivalent to fractions with a power of 10 in the denominator. Fractions could represent any number of equal parts of a whole.

5b.

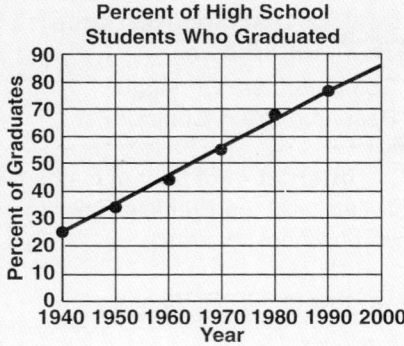

Percent of High School Students Who Graduated

EXERCISES *On Your Own*

Modeling **Model each number on a 10 × 10 grid.** 1–6. See back of book.

1. 0.8 **2.** 91% **3.** 0.72 **4.** $\frac{2}{5}$ **5.** 6% **6.** $\frac{11}{20}$

Write each percent as a decimal and then as a fraction in simplest form.

7. 15% 0.15; $\frac{7}{20}$ **8.** 75% 0.75; $\frac{3}{4}$ **9.** 88% 0.88; $\frac{22}{25}$ **10.** 18% 0.18; $\frac{9}{50}$ **11.** 50% 0.5; $\frac{1}{2}$ **12.** 14% 0.14; $\frac{7}{50}$

13. 7% 0.07; $\frac{7}{100}$ **14.** 70% 0.7; $\frac{7}{10}$ **15.** 62.5% 0.625; $\frac{5}{8}$ **16.** 33% 0.33; $\frac{33}{100}$ **17.** 27.4% 0.274; $\frac{137}{500}$ **18.** 2% 0.02; $\frac{1}{50}$

19. 42% 0.42; $\frac{21}{50}$ **20.** 22% 0.22; $\frac{11}{50}$ **21.** 17% 0.17; $\frac{17}{100}$ **22.** 0.5% 0.005; $\frac{1}{200}$ **23.** 44% 0.44; $\frac{11}{25}$ **24.** 5% 0.05; $\frac{1}{20}$

25. *Physical Science* The air we breathe is about 80% nitrogen and 20% oxygen. Write each percent as a fraction in simplest form and as a decimal. $\frac{4}{5}$, 0.8; $\frac{1}{5}$, 0.2

26. Write 58% as a decimal and as a fraction in simplest form. 0.58; $\frac{29}{50}$

Use the graph at the right for Exercises 27–29.

27. In what percent of lunch bags are you likely to find fruit? **23%**

28. Choose A, B, C, or D. Which of the following can you *not* conclude from the graph? **D**
   A. About one fourth of the lunch bags contained fruit.
   B. Almost 10% of the lunch bags contained a sandwich.
   C. Fruit was in almost twice as many lunch bags as cookies.
   D. Students don't take drinks in their lunch bags.

29. *Research* Take a lunch bag survey in your class. Make a graph to show your results.
Check students' work.

30. Copy and complete the table below. Write each fraction in simplest form.

Fraction	Decimal	Percent
$\frac{11}{50}$	0.22	22%
$\frac{39}{50}$	0.78	78%
$\frac{22}{25}$	0.88	88%
$\frac{11}{20}$	0.55	55%
$\frac{4}{5}$	0.8	80%

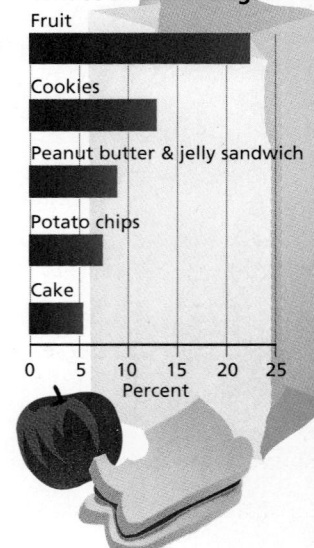

What's in Lunch Bags?

Fruit
Cookies
Peanut butter & jelly sandwich
Potato chips
Cake

0   5   10   15   20   25
Percent

302

WRAP UP

IDENTIFYING THE BIG IDEA Ask students to explain how to write percents as fractions and decimals. Also ask them to explain how to write decimals and fractions as percents.

LESSON QUIZ

Write each percent as a decimal and then as a fraction in simplest form. If necessary, round to the nearest hundredth.

1. 33% 0.33; $\frac{33}{100}$

2. 5% 0.05; $\frac{1}{20}$

3. 68% 0.68; $\frac{17}{25}$

4. 40% 0.4; $\frac{2}{5}$

Write each decimal or fraction as a percent.

5. 0.09 9%

6. 0.67 67%

7. $\frac{6}{30}$ 2%

8. $\frac{8}{25}$ 32%

Write each fraction or decimal as a percent.

31. $\frac{19}{20}$ 95%   32. 0.65 65%   33. $\frac{7}{50}$ 14%   34. $\frac{1}{4}$ 25%   35. 0.7 70%   36. 0.34 34%

37. 0.03 3%   38. $\frac{1}{8}$ 12.5%   39. 0.11 11%   40. $\frac{3}{200}$ 1.5%   41. 1.00 100%   42. $\frac{8}{20}$ 40%

43. 0.99 99%   44. $\frac{3}{10}$ 30%   45. 0.01 1%   46. 0.005 0.5%   47. $\frac{12}{30}$ 40%   48. $\frac{2}{25}$ 8%

49. *Writing* Describe how to write a decimal as a percent.
   Move the decimal point two places to the right and append the % sign.

50. *Reasoning* How are fractions, decimals, and percents alike? How are they different? **See margin p. 302.**

51. **a.** The table shows the fraction of high school students who graduated from 1940 to 1990. Write each fraction as a percent. **25%; 34%; 44%; 55%; 69%; 77%**

Year	1940	1950	1960	1970	1980	1990
Graduates	$\frac{1}{4}$	$\frac{17}{50}$	$\frac{11}{25}$	$\frac{11}{20}$	$\frac{69}{100}$	$\frac{77}{100}$

Source: *Universal Almanac*

b. Graph the data in the table. Make a line graph. **See margin p. 302.**

c. *Data Analysis* Use your graph to predict the percent of high school graduates in the year 2000.
   Answers may vary. Sample: 86%

Calculator **Write each fraction as a percent. Round percents to the nearest tenth.**

52. $\frac{2}{3}$ 66.7%   53. $\frac{4}{15}$ 26.7%   54. $\frac{7}{11}$ 63.6%   55. $\frac{12}{45}$ 26.7%   56. $\frac{78}{98}$ 80.0%   57. $\frac{1}{7}$ 14.3%

58. $\frac{6}{13}$ 46.2%   59. $\frac{17}{30}$ 56.7%   60. $\frac{4}{9}$ 44.4%   61. $\frac{2}{15}$ 13.3%   62. $\frac{7}{18}$ 38.9%   63. $\frac{18}{21}$ 85.7%

Mixed Review

Use <, =, or > to complete each statement. *(Lesson 3-3)*

64. 0.112 ▦ 0.121   65. 0.9985 ▦ 0.998   66. 0.0009 ▦ 0.001   67. 1.9 ▦ 11.9
   <   >   <   <

Simplify using the distributive property. *(Lesson 4-3)*

68. $(2.5 \times 16) + (2.5 \times 14)$ 69. $4 \times (6 - 2) - 23$ 70. $(2.08 \times 20) - (8.9 \times 20)$
   75   −7   −136.4

71. *Choose a Strategy* A hotel has 28 rooms at $74 per day, 152 rooms at $93 per day, 317 rooms at $112 per day, and 18 rooms at $136 per day. To the nearest dollar, what is the average cost of a room? **$105**

PRACTICE

Practice 7-7 *Percents, Fractions, and Decimals*

Write each fraction as a decimal and as a percent.

1. $\frac{3}{5}$ 0.6; 60%   2. $\frac{7}{10}$ 0.7; 70%   3. $\frac{13}{25}$ 0.52; 52%   4. $\frac{17}{20}$ 0.85; 85%

Write each decimal as a percent and as a fraction in simplest form.

5. 0.02 2%; $\frac{1}{50}$ 6. 0.45 45%; $\frac{9}{20}$ 7. 0.4 40%; $\frac{2}{5}$ 8. 0.92 92%; $\frac{23}{25}$

Write each percent as a decimal and as a fraction in simplest form.

9. 46% 0.46; $\frac{23}{50}$ 10. 17% 0.17; $\frac{17}{100}$ 11. 90% 0.9; $\frac{9}{10}$ 12. 5% 0.05; $\frac{1}{20}$

The table shows the fraction of students who participated in extracurricular activities from 1965 to 1995. Complete the table by writing each fraction as a percent.

Students' Extracurricular Choices

Year	1965	1970	1975	1980	1985	1990	1995
Student participation (fraction)	$\frac{3}{4}$	$\frac{8}{10}$	$\frac{17}{20}$	$\frac{39}{50}$	$\frac{21}{25}$	$\frac{19}{25}$	$\frac{87}{100}$
Student participation (percent)	75%	80%	85%	78%	84%	76%	87%

Write each fraction or decimal as a percent. Write the percent (without the percent sign) in the puzzle.

Across
1. $\frac{3}{5}$
2. $\frac{1}{5}$
3. 0.55
5. 0.23
6. $\frac{7}{20}$
7. 0.17
9. 0.4
10. $\frac{9}{25}$

Down
1. $\frac{13}{20}$
2. 0.25
3. $\frac{1}{2}$
4. $\frac{3}{20}$
5. $\frac{3}{10}$
6. $\frac{3}{10}$
7. 0.1
8. $\frac{4}{25}$

In copymaster and workbook formats

RETEACHING

Reteaching 7-7 *Percents, Fractions, and Decimals*

- To *write a percent as a fraction* in simplest form, first write a fraction with a denominator of 100. Then simplify.

  $74\% = \frac{74}{100} = \frac{37}{50}$

- To *write a percent as a decimal*, first write a fraction with a denominator of 100. Then write the decimal.

  $74\% = \frac{74}{100} = 0.74$

- To *write a decimal as a percent*, move the decimal point two places to the right.

  $0.23 = 23\%$

Here are two ways to *write a fraction as a percent.*

- Write an equivalent fraction with a denominator of 100, then write the percent.

  $\frac{3}{20} = \frac{15}{100} = 15\%$

- Divide the numerator by the denominator.

  $\frac{3}{8} = \begin{array}{r} 0.375 \\ 8)\overline{3.000} \\ -24 \\ \hline 60 \\ -56 \\ \hline 40 \\ -40 \\ \hline 0 \end{array} = 37.5\%$

  Move the decimal point two places to the right.

  So, $\frac{3}{8} = 37.5\%$.

Write each percent as a decimal and as a fraction in simplest form.

1. 30%   0.30, $\frac{3}{10}$
2. 14%   0.14, $\frac{7}{50}$
3. 16%   0.16, $\frac{4}{25}$
4. 5%   0.05, $\frac{1}{20}$
5. 92%   0.92, $\frac{23}{25}$
6. 80%   0.80, $\frac{4}{5}$
7. 21%   0.21, $\frac{21}{100}$
8. 38%   0.38, $\frac{19}{50}$

Write each fraction or decimal as a percent.

9. $\frac{17}{25}$ 68%   10. 0.85 85%   11. 0.16 16%   12. $\frac{5}{40}$ 12.5%
13. $\frac{7}{200}$ 3.5%   14. $\frac{1}{10}$ 10%   15. 0.64 64%   16. 0.008 0.8%
17. $\frac{9}{20}$ 45%   18. $\frac{6}{15}$ 40%   19. 0.32 32%   20. 0.07 7%
21. $\frac{13}{100}$ 13%   22. $\frac{45}{50}$ 90%   23. 0.010 1%   24. 0.60 60%

ENRICHMENT

Minds on Math Transparency

7-7

Rachel is thinking of a three-digit number. She tells Steven that when she divides her number by the sum of the digits of her number, the quotient is 26. She tells him that her number is the least one for which this is true. What is Rachel's number?

234

See *Solution Key* for worked-out answers.

303

PROBLEM SOLVING PRACTICE ★★

This page provides problems for students to solve using their knowledge of ratios, measurement, rates, number lines, percents, expressions, proportions, estimating the quotient of decimals, and scale drawings. Allow students to use any method they find helpful.

Exercise 2 Advise students first to write how many meters equal 1 km.

Exercise 3 Students should be able to demonstrate the truth of the statement they choose. Tell students to show their work.

Exercise 7 Challenge students to write a true statement of their own.

PROBLEM SOLVING PRACTICE

Choose the best answer.

1. The ratio of a team's wins to losses is exactly 4 to 3. The team could have— **C**
   A. 12 wins and 10 losses
   B. 16 wins and 9 losses
   C. 16 wins and 12 losses
   D. 30 wins and 40 losses

2. The distance between school and the library is 0.8 kilometers. How many meters is 0.8 kilometers? **J**
   F. 0.0008 meters   G. 8 meters
   H. 80 meters   J. 800 meters

3. Matthew wrote 24 letters in 15 seconds. Lydia wrote 18 letters in 10 seconds. Which statement is true? **B**
   A. Matthew writes faster than Lydia.
   B. Lydia writes faster than Matthew.
   C. Matthew wrote 6 more letters than Lydia during the same time period.
   D. Matthew and Lydia together wrote at a rate of 42 letters in 25 seconds.

4. Janelle is practicing for a shot put competition. Each day she plots on a number line the longest distance she threw for on that day. Which point best represents a distance of 9.05 meters? **F**

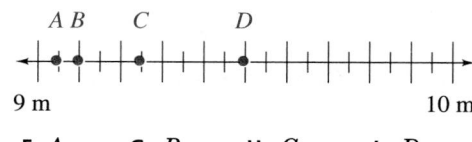

   F. A G. B H. C J. D

5. Which pair is equivalent to $\frac{2}{5}$? **D**
   A. 4% and 0.04   B. 25% and 0.025
   C. 25% and 0.25   D. 40% and 0.4

6. At one car dealer, $\frac{2}{5}$ of the vehicles sold during the year were sport utility vehicles. What percent of the vehicles sold were sport utility vehicles? **J**
   F. 2.5%   G. 20%   H. 25%   J. 40%

7. For the proportion $\frac{9}{20} = \frac{n}{100}$, which statement is *not* true? **C**
   A. $900 = 20n$ B. $\frac{900}{20} = n$
   C. $\frac{9}{100} = \frac{n}{20}$ D. $\frac{100}{n} = \frac{20}{9}$

Please note that items 8–10 each have *five* answer choices.

8. A car traveled 279.9 miles on 9.8 gallons of gasoline. A good estimate for the miles per gallon that the car traveled is— **J**
   F. less than 20 miles per gallon
   G. 20 miles per gallon
   H. 25 miles per gallon
   J. 30 miles per gallon
   K. 40 miles per gallon

9. A scale model of an airplane is 7.5 inches long. The scale used to make the model was 1 inch : 5 feet. What is the length of the original airplane? **D**
   A. 1.5 inches   B. 1.5 feet
   C. 37.5 inches   D. 37.5 feet
   E. Not Here

10. A garage charges $2.00 for the first 90 minutes and $1.00 for each additional half-hour. Which equation can you use to find the cost of parking for 4 hours? **H**
    F. $C = 2.00 + 4(1.00)$
    G. $C = 2.00 + 2.5(1.00)$
    H. $C = 2.00 + 5(1.00)$
    J. $C = 4(2.00 + 1.00)$
    K. Not Here

1 Focus

CONNECTING TO PRIOR KNOWLEDGE Ask students how they estimate sums and differences of whole numbers. **Answers may vary. Sample: Round numbers so they are easy to add or subtract mentally.** Ask: *How would you round 174 to the nearest ten?* **down to 170** *To the nearest hundred?* **up to 200**

2 Teach

THINK AND DISCUSS

ERROR ALERT! Question 3 Make sure students understand that the *value* of the ten boxes in the model totals $50. Students may think the model represents $100. **Remediation:** Make sure students understand that 100% of anything means *all* of the value. Tell students that in Question 3, 100% of the value is $50.

CONNECTING TO THE STUDENTS' WORLD Have students conduct a survey finding favorite foods. Then have them find the percent of classmates who like the foods listed.

VISUAL LEARNING Have students practice rounding numbers at the board. Have them explain why they rounded up or down.

7-8 Estimating with Percents

What You'll Learn

1 To estimate percents using models

2 To estimate a percent using mental math

...And Why

You often estimate percents when you shop or leave a tip in a restaurant.

Here's How

Look for questions that
- build understanding
- ✔ check understanding

1. sale price as percent of original price and the dollar amount of the sale price

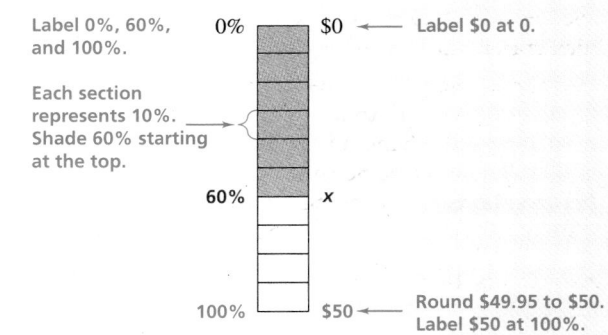

0% $0
30% x
100% $130

Now you may assign Exercises 1–33.

THINK AND DISCUSS

1 Estimating Percents Using Models

Estimating percents when you shop helps you make smart consumer decisions. You can use models to estimate percents.

■ **EXAMPLE 1** *Real-World Problem Solving*

A jacket is on sale for 60% of the regular price of $49.95 (or 40% off). Is $25 enough to buy the jacket?

Step 1 Make a model with ten equal sections.

Label 0%, 60%, and 100%.

Each section represents 10%. Shade 60% starting at the top.

0% → $0 ← Label $0 at 0.

60% x

100% → $50 ← Round $49.95 to $50. Label $50 at 100%.

Step 2 Find the dollar value of each section.

$$\text{100\% dollar value} \div \frac{\text{total number}}{\text{of sections}} = \frac{\text{dollar value of}}{\text{each section}}$$

$$\$50 \div 10 = \$5$$

Each section represents $5. Six sections represent 6 × 5, or $30. So $25 is not enough to buy the jacket.

1. What does the shading in the model in Example 1 represent? **See above left.**

2. Copy the model in Example 1 on graph paper. Write dollar amounts for 20%, 40%, 60% and 80%. **Check students' work for models. 20% = $10, 40% = $20, 60% = $30, 80% = $40**

3. ✔*Try It Out* What dollar amount does the shaded part of the model at the left represent? **$39**

Lesson Planning Options

Prerequisite Skills
- rounding and estimating decimals (3-6)
- adding and subtracting decimals (3-7)

Resources

Student Edition

Skills Handbook, p. 535
Extra Practice, p. 528
Glossary/Study Guide

Teaching Resources

Chapter Support File, Ch. 7
- Lesson Planner 7-8
- Practice 7-8, Reteaching 7-8
- Alternative Activity 7-8
- Answer Masters 7-8
- Teaching Aids Masters 20–25

Glossary, Spanish Resources

Transparencies
11, 12, 18, 22–29, 91, Minds on Math 7-8

Warm Up

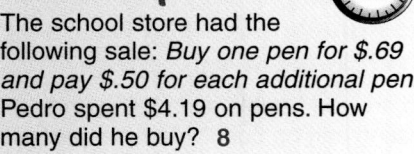

The school store had the following sale: *Buy one pen for $.69 and pay $.50 for each additional pen.* Pedro spent $4.19 on pens. How many did he buy? **8**

■ ADDITIONAL EXAMPLES

FOR EXAMPLE 1

A pair of jeans is on sale for 80% of the regular price of $34.99 (or 20% off). Is $30 enough to buy the jeans? **yes**

FOR EXAMPLE 2

Estimate a 15% tip for each amount given.

a. $35.75 **about $5.40**

b. $29.34 **about $4.50**

FOR EXAMPLE 3

Estimate the sales tax and final cost of a pair of sneakers that cost $34.99 with a sales tax of 5%. **sales tax: about $1.75; final cost: about $37**

AEP **Example 2** Write labels for *bill*, *tip*, and *percent* above the numbers shown to help students follow the steps.

EXTENSION Example 3 Have students research the history of the sales tax. Ask them to find how each state uses the money collected from the sales tax. Then have students share their reports with the class.

ASSESSMENT Have pairs of students work together to write the steps needed to estimate 15% of 130. Have them write a full example for each step.

Technology Options

Prentice Hall Technology

 **Software for Learners**
- Math Blaster® Mystery*
- Interactive Student Tutorial, Chapter 7*

 Teaching Resource Software
- Computer Item Generator 7-8
- Resource Pro™ Chapter 7*

Internet • For related mathematics activities, visit the Prentice Hall site at www.phschool.com/math

*Available on CD-ROM only

Assignment Options for Exercises On Your Own

To provide flexible scheduling, this lesson can be subdivided into parts.

▼ **Core** 1–15, 17, 19–33
Extension 16, 18

▼ **Core** 34–40, 42
Extension 41

Use Mixed Review to maintain skills.

❷ *Estimating Percents Using Mental Math*

You can use mental math to estimate the added cost of sales tax.

■ **EXAMPLE 2** *Real-World Problem Solving*

Music You buy a CD for $14.99. The sales tax is 6%. Estimate the sales tax and the final cost.

$14.99 ≈ $15.00	◄— Round to a convenient place.
6% ⟶ 6¢ per dollar	◄— Think of the percent as cents per dollar.
15 × 6 = 90	◄— Multiply mentally.
15 + 0.90 = 15.90	◄— Add the estimates.

The sales tax is about $.90. The final cost is about $15.90.

4. ✓*Try It Out* Estimate the sales tax and final cost for a hat that costs $18.59 with a sales tax of 5%.
Estimates may vary slightly. Sample: $.95; $19.54

5. ⬛*Think About It* Why wouldn't you want to round the price of an item down before estimating the sales tax?
You want to estimate high, so you know what amount is enough.

You can use mental math to determine the amount of a tip.

QUICKreview

Shortcut: To find 10% of a number, move the decimal point to the left one place.
10% of 34.70 is 3.47.

3.4.70

■ **EXAMPLE 3** *Real-World Problem Solving*

You and two friends eat at a local restaurant. Estimate a 15% tip for a bill of $16.22.

$16.22 ≈ $16.00 ◄— Round to a convenient place.

First estimate 10% of the bill.

10% = 0.10	◄— Think of the percent as a decimal.
0.10 × 16 = 1.60	◄— Multiply mentally.

Half of $1.60 is $.80. So $.80 is about 5%.

10% + 5% = 15%
↓   ↓   ↓
1.60 + 0.80 = 2.40

So a 15% tip is about $2.40.

6–7. Estimates may vary slightly. Samples are given.

6. ✓*Try It Out* Estimate a 15% tip for each bill amount given.   a. **$2.70**   b. **$3.45**
a. $18.29   b. $23.40   c. $41.63 **$6.30**

7. ⬛*Look Back* Estimate a 20% tip for the bill in Example 3. **$3.20**

Now you may assign Exercises 34–42.

3 Practice/Assess

EXERCISES *On Your Own*

ERROR ALERT! Exercises 1–4 Students may find the wrong value for x because they do not understand the models. **Remediation:** Tell students the model shows what a certain percent of a number looks like. Have them copy the models on their own paper. Show students each division of the bar represents 10%. Have them write what each division

represents on the percent side. Ask: *What does each division represent on the $ side?* **the total price divided by 10** Have them write what each division represents on the dollar side. The value of x should now be clear.

AUDITORY LEARNING Exercise 14 Point out that the mitt is not 75% *off*, but 75% of the original price. Make sure students understand the difference. Ask them to compare 75% of the original price and 75% off the original price.

CONNECTING TO THE STUDENTS' WORLD

Exercise 18 Suggest students try and find out how tall they were at age two. Suggest they look in baby books, call their pediatrician, or ask a family member for help. Have them estimate their expected adult height.

WRAP UP

IDENTIFYING THE BIG IDEA Ask students to describe how to estimate the percent of a number.

EXERCISES *On Your Own*

What dollar amount does each shaded part represent?

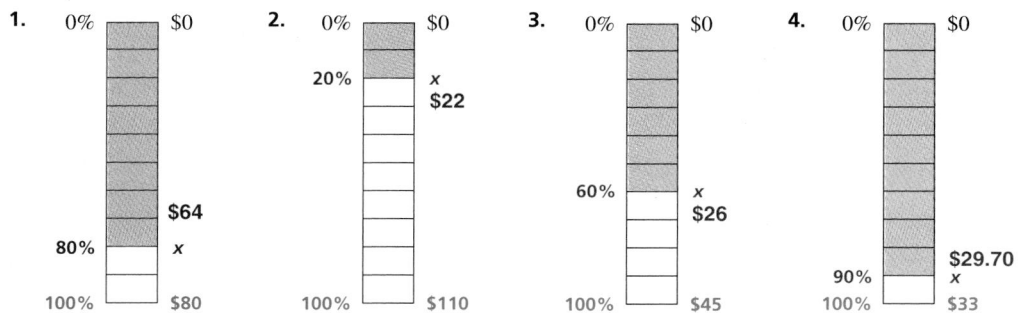

1. 0% $0 ... 80% $64 x ... 100% $80

2. 0% $0 ... 20% x $22 ... 100% $110

3. 0% $0 ... 60% x $26 ... 100% $45

4. 0% $0 ... 90% $29.70 x ... 100% $33

Draw a model to help you estimate each amount.

5–12. Estimates may vary slightly. Samples are given.

5. 90% of 41 **36**
6. 20% of 486 **100**
7. 10% of 129 **13**
8. 60% of 40 **24**

9. 25% of 53 **13**
10. 75% of 98 **75**
11. 15% of 21 **3**
12. 80% of 160 **128**

13. *Shopping* All items in a store are marked at 70% of the original price. Estimate the sale price of each item.
   a. a T-shirt regularly priced at $16.99
      $11.90
   b. a jacket regularly priced at $129
      $91

14. *Sports* A baseball mitt is on sale for 75% of the original price of $39.99. Estimate the sale price of the mitt. **$30**

15. The regular price for a pair of boots is $23.99. They are on sale for 80% of the regular price. Estimate the sale price.
   $16.20

16. *Reasoning* The regular price of a chair is $349. Estimate the amount saved at each sale below.
   a. 20% off **$70**
   b. 30% off **$105**
   c. 75% off **$262.50**

17. *Recreation* Use the skateboard ad at the right.
   a. *Reasoning* What percent of the regular price of the skateboard is the sale price? **80%**
   b. *Estimation* Estimate the cost of the skateboard. **b. See below.**
   c. Is $25 enough to buy the skateboard on sale?
      No; $22 < $24 or $25.60.

20% OFF $32

18. *Pediatrics* By the age of two, a child's height is usually about 50% of its full adult height. Estimate the adult height of a 2-year-old whose height is 2 ft 9 in. **5 ft 6 in.**

17b. Estimates may vary. $24 or $25.60

---

pages 306–308   On Your Own

34. $2.25, $77.25; $4.50, $79.50; $3, $78; $3.75, $78.75; $5.25, $80.25

35. $.45, $15.45; $.90, $15.90; $.60, $15.60; $.75, $15.75; $1.05, $16.05

36. $.30, $10.30; $.60, $10.60; $.40, $10.40; $.50, $10.50; $.70, $10.70

37. $.56, $19.06; $1.11, $19.61; $.74, $19.24; $.93, $19.43; $1.30, $19.80

38. $.63, $21.66; $1.26, $22.29; $.84, $21.87; $1.05, $22.08; $1.47, $22.50

39. $.03, $.82; $.06, $.85; $.04, $.83; $.05, $.84; $.07, $.86

PRACTICE

Practice 7-8 *Estimating with Percents*

Draw a model to help you estimate each amount.
Sample drawings shown.

1. 81% of 60 **48** 2. 20% of 490 **100** 3. 48% of 97 **50**

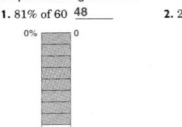
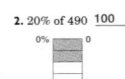
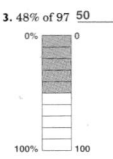

Circle A, B, C, or D. Determine the best estimate.

4. 72% of 80
   A. 64 **B.** 56
   C. 6 D. 5.6

5. 18% of 90
   A. 18 B. 9
   C. 27 D. 1.5

6. 21% of 80
   A. 20 B. 160
   C. 16 D. 1.6

7. 39% of 200
   A. 80 B. 60
   C. 100 D. 72

8. 81% of 150
   A. 80 **B.** 120
   C. 160 D. 60

9. 68% of 250
   A. 140 B. 210
   C. 170 D. 175

Solve.

10. Mr. Andropolis wants to leave the waitress a 12% tip.
    Estimate the tip he should leave if the family's bill is $32.46.
    Answers may vary. Sample: $3.50

11. Michael receives a 9.8% raise. He currently earns $1,789.46
    per month. Estimate the amount by which his monthly
    earnings will increase.
    $180

12. Estimate the sales tax and final cost of a book that costs
    $12.95 with a sales tax of 6%.
    Sample answers: $.65 tax, $13.65 total

13. A real estate agent receives a 9% commission for every house
    sold. Suppose she sold a house for $112,000. Estimate her
    commission. Answers may vary. Sample: $11,200

In copymaster and workbook formats

RETEACHING

Reteaching 7-8 *Estimating with Percents*

You can use a model to estimate a
percent of a number.

Estimate 40% of $70.

0%	50%	100%
$0	$35	$70

- The line segment represents 100%, or
  $70.
- The point marked on the line is 50% of
  $70 (half of $70), or $35.

40% of $70 is a little less than half.
A good estimate is $30.

You can estimate a percent of a number
using mental math.

Estimate 19% of $83.

① Round to convenient numbers.
   20% of 80
② Find 10% of 80.
   10% of 80 = 8.
③ 20% of 80 is 2 times as much.
   20% of 80 is 2 × 8 or 16.
19% of 83 is about 16.

Estimate the dollar amount that the point represents. Estimates may vary.

1. 0%   37%   100%
   $0 $200
   about $75

2. 0%   60%   100%
   $0 $40
   about $25

3. 0%   80% 100%
   $0 $150
   about $120

Estimate each amount. Estimates may vary.

4. 50% of 41 **20**
5. 20% of 99 **20**
6. 10% of 73 **7**
7. 40% of 59 **24**
8. 1% of 94 **1**
9. 5% of 313 **15**
10. 70% of 498 **350**
11. 15% of 172 **25**
12. 25% of 154 **38**
13. 90% of 81 **72**
14. 30% of 60 **18**
15. 15% of 401 **60**
16. 40% of 23 **9**
17. 20% of 178 **34**
18. 75% of 21 **15**
19. 25% of 216 **50**
20. 50% of 77 **40**
21. 15% of 39 **6**
22. 3% of 887 **27**
23. 70% of 419 **280**
24. 80% of 69 **56**

ENRICHMENT

Minds on Math Transparency

7-8

I am the least number that has factors of 1, 2, 3, 4, 5, 6, 7,
and 8. What number am I?

840

See *Solution Key* for worked-out answers.

308

LESSON QUIZ

What dollar amount does the shaded part
represent? **$70**

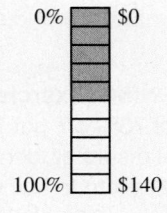

Draw a model to help you estimate each
amount.

1. 60% of 135 **about 80**
2. 10% of 80 **about 8**
3. 25% of 320 **about 80**
4. 75% of 200 **about 150**

Estimate each amount. 19–33. Estimates may vary slightly. Samples are given.

19. 50% of 89 **45** 20. 10% of 302 **30** 21. 25% of 43 **10** 22. 30% of 295 **90** 23. 1% of 512 **5**

24. 25% of 59 **15** 25. 60% of 789 **480** 26. 90% of 49 **45** 27. 10% of 872 **87** 28. 75% of 23 **18**

29. 15% of 201 **30** 30. 50% of 37 **19** 31. 5% of 411 **20** 32. 40% of 81 **32** 33. 25% of 78 **20**

**Use the sales tax chart at the right. Estimate the sales tax
and final cost of each item below in each state.**
34–39. See margin p. 307.

34. in-line skates: $75
35. dictionary: $14.59
36. poster: $9.99
37. calculator: $18.50
38. game: $21.03
39. erasers: $.79

State Sales Tax

State	Tax
Colorado	3%
Florida	6%
Georgia	4%
Massachusetts	5%
New Jersey	7%

Source: *The World Almanac and
Book of Facts*

40. *Eating Out* A meal costs $5.83. Estimate each tip.
    a. 10% tip b. 15% tip c. 20% tip
       $.60 $.90 $1.20

41. *Writing* Suppose 10% of a bill is $4.36. How can you use **Double the 10% tip to get the 20%**
    this to find a 20% tip? A 15% tip? **tip. Add half the 10% tip to the 10% tip to get the 15% tip.**

42. a. *Jobs* Miguel received the following tips. Estimate the
      value of each.
      i. 15% of $4.20 **$.60** ii. 10% of $4.75 **$.50** iii. 12% of $6.00 **$.72**
    b. Which tip was for the greatest amount? **iii**

Mixed Review

Find each product or quotient. *(Lessons 6-8 and 6-9)*

43. $3\frac{1}{3} \div 1\frac{1}{2}$ **$2\frac{2}{9}$** 44. $1\frac{1}{5} \times 4\frac{1}{3}$ **$5\frac{1}{5}$** 45. $7\frac{2}{3} \div 8\frac{7}{10}$ **$\frac{230}{261}$** 46. $12 \times 4\frac{8}{9}$ **$58\frac{2}{3}$** 47. $3\frac{5}{6} \div 3\frac{3}{10}$ **$1\frac{16}{99}$**

Find the GCF of each set of numbers. *(Lesson 5-3)*

48. 54, 72 **5** 49. 85, 95 **4** 50. 16, 20, 36 **18** 51. 30, 15, 60 **15** 52. 9, 27, 54 **9** 53. 14, 21, 84 **7**

54. What metric unit would you use to measure each item?
    (Lessons 3-8 and 3-9)
    a. length of a bridge **m** b. weight of a cat **kg** c. amount of juice **mL**

55. *Choose a Strategy* Suppose a team is out of a soccer
    tournament if it loses a game. If 63 games must be played to
    determine the champion, how many teams were entered? **64 teams**

1 Focus

CONNECTING TO PRIOR KNOWLEDGE
Review estimating percents. Ask students: *A bank pays between 7% and 10% interest per year on its savings accounts. You deposit $100 in an account. About how much interest would you earn in a year on your $100?*

between $7 and $10 Discuss strategies for finding the range.

2 Teach

THINK AND DISCUSS

VISUAL LEARNING Have students write on an index card the steps for finding a percent of a number. Have them keep the card on their desk for reference.

CONNECTION TO HEALTH Example 1 Ask students to discuss safe heart rates for people of various ages. Tell students to include reasons for changes in heart rate.

VISUAL LEARNING Example 1 Have students study the keys on their calculators. Tell students to use the percent key if their calculator has one. Ask students to change the percent to a decimal before multiplying if the calculator does not have the percent key.

ALGEBRA Connection

7-9   Finding a Percent of a Number

What You'll Learn

▼ To find a percent of a number using a model or a calculator

▼ To find a percent of a number using proportions

...And Why

Your safe exercise range can be found by calculating the percent of a number.

Here's How

Look for questions that
⊞ build understanding
✔ check understanding

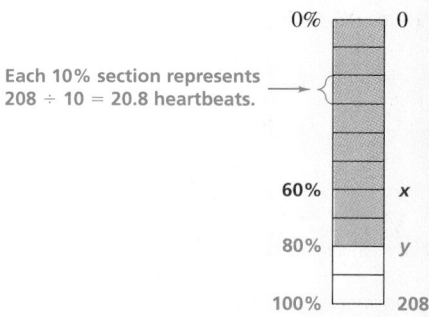

THINK AND DISCUSS

1   *Using Modeling or a Calculator*

Your heart rate increases when you exercise. A safe exercise range is between 60% and 80% of your maximum *safe heart rate*. Your maximum safe heart rate is 220 minus your age.

■ **EXAMPLE 1**   *Real-World Problem Solving*

Fitness Find the safe exercise range for a 12-year-old.
220 − 12 = 208 ◄── Find the maximum safe heart rate.

Method 1 Use a model.

Each 10% section represents
208 ÷ 10 = 20.8 heartbeats. ➞

	0%	0
60%	x
80%	y
100%	208

60% of 208 is 6 sections × 20.8 = 124.8 ≈ 125 heartbeats
80% of 208 is 8 sections × 20.8 = 166.4 ≈ 166 heartbeats

 Method 2 Use a calculator and the percent key to multiply.
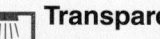
208 ⊠ 60 ▓ ▤ *124.8* ≈ 125
208 ⊠ 80 ▓ ▤ *166.4* ≈ 166

Both methods give the same result. The safe exercise range for a 12-year-old is about 125 to 166 heartbeats per minute.
1a. 120 to 160 beats/min; 102 to 136 beats/min

1. **a.** ✔*Try It Out* Find the safe exercise ranges for a 20-year-old and for a 50-year-old.
   b. How does the safe exercise range change as a person grows older? **The range decreases with age.**

Now you may assign Exercises 1–20, 26–30.

Lesson Planning Options

Prerequisite Skills
• multiplying fractions (6-7)

Materials/Manipulatives
• calculator

Resources

📖 **Student Edition**
Skills Handbook, p. 540
Extra Practice, p. 528
Glossary/Study Guide

📦 **Teaching Resources**
Chapter Support File, Ch. 7
• Lesson Planner 7-9
• Practice 7-9, Reteaching 7-9
• Answer Masters 7-9
• Teaching Aids Masters 20–25
Glossary, Spanish Resources

▨ **Transparencies**
18, 19, 22–29, Minds on Math 7-9

Warm Up
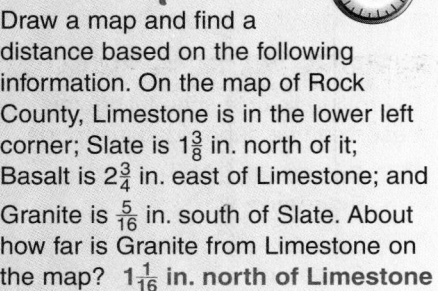
Draw a map and find a distance based on the following information. On the map of Rock County, Limestone is in the lower left corner; Slate is $1\frac{3}{8}$ in. north of it; Basalt is $2\frac{3}{4}$ in. east of Limestone; and Granite is $\frac{5}{16}$ in. south of Slate. About how far is Granite from Limestone on the map? $1\frac{1}{16}$ **in. north of Limestone**

309

FOR EXAMPLE 1

Find the safe exercise range for a 40-year-old and a 70-year-old. **108–144 beats per minute; 90–120 beats per minute**

FOR EXAMPLE 2

Find 60% of 45. **27**

ASSESSMENT Tell students: *A karat is a measure of purity in gold. Pure gold is 24 karats. However, jewelers often mix gold with other metals to give the jewelry strength.*

- *How many karats is a ring that is 75% gold?* **18 karats**

- *In some parts of the world, you can find gold jewelry that is 92% pure. How many karats is this?* **about 22 karats**

- *Which method would you use to solve each problem?* **Answers may vary. Sample: You can solve the first problem using**

fractions since 75% is equivalent to $\frac{3}{4}$. The second is easier to solve using decimals. You can use a visual model for both.

AEP Question 3 Pair students who have difficulty calculating decimals with those who do not. Ask pairs to share their reasons for choosing their methods. Encourage them to also discuss their mental math strategies.

Technology Options

Prentice Hall Technology

 **Software for Learners**
- Math Blaster® Mystery*
- Interactive Student Tutorial, Chapter 7*

 Teaching Resource Software
- Computer Item Generator 7-9
- Resource Pro™ Chapter 7*

Internet • For related mathematics activities, visit the Prentice Hall site at www.phschool.com/math

*Available on CD-ROM only

Assignment Options for Exercises On Your Own

To provide flexible scheduling, this lesson can be subdivided into parts.

 **Core** 1–20, 26–29
Extension 30

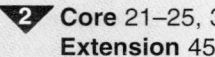 **Core** 21–25, 31–44
Extension 45

Use Mixed Review to maintain skills.

---

2 Using Proportions

You can also write a proportion to find the percent of a number.

■ **EXAMPLE 2**

Find 30% of 80.

$$30\% = \frac{30}{100}$$

Use a model to write a proportion.

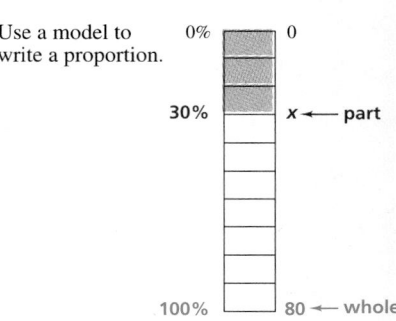

$$\frac{30}{100} = \frac{x}{80} \qquad \longleftarrow \text{Write a proportion.}$$
$$30 \times 80 = 100 \times x \qquad \longleftarrow \text{Write the cross products.}$$
$$2{,}400 = 100x \qquad \longleftarrow \text{Multiply.}$$
$$\frac{2{,}400}{100} = x$$
$$24 = x \qquad \longleftarrow \text{Divide.}$$

30% of 80 is 24.

2. ✓Try It Out Find each percent. Use any method.
- **a.** 75% of 84 **63**
- **b.** 37% of 140 **51.8**
- **c.** 80% of 255 **204**
- **d.** 10% of 56 **5.6**
- **e.** 50% of 786 **393**
- **f.** 43% of 61 **26.23**

For some problems, one method may be more appropriate or convenient than another.
a. Check students' work for method and reasoning.

3. a. ⬡*Choose* Which method would you use to answer each question? Explain your reasoning. Use a 24-hour day.
   i. Catherine spends 25% of her day in school. How many hours does Catherine spend in school each day?
   ii. Ian practices the piano for 5% of the day. For how many hours does Ian practice the piano each day?

b. ⬡*Reasoning* Describe how to calculate the percents in part (a) using mental math. **See margin p. 311.**

Now you may assign Exercises 21–25, 31–45.

3 Practice/Assess

EXERCISES *On Your Own*

Exercises 6–20 Have students work in pairs. Ask students to explain why they prefer one method over another.

ERROR ALERT! Exercises 6–20 Students may make careless errors when calculating percent. **Remediation:** Remind students to estimate the percent of a number. Tell students to use their estimates to check if their answers are reasonable.

AUDITORY LEARNING Exercises 21–23 Have students explain to the class how they would decide which method for finding percent to use.

CONNECTING TO THE STUDENTS' WORLD Exercises 21–23 Survey how many girls in the class swam, how many boys in the class swam, and how many girls sailboarded. Have students find the percentages for the data and compare them to the values in the table.

CONNECTION TO LANGUAGE Exercises 26–29 If you have block scheduling or extended class periods, pair the students and give each pair a paragraph from a newspaper or novel. Have them count the vowels and find the percentages of each vowel there are in the passage. Combine the data from all the students and find the total percentages. Have students compare these to the values in the table. Ask: *Which percentages are closer, the percentage for your paragraph or all the paragraphs? Why do you think this happened?*

EXERCISES *On Your Own*

Modeling **Use a model to find each percent.**

1. 20% of 48
   9.6
2. 50% of 288
   144
3. 90% of 72
   64.8
4. 30% of 305
   91.5
5. 25% of 112
   28

Find each percent. Use a model or a calculator.

6. 12% of 90
   10.8
7. 5% of 86
   4.3
8. 35% of 120
   42
9. 15% of 60
   9
10. 70% of 240
    168
11. 66% of 99
    65.34
12. 7% of 50
    3.5
13. 18% of 170
    30.6
14. 63% of 450
    283.5
15. 44% of 165
    72.6
16. 8% of 235
    18.8
17. 55% of 91
    50.05
18. 75% of 32
    24
19. 12% of 72
    8.64
20. 22% of 288
    63.36

Sports **Use the table at the right for Exercises 21–23. There were 250 boys and 250 girls surveyed. Use any method.**

21. How many girls swam? **190 girls**

22. How many boys swam? **155 boys**

23. How many girls sailboarded? **5 girls**

24. *Savings* During the summer Rosa earned $950. She saved 40%. How much money did she save?
    $380

25. Nail biting is a hard habit to kick. About 40% of children and teenagers bite their nails. A town has 1,618 children and teenagers. How many would you expect to be nail biters?
    647 children and teenagers

Teens Who Participated in Water Sports During One Year

Water Sport	Boys	Girls
Swimming	62%	76%
Waterskiing	13%	13%
Boating	15%	15%
Scuba Diving	9%	4%
Surfing	7%	3%
Sailboarding	4%	2%

Source: Teenage Research Unlimited

Language **Estimate the number of letters you expect in each passage given below. Use the table below.**

Frequency of Vowels in Written Passages

Letter	A	E	I	O	U	Y
Frequency	8%	13%	6%	8%	3%	2%

26. number of E's in a passage of 300 letters
    39 E's
27. number of A's in a passage of 1,400 letters
    112 A's
28. number of U's in a passage of 235 letters
    7 U's
29. number of I's in a passage of 695 letters
    42 I's
30. *Reasoning* Why don't the percents in the table above add up to 100%? **Words also contain consonants.**

pages 309–310   Think and Discuss

3b. i. 25% is $\frac{1}{4}$ of the whole, so 25% of a day is $24 \div 4 = 6$ h; ii. 5% is $\frac{1}{2}$ of 10%, which is $\frac{1}{10}$ of the whole. So 5% of a day is $(24 \div 10) \div 2 = 1.2$ h or 1 h and 12 min.

page 313   Checkpoint 2

1.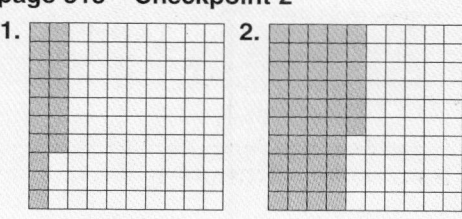
2.
3.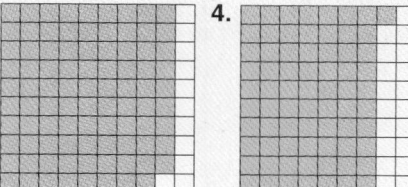
4.

CONNECTION TO SPORTS Exercise 43
Have students pick their favorite sports team and find what percentage of their games they won this year. Have them find how many games they played and how many they won. Have them check to make sure all these numbers match up mathematically.

CONNECTION TO STATISTICS Ask students to look in newspapers or magazines to find examples of percents used in statistics.

CONNECTION TO SCIENCE Exercise 44 Tell students their bodies consist of about 18.5% carbon and 3.3% nitrogen. Have students calculate the body weight of the percentages of carbon and nitrogen for a person weighing 114 lb. **about 21 lb; about 3.8 lb**

WRAP UP

IDENTIFYING THE BIG IDEA Ask students to describe four methods for finding the percent of a number.

JOURNAL Have students think of percents they have seen in their life. Have them write a real-world problem involving one of these percents. Ask them to work this problem four different ways.

Math at Work

If you have block scheduling or extended class periods, consider having small groups of students construct a model of a web page that shows how to find the percent of a

---

CHECKPOINT 2

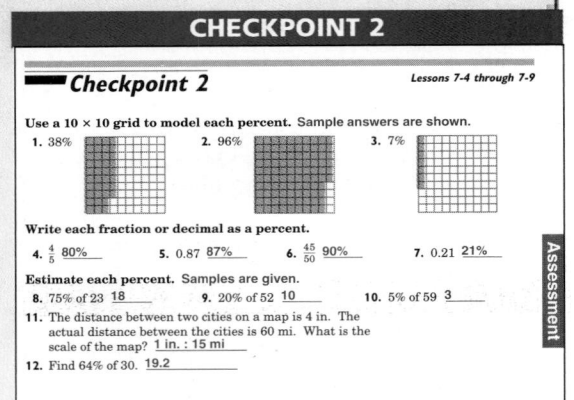

Checkpoint 2 *Lessons 7-4 through 7-9*

Use a 10 × 10 grid to model each percent. Sample answers are shown.
1. 38%   2. 96%   3. 7%

Write each fraction or decimal as a percent.
4. $\frac{4}{5}$ **80%**   5. 0.87 **87%**   6. $\frac{45}{50}$ **90%**   7. 0.21 **21%**

Estimate each percent. Samples are given.
8. 75% of 23 **18**   9. 20% of 52 **10**   10. 5% of 59 **3**
11. The distance between two cities on a map is 4 in. The actual distance between the cities is 60 mi. What is the scale of the map? **1 in. : 15 mi**
12. Find 64% of 30. **19.2**

Assessment

---

page 313   Checkpoint 2

5.
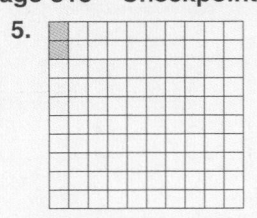

6.
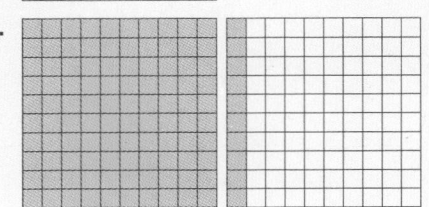

Use a proportion to find each percent.

31. 20% of 180 **36**	**32.** 55% of 160 **88**	**33.** 15% of 320 **48**	**34.** 5% of 230 **11.5**	**35.** 75% of 680 **510**
36. 15% of 90 **13.5**	**37.** 65% of 80 **48**	**38.** 11% of 600 **66**	**39.** 40% of 40 **16**	**40.** 72% of 325 **234**

41. In the United States, about 46% of the population wears glasses or contact lenses.
  a. In a group of 85 people, how many people would you expect to wear glasses or contact lenses? **39 people**
  b. *Writing* Explain how you found your answer to part (a) and why you chose that method.
  c. How many people in your classroom would you expect to wear glasses or contact lenses?
b–c. Check students' work.

42. *Entertainment* A dance club printed 400 tickets for its annual show and sold 85% of them. How many tickets did it sell? **340 tickets**

43. *Sports* The Lions won 75% of their 28 games this year. How many games did they win? **21 games**

44. About 67% of a person's body weight is water. Suppose a person weighs 114 lb. About how many pounds are water? **76 lb**

45. *Simple interest* earned on a savings account is found by multiplying the amount deposited, the interest rate, and the number of years. Suppose you deposited $1,000 at an interest rate of 4% for 5 years. Find the simple interest earned. **$200**

> **JOURNAL**
> Provide an example of each of the three methods shown for finding the percent of a number.

Mixed Review

Complete each statement. *(Lesson 4-10)*

46. 10.3 m = ▇ km **0.0103**   **47.** 56,930 mg = ▇ kg **0.05693**   **48.** 253 L = ▇ kL **0.253**   **49.** 36 mm = ▇ cm **3.6**

Estimate each sum or difference. *(Lesson 6-1)*

50. $2\frac{2}{5} + 2\frac{1}{4}$ **4**   **51.** $18\frac{1}{4} - 12\frac{3}{5}$ **5**   **52.** $2\frac{1}{20} + 1\frac{1}{3}$ **3**   **53.** $11\frac{7}{8} - \frac{5}{6}$ **11**   **54.** $8\frac{3}{4} + 4\frac{2}{3}$ **14**

55. *Choose a Strategy* Suppose one day you save 1 dime and the second day you save 2 dimes. Each day you save 1 more dime than the day before. How much money will you have after 2 weeks? **$10.50**

312

number. Each method for finding a percent could be on a separate page. Encourage students to create a flow chart to show how to move through the pages.

LESSON QUIZ

Find each percent. Use a model or a calculator.
1. 9% of 225 **20.25**
2. 62% of 387 **239.94**

Use any method to find each percent.
3. 6% of 175 **10.5**
4. 30% of 340 **102**

Use a proportion to find each percent.
5. 12% of 500 **60**
6. 62% of 425 **263.5**

✓ CHECKPOINT 2

Lessons 7-4 through 7-9

Modeling **Use a 10 × 10 grid to model each percent.**

1. 17%   2. 46%   3. 89%   4. 71%   5. 2%   6. 110%
1–4. See margin p. 311.   5–6. See margin p. 312.

Write each fraction or decimal as a percent.

7. $\frac{6}{8}$ **75%**   8. 0.45 **45%**   9. 0.67 **67%**   10. $\frac{15}{25}$ **60%**   11. $\frac{19}{20}$ **95%**   12. 0.07 **7%**

Estimation **Estimate each percent.**

13. 10% of 72 **7**   14. 80% of 41 **32**   15. 40% of 59 **24**   16. 25% of 191 **50**   17. 60% of 54 **30**

18. *Travel* A map has a scale of 1 cm : 75 km. The distance on the map from Hondo to Cheyenne is 3.5 cm. What is the actual distance? **262.5 km**

19. **Choose A, B, C, or D.** Which method should *not* be used to find 88% of 40? **D**

A. 0.88×40 B. $\frac{88}{100} \times 40$ C. 88 % ☒ 40 ▤   D. $\frac{40}{n} = \frac{88}{100}$

Math at Work

INTERNET HELP PROVIDER

If you enjoy surfing the Internet, making computer art, or exploring Web life, then a career as an Internet help provider might be for you. Help providers educate people about technical writing and are involved in Web page design. Consulting and technical drawing are also responsibilities of an Internet help provider.

Technical drawing and design require a knowledge of geometry and proportion. Technical writing requires good problem solving and logical reasoning skills.

Visit the Web sites suggested at www.yahoo.com/Business_and_Economy/ Companies/Internet_Services/Web_Services/ Hosting/ to learn more about Internet help providers.

PRACTICE

■ **Practice 7-9** *Finding a Percent of a Number*

Find each percent.

1. 15% of 20 ___3___	2. 40% of 80 ___32___	3. 20% of 45 ___9___	4. 18% of 70 ___12.6___
5. 90% of 120 ___108___	6. 65% of 700 ___455___	7. 25% of 84 ___21___	8. 63% of 80 ___50.4___
9. 60% of 50 ___30___	10. 45% of 90 ___40.5___	11. 12% of 94 ___11.28___	12. 15% of 52 ___7.8___
13. 37% of 80 ___29.6___	14. 25% of 16 ___4___	15. 63% of 800 ___504___	16. 72% of 950 ___684___
17. 55% of 250 ___137.5___	18. 18% of 420 ___75.6___	19. 33% of 140 ___46.2___	20. 53% of 400 ___212___

Solve each problem.

21. The Badgers won 75% of their 32 games this year. How many games did they win? **24 games**

22. Vivian earned $540 last month. She saved 30% of this money. How much did she save? **$162**

23. A survey of the students at Lakeside School yielded the results shown below. There are 1,400 students enrolled at Lakeside. Complete the table for the number of students in each activity.

How Lakeside Students Spend Their Time on Saturday

Activity	Percent of Students	Number of Students
Baby-sitting	22%	308
Sports	26%	364
Job	15%	210
At home	10%	140
Tutoring	10%	140
Other	17%	238

In copymaster and workbook formats

RETEACHING

■ **Reteaching 7-9** *Finding a Percent of a Number*

You can find 70% of 90 using different methods.

Use a fraction.
① Write the percent as a fraction in simplest form.
$70\% = \frac{70}{100} = \frac{7}{10}$
② Multiply by the fraction.
$\frac{7}{10} \times \frac{90}{1} = \frac{630}{10} = 63$
70% of 90 = 63.

Use a proportion.
① Write a proportion.
$\frac{70}{100} = \frac{c}{90}$
② Write cross products and simplify.
$100 \times c = 70 \times 90$
$100c = 6,300$
③ Solve.
$c = \frac{6,300}{100}$
$c = 63$
70% of 90 = 63

Use a fraction to find each percent.

1. 45% of 60 ___27___   2. 60% of 160 ___96___   3. 15% of 220 ___33___
4. 90% of 80 ___72___   5. 35% of 60 ___21___   6. 70% of 350 ___245___

Use a proportion to find each percent.

7. 40% of 60 ___24___   8. 85% of 300 ___255___   9. 15% of 160 ___24___
10. 22% of 500 ___110___   11. 37% of 400 ___148___   12. 68% of 250 ___170___

Find each percent.

13. 25% of 100 ___25___   14. 70% of 70 ___49___   15. 10% of 70 ___7___
16. 75% of 40 ___30___   17. 80% of 50 ___40___   18. 12% of 60 ___7.2___
19. 24% of 80 ___19.2___   20. 45% of 90 ___40.5___   21. 60% of 72 ___43.2___
22. 55% of 120 ___66___   23. 95% of 180 ___171___   24. 16% of 80 ___12.8___

ENRICHMENT

Minds on Math **T**ransparency

7-9

A restaurant supplier sells plastic forks in packages of 30 and plastic knives in packages of 24. Micah wants to buy the same number of forks and knives. What is the minimum number of packages of each he would have to buy?

4 packages of forks and 5 packages of knives

See *Solution Key* for worked-out answers.

---

1 Focus

CONNECTING TO PRIOR KNOWLEDGE Ask students where they have seen circle graphs. **Answers may vary. Sample: newspapers, magazines** Ask: *How are circle graphs different from line graphs?* **Answers may vary. Sample: Circle graphs show data** compared to a whole. Line graphs show changes over a period of time.

2 Teach

Work Together

TACTILE LEARNING **Question 6** Have students use their compasses to draw another circle the same size as the circle for Question 4. Tell them to cut the new circle in half. Label one of the halves 50%. Then cut the other half in half. Label one of these halves 25%.

THINK AND DISCUSS

AEP Ask students to bring in examples of circle graphs. Group students in pairs. Encourage students who have difficulty reading English to explain the information displayed in a graph to a partner. Have the partner record the information and try to copy the graph. Students discuss the process they use.

Lesson Planning Options

Prerequisite Skills
- finding equivalent fractions (5-5)
- measuring angles (precourse)

Vocabulary/Symbols
circle graphs

Materials/Manipulatives
- metric ruler
- tape
- calculator
- scissors
- compass

Resources

 Student Edition

Skills Handbook, p. 540

Extra Practice, p. 528

Glossary/Study Guide

 Teaching Resources

Chapter Support File, Ch. 7
- Lesson Planner 7-10
- Practice 7-10, Reteaching 7-10
- Answer Masters 7-10

Teaching Aids Masters 3, 10, 19

Glossary, Spanish Resources

 Transparencies

9, 19, 42–44, Minds on Math 7-10

Warm Up

What fraction of 2 dollars is represented by the total of these coins: 3 quarters, 2 dimes, and 2 nickels? $\frac{21}{40}$

DATA ANALYSIS Connection

7-10 Data and Circle Graphs

What You'll Learn

▼ To sketch circle graphs

...And Why

You can use circle graphs to display data about television, reading, and the environment.

Here's How

Look for questions that
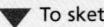 build understanding
✔ check understanding

1–6. Check students' work.

Work Together
Applying Data to Circle Graphs

Texas A&M University asked children between 4 years old and 12 years old how they received money. Here are the results.

Allowance	Doing Chores	Earned Outside the Home	Gifts
54%	20%	10%	16%

Source: *The Book of Lists for Kids*

Circle graphs provide a good visual display of percent data. Work with a partner to make a circle graph for the data above.

1. Make a strip 10 cm long. Leave a tab at the end as shown.

|←————————— 10 cm —————————→|
| 54% | 20% | 10% | 16% | ←Tab |
|←————————— 100% —————————→|

2. Since 10 cm = 100 mm, each millimeter represents 1% of the strip. Mark the strip with the percentages given in the table.

3. Shape the strip into a percent ring and tape the ends. Be sure to align the beginning and end of the strip.

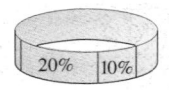

4. **Modeling** Use a compass. Draw a circle slightly larger than your percent ring. Place a dot at the center of the circle.

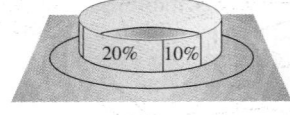

5. Use your percent ring to mark the percentages around the circumference of the circle. Use a ruler to connect the marks to the center of the circle.

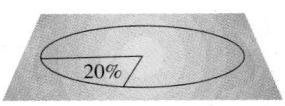

6. **Estimation** Label your graph and give it a title. Does each section appear to equal the percents in the table above?

314

FOR EXAMPLE

Sketch a circle graph showing how Rita budgets her money for a week.

Rita's Weekly Budget

Savings	Hobbies	Food	Other
43%	25%	14%	18%

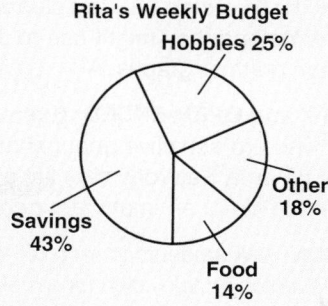

Rita's Weekly Budget

Hobbies 25%
Savings 43%
Food 14%
Other 18%

DIVERSITY Some students may have difficulty using a compass to draw circles.

Give these students circle manipulatives to trace around.

ASSESSMENT Have students form groups of three. Give each student a circle to draw a section of a circle graph on. Have each student sketch the section of the circle graph for one of these percents: 37%, 10%, and 53%. Have each student cut out their section. They can check their work by seeing if the sections form a circle when placed together. Have them discuss any errors.

$25\% = \frac{1}{4}$

THINK AND DISCUSS

Most of the time a sketch of a circle graph gives you adequate information. You can sketch a circle graph by estimating a percent and using its fraction equivalent. For example, $24\% \approx 25\%$, which equals $\frac{1}{4}$. So shade a section that is about $\frac{1}{4}$ of the whole.

7. Each percent is approximately what fraction of the whole?
   a. 52% $\frac{1}{2}$ b. 26% $\frac{1}{4}$ c. 32% $\frac{1}{3}$ d. 74% $\frac{3}{4}$

You can use math skills you already know to sketch a circle graph.

8a.

b.

■ **EXAMPLE**   *Real-World Problem Solving*

Environment Sketch a circle graph showing the willingness of teen drivers to use the bus more often.

What Teen Drivers Will Do for Air Quality

Option	Very Willing	Somewhat Willing	Not Very Willing	Don't Know
Use Bus More Often	22%	25%	50%	3%
Car Pool More Often	49%	26%	23%	2%

Source: Gallup Organization

Estimate the size of each section using the table above.

Very Willing ⟶ 22% is a little less than $\frac{1}{4}$ of the whole circle.

Somewhat Willing ⟶ 25% is $\frac{1}{4}$ of the whole circle.

Not Very Willing ⟶ 50% is $\frac{1}{2}$ of the whole circle.

Don't Know ⟶ 3% is the part of the circle left.

8c.

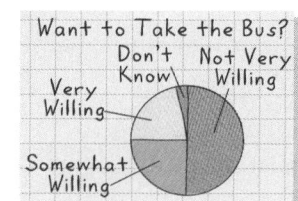

Want to Take the Bus?

Don't Know | Not Very Willing
Very Willing
Somewhat Willing

⟵ Draw a circle.

⟵ Divide the circle into two parts for the 50% section. The 25% section is half of the remaining section. Then estimate the 22% and 3% sections.

⟵ Label each section and give your graph a title.

8. *Estimation* Sketch a circle graph for the percentages given.
   a. 23%, 51%, 26%   b. 33%, 32%, 35%   c. 74%, 13%, 13%
   a–c. See above left.

Technology Options

Prentice Hall Technology

 **Software for Learners**
- Math Blaster® Mystery*
- Interactive Student Tutorial, Chapter 7*

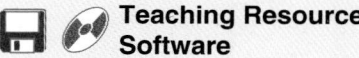 **Teaching Resource Software**
- Computer Item Generator 7-10
- Resource Pro™ Chapter 7*

Internet • For related mathematics activities, visit the Prentice Hall site at www.phschool.com/math

*Available on CD-ROM only

Assignment Options for Exercises On Your Own

Core 1–25, 27
Extension 26, 28–30

Use Mixed Review to maintain skills.

3 Practice/Assess

EXERCISES *On Your Own*

ERROR ALERT! Exercises 7–22 Students may leave out one of the percents in their circle graph. **Remediation:** Have students check to make sure they have one section for each percent. Show students the sum of the percents is 100% so the sections must cover 100% of the circle.

ESTIMATION Exercise 23 Ask students to describe a method they might use to check the sections on their graphs.

DIVERSITY and OPEN-ENDED Exercise 26 Students who are sensitive about sharing what they do on a Saturday may list activities for 24 h in the life of an imaginary person.

EXTENSION Ask students to record the time they spend watching television for a week. Then have them make a circle graph of the data.

WRAP UP

IDENTIFYING THE BIG IDEA Ask students to explain how to make circle graphs.

LESSON QUIZ

Sketch a circle graph for the percentages given.

1. 4%, 18%, 47%, 31%

---

pages 315–316 Think and Discuss

1.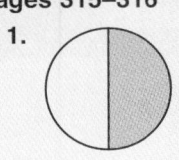
2.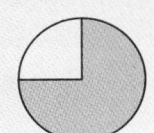
3.
4.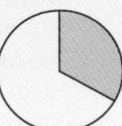
5.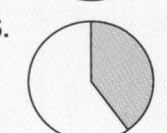
6.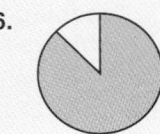
7.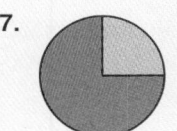
8.
9.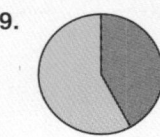
10.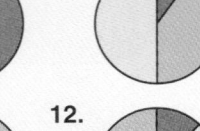
11.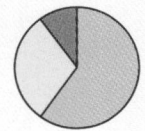
12.
13.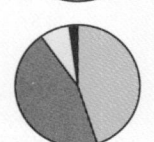
14.
15.
16.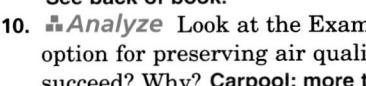
17.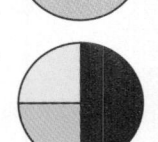
18.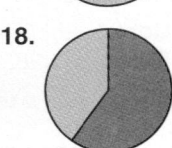

b. Sketch a circle. Mark $\frac{1}{4}$ of the circle. Then shade $\frac{1}{2}$ of the marked sector.

9. ✔ *Try It Out* Refer to the Example. Sketch a circle graph showing the willingness of teens to car pool more often. **See back of book.**

10. ♣ *Analyze* Look at the Example and Question 9. Which option for preserving air quality seems more likely to succeed? Why? **Carpool; more than half the teen drivers are willing to carpool more often.**

11. a. A section that is $\frac{1}{8}$ of a circle graph would be what percent of the whole? **12.5%**

b. Explain how you would sketch a circle graph with a shaded section equal to $\frac{1}{8}$ of the whole.

Now you may assign Exercises 1–30.

EXERCISES *On Your Own*

Sketch a circle graph with a shaded section equal to the fraction given. **1–6. See margin.**

1. $\frac{1}{2}$
2. $\frac{3}{4}$
3. $\frac{1}{6}$
4. $\frac{1}{3}$
5. $\frac{4}{10}$
6. $\frac{7}{8}$

Estimation Sketch a circle graph for the percentages given. **7–18. See margin.**

7. 25%, 75%
8. 36%, 64%
9. 42%, 58%
10. 10%, 40%, 50%
11. 60%, 30%, 10%
12. 12%, 26%, 62%
13. 45%, 45%, 8%, 2%
14. 5%, 14%, 33%, 48%
15. 24%, 76%
16. 34%, 32%, 34%
17. 48%, 25%, 27%
18. 59%, 41%
19. 42%, 19%, 39%
20. 55%, 45%
21. 20%, 75%, 5%
22. 8%, 92%

19–22. See back of book.

Data Analysis The table below shows the results of 1,000 adults surveyed. Use the table for Exercises 23 and 24.

Amount of Time Adults Think They Spend Reading for Pleasure

Too much	Too little	About right	Don't know
7%	73%	16%	4%

Source: Gallup Organization

23. *Estimation* Sketch a circle graph for the data. **See back of book.**

24. How many adults responded "Don't know"? "Too little"? "About right"? **40 adults, 730 adults, 160 adults**

PORTFOLIO

For your portfolio, choose one or two items from your work for this chapter. Here are some possibilities:
• corrected work
• decimal or percent models
• part of your project
Explain why you have included each selection.

316

2. 70%, 22%, 8%

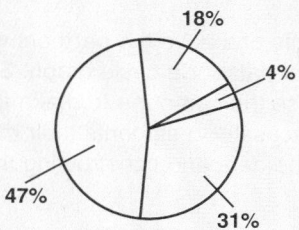

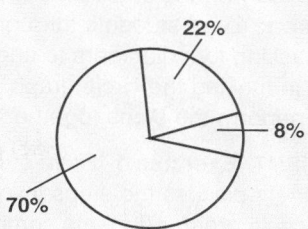

25. The graph at the right is labeled incorrectly. Trace the circle graph and move each percent label to the correct section. **See right.**

26. *Open-ended* List the things you do on a Saturday. Estimate the hours you spend on each activity. Write each time as a percent of a 24-hour day. Make a circle graph using your data. **Check students' work.**

27. *Fund-raising* Display the data below in a circle graph.
See back of book.

Percent of Money Raised from La Monte Middle School Fund-raisers

Car Wash	Paper Drive	Book Sale	Food Stand
42%	28%	18%	12%

28a–b. See back of book.

28. *Data Analysis* Use the graph at the right.
a. *Estimation* Estimate the percent of total ad hours spent on each type of product.
b. *Calculator* Find the percent of total ad hours spent on each type of product.
c. Compare your estimates in part (a) to the actual percents you found in part (b). How close were your estimates? **Check students' work.**

29. *Writing* Why should the percents that make up a circle graph always total 100%? **A circle graph always shows exactly 100% of the whole.**

30. *Sports* Out of 160 students, 22 play lacrosse, 41 play soccer, 19 play field hockey, and 78 don't play. Sketch a circle graph of the data.
See back of book.

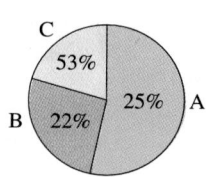

25.

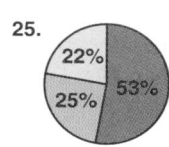

Kinds of Ads During 604 Hours of Kid's TV

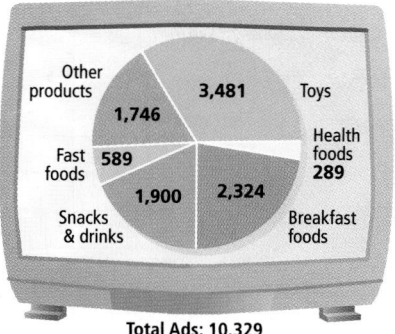

Total Ads: 10,329
Source: Dynamath

Mixed Review

Find the LCM of each set of numbers. *(Lesson 5-7)*

31. 15, 25, 75 — 75
32. 6, 10, 15 — 30
33. 3, 12, 19 — 228
34. 9, 12, 81 — 324
35. 24, 40, 60 — 120

Find the value of each expression. *(Lesson 4-2)*

36. $6^2 + 7^3$ — 379
37. $4^3 + 3^2 \times 8$ — 136
38. $10^3 - 5^2 + 2^3$ — 983
39. $3^3 + 5^2 \times 1^{10}$ — 52

40. *Choose a Strategy* Suppose you can arrange the chorus singers in rows of 10, 12, or 15 with no one left over. What is the least possible number of singers? **60 singers**

Practice 7-10 *Data and Circle Graphs*

Sketch a circle graph for the percentages given.

1. Ms. Murphy's Class's Favorite Foods

Pizza	Spaghetti	Hamburger
60%	30%	10%

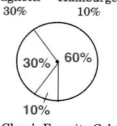

2. Mr. Chung's Class's Favorite Type of Book

Animal	Sports	Adventure	Mystery
20%	25%	10%	45%

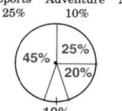

3. Mr. Fano's Class's Favorite Color

Blue	Purple	Red
40%	35%	25%

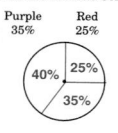

4. Ms. Ramon's Class's Favorite Sport

Swimming	Softball	Soccer	Hockey
20%	30%	5%	45%

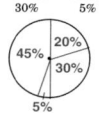

5. Number of TV Stations Received By Homes

1–6	7–10	11–14	15–40	41–60
7%	34%	34%	19%	6%

6. Tom Pin's Bowling Record

Games Won	Games Lost	Games Tied	Forfeits
50%	35%	5%	10%

In copymaster and workbook formats

Reteaching 7-10 *Data and Circle Graphs*

To *sketch* a circle graph, first estimate the percents. Then use the equivalent fractions.

Sketch these percents: 48%, 22%, 30%.

$48\% \approx 50\%$ $50\% = \frac{1}{2}$

$22\% \approx 20\%$ $20\% = \frac{1}{5}$

$30\% \approx 33\frac{1}{3}\%$ $33\frac{1}{3}\% = \frac{1}{3}$

Sketch the circle graph.

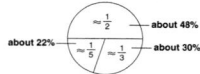

Sketch a circle graph with a shaded section equal to the fraction given. Answers may vary.

1. $\frac{1}{4}$ **2.** $\frac{2}{3}$ **3.** $\frac{4}{5}$

Sketch a circle graph for the percentages given.

4. 65%, 35%
5. 26%, 62%, 12%
6. 16%, 51%, 33%

7. 10%, 90%
8. 30%, 50%, 20%
9. 15%, 15%, 70%

Minds on Math Transparency

7-10

Eve sold candles to raise money for her school. After the first day, she sold 3 more candles than the day before for 6 days. If she sold 24 candles on the last day, how many candles did she sell on the first day?

6 candles

See Solution Key for worked-out answers.

In Lesson 7-10, students learned how to make circle graphs. This toolbox shows students how to construct circle graphs using a spreadsheet or geometry program on a computer.

ERROR ALERT! Students may need help getting started with the spreadsheet program. **Remediation:** Lead students through the Example, asking for volunteers to suggest each step in making the circle graph. The class can perform the steps together.

ASSESSMENT Exercise 1 Have students in pairs. Partners discuss the steps involved in making a circle graph. Students compare circle graphs with data to check that the graphs are reasonable.

■ **ADDITIONAL PROBLEM**

Pair students and have the partners write their own table of data for a circle graph. Students can then use the computer to make their graphs. Discuss with students their methods for listing the data and constructing their graphs.

Materials/Manipulatives

• spreadsheet software

page 318   Math Toolbox

1.   Ages of People Eating At Freddy's Fast Food

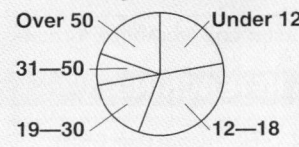

2.   How Theo Spends His Weekly Allowance

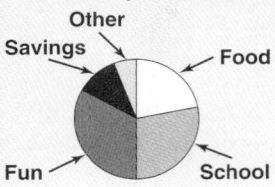

3.   How Often Adults Need to Search for Keys

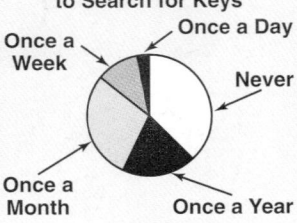

TECHNOLOGY

MATH TOOLBOX

Constructing Circle Graphs

After Lesson 7-10

Many spreadsheet applications have graphing capabilities. To make a circle graph on a computer, enter the data in a spreadsheet. Highlight the data you wish to graph. Then choose "circle graph" from the menu.

■ **EXAMPLE**

The data in the table below were entered in a spreadsheet program. Use a computer to graph the data.

How Sierra Spends Her Time on Weekdays

Activity	Amount of Time
At School	6 hours
Chores	1 hour
Homework	2 hours
Play/Recreation	4 hours
Eating	3 hours
Sleeping	8 hours

How Sierra Spends Her Time on Weekdays

Use a graphing program to make a circle graph for each set of data.   1–3. See margin.

1. Ages of People Eating at Freddy's Fast Food

Age	Under 12	12–18	19–30	31–50	Over 50
Number of People	80	120	60	30	70

2. How Theo Spends His Weekly Allowance

Categories	Food	School	Fun	Savings	Other
Amount Spent	$4	$5	$6	$2	$1

3. How Often Adults Need to Search for Keys

Categories	Never	Once a Year	Once a Month	Once a Week	Once a Day
Number of Responses	31	15	23	9	2

FINISHING THE CHAPTER PROJECT

PROJECT DAY You may wish to plan a project day on which students share their completed projects. Encourage students to explain their processes as well as their products.

PROJECT NOTEBOOK Ask students to review their project work and bring their notebooks up to date.

Have students review their methods for using ratios, making two-dimensional drawings, and writing scale distances for the project.

SCORING RUBRIC

3 You correctly write ratios for planet diameters and distances to the sun. All scaled dimensions are accurate. You neatly show your calculations and draw your two assigned planets to scale. You use distances familiar to your classmates to describe where in your model your planets would be relative to the sun.

2 You correctly write all ratios, and most of your calculations are correct. You draw your two assigned planets to scale, and you calculate the distances from the sun to these planets. Your work is neat and easy to follow.

1 Your ratios are not correctly written, many of your calculations are inaccurate, or your drawings or explanations are incomplete or not organized.

0 You do not complete the project, or you leave out a large part of the required work.

FINISHING THE CHAPTER PROJECT

CHAPTER PROJECT

Planet of the Stars

Make a Scale Model The Project Link questions on pages 284, 288, and 295 will help you complete your project. Here is a checklist to help you gather the parts of your project together.

- ✔ ratios of the diameter of each of your two planets to the real diameter of Pluto
- ✔ two-dimensional drawings of your two planets
- ✔ scaled distances from the sun to your two planets

Present your scale model of your two planets and all your calculations to the class. Include all necessary dimensions. You may want to describe the distance each of your planets is from the sun in terms of distances your classmates would understand.

Reflect and Revise
Meet with other students who also chose one of your planets to compare data. Compare any differences that you find and revise your calculations if necessary. Is your model neat and legible? Is it attractive but informative? Could your scale model be improved? If necessary, revise parts of your project.

Web Extension
Prentice Hall's Internet site contains information you might find helpful as you complete your project. Visit www.phschool.com/mgm1/ch7 for some links and ideas related to astronomy.

STUDENT SELF-ASSESSMENT SURVEY

▬ *Chapter 7 Student Self-Assessment Survey*

1. Now that you have finished this chapter, think about what you have learned about ratios, proportions, and percents. Check each topic that you feel confident you understand.
   _____ write ratios in three ways (7-1)
   _____ find unit rates and write equal ratios (7-2)
   _____ use cross products to solve proportions (7-3)
   _____ solve problems by solving a simpler problem (7-4)
   _____ enlarge and reduce designs by making scale drawings (7-5)
   _____ use scale drawings to find actual measurements (7-5)
   _____ model percents (7-6)
   _____ convert among percents, fractions, and decimals (7-7)
   _____ estimate a percent of a number (7-8)
   _____ find a percent of a number (7-9)
   _____ make circle graphs to display data (7-10)

2. Before the Chapter Assessment, I need to review _____

3. a. Check one. In general, I thought this chapter was
   _____ a snap _____ easy _____ average _____ hard _____ a monster
   b. Why do you feel this way?

4. In this chapter, I did my best work on _____

5. In this chapter, I had trouble with _____

6. Check each one that applies. Now that I've spent some time studying proportions, I think they are
   _____ important _____ boring _____ useful _____ fun
   _____ a waste of time _____ confusing _____ tricky _____ interesting

7. Many people use scale drawings as part of their jobs. List several jobs in which people use scale drawings. _____
   What did you like about making scale drawings? _____

Vocabulary/Symbols

cross products, equal ratios, percent, proportion, rate, ratio, scale, unit rate

Materials/Manipulatives

- centimeter ruler   • calculator
- compass

Resources

 Student Edition

Extra Practice, p. 528
Glossary/Study Guide

 **Teaching Resources**

Chapter Support File, Ch. 7
• Student Self-Assessment Survey
Glossary, Spanish Resources
Tools for Studying Smarter

320

WRAP UP

Exercises 6 and 7 Encourage students to draw diagrams or pictures to help them complete the exercises.

Exercises 8–17 Tell students to circle the cross products before solving each proportion.

ASSESSMENT Exercises 1–14 Have students work with partners. One partner can do the odd-numbered exercises, the other partner can do the even-numbered exercises. Have partners exchange papers and check their answers.

Exercises 18 and 19 Remind students to write out a proportion after measuring and before they try to solve the problem.

Exercises 24–29 Some students may find that the most efficient way to complete each exercise is to find the answers in the following order: fractions, decimals, percents.

7 WRAP UP

Ratios and Rates   7-1, 7-2

A **ratio** is a comparison of two numbers.

A **rate** is a ratio that compares two measures with different units.

Write each ratio as a fraction in simplest form.

1. 20 to 80 $\frac{1}{4}$ 2. 15 : 35 $\frac{3}{7}$ 3. 33 : 77 $\frac{3}{7}$ 4. 14 to 56 $\frac{1}{4}$ 5. 17 : 51 $\frac{1}{3}$

6. A moonrat is a member of the hedgehog family. An adult male's body is about 45 cm long. In three different ways, write the ratio to compare a moonrat's body length to 1 m. (1 m = 100 cm)
   $\frac{45}{100}$, 45 : 100, 45 to 100

7. A package of three videotapes is on sale for $5.97. A package of two videotapes is on sale for $3.76. Find the unit rate for each. Which package has the higher unit cost?
   $1.99; $1.88; package of 3 tapes

Proportions and Scale Drawings   7-3, 7-5

A **proportion** is an equation stating that two ratios are equal. You can use cross products to find the missing term in a proportion.

A **scale** is a ratio that compares length on a drawing or model to the actual length of an object.

Find the value of n.

8. $\frac{3}{5} = \frac{n}{35}$ 21   9. $\frac{6}{9} = \frac{18}{n}$ 27   10. $\frac{n}{6} = \frac{12}{24}$ 3   11. $\frac{32}{n} = \frac{8}{4}$ 16   12. $\frac{n}{15} = \frac{5}{25}$ 3

13. $\frac{17}{51} = \frac{3}{n}$ 9   14. $\frac{n}{28} = \frac{9}{12}$ 21   15. $\frac{45}{n} = \frac{30}{48}$ 72   16. $\frac{0}{108} = \frac{n}{9}$ 0   17. $\frac{96}{144} = \frac{4}{n}$ 6

Use a centimeter ruler and the scale drawing at the right.

18. Find the actual length of the bicycle.   3 m

19. Find the actual diameter of the front wheel.   1 m

1 cm : 1 m

20. The scale on a landscape blueprint is 1 in. : 6 ft. A stone wall is 4 in. long on the blueprint. How long is the wall?   24 ft

21. A drawing of a leatherback turtle has a scale of 2 cm : 1 m. The drawing of the turtle is 3 cm long. How long is the turtle?
   1.5 m

Exercise 32 Students can use rounding or reasoning to help them with their choices.

Remind students that the new mathematical terms in this chapter are defined in the Glossary/Study Guide in the back of the book.

Problem Solving Strategies 7-4

Solving a similar, simpler problem can help you see new ways to solve a given problem.

22. A clock chimes once every 30 min. How many times will it chime in the month of June? **1,440 times**

23. How many days have passed since you were born? **Check students' work.**

Percents, Fractions, and Decimals 7-6, 7-7, 7-8

A **percent** is a ratio that compares a number to 100. You can write a percent as a decimal or as a fraction.

Write each as a percent, as a fraction in simplest form, and as a decimal.

24. 24 cm out of 100 cm $24\%; \frac{6}{25}; 0.24$

25. 55 students out of 100 students $55\%; \frac{11}{20}; 0.55$

26. 3 hats out of 25 hats $12\%; \frac{3}{25}; 0.12$

27. 5 pens out of 20 pens $25\%; \frac{1}{4}; 0.25$

28. 40 heads out of 100 coin tosses $40\%; \frac{2}{5}; 0.40$

29. 2 days out of 10 days $20\%; \frac{1}{5}; 0.20$

30. Write 65% as a decimal and as a fraction in simplest form. $0.65; \frac{13}{20}$

31. An office chair is on sale for 80% of the regular price of $87.95. Estimate the sale price. **about $72**

32. Choose A, B, C, or D. Find the best estimate for 72% of 90. **C**

A. 72 B. 45 C. 63 D. 90

Percent of a Number and Circle Graphs 7-9, 7-10

You can use a model, a calculator, or a proportion to find a percent of a number.

You can make a circle graph to show percent data.

Find each percent.

33. 75% of 40 **30**

34. 23% of 19 **4.37**

35. 60% of 80 **48**

36. 10% of 235 **23.5**

37. 5% of $15.98 **$.80**

38. Use the data at the right to sketch a circle graph. **See back of book.**

Ways We Get to School

Car	Bus	Bike	Walk
24%	57%	4%	15%

Chapter 7 Assessment • Form A

Answers

1. Write the ratio of footballs to baseballs in three ways.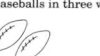

1. $\frac{2}{5}$, 2:5, 2 to 5

2. Find the value of n that makes the ratios equal.
$\frac{4}{9} = \frac{n}{27}$

2. 12

3. Write three equal ratios for $\frac{30}{40}$.

3. Answers may vary.
Sample: $\frac{3}{4}, \frac{6}{8}, \frac{9}{12}$

4. Write 124 mi on 4 gal as a unit rate.

4. 31 mi/gal

5. If $\frac{7}{10} = \frac{28}{x}$, what is the value of x?

5. 40

6. Choose A, B, C, or D. Which pair of ratios does *not* form a proportion?

A. $\frac{2}{3}, \frac{4}{5}$ B. $\frac{5}{6}, \frac{15}{18}$
C. $\frac{14}{16}, \frac{7}{8}$ D. $\frac{3}{21}, \frac{1}{7}$

6. A

7. Patrick makes $14.00 for every 3 h he works. Last week he made $43.00. How many hours did he work, rounded to the nearest whole hour?

7. 9 h

8. Use the scale drawing to find the actual length of the car.

1 in. : 5 ft

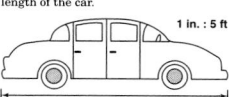

8. 15 ft

Assessment

Chapter 7 Assessment • Form A (continued)

9. The length of a wall in a blueprint is 5 in. The actual wall is 25 ft long. What is the scale of the blueprint?

9. 1 in. : 5 ft

10. How do you write "9 out of every 100 students were absent," as a percent?

10. 9%

11. Write $\frac{9}{10}$ as a percent and as a decimal.

11. 90%, 0.9

12. Write 0.75 as a percent and then as a fraction in simplest form.

12. 75%, $\frac{3}{4}$

13. Write 5% as a decimal and then as a fraction in simplest form.

13. 0.05, $\frac{1}{20}$

14. Estimate a 15% tip for a bill of $19.20.

14. Sample: $3.00

15. Use mental math to find 12% of 200.

15. 24

16. Find 25% of 65.

16. 16.25

17. Kersey knows that every school week, she spends 30 h at school, 18 h watching TV, 48 h sleeping, and the remaining hours practicing basketball. Sketch a circle graph showing how Kersey spends her week.

17. Kersey's Week
School 25%, TV 15%, Sleep 40%, Practice 20%

Choose a Strategy

18. Two numbers have a sum of 29 and a product of 154. What are the two numbers?

18. 22 and 7

Writing

19. What do the percents in a circle graph always add to? Explain. The percents add up to 100. The parts represent one whole.

321

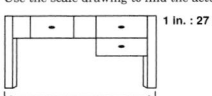

■ Chapter 7 Assessment • Form B

Choose the best answer. Circle A, B, C, or D.

1. Which ratio is *not* the same as the ratio of 8 girls to 6 boys?
   - (A) 3 to 4
   - B. 4 to 3
   - C. $\frac{8}{6}$
   - D. 4 : 3

2. Find the value of n that makes the ratios $\frac{6}{n}$ and $\frac{9}{15}$ equal.
   - A. 15
   - (B) 10
   - C. 9
   - D. 6

3. Which set has equal ratios?
   - A. $\frac{3}{10}, \frac{2}{5}, \frac{6}{20}$
   - B. $\frac{2}{6}, \frac{6}{8}, \frac{1}{3}$
   - (C) $\frac{15}{20}, \frac{3}{4}, \frac{9}{12}$
   - D. $\frac{1}{2}, \frac{3}{6}, \frac{4}{7}$

4. You drove 100 mi in 2 h. What is the unit rate?
   - A. 200 mi/h
   - B. 100 mi/h
   - (C) 50 mi/h
   - D. 2 mi/h

5. Use mental math to find the value of x. $\frac{6}{15} = \frac{x}{60}$
   - (A) 24
   - B. 18
   - C. 12
   - D. 6

6. Which pair of ratios forms a proportion?
   - A. $\frac{6}{10}, \frac{3}{4}$
   - (B) $\frac{4}{8}, \frac{5}{10}$
   - C. $\frac{2}{9}, \frac{5}{9}$
   - D. $\frac{3}{4}, \frac{3}{8}$

7. Wanda made $9.00 last night babysitting for 2 h. At that rate, how much would Wanda make if she babysat for 6 h?
   - A. $54.00
   - (B) $27.00
   - C. $12.00
   - D. $4.50

8. Use the scale drawing to find the actual length of the desk.

   1 in. : 27 in.

   - A. 13 in.
   - B. 27 in.
   - (C) 54 in.
   - D. 81 in.

9. The length of a trail on a map is 4 in. The actual length of the trail is 24 mi. What is the scale of the map?
   - A. 1 in. : 4 mi
   - B. 1 in. : 24 mi
   - C. 1 in. : 12 mi
   - (D) 1 in. : 6 mi

10. Eighteen out of every 100 games expressed as a percent is ____.
    - A. 1.8%
    - B. 9%
    - (C) 18%
    - D. 100%

Chapter 7 Assessment • Form B (continued)

11. Which pair of numbers shows $\frac{4}{5}$ written as a percent and as a decimal?
    - A. 45%, 0.45
    - B. 54%, 0.54
    - C. 40%, 0.4
    - (D) 80%, 0.8

12. Which pair of numbers shows 0.35 written as a percent and as a fraction in simplest form?
    - A. 35%, $\frac{35}{100}$
    - B. 0.35%, $\frac{7}{20}$
    - (C) 35%, $\frac{7}{20}$
    - D. 3.5%, $\frac{35}{100}$

13. Which pair of numbers shows 2% written as a decimal and as a fraction in simplest form?
    - A. 0.2, $\frac{1}{2}$
    - (B) 0.02, $\frac{1}{50}$
    - C. 0.02, $\frac{2}{100}$
    - D. 0.02, $\frac{2}{50}$

14. About how much would you leave if you wanted to give a 15% tip for a dinner bill of $20.87?
    - A. $2.00
    - B. $2.50
    - (C) $3.00
    - D. $3.50

15. Use mental math to find 18% of 300.
    - A. 18
    - B. 36
    - (C) 54
    - D. 72

16. What is 65% of 82?
    - A. 533
    - B. 524.8
    - (C) 53.3
    - D. 53

Use the circle graph for Exercises 17 and 18. Circle A, B, C, or D.

17. How many hours per day does Jenny work?
    - (A) 6 h
    - B. 7 h
    - C. 8 h
    - D. 9 h

    Jenny's Day
    Work 25%
    Practice 25%
    TV 17%
    Sleep 33%

18. Estimate the number of hours per day that Jenny spends sleeping.
    - A. 3 hours
    - (B) 8 hours
    - C. 10 hours
    - D. 12 hours

Choose a Strategy

19. Two numbers have a sum of 84 and a product of 1,764. What are the two numbers?
    - A. 50, 34
    - B. 29, 55
    - C. 40, 44
    - (D) 42, 42

■ Teaching Resources

Chapter Support File, Ch. 7, and Spanish Resources

 Teacher's Edition

See pp. 276C–D for Assessment Options.

 Teaching Resource Software

• Computer Item Generator, Ch. 7

322

ASSESSMENT

WRITING EXERCISES allow students to describe more fully their thinking and understanding of the concepts they've learned. **Exercise 2** is a writing exercise.

7 ASSESSMENT

1. Which is another way to write the ratio 6 : 3? **D**
   - A. 3 : 6
   - B. 6, 3
   - C. $\frac{3}{6}$
   - D. 6 to 3

2. *Writing* Are the ratios 9 apples to 12 apples and 6 apples to 10 apples equal? Explain your answer. **no; $\frac{9}{12} \neq \frac{6}{10}$**

3. Use the figure below. Write a ratio comparing the shaded regions to the unshaded regions as a fraction in lowest terms. $\frac{2}{3}$

   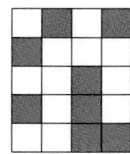

4. Find a ratio equal to $\frac{3}{12}$. **C**
   - A. $\frac{9}{24}$
   - B. $\frac{4}{1}$
   - C. $\frac{8}{32}$
   - D. $\frac{5}{15}$

5. Solve for n.
   - a. $\frac{21}{35} = \frac{9}{n}$ **15**
   - b. $\frac{n}{63} = \frac{4}{14}$ **18**

6. *Geometry* A scale drawing has a scale of 1 cm to 1.5 m. A tree in the drawing measures 4.5 cm. Find the height of the tree. **6.75 m**

7. Write each as a percent.
   - a. $\frac{11}{20}$ **55%**
   - b. 0.7 **70%**

8. Write each as a fraction in lowest terms.
   - a. 38% $\frac{19}{50}$
   - b. 0.62 $\frac{31}{50}$

10. Reasoning may vary. Sample: B; $\frac{5}{12}$ is halfway between $\frac{4}{12} = \frac{1}{3} \approx 33\%$ and $\frac{6}{12} = \frac{1}{2} = 50\%$.

9. Express each as a decimal.
   - a. $\frac{6}{20}$ **0.3**
   - b. 55% **0.55**
   - c. 6% **0.06**
   - d. $\frac{78}{100}$ **0.78**

10. *Estimation* Choose the best estimate for $\frac{5}{12}$. Explain how you arrived at your estimate. **See below left.**
    - A. 50%
    - B. 40%
    - C. 30%

11. Draw a model to show each percent.
    - a. 75% of 200 **a–b. See back of book.**
    - b. 30% of 210

12. Find each percent.
    - a. 52% of 96 **49.92**
    - b. 20% of 400 **80**
    - c. 38% of 150 **57**

13. Use the data in the table below to make a circle graph. **See back of book.**

    Favorite Types of Books

Mysteries	Biographies	Fiction	Humor
22%	13%	55%	10%

14. Marisa spent $4.25 on 16 stamps. She bought some for $.32 each and some for $.03 each. How many of each type did she buy? **13 32¢-stamps and 3 3¢-stamps**

15. Gerald bought art supplies that totaled $15.78. The sales tax is 3%. Estimate the amount of the tax and the total cost of the art supplies. **Estimates may vary. $.48; $16.48**

16. Estimate a 15% tip on each bill.
    - a. $25.35 **$3.90**
    - b. $9.35 **$1.50**

Item	Review Topic	Ch
1	Prime factors	5
2	Evaluating expressions	2
3	Subtracting fractions and mixed numbers	6
4	Measuring elapsed time	3
5	Order of operations	2
6	Finding mean	1

Item	Review Topic	Ch
7	Multiplying decimals	4
8	Measuring metric units	3
9	Percents	7
10	Evaluating patterns	2
11	Finding unit cost	4
12	Fractions	5

7 CUMULATIVE REVIEW

Choose the best answer.

1. Which number is *not* a prime factor of 2,420? **B**

A. 2   B. 3
C. 5   D. 11

2. Find the value of the expression $3 + b^2$ when $b = 5$. **B**

A. 64   B. 28
C. 16   D. 13

3. What is a step to find the difference $5\frac{1}{4} - 3\frac{2}{3}$? **B**

A. Subtract $\frac{1}{4}$ from $\frac{2}{3}$.
B. Write $5\frac{1}{4}$ as $4\frac{5}{4}$.
C. Find the difference $5 - 3\frac{2}{3}$.
D. Write $3\frac{2}{3}$ as $2\frac{5}{3}$.

4. Sukie boarded the school bus at 7:48 A.M. and arrived at school at 8:13 A.M. How many minutes did she spend on the bus? **C**

A. 13 min
B. 15 min
C. 25 min
D. 65 min

5. Which expression is equivalent to 35×10? **A**

A. $35(100 \div 10)$
B. $35(100 \times 10)$
C. $35 + (100 \times 10)$
D. $35 + (100 + 10)$

6. Find the mean of the following allowances: $4, $2, $2.50, $4, $3. **D**

A. $4.00   B. $2.50
C. $2.75   D. $3.10

7. Which number is the *best estimate* for 21.7×0.03? **C**

A. 66   B. 6.6
C. 0.66   D. 0.066

8. The mass of a package is 1.1 kilograms. How many grams are equivalent to 1.1 kilograms? **D**

A. 0.11 g   B. 11 g
C. 110 g   D. 1,100 g

9. The regular price of a jacket is $46.95. However, during a sale there is a 20% discount off the regular price. It is reasonable to assume that the sale price will be — **C**

A. more than $10 but less than $20
B. more than $20 but less than $30
C. more than $30 but less than $40
D. more than $40 but less than $50

10. If you continue the pattern below, which figure will have 51 blocks? **B**

A. the 25th   B. the 26th
C. the 50th   D. the 100th

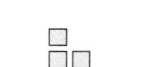

11. Which is the best buy? **B**

A. a half-dozen muffins, if a dozen cost $6.59
B. a half-dozen muffins for $3.19
C. a half-dozen muffins if each costs $.59
D. a half-dozen muffins if muffins cost $1.19 for 2

12. What is the reciprocal of $4\frac{2}{5}$? **D**

A. $2\frac{4}{5}$ B. $\frac{5}{2}$ C. $\frac{1}{4}$ D. $\frac{5}{22}$

CUMULATIVE REVIEW

■ Chapter 7 Cumulative Review

Choose the best answer. Circle A, B, C, or D.

1. Which equation is true?
A. $13 + 8 \div 2 \times (3 - 1) = 24$
B. $(13 + 8) \div 2 \times (3 - 1) = 24$
C. $13 + (8 \div 2) \times (3 - 1) = 24$
D. $13 + 8 \div 2 \times 3 - 1 = 24$

2. Fill in the missing numbers.
$8 \times (14 + \blacksquare) = (8 \times \blacksquare) + (\blacksquare \times 3)$
A. 8, 14, 3   B. 3, 14, 8
C. 14, 8, 3   D. 3, 8, 14

3. Use mental math to find the product 0.034×100.
A. 0.34   B. 3.4
C. 34.0   D. 340

4. Use mental math to find the quotient $14.35 \div 0.7$.
A. 0.205   B. 2.05
C. 20.5   D. 2,050

5. Which is the prime factorization tree of 270?

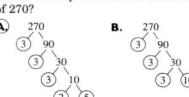

A. B. C. D.

6. Find the GCF of 60 and 96.
A. 2   B. 6
C. 12   D. 32

7. Which fraction is *not* an equivalent fraction to $\frac{6}{9}$?
A. $\frac{9}{12}$ B. $\frac{4}{6}$
C. $\frac{2}{3}$ D. $\frac{12}{18}$

8. Write $\frac{17}{5}$ as a mixed number in simplest form.
A. $2\frac{2}{5}$ B. $3\frac{2}{5}$
C. $1\frac{7}{5}$ D. $3\frac{3}{5}$

9. Write 0.75 as a fraction in simplest form.
A. $\frac{7}{10}$ B. $\frac{70}{100}$
C. $\frac{3}{4}$ D. $\frac{16}{20}$

10. Find the sum. Write the answer in simplest form.
$\frac{1}{5} + \frac{1}{6}$
A. $\frac{2}{11}$ B. $\frac{1}{11}$
C. $\frac{1}{30}$ D. $\frac{11}{30}$

11. Find the difference $11\frac{1}{3} - 8\frac{1}{2}$.
A. $3\frac{5}{6}$ B. $3\frac{1}{3}$
C. $2\frac{1}{6}$ D. $2\frac{5}{6}$

12. Jason has $4\frac{3}{8}$ yd of fabric. How many bandanas can he make if each one requires $\frac{5}{8}$ yd of fabric?
A. 6 bandanas   B. 7 bandanas
C. $5\frac{1}{2}$ bandanas   D. $6\frac{1}{5}$ bandanas

Assessment

CUMULATIVE REVIEW

Chapter 7 Cumulative Review (continued)

13. Find the total area of the two rectangles shown. Write the answer in simplest form.

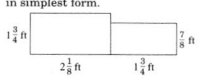

A. $3\frac{5}{8}$ ft² B. $5\frac{1}{4}$ ft²
C. $2\frac{3}{4}$ ft² D. $4\frac{2}{3}$ ft²

14. Add. Write the answer in simplest form.
    12 gal 3 qt
 + 11 gal 2 qt
A. 24 gal 1 qt   B. 25 gal
C. 23 gal 1 qt   D. 23 gal 7 qt

15. To qualify for a keyboarding job, Karen needs to type 95 words per min. She timed herself at 450 words for 5 min. What is her rate in comparison to the required rate?
A. She types 5 words per min faster.
B. She types exactly the required rate.
C. She types 5 words per min too slow.
D. She types 15 words per min too slow.

16. Find the value of y in $\frac{33}{y} = \frac{22}{8}$.
A. 6   B. $7\frac{1}{2}$
C. 9   D. 12

17. On a blueprint, you measure the width of a door to be $\frac{3}{4}$ in. The scale on the map is $\frac{1}{4}$ in. : 12 in. What is the actual width of the door?
A. 3 ft   B. 30 in.
C. 2 ft   D. 32 in.

18. Write 44 pens out of 200 pens as a percent, a decimal, and a fraction in simplest form.
A. 44%, 0.22, $\frac{22}{100}$ B. 33%, 0.33, $\frac{33}{100}$
C. 22%, 0.22, $\frac{11}{50}$ D. 22%, 0.2, $\frac{22}{100}$

19. The cost of dinner for you and three of your friends is $48.24. You decide to leave a 17% tip for excellent service. How much of the tip do each of you have to pay to the nearest cent?
A. $2.05   B. $3.00
C. $2.10   D. $8.20

20. People are lined up for the first tour at 8 A.M. Every 15 minutes, a guide takes 40 people. The tours end just before noon. How many people will be taken on the tour?
A. 40 people   B. 160 people
C. 20 people   D. 640 people

Resources

■ Teaching Resources

Chapter Support File, Ch. 7
• Cumulative Review

Teacher's Edition

See also pp. 276C–D for Assessment Options.

CHAPTER OVERVIEW

To accommodate flexible scheduling, most lessons are divided into parts. Assignment Options are given in the Teacher's Edition for each lesson.

Pages 326–330	**Lesson 8-1** **Points, Lines, and Planes**
NCTM 1, 2, 3, 4, 7, 12	Part 1 Exploring Points, Lines, Segments, and Rays Part 2 Special Pairs of Lines **Key terms:** point, plane, segment, ray, collinear, noncollinear, parallel lines, parallel segments, vertical, horizontal, skew lines **Alternative Activity** 8-1

Pages 331–335	**Lesson 8-2** **Measurement:** **Exploring Angles**
NCTM 1, 2, 3, 4, 7, 12, 13	Part 1 Estimating and Measuring Angles Part 2 Classifying Angles **Key terms:** degree, angle, acute angle, right angle, sides, obtuse angle, straight angle, perpendicular, vertex

Pages 337–339	**Lesson 8-3** **Algebra: Special** **Pairs of Angles**
NCTM 1, 2, 3, 4, 9, 12	**Key terms:** transversal, congruent angles ▼ **Project Link** **Key terms:** complementary angles, supplementary angles, transversal, exterior angles, interior angles, congruent angles

Pages 353–355	**Lesson 8-7** **Problem Solving Strategy**
NCTM 1, 3, 4, 13	**Use Logical Reasoning**

Pages 356–359	**Lesson 8-8** **Measurement: Congruent** **and Similar Figures**
NCTM 1, 3, 6, 12, 13	Part 1 Identifying Congruent Figures Part 2 Identifying Similar Figures **Key terms:** congruent, similar, corresponding parts **Alternative Activity** 8-8 ▼ **Project Link**

Pages 360–363	**Lesson 8-9** **Line Symmetry**
NCTM 1, 2, 3, 7, 12	**Key terms:** line symmetry, line of symmetry **Journal**

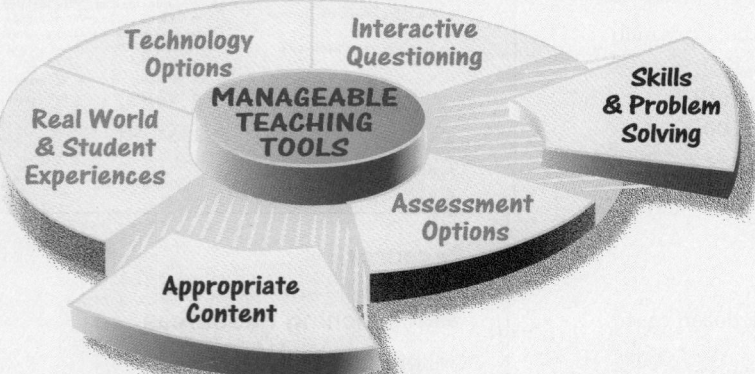

MANAGEABLE TEACHING TOOLS

Technology Options · Interactive Questioning · Skills & Problem Solving · Assessment Options · Appropriate Content · Real World & Student Experiences

Pacing Options

This chart suggests pacing only for the core lessons and their parts. It is provided merely as a possible guide. It will help you determine how much time you have in your schedule to cover other features, such as the Chapter Project, Math Toolboxes, Wrap Up, and Assessment.

	1 Class Period	1 Class Period	1 Class Period	1
Traditional (40–45 min class periods)	8–1 ▼	8–1 ▼2	8–2 8–2 ▼ ▼2	
Block Scheduling (90 min class periods)	8–1 8–1 ▼ ▼2	8–2 8–2 8–3 ▼ ▼2	8–4 8–5 8–5 ▼ ▼2	8–6 ▼

NCTM STANDARDS

1	Problem Solving	6	Number Systems and Number Theory	10	Statistics
2	Communication	7	Computation and Estimation	11	Probability
3	Reasoning	8	Patterns and Functions	12	Geometry
4	Mathematical Connections	9	Algebra	13	Measurement
5	Number and Number Relationships				

Pages 340–343

Lesson 8-4
Identifying Triangles

NCTM 1, 2, 3, 7, 12, 13

Key terms: congruent segments, acute triangle, obtuse triangle, right triangle, equilateral triangle, isosceles triangle, scalene triangle

Journal

▼ **Project Link**

Pages 344–348

Lesson 8-5
Exploring Polygons

NCTM 2, 3, 4, 7, 12

Key terms: polygons, convex

Alternative Activity 8-5

Math at Work

☑ **Checkpoint 1**

Pages 349–352

Lesson 8-6
Classifying Quadrilaterals

NCTM 1, 2, 3, 12

Part 1   Identifying Quadrilaterals
Part 2   Classifying Quadrilaterals
Key terms: parallelogram, rhombus, trapezoid

▼ **Project Link**

Pages 364–367

Lesson 8-10
Measurement: Investigating Circles

NCTM 1, 2, 3, 4, 12

Key terms: radius, diameters, chords, central angles

☑ **Checkpoint 2**

Pages 370–374

Lesson 8-11
Slides, Flips, and Turns

NCTM 1, 2, 3, 4, 12

Part 1   Exploring Translations and Reflections
Part 2   Exploring Rotations
Key terms: translation, image, reflection, line of reflection, rotation, point of rotation

---

Optional Materials and Manipulatives

straightedge (8-1)
protractor (8-2, 8-3, 8-10)
index cards (8-11)
ruler (8-3, 8-8, 8-10)

geoboards (8-4, 8-6)
dot paper (8-4, 8-6, 8-8)
geoboard bands (8-4, 8-6)
compass (8-7, 8-10)

scissors (8-8, 8-9, 8-11)
Optional calculator use is integrated
    throughout the course.

---

ss d	1 Class Period	1 Class Period	1 Class Period	1 Class Period	1 Class Period	1 Class Period	1 Class Period	1 Class Period	1 Class Period	1 Class Period
	8–5 8–5 ▼ ②	8–6 8–6 ▼ ②	8–7	8–8 ▼	8–8 ②	8–9	8–10	8–10	8–11 8–11 ▼ ②	

| –8 ▼ | 8–9 8–10 | 8–10 8–11 8–11 ▼ ② | | | | | | | | |

MEETING INDIVIDUAL NEEDS

Accommodating Diverse Learning Styles

In your Teacher's Edition, you will find suggestions as to how you can help students complete mathematical tasks in Chapter 8 by meeting individual needs and supporting various learning styles. Here are some examples:

VISUAL LEARNING
illustrating the solar eclipse with a diagram or model (p. 328)

TACTILE LEARNING
modeling shapes with clay and straws (p. 328)

AUDITORY LEARNING
creating mnemonics to remember definitions (p. 340)

KINESTHETIC LEARNING
modeling angles using rope (p. 332)

EARLY FINISHERS
Performance-Based Project, MathBlaster® Mystery, Interdisciplinary Units

GIFTED AND TALENTED
researching how points, lines, and angles are used in art (p. 328)

DIVERSITY looking for points, lines, and planes in house designs (p. 326)

ACQUIRING ENGLISH PROFICIENCY (AEP)
drawing models for points, lines, planes, etc. on index cards (p. 326)

ASSESSING PROGRESS

A broad range of assessment tools are available to reach a variety of learners.

INFORMAL ASSESSMENT

Informal assessments provide day-to-day feedback to help give you a picture of conceptual understanding and skill development.

ONGOING ASSESSMENT is built into lesson instruction and the Teaching Notes of the Teacher's Edition.

In the Teacher's Edition
Lesson Quiz for every lesson

In the Student Edition
On Your Own, Mixed Review, Journal, Portfolio, Project Link, Chapter Wrap Up

Look for **Interactive Questions** within lessons that

- **BUILD UNDERSTANDING** with labels such as Analyze, Reasoning, Estimation, Writing, and Summarize
- ✔ **CHECK UNDERSTANDING** with the Try It Out label.

FORMAL ASSESSMENT

Formal assessment can occur before and after the chapter, as well as at natural breaking points in the chapter.

Checkpoints
Two forms of each self-assessment Checkpoints are available: one in the Student Edition and another in the Chapter Support File in the Teaching Resources box.

- Mid-Chapter Checkpoint 1, page 348
- End-of-Chapter Checkpoint 2, page 367

Chapter 8 Assessment, page 378.
Two alternative forms are available in the Chapter Support File. They may be used after a chapter has been completed, or as a pre-test and post-test comparison.

Cumulative Review, page 379.
Assesses skills and concepts in Chapters 1–8.
An alternative form is available in Chapter Support File.

Computer Item Generator for Chapter 8
Customized tests can be generated for each lesson and for mid-chapter and end-of-chapter assessments, and for pre- and post-test comparisons of achievement.

Interactive Questioning

Technology Options

MANAGEABLE TEACHING TOOLS

Real World & Student Experiences

Skills & Problem Solving

Appropriate Content

Assessment Options

CHAPTER PROJECT

The Chapter Project in the student edition provides a real-world connection to the math context of the chapter. The Teacher's Edition contains a scoring rubric.

Another performance-based Chapter Project with a scoring rubric can be found in the Chapter Support File in the Teaching Resources Box.

Name _____ Class _____ Date _____

Chapter 8 Performance Assessment

Triangles Everywhere

Look at the two triangles below. Notice how you can put them together to form a rectangle.

Now look at these two triangles. Notice how you can put them together to form a square.

Show all your work. Use a separate sheet of paper if needed.

1. Use one line to divide each of these figures into triangles.

2. How many triangles did you make from each figure? Is there more than one way to divide each figure? How many ways?

3. Do you think the triangles from each figure are congruent? Explain.

4. Use two segments to divide each figure into triangles. Make your two segments the same length.

5. How many triangles did you make from each figure? Be sure to count all the triangles, big and small.

6. Do you think these triangles are congruent? Explain.

Course 1 Chapter 8   50

Chapter 8 Performance Assessment Scoring Rubric

Exercise	Points	Explanation
1.	1	Figures correctly divided into triangles
	0	No response OR other response
2.	1	Two triangles; yes, two ways to do it
	0	No response OR other response
3.	1	Triangles considered congruent and justification given
	0	No response OR other response
4.	1	Figures correctly divided into triangles
	0	No response OR other response
5.	1	Response of eight triangles (not all the same size) for triangles formed by diagonals; judge other responses on their merits.
	0	No response OR other response that lacks merit
6.	1	Same sizes: yes; different sizes: no; justification given
	0	No response OR other response
7.	1	Figure divided into triangles, using three lines
	0	No response OR other response
8.	1	Responses should be accurate in terms of drawing.
	0	No response OR other response
9.	1	Responses will vary; explanation of the method given
	0	No response OR other response
10.	1	Explanation of how lines can be added indefinitely
	0	No response OR other response
Excursion	5	Complex puzzle with good explanation of answer
	4	Complex puzzle with adequate explanation OR less complex puzzle with good explanation
	3	Less complex puzzle with adequate explanation OR complex puzzle with weak explanation
	2	Less complex puzzle with weak explanation
	1	Puzzle with no explanation
	0	No response

Course 1 Chapter 8   52

Correlation to Standardized Tests

		STANDARDIZED TEST ITEMS					
Lesson		**CAT5**	**CTBS/5 Terra Nova**	**ITBS**	**MAT7**	**SAT9**	**Your Local Test**
8-1	Points, Lines, and Planes	■		■	■		
8-2	Measurement: Exploring Angles	■	■			■	
8-3	Algebra: Special Pairs of Angles	■	■			■	
8-4	Identifying Triangles	■		■	■		
8-5	Exploring Polygons	■			■	■	
8-6	Classifying Quadrilaterals	■			■	■	
8-7	Problem Solving Strategy: Using Logical Reasoning	■	■		■	■	
8-8	Measurement: Congruent and Similar Figures		■				
8-9	Line Symmetry		■			■	
8-10	Measurement: Investigating Circles					■	
8-11	Slides, Flips, and Turns				■	■	

CAT5 California Achievement Test, 5th Edition
CTBS/5 Comprehensive Test of Basic Skills, 5th Edition

ITBS Iowa Test of Basic Skills, Form B
MAT 7 Metropolitan Achievement Test, 7th Edition

SAT9 Stanford Achievement Test, 9th Edition

MAKING CONNECTIONS

Technology Options
Interactive Questioning
MANAGEABLE TEACHING TOOLS
Skills & Problem Solving
Real World & Student Experiences
Assessment Options
Appropriate Content

TEAM TEACHING WITH PRENTICE HALL MATERIALS

MIDDLE GRADES MATH INTERDISCIPLINARY UNITS

- **The Great Outdoors: Activity 12**
- **Sports: Activities 3 & 8**
- **Travel and Geography: Activity 7**

INTERDISCIPLINARY EXPLORATIONS

- *Sleuth's Supper* **p. 42**

SCIENCE EXPLORER

L Life Science **E** Earth Science **P** Physical Science

E Sec. 13-2 (Shapes of Crystals)

Lesson	Interdisciplinary Connections	Real World Connections	Math Integration
8-1	Earth Sciences Science	Astronomy Games	Geometry
8-2	Physical Education Science	Football Photography	Geometry Measurement
8-3	Architecture	Cheese Art Consumer Issues	Algebra Geometry
8-4	Drafting	Games Optics Sailing	Geometry Measurement
8-5	Language Art	Botany Cartoons Soccer	Geometry
8-6	Geometry	Geometry	Geometry
8-7	Sports	Weather Clothes Food	Measurement Data Analysis
8-8	Architecture Business	Bridges Home Improvement	Geometry Measurement
8-9	Design	World Flags	Geometry
8-10	Swimming History	Leisure Amusement Parks Industry	Algebra Data Analysis Measurement
8-11	Language	Interior Design	Geometry

School to Home

MATERIALS:

measuring cup (marked in fluid ounces), teacup, coffee mug, drinking glass, 3 kitchen storage containers (tall, round, and rectangular bowl), construction paper (one white sheet and 5 colored sheets), straightedge, scissors, paper, pencil

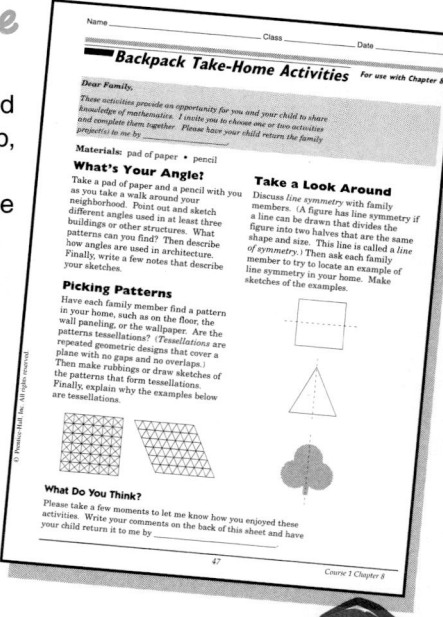

English and Spanish versions are available in the Teacher's Communication Kit, Teacher's Resource box.

Using Technology to Enhance Instruction

For the Student

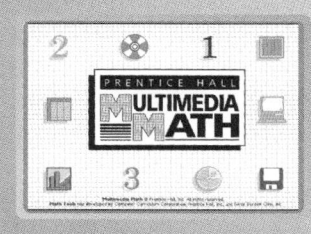

Multimedia Math Hot Pages™
This interactive software and video package on CD-ROM integrates solid math content through a variety of media.

- Hot Page™ 22 (8-2)

Math Labs
This software, available on both diskette and CD-ROM, includes on-screen Math Lab activities. Students use linkable, interactive tools to explore math concepts.

- Math Lab: Congruent Angles (8-8)

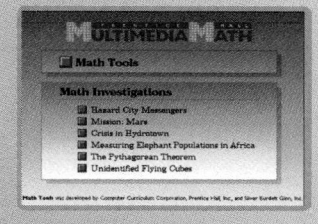

Multimedia Math Investigations
These in-depth interactive activities on CD-ROM develop real-world applications of mathematics. They allow students the opportunity to reinforce key concepts.

- Mission: Mars
- The Pythagorean Theorem

Interactive Student Tutorial
Available on CD-ROM, this test preparation program contains self-tests with questions in standardized test format. Software includes electronic versions of the text lessons and the Math Tools and Math Labs.

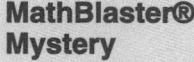

MathBlaster® Mystery
This award-winning, interactive software program on CD-ROM can be used to maintain skills or to accommodate early finishers.

- Level: Earn 2 coins; Pay 6 coins
- Mission Mode (all lessons)
- Kitchen Comparisons (8-2, 8-8)
- Number Guesser (8-3, 8-7, 8-11)
- Equation Maker (8-5, 8-9)
- Word Problems (8-1, 8-4, 8-6, 8-10, Problem Solving Practice)

Internet Connection

For Students
Support for the Chapter Project
A career-oriented link for Math at Work feature

www.phschool.com/math

For teachers
Curriculum Support
Product Information
Regional Support Information

For the Teacher

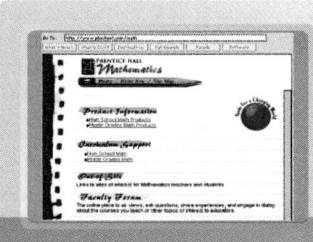

Computer Item Generator
Available on both CD-ROM and diskette, this software generates customized practice sheets, quizzes, and tests. It generates an unlimited supply of questions with varying levels of difficulty.

The Resource Pro™
Available on CD-ROM, this software can be used to customize and plan lessons.

Technology Options

MANAGEABLE TEACHING TOOLS
- Interactive Questioning
- Skills & Problem Solving
- Assessment Options
- Appropriate Content
- Real World & Student Experiences

CHAPTER 8 TOOLS OF GEOMETRY

CONNECTING TO PRIOR LEARNING Ask students if they have ever put together a puzzle that was made up of regular shapes. Ask students to name the shapes. **Answers may vary. Sample: triangles, squares, rectangles** Then discuss with students how to make such shapes fit together. Students can draw diagrams for the class.

CULTURAL CONNECTIONS Different cultures have created variations of puzzles. For example, the Chinese make puzzle boxes that fit together in interesting ways. In Russia, they make dolls that stack inside one another. Discuss with the class puzzle-like items from other cultures.

INTERDISCIPLINARY CONNECTIONS Have students research how straight lines may be used for boundaries between counties and states. You may want to have students discuss when and why boundaries other than straight lines are used.

ABOUT THE PROJECT The Chapter Project allows students to use their knowledge of geometric shapes to make a challenging puzzle.

Internet • For information and activities related to the Chapter Project, visit the Prentice Hall site at www.phschool.com/mgm1/ch8

Tools of Geometry

8

| WHAT YOU WILL LEARN IN THIS CHAPTER | • How to identify points, lines, planes and angles | • How to identify and classify triangles and other polygons | • How to identify similarity, symmetry, and congruency |

Ask students:

- *Have you ever solved a jigsaw puzzle? How do you determine which pieces fit together?*

- *Have you ever seen a tangram puzzle? How is it similar and how is it different from a jigsaw puzzle?*

- *What shapes could you use for a tangram puzzle? How would they fit together?*

PROJECT NOTEBOOK Encourage students to keep all project-related materials in a separate folder or notebook.

TRACKING THE PROJECT You may wish to have students read Finishing the Chapter Project on page 375 to help them get an overview of the project. Set benchmark deadlines for students to show you their work in progress.

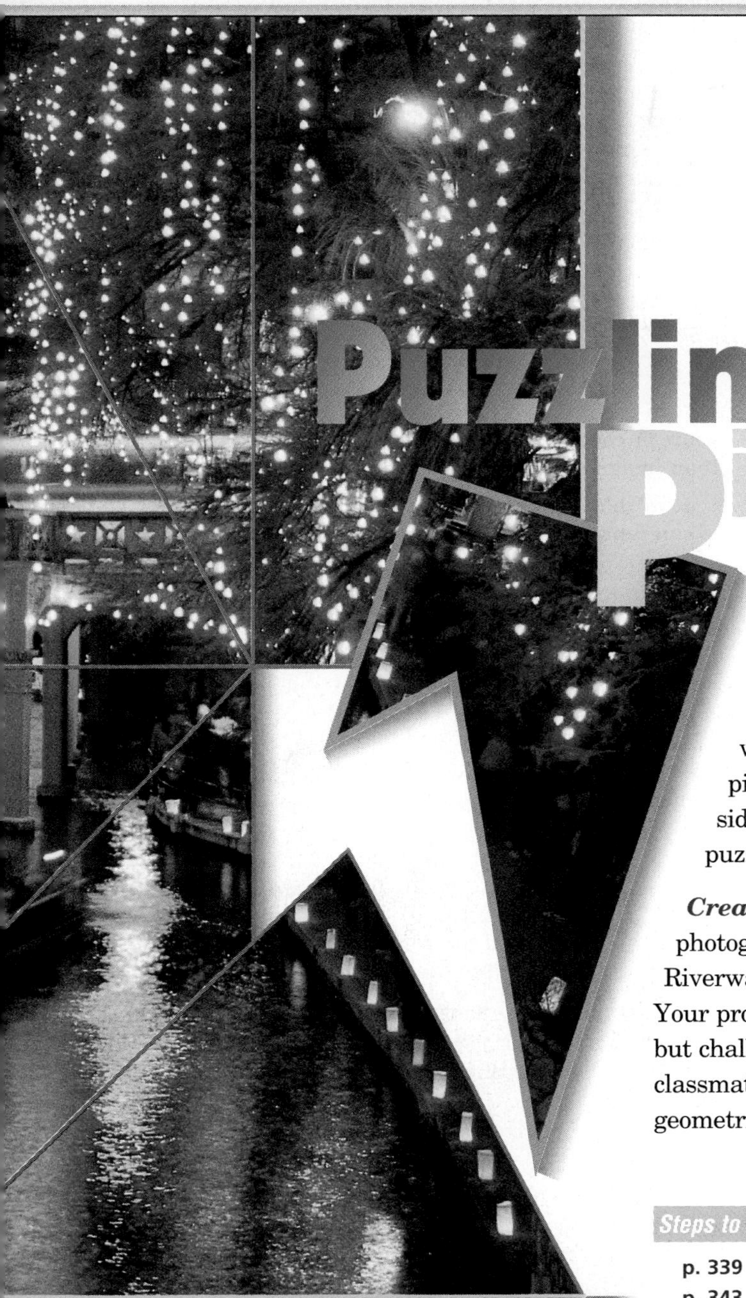

CHAPTER PROJECT

THEME:
PUZZLES

Puzzling Pictures

Do you remember putting together simple puzzles when you were younger? Those designed for little children are often made of wood and are made of large pieces. The pieces have straight sides so that the child can put the puzzle together easily.

Create a Puzzle Imagine that the photograph of the San Antonio, Texas, Riverwalk at the left was a puzzle. Your project is to make an attractive but challenging puzzle for your classmates to solve. Include as many geometric shapes as you can.

Steps to help you complete the project:

- **How to solve problems using logical reasoning**

SCORING RUBRIC

3 Your puzzle includes the ten required shapes as well as the necessary congruent and similar triangles. Your puzzle is carefully made and includes a list of the triangles and polygons you used.

2 Your puzzle meets at least nine of the twelve requirements listed in the project links. Your list of the triangles and polygons in your puzzle is adequate, and your puzzle is attractive.

1 You leave out more than three of the required shapes in your puzzle, you incorrectly identify shapes in your list, or you pay little attention to the appearance of your finished puzzle.

0 You do not complete a puzzle, or you leave out most of the required triangles and polygons.

1 Focus

CONNECTING TO PRIOR KNOWLEDGE Ask students if they have ever looked up in the night sky and observed the Big Dipper. Ask: *Why do we call it the Big Dipper? If you draw a line connecting the stars, it forms a ladle, or dipper.* Tell students that in this lesson they will learn about the geometric concepts of points and lines.

Lesson Planning Options

Prerequisite Skills
• drawing lines (precourse)

Vocabulary/Symbols
point, plane, segment, ray, collinear, noncollinear, parallel lines, parallel segments, vertical, horizontal, skew lines

Materials/Manipulatives
• straightedge

Resources

 Student Edition

Skills Handbook, p. 536
Extra Practice, p. 529
Glossary/Study Guide

 Teaching Resources

Chapter Support File, Ch. 8
• Lesson Planner 8-1
• Practice 8-1, Reteaching 8-1
• Alternative Activity 8-1
• Answer Masters 8-1
Teaching Aids Masters 3, 26
Glossary, Spanish Resources

 Transparencies
15, 18, Minds on Math 8-1

Warm Up

Multiply.
4.23 × 13.8 **58.374**

326

2 Teach

THINK AND DISCUSS

VISUAL LEARNING **Question 4** The board, a desk, a sheet of paper, and a book are all approximate physical models of a plane. Ask: *What is the difference between these models and a plane?* **Answers may vary. Sample: A plane extends indefinitely and has no thickness.**

AEP Have students draw models for a point, line, plane, segment, and ray on an index card. Then have them write the geometric name for each model on the cards.

DIVERSITY Ask students to sketch the shapes of kinds of dwellings such as tents, teepees, hogans, and A-frame houses. Have them identify models of points, lines, and planes in each dwelling. Challenge students to locate places in the world where such dwellings exist. Ask students to note the reasons for using these structures.

8-1 **Points, Lines, and Planes**

What You'll Learn

1️⃣ To identify and work with points, lines, segments, and rays

2️⃣ To investigate relationships between special pairs of lines

...And Why

You can accurately describe and identify geometric figures.

Here's How

Look for questions that
🔹 build understanding
✔ check understanding

THINK AND DISCUSS

1️⃣ *Exploring Points, Lines, Segments, and Rays*

You can easily find a particular star in the sky if you can see the group, or constellation, to which it belongs. The stars are points on an imaginary geometric figure.

A **point** has no size, only location. A small dot made by a pencil tip can represent a point. Points *A*, *B*, and *C* are shown.

1. ✓*Try It Out* Give an example of a physical model of a point.
Answers may vary. Sample: a city on a map

A **line** continues without end in opposite directions. It has no thickness. You can name a line by using two points on the line. For example, one name for this line is $\overleftrightarrow{DE}$ (read as "line *DE*").

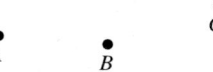

2. ✓*Try It Out* What are some other names for the line above?
Answers may vary. Samples: $\overleftrightarrow{ED}$, $\overleftrightarrow{DF}$, $\overleftrightarrow{EF}$
3. Name something that could be a physical model of a line.
Answers may vary. Sample: writing rule on notebook paper

A **plane** is a flat surface that extends indefinitely in four directions. It has no thickness.

4. Name something that could be a physical model of a plane.
Answers may vary. Sample: window

A **segment** is part of a line. It is made up of two points and all the points of the line that joins the two points. You name a segment by the two *endpoints*. This is $\overline{RS}$ (read as "segment *RS*").

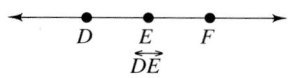

5. ✓*Try It Out* Give another name for $\overline{RS}$. $\overline{SR}$

Work Together

Have pairs of students attempt to complete this activity. Students can use the same paper to draw the points and lines. Have students discuss how arranging the points affects the number of lines.

■ ADDITIONAL EXAMPLE

FOR EXAMPLE

Does each pair of lines appear to be parallel or intersecting?

a.

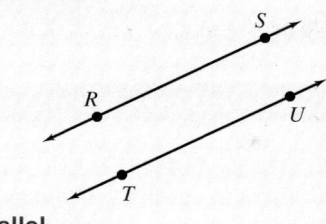

parallel

b.

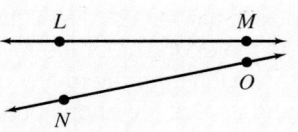

intersecting

CONNECTION TO SCIENCE Ask students to find pictures of constellations. Have them letter the major stars. Then have them name the line segments that connect these stars.

ERROR ALERT! Question 8 Students may incorrectly name the ray. **Remediation:** Have

6. ✓*Try It Out* Draw $\overleftrightarrow{JK}$ and $\overline{JK}$. Explain the difference.

Check students' work for diagrams; $\overline{JK}$ has endpoints and $\overleftrightarrow{JK}$ does not.

7. ⚏*Open-ended* Draw a line and label several points on it. Name your line. Name four different segments.

Check students' work.

A **ray** is part of a line. It consists of one endpoint and all the points of the line on one side of the endpoint. To name a ray, you name the endpoint first and then any other point on the ray. This is $\overrightarrow{GH}$ (read as "ray *GH*").

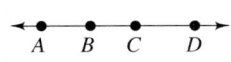

8. ✓*Try It Out* Give another name for $\overrightarrow{GH}$. $\overrightarrow{GK}$

9. ⚏*Think About It* Describe $\overrightarrow{YX}$. How is $\overrightarrow{YX}$ different from $\overrightarrow{XY}$? What part of $\overleftrightarrow{XY}$ do $\overrightarrow{YX}$ and $\overrightarrow{XY}$ have in common?

$\overrightarrow{YX}$ is a ray whose endpoint is Y; Y is the endpoint of $\overrightarrow{YX}$ and X is the endpoint of $\overrightarrow{XY}$; $\overline{XY}$

If a line can be drawn through a set of points, the points are **collinear.** If no one line can be drawn through all the points, the points are **noncollinear.**

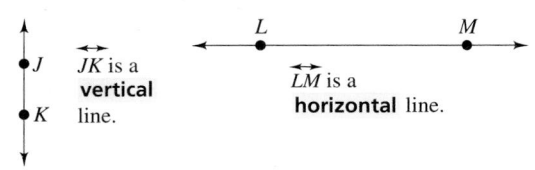

collinear points   noncollinear points

Now you may assign Exercises 1–10, 13–16, 20, 22–25, 28.

▼2 Special Pairs of Lines

There are two possible relationships between two lines that lie in a plane: either they intersect or they are parallel. **Parallel lines** are lines in the same plane that do not intersect. **Parallel segments** lie in parallel lines.

Some lines are horizontal or vertical.

$\overleftrightarrow{JK}$ is a **vertical** line.

$\overleftrightarrow{LM}$ is a **horizontal** line.

The stars...

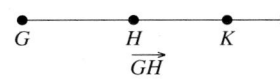

The stars that form the constellation Cetus can be represented by points. These points are connected here with segments to help you see the shape of Cetus.

Source: *Encyclopedia Americana*

Technology Options

Prentice Hall Technology

💾 💿 **Software for Learners**
- Math Blaster® Mystery*
- Interactive Student Tutorial, Chapter 8*

💾 💿 **Teaching Resource Software**
- Computer Item Generator 8-1
- Resource Pro™ Chapter 8*

🌐 **Internet** • For related mathematics activities, visit the Prentice Hall site at www.phschool.com/math

*Available on CD-ROM only

Assignment Options for Exercises On Your Own

To provide flexible scheduling, this lesson can be subdivided into parts.

▼1 **Core** 1–10, 13–15, 20, 22–25
Extension 16, 28

▼2 **Core** 11, 12, 17–19, 21, 26, 27, 31–36
Extension 29, 30

Use Mixed Review to maintain skills.

students look at the ray *GH*. Have them identify *G* as the endpoint for the ray. Students can then trace along the ray to any other point. Remind students that the endpoint always comes first in the name of the ray.

ASSESSMENT Have students define a line, a line segment, and a ray. Ask students to draw an example of each.

EXTENSION and CONNECTION TO ART Tell students that painting involves the study of the lines, angles, and points they are learning about. If you have block scheduling or extended class

periods, have students research how Renaissance artists discovered the use of the vanishing point to make objects in 2-dimensional paintings look as they appear in nature.

3 Practice/Assess

TACTILE LEARNING and OPEN-ENDED Exercise 16 Provide students with clay and straws to model the four points and two lines.

EXTENSION Exercise 18 Have students find other geometric figures that contain parallel lines.

VISUAL LEARNING Exercise 28a Ask students to draw a diagram or make a model to illustrate the solar eclipse.

KINESTHETIC LEARNING and CONNECTION TO SCIENCE Interested students may want to look in an almanac to find the dates of the next solar or lunar eclipse that they can see in their area. Challenge them to use clay, straws, and string to model an eclipse. Have

---

This game involves sticks that can be parallel or intersecting. The sticks are removed one by one. The object of the game is to not let the marbles fall between the sticks.

Skew lines are lines that lie in different planes. They are neither parallel nor intersecting.

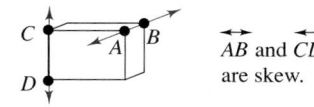

$\overleftrightarrow{AB}$ and $\overleftrightarrow{CD}$ are skew.

■ **EXAMPLE**

Does each pair of lines appear to be parallel or intersecting?

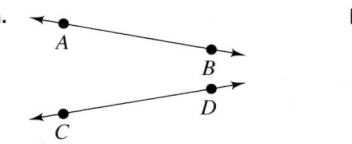 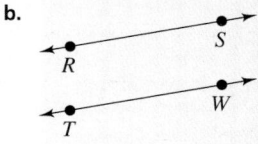

a. $\overleftrightarrow{AB}$ and $\overleftrightarrow{CD}$ are intersecting lines, even though the point of intersection is not shown.

b. $\overleftrightarrow{RS}$ and $\overleftrightarrow{TW}$ are parallel. No matter how far you extend them, they will not intersect.

Work Together

Drawing Points and Lines

10. Draw a point. How many lines can you draw through a point? How many vertical lines can you draw through a point?
too many to count; 1 vertical line

12. Check students' work; answers should show that only 1 line can be drawn through the points if they are in one row, and otherwise 3 lines can be drawn through them.

11. ⚓*What If . . .* Draw two points. How many lines can you draw through two points? Can you draw a horizontal line through your two points? Explain.
Check students' work for diagrams and reasoning; 1 line.

12. ⚓*Go a Step Further* Draw three points. Then draw all the lines that go through any two points. Arrange the three points so that you get a different number of lines.

Now you may assign Exercises 11–12, 17–19, 21, 26–27, 29–36.

Match each figure with its name.

1. 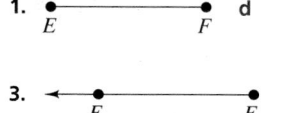 d
   E   *F*

2. a
   E   *F*

3. c
   E   *F*

4. b
   E   *F*

a. $\overleftrightarrow{EF}$ b. $\overrightarrow{EF}$ c. $\overrightarrow{FE}$ d. $\overline{EF}$

328

students describe their models in geometric terms.

REASONING **Exercise 28b** Ask students to name other items that they often think of as points but that are actually models of points. **Answers may vary. Sample: cities on a map**

WRITING **Exercise 29** Before students begin, ask them what they think will be most difficult in writing this description. Giving directional clues can often be difficult. Discuss ways to overcome these difficulties. Encourage students to use what they have learned about naming segments and rays.

WRAP UP

IDENTIFYING THE BIG IDEA Ask students to describe a point, a line, a ray, and a plane. Have them describe two relationships between pairs of lines and sets of points.

LESSON QUIZ

Use the diagram for Questions 1 and 2.

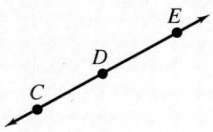

1. Give three names for this line.
$\overleftrightarrow{CD}$, $\overleftrightarrow{DE}$, $\overleftrightarrow{CE}$

2. Name four different rays.
$\overrightarrow{DE}$; $\overrightarrow{CD}$ or $\overrightarrow{CE}$; $\overrightarrow{EC}$ or $\overrightarrow{ED}$; $\overrightarrow{DC}$

Use the diagram at the right for Exercises 5 and 6.

5. Name the line in several different ways.
Answers may vary. Samples: $\overleftrightarrow{AB}$, $\overleftrightarrow{BA}$, $\overleftrightarrow{AC}$, $\overleftrightarrow{BC}$
6. Name four different rays.
Answers may vary. Samples: $\overrightarrow{AB}$, $\overrightarrow{AC}$, $\overrightarrow{BA}$, $\overrightarrow{BC}$

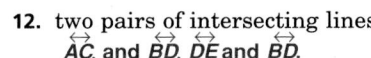

Refer to the diagram below for Exercises 7–12. Name each of the following.

7. three collinear points
A, B, C
8. three noncollinear points
Answers may vary. Sample: A, C, E
9. three segments
Answers may vary. Sample: $\overline{AB}$, $\overline{DE}$, $\overline{AC}$
10. three rays
Answers may vary. Sample: $\overrightarrow{AB}$, $\overrightarrow{ED}$, $\overrightarrow{BD}$
11. two lines that appear to be parallel
$\overleftrightarrow{AC}$, $\overleftrightarrow{DE}$

12. two pairs of intersecting lines
$\overleftrightarrow{AC}$ and $\overleftrightarrow{BD}$, $\overleftrightarrow{DE}$ and $\overleftrightarrow{BD}$.

13. • • • • •
   A   B C   D   E

14. •
     • B
   • A   • C

Draw each of the following.

13. five collinear points
13–14. See above right.
14. three noncollinear points
15. two noncollinear points
not possible

16. a. *Open-ended* Arrange four points in as many different positions as you can. For each arrangement, draw all lines that go through at least two of the points. **Check students' work.**
   b. *Reasoning* If you have four points on a plane, how many lines go through at least two of the points? **1 line, 4 lines, or 6 lines**

Name each pair of segments in each figure that appear to be parallel.

17.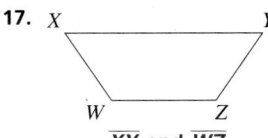
$\overline{XY}$ and $\overline{WZ}$

18.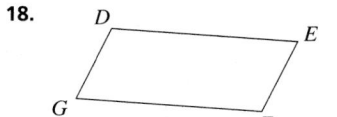
$\overline{DG}$ and $\overline{EF}$, $\overline{DE}$ and $\overline{GF}$

19.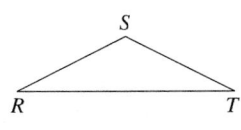
no parallel segments

Complete each sentence with *sometimes*, *always*, or *never*.

always
20. Two points are ■ collinear.
sometimes
22. Four points are ■ collinear.
never
24. A ray ■ has two endpoints.
always
26. Horizontal lines are ■ parallel.

never
21. Two parallel lines are ■ intersecting.
always
23. A segment ■ has two endpoints.
never
25. A line ■ has two endpoints.
never
27. Skew lines ■ intersect.

pages 328–330   On Your Own

28b. Although the planets are large, their dimensions are very small compared to the dimensions of their orbits.

29. Draw $\overleftrightarrow{AB}$. Draw $\overline{CD}$ through point B, so that C is above $\overleftrightarrow{AB}$ and D is farther from A than from B. Draw $\overrightarrow{BE}$, so that E is closer to B than to A and is above $\overleftrightarrow{AB}$.

30. 4 ways

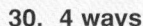
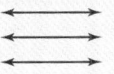

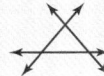

PRACTICE

Practice 8-1 Points, Lines, and Planes

Refer to the diagram at the right for Exercises 1–6. Name each of the following.

1. three collinear points
   M, N, O

2. three noncollinear points
   Sample: Q, N, O

3. three segments
   Sample: MN, MO, NO

4. three rays
   Sample: NM, NO, PQ

5. two lines that appear to be parallel
   OM and PQ

6. two pairs of intersecting lines
   OM and NP, NP and PQ

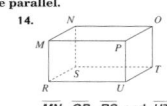

7. Draw four collinear points.
   Sample drawing shown.

   G   H   I   J

8. Draw five noncollinear points.
   Sample drawing shown.

Complete each sentence with *sometimes, always,* or *never.*

9. Three points are __sometimes__ collinear.

10. Four points are __sometimes__ noncollinear.

11. A ray __always__ has one endpoint.

12. A line __never__ has an endpoint.

Name the segments that appear to be parallel.

13.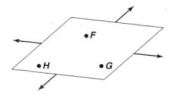
    AB, FC, DE; CD, EB, FA; FE, AD, BC

14.
    MN, OP, RS, and UT; MP, NO, RU, and ST; MR, PU, OT, and NS

In copymaster and workbook formats

RETEACHING

Reteaching 8-1 Points, Lines, and Planes

Each **point** F, G, and H, indicates an exact location in space.

Plane FGH is flat and extends indefinitely as suggested by the arrows.

Line KM (KM) is straight and continues without end in opposite directions.

Segment LM (LM) is part of KM. The points L and M are endpoints of LM.

Ray LM (LM) is part of a line. Point L is its only endpoint.

ST and UV are **parallel lines.** They are in the same plane but do not intersect.

Parallel segments are parts of parallel lines.

Skew lines are neither parallel nor intersecting.

Read each statement. Write *true* or *false.*

1. A line has 2 endpoints __false__
2. A plane has only 2 points. __false__
3. A segment is part of a line. __true__
4. A plane is flat. __true__
5. A segment has 2 endpoints. __true__
6. A ray has 2 endpoints. __false__
7. A ray has no beginning or end. __false__
8. A plane contains only one line. __false__
9. Parallel segments do not intersect. __true__
10. Skew lines intersect each other. __false__

Match each figure with its name.

11. ___b___
12. ___c___
13. ___d___
14. ___a___

a. ray
b. plane
c. line
d. segment

ENRICHMENT

Minds on Math Transparency

8-1

I am the least three-digit number that is divisible by 22 and the sum of whose ones digit and tens digit is 11. What number am I?

374

See *Solution Key* for worked-out answers.

330

Use the diagram for Questions 3–6. Name each of the following.

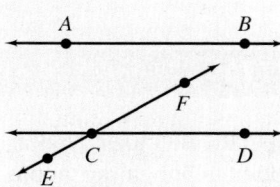

5. intersecting lines CD and EF

6. two lines that appear parallel
   AB and CD

3. three collinear points E, C, F

4. two segments Answers may vary.
   Sample: AB, CD

Use the article below to answer Exercise 28.

28. a. *Astronomy* How could you describe geometrically the position of the moon, Earth, and sun during a solar eclipse? collinear

    b. *Reasoning* These planets are very large. Why can we think of them as points? See margin p. 329.

(((Eclipses)))

EARTH IS ABOUT 248,550 mi from the moon and 93,000,000 mi from the sun. The diameters of Earth and the moon are about 7,910 mi and 2,200 mi, respectively. The diameter of the sun is about 865,400 mi. A solar eclipse occurs when the moon comes between the sun and Earth.

29. *Writing* Write a description of the figure at the right that would help someone to draw a copy of the figure.
    See margin p. 329.

30. *Reasoning* In how many ways can three lines that lie on one plane be related? Draw sketches to show some ways.
    See margin p. 329.

Look at the diagram at the right for Exercises 31–36.
Name each of the following. 31–36. Answers may vary. Samples are given.

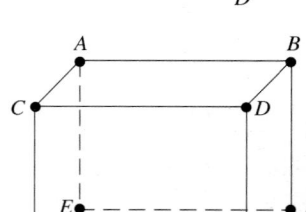

31. a pair of parallel lines
    AB, GH

32. a pair of intersecting lines
    AB, AC

33. a pair of skew lines
    AB, CG

34. a vertical line
    DH

35. a horizontal line
    AB

36. a pair of vertical lines
    DH, BF

Mixed Review

Simplify each expression. *(Lesson 4-2)*

37. 17^2 289
38. 4.2^2 17.64
39. $3(2+6)^2$ 192
40. $359 - 6^3$ 143
41. $(52 \div 2) - 2^4$ 10

Estimate each sum or difference. *(Lesson 6-1)*

42. $6\frac{1}{5} - 2\frac{7}{8}$ 3
43. $4\frac{1}{2} + 5\frac{7}{10}$ 11
44. $3\frac{5}{16} + \frac{7}{8}$ 4
45. $2\frac{7}{12} - 1\frac{2}{3}$ 1
46. $9\frac{5}{8} - 4\frac{1}{5}$ 6

47. *Choose a Strategy* The chorus director can arrange singers in rows of 10, 12, or 15 with no one left over. What is the fewest possible number of singers in the chorus? 60 singers

Extra Practice, Lesson 8-1, page 529

1 Focus

CONNECTING TO PRIOR KNOWLEDGE Ask: *Where do you see examples of angles in the classroom? Outside the classroom?* **Answers may vary. Sample: corners of the wall, board, tile; intersections of roads, houses**

2 Teach

THINK AND DISCUSS

AEP Draw the following angle on the board. Have students provide as many names for the angle as they can. ∠*ABC*, ∠*CBA*, ∠*B*, ∠*1*

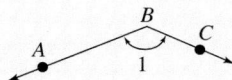

CONNECTION TO SCIENCE Have students research sundials. Discuss how the angle of the rays of the sun tells the time of day.

REASONING Question 3b Have students state a guideline for using a single letter to name an angle.

DIVERSITY Question 6 Students with visual impairments may have trouble reading the scale on the protractor. Allow these students to measure angles with a partner.

MEASUREMENT Connection

8-2 Exploring Angles

What You'll Learn

▼ To estimate and measure angles
▼ To classify angles as acute, right, obtuse, or straight

...And Why

You can understand exercise directions involving angle measures.

Here's How

Look for questions that
▪ build understanding
✔ check understanding

THINK AND DISCUSS

1 Estimating and Measuring Angles

More than 3,000 years ago, the Babylonians discovered that it takes about 360 days for the sun to travel in a circular path. They divided the path into 360 equal parts. We now call each of these parts a **degree.**

An **angle** is made up of two rays with a common endpoint.

∠YXZ

1b. *X* is the vertex, and *Y* and *Z* are points on the sides of ∠*XYZ*.

1. a. ✔*Try It Out* Name the vertex and sides of the angle. **X; $\overrightarrow{XY}$, $\overrightarrow{XZ}$**
   b. Describe what the three letters represent in ∠*YXZ*.
   c. Use three letters to give the angle another name. **∠ZXY**

2. ▪*Look Back* Sometimes you can name an angle with a number, like ∠1, or by the name of the vertex. What one-letter name would you use for ∠*YXZ*? Explain. **∠X; X is the label of the vertex.**

3. a. ✔*Try It Out* How many angles are shown at the right? Name them.
   b. ▪*Reasoning* Why can't you use a single letter to name any of the angles?

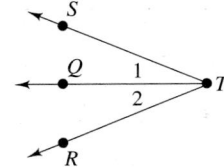

The legs of this camera tripod form angles with each other and meet at the vertex. The legs are sides of the angles.

3a. 3 angles; ∠*STR*, ∠1, ∠2
b. The angles have the same vertex, so they would all have the same name.

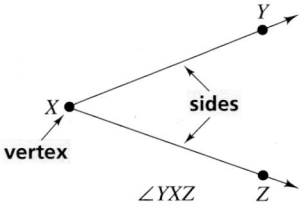

Lesson Planning Options

Prerequisite Skills
- naming points (8-1)
- naming rays (8-1)

Vocabulary/Symbols
degree, angle, vertex, sides, acute angle, right angle, obtuse angle, straight angle, perpendicular

Materials/Manipulatives
- protractor

Resources

Student Edition

Skills Handbook, p. 536
Extra Practice, p. 529
Glossary/Study Guide

Teaching Resources

Chapter Support File, Ch. 8
- Lesson Planner 8-2
- Practice 8-2, Reteaching 8-2
- Answer Masters 8-2
Teaching Aids Masters 3, 6, 26
Glossary, Spanish Resources

Transparencies
6, 15, 18, Minds on Math 8-2

Warm Up

What is the result if you divide 50 by $\frac{1}{2}$ and then subtract 25?
75

331

■ **ADDITIONAL EXAMPLES**

FOR EXAMPLE 1

Make an angle using your forearm and the top of your desk. Then estimate and measure the angle. **Answers may vary.**

FOR EXAMPLE 2

Classify each angle as acute, right, obtuse, or straight.

a.

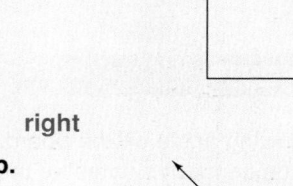

right

b.

obtuse

c.

acute

KINESTHETIC LEARNING and ESTIMATION
Provide a group of three students with a rope 5 ft in length. One student pulls the rope at the midpoint, while two students hold the rope taut at either end. Have classmates classify various angles.

Technology Options

Prentice Hall Technology

  Software for Learners

- Hot Page™ 22*
- Math Blaster® Mystery*
- Interactive Student Tutorial, Chapter 8*

Teaching Resource Software

- Computer Item Generator 8-2
- Resource Pro™ Chapter 8*

Internet • For related mathematics activities, visit the Prentice Hall site at www.phschool.com/math

*Available on CD-ROM only

Assignment Options for Exercises On Your Own

To provide flexible scheduling, this lesson can be subdivided into parts.

▼1 **Core** 1–17
Extension 18–23

▼2 **Core** 24–29, 31, 32, 34, 35
Extension 30, 33, 36

Use Mixed Review to maintain skills.

You can use a *protractor* to measure the size of an angle. The units of measurement are degrees. Use the symbol ° for degrees.

■ **EXAMPLE 1**   *Real-World Problem Solving*

Physical Education Measure the angle formed by the football player's leg and the ground.

First, extend the sides of the angle so that they will intersect the scale on the protractor.

③ Read the scale where it intersects the second side of the angle.

4. Use the scale that aligns zero with one side of the angle.
5. No; degrees are units measuring the opening of an angle, not the lengths of its sides.

② Make sure that one side of the angle passes through zero on the protractor scale.

① Place the center point of the protractor on the vertex of the angle.

The angle measures 50°.

4. ⁙*Reasoning* Most protractors have two scales. How do you decide which number to read?
4–5. See above left.

5. ⁙*Reasoning* Does changing the lengths of the sides of the angle change the measurement of the angle? Explain.

6. ✔*Try It Out* Use a protractor to measure each angle.
   a. 115°
   b. 71°

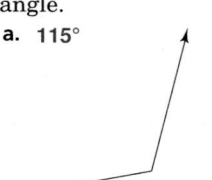

Now you may assign Exercises 1–23.

ASSESSMENT Draw several angles for the class. Have students record each angle as acute, right, obtuse, or straight. Then have students estimate the angle measure. Ask students to use a protractor to draw a similar angle on their papers.

CONNECTION TO SPORTS Ask students how they might use angles when participating in sports. **Answers may vary. Sample: rolling a bowling ball at a desired angle; return a tennis ball at the best angle**

3 Practice/Assess

EXERCISES *On Your Own*

Exercise 5 Ask students to name the angle in the diagram that forms a right angle and the two rays that are perpendicular. ∠*KLM*; $\overrightarrow{LK}$, $\overrightarrow{LM}$

ERROR ALERT! Exercises 6–17 Students may read the wrong scale on the protractor when drawing angles. **Remediation:** Have students classify each angle as acute, obtuse, right, or straight. Then compare the drawing to its classification.

pages 334–335   On Your Own

6.   7.

8.   9.

10.   11.

12.   13.

14.   15.

16.   17.

❷ *Classifying Angles*

You can use measures to classify angles.

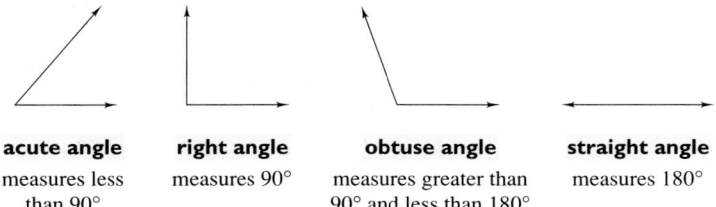

acute angle	**right angle**	**obtuse angle**	**straight angle**
measures less than 90°	measures 90°	measures greater than 90° and less than 180°	measures 180°

■ EXAMPLE 2   *Real-World Problem Solving*

Art In this drawing, what type of angle does the dinosaur make with the ground?

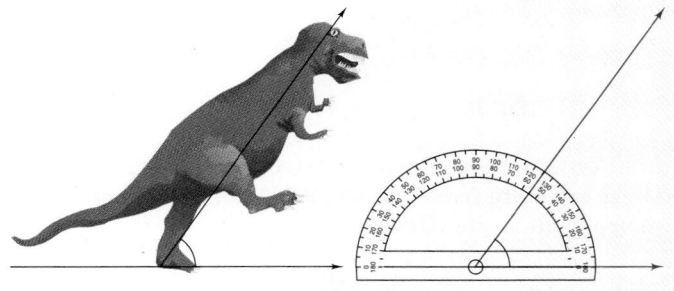

The angle measures 55°. Since 55° < 90°, the dinosaur makes an acute angle with the ground.

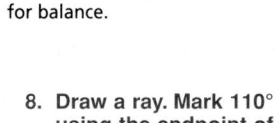 Many museum models of *Tyrannosaurus rex* show the dinosaur in an upright, tail-dragging position. Scientists now believe that *Tyrannosaurus rex* actually walked at an angle, using its tail for balance.

7. ✓*Try It Out* Classify the angles in Question 6 on page 332 as acute, right, obtuse, or straight.
7a. obtuse   b. acute   c. right

8. How would you use your protractor to draw a 110° angle?

8. Draw a ray. Mark 110° using the endpoint of the ray for the vertex. Draw a ray from the endpoint of the first ray through the mark.

Lines that intersect to form right angles are **perpendicular.** The symbol ⌐ on a diagram indicates that lines are perpendicular and that an angle is a right angle.

9. Name all the right angles formed by the perpendicular lines, $\overleftrightarrow{AB}$ and $\overleftrightarrow{CD}$, shown.
∠*AEC*, ∠*AED*, ∠*BED*, ∠*BEC*

10. Answers may vary. Samples: corner of a door, corner of the ceiling, corners of pages in textbooks

10. ♣*Open-ended* Find examples of perpendicular lines in your classroom.

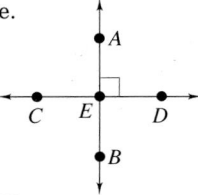

Now you may assign Exercises 24–36.

Exercises 18–23 Have students make sure that one side of the angle passes through zero on the protractor.

WRITING Exercise 30 Ask students to draw examples to help prove their answers.

Exercise 35 Students should be able to answer the question without using a protractor.

KINESTHETIC LEARNING Exercise 49 Have students use quart containers to demonstrate the problem to the rest of the class.

WRAP UP

IDENTIFYING THE BIG IDEA Ask students to describe four types of angles and explain how to estimate, measure, and draw angles.

LESSON QUIZ

Use a protractor to draw the following angles. Classify each angle as acute, right, obtuse, or straight.

1. 30° acute

2. 162° obtuse

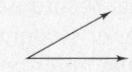

---

30. No; yes; no; yes; the measure of a right angle must be 90°. The measure of a straight angle must be 180°. An acute angle can have any measure between 0° and 90°. An obtuse angle can have any measure between 90° and 180°.

34. Answers may vary. Sample:

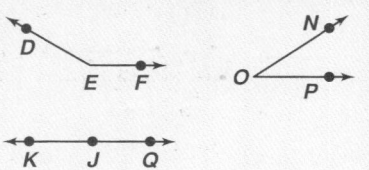

49. Fill the 3-qt container and empty it into the 5-qt container. Refill the 3-qt container and empty as much as possible (2 qt) into the 5-qt container. One quart remains in the 3-qt container.

EXERCISES *On Your Own*

Name the vertex and sides of each angle.

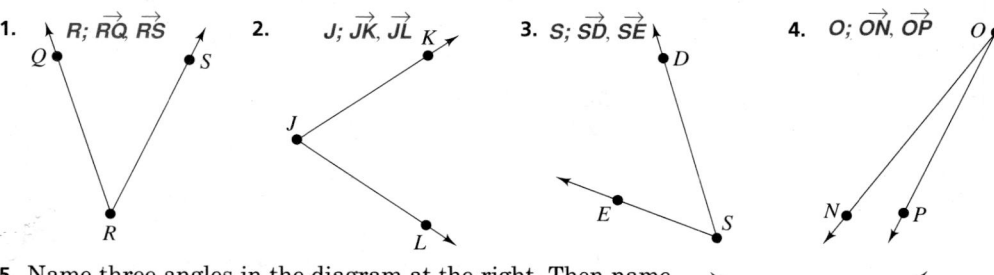

1. R; $\vec{RQ}$, $\vec{RS}$ **2.** J; $\vec{JK}$, $\vec{JL}$ **3.** S; $\vec{SD}$, $\vec{SE}$ **4.** O; $\vec{ON}$, $\vec{OP}$

5. Name three angles in the diagram at the right. Then name each angle in a different way.
∠KLM, ∠KLN, ∠MLN; ∠MLK, ∠NLK, ∠NLM

Use a protractor to draw angles with the following measures.   6–17. See margin p. 333.

6. 30°   **7.** 135°   **8.** 90°   **9.** 45°   **10.** 120°   **11.** 60°

12. 125°   **13.** 75°   **14.** 82°   **15.** 154°   **16.** 52°   **17.** 165°

Estimation **Estimate the measure of each angle. Choose the best estimate from 30°, 60°, 90°, 120°, 150°. Then measure each angle with a protractor.**

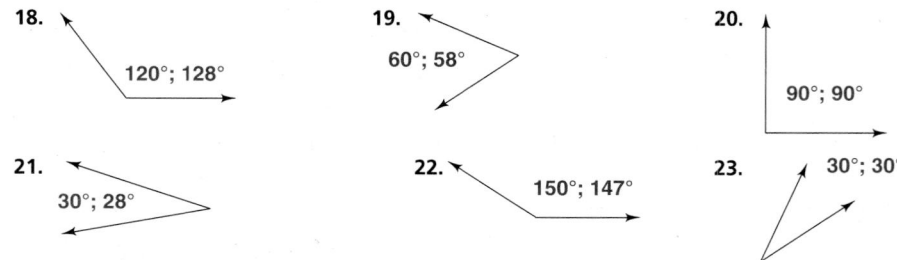

18. 120°; 128°   **19.** 60°; 58°   **20.** 90°; 90°

21. 30°; 28°   **22.** 150°; 147°   **23.** 30°; 30°

Classify each angle as *acute, right, obtuse,* or *straight*.

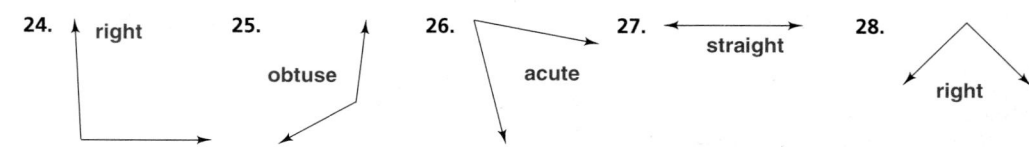

24. right   **25.** obtuse   **26.** acute   **27.** straight   **28.** right

334

3. 90° **right**

4. Name the vertex and rays of the angle shown. **vertex: Y; rays: $\overrightarrow{YX}$; $\overrightarrow{YZ}$**

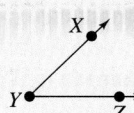

29. *Photography* A 50-mm camera lens has a 45° viewing angle. What kind of angle is this? **acute**

30. *Writing* Must two acute angles have the same measure? Must two right angles? Two obtuse angles? Two straight angles? Explain. **See margin p. 334.**

31. **a.** Draw two perpendicular lines, $\overleftrightarrow{RS}$ and $\overleftrightarrow{TW}$.
  b. How many right angles are formed?
     4 right angles

31a.
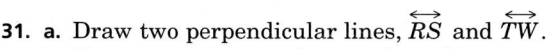

32. Name all the right angles formed by the perpendicular lines $\overleftrightarrow{ST}$ and $\overleftrightarrow{WX}$ at the right. **∠SOW, ∠SOX, ∠TOX, ∠TOW**

33. *Reasoning* What angles can you draw accurately without using a protractor? Explain. **Straight angles; you can draw a straight angle by drawing a line through a point.**

34. *Open-ended* Draw an obtuse ∠DEF, an acute ∠NOP, and a straight ∠KJQ. **See margin p. 334.**

35. **Choose A, B, C, or D.** Which measure is *not* a measure of one of the angles shown at the right? **A**

  A. 60°   **B.** 90°   **C.** 120°   **D.** 150°

36. **a.** *Measurement* Find the measure of each angle in the figure at the right.   **i. 180° ii. 70° iii. 120° iv. 90°**

     i. ∠AGF   **ii.** ∠DGB   **iii.** ∠BGE   **iv.** ∠EGC
  b. List all the obtuse angles shown.
  c. List all the right angles shown.
  d. List all the straight angles shown.   **∠AGF**
  b. ∠AGE, ∠BGF, ∠BGE, ∠CGF   **c.** ∠AGD, ∠FGD, ∠CGE

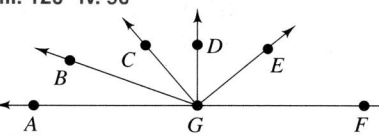

Mixed Review

37–42. Answers may vary. Samples are given.
Write three equal ratios for each given ratio. *(Lesson 7-2)*

37. 6 : 10, 9 : 15, 12 : 20   **40.** 7 : 16, 21 : 48, 28 : 64   **42.** $\frac{3}{5}, \frac{6}{10}, \frac{9}{15}$

37. 3 : 5   **38.** 5 to 9   **39.** $\frac{1}{6}$ **40.** 14 : 32   **41.** 16 to 20   **42.** $\frac{48}{80}$
  38. 10 to 18, 15 to 27, 20 to 36   **39.** $\frac{2}{12}, \frac{3}{18}, \frac{4}{24}$ **41.** 4 to 5, 8 to 10, 32 to 40

Find the GCF. *(Lesson 5-3)*

43. 18, 27   **44.** 52, 78   **45.** 84, 28   **46.** 10, 15, 25   **47.** 4, 18, 144   **48.** 9, 36, 56
   9   **26**   **28**   **5**   **2**   **1**

49. *Choose a Strategy* Suppose you have a 3-qt container and a 5-qt container. Without marking the containers, how could you measure exactly 1 qt of water? **See margin p. 334.**

PRACTICE

Practice 8-2 *Exploring Angles*

In copymaster and workbook formats

RETEACHING

Reteaching 8-2 *Exploring Angles*

ENRICHMENT

M inds on Math Transparency

8-2

Find the missing numbers if each number after the first two is the sum of the two preceding numbers.
5.5 , 8, 13.5 , 21.5, 35 , 56.5

See Solution Key for worked-out answers.

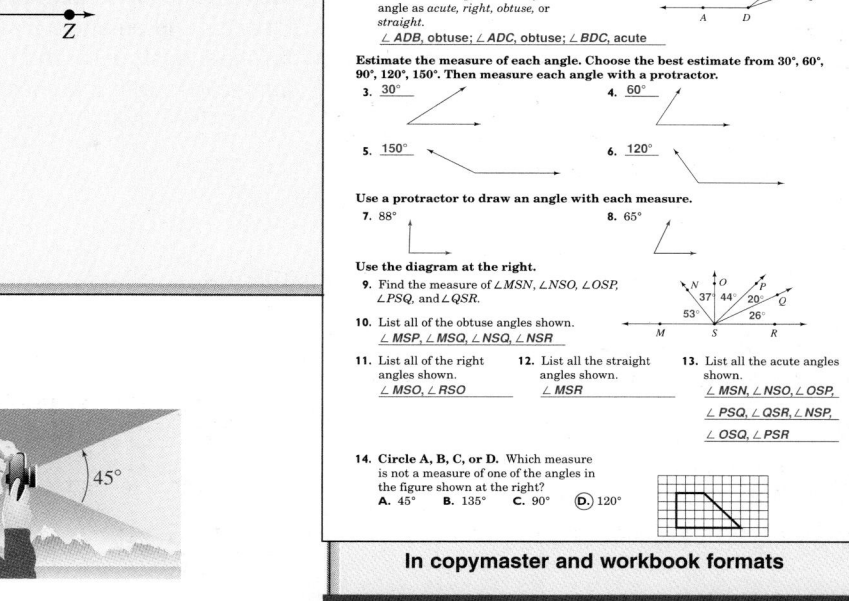

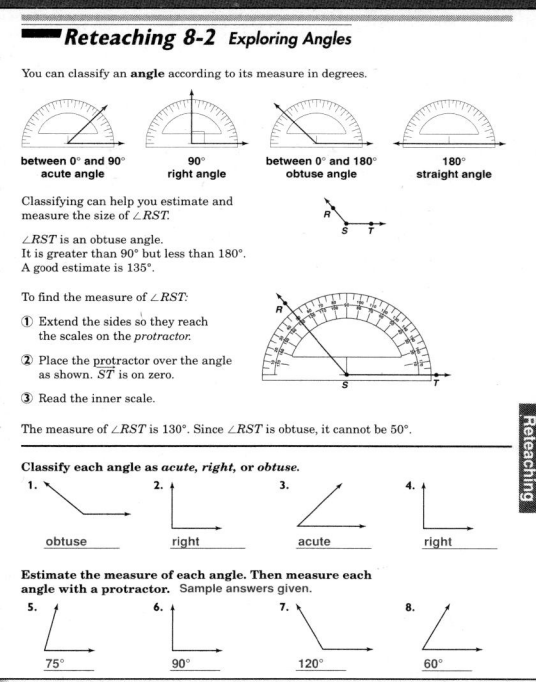

335

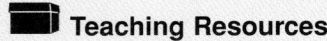

In Lesson 8-2, students learned how to estimate, measure, and classify angles. This toolbox allows students to explore constructing angles.

ERROR ALERT! Students may not be able to follow the step-by-step instructions in the examples. **Remediation:** Have students perform the steps with a partner. Partners can

compare their constructions and discuss the goals of each step.

ASSESSMENT Without looking at the book, have students work with a partner to write instructions for constructing a segment bisector and an angle bisector. When they are finished, each pair can compare their instructions with the ones in the book and correct their instructions.

■ ADDITIONAL PROBLEM

Use a straightedge to draw and label a line segment. Draw a segment bisector. Then draw an angle bisector of one of the right angles formed by the segment bisector and the segment. Check your work by measuring the segment with a ruler and the angles with a compass.

Materials/Manipulatives

• compass   • straight edge

Resources

Teaching Resources

Teaching Aids Masters 3, 6, 26

Transparencies
6, 15

page 336   Math Toolbox

1.

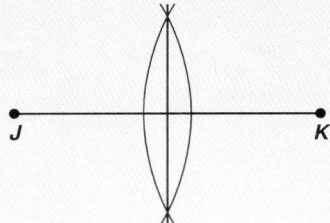

2.

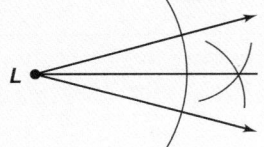

3. First construct the perpendicular bisector of a segment. This will form 90° angles. Then construct the angle bisector of one of the 90° angles to make a 45° angle.

336

EXPLORATION

Basic Constructions

After Lesson 8-2

A *bisector* is a line perpendicular to a segment and passing through the midpoint of the segment.

An *angle bisector* is a ray that divides the angle into two congruent angles.

■ EXAMPLE 1

Use a compass and straightedge to construct the perpendicular bisector of $\overline{AB}$.

Open the compass to more than half the length of $\overline{AB}$. Put the tip of the compass at A. Draw a part of a circle that intersects $\overline{AB}$.

Put the tip of the compass at B, keeping the compass open to the same width. Then draw a part of a circle that intersects $\overline{AB}$. The curves intersect at two points. Label these points C and D. $\overleftrightarrow{CD}$ intersects $\overline{AB}$ at its midpoint M.

Point M is the midpoint of $\overline{AB}$.

■ EXAMPLE 2

Use a compass and straightedge to construct the angle bisector of $\angle E$.

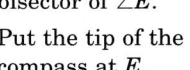

Put the tip of the compass at E. Draw a part of a circle that intersects the sides of $\angle E$. Label the points of intersection F and G.

Put the compass tip at F and then at G. With the same compass opening, draw intersecting parts of circles. Label the point of intersection H. Draw $\overleftrightarrow{EH}$.

$\overleftrightarrow{EH}$ is the bisector of $\angle FEG$.

1–3. See margin.

1. Copy $\overline{JK}$ at the right. Then construct the perpendicular bisector of $\overline{JK}$.

2. Copy $\angle L$ at the right. Then construct the angle bisector of $\angle L$.

3. *Writing* Explain how you can use what you know about perpendicular bisectors and angle bisectors to construct angles of 90° and 45°.

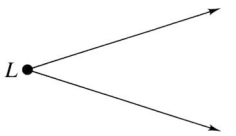

Teaching Notes

1 Focus

CONNECTING TO PRIOR KNOWLEDGE
Draw this angle on the board.

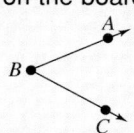

Ask students to name the angle three ways.
∠ABC, ∠CBA, ∠B

2 Teach

Work Together

Students can easily draw a pair of parallel lines if they use both sides of a straightedge.

THINK AND DISCUSS

VISUAL LEARNING Question 5a Students can trace the angles onto tracing paper and move them around on the picture to find congruent angles.

ERROR ALERT! Students may confuse the terms *complementary* and *supplementary*.
Remediation: Ask students to think of mnemonics to help them remember the terms. For example, *c* is before *s* in the alphabet, so complementary angles are smaller than supplementary angles.

EXTENSION Question 5 Tell students when two lines intersect, four angles are formed. The angles next to each other are adjacent angles. The angles across from each other are vertical angles. In the diagram, ∠2 and ∠3 are

---

ALGEBRA Connection

8-3 Special Pairs of Angles

What You'll Learn

▼ To identify congruent, complementary, supplementary, interior, and exterior angles

...And Why

You can find the measure of unknown angles based on the measures of other angles.

Here's How

Look for questions that
▪▪ build understanding
✔ check understanding

1–2.

Work Together
Investigating Angles

1. Use a ruler to draw a straight line on your paper. Then draw a second line parallel to the first.
   1–2. See left.
2. Now draw a line that intersects the pair of parallel lines.

3. ▪▪*Analyze* Measure the four angles formed at each intersection. What do you notice? **Each angle is one of two different measures and the sum of the two different measures is 180°.**

THINK AND DISCUSS

Sometimes, two angles have a special relationship.

Complementary angles

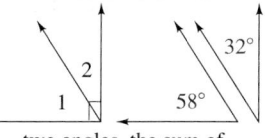

two angles, the sum of whose measures is 90°

Supplementary angles

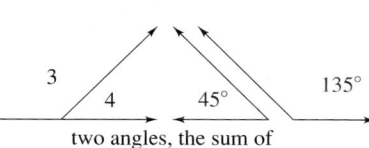

two angles, the sum of whose measures is 180°

■ EXAMPLE

Find the measure of ∠AEB.

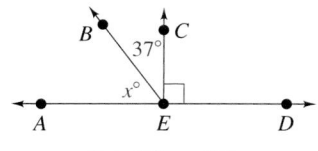

∠AEB and ∠BEC are complementary. The sum of their measures is 90°.

$x° + 37° = 90°$ ← Write an equation.
$x° + 37° - 37° = 90° - 37°$ ← Subtract 37° from each side.
$x° = 53°$

The measure of ∠AEB is 53°.

4. ✔*Try It Out* Refer to the Example. Find the measure of the angle that is supplementary to ∠AEB. **127°**

Lesson Planning Options

Prerequisite Skills
• writing equations (2-6)

Vocabulary/Symbols
complementary angles, supplementary angles, transversal, exterior angles, interior angles, congruent angles

Materials/Manipulatives
• ruler   • protractor

Resources

 Student Edition
Skills Handbook, p. 537
Extra Practice, p. 529
Glossary/Study Guide

Teaching Resources
Chapter Support File, Ch. 8
• Lesson Planner 8-3
• Practice 8-3, Reteaching 8-3
• Answer Masters 8-3
Teaching Aids Masters 3, 6, 26
Glossary, Spanish Resources

 Transparencies
6, 15, Minds on Math 8-3

Warm Up

Jan's bicycle wheel makes one turn every 2 m. How many complete turns will it make during a 5 km bike ride? **2,500**

adjacent angles; ∠1 and ∠3 are vertical angles. Have students identify a pair of each kind of angle. **Answers may vary. Sample: adjacent: ∠6 and ∠7; vertical: ∠5 and ∠7**

■ **ADDITIONAL EXAMPLE**

FOR EXAMPLE

Find the measure of ∠HIK. **48°**

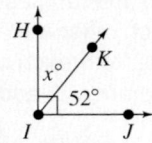

Technology Options

Prentice Hall Technology

  Software for Learners

• Math Blaster® Mystery*
• Interactive Student Tutorial, Chapter 8*

  Teaching Resource Software

• Computer Item Generator 8-3
• Resource™ Pro Chapter 8*

Internet • For related mathematics activities, visit the Prentice Hall site at www.phschool.com/math

*Available on CD-ROM only

Assignment Options for Exercises On Your Own

Core 1–7, 11, 12, 14–17
Extension 8–10, 13

Use Mixed Review to maintain skills.

338

AEP You can help students remember the term *transversal* by telling them that *trans-* means "across" in Latin. A transversal is a line that goes across two other lines. Ask what other words they know containing the prefix *trans-*. **Answers may vary. Sample: transportation, translate**

ASSESSMENT Have students draw a pair of supplementary angles by drawing a line, picking a point on the line, and drawing a ray from that point. Have students measure one of the angles with a protractor. Then find the measure of the

other angle by writing an equation and solving it. They can check their answer by measuring.

3 Practice/Assess

EXERCISES *On Your Own*

RESEARCH Exercise 13 Students should be able to find this information in books on carpentry in the library.

In the Work Together, you drew a line intersecting a pair of parallel lines. This line is a **transversal.** The transversal forms eight angles with the pair of parallel lines.

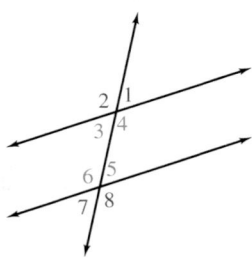

∠s 1, 2, 7, and 8 are outside the parallel lines. They are **exterior angles.**

∠s 3, 4, 5, and 6 are between the parallel lines. They are **interior angles.**

Congruent angles are angles that have the same measure.

5. ✓*Try It Out* Use the diagram above to name each of the following. **Answers may vary. Samples are given.**
   a. a pair of congruent angles **∠1 and ∠3**
   b. two pairs of supplementary angles **∠1 and ∠4, ∠5 and ∠6**
   c. two supplementary angles that are both exterior **∠1 and ∠2**
   d. two supplementary angles, one of which is interior and one of which is exterior **∠1 and ∠4**

Now you may assign Exercises 1–17.

EXERCISES *On Your Own*

Complete each sentence with *sometimes*, *always*, or *never*.

1. Two acute angles are ■ complementary.
   sometimes

2. Two obtuse angles are ■ complementary.
   never

3. Two obtuse angles are ■ supplementary.
   never

4. Two right angles are ■ supplementary.
   always

Algebra **Find the measure of each angle marked $x°$.**

5.
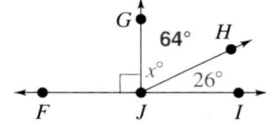

6.

7.
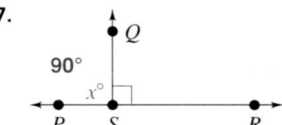

8. *Cheese* One half of a cheese wheel is cut into two unequal wedges. One wedge forms an angle whose measure is 65°. Find the angle formed by the other wedge. (*Hint:* The sum of the angles formed by all three wedges is 360°.) **115°**

WRAP UP

IDENTIFYING THE BIG IDEA Ask students how to find the measures of complementary and supplementary angles.

▽ **PROJECT LINK** Inform students that the tangram puzzle originated in China. Suggest they review the names of the geometric shapes. They may want to look ahead to Lesson 6.

LESSON QUIZ

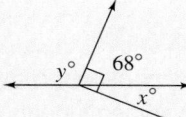

1. Find the measure of the angle marked *x*°.
   22°
2. Find the measure of the angle marked *y*°.
   112°

---

9. *Architecture* The Leaning Tower of Pisa makes an angle of about 5° with a vertical line. What is the measure of the acute angle that the tower makes with the ground? What is the measure of the obtuse angle?   **85°**

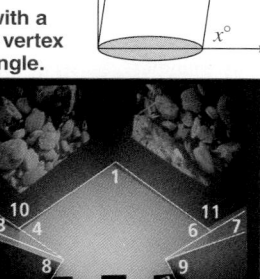

10. *Writing* Explain how to draw a pair of supplementary angles without using a protractor. **Draw a straight angle with a straightedge. Then draw a ray whose endpoint is at the vertex**

11. *Art* The photograph at the right shows **of the straight angle.** *Oblique House* by American artist Mary Lucier. Which angles are congruent? Complementary? Supplementary?   **See back of book.**

12. *Open-ended* Draw a pair of complementary angles. What is the measure of each angle?
    12–13. Check students' work.

13. *Research* Find out how complementary and supplementary angles are used in carpentry.

Use the diagram at the right to name each of the following.   **15–17. Answers may vary. Samples are given.**

14. the transversal $\overleftrightarrow{CE}$ 15. two interior angles   **∠3, ∠4, ∠6, ∠8**

16. two exterior angles   17. two pairs of supplementary angles
    ∠1, ∠2, ∠5, ∠7   **∠1 and ∠3, ∠3 and ∠4**

Mixed Review

Draw a model to find each quotient. *(Lesson 4-6)*

18. 0.2 ÷ 0.04   19. 0.9 ÷ 0.03   20. 1.5 ÷ 0.1   21. 0.08 ÷ 0.2   22. 0.24 ÷ 0.04
    5   **30**   **15**   **0.4**   **6**

23. *Choose a Strategy* To purchase a car that cost $12,800, Ms. Jackson paid $2,400 in cash and agreed to pay $535 each month for 24 months. How much interest did she pay by purchasing the car this way?   **$2,440**

▽ **CHAPTER PROJECT**

PROJECT LINK: IDENTIFYING

The diagram shows a puzzle known as a tangram. Identify the geometric shapes used to form the large square.

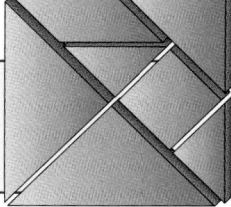

5 triangles, 1 square, 1 parallelogram

PRACTICE

Practice 8-3 *Special Pairs of Angles*

Complete each sentence with *sometimes*, *always*, or *never*.

1. Two right angles are **never** complementary.
2. Two acute angles are **never** supplementary.
3. One obtuse angle and one acute angle are **sometimes** supplementary.
4. One obtuse angle and one right angle are **never** supplementary.

Find the measure of each angle marked *x*°.

5.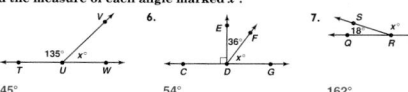
   45°
6. **54°**
7. **162°**
8. **22°**
9. **93°**
10. **71°**

Use the diagram at the right. Name each of the following.   Answers may vary.

11. two interior angles   **∠3 and ∠4**
12. two exterior angles   **∠1 and ∠2**
13. two pairs of supplementary angles
    ∠5 and ∠6; ∠7 and ∠8
14. the transversal   **$\overleftrightarrow{OP}$**

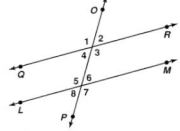

Use the figure at the right to solve.

15. Find the measure of the angle marked *x*° at the corner of the picture frame.
    118°

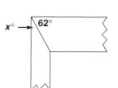

In copymaster and workbook formats

RETEACHING

Reteaching 8-3 *Special Pairs of Angles*

Complementary angles: sum of measures = 90°.	Supplementary angles: sum of measures = 180°.	Congruent angles have the same measure.
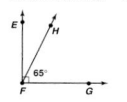	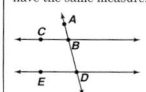	
To find the measure of a complement, subtract from 90°.	To find the measure of a supplement, subtract from 180°.	Angles *ABC* and *BDE* are formed by two parallel lines cut by a **transversal**.
90° − 65° = 35°	180° − 130° = 50°	∠*ABC* and ∠*BDE*
The complement of ∠*HFG* has measure 35°.	The supplement of ∠*USR* has measure 130°.	have the same measure; they are congruent.

Find the measure of each angle marked *x*°.

1.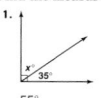
   55°
2.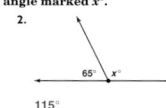
   115°
3.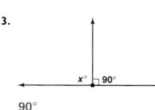
   90°

Use the diagram at the right. Complete each sentence with *complementary*, *supplementary*, or *congruent*. Some exercises use more than one word.

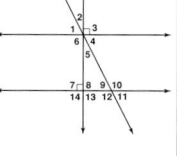

4. Angles 1 and 2 are **complementary**.
5. Angles 9 and 10 are **supplementary**.
6. Angles 3 and 7 are **supplementary and congruent**.
7. Angles 4 and 5 are **complementary**.
8. Angles 10 and 11 are **supplementary**.
9. Angles 7 and 14 are **supplementary and congruent**

ENRICHMENT

Minds on Math Transparency

8-3

A number has 4 digits.
The sum of the first digit and the last digit is twice the second digit.
The second digit is 2 less than the third digit.
The last digit is twice the first digit.
Some of the digits are alike.
What is the number?

4,688

See *Solution Key* for worked-out answers.

1 Focus

CONNECTING TO PRIOR KNOWLEDGE Draw a variety of triangles for the class. Ask students to identify any acute, right, or obtuse angles they see. Challenge students to make statements about triangles. **Answers may vary. Sample: Triangles always have three sides and three angles.**

Lesson Planning Options

Prerequisite Skills
- classifying angles (8-2)

Vocabulary/Symbols
congruent segments, acute triangle, obtuse triangle, right triangle, equilateral triangle, isosceles triangle, scalene triangle

Materials/Manipulatives
- geoboards   • dot paper
- geoboard bands   • metric ruler
- protractor

Resources

 Student Edition

Skills Handbook, p. 537
Extra Practice, p. 529
Glossary/Study Guide

 Teaching Resources

Chapter Support File, Ch. 8
- Lesson Planner 8-4
- Practice 8-4, Reteaching 8-4
- Answer Masters 8-4
Teaching Aids Masters 3, 7, 8
Glossary, Spanish Resources

 Transparencies
6, 20, 21, 92, Minds on Math 8-4

Warm Up

List the possible values for
y, if $|y| = 5$. $-5, +5$

---

2 Teach

Work Together

CONNECTION TO TECHNOLOGY Question
If available, have some students use geometry software to explore the shapes of triangles.

KINESTHETIC LEARNING Have groups of three students model the triangles using rope. Each student stands for a vertex of the triangle; the rope forms the sides.

THINK AND DISCUSS

AEP Write *equilateral* for the class. Tell students: *All sides of an equilateral triangle are equal.*

AUDITORY LEARNING To help students remember the definition of *scalene,* say: *Scalene, none of your sides are equal.* Have students come up with similar phrases as memory devices.

8-4 Identifying Triangles

What You'll Learn
▼ To identify triangles by their angles or by their sides

...And Why
Different types of triangles are used in games, drafting, and optics.

Here's How
Look for questions that
⁘ build understanding
✔ check understanding

Work Together _____ *Forming Different Triangles*

On geoboards, form as many of the triangles described below as you can. Try to form two triangles with different shapes that fit each description.
a, c, e–f. See below left.

1. Draw each triangle on dot paper.
   a. a triangle with three acute angles
   b. a triangle with one right angle
   c. a triangle with one obtuse angle
   d. a triangle with one right angle and one obtuse angle
   e. a triangle with no sides that have the same length
   f. a triangle with two sides that have the same length

   b.
   d. not possible

2. ⁘*Look Back* Which of the above triangle(s) could you *not* form on your geoboard? Explain. **A triangle with one right angle and one obtuse angle; check students' work for reasoning.**

THINK AND DISCUSS

Segments that have the same length are called **congruent segments.**

You can classify triangles by angle measures or by the number of congruent sides.

Classifying by Angles

acute triangle	**obtuse triangle**	**right triangle**
three acute angles	one obtuse angle	one right angle

Classifying by Sides

equilateral triangle	**isosceles triangle**	**scalene triangle**
three congruent sides	at least two congruent sides	no congruent sides

1a.
c.
e.
f.

REASONING **Question 6** Ask students: *What makes the best name for something the best?* **Answers may vary. Sample: plenty of specific information**

CONNECTION TO HISTORY Historians think that dominoes arrived in Italy from China in the fourteenth century.

■ **ADDITIONAL EXAMPLE**

FOR EXAMPLE
Name the triangles in the tangram puzzle. **isosceles, right**

ASSESSMENT List the six types of triangles. Give students time to sketch each type after you name it. Have students check each other's drawings.

3 Practice/Assess

EXERCISES *On Your Own*

Exercises 1–12 Remind students that the best name is the correct name.

TACTILE LEARNING **Exercises 1–12** Give students pieces of uncooked spaghetti. They can break the spaghetti into different lengths and create each triangle. Creating the triangles may make them easier for some students to classify.

3. ⚑ *Think About It* Can an isosceles triangle be an acute triangle? Can a right triangle be an acute triangle? Explain.
   Yes; no; check students' work for reasoning.

4. Can a scalene triangle be an acute triangle? Can it be an obtuse triangle? **yes; yes**

5. Can an equilateral triangle be an acute triangle? Can it be a right triangle? Explain.
   Yes; no; check students' work for reasoning.

6. ⚑ *Reasoning* Suppose a triangle is both isosceles and obtuse. What is the best name for such a triangle?
   obtuse isosceles triangle

■ **E X A M P L E**   *Real-World Problem Solving*

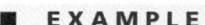

Games Judging by appearance, give all the names you can for the triangle formed by each triomino. What is the best name?

The triangle has three acute angles. It is acute.

The triangle has at least two congruent sides. It is isosceles.

The triangle has three congruent sides. It is equilateral.

The best name is equilateral because every equilateral triangle is both acute and isosceles.

 Triominoes is a game similar to dominoes. It is played with triangular pieces instead of the rectangles used in dominoes.

7. ⚑ *Visual Thinking* Why do you think triominoes are equilateral triangles? **Each side of a triomino has the same length as each side of any other triomino.**

Now you may assign Exercises 1–41.

EXERCISES *On Your Own*

Classify each triangle with given side lengths as *scalene*, *isosceles*, or *equilateral*.

1. 3, 3, 5 **isosceles**	**2.** 8, 8, 8 **equilateral**	**3.** 6, 9, 4 **scalene**	**4.** 7, 9, 14 **scalene**	**5.** 5, 8, 5 **isosceles**	**6.** 6, 8, 6 **isosceles**
7. 12, 7, 9 **scalene**	**8.** 3, 4, 5 **scalene**	**9.** 6, 8, 10 **scalene**	**10.** 11, 11, 11 **equilateral**	**11.** 4, 4, 9 **isosceles**	**12.** 3, 6, 7 **scalene**

Classify each triangle with given angle measures as *acute*, *right*, or *obtuse*.

13. 90°, 35°, 55° **right**	**14.** 15°, 60°, 105° **obtuse**	**15.** 30°, 90°, 60° **right**	**16.** 120°, 35°, 25° **obtuse**
17. 85°, 70°, 25° **acute**	**18.** 45°, 45°, 90° **right**	**19.** 100°, 30°, 50° **obtuse**	**20.** 60°, 60°, 60° **acute**

Technology Options

Prentice Hall Technology

💾 💿 **Software for Learners**
• Hot Page™ 23*
• Math Blaster® Mystery*
• Interactive Student Tutorial, Chapter 8*

💾 💿 **Teaching Resource Software**
• Computer Item Generator 8-4
• Resource Pro™ Chapter 8*

Internet • For related mathematics activities, visit the Prentice Hall site at www.phschool.com/math

*Available on CD-ROM only

Assignment Options for Exercises On Your Own

Core 1–27, 29, 32–41
Extension 28, 30, 31

Use Mixed Review to maintain skills.

EXTENSION Exercises 13–20 Ask: *What do you notice about the sum of the angle measures?* **The sum of the measures is 180°.**

ERROR ALERT! **Exercise 21** Students may forget an equilateral triangle is also isosceles. **Remediation:** Discuss with students similar relationships such as a square is also a rectangle.

WRAP UP

IDENTIFYING THE BIG IDEA Ask students to describe how to classify triangles.

JOURNAL Students may want to look through magazines for pictures with triangles in them. They can paste these pictures into their journal.

PROJECT LINK To construct the puzzle, students can start by drawing a rectangle. Have them draw lines to divide the rectangle into triangles. Challenge them to make as many different types of triangles as they can.

---

pages 341–343 **On Your Own**

32. 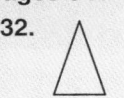 33.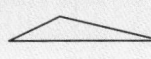

34. 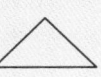 35.

36.

37. **Not possible; a right triangle has one right angle and two acute angles so it cannot have an obtuse angle.**

38.

39.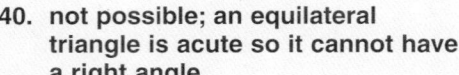

40. **not possible; an equilateral triangle is acute so it cannot have a right angle.**

41. **Not possible; an equilateral triangle is acute so it cannot have an obtuse angle.**

Judging by appearance, name all the triangles shown below that fit each description.

21. equilateral triangle **e**   22. isosceles triangle **a, c, e**   23. scalene triangle **b, d, f**

24. acute triangle **d, e**   25. right triangle **a, b, c**   26. obtuse triangle **f**

a.    b.    c.

d. 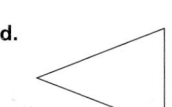   e.    f.

27. *Sailing* A triangular sail allows a boat to sail in any direction—even into the wind. Judging by appearance, give all the names you can for the triangle in the photo at the right. What is the best name for it?
acute, isosceles, equilateral; equilateral

28. *Writing* Must an equilateral triangle be an isosceles triangle? Why or why not? Must an isosceles triangle be an equilateral triangle? Why or why not? **Yes; at least two sides are congruent; no; only two sides need to be congruent.**

29. *Reasoning* Use a metric ruler and protractor to measure the sides and angles of each triangle below. Classify each of the triangles by side lengths. What do you notice?
Isosceles, isosceles, isosceles; isosceles triangles have two angles with equal measure.

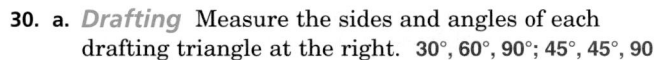

30. a. *Drafting* Measure the sides and angles of each drafting triangle at the right. **30°, 60°, 90°; 45°, 45°, 90°**
    b. Classify each triangle according to its angle measures and side lengths. Then choose the best name for each triangle. **scalene right, isosceles right**
    c. How are the triangles alike? How are they different? **Each triangle has a right angle; one triangle is scalene, the other is isosceles.**

342

Classify each triangle with given side lengths as scalene, isosceles, or equilateral.

1. 4, 4, 6   **isosceles**

2. 7, 7, 7   **equilateral**

3. 6, 9, 5   **scalene**

Classify each triangle with given angle measures as acute, right, or obtuse.

4. 40°, 50°, 90°   **right**

5. 115°, 35°, 30°   **obtuse**

6. 70°, 65°, 45°   **acute**

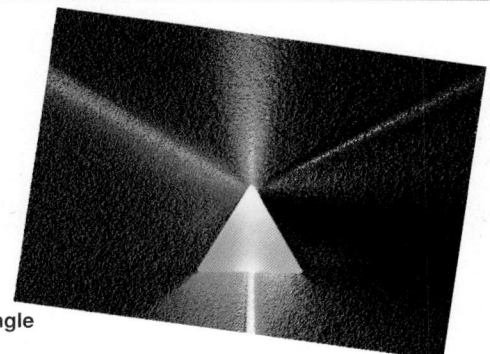

31. *Optics* A triangular prism can be used to bend rays of light. Give all the names you can to this triangle. What is the best name?

right triangle, isosceles triangle; isosceles right triangle

Sketch each triangle. If you can't sketch a triangle, explain why. 32–41. See margin p. 342.

32. an acute isosceles triangle

33. an obtuse scalene triangle

34. a right isosceles triangle

35. an acute equilateral triangle

36. an acute scalene triangle

37. an obtuse right triangle

38. a right scalene triangle

39. an obtuse isosceles triangle

40. a right equilateral triangle

41. an obtuse equilateral triangle

> **JOURNAL**
> Make a list of the places in which you might see triangles in everyday life. Classify the triangles used in each situation. Are some types more common than others?

Mixed Review

Estimate using mental math. *(Lesson 7-9)*

42. 80% of 20   16

43. 96% of 32   30

44. 30% of 192   60

45. 68% of 90   63

46. 17% of 500   80

Compare. Use >, <, or =. *(Lesson 5-8)*

47. $\frac{3}{8}$ < $\frac{2}{4}$

48. $\frac{2}{3}$ > $\frac{6}{15}$

49. $\frac{7}{10}$ = $\frac{84}{120}$

50. $\frac{19}{25}$ > $\frac{9}{15}$

51. $\frac{99}{100}$ < $\frac{199}{200}$

52. *Choose a Strategy* Dwania is saving dimes. The first day she saves 1 dime, and the second day she saves 2 dimes. Each day she saves 1 more dime than the day before. How much money will she have after 2 weeks? $10.50

CHAPTER PROJECT

PROJECT LINK: DRAWING

Your puzzle must include at least one of each of the following triangles: right, equilateral, isosceles, and scalene. Try drawing a rectangular puzzle on a piece of paper.

Check students' work.

PRACTICE

Practice 8-4 Identifying Triangles

Use a centimeter ruler and protractor to measure the sides and angles of each triangle. Classify each triangle according to its angle measures and side lengths.

1. right, scalene
2. acute, isosceles
3. obtuse, scalene

Classify each triangle with given side lengths as *scalene, isosceles,* or *equilateral.*

4. 8, 9, 8   isosceles
5. 3, 4, 5   scalene
6. 15, 15, 15   equilateral
7. 4, 7, 9   scalene

Classify each triangle with given angle measures as *acute, right,* or *obtuse.*

8. 60°, 60°, 60°   acute
9. 25°, 14°, 141°   obtuse
10. 90°, 63°, 27°   right
11. 90°, 89°, 1°   right

Sketch each triangle. If you can't sketch a triangle, explain why.

12. a right obtuse triangle
13. an acute equilateral triangle
14. an isosceles scalene triangle

Can't be done. A right triangle always has two acute angles.

Can't be done. A scalene triangle has no congruent sides, so it cannot be isosceles.

In copymaster and workbook formats

RETEACHING

Reteaching 8-4 Identifying Triangles

Triangles can be classified by the measures of their angles.

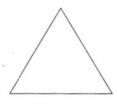

Triangles can be classified by their number of congruent sides.

Classify each triangle as *acute, right,* or *obtuse.*

1. right
2. obtuse
3. acute
4. acute

Classify each triangle with the given angle measures as *acute, right,* or *obtuse.*

5. 90°, 40°, 50°   right
6. 38°, 72°, 70°   acute
7. 115°, 30°, 35°   obtuse
8. 70°, 60°, 50°   acute

Classify each triangle with the given side lengths as *scalene, isosceles,* or *equilateral.*

9. scalene
10. isosceles
11. equilateral
12. isosceles

ENRICHMENT

Minds on Math Transparency

8-4

Nathan is weighing blocks and balls. Each of the blocks weighs the same and each of the balls weighs the same. The weight of 4 blocks and 1 ball is the same as the weight of 2 blocks and 2 balls. Which is heavier: a block or a ball? How much heavier?

A ball is twice as heavy as a block.

See *Solution Key* for worked-out answers.

343

1 Focus

CONNECTING TO PRIOR KNOWLEDGE Have students sketch various road signs they have seen. Have them describe their shapes. Answers may vary. Sample: A stop sign has eight sides; a one-way sign is a rectangle; a yield sign is a triangle.

Lesson Planning Options

Prerequisite Skills
• identifying angles (8-2)

Vocabulary/Symbols
polygon, convex

Resources

 Student Edition

Skills Handbook, p. 536
Extra Practice, p. 529
Glossary/Study Guide

 Teaching Resources

Chapter Support File, Ch. 8
• Lesson Planner 8-5
• Practice 8-5, Reteaching 8-5
• Alternative Activity 8-5
• Answer Masters 8-5
Teaching Aids Masters 3, 7, 8, 9
Glossary, Spanish Resources

 Transparencies

6, 20, 21, Minds on Math 8-5

Warm Up

A video store has two membership plans. Plan A costs $15 to join and $2.50 per video. Plan B costs $20 to join and $1.75 per video. How many videos must a customer rent before plan B is the better deal?

344

2 Teach

 **Work Together**

TACTILE LEARNING Have students form some of the figures on geoboards. Students can touch the figures to explore their characteristics. Students can use pipe cleaners and twist ties to model polygons as well as figures that are not polygons.

ALTERNATIVE METHOD Question 3
Suggest students extend the sides of each polygon. If any extended side falls inside the polygon, the polygon is not convex.

AEP Have students compare the names of the polygons with the names of numbers in French, Spanish, and Italian. In these languages, *triangle*, *quadrilateral*, *octagon*, and *decagon* come from the same roots as the numbers 3, 4, 8, and 10.

8-5 Exploring Polygons

What You'll Learn
▼ To identify types of convex polygons

...And Why
Polygons play an important role in the study of geometry.

Here's How
Look for questions that
⚫ build understanding
✔ check understanding

1a. Each polygon has exactly one inside region and its edges are segments.

b. The figures that are not polygons may have a curved edge, sides that cross each other, no inside region, or more than one inside region.

Work Together

Investigating Polygons

Some of the figures shown are polygons.

polygon   polygon

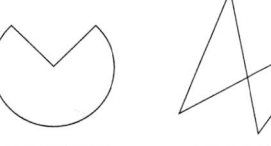   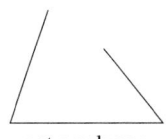

not a polygon   not a polygon   not a polygon

1. a. ⚫*Analyze* How are the polygons alike?
   b. How do the polygons differ from the figures that are not polygons?
   c. ⚫*Writing* Write a definition for a polygon. Share your definition with the class.   Check students' work.

2. Use your definition to tell which of these figures are polygons. Does your definition work? If not, how would you change it?   Check students' work for definition.

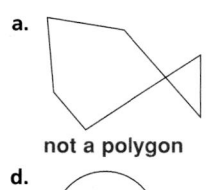

a. not a polygon   **b.** polygon   **c.** polygon

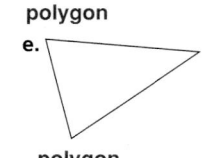

d. not a polygon   **e.** polygon   **f.** not a polygon

ASSESSMENT Have students create convex polygons on their geoboard. Ask them to find the number of sides each convex polygon has. **Answers may vary. Sample: 8** Ask: *What do we call this polygon?* **Sample: octagon** Have students share their polygons with each other. Ask them to check to make sure the polygons are convex.

■ **ADDITIONAL EXAMPLE**

FOR EXAMPLE
Name each polygon.

a.

quadrilateral

b.

octagon

c.

hexagon

d.

triangle

THINK AND DISCUSS

A **polygon** is a closed shape formed by line segments that do not cross.

A **convex** polygon is one that a rubber band could fit around snugly, without any gaps and without crossing itself.

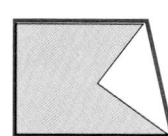

The red band does not fit snugly. This polygon is not convex.

3a. Convex; a rubber band would fit snugly.

b. Not convex; a rubber band would leave a gap.

c. Not convex; a rubber band would leave a gap

d. Convex; a rubber band would fit snugly.

3. Which of the following polygons are convex? Explain.

a.  **b.** 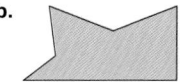 **c.**   **d.** (hexagon)

From now on, unless stated otherwise, assume that the polygons discussed are convex.

You can name a polygon according to the number of sides.

Polygon	Number of Sides
Triangle	3
Quadrilateral	4
Pentagon	5
Hexagon	6
Octagon	8
Decagon	10

The surface of this soccer ball is made up of hexagons and pentagons.

■ **EXAMPLE**

Name each polygon.

a. 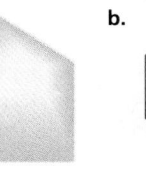 **b.**  **c.**

This polygon has five sides. It is a pentagon.

This polygon has eight sides. It is an octagon.

This polygon has four sides. It is a quadrilateral.

Technology Options

Prentice Hall Technology

Software for Learners
- Math Blaster® Mystery*
- Interactive Student Tutorial, Chapter 8*

Teaching Resource Software
- Computer Item Generator 8-5
- Resource Pro™ Chapter 8*

Internet • For related mathematics activities, visit the Prentice Hall site at www.phschool.com/math

*Available on CD-ROM only

Assignment Options for Exercises On Your Own

Core 1–15
Extension 16–20

Use Mixed Review to maintain skills.

CONNECTION TO ART Look in your school library for art books containing reproductions of Cubist paintings from artists such as Pablo Picasso, Georges Braque, and Jean Metzinger. Have students look at the geometric shapes in the paintings. They may wish to research Cubism.

EXTENSION Ask students to draw a heptagon (a polygon with 7 sides), a nonagon (a polygon with 9 sides), and a dodecagon (a polygon with 12 sides).

3 Practice/Assess

EXERCISES *On Your Own*

ERROR ALERT! **Exercises 1–5** Students may not recognize the convex polygon. **Remediation:** Have students cut out cardboard shapes for each of the exercises. Ask them to wrap the rubber band around the edges. If the rubber band fits snugly then the polygon is convex.

WRITING **Exercise 16b** Suggest students use toothpicks to model figures that will help them answer this question.

REASONING **Exercise 17** Students may want to draw a triangle, parallelogram, and pentagon to explore this problem.

TACTILE LEARNING **Exercise 18** Allow students the option of using pattern blocks or geoboards to help them with the exercise.

MENTAL MATH **Exercises 26–29** Have students check their answers for reasonableness after completing each exercise.

4. ✔ *Try It Out* Name each polygon.

a. octagon b. hexagon c. triangle

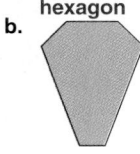

Now you may assign Exercises 1–20.

EXERCISES *On Your Own*

State whether each polygon is convex.

1.   2.   3.   4.   5.

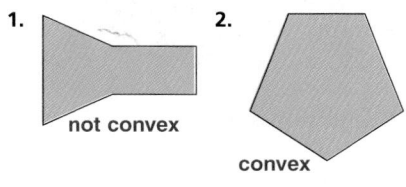
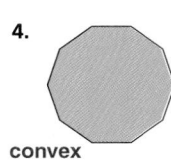
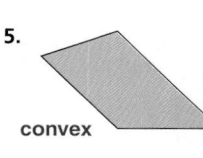

not convex convex not convex convex convex

6. Is a circle a polygon? Explain.
No; its sides are not segments.

7. *Open-ended* Draw two nonconvex polygons.
Check students' work.

Name each polygon.

8.   9.   10.   11.

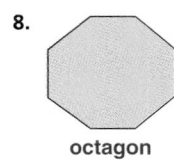

octagon triangle pentagon hexagon

12.   13.   14.   15.

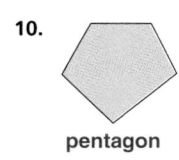
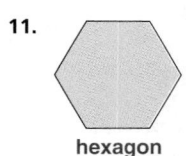

quadrilateral quadrilateral quadrilateral quadrilateral

16. a. An *interior* angle is formed by two sides of a polygon that share a common vertex. How many interior angles does each polygon have?

  i. triangle 3 **ii.** quadrilateral 4 **iii.** pentagon 5
  iv. hexagon 6 **v.** octagon 8 **vi.** decagon 10

  b. *Writing* What is the relationship between the number of sides and the number of interior angles in a polygon? Why does this relationship exist? They are the same; check students' work for reasoning.

17. *Reasoning* What characteristics do triangles, quadrilaterals, and pentagons have in common?
Answers may vary. Sample: Each is a polygon.

346

WRAP UP

IDENTIFYING THE BIG IDEA Ask students how to determine whether a figure is a polygon. Have students name six types of polygons. Ask them to explain the names for the polygons.

Math at Work

If you have block scheduling or extended class periods, consider having each member of the class bring in a cartoon or comic strip. Students can pick a frame or character to sketch. Ask them to try to draw the frame or character two times its actual size.

LESSON QUIZ

State whether the figure is a polygon.

1.

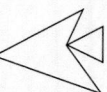

not a polygon

2.

polygon

---

18. *Botany* The Raft of the Treetops allows botanist Francis Hallé and his team to investigate the top of the rain forest without having to climb the trees.   **hexagon**
    a. What shape is the platform?
    b. Draw a polygon shaped like the platform. Instead of dividing it into six triangles, divide it into four triangles.
    c. Draw a polygon shaped like the platform. Divide it into a quadrilateral and two triangles.
    b–c. Check students' work.

19. The *diagonal* of a polygon is a segment that connects two vertices that are not next to each other. The quadrilateral at the right has two diagonals.
    a. Draw a hexagon. How many diagonals does it have?
    b. How many diagonals does a triangle have? Explain.   **a. 9 diagonals**

Diagonals

19b. None; a segment from any vertex to any other vertex is a side of the triangle.

20. *Language* A prefix is a syllable at the beginning of a word that helps describe the object.   **a–b. Samples are given.**
    a. List three words, besides *triangle*, that have the prefix *tri-*.   **tricycle, triathlon; triceps**
    b. List three words, besides *quadrilateral*, that have the prefix *quad-*.   **quadrennial, quadruple, quadruped**
    c. For each of your words, state what the prefix tells you about it.   **Check students' work.**

Mixed Review

Find each product or quotient. Write each answer in simplest form. *(Lessons 6-8 and 6-9)*

21. $6\frac{1}{2} \times \frac{1}{10}$ $\frac{13}{20}$ **22.** $1\frac{5}{6} \div 3\frac{2}{3}$ $\frac{1}{2}$ **23.** $7\frac{1}{5} \times 7\frac{1}{5}$ $51\frac{21}{25}$ **24.** $3\frac{3}{4} \div 6\frac{3}{10}$ $\frac{25}{42}$ **25.** $6\frac{2}{3} \times 2\frac{7}{10}$ 18

Use mental math to complete each statement. *(Lesson 4-10)*

26. $2.07 \text{ g} = \blacksquare \text{ mg}$ **27.** $0.6 \text{ L} = \blacksquare \text{ kL}$ **28.** $89 \text{ m} = \blacksquare \text{ mm}$ **29.** $440 \text{ cm} = \blacksquare \text{ km}$
    2,070   **0.0006**   **89,000**   **0.0044**

30. *Choose a Strategy* Suppose you have 20 dimes and nickels altogether. The total value of the coins is $1.35. How many dimes do you have?   **7 dimes, 13 nickels**

CHECKPOINT 1

▬ *Checkpoint 1*   *Lessons 8-1 through 8-5*

Use the figure at the right for Exercises 1–7.   Answers may vary.
Name each of the following.   Samples given.
1. two intersecting lines   XT , QR
2. three segments   XY, QY, SY
3. a right angle   ∠RYS
4. an obtuse angle   ∠XYS
5. a straight angle   ∠QYR
6. three collinear points   X, Y, T
7. two complementary angles   ∠QYT, ∠TYS

8. Sketch an acute isosceles triangle.   Sample:

Write a name for a polygon with the given number of sides.
9. 6   hexagon   10. 5   pentagon   11. 8   octagon

PRACTICE

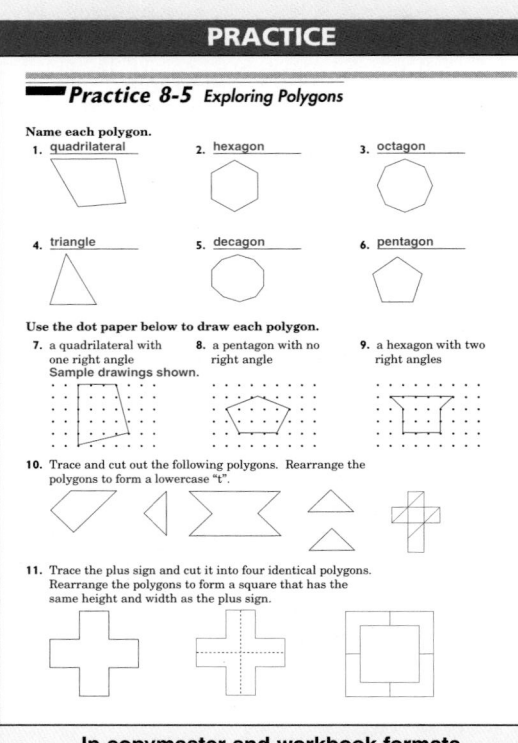

Practice 8-5 *Exploring Polygons*

Name each polygon.
1. quadrilateral   2. hexagon   3. octagon
4. triangle   5. decagon   6. pentagon

Use the dot paper below to draw each polygon.
7. a quadrilateral with one right angle   8. a pentagon with no right angle   9. a hexagon with two right angles
Sample drawings shown.

10. Trace and cut out the following polygons. Rearrange the polygons to form a lowercase "t".

11. Trace the plus sign and cut it into four identical polygons. Rearrange the polygons to form a square that has the same height and width as the plus sign.

In copymaster and workbook formats

RETEACHING

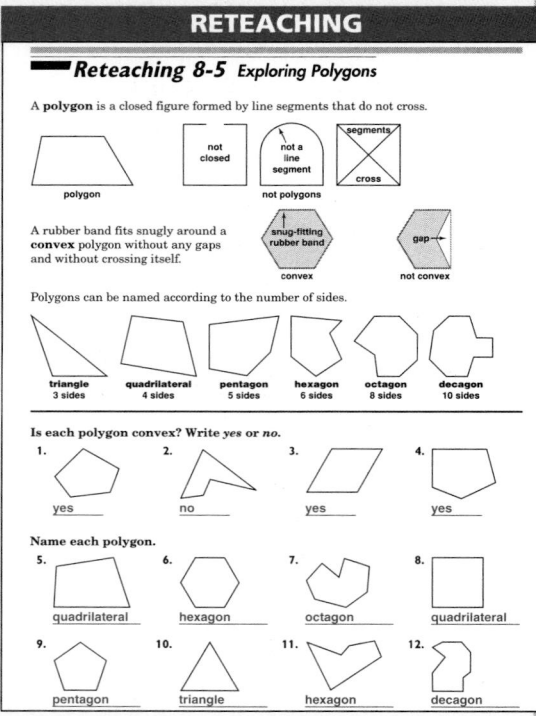

Reteaching 8-5 *Exploring Polygons*

A **polygon** is a closed figure formed by line segments that do not cross.

polygon

not closed   not a line segment   segments   cross
not polygons

A rubber band fits snugly around a **convex** polygon without any gaps and without crossing itself.

snug-fitting rubber band   gap
convex   not convex

Polygons can be named according to the number of sides.

triangle 3 sides   quadrilateral 4 sides   pentagon 5 sides   hexagon 6 sides   octagon 8 sides   decagon 10 sides

Is each polygon convex? Write *yes* or *no*.
1. yes   2. no   3. yes   4. yes

Name each polygon.
5. quadrilateral   6. hexagon   7. octagon   8. quadrilateral
9. pentagon   10. triangle   11. hexagon   12. decagon

ENRICHMENT

Minds on Math Transparency

8-5

Which six sides of the small squares would you remove to leave 2 squares?

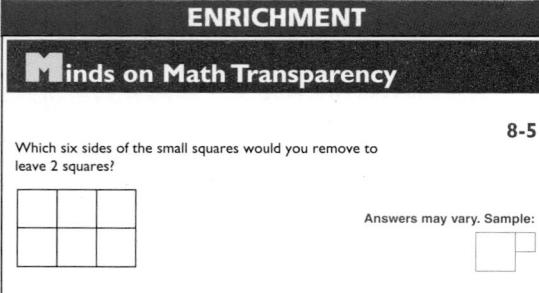

Answers may vary. Sample:

See *Solution Key* for worked-out answers.

348

Name each polygon.

3.

octagon

4.

triangle

5.

hexagon

6.

pentagon

✓ CHECKPOINT 1

Use the figure at the right for Exercises 1–10. Name each of the following. 2–7. Answers may vary. Samples are given.

1. two lines $\overleftrightarrow{KN}$, $\overleftrightarrow{LM}$ 2. a right angle $\angle PJL$

3. three collinear points K, J, N   4. an acute angle $\angle PJK$

5. an obtuse angle $\angle PJN$ 6. a straight angle $\angle KJN$

7. three noncollinear points K, J, P   8. an angle that measures 133° $\angle LJN$

9. a pair of parallel lines not possible   10. a pair of perpendicular lines $\overleftrightarrow{LM}$, $\overleftrightarrow{PJ}$

11. **Choose A, B, C, or D.** Judging by appearance, classify the triangle at the right. B

   A. right scalene   **B.** acute isosceles
   C. equilateral   **D.** obtuse isosceles

How many sides does each of the following polygons have?

12. a decagon
10 sides
13. an octagon
8 sides
14. a quadrilateral
4 sides
15. a hexagon
6 sides

Math at Work

CARTOONIST

If you enjoy reading comics and draw well, a career as a cartoonist may be right for you. Some cartoonists produce comic strips meant for amusement. Others create illustrations for stories, articles, books, or advertisements. Editorial cartoons can dramatize the news. Cartoonists can work for newspapers, advertising agencies, or other commercial firms. They use their mathematics skills to create cartoons using lines, angles, measures, and perspective.

Visit the Association of American Editorial Cartoonists Home Page for more information:
www.detnews.com/AAEC/index.html

1 Focus

CONNECTING TO PRIOR KNOWLEDGE Draw a parallelogram for the class. Ask: *What do you notice about this quadrilateral?* **Answers may vary. Sample: The opposite sides look parallel and congruent; two angles are acute; two are obtuse.**

2 Teach

Work Together

Question 2 Compare characteristics and see how many the class can name.

THINK AND DISCUSS

TACTILE LEARNING Students can use cardboard strips and brass fasteners to model the quadrilaterals. To compare a square and a rhombus, have them connect four congruent strips of cardboard with the fasteners. By adjusting the angles, they can create the different shapes.

AEP Have students make index cards with the names of special quadrilaterals on one side and diagrams of the shapes on the other side.

VISUAL LEARNING **Question 5** Ask students to create diagrams to show the relationship of squares and rhombuses, and rhombuses and parallelograms. Check students' work.

8-6 Classifying Quadrilaterals

What You'll Learn

▼ To identify quadrilaterals
▼ To classify quadrilaterals

...And Why

There are many different types of four-sided figures, some of which have special names.

Here's How

Look for questions that
⚒ build understanding
✔ check understanding

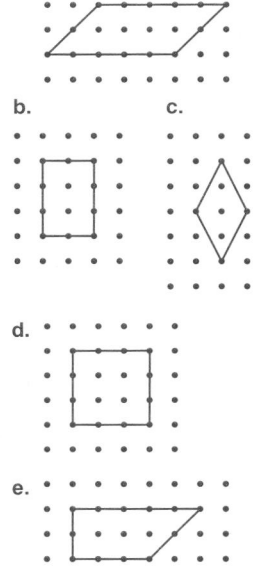

1a.

b.   c.

d.

e.

Work Together

Drawing Quadrilaterals

1. Using a geoboard or dot paper, show each of the following.
   a. a quadrilateral with two pairs of parallel sides and no right angles   **a–e. See below left.**
   b. a quadrilateral with four right angles and two pairs of congruent sides
   c. a quadrilateral with four congruent sides and no right angles
   d. a quadrilateral with four congruent sides and four right angles
   e. a quadrilateral with one pair of parallel sides

2. Name 3 characteristics your quadrilaterals have in common. **They are made of segments; they have 4 sides; they have 4 angles.**

THINK AND DISCUSS

▼ *Identifying Quadrilaterals*

Certain quadrilaterals have special names because they have characteristics that differ from those of other quadrilaterals.

Parallelogram	Rectangle	Rhombus
a quadrilateral with both pairs of opposite sides parallel	a parallelogram with four right angles	a parallelogram with four congruent sides

3. *Open-ended* Find several examples of rectangles in your classroom.
   Answers may vary. Samples: notebook paper, door, wall

4. *Reasoning* Can a rhombus be a rectangle? Explain.
   Yes; a square is a rhombus that is a rectangle.

Lesson Planning Options

Prerequisite Skills
• classifying angles (8-2)

Vocabulary/Symbols
parallelogram, rhombus, trapezoid

Materials/Manipulatives
• geoboard   • dot paper

Resources

📖 **Student Edition**
Skills Handbook, p. 536
Extra Practice, p. 529
Glossary/Study Guide

▪ **Teaching Resources**
Chapter Support File, Ch. 8
• Lesson Planner 8-6
• Practice 8-6, Reteaching 8-6
• Answer Masters 8-6
Teaching Aids Masters 3, 7, 8, 9
Glossary, Spanish Resources

📽 **Transparencies**
20, 21, Minds on Math 8-6

Warm Up

Use $<$, $>$, or $=$.
If $x < 0$, then 0 ■ x. $>$
If x is any positive integer, then x ■ 0. $>$
If x is any negative integer, then 0 ■ x. $>$

FOR EXAMPLE

Give all the names that apply to this polygon made from six toothpicks. Then choose the best name.

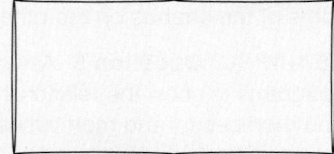

quadrilateral, parallelogram, rectangle; rectangle

ASSESSMENT Pair students. One student names a type of quadrilateral. The partner draws this shape then names another quadrilateral. The first student then describes the changes required to change the first quadrilateral into the second. Have students switch roles and repeat.

CONNECTION TO LANGUAGE Tell students the Latin word *lateral* means "side." Ask them: *What do you think quad means?* **four**

3 Practice/Assess

EXERCISES *On Your Own*

ERROR ALERT! Exercises 10–19 Students may not understand whether the answer is *some* or *all*. **Remediation:** Have students consider the statement: "All chickens are birds, but not all birds are chickens." Tell students that if they can think of two rectangles, one that is a square and one that is not, then the answer is *some*. Have

Technology Options

Prentice Hall Technology

  Software for Learners

• Math Blaster® Mystery*
• Interactive Student Tutorial, Chapter 8*

  Teaching Resource Software

• Computer Item Generator 8-6
• Resource Pro™ Chapter 8*

Internet • For related mathematics activities, visit the Prentice Hall site at www.phschool.com/math

Available on CD-ROM only

Assignment Options for Exercises On Your Own

To provide flexible scheduling, this lesson can be subdivided into parts.

▼1 **Core** 1–8
   Extension 9, 25

▼2 **Core** 10–23, 26–28
   Extension 24, 29, 30

Use Mixed Review to maintain skills.

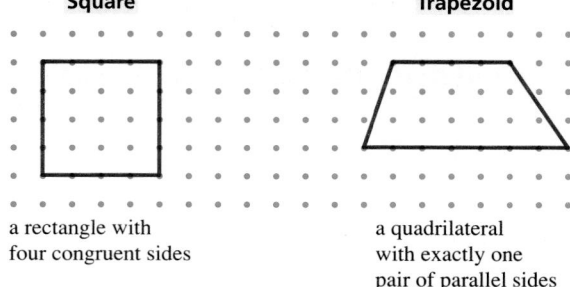

Square   Trapezoid

a rectangle with   a quadrilateral
four congruent sides   with exactly one
                           pair of parallel sides

5a. Yes; no; not every rectangle has 4 congruent sides.

5. a. ⬛*Think About It* Is every square a rectangle? Is every rectangle a square? Explain.

   b. Is every square a rhombus? Is every rhombus a square? Explain. **Yes; no; not every rhombus has 4 right angles.**

   c. ⬛*Reasoning* What is the best name for a rhombus that is also a rectangle? **square**

6. No; a trapezoid has exactly one pair of parallel sides and a parallelogram has two pairs.

6. ⬛*Reasoning* Can a trapezoid be a parallelogram? Explain.

Now you may assign Exercises 1–9, 25.

2 *Classifying Quadrilaterals*

You can classify quadrilaterals as you classified triangles in Lesson 8-4. First look at all the characteristics. Then decide on the best name.

■ **EXAMPLE** *Real-World Problem Solving*

Judging by appearance, give all the names you can for the quadrilateral in the picture at the right. What is the best name?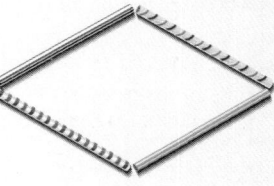

Both pairs of opposite sides are parallel. It is a parallelogram.

The four sides are congruent. It is a rhombus.

The best name is rhombus, because every rhombus is a quadrilateral and a parallelogram.

7. ✓*Try It Out* Give all the names you can for the polygon at the right. What is the best name?
   quadrilateral, parallelogram, rectangle, rhombus, square; square

students use the definitions to make drawings for each problem.

Exercise 25a Students should be able to see the nonparallel sides are congruent. If they have difficulty, suggest they investigate the side lengths with a ruler.

Exercise 29 Have students label the quadrilaterals in their drawings.

IDENTIFYING THE BIG IDEA Ask students to name and describe five special types of quadrilaterals.

PROJECT LINK Students may need to draw this new puzzle on a larger rectangle. They may want to use stencils as patterns for some of the pieces. When they have drawn their new puzzle, suggest they cut out the pieces and try to reassemble it.

EXERCISES *On Your Own*

Use the shapes at the right for Exercises 1 and 2.
a. i, ii, iii, v, vi, vii, viii, ix   b. i, v, vi, vii, viii, ix

1. Identify the polygons that have each name.
   a. quadrilateral **b.** parallelogram **c.** rhombus
   d. rectangle **e.** square **f.** trapezoid
c. i, vii, viii   d. i, v, vii   e. i, vii   f. ii

2. Which shape is not used? Why?
   iv; it is a pentagon.

Sketch an example of each quadrilateral.
3–9. See margin.

3. a parallelogram 4. a square 5. a trapezoid

6. a rectangle   7. a rectangle that is not a square

8. a rhombus that is not a square

9. a quadrilateral that is not a trapezoid or a parallelogram

Complete each sentence with *All, Some,* or *No*.

10. ▦ quadrilaterals are parallelograms.
    Some
11. ▦ trapezoids are parallelograms.
    No
12. ▦ parallelograms are quadrilaterals.
    All
13. ▦ squares are rectangles.
    All
14. ▦ rhombuses are rectangles.
    Some
15. ▦ rectangles are trapezoids.
    No
16. ▦ quadrilaterals are trapezoids.
    Some
17. ▦ rectangles are parallelograms.
    All
18. ▦ parallelograms are trapezoids.
    No
19. ▦ rectangles are rhombuses.
    Some

List all the names that apply to each quadrilateral.
**Choose from *parallelogram, rectangle, rhombus, square,*
and *trapezoid*. Then circle the best name.**

20.
    trapezoid

21.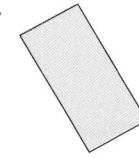
    parallelogram, rectangle

22.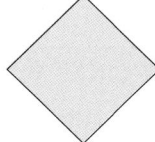
    parallelogram, rectangle, rhombus, square

23.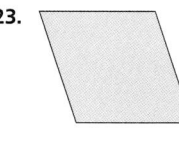
    parallelogram, rhombus

24. *Writing* Describe the relationships among the following figures: rectangle, rhombus, square. They are all parallelograms. A square is a rhombus that is also a rectangle.

---

pages 351–352   On Your Own
3. 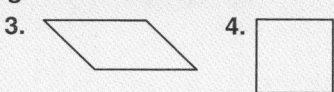 4.
5. 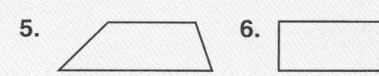 6.
7.  8.
9.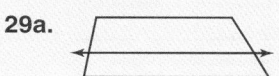

25c. Isosceles trapezoid; an isosceles triangle and an isosceles trapezoid each have 2 congruent sides.

29a.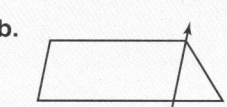

b.

c.

PRACTICE

Practice 8-6 *Classifying Quadrilaterals*

Use the diagram at right for Exercises 1–14. Identify all the polygons that have each name.

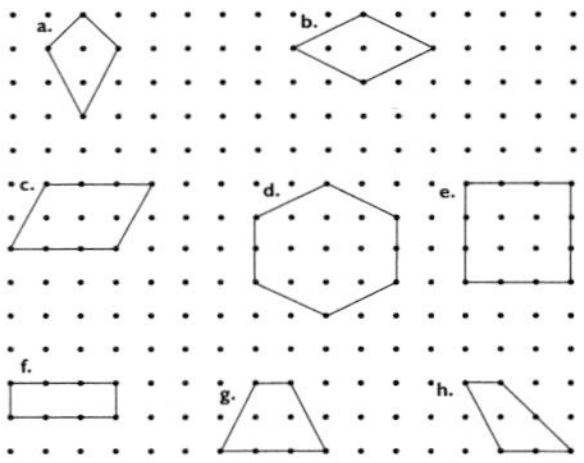

1. quadrilateral
   a, b, c, e, f, g, h

2. parallelogram
   b, c, e, f

3. rhombus
   b, e

4. rectangle
   e, f

5. square
   e

6. trapezoid
   g

State the *best* name for each polygon.

7. a   8. b   9. c   10. d
   quadrilateral   rhombus   parallelogram   hexagon

11. e   12. f   13. g   14. h
    square   rectangle   trapezoid   quadrilateral

Sketch an example of each quadrilateral. Sample drawings shown.

15. a parallelogram that   16. a quadrilateral that   17. a rectangle
    is not a rectangle   is not a parallelogram

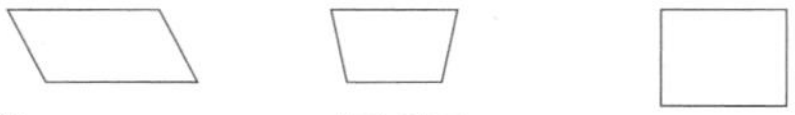

18. How many squares can you
    find in the figure?
    14

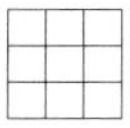

19. Move four of the line segments from the
    large square so that three squares result.

In copymaster and workbook formats

RETEACHING

Reteaching 8-6 *Classifying Quadrilaterals*

All four-sided polygons are quadrilaterals.

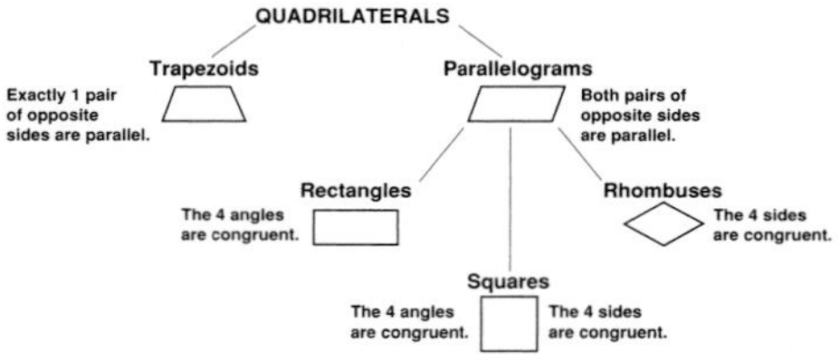

QUADRILATERALS

Trapezoids   Parallelograms
Exactly 1 pair   Both pairs of
of opposite   opposite sides
sides are parallel.   are parallel.

        Rectangles   Rhombuses
        The 4 angles   The 4 sides
        are congruent.   are congruent.

                Squares
        The 4 angles   The 4 sides
        are congruent. are congruent.

List all the names that apply to each quadrilateral. Choose from *parallelogram, rectangle, rhombus, square,* and *trapezoid.*

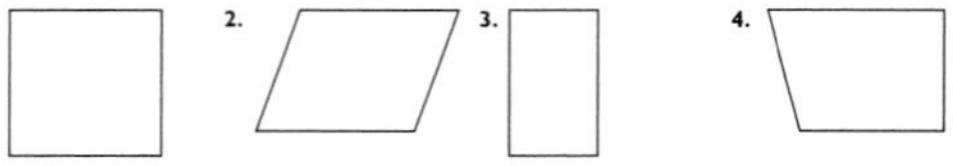

1. parallelogram, rectangle, rhombus, square
2. parallelogram, rectangle
3. parallelogram, rectangle
4. trapezoid
5. parallelogram, rhombus 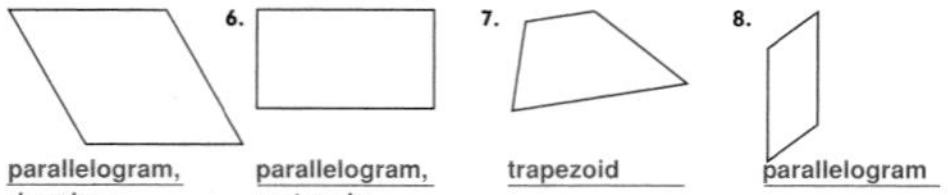
6. parallelogram, rectangle
7. trapezoid
8. parallelogram

ENRICHMENT

Minds on Math Transparency

8-6

Fred said to Tara, "Give me eight books and we'll have an equal number." Tara answered, "If you give me eight books, then I will have twice as many as you." If both Fred and Tara are correct, how many books did each have?

Fred had 40 books and Tara had 56 books.

See *Solution Key* for worked-out answers.

352

LESSON QUIZ

List all the names that apply to each quadrilateral. Choose from parallelogram, rectangle, rhombus, square, and trapezoid.

1.

trapezoid

2.

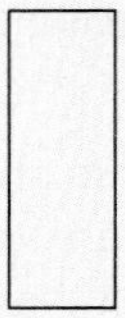

parallelogram, rectangle

3.

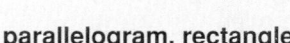

rhombus

---

25. **a.** Four trapezoids are shown at the right. What do you notice about each pair of nonparallel sides?
    b. When sides of a triangle have this same characteristic, what special name do you give the triangle? **isosceles**
    c. *Reasoning* What special name could you use for See trapezoids like this? Why does this name fit? margin p. 351.

25a. **They are congruent.**

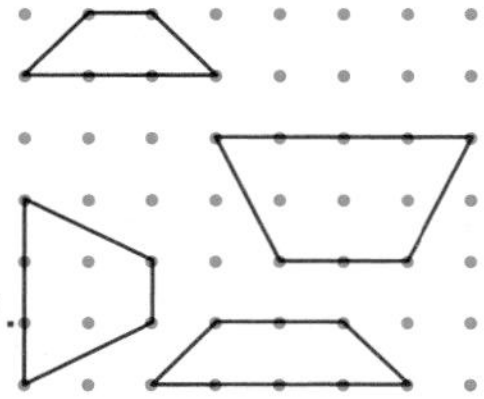

Name all the types of quadrilaterals that fit each description.

26. four congruent sides   27. four right angles   28. parallelogram, rhombus, rectangle, square
    rhombus, square   rectangle, square   28. **parallelogram**

29. Draw three copies of the trapezoid at the right.
    a. Draw a line on one trapezoid that divides it into two trapezoids.
    b. Draw a line on the second trapezoid that divides it into a parallelogram and a triangle.
    c. Draw a line on the third trapezoid that divides it into a rhombus and a trapezoid.

29a–c. See margin p. 351.

30. **Choose A, B, C, or D.** Which name does *not* appear to describe quadrilateral *RSTU*? **C**

    A. square   **B.** rhombus   **C.** trapezoid   **D.** parallelogram

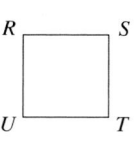

Mixed Review

Find the value of *n*. *(Lesson 7-3)*

31. $\frac{1}{2} = \frac{n}{10}$ 5   32. $\frac{15}{25} = \frac{3}{n}$ 5   33. $\frac{7}{9} = \frac{21}{n}$ 27   34. $\frac{n}{5} = \frac{20}{60}$ 35. $\frac{n}{3} = \frac{9}{18}$

$\frac{5}{3}$, or $1.\overline{6}$ $\frac{3}{2}$, or 1.5

36. *Choose a Strategy* Payat bought 3 shirts for $14 each and a pair of pants for $23. How much of his clothing budget does Payat have left? **There is not enough information to solve this problem.**

CHAPTER PROJECT

PROJECT LINK: PLANNING

Your puzzle must also include at least one of each of the following polygons: quadrilateral, pentagon, hexagon, rhombus, trapezoid, and parallelogram. Draw a new puzzle that includes these shapes as well as the four triangle types.

Check students' work.

8-7 Teaching Notes

1 Focus

CONNECTING TO PRIOR KNOWLEDGE Ask students to name some clothing they own. Record their responses. Then ask students to categorize the clothing by cold weather or hot. Write the categories for the class. For example, write *Summer, Winter,* or *Both.* Have students provide examples for each category.

2 Teach

THINK AND DISCUSS

TACTILE LEARNING Question 1 Provide students with rings and attribute blocks to use for modeling the exercise.

ERROR ALERT! Question 6b Some students may become confused if the total represented in the circles does not equal the total survey population. **Remediation:** Remind students

that some members of the population do not fit in any of the circles. Tell students to think of the area outside the circles as the *remainder.*

ASSESSMENT Have students make their own diagrams for the clothing categories from Connecting to Prior Knowledge. Ask students what each part of the diagram represents.

PROBLEM SOLVING STRATEGY

8-7 Use Logical Reasoning

Problem Solving Strategies

Draw a Diagram
Guess and Test
Look for a Pattern
Make a Model
Make a Table
Simulate a Problem
Solve a Simpler Problem
Too Much or Too Little
   Information
✔ Use Logical Reasoning
Use Multiple Strategies
Work Backward

 **READ**

Read for understanding. Summarize the problem.

 PLAN

Decide on a strategy.

1c. how many students earn money by baby-sitting, doing yard work, or both, and how many students do not earn money

THINK AND DISCUSS

You often can use logical reasoning to solve problems involving relationships among groups of objects or people.

SAMPLE PROBLEM..
The 6th-grade class at Fairfield Middle School surveyed 130 7th- and 8th-grade students to find out how they earn money. The survey showed that 45 students baby-sit, 32 have paper routes, 28 do yard work, and 12 have after-school office jobs. Each student who works does only one kind of work, except for 15 who baby-sit *and* do yard work. How many students earn money by either baby-sitting or doing yard work (or both)? How many students do not earn money?

....

1. Think about the information you are given and what you are asked to find.
   a. How many students were surveyed? How did they earn money? **130 students**   b. **15 students**
   b. How many students did two different kinds of work?
   c. What does the problem ask you to find? **See below left.**

Logical Reasoning is a good strategy to use here. You can draw a diagram to show the different ways students earn money. Draw a rectangle to represent all the 7th- and 8th-grade students.

In the rectangle, draw a circle to represent each type of work. Label your circles *B* (for baby-sitting), *P* (for paper routes), *Y* (for yard work), and *O* (for office jobs).

2. Which circles should overlap? Why? **B and Y; they represent the students who baby-sit *and* do yard work.**

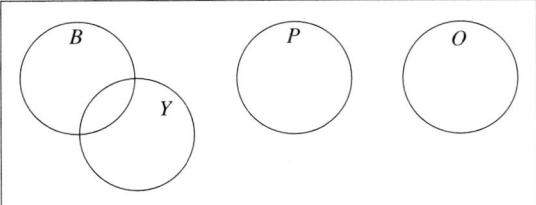

Write 15 where *B* and *Y* overlap. Write 32 in *P* and 12 in *O*.

8-7 Use Logical Reasoning   353

Lesson Planning Options

Prerequisite Skills
- drawing diagrams (6-6)

Materials/Manipulatives
- compass

Resources

📖 **Student Edition**

Skills Handbook, p. 538
Extra Practice, p. 529
Glossary/Study Guide

🗄 **Teaching Resources**

Chapter Support File, Ch. 8
- Lesson Planner 8-7
- Practice 8-7, Reteaching 8-7
- Answer Masters 8-7

Glossary, Spanish Resources

🖥 **Transparencies**
7, Minds on Math 8-7

Warm Up

Write $3\frac{1}{7}$ as an improper fraction. Then find the decimal equivalent. Use a calculator to determine which is larger, $3\frac{1}{7}$ or π.
$\frac{22}{7}$; 3.1428571; 3.1428571
is larger than π, which is 3.1415927.

The 6th-grade class at Sunnyvale Middle School surveyed 155 7th- and 8th-grade students to find out what sports they play. The survey showed that 45 students play baseball, 56 play basketball, and 39 play football. Each student plays only one sport, except for 9 students who play both baseball and basketball. How many students play either baseball or basketball (or both)? How many students do not play a sport? **92; 24**

3 Practice/Assess

EXERCISES *On Your Own*

Exercises 3–8 When students have completed the exercises, allow them to work in pairs to compare the strategies used. If students have used different strategies, ask them to discuss the pros and cons of each strategy.

IDENTIFYING THE BIG IDEA Ask: *How can you use logical reasoning to solve problems?*

Technology Options

Prentice Hall Technology

  Software for Learners

- Math Blaster® Mystery*
- Interactive Student Tutorial, Chapter 8*

  Teaching Resource Software

- Computer Item Generator 8-7
- Resource Pro™ Chapter 8*

Internet • For related mathematics activities, visit the Prentice Hall site at www.phschool.com/math

*Available on CD-ROM only

Assignment Options for Exercises On Your Own

> **Core** 1, 2
> **Extension** 3–8

Use Mixed Review to maintain skills.

SOLVE
Try the strategy.

3–4.
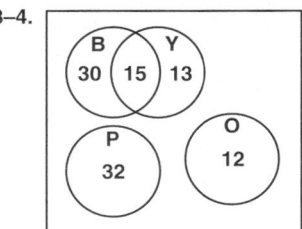

LOOK BACK
Think about how you solved the problem.

3. What number should be in *B*? How many students have you included already? What number should be in the part of *B* that does not overlap *Y*? Write it in. 45; 15; 30

4. How many students earn money only by doing yard work? What number should be in the part of *Y* not overlapping *B*? Place all known data in the diagram. 28; 13

Use the information above to answer the questions in the problem.

58 students
5. Find the total number of students who earn money by either baby-sitting or doing yard work (or both).

6a. 102; it is less than the number surveyed; some students do not earn money.
6. **a.** Add the numbers on your diagram. How does this number compare to the number of students surveyed? Explain.
   b. If you subtract the sum from 130, what does the result represent? Where would you write that number? Why?
   See back of book.

Make sure that you have clearly stated your answers to the questions in the problem.

7. Draw a diagram like the one shown at the right. Label it to show the relationships among quadrilaterals.
   See back of book.

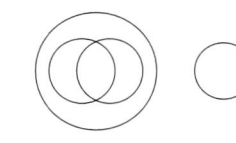

Now you may assign Exercises 1–8.

EXERCISES *On Your Own*

Use *Logical Reasoning* to solve each problem.

1. *Sports* There are 20 students on the intramural tennis team. Eight students play only singles and eight students play both singles and doubles. How many students play only doubles? **4 students**

2. *Buttons* In a box of 39 buttons, 25 buttons have four holes, 18 are red, and 13 have four holes and are also red. The rest of the buttons have two holes or are colors other than red.
   a. How many buttons have four holes but are not red? **12 buttons**
   b. How many red buttons have two holes? **5 buttons**
   c. How many buttons do not have four holes and are not red? **9 buttons**

354

Use Logical Reasoning to solve each problem.

1. In baseball intramurals, 14 students play infield, 14 students play outfield. Of all students, 5 play both infield and outfield. How many students are on the team? **23**

2. Of 135 juniors in high school, 45 students are in the chess club, 28 are in the science club, and 35 are in the photography club. Each student is in only one club, except for 14 students who are in both the chess and science clubs. How many students are in chess or science or both? How many of the junior students are not in any club? **59; 41**

Use any strategy to solve each problem. Show your work.

3. *Weather* Did you know that $\frac{1}{2}$ in. of rain is equal to about 4 in. of snow? In April 1921, 6 ft 4 in. of snow fell during a 24-h period in Silver Lake, Colorado. How much rain would have fallen if it had not been cold enough to snow? **$9\frac{1}{2}$ in.**

4. *Clothes* Suppose you have three pairs of pants, four sweaters, and five shirts. How many days can you wear an outfit consisting of a pair of pants, a sweater, and a shirt before you wear the same outfit again? **60 days**

5. *Food* In a restaurant, 37 customers ordered lunch between 11:30 A.M. and 12:30 P.M. Of those customers, 25 ordered soup with their lunch, 16 ordered salad with their lunch, and 8 ordered both soup and salad. **17 customers**
 a. How many customers ordered soup but no salad?
 b. How many customers did not order soup or salad?
  4 customers

6. *Baseball Cards* Suppose you have a baseball card collection and you decide to sort your cards. When you put your cards in piles of two, you have one card left over. You also have one left over when you put the cards in piles of three or piles of four. But when you put them in piles of seven, you have none left over. What is the least possible number of cards in your collection? **49 cards**

7. *Money* How many coin combinations total exactly 17¢? **6 combinations**

8. *Lemonade* To make lemonade, you need 3 c water for every 2 c lemon juice. Suppose you want to make 10 gal of lemonade. How many cups of lemon juice do you need? **64 c lemon juice**

Mixed Review

Complete each statement. *(Lesson 6-10)*

9. 8,800 lb = ▒ T ▒ lb
  4   800

10. 18 qt = ▒ gal ▒ qt
  4   2

11. 60 fl oz = ▒ c ▒ fl oz
  7   8

Find each quotient. *(Lesson 4-8)*

12. 53.7 ÷ 1.2
 44.75

13. 46.2 ÷ 2.4
 19.25

14. 101.536 ÷ 3.8
 26.72

15. 38.13 ÷ 8.2
 4.65

16. 250.56 ÷ 11.6
 21.6

17. The temperature is 70°F at 10:00 A.M. It increases 2 degrees every hour. What is the temperature at 4:00 P.M.? *(Lesson 3-10)* **82°F**

Practice 8-7 *Problem-Solving Strategy: Use Logical Reasoning*

Solve each problem using *logical reasoning*. Show all your work.

1. A local restaurant features a three-course meal. For the first course, you can choose from soup, salad, cottage cheese, or coleslaw. For the second course, you can choose from beef, pork, chicken, or a vegetarian pasta dish. For the third course, you can choose from sherbet, rice pudding, or ice cream. How many different meals could you choose if you choose one item from each course?
 48 meals

2. In a sixth-grade class of 28 students, 23 like to watch basketball. Also, 15 like to watch baseball. Twelve in the class said they like to watch both sports. How many in the class do not like to watch either sport?
 2 students

Use any strategy to solve. Show all your work.

3. Don has a pile of pennies. When he separates the pennies into stacks of two, he has one left over. When he separates the pennies into stacks of five, he has four left over. When he separates the pennies into stacks of seven, there are none left over. What is the least number of pennies that Don could have?
 49 pennies

4. Mara bought some flowers to plant in her garden. When she separated the plants into groups of three or five, she had one plant left over. When she separated the plants into groups of eight, she had none left over. What is the smallest number of plants that Mara could have bought?
 16 plants

5. Rearrange these numbers so that the sum of the three numbers along each segment is 12.

In copymaster and workbook formats

Reteaching 8-7 *Problem-Solving Strategy: Use Logical Reasoning*

In a survey, 46 students were asked to choose their favorite subject from English, math, and science. Nine named English, 26 named math, and 19 named science. Of these students, 12 could not name just one favorite but named both math and science. How many students did not name a favorite subject?

Read How many students appear to have answered? *9 + 26 + 19 = 54 plus the students who did not respond.* How many students named more than one subject? *12 students* What does the problem ask you to find? *How many students did not name a subject?*

Plan Use logical reasoning. Draw a rectangle to represent all 46 students. Draw overlapping circles for math and science.

Solve 12 students named both math and science. Write 12 in the overlap.
 26 − 12, or 14, named math only.
 19 − 12, or 7, named science only.

  | Math Science | English |
  | 14 (12) 7 | 9 |

 46 − (14 + 12 + 7 + 9) = 4 students did not name a favorite subject.

Look Back How can I check my solution? *Be sure that your diagram and answer fit each condition in the problem.*

Use *logical reasoning* to solve each problem.

1. Seventy students were asked to choose their favorite subject from English, math, and science. Thirteen chose English, 31 chose math, and 24 chose science. Of these students, 8 could not name just one and chose both math and science. How many students did not pick a favorite subject? 10 students

2. There are 50 members in the school orchestra who play brass, string, or drum instruments. Fifteen play only brass instruments. Fifteen play brass and drums. Fourteen play only strings. The others play only drums. How many play only drums? 6 students

3. There are 15 students who tutor English, history, and math. Six tutor only math and 3 tutor only English. Four students tutor English and history. The others tutor only history. How many students tutor only history? 2 students

4. Of the students who have school jobs, 12 work in the library and 8 work in the office. Four students work only in the cafeteria. Three of the students work in both the library and office. How many students have school jobs? 21 students

---

Minds on Math Transparency

8-7

Marcus makes three flower arrangements in four hours. At this rate, how long will it take him to make five flower arrangements?

$6\frac{2}{3}$ h

See *Solution Key* for worked-out answers.

Teaching Notes

1 Focus

CONNECTING TO PRIOR KNOWLEDGE Ask students to name two objects in the classroom that are identical. Ask students why they think the objects are identical, and how they could verify their opinions. **Answers may vary. Sample: machines using the same mold**

Lesson Planning Options

Prerequisite Skills
• identifying triangles (8-4)

Vocabulary/Symbols
congruent, similar, corresponding parts

Materials/Manipulatives
• dot paper   • scissors
• ruler

Resources

 Student Edition

Skills Handbook, p. 537
Extra Practice, p. 529
Glossary/Study Guide

 Teaching Resources

Chapter Support File, Ch. 8
• Lesson Planner 8-8
• Practice 8-8, Reteaching 8-8
• Alternative Activity 8-8
• Answer Masters 8-8
Teaching Aids Masters 1–3, 7–9, 19
Glossary, Spanish Resources

 Transparencies
1, 9, 20, 21, 93, Minds on Math 8-8

Warm Up

What is similar and different about the distances from +9 and –9 to 0 on a number line? **Both are the same distance from 0, but the directions are different.**

made them; compare dimensions of objects using measuring devices

2 Teach

Work Together

Ask students:

• *Name some triangles that are nonscalene.* **isosceles, equilateral**

• *Define nonscalene triangle.* **at least two equal sides**

THINK AND DISCUSS

REASONING Question 4 Emphasize that students may need to flip or rotate the trapezoids to make them match. After flipping or rotating, however, the trapezoids are still congruent.

AEP Relate the symbol for *congruent* (≅) to its definition. The symbol for similar (~) means the same shape. The equal sign (=) means everything has equal measures. Thus, congruent means same shape and size.

MEASUREMENT Connection

8-8 Congruent and Similar Figures

What You'll Learn

▼ To determine if figures are congruent
▼ To determine if figures are similar

...And Why

You can use congruent and similar figures in architecture and construction.

Here's How

Look for questions that
▪ build understanding
✔ check understanding

2a.

Work Together
Investigating Similarity

1. ▪*Modeling* Draw four identical triangles on dot paper. Cut out the four triangles. Put the triangles on top of each other. Check that they have the same size and shape. **Check students' work.**

2. a. Arrange the four triangles so that they form a larger triangle that has the same shape as the original triangle. None of the triangles should overlap. **See below left.**

   b. Draw your arrangement on dot paper. How do the lengths of the sides of the original triangle and the lengths of the sides of the larger triangle compare? **The lengths of the sides of the larger triangle are twice the lengths of the sides of the smaller triangle.**

3. ▪*Analyze* Show how to arrange nine identical triangles to form a larger triangle with the same shape. How do the lengths of the sides of the larger triangle compare to the lengths of the sides of the original triangle? **The lengths of the sides of the larger triangle are triple the lengths of the sides of the smaller triangle.**

THINK AND DISCUSS

▼ *Identifying Congruent Figures*

Figures that have the same size and shape are **congruent.** Congruent figures have congruent *corresponding* sides and angles.

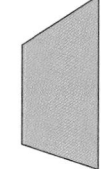

Two figures can be congruent even if one of the figures is turned.

Two figures can also be congruent even if one appears to be flipped over.

4. ▪*Reasoning* How could you check that the trapezoids shown are congruent? **Measure the sides and angles.**

356

ASSESSMENT Have students work in pairs. One student forms a pair of congruent rectangles on a geoboard. A partner changes one of the rectangles so that the two rectangles are similar. The first student then forms two rectangles that are neither congruent nor similar. Students exchange roles.

■ **ADDITIONAL EXAMPLE**

FOR EXAMPLE
Which rectangle is similar to the given one? **a.**

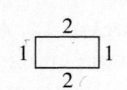

a.  **b.**

ERROR ALERT! Students may have difficulty recognizing congruence or similarity after the figures have been flipped or rotated.
Remediation: Allow students to trace the figures onto paper. They can then flip or rotate the paper as necessary.

CONNECTION TO BUSINESS Ask students to give examples of procedures in the business world that involve congruence or similarity. **Answers may vary. Sample: Manufacturing involves congruent parts on assembly lines and when making patterns for clothing.**

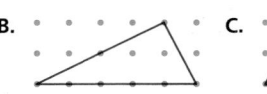

5. ✓*Try It Out* Which of the triangles below are congruent to the triangle at the right? **A, C**

A. **B.** **C.**

Now you may assign Exercises 1–5.

2 *Identifying Similar Figures*

Similar figures have the same shape, but are not necessarily the same size. Similar figures have congruent angles.

The matching parts of similar figures are called **corresponding parts.** Corresponding parts of similar figures are proportional.

6. ■*Reasoning* Must two congruent figures be similar? Why or why not? **Yes; the corresponding angles are congruent and corresponding sides have the ratio 1 : 1.**

■ **EXAMPLE**

Which triangles below are similar to the triangle at the right?

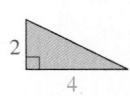

a. 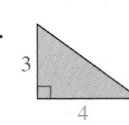 **b.** 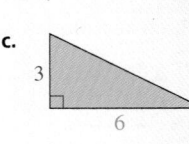 **c.**

$\frac{2}{1} \stackrel{?}{=} \frac{4}{2}$ $\frac{2}{3} \stackrel{?}{=} \frac{4}{4}$ $\frac{2}{3} \stackrel{?}{=} \frac{4}{6}$

$2 = 2$ ✓ $\frac{2}{3} \neq 1$ $\frac{2}{3} = \frac{2}{3}$ ✓

similar   not similar   similar

7. ✓*Try It Out* Which of the following triangles are also similar to the one in the Example above? **b**

a. 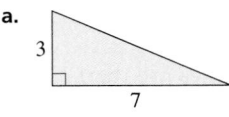 **b.**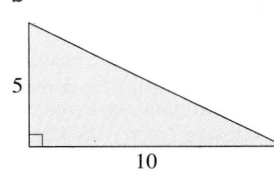

Now you may assign Exercises 6–16.

You can see congruent and similar triangles in Arizona's Navajo Bridge. The bridge crosses the Colorado River.

Technology Options

Prentice Hall Technology

💾 💿 **Software for Learners**
• Math Lab: Congruent Angles
• Math Blaster® Mystery*
• Interactive Student Tutorial, Chapter 8*

💾 💿 **Teaching Resource Software**
• Computer Item Generator 8-8
• Resource Pro™ Chapter 8*

🔄 **Internet** • For related mathematics activities, visit the Prentice Hall site at www.phschool.com/math

*Available on CD-ROM only

Assignment Options for Exercises On Your Own

To provide flexible scheduling, this lesson can be subdivided into parts.

🔻**Core** 1, 2, 4, 5
Extension 3

🔻**Core** 6–10, 13
Extension 11, 12, 14–16

Use Mixed Review to maintain skills.

357

to show that they are congruent.

VISUAL LEARNING **Exercise 13** Tell students to imagine the smaller figures enlarged on a photocopying machine.

REASONING **Exercise 14** Ask students to change each question into a statement using *always*, *sometimes*, or *never*.

WRAP UP

IDENTIFYING THE BIG IDEA Ask students to explain how to determine whether two figures are congruent or similar.

PROJECT LINK Students may need to adjust the sizes and shapes of previous puzzle pieces to accommodate the new shapes. Students can prepare plans by sketching with pencil and tracing paper.

3 Practice/Assess

EXERCISES *On Your Own*

Exercises 1 and 4 Students can trace the figures to check their answers. Then have students explain how to flip or turn the figures

---

pages 358–359   On Your Own

3. If the figures appear to have the same shape, compare the lengths of corresponding sides. If the lengths in each pair are equal, and the corresponding angles have the same measure, then the figures are congruent.

15b. No; some rhombuses have four right angles and some do not.

  c. Yes; all squares have four right angles and their sides are always proportional.

EXERCISES *On Your Own*

1. Which of the figures below appear to be congruent to the trapezoid at the right? **A, D**

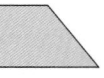

A. **B.** **C.** **D.**

2. *Open-ended* Use dot paper to draw four congruent triangles in different positions. **Check students' work.**

3. *Writing* Explain how you decide if two figures are congruent. **See margin.**

4. List the pairs of triangles below that appear to be congruent. **A and D, B and F, C and E**

A. **B.** **C.** **D.** **E.** **F.**

5. **Choose A, B, C, or D.** Which figure below is not congruent to the figure at the right? **C**

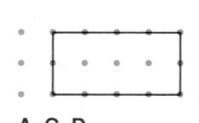

A. **B.** **C.** **D.**

6. Which rectangles are similar to the rectangle at the right?

A. **B.** **C.** **D.**

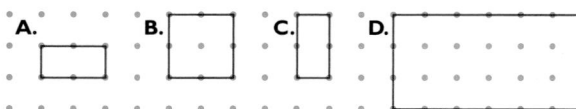

A, C, D

Tell whether the triangles appear to be *congruent*, *similar*, or *neither*.

7. 8. 9. 10.
  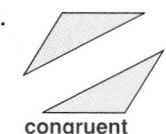 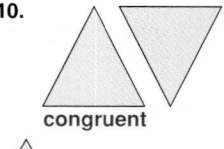

similar neither congruent congruent

11. *Patterns* How many congruent triangles are in the diagram at the right? How many similar triangles are there?
4 triangles; 5 triangles

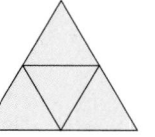

12. *Home Improvement* Suppose you are replacing a window. Should the replacement be congruent to or similar to the original? Explain your reasoning. **Congruent; the new window should be the same size and shape so it will fit the old opening.**

358

LESSON QUIZ

1. List the figures that are congruent.

a.

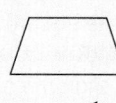

b.

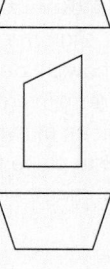

c.

a. and c.

2. List the figures that are similar.

a.

b.

c.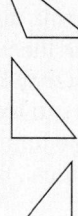

d.

c. and d.

---

13. *Measurement* List the pairs of figures below that are similar. **A and E, I and L**

A. 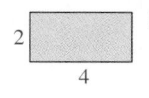 **B.**   **C.** 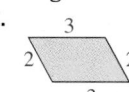 **D.** 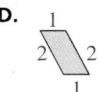 **E.** 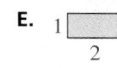 **F.**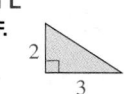

G. 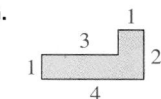 **H.** 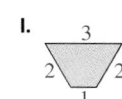 **I.** 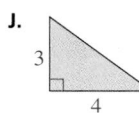 **J.** 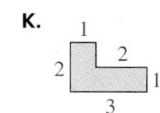 **K.** 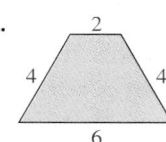 **L.**

14. *Reasoning* Are congruent figures similar? Are similar figures congruent? Explain. **Yes; no; the ratio of corresponding parts of congruent figures is 1:1, but not all similar figures are the same size.**

15. a. Use dot paper to draw several rhombuses, none of which are congruent. Include squares and nonsquares. If possible, make each one a different shape. **Check students' work.**
b. Are all rhombuses similar? Explain.
c. Are all squares similar? Explain.
b–c. See margin.

16. Use a protractor to draw a triangle with two angles measuring 45° and 60°. Then draw a second triangle that is not congruent to the first triangle, but that has angles measuring 45° and 60°. What appears to be true of the two triangles? **They are similar.**

Mixed Review

Write each improper fraction as a mixed number.
(Lesson 5-6)

17. $\frac{38}{6}$ $6\frac{1}{3}$ **18.** $\frac{49}{8}$ $6\frac{1}{8}$ **19.** $\frac{47}{3}$ $15\frac{2}{3}$ **20.** $\frac{63}{4}$ $15\frac{3}{4}$ **21.** $\frac{18}{5}$ $3\frac{3}{5}$ **22.** $\frac{29}{12}$ $2\frac{5}{12}$

Write each as a percent. *(Lesson 7-7)*

23. 18 boards out of 100 boards are warped. **18%**
24. 86 seats out of 100 seats are occupied. **86%**

25. *Choose a Strategy* In a class of 40 students, 29 wore jeans, 18 wore sneakers, and 10 wore both jeans and sneakers. How many wore neither jeans nor sneakers? **3 wore neither.**

CHAPTER PROJECT

PROJECT LINK: DESIGNING

Prepare the plan for your puzzle. Make sure it includes two triangles that are congruent and two triangles that are similar but not congruent. **Check students' work.**

PRACTICE

Practice 8-8 *Congruent and Similar Figures*

State whether each figure appears to be congruent to the parallelogram at the right.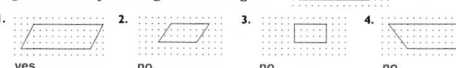

1. yes   **2.** no   **3.** no   **4.** no

State whether each trapezoid appears to be similar to the trapezoid at the right.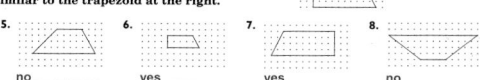

5. no   **6.** yes   **7.** yes   **8.** no

Tell whether the triangles appear to be *congruent*, *similar*, or *neither*.

9. neither   **10.** congruent   **11.** similar

12. List the pairs of figures that appear to be similar. **a, f; b, h; c, g**
a. □ **b.** **c.** △ **d.** ▭
e. ▱ **f.** □ **g.** ▽ **h.**

13. The figure below contains eight small congruent triangles. Redraw the figure with four fewer segments, so that only four small congruent triangles remain.
Answers may vary. Sample is given.

In copymaster and workbook formats

RETEACHING

Reteaching 8-8 *Congruent and Similar Figures*

Congruent figures have the same size and shape. Matching sides and matching angles are congruent. These are *corresponding parts*. Here, quadrilaterals *ABCD* and *EFGH* are congruent.

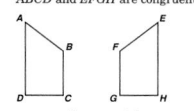

$\cong$ means "congruent."

Thus, we know that the following pairs of corresponding sides and corresponding angles are congruent:
$\overline{AB}$ and $\overline{EF}$
$\overline{CD}$ and $\overline{GH}$ $\overline{AD}$ and $\overline{EH}$
$\angle A$ and $\angle E$ $\angle B$ and $\angle F$
$\angle C$ and $\angle G$ $\angle D$ and $\angle H$

Similar figures have the same shape but may not be the same size. They have congruent corresponding angles and proportional corresponding sides. Here, triangles *RST* and *UVW* are similar.

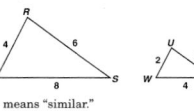

$\sim$ means "similar."

$\triangle RST \sim \triangle UVW$

Thus, we know, for example, that $\angle R$ and $\angle U$ are congruent and
$\frac{RS}{UV} = \frac{RT}{UW}$

$\triangle RST$ is congruent to $\triangle NPO$ and $\triangle ABC$ is congruent to $\triangle DEF$.

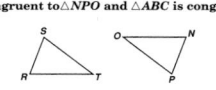 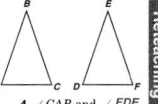

1. $\overline{AB}$ and $\overline{DE}$ **2.** $\angle DEF$ and $\angle ABC$ **3.** $\overline{BC}$ and $\overline{EF}$ **4.** $\angle CAB$ and $\angle FDE$
5. $\overline{DF}$ and $\overline{AC}$ **6.** $\angle ACB$ and $\angle DFE$ **7.** $\overline{RS}$ and $\overline{NP}$ **8.** $\angle SRT$ and $\angle PNO$
9. $\overline{ST}$ and $\overline{PO}$ **10.** $\angle RST$ and $\angle NPO$ **11.** $\overline{RT}$ and $\overline{NO}$ **12.** $\angle RTS$ and $\angle NOP$

Which figures appear to be similar to the first figure?

13. 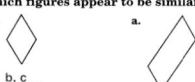 **a.**   **b.** **c.**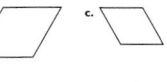

b, c

ENRICHMENT

Minds on Math Transparency

8-8

I am a fraction in simplest form. One-sixth of me is the same as one-half of one-fourth. What fraction am I?

$\frac{3}{4}$

See *Solution Key* for worked-out answers.

8-9 Teaching Notes

1 Focus

CONNECTING TO PRIOR KNOWLEDGE
Provide students with scissors and paper. Ask them to fold the paper in half and cut out a shape, making sure not to cut along the fold. Then open their folded papers. Ask: *What do you notice about the halves of the paper?* **Both halves are equal, or congruent.**

Lesson Planning Options

Prerequisite Skills
• recognizing congruent figures (8-8)

Vocabulary/Symbols
line symmetry, line of symmetry

Materials/Manipulatives
• scissors

Resources

 Student Edition

Skills Handbook, p. 536
Extra Practice, p. 529
Glossary/Study Guide

 Teaching Resources

Chapter Support File, Ch. 8
• Lesson Planner 8-9
• Practice 8-9, Reteaching 8-9
• Answer Masters 8-9
Teaching Aids Masters 1–3, 7, 8, 19
Glossary, Spanish Resources

 Transparencies
1, 9, 20, 21, Minds on Math 8-9

Warm Up

On a number line, find the integer at point *A*, if point *A* is 12 units to the left of 4. −8

2 Teach

THINK AND DISCUSS

Ask students if they think human faces are symmetrical. If so, ask them to describe where the lines of symmetry may be. Ask them how they might use mirrors to test their conjectures. Tell students that while human faces may appear to be symmetrical, they are not.

TACTILE LEARNING Questions 2 and 3
Have students make two photocopies of an equilateral triangle and a square. Tell students to cut out one copy of the square and triangle and fold back each to discover lines of symmetry. Then have students align the folded half on top of the other copy. Show students that the folded paper matches the remaining side. You can also have students find lines of symmetry using mirrors. Have students place the mirror on one of the figures so the image and visible pattern match the copy.

8-9 Line Symmetry

What You'll Learn

▼ To determine whether a figure has line symmetry

...And Why

Symmetry is very important in art, design, and photography.

Here's How

Look for questions that
 build understanding
✔ check understanding

THINK AND DISCUSS

You often see symmetry in nature—in the human body, in flowers, insects, birds, and in many other living things. Symmetrical designs are appealing to the eye. They often are used in fabrics, flags, architecture, masks, art, and pottery.

A figure has **line symmetry** if a line could be drawn to divide the figure into two congruent halves. The line is called a **line of symmetry.**

1. Does the butterfly at the left below have any lines of symmetry? How many? **yes; 1 line of symmetry**

2. ⚎*Modeling* Draw an equilateral triangle. Sketch all the lines of symmetry. How many lines of symmetry does an equilateral triangle have? **3 lines of symmetry**

3. How many lines of symmetry does a square have?
   4 lines of symmetry

■ **EXAMPLE** *Real-World Problem Solving*

Nature How many lines of symmetry does each figure have? Describe each line of symmetry as horizontal, vertical, or neither.

a.

b.

The leaf has one vertical line of symmetry.

The snowflake has one horizontal line of symmetry, one vertical, and four that are neither horizontal nor vertical.

AEP Group students in pairs. Ask students to fold a sheet of paper several times. Then ask students to identify and label the lines of symmetry as horizontal, vertical, or neither.

ERROR ALERT! Some students may confuse a line of symmetry with any line that divides a figure in half. **Remediation:** Remind students that a line of symmetry divides a figure into two congruent halves. Each side of the line should be an exact reflection of the other.

■ **ADDITIONAL EXAMPLE**

FOR EXAMPLE
How many lines of symmetry does each figure have? Describe each line of symmetry as horizontal, vertical, or neither.

a.

one; horizontal

b.

one; vertical

DIVERSITY and EXTENSION Inform students that in traditional Iroquois culture, there was a False Face society. The members of the Society wore expressive carved masks during religious ceremonies. Ask students to find pictorial examples of these masks. Have them identify any lines of symmetry they see in the masks.

---

4. ⚖*Reasoning* How could you check whether a figure has line symmetry? **Try to find two halves that are the same shape and size.**

5. ✓*Try It Out* How many lines of symmetry does each figure have? Describe each line of symmetry as horizontal, vertical, or neither. **one; vertical**

no symmetry

a.

b.

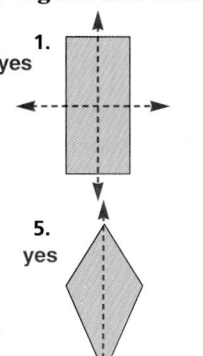

Work Together

Looking at Symmetry

6. Fold a sheet of paper. Cut out a shape that will have the fold line as a line of symmetry.
6–7. Check students' work.

7. Fold a sheet of paper into quarters. Cut out a shape that will have two perpendicular lines of symmetry.

Now you may assign Exercises 1–24.

EXERCISES *On Your Own*

Does each figure have line symmetry? If it does, trace the figure and draw all the lines of symmetry.

1. yes

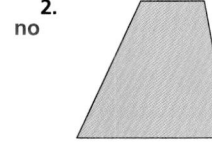

2. no

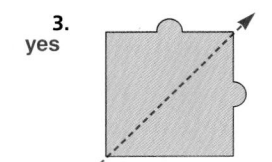

3. yes

4. yes

5. yes

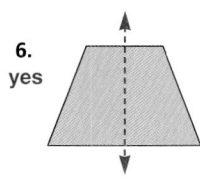

6. yes

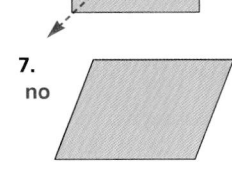

7. no

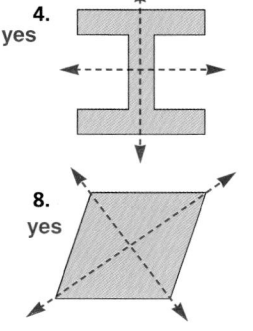

8. yes

Technology Options

Prentice Hall Technology

Software for Learners
- Math Blaster® Mystery*
- Interactive Student Tutorial, Chapter 8*

Teaching Resource Software
- Computer Item Generator 8-9
- Resource Pro™ Chapter 8*

Internet • For related mathematics activities, visit the Prentice Hall site at www.phschool.com/math

*Available on CD-ROM only

Assignment Options for Exercises On Your Own
> **Core** 1–14, 17–19, 21–24
> **Extension** 15, 16, 20
> Use Mixed Review to maintain skills.

ASSESSMENT Have students work in pairs to write their own definitions for a line of symmetry. Then have students draw figures with examples of horizontal and vertical lines of symmetry. Then draw a figure that has no line of symmetry.

3 Practice/Assess

EXERCISES *On Your Own*

DIVERSITY Exercise 17 Have students investigate letters in the alphabets of other languages and determine if the letters have lines of symmetry.

DIVERSITY Exercise 20 Display books showing nautical signal flags or flags from other states or countries. Ask students to find and describe flags with lines of symmetry.

IDENTIFYING THE BIG IDEA Have students tell what it means for a figure to have a line of symmetry.

JOURNAL Ask students to look around their homes and neighborhoods for examples of symmetry. List as many examples as they can in their journal.

---

pages 361–363   On Your Own

12.

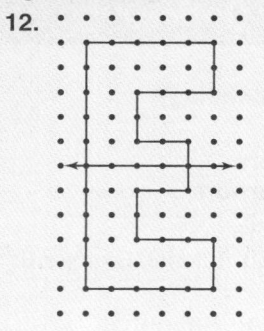

13.

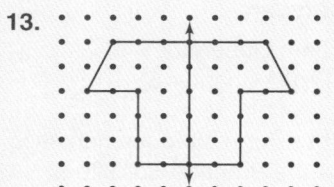

14.

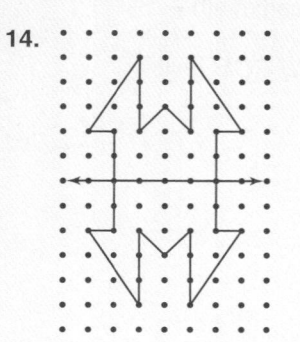

16c. no lines of symmetry; the line through the center of the non-congruent side and the opposite vertex; 3 lines through each vertex and the center of its opposite side

How many lines of symmetry does each figure have? Describe each line of symmetry.

9.

10.

One; check students' work.

11.

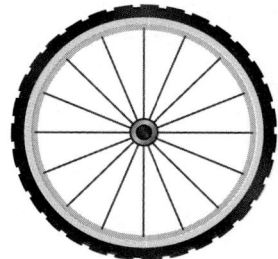

16; a line through each spoke and a line between every two consecutive spokes

Copy each figure on dot paper. Complete the figure so that the line is a line of symmetry.

12.

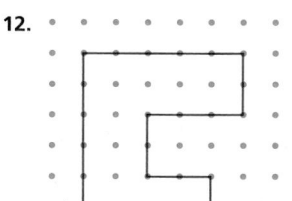

13.

14.

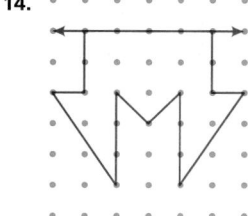

12–14. See margin.

15. Trace the hexagon at the right. Draw each line of symmetry.

16. **a.** Draw three isosceles triangles like those shown below. Draw all the lines of symmetry for each triangle.

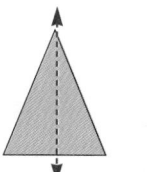 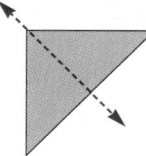 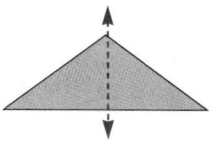

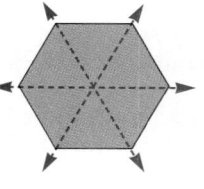

b. *Open-ended* Draw three scalene triangles. Draw all the lines of symmetry for each triangle. **Check students work for diagram; scalene triangles have no line of symmetry.**

c. *Writing* Describe the lines of symmetry of scalene, equilateral, and isosceles triangles. **See margin.**

17. Which capital letters have line symmetry?
 A B C D E F G H I J K L M A, B, C, D, E, H, I, M, O, T, U, V, W, X, Y
 N O P Q R S T U V W X Y Z

362

LESSON QUIZ

Draw the lines of symmetry on the figures. How many lines of symmetry does each figure have?

1.

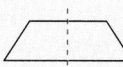

one

2.

three

3. The vertical line is a line of symmetry. Complete the other half of the figure.

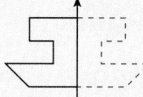

18. The word **CODE** has a horizontal line of symmetry. Find another word that has a horizontal line of symmetry.
Answers may vary. Samples: BOX, HIDE

19. The word **MOW**, written vertically, has a vertical line of symmetry. Find another word like that.
Answers may vary. Samples: MOM, HIM

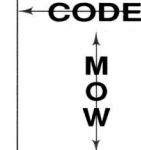

20. a. *World Flags* Find all the lines of symmetry of each flag.

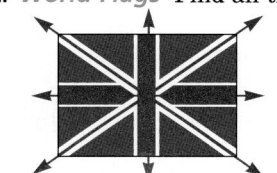 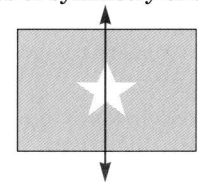 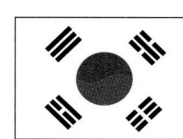

no line of symmetry

b–c. Check students' work.
b. Design a flag that has at least one line of symmetry.
c. Design a flag that has no line of symmetry.

Tell whether each dashed line is a line of symmetry.

21.

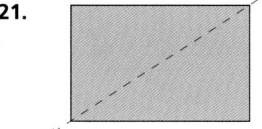

22.

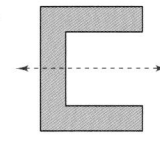

22. Yes; ; if you fold the figure along the line, the two sides align.

23.

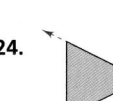

24.

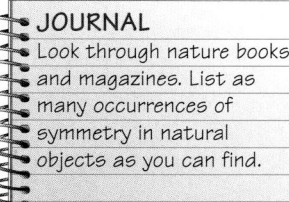

21, 23–24. No; if you fold the figure along the line, the two sides do not align.

JOURNAL
Look through nature books and magazines. List as many occurrences of symmetry in natural objects as you can find.

Mixed Review

Find each product. *(Lesson 4-5)*

25. 70.3 × 70.55
4,959.665

26. 9.07 × 0.025
0.22675

27. 21.51 × 21.49
462.2499

28. 1.7 × 1.78
3.026

29. 0.0145 × 0.12
0.00174

Estimate each sum or difference. *(Lesson 6-1)*

30. $\frac{1}{10} + \frac{1}{3}$ $\frac{1}{2}$

31. $\frac{1}{2} - \frac{1}{6}$ $\frac{1}{2}$

32. $\frac{4}{9} + \frac{1}{6}$ $\frac{1}{2}$

33. $\frac{5}{8} - \frac{1}{6}$ $\frac{1}{2}$

34. $\frac{3}{4} - \frac{9}{16} + \frac{1}{2}$ $\frac{3}{4}$

35. *Choose a Strategy* Thirty-two teams are competing in a single-elimination tournament. How many games will the winning team have to play? 5 games

---

PRACTICE

Practice 8-9 *Line Symmetry*

Does each figure have line symmetry? If it does, draw all the lines of symmetry. If not, write *none*.

1.   **2.**   **3.**

4.   **5.** **6.** none

Complete each figure so that the line is a line of symmetry.

7. **8.** **9.**

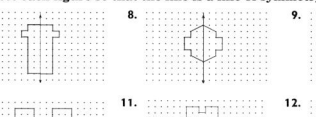

10. **11.** **12.**

Is there a line of symmetry for each word? If so, draw it.

13. BOX **14.** TOOT **15.** CHICO **16.** MOM

17. Many logos such as the one at the right have both horizontal line symmetry and vertical line symmetry. Design three other logos, one with horizontal line symmetry only, one with vertical line symmetry only, and one with both horizontal and vertical line symmetry. Sample designs shown.

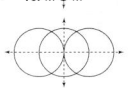

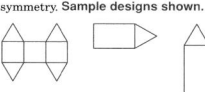

In copymaster and workbook formats

RETEACHING

Reteaching 8-9 *Line Symmetry*

A figure has **line symmetry** if you can fold it in half so that the two halves match exactly. The line is called a **line of symmetry.**

This figure *has* line symmetry. Trace the figure and the line through it. Cut out the figure and fold it on the line. The two halves match exactly.

This figure *does not* have line symmetry. Trace the figure and the line through it. Cut out the figure and fold it on the line (or on any other line). The two halves do not match exactly.

Some figures have many lines of symmetry. Draw a circle and try to find all the lines of symmetry.

Does the figure have line symmetry? Write *yes* or *no*. If yes, draw all the lines of symmetry.

1. yes **2.** no **3.** yes

4. no **5.** yes **6.** yes

Can you find a line of symmetry for each word? Write *yes* or *no*. If yes, then draw the line of symmetry.

7. DAD no **8.** HAH yes **9.** DAY no **10.** COB yes

ENRICHMENT

Minds on Math Transparency

8-9

I am a quadrilateral with two right angles, one obtuse angle, and one acute angle. What kind of quadrilateral am I?

trapezoid

See *Solution Key* for worked-out answers.

363

1 Focus

CONNECTING TO PRIOR KNOWLEDGE Ask students to tell why they think the invention of the wheel was so important. **Answers may vary. Sample: Wheels make the moving of objects easier and faster.** Tell students they will learn about the circle in this lesson.

2 Teach

THINK AND DISCUSS

Make sure students give reasons for their answers. For example, in diameter $\overline{AE}$, the endpoints A and E are on the circle.

CONNECTION TO HISTORY The first Ferris Wheel appeared at the Chicago World's Fair in 1893. Designed by George Washington Ferris, it was 265 ft high and had a diameter of 250 ft. The 36 cars were able to carry 2,160 passengers. A single spin took 20 min.

Question 4a Make sure students are aware that as they rotate the compass to make a circle, the pencil point should stay the same distance from the center, or the pivot point.

REASONING Question 4d Help students understand why a circle has an infinite number of radii. Discuss with students how many points are on a number line. Tell

Lesson Planning Options

Prerequisite Skills
- using a compass (precourse)
- solving equations (2-7)

Vocabulary/Symbols
radius, diameters, chords, central angles

Materials/Manipulatives
- compass
- ruler
- protractor

Resources

 Student Edition

Skills Handbook, p. 541
Extra Practice, p. 529
Glossary/Study Guide

 Teaching Resources

Chapter Support File, Ch. 8
- Lesson Planner 8-10
- Practice 8-10, Reteaching 8-10
- Answer Masters 8-10
Teaching Aids Masters 3, 10
Glossary, Spanish Resources

 Transparencies
6, 10, Minds on Math 8-10

Warm Up

Find two even integers whose sum is 20 and whose product is 96. **8 and 12**

8-10 Investigating Circles

What You'll Learn
▼ To identify parts of a circle and identify central angles

...And Why
Circles have played an important role in industry, transportation, and entertainment.

Here's How
Look for questions that
⚬ build understanding
✔ check understanding

THINK AND DISCUSS

Designers and engineers use geometric figures to model real objects.

A **circle** is the set of points in a plane that are the same distance from a given point, the *center*. You name a circle by its center.

Circle O

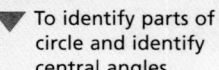

$\overline{OG}, \overline{OA}, \overline{OD}$ and $\overline{OE}$ are radii (plural of **radius**) of circle O.

$\overline{AE}$ and $\overline{DG}$ are **diameters** of circle O.

$\overline{AD}, \overline{DE}$, and $\overline{GE}$ are **chords** of circle O.

You can model a Ferris wheel with a circle and segments inside the circle. **1–3. Answers may vary. Samples are given.**

1. ✔*Try It Out* Name a radius of the model of the Ferris wheel at the right. $\overline{OA}$

2. ✔*Try It Out* Name a diameter of the model. $\overline{AE}$

3. ✔*Try It Out* Name a chord of the model. $\overline{AE}, \overline{AB}$

4c. **Check students' work.**

4. a. Use a compass to draw a circle. Label the center S. **a–b. See margin p. 366.**
   b. Draw a radius of your circle. Label it $\overline{ST}$.
   c. Did you and your classmates draw $\overline{ST}$ the same way?
   d. ⚬*Reasoning* How many different radii can a circle have? How many diameters can a circle have? **too many to count; too many to count**

students any two points can have a point between them. The same is true for the points on the outside of a circle.

■ ADDITIONAL EXAMPLE

FOR EXAMPLE
The diameter of a can of soup is 8 cm. What is its radius? **4 cm**

CONNECTION TO ALGEBRA Question 6
Discuss with students which equation would be easier to use to solve the problem,
$d = 2r$ or $r = \frac{d}{2}$.

ASSESSMENT Have students use a compass to draw a circle. Then have them use a ruler to draw and label a radius, a diameter, and a chord. Ask students to describe a central angle.

3 Practice/Assess

EXERCISES *On Your Own*

ERROR ALERT! Exercise 3 Students may see only one chord $\overline{ST}$. **Remediation:** Tell students a chord is a line segment whose

endpoints are on the circle. Ask: *Is a diameter a chord?* Yes; it is the longest chord.

ERROR ALERT! Exercises 6–17 Some students may mix up radius and diameter. They may half the radius to find the diameter or double the diameter to find the radius. **Remediation:** Help students remember a circle's diameter is longer than its radius by telling them diameter has more letters than radius. Have them check their answers to make sure the diameters are greater than the radii.

The length of a radius r is the distance from the center to any point on the circle. The length of a diameter d is the distance from a point on the circle, through the center, to another point on the circle.

See margin p. 366.

5. **a.** Choose a point on your circle other than T. Label it U. Draw diameter $\overline{UV}$. Compare the lengths of $\overline{UV}$ and $\overline{ST}$.

   b. ⚓*Reasoning* What is the relationship between the length of a radius and the length of a diameter for any given circle? Explain. **The length of a radius will always be half the length of a diameter because a diameter is made of two radii.**

CIRCLES

The length of the diameter of a circle is equal to twice the length of the radius. ($d = 2r$ or $r = \frac{d}{2}$)

■ **EXAMPLE**   *Real-World Problem Solving*

Amusement Parks The first Ferris wheel had a diameter of 250 ft. What was its radius?

$$d = 250 \quad \longleftarrow \text{Write an equation.}$$
$$2r = 250 \quad \longleftarrow \text{Substitute } 2r \text{ for } d.$$
$$\frac{2r}{2} = \frac{250}{2} \quad \longleftarrow \text{Divide each side by 2.}$$
$$r = 125 \quad \longleftarrow \text{Simplify.}$$

The length of the radius was 125 ft.

6. ✓*Try It Out* Find the length of the radius of a circle whose diameter is 8 cm. **4 cm**

7. **diameter**

7. ⚓*Measurement* Draw and measure several chords of circle T above. What is the longest chord of a circle called?

8. **The vertex of a central angle is at the center of the circle.**

8. ⚓*Explain* A model of a Ferris wheel, like the one at the right, contains many angles. Some of the angles, like $\angle APB$, are **central angles.** Why do you think they have this name?

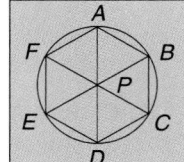

9a. **$\angle APB, \angle BPC, \angle CPD, \angle DPE, \angle EPF,$ and $\angle FPA$**

9. **a.** Name the 6 acute central angles shown in circle P above.

   b. ⚓*Measurement* Measure one acute central angle. **60°**

   c. ⚓*Reasoning* The 6 central angles are congruent. What is **360°** the sum of their measures?

Technology **Options**

Prentice Hall Technology

Software for Learners
• Math Blaster® Mystery*
• Interactive Student Tutorial, Chapter 8*

Teaching Resource Software
• Computer Item Generator 8-10
• Resource Pro™ Chapter 8*

Internet • For related mathematics activities, visit the Prentice Hall site at www.phschool.com/math

*Available on CD-ROM only

Assignment Options for Exercises On Your Own
Core 1–17, 19
Extension 18, 20–23
Use Mixed Review to maintain skills.

WRITING Exercise 18 Have students use other words, such as *horizontal,* to describe the orientation of the drawing.

EXTENSION Ask students to find the formulas for the diameter and area of a circle. Then have them research the meaning and origin of pi.

WRAP UP

IDENTIFYING THE BIG IDEA Ask students to name the parts of a circle. Then list the conditions for each part.

LESSON QUIZ

Find the unknown length in each circle.

1. $r = 12$ cm; $d = \blacksquare$ 24 cm

2. $d = 46$ in.; $r = \blacksquare$ 23 in.

3. $r = .5$ ft; $d = \blacksquare$ 1 ft

CHECKPOINT 2

█Checkpoint 2   *Lessons 8-6 through 8-10*

1. **Writing** In your own words, describe a circle and its parts. Answers may vary.
   _____
   _____

2. Six soccer teams are in a tournament. Each team plays every other team once. How many games will be played? 15 games

3. Which figures below appear to be congruent? B, D

   A. 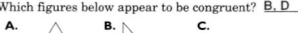 **B.** **C.** **D.**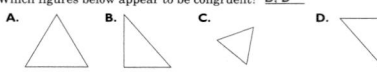

4. Which figures above appear to be similar but not congruent? A, C

5. Circle A, B, C, or D. Which figure has more than two lines of symmetry?
   A. a rectangle that is not a square   **B.** a right triangle
   Ⓒ an equilateral triangle   **D.** a pentagon with sides of unequal length

---

pages 364–365   Think and Discuss

4a–b.

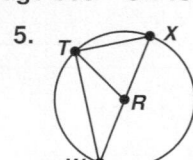

5a. Diagrams may vary. Sample:

The length of $\overline{ST}$ is half the length of $\overline{UV}$.

page 366   On Your Own

5.

18. △*ABC* is inscribed in a circle with center *O*. $\overline{AB}$ is a diameter and $\overline{AC}$ and $\overline{BC}$ are chords.

366

EXERCISES *On Your Own*

Name each of the following for circle *O*.

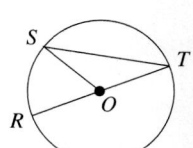

1. three radii
$\overline{OR}, \overline{OS}, \overline{OT}$

2. a diameter
$\overline{RT}$

3. two chords
$\overline{ST}, \overline{RT}$

4. two central angles
$\angle ROS, \angle SOT$

5. Draw a circle that has radius $\overline{RT}$, diameter $\overline{WX}$, and chords $\overline{WT}$ and $\overline{TX}$. See margin.

Find the unknown length for each circle.

6. $r = 10$ in.; $d = \blacksquare$ 20 in.

7. $d = 140$ ft; $r = \blacksquare$ 70 ft

8. $d = 5$ m; $r = \blacksquare$ 2.5 m

9. $r = 46$ cm; $d = \blacksquare$ 92 cm

10. $d = 22$ cm; $r = \blacksquare$ 11 cm

11. $r = 12$ m; $d = \blacksquare$ 24 m

12. $r = 35$ mi; $d = \blacksquare$ 70 m

13. $d = 4$ mm; $r = \blacksquare$ 2 mm

14. $r = 7$ km; $d = \blacksquare$ 14 km

15. $d = 0.25$ ft; $r = \blacksquare$ 0.125 ft

16. $r = 0.6$ mi; $d = \blacksquare$ 1.2 mi

17. $d = 12.4$ m; $r = \blacksquare$ 6.2 m

18. *Writing* A graphic designer wants to describe the drawing at the right in words. Write a description for him. Remember to use geometric terms such as *radius*, *diameter*, and *chord*. See margin.

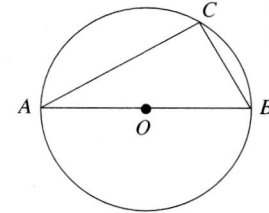

19. *Leisure* The diameter of a circular swimming pool is 20 ft. What is the radius?   10 ft

20. *Open-ended* Draw a circle and several chords with different lengths. Measure the distance from the center of the circle to each chord. Describe the relationship between the lengths of the chords and the distances from the center of the circle.   The longer the chord, the shorter the distance to the center of the circle.

21. a. *Measurement* Find the measure of $\angle AXB$.   60°
   b. Judging by appearance, classify the triangles shown for circle *X*.   equilateral

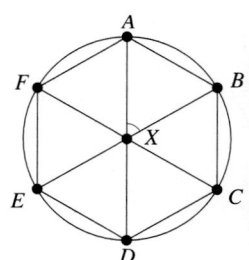

22. *Reasoning* Draw and label a circle. Then draw a central angle of your circle. If you increase or decrease the size of your circle, what happens to the measure of the central angle?   It stays the same.

23. **Choose A, B, C, or D.** Circle *P* has 8 congruent central angles. What is the measure of $\angle APC$?   C
   A. 45°   **B.** 60°
   C. 90°   **D.** 120°

Name each of the following for circle A.

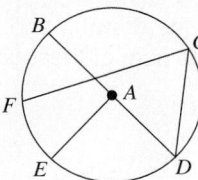

4. three radii $\overline{BA}, \overline{EA}, \overline{AD}$

5. three chords $\overline{BD}, \overline{FC}, \overline{CD}$

6. a diameter $\overline{BD}$

7. two central angles $\angle EAD, \angle BAE$

Mixed Review

24. *Data Analysis* Make a circle graph that shows the information at the right. *(Lesson 7-10)*

Favorite Fruit	
Apples	50%
Oranges	25%
Other	25%

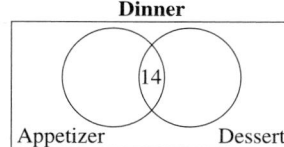

Find the prime factorizations using a factor tree.
(Lesson 5-2)

25. 60 $2^2 \times 3 \times 5$

26. 144 $2^4 \times 3^2$

27. 500 $2^2 \times 5^3$

28. 496 $2^4 \times 31$

29. 1,240 $2^3 \times 5 \times 31$

30. 5,070 $2 \times 3 \times 5 \times 13^2$

31. *Choose a Strategy* There are 30 students in a math class. Of these students, 12 belong to the computer club, 8 to the hiking club, and 3 to both. How many belong to neither? **13 students**

✓ CHECKPOINT 2

Lessons 8-6 through 8-10

1. *Writing* In your own words, describe a square.
A square is a parallelogram with four congruent sides and four right angles.

2. The Cool Café had 63 customers. All of them had dinner. Twenty of the customers ordered an appetizer, and 36 had dessert. Complete the diagram at the right.
  a. How many customers ordered an appetizer but no dessert with their dinner? **6 customers**
  b. How many customers had dinner only? **21 customers**

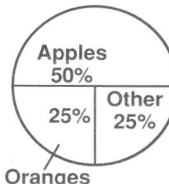

3. a. Which of the figures shown below appear to be congruent? **A, B, E**
  b. Which figures appear to be similar? **A, B, D E**

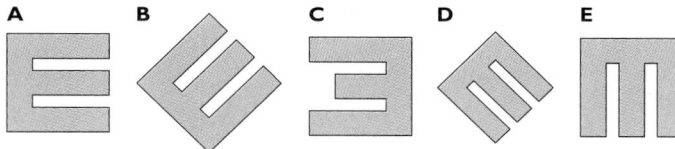

A   B   C   D   E

4. Choose A, B, C, or D. Which figure has the most lines of symmetry? **A**

  A. a square   **B.** a right isosceles triangle
  C. a scalene triangle **D.** an equilateral triangle

Find the unknown length for each circle.

5. $r = 10$ in.; $d = \blacksquare$ **20 in.**
6. $d = 140$ ft; $r = \blacksquare$ **70 ft**
7. $d = 5$ m; $r = \blacksquare$ **2.5 m**
8. $r = 46$ cm; $d = \blacksquare$ **92 cm**

Practice 8-10 *Investigating Circles*

Name each of the following for circle O.

1. three radii
  $\overline{OJ}, \overline{OL}, \overline{OK}$

2. a diameter
  $\overline{JK}$

3. two chords
  $\overline{JK}, \overline{LK}$

4. two central angles
  $\angle JOK, \angle LOK, \angle JOL$

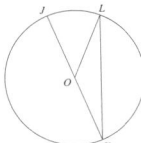

Find the unknown length in each circle. $r =$ length of radius; $d =$ length of diameter.

5. $r = 4$ in.; $d = \blacksquare$ **8 in.**
6. $d = 15$ cm; $r = \blacksquare$ **7.5 cm**
7. $d = 9$ mm; $r = \blacksquare$ **4.5 mm**
8. $r = 12$ mm; $d = \blacksquare$ **24 mm**

9. $d = 35$ ft; $r = \blacksquare$ **17.5 ft**
10. $r = 22$ in.; $d = \blacksquare$ **44 in.**
11. $r = 6$ m; $d = \blacksquare$ **12 m**
12. $d = 8$ ft; $r = \blacksquare$ **4 ft**

Choose A, B, C, or D. What is the measure of each angle?

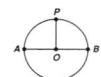

13. $\angle LUZT$
  (A.) 60°   **B.** 120°   **C.** 150°   **D.** 180°

14. $\angle TZW$
  A. 60°   **B.** 120°   **C.** 150°   **(D.)** 180°

15. $\angle LUZY$
  A. 60°   **(B.)** 120°   **C.** 150°   **D.** 180°

16. $\angle TYV$
  (A.) 60°   **B.** 120°   **C.** 150°   **D.** 180°

17. A toy race car has a wheel with a diameter of 10 in. A larger car has a wheel with a diameter of 14 in. A designer plans to include 9 spokes from the center of each wheel. What will be the measure of the central angle formed by two consecutive spokes of the 10-in. wheel? of the 14-in. wheel? What can you conclude?
  40°; 40°; the measure of a central angle is not dependent on the length of the diameter.

In copymaster and workbook formats

Reteaching 8-10 *Investigating Circles*

Point O is the **center** of the circle.
$\overline{AB}$ is the **diameter**.
$\overline{OA}$ is a **radius**. $\overline{OP}$ is also a radius.

$\overline{CD}$ and $\overline{EF}$ are **chords**.
The longest chord is a diameter.

In any circle, the length of the diameter is twice the length of the radius.
$$d = 2r$$

The radius is half the diameter.
$$r = \frac{d}{2}$$

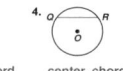

$\angle AOP$ and $\angle AOQ$ are **central angles**.

Label the parts shown. Write *diameter, radius, chord,* **or** *center.* **Some exercises have more than one answer.**

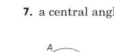

1. center, radius   **2.** center   **3.** diameter, chord   **4.** center, chord

Draw a circle and each named part. Sample drawings shown.

5. a diameter and a different radius
6. three chords that are not diameters
7. a central angle

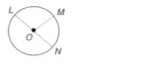
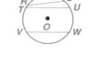

Find the unknown length in each circle.

8. $r = 8$ cm $d =$ **16 cm**
9. $d = 110$ in. $r =$ **55 in.**
10. $d = 48$ ft $r =$ **24 ft**
11. $r = 23$ mm $d =$ **46 mm**
12. $d = 55$ cm $r =$ **27.5 cm**
13. $r = 18$ in. $d =$ **36 in.**

Minds on Math Transparency

8-10

I am a polygon that can be called a rectangle or a rhombus. What polygon am I?

square

See *Solution Key* for worked-out answers.

In Lesson 8-10, students learned how to identify parts of a circle and identify central angles. This toolbox shows students how to use geometry software to investigate angles of a triangle.

ERROR ALERT! Students may skip steps when investigating the angles of a triangle. **Remediation:** Have students read the directions carefully and make a list of the

things they need to do. Suggest students number the list. Have them check off each item as they complete it.

ASSESSMENT Have students use the program to draw all three exterior angles of a triangle. **See students' work.**

■ **ADDITIONAL PROBLEM**

Have them use the drawing and spreadsheet to investigate the sum of these three exterior angles. **360°**

Materials/Manipulatives

- computer
- geometry software

Investigating Angles of a Triangle

After Lesson 8-10

You can use geometry software to investigate relationships among angles of a triangle.

Open a new geometry window. Use the polygon feature to draw a triangle. Label the vertices A, B, and C. Use the angle-marking feature to mark the three interior angles.

🔲 **polygon feature**

🔲 **angle-marking feature**

🔲 **color-linking feature**

Open a new spreadsheet window. Use the color-linking feature to link each interior angle to a cell in the spreadsheet.

	A	B	
1	Angle A	54	
2	Angle B	66	
3	Angle C	60	
4	Sum	=B1+B2+B3	

Drag the vertex of one angle so that the angle measure changes.

Enter the formula to find the sum of the three angles.

1. How does this affect the other angle measures? **When the measure of the dragged angle decreases, the measures o the other angles increase. When the measure of the dragged angle increases, the measures of the other angles decrease.**

2. How does it affect the sum of the angle measures? **The sum stays the same.**

3. Drag the vertex of another angle. What do you notice? **The results are the same.**

4. What can you conclude about the sum of the measures of the interior angles of a triangle? **The sum is always 180°.**

Use the segment tool to extend one of the sides of the triangle. Mark the exterior angle ($\angle ACF$) it forms with the other side. Open a new spreadsheet window. Link this angle to a cell in the spreadsheet.

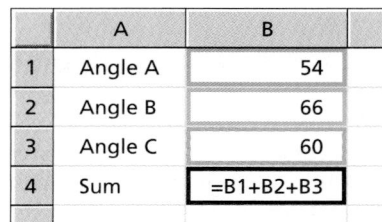

Study the relationship between the measure of the exterior angle and the sum of the measures of the two opposing interior angles.

5. What do you notice? **Their measures are the same.**

6. What can you conclude about the exterior angle and the two opposing interior angles?

	A	B
1	Angle A	55
2	Angle B	65
3	Sum Angles A and B	=B1+B2
4	Angle ACF	120

The sum of the measures of the two interior angles equals the measure of the exterior angle.

PROBLEM SOLVING PRACTICE ★★

This page provides problems for students to solve using their knowledge of geometry, measurement, using number lines, and using proportion. Allow students to use any method they find helpful.

USING MANIPULATIVES Exercises 1 Suggest students cut out a rectangle that is not a square. Have them fold the paper to find all the lines of symmetry.

Exercises 3 Encourage students to draw figures to help them solve the problems.

COOPERATIVE GROUPS Exercise 7 Have students form groups of four. Each person in the group chooses one of the four shapes. Then decides how many lines of symmetry their shape can have. Have group members discuss their answers and decide together how to answer the problem.

Exercises 9 and 10 Have students write the proportions they can use to find each answer.

PROBLEM SOLVING PRACTICE ★★★★★

Choose the best answer.

1. How many lines of symmetry does a nonsquare rectangle have? **C**

  A. 0   **B.** 1   **C.** 2   **D.** 4

2. A nickel is approximately 21 mm across. What is this distance expressed in centimeters? **J**

  F. 21,000 cm   **G.** 2,100 cm
  H. 210 cm   **J.** 2.1 cm

3. Which of the following polygons is *not* a quadrilateral? **D**

  A. trapezoid   **B.** parallelogram
  C. rhombus   **D.** pentagon

4. What is the area of a rectangle 9 m wide and 70 cm high? **J**

  F. 6,300 cm^2 **G.** 630 cm^2
  H. 63 m^2 **J.** 6.3 m^2

5. Name two triangles in the diagram that are not congruent. **C**

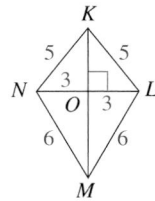

  A. triangles *KNO* and *KLO*
  B. triangles *MON* and *MOL*
  C. triangles *NKL* and *NML*
  D. triangles *KMN* and *KML*

6. What are all the factors of 100? **J**

  F. 2 and 5   **G.** $2^2 \times 5^2$
  H. 2, 4, 5, 10, 20, 25, and 50
  J. 1, 2, 4, 5, 10, 20, 25, and 100

7. If a quadrilateral has at least two lines of symmetry, then it *cannot* be which of the following? **D**

  A. rhombus   **B.** square
  C. rectangle   **D.** trapezoid

8. In a fishing contest, the weights of the four heaviest fish are plotted on a number line. Which point shows the weight for a fish weighing $4\frac{3}{8}$ pounds? **H**

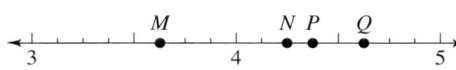

  F. point *M*   **G.** point *N*
  H. point *P*   **J.** point *Q*

Please note that items 9 and 10 each have *five* answer choices.

9. On a scale drawing, the scale shown is 1 in. : 10 ft. The length of a room is 2.5 in. on the drawing. How long is the actual room? **B**

  A. 4 in.   **B.** 25 in.   **C.** 4 ft

  D. 25 ft   **E.** Not Here

10. A triangular table top has the dimensions shown below. **F**

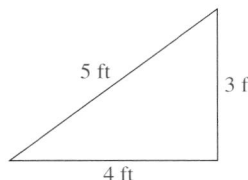

A smaller table is similar in shape, but the longest side is 2.5 feet long. How long is the shortest side of the smaller table?

  F. 1.5 ft   **G.** 2 ft
  H. 6 ft   **J.** 8 ft
  K. Not Here

1 Focus

CONNECTING TO PRIOR KNOWLEDGE
Review the meaning of the term *congruent*. Then ask: What are some methods you can use to determine if two figures are congruent? **Answers may vary. Sample: Trace one figure and place it on top of the other.**

2 Teach

Work Together

To help students complete the activity, create your own cutout and model the steps of the Work Together on the overhead projector.

DIVERSITY Have students work in pairs to accommodate students who have visual or fine-motor impairments.

THINK AND DISCUSS

As you work through the examples in this section, use a large letter E to model translations, rotations, and reflections on the overhead projector.

CONNECTING TO THE STUDENTS' WORLD
Examples 1 and 2 Ask students to give examples of reflections and rotations in the real world. **Answers may vary. Sample: reflections—images reflecting off the water**

Lesson Planning Options

Prerequisite Skills
• recognizing congruent shapes (8-8)

Vocabulary/Symbols
translation, image, reflection, line of reflection, rotation, point of rotation

Materials/Manipulatives
• index cards   • scissors

Resources

 Student Edition

Skills Handbook, p. 536
Extra Practice, p. 529
Glossary/Study Guide

 Teaching Resources

Chapter Support File, Ch. 8
• Lesson Planner 8-11
• Practice 8-11, Reteaching 8-11
• Answer Masters 8-11
Teaching Aids Masters 1–3, 7, 8, 19
Glossary, Spanish Resources

 Transparencies
1, 9, 20, 21, Minds on Math 8-11

Warm Up

Name a number between 6 and 7. **Answers may vary. Sample: 6.3**

370

 **8-11** **Slides, Flips, and Turns**

What You'll Learn

▼ To explore translations and reflections
▼ To explore rotations

...And Why

Translations, reflections, and rotations are widely used in interior design.

Here's How

Look for questions that
⬛ build understanding
✔ check understanding

6. All the shapes are congruent; they are in different positions; yes; they are the same shape and size.

Work Together _____ *Investigating Slides, Flips, and Turns*

1. Fold an index card in half. Cut out a geometric shape along the fold line. Cut an extra piece from one side of the fold.
1–5. Check students' work.

2. Unfold the index card.
   a. Use the card as a stencil. Draw the shape on a sheet of paper.
   b. Without turning or lifting the stencil, slide it to the right. Draw the shape again.

3. Flip the stencil over, so that the front is face down. Draw the shape again.

4. Turn your stencil so the top is now at the bottom. Draw the shape.

5. Flip the shape again so the front is face up again. Draw the shape.

6. ⬛*Analyze* How are the shapes alike? How are they different? Are all of your drawings congruent? Explain.

 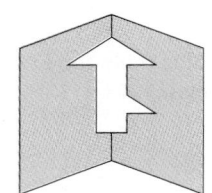 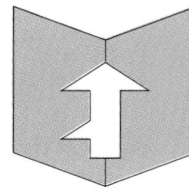 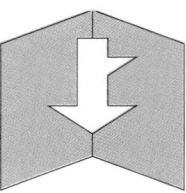 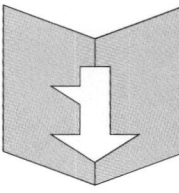

THINK AND DISCUSS

▼ *Exploring Translations and Reflections*

You can say that the first shape was moved to the right to become the second shape. A **translation** moves a figure so that every point moves the same distance in the same direction. The new shape is called the **image** of the original shape.

of a pond; rotations—the beams of a search light, spokes on a wheel

CONNECTION TO LANGUAGE ARTS Have students look up the words *translate*, *rotate*, and *reflect* in a dictionary. Have them write the nonmathematical definitions of the words in their math journals. Have students explain how these definitions apply to the mathematical meanings of the words.

■ **ADDITIONAL EXAMPLES**

FOR EXAMPLE 1

Draw a translation and a reflection of the shape.

Check students' work.

FOR EXAMPLE 2

Which of the following is a rotation of the shape below? a.

a.

b.

c.

7. ▪*Reasoning* Why is a translation also called a *slide?*
   You slide it from the original position.

■ **EXAMPLE 1**

Draw two translations of the shape at the right.

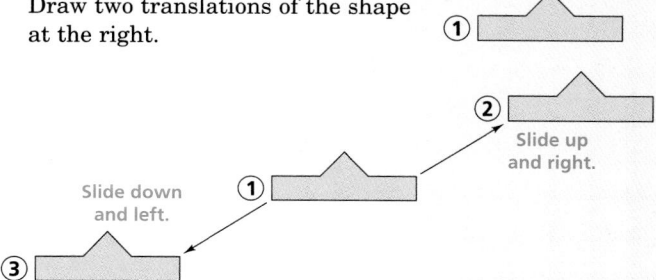

Slide up and right.

Slide down and left.

Shapes ② and ③ are translations of shape ①.

8. ✓*Try It Out* Draw two translations of the shape at the right.
   Check students' work.

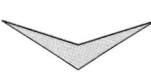

Another way of moving a figure is to reflect it. A **reflection** is a figure flipped across a line. The new figure is a mirror image of the original figure.

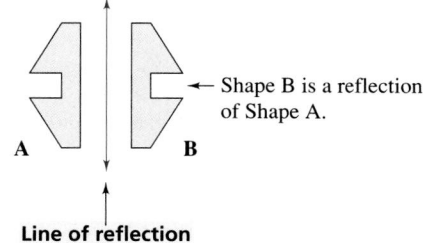

← Shape B is a reflection of Shape A.

A   B

Line of reflection

9. ✓*Try It Out* Place a mirror on the line of reflection above, perpendicular to the page. What do you notice?
   The mirror image matches the second shape.

10. ✓*Try It Out* Draw the reflection of each shape over the line of reflection.

a. 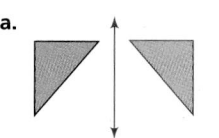   b. 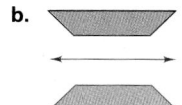   c.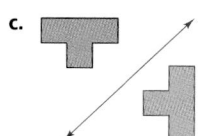

Now you may assign Exercises 1–14.

Technology Options

Prentice Hall Technology

Software for Learners
• Math Blaster® Mystery*
• Interactive Student Tutorial, Chapter 8*

Teaching Resource Software
• Computer Item Generator 8-11
• Resource Pro™ Chapter 8*

Internet • For related mathematics activities, visit the Prentice Hall site at www.phschool.com/math

*Available on CD-ROM only

Assignment Options for Exercises On Your Own

To provide flexible scheduling, this lesson can be subdivided into parts.

▼ **Core** 1–9, 12–14
   Extension 10, 11

▼ **Core** 15–21
   Extension 22, 23

Use Mixed Review to maintain skills.

ERROR ALERT Students may confuse translations and reflections. **Remediation:** Relate *sl*ide to trans*l*ation and *fl*ip to re*fl*ection. Use everyday objects such as books to visually demonstrate these concepts.

TACTILE LEARNING Some students may have difficulty visualizing rotations. Demonstrate rotations by having a volunteer tie one end of a piece of string to a tack and push the tack into the bulletin board. Another volunteer cuts a shape out of construction paper and tapes it to the other end of the

string. A third student moves the shape to different positions on the bulletin board, keeping the string taut.

ASSESSMENT Have students work in groups of three. Each student chooses one term: *rotation, translation,* or *reflection.* They write a description of the term in their own words, then create a drawing to illustrate the word. Group members then share and evaluate their definitions and illustrations.

3 Practice/Assess

EXERCISES *On Your Own*

Exercises 1–4 Challenge students to use a computer graphics program to draw their responses.

Exercises 6–9 Students may also enjoy using a computer graphics program to draw the answers to these exercises. If students draw answers by hand, allow them to use mirrors to check their answers.

▼2 *Exploring Rotations*

A **rotation** turns, or rotates, a shape. Imagine you have a cutout of the letter E, which you place on a piece of cardboard. Suppose you insert a pin through the corner, as shown by the black dot at the right.

Point of Rotation

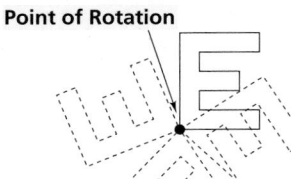

11. ▪*Writing* Describe each image of the letter E as you rotate the cutout once around the point of rotation. Each image is congruent to the original figure.

A rotation can be described in terms of the number of degrees by which the original figure has been rotated.

12. ▪*Reasoning* Suppose you rotate the letter E so it is back where it started. How many degrees have you turned it? 360°

■ **EXAMPLE 2**

Which of the following is a rotation of the shape at the right?

A.  **B.**  **C.**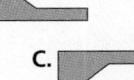

Imagine you place a pin at any point on the shape. Picture some stages of the rotation.

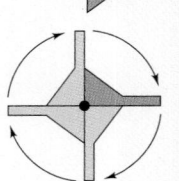

Shape B is the only one that you will see. Shape A is a reflection over a vertical line. Shape C is a reflection over a horizontal line.

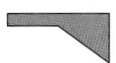 is a rotation of .

13. ✓*Try It Out* Which of the following is a rotation of the figure at the right? C

A.  **B.** **C.**

Now you may assign Exercises 15–23.

WRITING **Exercise 11** Discuss with students which examples would best illustrate translation and reflection. For instance, a square would not be a good example to use.

EXTENSION If you have block scheduling or extended class periods, challenge students to draw three-dimensional models of rotations and reflections on a two-dimensional surface. They may want to use connecting cubes, modeling clay, or some other material to create the three-dimensional models.

WRAP UP

IDENTIFYING THE BIG IDEA Ask students to explain translations, reflections, and rotations and to draw examples of each.

PORTFOLIO Share with students the criteria you will use to assess their work in portfolios, as well as how you plan to use the results. Students should understand how the rubrics are used to assess their work, how each piece in the portfolio counts, and how

the scores they get in their portfolios will affect their overall evaluation.

LESSON QUIZ

1. Draw two translations of the shape.

Check students' drawings.

EXERCISES *On Your Own*

1–4. Check students' work. Solutions should show each figure in two different upright positions.
Draw two translations of each shape.

1.  **2.**  **3.**  **4.**

5. *Interior Design* Describe all the translations of the figure in the fabric shown below.   up and left, up and right, down and left, down and right

Draw a reflection of each shape. Use the dashed line as the line of reflection.   7, 9. See margin.

6. 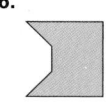 **7.** 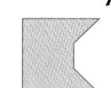 **8.** 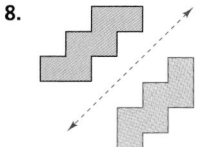 **9.**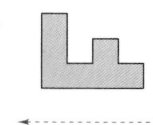

10. The art at the right shows part of a figure and part of its reflection. Copy the diagram. Complete the figure. Then complete the image.

11. *Writing* Describe how translations and reflections are alike and how they are different. Include examples.
See margin.

Tell whether each shows a translation or a reflection.

12. 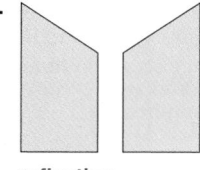 **13.**  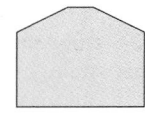 **14.**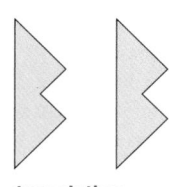

reflection   translation   translation

pages 373–374   On Your Own

7.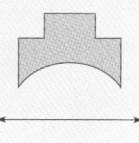

9.

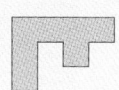

11. They are alike in that their images are congruent to the original figure and they occupy a new space. They are different in that a reflection is a mirror image of the original and a translation is the original figure moved, but not flipped.

373

PRACTICE

Practice 8-11 *Slides, Flips, and Turns*

Draw two translations of each shape. Sample answers shown.

1. 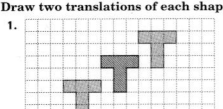   2.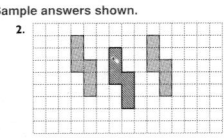

Draw the reflection of each shape. Use the dashed line as the line of reflection.

3. 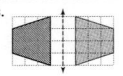   4.   5.

Tell whether each shows a translation or a reflection.

6.   7. 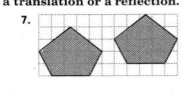   8.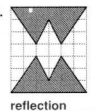

   reflection   translation   reflection

Are the shapes of each of the following rotations the shape at the right? Write *yes* or *no*.

9.   10.   11.   12.

   yes   no   yes   no

In copymaster and workbook formats

RETEACHING

Reteaching 8-11 *Slides, Flips, and Turns*

In a **translation**, or slide, every point on a figure moves in the same direction and the same distance.

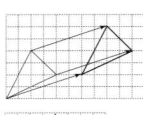

In a **reflection**, or flip, a figure is flipped across a line. The new image is a mirror image of the original figure.

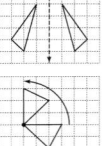

In a **rotation**, a figure is turned, or rotated about a point. To draw the **image** of this triangle, first draw the image of each vertex point. Then connect the three image points.

Draw a translation of each triangle. See sample drawings.

1. 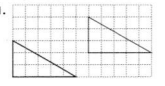   2.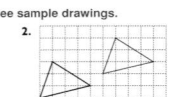

For each triangle, draw the reflection over the line shown. See sample drawings.

3. 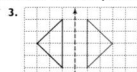   4.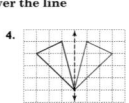

Circle all rotations of the first shape.

5.

ENRICHMENT

ⓜinds on Math Transparency

8-11

How many parallelograms can you find in the figure below?

13 parallelograms

See *Solution Key* for worked-out answers.

374

2. Draw a reflection of the shape. Use the dashed line as the line of reflection.

a.

b.

3. Decide which figures are a rotation of the shape. **a. and b.**

c.

Decide if each figure is a rotation of the shape at the right.

15. 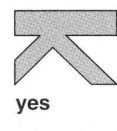   16.  **no**   17.  **yes**

   yes

18.    19.    20.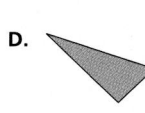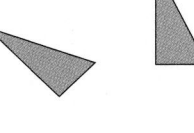

   yes   **no**   **no**

21. Identify all rotations of the shape at the right.   **A, B, C, D, E**

A. 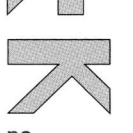   B.   C.   D.

E.   F.    G. 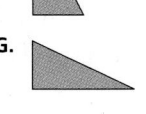   H.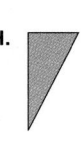

22. *Open-ended* Design a wallpaper pattern that consists of translations, reflections, and rotations of one basic figure. **Check students' work.**

23. *Reasoning* Why are rotations also called *turns*? **You turn a shape to show a rotation.**

> **◆ PORTFOLIO**
> Make a summary of the new terms you have learned in this chapter. Illustrate each term with a labeled diagram when possible.

Mixed Review

Find each difference. Write the answer in simplest form.
(Lesson 6-5)

24. $14\frac{1}{3} - 5\frac{2}{9}$ $9\frac{1}{9}$ 25. $25 - 17\frac{2}{3}$ $7\frac{1}{3}$ 26. $27\frac{1}{2} - 5\frac{3}{4}$ $21\frac{3}{4}$ 27. $9\frac{3}{5} - 4\frac{1}{5}$ $5\frac{2}{5}$ 28. $19\frac{3}{5} - 6\frac{7}{10}$ $12\frac{9}{10}$

Write each number in words. *(Lesson 3-2)*

29. seventy-three hundredths
30. nine thousandths
31. three hundred eighty-six and nine hundred eight thousandths
32. four thousand, two hundred seventy-three and fifteen hundred
33. four hundred seven thousand, six hundred eighty-three and seven hundredths
34. three thousand, nine hundred two hundred-thousandths

29. 0.73   30. 0.009   31. 386.908   32. 4,273.15   33. 407,683.07   34. 0.03902

35. *Choose a Strategy* Eight people shake hands with each of the others exactly once. What is the total number of handshakes exchanged? **28 handshakes**

PROJECT DAY You may wish to plan a project day on which students share their completed projects. Encourage students to explain their process as well as their product.

PROJECT NOTEBOOK Ask students to review their project work and bring their notebooks up to date.

Have students review their methods for designing and constructing their puzzles.

SCORING RUBRIC

3 Your puzzle includes the ten required shapes as well as the necessary congruent and similar triangles. Your puzzle is carefully made and includes a list of the triangles and polygons you used.

2 Your puzzle meets at least nine of the twelve requirements listed in the project links. Your list of the triangles and polygons in your puzzle is adequate, and your puzzle is attractive.

1 You leave out more than three of the required shapes in your puzzle, you incorrectly identify shapes in your list, or you pay little attention to the appearance of your finished puzzle.

0 You do not complete a puzzle, or you leave out most of the required triangles and polygons.

FINISHING THE CHAPTER PROJECT

CHAPTER PROJECT

Puzzling Pictures

Materials/Manipulatives
- cardboard
- picture or photograph
- scissors
- paste or glue

Create a Puzzle The Project Link questions on pages 343, 347, 356, and 363 will help you to complete your project. Here is a checklist to help you gather the parts of your project together.

- ✔ list of geometric shapes
- ✔ different types of triangles
- ✔ list of polygons
- ✔ congruent and similar triangles

Your finished tangram should have 8–12 polygonal pieces. Your practice puzzles were drawn on paper. Redraw your final design on a rectangular piece of thin cardboard. Paste a piece of wall paper, a magazine picture, a photograph, or a drawing on the other side of the cardboard. Cut out the pieces of your puzzle.

Reflect and Revise

Make a checklist of the requirements for your puzzle. Use the checklist to see if your tangram satisfies all the requirements. How few pieces can you have and still satisfy all the requirements?

Exchange puzzles with a classmate and put them together as quickly as possible.

Web Extension

Prentice Hall's Internet site contains information you might find helpful as you complete your project. Visit www.phschool.com/mgm1/ch8 for some links and ideas related to puzzles.

STUDENT SELF-ASSESSMENT SURVEY

Chapter 8 Student Self-Assessment Survey

1. Now that you have finished this chapter, think about what you have learned about geometry. Check each topic that you feel confident you understand.

_____ identify and use points, lines, segments, and rays (8-1)
_____ investigate parallel and skew lines (8-1)
_____ estimate and measure angles (8-2)
_____ classify angles as acute, right, obtuse, or straight (8-2)
_____ identify congruent, complementary, supplementary, interior, and exterior angles (8-3)
_____ identify triangles as right, obtuse, or acute (8-4)
_____ identify triangles as equilateral, isosceles, or scalene (8-4)
_____ identify different types of polygons (8-5)
_____ classify quadrilaterals (8-6)
_____ use logical reasoning to solve problems (8-7)
_____ decide whether figures are similar or congruent (8-8)
_____ decide whether a figure has line symmetry (8-9)
_____ identify and work with parts of a circle (8-10)
_____ work with translations, reflections, and rotations (8-11)

2. Before the Chapter Assessment, I need to review _____

3. a. Check one. In general, I thought this chapter was

_____ a snap _____ easy _____ average _____ hard _____ a monster
   b. Why do you feel this way?

4. In this chapter, I did my best work on _____

5. In this chapter, I had trouble with _____

6. Check each one that applies. Now that I've spent some time studying geometric figures, I think they are
_____ important _____ boring _____ useful _____ fun
_____ a waste of time _____ confusing _____ tricky _____ interesting

7. One place outside the classroom where people use geometry is

Vocabulary/Symbols

acute angle, acute triangle, angle, central angles, chords, collinear, complementary angles, congruent angles, congruent segments, congruent, convex, corresponding parts, degree, diameters, equilateral triangle, exterior angles, horizontal, image, interior angles, isosceles triangle, line, line of reflection, line of symmetry, line symmetry, noncollinear, obtuse angle, obtuse triangle, parallel lines, parallel segments, parallelogram, perpendicular, plane, point, point of rotation, polygon, radius, ray, reflection, rhombus, right angle, right triangle, rotation, scalene triangle, segment, sides, similar, skew lines, straight angle, supplementary angles, translation, transversal, trapezoid, vertex, vertical

Materials/Manipulatives

- dot paper

Resources

 Student Edition

Extra Practice, p. 529
Glossary/Study Guide

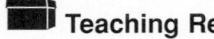 **Teaching Resources**

Chapter Support File, Ch. 8
- Student Self-Assessment Survey
Glossary, Spanish Resources
Tools for Studying Smarter

376

WRAP UP

Exercises 1 and 2 Have students list the new terms in these two exercises from this chapter. Then ask them to write their definitions before answering the exercises.

ASSESSMENT Have students sketch six triangles, one for each classification—acute, obtuse, right, equilateral, isosceles, and scalene.

Exercise 7 Students can work backward and draw two equilateral triangles that share a side.

WRITING Exercise 11 Ask students to draw a rhombus and a square and label their lines of symmetry. Have them include the drawings with their written descriptions.

Exercise 15 Have students compare their drawings and tell how they are different or the same.

Remind students that the new mathematical terms in this chapter are defined in the Glossary/Study Guide in the back of the book.

---

8 WRAP UP

Points, Lines, Planes, and Angles 8-1, 8-2, 8-3

A **point** has no size, only location. A **line** continues without end in opposite directions. A **plane** is a flat surface that extends indefinitely in four directions. A **segment** has two endpoints. A **ray** is a part of a line with one endpoint.

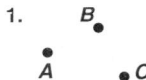

If a line can be drawn through a set of points, the points are **collinear**. **Parallel lines** are lines in the same plane that do not intersect. **Skew lines** are lines that lie in different planes.

An **angle** is made up of two rays with a common endpoint. **Complementary angles** have measures whose sum is 90°. **Supplementary angles** have measures whose sum is 180°. **Congruent angles** are angles that have the same measure.

You can classify angles as **acute**, **right**, **obtuse**, or **straight**.

1. Draw three noncollinear points A, B, and C.   2. Draw parallel lines $\overleftrightarrow{JK}$ and $\overleftrightarrow{MN}$.

3. How many segments are in the figure at the right? How many rays are in the figure? How many lines are in the figure?

3 segments; 6 rays; 1 line

Classify each angle as *acute, right, obtuse,* or *straight*.

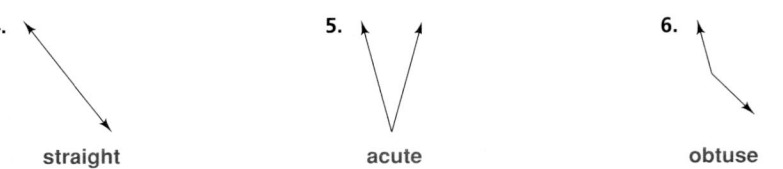

4. straight   5. acute   6. obtuse

Triangles, Polygons, and Quadrilaterals 8-4, 8-5, 8-6

You can classify triangles by their angles as **acute**, **obtuse**, or **right**, and by their sides as **equilateral**, **isosceles**, or **scalene**.

A **polygon** is a closed shape formed by line segments that do not cross.

7. **Choose A, B, C, or D.** When $\overline{XZ}$ is drawn in parallelogram $WXYZ$, two congruent equilateral triangles are formed. What kind of figure is $WXYZ$?   **B**

A. rectangle   B. rhombus   C. trapezoid   D. square

━━ Chapter 8 Assessment • Form A

Use the figure below to answer Exercises 1–3.
Sample answers given.

Answers

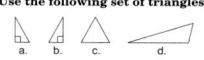

1. Name 3 different rays.

   1. $\overrightarrow{AB}$ or $\overrightarrow{AC}$, $\overrightarrow{BC}$, $\overrightarrow{BD}$, $\overrightarrow{BE}$

2. Name 3 different angles.

   2. ∠ABD, ∠ABE, ∠ABC, ∠DBE, ∠DBC, ∠EBC

3. Identify one acute angle and one obtuse angle.

   3. ∠EBC acute
      ∠DBE acute
      ∠ABE obtuse

4. Draw a trapezoid with two acute angles and two obtuse angles.

   4.
      obtuse   obtuse
      acute   acute

5. List all the names that apply to a quadrilateral with four congruent sides and four right angles. Choose from parallelogram, rectangle, rhombus, square, and trapezoid.

   5. parallelogram
      rectangle
      rhombus
      square

Complete Exercises 6–8 with *sometimes*, *always*, or *never*.

6. Three points are ■ collinear.

   6. sometimes

7. An acute triangle ■ has 3 acute angles.

   7. always

8. Two obtuse angles are ■ complementary.

   8. never

Use the following set of triangles to answer Exercises 9–11.

a.   b.   c.   d.

9. List a pair of triangles that appear to be similar.

   9. a, b

10. Classify each triangle as *acute*, *obtuse*, or *right*.

    10. a, b rt; c acute; d obtuse

11. Which of the triangles appears to have line symmetry? Sketch in the lines of symmetry.

    11. c

Assessment

Chapter 8 Assessment • Form A (continued)

Use the figure at the right to answer Exercises 12–14.

12. Name a diameter.

    12. $\overline{AC}$

13. If the length of $\overline{BF}$ is 4 cm, how long is a diameter of circle F?

    13. 8 cm

14. Name 3 different central angles.

    14. Samples: ∠AFB, ∠BFC, ∠CFD, ∠DFE, ∠EFA

Choose A, B, C, or D.

15. Which figure is not a rotation of this figure?

    15. C

    A.   B.

    C.   D.

Choose a Strategy

16. Of the 25 students in Ms. Duke's Spanish class, 9 play in the school band and 8 are in the choir. Four have formed their own quartet and do not participate in either the school choir or band. If 3 of the students are in both the choir and the band, how many students do not participate in any of the three activities?

    16. 7 students do not participate in any of the three activities

    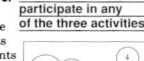

Writing

17. Draw two lines and a transversal. Label your diagram. Then identify two supplementary interior angles. Explain your choice.

    Sample: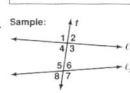

    ∠4 and ∠3, ∠5 and ∠6; they are supplementary because their sum is 180° and interior because they are inside ℓ_1 and ℓ_2.

You can often use *Logical Reasoning* to solve problems.

8. Of 26 students, 3 read *The Yearling* and *Where the Red Fern Grows*, 11 read only the first book, and 7 students read neither book. How many read only the second book?
   5 students

Figures that have the same size and shape are **congruent**. **Similar** figures have the same shape, but not necessarily the same size. A **line of symmetry** divides a figure into two congruent parts.

Do the triangles appear to be congruent, similar, or neither?

9.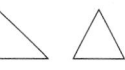

   similar

10.

    neither

11. *Writing* Describe the lines of symmetry of a rhombus and a square. **Each diagonal of a rhombus is its line of symmetry. A square also has two lines of symmetry which are the perpendicular bisectors of each pair of opposite sides.**

A **circle** is the set of points in a plane that are the same distance from a given point. A **radius** has one endpoint at the center and one endpoint on the circle. A **diameter** has two endpoints on the circle and passes through the center. A **chord** has two endpoints on the circle.

Name the following for circle *O*.

12. three radii
    OV, OX, OY

13. a diameter
    VX

14. three chords
    VW, VX, WY

A figure can be moved to make a **translation** (slide), a **reflection** (flip), or a **rotation** (turn).

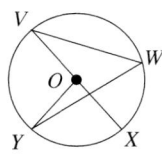

15. *Open-ended* Draw a translation, a reflection, and a rotation of the shape at the right.
    Check students' work.

377

Chapter 8 Assessment • Form B

Choose the best answer. Circle A, B, C, or D.

1. Which set of line segments are pictured in the figure?
   A. $\overline{BD}, \overline{BE}, \overline{BC}$
   B. $\overline{AB}, \overline{ED}, \overline{BC}$
   C. $\overline{BA}, \overline{AE}, \overline{AD}$
   D. $\overline{EB}, \overline{ED}, \overline{EA}$

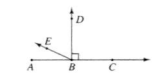

2. Which is an obtuse angle in the figure?
   A. $\angle ABD$ **B.** $\angle ABE$ **C.** $\angle ABC$ **D.** $\angle EBC$

3. Which is a right angle in the figure?
   A. $\angle ABD$ **B.** $\angle ABE$ **C.** $\angle ABC$ **D.** $\angle EBC$

4. Which is impossible to draw?
   A. a trapezoid with 1 acute angle and 1 obtuse angle
   B. a trapezoid with 2 acute angles
   C. a trapezoid with 3 acute angles
   D. a trapezoid with 2 obtuse angles

5. Which name does not appear to describe the polygon *JKLM* below?
   A. parallelogram **B.** square
   C. quadrilateral **D.** rhombus

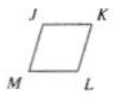

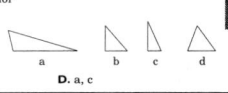

6. Which figures appear to be similar?

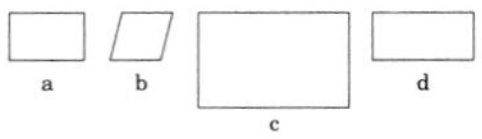

   a b c d

   A. a, b **B.** a, c **C.** c, d **D.** b, c

7. Which of the following is not a type of triangle?
   A. acute **B.** equilateral
   C. quadrilateral **D.** right isosceles

8. Which word describes two angles with measures 65 and 25?
   A. exterior **B.** complementary
   C. supplementary **D.** interior

9. Which figures appear to be right triangles?

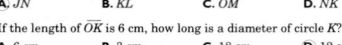

   a b c d

   A. a, b **B.** b, c **C.** c, d **D.** a, c

Chapter 8 Assessment • Form B (continued)

10. Which of the following words does not have a line of symmetry?
    A. COB **B.** MUM **C.** DUDE **D.** DICE

11. Which are all radii of circle *K*?
    A. $\overline{JK}, \overline{JN}, \overline{JO}$ **B.** $\overline{KJ}, \overline{KN}, \overline{KM}$
    C. $\overline{JO}, \overline{JL}, \overline{MN}$ **D.** $\overline{OL}, \overline{LM}, \overline{MN}$

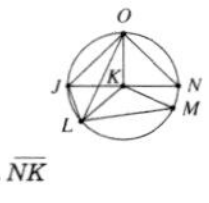

12. Which names a diameter in the figure?
    A. $\overline{JN}$ **B.** $\overline{KL}$ **C.** $\overline{OM}$ **D.** $\overline{NK}$

13. If the length of $\overline{OK}$ is 6 cm, how long is a diameter of circle *K*?
    A. 6 cm **B.** 3 cm **C.** 18 cm **D.** 12 cm

14. Which are both central angles of circle *K*?
    A. $\angle JKL, \angle KMN$ **B.** $\angle KLJ, \angle KNM$
    C. $\angle JKL, \angle MKN$ **D.** $\angle JKO, \angle JLK$

15. Which are both chords of circle *K*?
    A. $\overline{JN}, \overline{KM}$ **B.** $\overline{ML}, \overline{NM}$ **C.** $\overline{JK}, \overline{KO}$ **D.** $\overline{JO}, \overline{JK}$

16. What is the name given a polygon with 10 sides?
    A. hexagon **B.** tenagon
    C. pentagon **D.** decagon

17. Which of the following is a reflection of ?

    A. **B.**

    C. **D.**

Choose a Strategy

18. Of a class of 23 students, 10 are in the science club. Eight of the students are in the math club and 3 are in only the English club. If 2 of the students in the science club are also in the math club, how many students do not belong to a club at all?
    A. 19 **B.** 4 **C.** 2 **D.** 21

 **Teaching Resources**

Chapter Support File, Ch. 8, and Spanish Resources

 Teacher's Edition

See pp. 324C–D for Assessment Options.

 **Teaching Resource Software**
• Computer Item Generator, Ch. 8

378

ASSESSMENT

WRITING EXERCISES allow students to describe more fully their thinking and understanding of the concepts they've learned. **Exercise 5** is a writing exercise.

8 ASSESSMENT

1. Draw three noncollinear points and label them *X*, *Y*, and *Z*. Draw $\overleftrightarrow{XY}$. Then draw a line through *Z* that appears to be parallel to $\overleftrightarrow{XY}$. **See back of book.**

2. What is the best estimate for the measure of $\angle PQR$? **B**
   A. 80°
   B. 100°
   C. 135°
   D. 150°

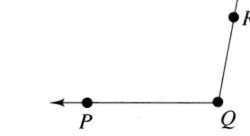

3. Measure each angle. Classify each as *acute*, *obtuse*, or *right*.

   a. **90°, right**   b. **72°, acute**

   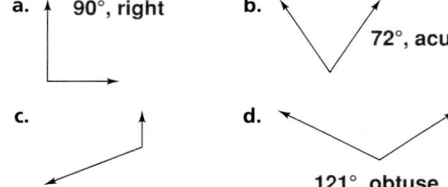

   c. **112°, obtuse**   d. **121°, obtuse**

4. What is the best classification for triangle *ABC*?

   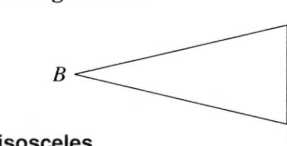

   isosceles

5. *Writing* In the polygons below, *diagonals* are drawn from one vertex. How many diagonals can you draw from one vertex of a hexagon? From one vertex of a 7-sided polygon? From one vertex of a 100-sided polygon? Explain your reasoning. **See back of book.**

   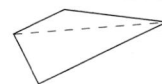

6. Draw a circle *O* and any chord $\overline{AB}$ that is not a diameter. Draw $\overline{OA}, \overline{OB}$, and the radius that is perpendicular to $\overline{AB}$. Make as many statements as you can about the angles, segments, and triangles in your diagram.
   See back of book.

7. In order to conclude that *MNOP* is a rhombus, what do you have to know? **C**

   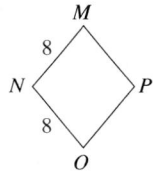

   A. $\overline{MO}$ is perpendicular to $\overline{NP}$.
   B. $\overline{MO}$ has length 8.
   C. $\overline{MP}$ and $\overline{PO}$ have length 8.
   D. $\overline{NP}$ and $\overline{MO}$ are congruent.

8. Of the 16 boys in Mrs. Stern's math class, seven play soccer and five are in the band. Four play football, but they do not participate in any other activity. Two students play soccer *and* play in the band. How many students participate in none of the three activities? **2 students**

9. a. Draw two triangles that appear to be congruent.
   b. Draw two triangles that appear to be similar but not congruent.
   9a–b. Check students' work.

10. Draw a quadrilateral with the given number of lines of symmetery.
    a. 0 b. 1 c. 2 d. 4
    10a–d. See back of book.

11. Draw a translation, a reflection, and a rotation of the shape at the right.
    See back of book.

Item	Review Topic	Ch
1, 10	Reading and understanding graphs	1
2	Writing number expressions	2
3	Ordering decimals	3
4	Relating fractions and percents	7
5	Multiplying decimals	4

Item	Review Topic	Ch
6	Order of operations	4
7	Solving problems with too much information	4
8	Solving equations	2
9	Using proportions	7

8 CUMULATIVE REVIEW

Choose the best answer.

1. What information does the circle graph below *not* tell you?　**C**

A. Jen purchased lunch more often than she brought it from home.
B. Jen purchased hot and cold lunches about as often.
C. Jen brought lunch from home more often than she purchased cold lunch.
D. Jen purchased hot lunch more often than she brought lunch from home.

Jen's School Lunches

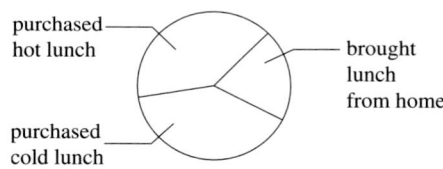

purchased hot lunch — brought lunch from home — purchased cold lunch

2. If bagels cost $2 per dozen, how would you find the cost of 5 bagels?　**B**

A. $2 × 5 × 12　　B. $2 ÷ 12 × 5
C. $2 × 12 ÷ 5　　D. $2 ÷ 5 × 12

3. Which set of decimals below is ordered from least to greatest?　**B**

A. 0.2, 0.02, 0.22　　B. 0.15, 0.51, 1.05
C. 0.24, 0.3, 0.05　　D. 0.49, 0.4, 0.05

4. The Amazon River in South America carries one sixth of Earth's water that flows into oceans. About what percent of the water that flows into oceans is this?　**A**

A. 17%　B. 12.5%　C. 10%　D. 6%

5. If $31.2 × \blacksquare = 0.00312$, $\blacksquare$ must be—　**D**

A. 10,000　B. 1,000　C. 0.001　D. 0.0001

6. What is the value of $3 + 4 × 2^3$?　**C**

A. 515　B. 56　C. 35　D. 27

7. What information do you *not* need to know in order to solve the problem?　**B**

At Ma's Restaurant, a cheese sandwich costs 99¢, a salad costs 20¢ less than a cheese sandwich, and milk costs 75¢. If you have $3.00, can you buy two cheese sandwiches and milk for lunch?

A. the cost of a cheese sandwich
B. the cost of a salad
C. the cost of milk
D. You have $3.00.

8. To solve a puzzle, you must solve the equation $4x = 8.8$. The solution is—　**A**

A. 2.2　B. 4.8　C. 22　D. 35.2

9. Which of the following is *not* equivalent to a rate of 60 miles per hour?　**C**

A. 180 miles in 3 hours
B. 90 miles in 1.5 hours
C. 240 miles in 3 hours
D. 30 miles in 30 minutes

10. What can you conclude from the line plot below?　**A**

A. Most absences occurred on Monday and Friday.
B. The mean number of absences per day was 2.5.
C. Only one person was absent on Wednesday because of a field trip.
D. At least one person was absent twice that week.

Number of Students Absent

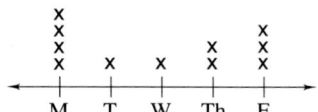

M　T　W　Th　F

Choose the best answer. Circle A, B, C, or D.

1. What is the LCM (least common multiple) of 5 and 6?
A. 11　　**B.** 30
C. 60　　D. 90

2. Which list shows the fractions $\frac{3}{5}, \frac{2}{9}, \frac{5}{9}, \frac{4}{5}$ from least to greatest?
A. $\frac{2}{9}, \frac{3}{5}, \frac{4}{5}, \frac{5}{9}$　　B. $\frac{3}{5}, \frac{2}{9}, \frac{5}{9}, \frac{4}{5}$
C. $\frac{4}{5}, \frac{3}{5}, \frac{5}{9}, \frac{2}{9}$　　**D.** $\frac{2}{9}, \frac{3}{5}, \frac{5}{9}, \frac{4}{5}$

Use the figure below to answer Exercises 7–10.

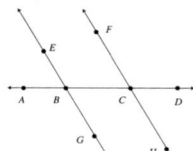

Use the table for Exercises 3 and 4.

Number on Number Cube	Tally
1	卌 卌
2	卌 ||
3	卌 卌
4	卌 |||
5	卌	
6	卌 卌

3. How many times was the number cube rolled?
A. 10　　**B.** 50
C. 21　　D. 30

4. What was the greatest number of times any one number was rolled?
A. 6　　B. 20
C. 10　　D. 4

5. Use mental math to find 14% of 200.
A. 14　　**B.** 28
C. 56　　D. 70

6. Which two fractions are equivalent to $\frac{2}{6}$?
A. $\frac{1}{3}, \frac{4}{12}$　　B. $\frac{4}{12}, \frac{8}{18}$
C. $\frac{6}{18}, \frac{10}{24}$　　D. $\frac{8}{18}, \frac{12}{24}$

7. Which are noncollinear points?
A. A, B, D　　B. E, B, G
C. F, C, H　　**D.** A, G, F

8. Which angles appear to be obtuse?
A. $\angle ABG, \angle ABE$　　B. $\angle BCH, \angle BCF$
C. $\angle FCD, \angle EBC$　　D. $\angle EBA, \angle FCB$

9. Which are intersecting lines?
A. $\overrightarrow{EG}$ and $\overrightarrow{FH}$　　**B.** $\overrightarrow{EG}$ and $\overrightarrow{AD}$
C. $\overrightarrow{EB}$ and $\overrightarrow{FC}$　　D. $\overrightarrow{BG}$ and $\overrightarrow{CH}$

10. Which angles are supplementary?
A. $\angle ABG, \angle BCH$　　B. $\angle DCH, \angle DCB$
C. $\angle ABE, \angle ABG$　　D. $\angle ABE, \angle DCH$

11. Which of the following describes a scalene triangle?
A. A triangle with 2 congruent sides
B. A triangle with 3 congruent sides
C. A triangle with no congruent sides
D. A triangle with 4 congruent sides

Assessment

Chapter 8 Cumulative Review (continued)

12. Suppose $\frac{5}{8}$ of the area of a garden is flowers. Zinnias cover $\frac{3}{4}$ of the flower area. What portion of the garden is zinnias?
A. $\frac{8}{12}$　　**B.** $\frac{15}{32}$
C. $\frac{20}{24}$　　D. $\frac{20}{32}$

13. Find the difference $\frac{11}{12} - \frac{9}{12}$.
A. $\frac{2}{6}$　　B. $\frac{1}{3}$
C. $\frac{3}{12}$　　**D.** $\frac{1}{6}$

14. A cookie recipe calls for $2\frac{3}{4}$ c of flour. Hedi plans to triple the recipe. How much flour will she need? Write the answer as a mixed number in simplest form.
A. $4\frac{1}{4}$ c　　B. $6\frac{3}{4}$ c
C. $8\frac{1}{4}$ c　　D. 9 c

15. 24 c is how many quarts?
A. 2 qt　　B. 4 qt
C. 6 qt　　D. 12 qt

16. Which ratio compares 10 girls to 12 boys?
A. 5 to 6　　B. 5 to 11
C. $\frac{6}{5}$　　D. 10:22

17. What pair shows $\frac{3}{5}$ as a percent and as a decimal?
A. 35%, 0.35　　B. 30%, 0.3
C. 53%, 0.53　　**D.** 60%, 0.6

Use the figure below for Exercises 18–19.

18. Which are *not* chords of circle E?
A. $\overline{AB}, \overline{AE}$　　B. $\overline{AB}, \overline{BC}$
C. $\overline{AD}, \overline{AB}$　　D. $\overline{BC}, \overline{DC}$

19. Which is an obtuse central angle of circle E?
A. $\angle AEB$　　B. $\angle AED$
C. $\angle DEC$　　D. $\angle DEA$

20. The length of a road on a map is 6 in. The actual length of the road is 36 mi. What is the scale of the map?
A. 1 in.:6 mi　　B. 1 in.:12 mi
C. 1 in.:18 mi　　D. 1 in.:36 mi

Choose a Strategy

21. Six students plan to work in pairs on their science projects, but they cannot decide on a partner. Their teacher told Tim, Susan, Anna, Maria, Matt, and Jake to figure out all the different pairs they could make. How many different pairs did they find?
A. 9 pairs　　B. 3 pairs
C. 15 pairs　　D. 21 pairs

Resources

 Teaching Resources

Chapter Support File, Ch. 8
• Cumulative Review

 Teacher's Edition

See pp. 324C–D for Assessment Options.

379

CHAPTER OVERVIEW

To accommodate flexible scheduling, most lessons are divided into parts. Assignment Options are given in the Teacher's Edition for each lesson.

Pages 382–385	**Lesson 9-1** **Estimating Area**
NCTM 1, 2, 3, 4, 5, 7, 12, 13	**Key term:** square units

Pages 387–391	**Lesson 9-2** **Algebra: Perimeters and Areas of Rectangles**
NCTM 2, 3, 4, 5, 8, 12, 13	Part 1 Measuring Rectangles Part 2 Measuring Squares **Alternative Activity** 9-2 ▼ **Project Link**

Pages 392–396	**Lesson 9-3** **Areas of Parallelograms and Triangles**
NCTM 2, 3, 4, 5, 8, 12, 13	Part 1 Areas of Parallelograms and Triangles Part 2 Areas of Complex Figures **Key term:** altitude **Journal** ☑ **Checkpoint 1**

Pages 414–417	**Lesson 9-7** **Exploring Surface Area**
NCTM 2, 3, 5, 8, 12, 13	**Key term:** surface area (SA) **Alternative Activity** 9-7 **Journal**

Pages 418–422	**Lesson 9-8** **Algebra: Volume of a Rectangular Prism**
NCTM 3, 4, 5, 7, 8, 12	Part 1 Finding Volume Part 2 Finding a Dimension **Key term:** volume (V) ☑ **Checkpoint 2**

Pages 424–426	**Lesson 9-9** **Problem Solving Strategy**
NCTM 1, 4, 6, 12	Make a Model

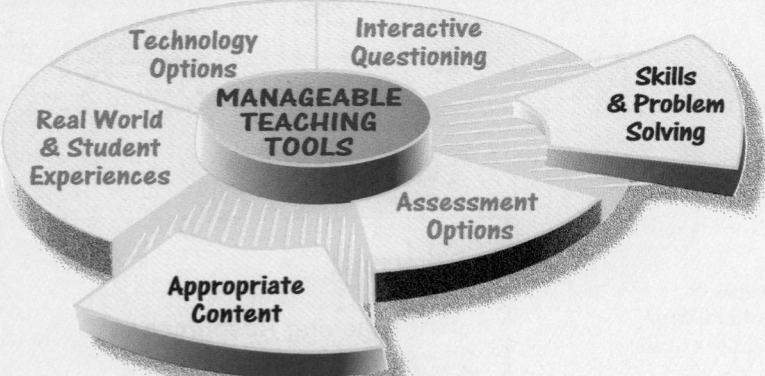

Technology Options · Interactive Questioning · MANAGEABLE TEACHING TOOLS · Skills & Problem Solving · Real World & Student Experiences · Assessment Options · Appropriate Content

Pacing Options

This chart suggests pacing only for the core lessons and their parts. It is provided merely as a possible guide. It will help you determine how much time you have in your schedule to cover other features, such as the Chapter Project, Math Toolboxes, Wrap Up, and Assessment.

	1 Class Period	1 Class Period	1 Class Period
Traditional (40–45 min class periods)	9–1	9–2 ▼ 9–2 ②	9–3 ▼
Block Scheduling (90 min class periods)	9–1 9–2 ▼	9–2 ② 9–3 ▼	9–3 ② 9–4 ▼ 9–4 ②

NCTM STANDARDS

1 Problem Solving	6 Number Systems and Number Theory	10 Statistics
2 Communication	7 Computation and Estimation	11 Probability
3 Reasoning	8 Patterns and Functions	12 Geometry
4 Mathematical Connections	9 Algebra	13 Measurement
5 Number and Number Relationships		

Pages 398–402

Lesson 9-4
Technology: Gathering Data to Explore π

NCTM
1, 2, 3, 4, 5, 7, 8, 12, 13

Part 1   Estimating π and Circumference
Part 2   Using π to Find Circumference
Key terms: circumference, pi (π)

Alternative Activity 9-4

▼ **Project Link**

Pages 403–407

Lesson 9-5
Area of a Circle

NCTM
1, 2, 3, 4, 5, 7, 8, 12, 13

Part 1   Finding Area of a Circle
Part 2   Finding Areas of Circles and Polygons

▼ **Project Link**

Pages 408–412

Lesson 9-6
Three-Dimensional Figures

NCTM
2, 3, 12

Key terms: three-dimensional figures, faces, prism, bases, edge, vertex, cube, pyramid, cylinder, cone, sphere, net

▼ **Project Link**

Math at Work

Optional Materials and Manipulatives

centimeter graph paper (9-1, 9-2, 9-3, 9-5, 9-6)	dot paper (9-3)	centimeter cubes (9-8)
square tiles (9-2)	string (9-4)	empty box (9-8)
ruler (9-2, 9-3, 9-4, 9-5, 9-7, 9-9)	compass (9-5)	pennies (9-9)
scissors (9-3, 9-5, 9-6)	tape (9-6)	Optional calculator use is integrated
	yardstick (9-7)	throughout the course.

---

ss d	1 Class Period	1 Class Period	1 Class Period	1 Class Period	1 Class Period	1 Class Period	1 Class Period	1 Class Period	1 Class Period	1 Class Period
	9–4 ▼2	9–5 ▼1	9–5 ▼2	9–6	9–7	9–7	9–8 ▼1	9–8 ▼2	9–9	
-7	9–8 ▼1 9–8 ▼2	9–9								

MEETING INDIVIDUAL NEEDS

Accommodating Diverse Learning Styles

In your Teacher's Edition, you will find suggestions as to how you can help students complete mathematical tasks in Chapter 9 by meeting individual needs and supporting various learning styles. Here are some examples:

VISUAL LEARNING
drawing cubes in two dimensions *(p. 409)*

TACTILE LEARNING
comparing circles cut out of paper *(p. 405)*

AUDITORY LEARNING
describing figures out loud *(p. 384)*

KINESTHETIC LEARNING
arranging carpet or floor tiles to create rectangles *(p. 387)*

EARLY FINISHERS
Performance-Based Project, MathBlaster® Mystery, Interdisciplinary Units

GIFTED AND TALENTED
designing house floor plans and calculating area *(p. 388)*

DIVERSITY researching ways other civilizations used math *(p. 406)*

ACQUIRING ENGLISH PROFICIENCY (AEP)
creating word maps for new terms *(p. 392)*

ASSESSING PROGRESS

A broad range of assessment tools are available to reach a variety of learners.

INFORMAL ASSESSMENT

Informal assessments provide day-to-day feedback to help give you a picture of conceptual understanding and skill development.

ONGOING ASSESSMENT is built into lesson instruction and the Teaching Notes of the Teacher's Edition.

In the Teacher's Edition
Lesson Quiz for every lesson

In the Student Edition
On Your Own, Mixed Review, Journal, Portfolio, Project Link, Chapter Wrap Up

Look for **Interactive Questions** within lessons that

▪ **BUILD UNDERSTANDING** with labels such as Analyze, Reasoning, Estimation, Writing, and Summarize

✔ **CHECK UNDERSTANDING** with the Try It Out label.

FORMAL ASSESSMENT

Formal assessment can occur before and after the chapter, as well as at natural breaking points in the chapter.

Checkpoints
Two forms of each self-assessment Checkpoints are available: one in the Student Edition and another in the Chapter Support File in the Teaching Resources box.

- Mid-Chapter Checkpoint 1, page 396
- End-of-Chapter Checkpoint 2, page 422

Chapter 9 Assessment, page 430.
Two alternative forms are available in the Chapter Support File. They may be used after a chapter has been completed, or as a pre-test and post-test comparison.

Cumulative Review, page 431.
Assesses skills and concepts in Chapters 1–9.
An alternative form is available in Chapter Support File.

Computer Item Generator for Chapter 9
Customized tests can be generated for each lesson and for mid-chapter and end-of-chapter assessments, and for pre- and post-test comparisons of achievement.

Interactive Questioning

Technology Options

MANAGEABLE TEACHING TOOLS

Skills & Problem Solving

Real World & Student Experiences

Appropriate Content

Assessment Options

CHAPTER PROJECT

The Chapter Project in the student edition provides a real-world connection to the math context of the chapter. The Teacher's Edition contains a scoring rubric.

Another performance-based Chapter Project with a scoring rubric can be found in the Chapter Support File in the Teaching Resources Box.

Name _____ Class _____ Date _____

Chapter 9 Performance Assessment

Park Design Contest

Jeanne Chilson has given her town a piece of land for a park. The land is in the shape of a rectangle 2,000 ft long and 1,000 ft wide. Jeanne is sponsoring a contest for the design of the park, with a generous prize for the winning design. The winning design must include the following:

- A place for people to picnic
- A place for people to play games
- An area with playground equipment for young children
- Trees for shade and flowers to make things beautiful
- Paths to walk on, baskets to throw trash in, and water fountains to drink from

Following is a list of some of the minimum space requirements for possible games and pieces of equipment:

- horseshoe court: 6 ft by 50 ft
- badminton court: 20 ft by 44 ft
- tennis court: 78 ft by 36 ft
- basketball court: 84 ft by 46 ft
- Olympic-size swimming pool: 165 ft by 69 ft
- soccer field: 330 ft by 240 ft
- swing set: 15 ft by 10 ft
- picnic table: 8 ft by 6 ft
- trash basket circle: 3 ft in diameter
- sand box: 12 ft by 12 ft

1. On a separate sheet of paper, draw your design for the park. Be sure to label the objects you include in your design.

2. You need to show Ms. Chilson that your design meets each of her requirements. Complete each exercise below.
  a. How many picnic tables did you include? _____
  b. Describe the areas that you have set aside for games.

Course 1 Chapter 9   44

Chapter 9 Performance Assessment Scoring Rubric

Exercise Points	Explanation
1.	(Note: All designs should include some labeling. Designs with no labels should receive one less point than they would otherwise earn.)
5	Design includes all five requirements and has a reasonable sense of scale.
4	Design includes all five requirements, but sense of scale weak or lacking OR design includes four requirements and has good sense of scale.
3	Design includes four requirements, but lacks scale OR has three requirements and good sense of scale.
2	Design includes three requirements, but lacks scale OR includes two requirements and sense of scale.
1	Design ignores most requirements and has weak or no scale.
0	No response
2.a.–e. 1	Relates design to requirement
0	No response OR no relationship

Excursion

(Note: All designs should include some labeling. Designs with no labels should receive one fewer point than they would otherwise earn.)

5	Identification of plan and location, a list of features, a design that includes the listed features; response is a reasonable/creative solution.
4	Response includes required elements, but is either not creative OR not particularly reasonable.
3	Response lacks one required element.
2	Response lacks two required elements.
1	Response does not contain required elements, but some effort has been made.
0	No response

Course 1 Chapter 9   46

Correlation to Standardized Tests

Lesson	STANDARDIZED TEST ITEMS					
	CAT5	CTBS/5 Terra Nova	ITBS	MAT7	SAT9	Your Local Test
9-1	Estimating Area			■	■	■	
9-2	Algebra: Perimeters and Areas of Rectangles	■	■	■	■	■	
9-3	Areas of Parallelograms and Triangles			■	■	■	
9-4	Technology: Gathering Data to Explore π					■	
9-5	Area of a Circle			■	■	■	
9-6	Three-Dimensional Figures				■		
9-7	Exploring Surface Area			■		■	
9-8	Algebra: Volume of a Rectangular Prism				■		
9-9	Problem Solving Strategy: Make a Model			■	■	■	

CAT5 California Achievement Test, 5th Edition
CTBS/5 Comprehensive Test of Basic Skills, 5th Edition
ITBS Iowa Test of Basic Skills, Form B
MAT 7 Metropolitan Achievement Test, 7th Edition
SAT9 Stanford Achievement Test, 9th Edition

MAKING CONNECTIONS

Technology Options
Interactive Questioning
MANAGEABLE TEACHING TOOLS
Skills & Problem Solving
Real World & Student Experiences
Appropriate Content
Assessment Options

TEAM TEACHING WITH PRENTICE HALL MATERIALS

MIDDLE GRADES MATH INTERDISCIPLINARY UNITS	INTERDISCIPLINARY EXPLORATIONS	SCIENCE EXPLORER L Life Science E Earth Science P Physical Science

• Sports: Activity 4
• Space Exploration: Activity 12
• Travel and Geography: Activity 5
	• *The Power of Patterns* pp. 26 & 27
	• *India Beyond the Golden Age* p. 26
		E Shapes of Crystals p. 406
		  Relative Humidity p. 504
		P Sec. 1-4 Tools of Measurement
		  Sec. 2-3 Volume and Density

Lesson	Interdisciplinary Connections	Real World Connections	Math Integration
9-1	Geography	Gardening	Geometry Measurement
9-2	Interior Design	Stamp Collecting Gardening Home Improvement Baby-sitting	Geometry Measurement
9-3	Geometry	Conservation	Geometry Measurement
9-4	Drafting	Entertainment Archery Technology Bicycles Pets	Geometry Measurement
9-5	Basketball	Communications Calendars Games	Geometry Measurement
9-6	Architecture	Sales	Geometry
9-7	Geometry	Package Design Construction	Geometry Measurement
9-8	Design	Food Swimming Pools Gardening	Algebra Geometry
9-9	Woodworking Literature	Coins Jobs Gardening Savings	Geometry

School to Home

MATERIALS:
tape
paper
pencil

English and Spanish versions are available in the Teacher's Communication Kit, Teacher's Resource box.

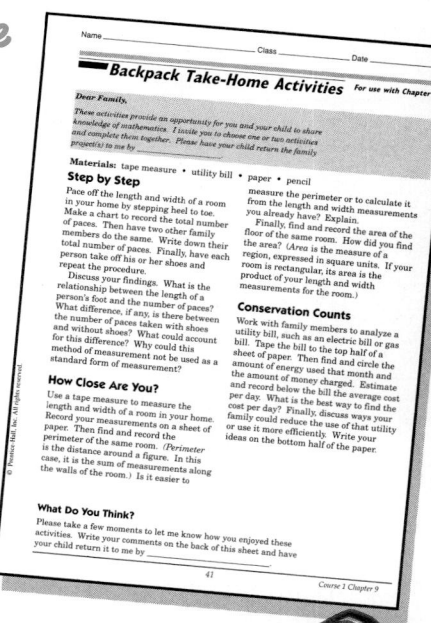

FOR THE STUDENT

Multimedia Math Hot Pages™
This interactive software and video package on CD-ROM integrates solid math content through a variety of media.

- Hot Page™ 24 (9-1)
- Hot Page™ 25 (9-3)
- Hot Page™ 26 (9-5)
- Hot Page™ 27 (9-6)

Math Labs
This software, available on both diskette and CD-ROM, includes on-screen Math Lab activities. Students use linkable, interactive tools to explore math concepts.

- Math Lab: Area of Rectangles and Squares

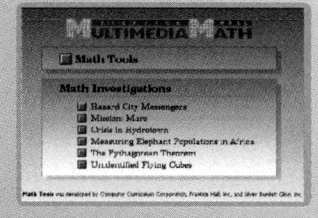

Multimedia Math Investigations
These in-depth interactive activities on CD-ROM develop real-world applications of mathematics. They allow students the opportunity to reinforce key concepts.

- Crisis in Hydrotown
- Unidentified Flying Cubes

Interactive Student Tutorial
Available on CD-ROM, this test preparation program contains self-tests with questions in standardized test format. Software includes electronic versions of the text lessons and the Math Tools and Math Labs.

MathBlaster® Mystery
This award-winning, interactive software program on CD-ROM can be used to maintain skills or to accommodate early finishers.

- Level: Earn 2 coins; Pay 6 coins
- Mission Mode (all lessons)
- Kitchen Comparisons (9-6, 9-8)
- Number Guesser (9-1)
- Equation Maker (9-2, 9-4, 9-7)
- Word Problems (9-3, 9-5, 9-9, Problem Solving Practice)

For Students
Support for the Chapter Project
A career-oriented link for Math at Work feature

www.phschool.com/math

For teachers
Curriculum Support
Product Information
Regional Support Information

FOR THE TEACHER

Computer Item Generator
Available on both CD-ROM and diskette, this software generates customized practice sheets, quizzes, and tests. It generates an unlimited supply of questions with varying levels of difficulty.

The Resource Pro™
Available on CD-ROM, this software can be used to customize and plan lessons.

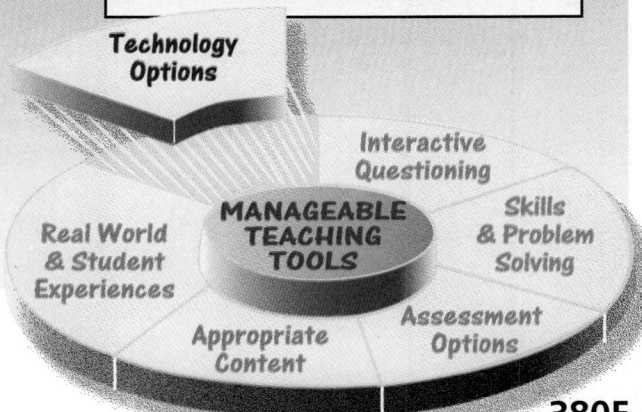

Technology Options

MANAGEABLE TEACHING TOOLS
- Interactive Questioning
- Skills & Problem Solving
- Assessment Options
- Appropriate Content
- Real World & Student Experiences

GEOMETRY AND MEASUREMENT

CONNECTING TO PRIOR LEARNING Ask students to share their experiences of finding information on the World Wide Web. Discuss with students their methods of searching for information on a topic. You may want to bring to class printouts of sample Web pages.

CULTURAL CONNECTIONS The development of the computer has drawn on centuries of mathematical thought and technological progress, from the ancient Chinese abacus to the modern-day silicon chip. Encourage students to look at a diverse range of Web sites when researching for their projects. Current applications of the computer are as diverse as its origins. Students can report their findings to the class.

INTERDISCIPLINARY CONNECTIONS Ask students: *How are geometry and measurement used to design newspaper pages?* Answers may vary. Sample: There is a given amount of space for text, advertisements, and graphics on the page. Pages are designed by the size of columns and space for art.

ABOUT THE PROJECT The Chapter Project allows students to use their understanding of geometry and measurement to evaluate and design a mock site for the World Wide Web.

Internet • For information and activities related to the Chapter Project, visit the Prentice Hall site at www.phschool.com/mgm1/ch9

Geometry and Measurement

9

WHAT YOU WILL LEARN IN THIS CHAPTER

• How to estimate and find areas of geometric figures

• How to find and use pi

• How to find surface area and volume of rectangular prisms

Ask students:

• *Have you ever used the World Wide Web to research a topic? What did you find?*

• *How do you think people who design Web sites can make their sites better?*

• *How would you design a Web site? What would be the topic of your site?*

PROJECT NOTEBOOK Encourage students to keep all project-related materials in a separate folder or notebook.

TRACKING THE PROJECT You may wish to have students read Finishing the Chapter Project on page 427 to help them get an overview of the project. Set benchmark deadlines for students to show you their work in progress.

CHAPTER PROJECT

THEME:
TECHNOLOGY

Home on the Web

Have you ever "surfed" the Internet? If so, you may see a dolphin like the one at the left. Such pictures are so attractive that they almost beg you to read the page. Other pages do not look as exciting. The World Wide Web can provide quick access to useful information. Unfortunately, many Web pages use lots of space to say very little.

Design a Home Page For this project you will research Web home pages. You will then create your own home page.

Steps to help you complete the project:

p. 391   **Project Link:** *Researching*
p. 402   **Project Link:** *Diagraming*
p. 407   **Project Link:** *Calculating*
p. 412   **Project Link:** *Designing*
p. 427   ***Finishing the Chapter Project***

• **How to solve a problem by making a model**

SCORING RUBRIC

3 You produce two well-sketched diagrams of the Web pages you analyzed. You provide clear and accurate calculations of areas of useful information. You accurately calculate the percent of useful information on each page. You also provide your own well-thought-out home page design along with notes describing what you learned from analyzing Web pages.

2 You provide two diagrams of Web home pages. You correctly calculate the percent of useful information on at least one of these pages. You also provide your own home page design that shows what you learned from other Web pages.

1 You provide an incomplete sketch of two Web home pages. You omit areas of useful information or incorrectly calculate areas of useful information on each page. Your own home page design is incomplete.

0 You show little evidence that you analyzed several Web pages, and you do not design a home page.

381

Teaching Notes

1 Focus

CONNECTING TO PRIOR KNOWLEDGE Ask students to name the units of measure they would use to describe the area of a book cover, the classroom, or a football field. **Answers may vary. Sample: in.², ft², yd²**

2 Teach

THINK AND DISCUSS

Example You may wish to label the squares in the drawing in the following manner.

9	1	2	10
3	4	5	6
9	7	8	10

Make sure students notice that each of the half squares in the corners has another half square with the same number. This number indicates that the two half squares together make one whole square.

Lesson Planning Options

Prerequisite Skills
• identifying area (precourse)

Vocabulary/Symbols
square units

Materials/Manipulatives
• centimeter graph paper

Resources

 Student Edition

Skills Handbook, p. 537
Extra Practice, p. 530
Glossary/Study Guide

 Teaching Resources

Chapter Support File, Ch. 9
• Lesson Planner 9-1
• Practice 9-1, Reteaching 9-1
• Answer Masters 9-1
Teaching Aids Masters 1, 2, 7, 8, 19
Glossary, Spanish Resources

 Transparencies
1, 9, 20, 21, Minds on Math 9-1

Warm Up

Rounded to the nearest ounce, Jack's basketball weighs 22 oz. What is the least and most it could weigh, in tenths of an ounce? **21.5 oz and 22.4 oz**

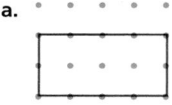

9-1 Estimating Area

What You'll Learn

▼ To estimate area

...And Why

You can solve problems involving gardening and geography by estimating area.

Here's How

Look for questions that
⚏ build understanding
✔ check understanding

1a. Reasoning may vary.
Sample: 8 units²; draw grid lines and count the number of unit squares.

b. Reasoning may vary.
Sample: 2 units²; draw grid lines. There is 1 unit square and two triangles that are each half a unit square.

c. Reasoning may vary.
Sample: 8 units²; draw grid lines. There are 4 half-unit-square triangles.

3c. Count the number of unit squares. Then count the number of half-unit-square triangles. Add half the number of triangles to the number of squares.

THINK AND DISCUSS

You can find the area of any figure by finding the number of *square units* that cover it.
1a–c. See below left.

1. ✔*Try It Out* How many square units are in each figure? Describe your method for finding each area.

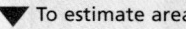

a.   b.   c.

Some of the standard units of area are square centimeters (cm²), square meters (m²), square inches (in.²), square feet (ft²), square yards (yd²), and square miles (mi²).

2. ⚏*Open-ended* Name some other units of area.
Sample: mm², km²

The figure below is on centimeter graph paper.

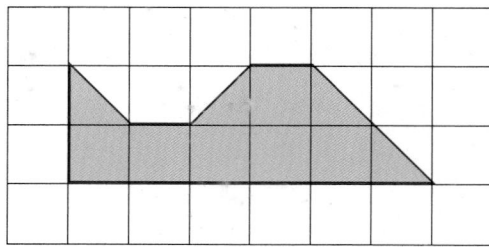

3. a. What is the area of each square of the graph paper? **1 cm²**
   b. ✔*Try It Out* What is the area of the shaded figure? **8 cm²**
   c. ⚏*Explain* How did you find the area? **See left.**
   d. ⚏*Go a Step Further* Suppose each square represents 9 m². What is the area of the figure? **72 m²**

You can estimate area by using a grid. Decide whether each square is full, almost full, about half full, or almost empty.

■ **ADDITIONAL EXAMPLE**

Estimate the area of this portion of a plant. Each square is 1 mm on each side.
about 12 mm²

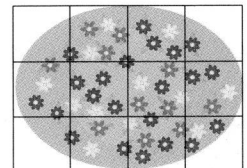

Work Together

Group students in pairs. Suggest that students use tracing paper to copy the map of Australia. Have students write an estimate of the number of square miles in each map square. Have students compare their estimates. Discuss different techniques that students used for estimating the area of Australia.

ASSESSMENT Have students use grid paper to draw a figure that covers whole and half squares. Ask students to switch drawings with a partner. Have students estimate the area of each figure. Then have students check each other's answers.

■ **EXAMPLE** *Real-World Problem Solving*

Gardening Estimate the area of the flower bed in the drawing below. Each square represents 1 m².

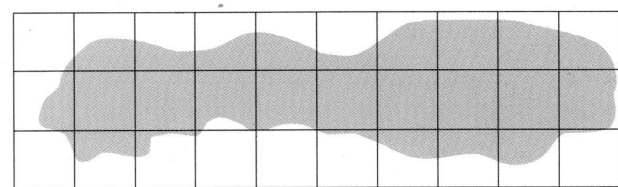

The 2 center squares are full. The 6 squares in the middle of the sides are almost full. The 4 corner squares are about half full.

$$2 + 6 + (4 \times \tfrac{1}{2}) = 2 + 6 + 2$$
$$= 10$$

The area is about 10 m².

4. ✔*Try It Out* Below is a drawing of a lake. Each square represents 4 mi². Estimate the area of the lake.

5. Answers may vary. Sample: about 3,110,400 mi²

4. Answers may vary. Sample: about 64 mi²

Work Together
See left.

Estimating Area from Maps

5. *Geography* Work with a partner. Each square represents an area 240 mi by 240 mi. Estimate the area of Australia.

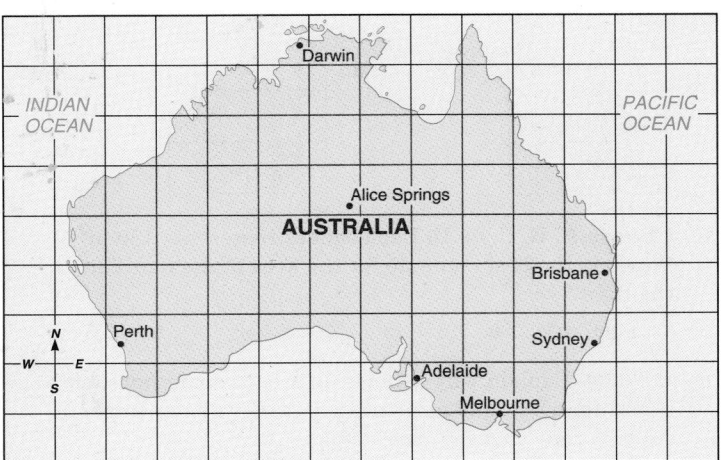

Sydney, Australia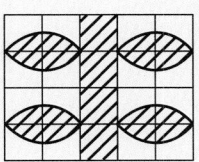

Now you may assign Exercises 1–14.

Technology Options

Prentice Hall Technology

Software for Learners
- Hot Page™ 24*
- Math Blaster® Mystery*
- Interactive Student Tutorial, Chapter 9*

Teaching Resource Software
- Computer Item Generator 9-1
- Resource Pro™ Chapter 9*

Internet • For related mathematics activities, visit the Prentice Hall site at www.phschool.com/math

*Available on CD-ROM only

Assignment Options for Exercises On Your Own

Core 1–6, 12, 13
Extension 7–11, 14

Use Mixed Review to maintain skills.

3 Practice/Assess

EXERCISES *On Your Own*

AUDITORY LEARNING and DIVERSITY
Exercises 1–9 Have students with visual impairments work with a partner. Have the partner describe the figures. Also have the partner tell the amount shaded in each square. Remind students to combine incomplete squares to form as many complete squares as they can.

ERROR ALERT! Students may lose track of the number of whole and partial squares in figures. **Remediation:** Have students use tracing paper to draw each figure. Have them mark each grid they count. Suggest that they record the number of whole and partial grids as they count.

VISUAL LEARNING and REASONING
Exercise 14 Have students use four yard sticks and make a square yard on the floor.

WRAP UP

IDENTIFYING THE BIG IDEA Have students explain how to estimate the area of a figure.

---

pages 384–385   On Your Own

11. Answers may vary. Sample: Estimating an area is faster than measuring it and it can be almost as accurate. For example, finding the area of an island may be difficult because the edges of the figure are not straight.

EXERCISES *On Your Own*

The area of each square is 1 cm². Find the area of each figure.

1.
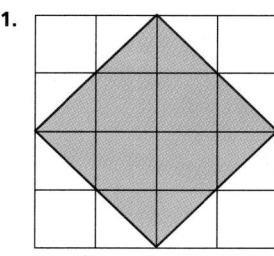
8 cm²

2.
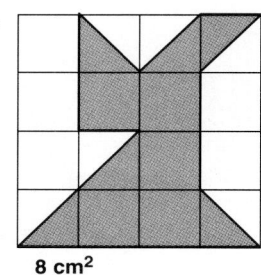
8 cm²

3.
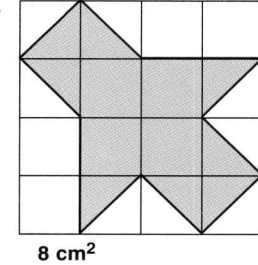
8 cm²

Each square represents 1 in.² Estimate the area of each figure.   4–9. Estimates may vary. Samples are given.

4.
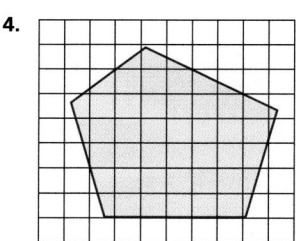
40 in.²

5.
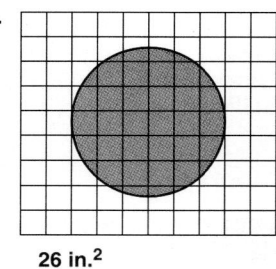
20 in.²

6.

26 in.²

Each square represents 4 cm². Estimate the area of each figure.

7.
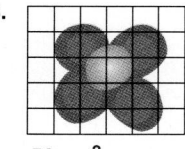
52 cm²

8.
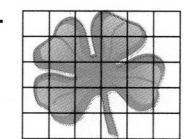
56 cm²

9.
36 cm²

10. **Choose A, B, C, or D.** Each square represents 100 m². Which is the best estimate for the area of the figure at the right? **B**

    A. 3,000 m²   **B.** 1,550 m²   **C.** 15.5 m²   **D.** 15.5 cm²

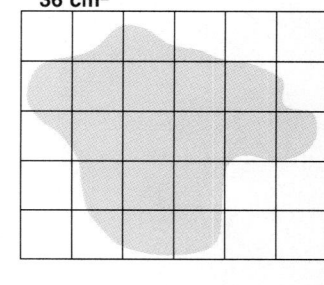

11. *Writing* Explain why estimating area is sometimes more useful than actually measuring area. Give an example to support your answer. **See margin.**

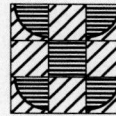

1. Estimate the dark grey area of the figure.
6 units²

2. Estimate the light grey area of the figure.
3 units²

12. Which region has the greatest area? The least area? Explain.
B; D; Area B is about 35 unit squares. Area D is about 32 unit squares.

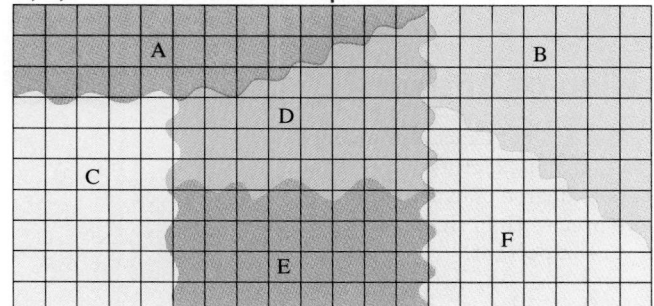

13. *Open-ended* Place your hand, with your fingers touching, on centimeter graph paper. Trace around your hand. On a second sheet of centimeter graph paper, trace around your hand with your fingers spread apart.
  a. Estimate the area of each hand. **Check students' work.**
  b. *Reasoning* Why might there be differences in your two estimates for part (a)? **Spreading the fingers apart covers more parts of squares than whole squares.**

14. *Reasoning* How many square feet are in a square yard? How many square inches are in a square yard? Use drawings to illustrate your answer. **9 ft²; 1,296 in.²; see back of book for diagram.**

Mixed Review

Find each sum or difference. Use equivalent fractions.
(Lessons 6-2 and 6-3)

15. $\frac{1}{5} + \frac{3}{5}$ **$\frac{4}{5}$** **16.** $\frac{4}{9} - \frac{3}{9}$ **$\frac{1}{9}$** **17.** $\frac{7}{8} + \frac{1}{4}$ **$1\frac{1}{8}$** **18.** $\frac{14}{21} - \frac{3}{7}$ **$\frac{5}{21}$** **19.** $\frac{5}{12} + \frac{4}{6}$ **$1\frac{1}{12}$** **20.** $\frac{23}{25} - \frac{1}{5}$ **$\frac{18}{25}$**

Write a ratio in three ways for each statement. *(Lesson 7-1)*

21. two black kittens in a litter of 6
  1 to 3; 1 : 3; $\frac{1}{3}$

22. eight A-students in a class of 24
  1 to 3; 1 : 3; $\frac{1}{3}$

23. 1 cup butter for every 2 cups sugar
  1 to 2; 1 : 2; $\frac{1}{2}$

24. 4 cartons for 24 bottles
  1 to 6; 1 : 6; $\frac{1}{6}$

25. *Choose a Strategy* Mr. Delgado is growing sunflowers to sell at the school plant sale. He plants $2\frac{1}{2}$ dozen seeds each day, but $\frac{3}{4}$ dozen seeds of each $2\frac{1}{2}$ dozen seeds planted do not grow. On how many days must Mr. Delgado plant to have a total of at least 8 dozen sunflower plants? **5 days**

PRACTICE

Practice 9-1 *Estimating Area*

The area of each square is 1 cm². Find the area of each figure.

1. **2.** **3.**

12 cm²   10 cm²   9 cm²

Each square represents 1 in.². Estimate the area of each figure.

4. **5.** **6.**

about 28 in.²   about 45 in.²   about 34 in.²

7. Circle **A, B, C,** or **D.** Each square represents 100 m². Which is the best estimate for the area of the figure?

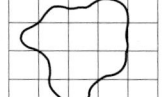

A. 250 m²   **B.** 2,500 m²
C. 2,000 m²   **D.** 1,500 m²

8. Outline the letters of your first name on the graph paper below. Make the letters as large as possible. Shade in the letters and then find the area. Each square represents 1 cm². Sample drawing shown. Area = about 38 cm²

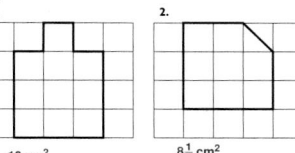

In copymaster and workbook formats

RETEACHING

Reteaching 9-1 *Estimating Area*

The area of a figure is the number of *square units* that cover it. Area is always measured in square units.

The area is 9 square units.

To estimate an area, count the number of squares that cover it.

① Count the full squares. *4 squares*
② Count the almost full squares. *2 squares*
③ Count what remains, combining parts of squares to make whole squares. *about 3 squares*
④ Add: 4 + 2 + 3 = 9 squares

Each square is 1 cm². The area is about 9 cm².

The area of each square is 1 cm². Find the area of each figure.

1. **2.** **3.**

10 cm² $8\frac{1}{2}$ cm²   8 cm²

Each square represents 1 in.². Estimate the area of each figure.

4. 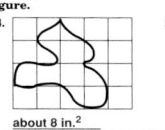 **5.** 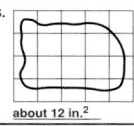 **6.**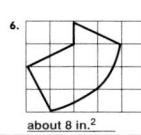

about 8 in.²   about 12 in.²   about 8 in.²

ENRICHMENT

Minds on Math Transparency

9-1

In September, $\frac{1}{2}$ of the customers at Tommy's Discount Store paid for their purchases by check. Of the remaining customers, $\frac{2}{3}$ paid with a credit card and the rest paid cash. What fraction of the customers paid cash?

$\frac{1}{6}$

See *Solution Key* **for worked-out answers.**

385

In Lesson 9-1, students learned how to estimate area. This toolbox allows students to explore the precision of measurements.

ERROR ALERT! **Exercise 4** Students may say the line is 2.5 or $2\frac{1}{2}$ inches long.
Remediation: Remind students the lines on the ruler determine how precise their measurement can be. Tell them to round their answer to the closest mark on the ruler they use.

ASSESSMENT Group students in pairs. Give each student a ruler that measures centimeters and inches. Have each student draw a line segment and give the segment to their partner to measure. Have each student measure the line segment in inches and in centimeters as precise as their ruler is. Have partners check each others' work and discuss how precise they were able to measure and why.

■ ADDITIONAL PROBLEM

Have students remeasure the lines in Exercises 4–6 with their ruler to a different degree of exactness.

Resources

 Transparencies
18

MATH TOOLBOX — EXPLORATION

Before Lesson 9-2

Precision of Answers

Sometimes you use numbers that are not exact. For example, measurements are *approximate*, or not exactly *precise*. The *precision* of a number refers to its degree of exactness. Measurements cannot be more precise than the measuring tool used. In science, precision is very important.

■ EXAMPLE 1

To what degree of precision can you measure a length using the ruler at the right?

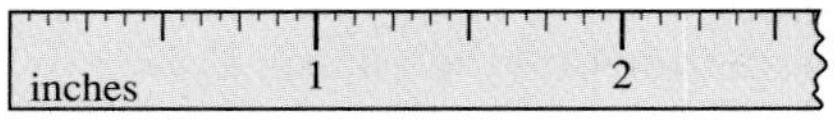

The ruler is divided into sixteenths of an inch, so you can measure a length to the nearest sixteenth of an inch.

■ EXAMPLE 2

Find the length of the line segment at the right using the given measuring tool.

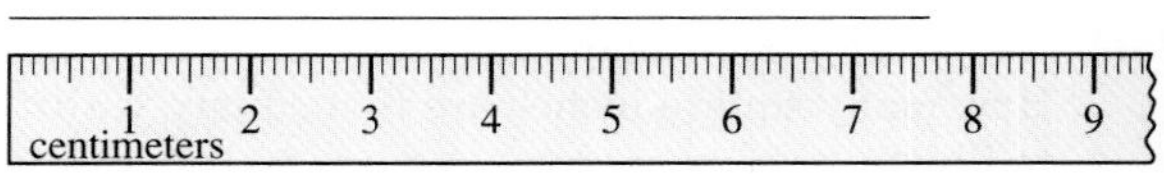

The centimeter ruler is divided into tenths of a centimeter, or millimeters. Since the line segment is closer to 7.6 cm or 76 mm than it is to 7.7 cm or 77 mm, its length is 7.6 cm or 76 mm.

To what degree of precision can you measure a given length using each measuring tool?

1. 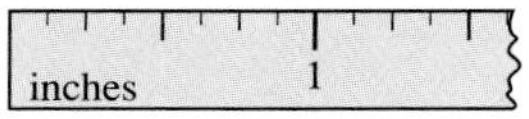
$\frac{1}{8}$ in.

2. 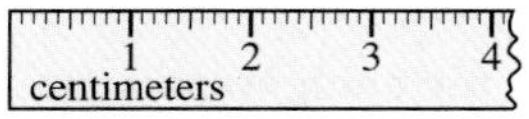
1 mm

3. 
$\frac{1}{16}$ in.

Find the length of each line segment using the measuring tool directly below it.

4. 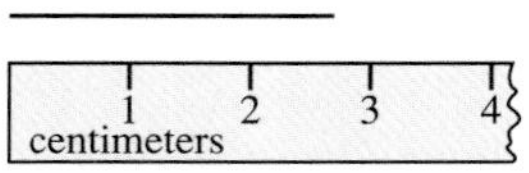
about 3 cm

5. 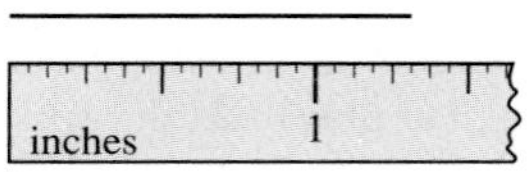
$1\frac{5}{16}$ in.

6. 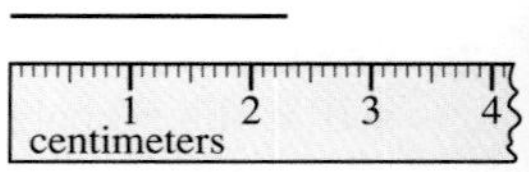
2.3 cm or 23 mm

7. *Writing* Describe five items for which a centimeter measure would be reasonable. For example, a pencil could reasonably be described as 7.5 cm long.
Sample: a notebook, a spoon, a knitting needle, a bicycle wheel, a skateboard

Teaching Notes

1 Focus

CONNECTING TO PRIOR KNOWLEDGE
Have students explain how to find the area of a 5×5 cm square on grid paper. **Count the number of squares.** Have students discuss how they would find the area of the grid outside the square. **Count the squares not counted for the square.**

2 Teach

THINK AND DISCUSS

AEP Review the meanings of *perimeter* and *area.* Have students recall definitions for both words as you show them how to find the perimeter and area of a 7×7 square on centimeter grid paper. Make certain students understand that *l* and *w* are abbreviations for length and width.

REASONING Question 1a Suggest that students try a variety of methods to find the answer. For example, some students may wish to use tiles or draw a picture on grid paper.

KINESTHETIC LEARNING If you have block scheduling or extended class periods, have students use carpet squares or floor tiles to create rectangles with the following dimensions: 3×4; 2×6. Have students stand around the perimeter of the rectangles they form. Ask one student to stand on each tile. Have them compare the perimeters.

ALGEBRA Connection

9-2 Perimeters and Areas of Rectangles

What You'll Learn

1 To find perimeters and areas of rectangles

2 To find perimeters and areas of squares

...And Why

Finding the area of a figure helps you solve problems involving landscaping.

Here's How

Look for questions that
⚬ build understanding
✔ check understanding

2c. No; the area of each plot does not change. The same amount of space is covered no matter how it is arranged.

THINK AND DISCUSS

1 *Measuring Rectangles*

Suppose you are planning a vegetable garden. You plan to have 12 square garden plots arranged into a rectangle. Each plot measures 1 meter along each side.

1. a. ⚬*Reasoning* How can you arrange the 12 plots to have the least perimeter? **3 plots by 4 plots**
   b. How can you arrange the plots to have the greatest perimeter? **12 plots by 1 plot**

2. a. What is the area of the arrangement with the least perimeter? **12 m²**
   b. What is the area of the arrangement with the greatest perimeter? **12 m²**
   c. ⚬*Explain* Will the area change if you arrange the plots in a nonrectangular shape? Why or why not? **See left.**

Perimeter measures the distance around a figure. When you do not have sides or squares to count, you can find the perimeter P of a rectangle by adding each length ℓ and width w: $\ell + w + \ell + w$, which is $2\ell + 2w$, or $2(\ell + w)$.

The area of a figure is the amount of surface it covers. It is measured in square units. You can find the area A of a rectangle by multiplying the length ℓ and the width w.

PERIMETER AND AREA OF A RECTANGLE

$$P = 2(\ell + w)$$

$$A = \ell \times w$$

Lesson Planning Options

Prerequisite Skills
- multiplying decimals (4-5)
- using metric units of length (3-8)

Materials/Manipulatives
- square tiles
- centimeter ruler
- calculator
- graph paper

Resources

📖 **Student Edition**

Skills Handbook, p. 540
Extra Practice, p. 530
Glossary/Study Guide

📦 **Teaching Resources**

Chapter Support File, Ch. 9
- Lesson Planner 9-2
- Practice 9-2, Reteaching 9-2
- Alternative Activity 9-2
- Answer Masters 9-2
Teaching Aids Masters 1, 2, 7, 8, 19
Glossary, Spanish Resources

📽 **Transparencies**

1, 9, 18, 20, 21, 94, Minds on Math 9-2

Warm Up

The length of a computer lab is 11 ft more that half of its width. What is the perimeter of the lab if it is 18 ft wide? **76 ft**

Example 1 Ask students: *Explain why you multiply (70 + 25) by 2.* **The rectangle has two sides that are 70 ft long and two s...**

[handwritten note]
Homework 6/3
Level 1 $5\frac{2}{7} - 3\frac{3}{4}$

Teaching Resource Software
• Computer Item Generator 9-2
• Resource Pro™ Chapter 9*

Internet • For related mathematics activities, visit the Prentice Hall site at www.phschool.com/math

*Available on CD-ROM only

Assignment Options for Exercises On Your Own

To provide flexible scheduling, this lesson can be split into parts.

▼1 **Core** 1, 3–15, 32
   Extension 16–20, 29–31

▼2 **Core** 2, 21–28
   Extension 33–38

Use Mixed Review to maintain skills.

388

■ **ADDITIONAL EXAMPLES**

FOR EXAMPLE 1

Find the perimeter and area of a picture frame ... n. long. **P = 17 in.;**

...ter is 52 cm. Find its area.

...xample 2 Ask students: ...area of a square whose

5a. The area would reduce by half.
b. The perimeter would reduce by 70 ft.

---

perimeter is 24 cm? Explain how. **Yes, divide 24 cm by 4 to find the length of one side, then square that number.**

EXTENSION and CONNECTION TO INTERIOR DESIGN You may wish to discuss with students how interior designers use area and perimeter to order floor coverings. Give students grid paper. Have students design a floor plan of a house. Ask students to plan how much carpeting they need based on their drawings. Ask them to explain how they used math skills to plan their rooms.

■ **EXAMPLE 1**   *Real-World Problem Solving*

Landscaping Find the perimeter and area of the backyard.

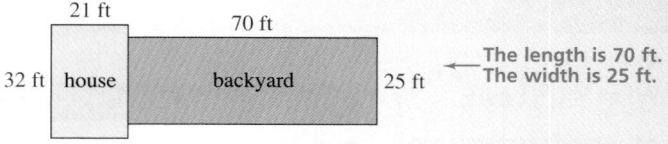

$P = 2(\ell + w)$ ◄——Use the formula for perimeter.
$= 2(70 + 25)$
$= 2 \times 95 = 190$ ft

$A = \ell \times w$ ◄——Use the formula for area.
$= 70 \times 25 = 1{,}750$ ft^2

The perimeter is 190 ft. The area of the backyard is 1,750 ft^2.

3. ♣*Number Sense* In Example 1, why was the area given in square feet and the perimeter in feet? **The area is the product of lengths. The perimeter is the sum of lengths.**
4. ✔*Try It Out* Find the perimeter and area of each rectangle.
   a. $\ell = 8$ ft, $w = 5$ ft   b. $\ell = 12$ in., $w = 7$ in.
   26 ft; 40 ft^2   **38 in.; 84 in.^{2}**
5. ♣*What If . . .* Suppose the length of the backyard in Example 1 were cut by one half.
   a. How would the area of the backyard change?
   b. How would the backyard's perimeter change?

Now you may assign Exercises 1, 3–20, 29–32.

2 *Measuring Squares*

A square is a rectangle with 4 sides of equal measure. The perimeter P is 4 times the length of each side s, or $4s$. You can find the area A by squaring the length of a side, or s^2.

PERIMETER AND AREA OF A SQUARE

$P = 4s$
(Perimeter = 4 × side)

$A = s \times s = s^2$
(Area = side × side)

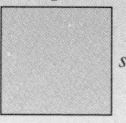

Work Together

You may wish to have students work in groups of three or four. Give each group 32 tiles.

VISUAL LEARNING and ALTERNATIVE METHOD Questions 7–9 Have students use grid paper to draw rectangles. Remind students to label the lengths and widths.

3 Practice/Assess

EXERCISES On Your Own

Exercises 1–4 Remind students to write area measurement as square units.

Exercise 5 Suggest that students draw a picture to find the perimeter of the pool.

TACTILE LEARNING Exercise 16 Suggest students use square tiles to solve this problem. Give each student 24 tiles. Have

them create a rectangle with all the tiles that will fulfill the requirements of the problem.

ERROR ALERT! Exercise 17 Students may fail to multiply the width by 2 before they subtract it from the perimeter. **Remediation:** Remind students that the rectangle has *2 sides* that are 4 ft. Make sure they multiply 2×4 *before they subtract* $22 - 8 = 14$. Also be sure they understand that they need *to divide the length by 2* to find the length of the side $14 \div 2 = 7$.

7. Sample:

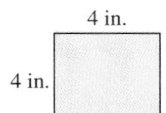

8. Sample:

9. Sample:

■ **EXAMPLE 2**

A square's perimeter is 32 cm. Find its area.

$$P = 4s$$
$$32 = 4s$$

⟵ Use the formula for perimeter to find the measure of a side.

$$\frac{32}{4} = \frac{4s}{4}$$

⟵ Solve for *s*.

$$8 = s$$

$$A = s^2$$

⟵ Use the formula for area.

$$A = 8^2 = 64$$

The area of the square is 64 cm^2.

6. ✔*Try It Out* Find the area of a square with perimeter 8 ft.
4 ft^2

Work Together
Relating Perimeter and Area

Use square tiles to form the following rectangles. Record the results on graph paper. **7–9. See left.**

7. ⬛*Modeling* Form at least two rectangles whose areas (in square units) are less than their perimeters (in units).

8. Form at least one rectangle whose area is equal to its perimeter.

9. Form at least two rectangles whose areas are greater than their perimeters.

Now you may assign Exercises 2, 21–28, 33–38.

EXERCISES On Your Own

Find the perimeter and area of each rectangle.

1.

3 cm   10 cm

26 cm; 30 cm^2

2.

4 in.

4 in.

16 in.; 16 in.^{2}

3.

4 ft

9 ft

26 ft; 36 ft^2

4.

16 m

8 m

48 m; 128 m^2

5. a. *Landscaping* How much fencing do you need to enclose a rectangular pool area that is 24 ft by 66 ft? **180 ft**

b. Suppose you use fence sections 3 ft wide. How many sections will you need? **60 sections**

CONNECTION TO STAMP COLLECTING
Exercise 18 Have students find the perimeter and area of a stamp they have at home. Have students share their measurements and compare them with the stamp in Exercise 18.

EXTENSION Exercises 21–28 Tell students they can check their work by dividing the area by the perimeter for each problem. The quotient is $\frac{s}{4}$. Ask: *Why is this true?* **because** $\frac{\text{area}}{\text{perimeter}} = \frac{s^2}{4s} = \frac{s}{4}$

WRITING Exercise 31 Have students use a geoboard to experiment with different rectangles. Ask students if they can find two rectangles with completely different dimensions, but the same area.

ESTIMATION Exercise 32 Remind students to round the measurements to numbers that are easy to work with mentally.

WRAP UP

IDENTIFYING THE BIG IDEA Ask students to explain how to find the perimeters and areas of squares and rectangles.

PROJECT LINK Ask students to explain how designers for Web sites on the Internet use area and perimeter to help create pages that use a minimum amount of space.

Find the perimeter and area of each rectangle.

6. $\ell = 6$ cm, $w = 3$ cm
   18 cm; 18 cm^2

7. $\ell = 15$ yd, $w = 10$ yd
   50 yd; 150 yd^2

8. $\ell = 5$ mm, $w = 20$ mm
   50 mm; 100 mm^2

9. $\ell = 7$ yd, $w = 12$ yd
   38 yd; 84 yd^2

10. $\ell = 1.5$ m, $w = 0.25$ m
    3.5 m; 0.375 m^2

11. $\ell = 7.2$ cm, $w = 3.7$ cm
    21.8 cm; 26.64 cm^2

Use a centimeter ruler to measure the length and width of each rectangle. Then find the perimeter and area.

2.5 cm and 2.2 cm; 9.4 cm; 5.5 cm^2

12.

4 cm and 1 cm;
10 cm; 4 cm^2

13.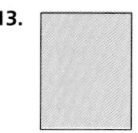

1.5 cm and 2 cm
7 cm; 3 cm^2

14.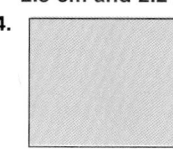

15.

2.5 cm and 1.5 cm;
8 cm; 3.75 cm^2

▦ *Choose* **Use a calculator, paper and pencil, or mental math to solve.**

16. The area of a rectangle is 24 in.^{2} One side is 6 in. What is the perimeter? **20 in.**

17. The perimeter of a rectangle is 22 ft. The width is 4 ft. What is the length? The area?
    7 ft; 28 ft^2

18. *Stamp Collecting* The world's smallest stamp, shown at right, was issued in Colombia from 1863 to 1866. It measured 0.31 in. by 0.37 in. Find the stamp's area. **0.1147 in.^{2}**

19. *Gardening* Suppose you would like a garden with an area of 18 ft^2. You have a garden space 6 ft long. How wide should it be? **3 ft**

20. **Choose A, B, C, or D.** A rectangle is 15.95 m by 8.25 m. Which of the following is the best estimate for the area? **D**

    A. about 48 m   B. about 48 m^2 C. about 128 m   D. about 128 m^2

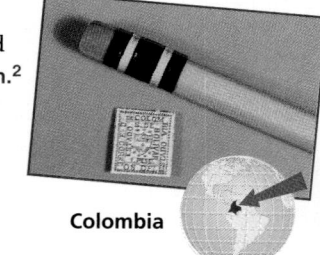

Colombia

Find the perimeter and area of each square.

21. $s = 4.5$ in.
    18 in.; 20.25 in.^{2}

22. $s = 13$ m
    52 m; 169 m^2

23. $s = 21$ mm
    84 mm; 441 mm^2

24. $s = 50$ mi
    200 mi; 2,500 mi^2

25. $s = 1.5$ cm
    6 cm; 2.25 cm^2

26. $s = 4.1$ km
    16.4 km; 16.81 km^2

27. $s = 100$ ft
    400 ft; 10,000 ft^2

28. $s = 12.5$ in.
    50 in.; 156.25 in.^{2}

29. The area of a rectangular parking lot is 24 yd^2. Find all the possible whole-number dimensions in yards. **1 yd × 24 yd, 2 yd × 12 yd, 3 yd × 8 yd, 4 yd × 6 yd**

30. The perimeter of a rectangle is 10 m. Find all the possible whole-number dimensions in meters. **1 m × 4 m, 2 m × 3 m**

31. *Writing* Suppose you know the area of a rectangle. Can you then find its perimeter? Why or why not? Use examples to illustrate your answer. **No; there are many different rectangles with the same area.** **Examples may vary. Sample: For example, 2 cm × 6 cm and 3 cm × 4 cm rectangles have the same area yet different perimeters.**

390

LESSON QUIZ

1. Find the perimeter and area of a rectangle with a length of 14 cm and width of 25 cm.
   78 cm; 350 cm²

2. Find the area of a square that has a perimeter of 92 cm. **529 cm²**

---

32. *Mental Math* Estimate the area of the rectangle at the right.
Estimates may vary. Sample: 240 m²

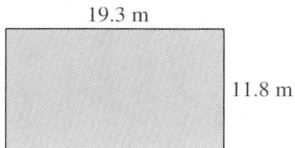
19.3 m
11.8 m

Find the area of each square with the given perimeter.

33. 8 cm **4 cm²**

34. 20 m **25 m²**

35. 48 in. **144 in.²**

36. 10 mi **6.25 mi²**

37. The perimeter of a square is 16 in.
   a. What is its area? **16 in.²**
   b. Suppose the length of the square's sides was cut in half. How would the perimeter and area change?
   The perimeter would be 8 in.; the area would be 4 in.².

38. *Home Improvement* A homeowner is buying square tiles for her dining room floor. The room is 10 ft by 15 ft. She can choose tiles that are 1 ft on a side or 2 ft on a side.
   a. How many tiles does she need if she chooses 1-ft² tiles? **150 tiles**
   b. How many 1-ft² tiles does it take to cover the same area as one 4-ft² tile? **4 tiles**

Mixed Review

Find each quotient. *(Lessons 4-7 and 4-8)*

39. $90\overline{)360}$ **4**

40. $11.85 \div 7.9$ **1.5**

41. $45\overline{)58.5}$ **1.3**

42. $2.262 \div 8.7$ **0.26**

43. $7\overline{)0.161}$ **0.023**

44. *Baby-sitting* Sheila baby-sits for $4\frac{3}{4}$ hour each Saturday and each Sunday. She plans to baby-sit for $3\frac{1}{2}$ weekends next month. Find the total number of hours she will work next month. *(Lesson 6-7)* $33\frac{1}{4}$

CHAPTER PROJECT
PROJECT LINK: RESEARCHING

Visit the home pages of several Web sites. Find an example of a home page that has a lot of words and pictures. Also find a home page that *does not* have a lot of words or pictures. Create a bookmark or record the addresses of the sites so you can return to them later.

Check students' work.

PRACTICE

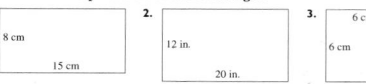

Practice 9-2 *Perimeters and Areas of Rectangles*

Find the area and perimeter of each rectangle.

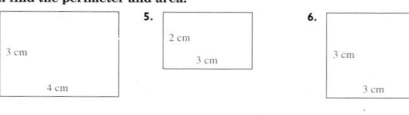

1. 8 cm, 15 cm
120 cm², 46 cm

2. 12 in., 20 in.
240 in.², 64 in.

3. 6 cm, 6 cm
36 cm², 24 cm

Use a centimeter ruler to measure the length and width of each rectangle. Mark the length and width on each figure. Then find the perimeter and area.

4. 3 cm, 4 cm
14 cm, 12 cm²

5. 2 cm, 3 cm
10 cm, 6 cm²

6. 3 cm, 3 cm
12 cm, 9 cm²

Choose a calculator, paper and pencil, or mental math to solve.

7. The length of the rectangle is 8 cm. The width is 6 cm.
   a. What is the area? **48 cm²**
   b. What is the perimeter? **28 cm**

8. The area of a rectangle is 45 in.². One dimension is 5 in. What is the perimeter? **28 in.**

9. The perimeter of a square is 36 cm. What is the area of the square? **81 cm²**

10. The perimeter of a rectangle is 38 cm. The length is 7.5 cm. What is the width? **11.5 cm**

11. The figure at the right contains only squares. Each side of the shaded square is 1 unit. What is the length, width, and area of the figure?
34 units long, 21 units wide, 714 square units

In copymaster and workbook formats

RETEACHING

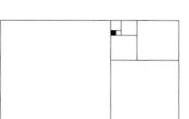

Reteaching 9-2 *Perimeters and Areas of Rectangles*

Perimeter
The *perimeter* of a figure is the sum of the lengths of its sides. Opposite sides of a rectangle are equal. To find the perimeter, add the 2 lengths (l) and the 2 widths (w).
$$P = l + l + w + w \quad \text{or} \quad P = 2l + 2w$$
Find the perimeter.

w 9 cm
l
14 cm

$$P = 2l + 2w$$
$$= 2(14) + 2(9)$$
$$= 28 + 18 = 46 \text{ cm}$$
The perimeter is 46 cm.

Area
The *area* of a figure is the number of square units needed to cover the figure. To find the area of a rectangle, multiply the length (l) and the width (w).
$$A = l \times w$$
Find the area.

5 m
w
6 m

$$A = l \times w$$
$$= 6 \times 5$$
$$= 30 \text{ m}^2$$
The area is 30 m².

Find the perimeter and area of each rectangle.

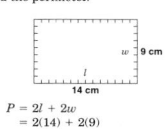 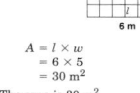

1. 4 m, 10 m
28 m; 40 m²

2. 5 cm, 5 cm
20 cm; 25 cm²

3. 10 cm, 20 cm
60 cm; 200 cm²

Find the perimeter and area of each rectangle.

4. $l = 12$ cm, $w = 2$ cm
28 cm; 24 cm²

5. $l = 9$ ft, $w = 7.5$ ft
33 ft; 67.5 ft²

6. $l = 2.5$ m, $w = 1.5$ m
8 m; 3.75 m²

7. $l = 5.5$ in., $w = 5.5$ in.
22 in.; 30.25 in.²

8. $l = 6.2$ in., $w = 3.4$ in.
19.2 in.; 21.08 in.²

9. $l = 4.5$ ft, $w = 0.75$ ft
10.5 ft; 3.375 ft²

10. $l = 17$ cm, $w = 8$ cm
50 cm; 136 cm²

11. $l = 10.5$ m, $w = 5.2$ m
31.4 m; 54.6 m²

12. $l = 22$ in., $w = 9$ in.
62 in.; 198 in.²

ENRICHMENT

Minds on Math Transparency

9-2

I am a percent that is less than 100%. As a decimal I can be written with one digit to the right of the decimal point. When I am written as a fraction in simplest form, the numerator and denominator are single digits and their difference is 3. What percent am I?

40%

See Solution Key for worked-out answers.

1 Focus

CONNECTING TO PRIOR KNOWLEDGE Have students draw an 8 × 8 square on cm grid paper. Ask students to determine the area. **64 cm²** Have them draw a vertical line down the middle of the square. Ask them to determine the area of each of the two rectangles they formed. **32 cm² each**

Lesson Planning Options

Prerequisite Skills

- classifying quadrilaterals (8-6)
- recognizing perpendicular segments (precourse)

Vocabulary/Symbols

altitude

Materials/Manipulatives

- graph paper
- centimeter ruler
- scissors
- dot paper

Resources

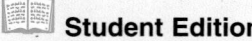 **Student Edition**

Skills Handbook, p. 538
Extra Practice, p. 530
Glossary/Study Guide

 **Teaching Resources**

Chapter Support File, Ch. 9
- Lesson Planner 9-3
- Practice 9-3, Reteaching 9-3
- Answer Masters 9-3
Teaching Aids Masters 1, 2, 8, 9, 19
Glossary, Spanish Resources

 Transparencies
1, 9, 18, 94, Minds on Math 9-3

Warm Up

Write the decimal for two hundred six hundred-thousandths.
0.02006

2 Teach

Work Together

Have students work with a partner. Give students graph paper and scissors.

Question 3 Remind students that congruent triangles have the same size and shape.

AEP Create a word map for each of the following words: *non-rectangular, vertex, base, perpendicular.* Have students include examples and non-examples as you discuss each word.

THINK AND DISCUSS

Example 1 Ask students to find the area of the land if it has a height of 200 yd. **30,000 yd²**

VISUAL LEARNING Ask each student to write on an index card the formulas for the area of a parallelogram and a triangle. Have the students place the cards on their desks for reference. Encourage students to add

---

9-3 Areas of Parallelograms and Triangles

What You'll Learn

▼ To find the areas of parallelograms and triangles

▼ To find the areas of complex figures

...And Why

You can use the areas of parallelograms and triangles to solve conservation problems.

Here's How

Look for questions that
- build understanding
- ✔ check understanding

Work Together

Comparing Areas

1a–c. Check students' work.
1. a. Draw a nonrectangular parallelogram on graph paper. Draw a perpendicular segment from one vertex to the base.
   b. Cut the parallelogram out. Cut along the perpendicular segment.
   c. **Patterns** Rearrange the two figures to form a rectangle.

2a–c. Check students' work.
2. a. What is the area of the rectangle?
   b. **Explain** What do you think was the area of the original parallelogram? Why?
   c. **Analyze** Repeat this activity. Make three different-sized parallelograms. Are the results similar?

3. **Patterns** Draw two congruent triangles on centimeter graph paper. Cut out and arrange the triangles to form a parallelogram. How does the area of each triangle compare to the area of the parallelogram? **Check students' work for diagrams.**
The area of each triangle is half of the area of the parallelogram.

THINK AND DISCUSS

▼ *Areas of Parallelograms and Triangles*

Any side of a parallelogram or triangle can be considered the base, with length b. The height h of the parallelogram or triangle is the length of a perpendicular segment, or *altitude,* from a vertex to the line containing the base.

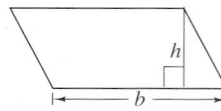

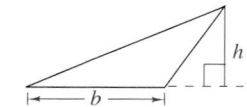

these formulas to any lists they may have in their notebooks.

■ ADDITIONAL EXAMPLES

FOR EXAMPLE 1

A city park is on a triangular piece of land that has a base length of 214 yd and a height of 70 yd. What is the area of the city park?
7,490 yd²

FOR EXAMPLE 2

Find the area of the figure. **26.5 cm²**

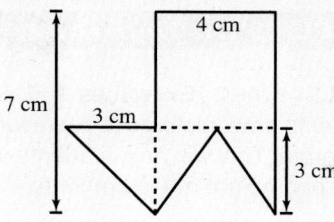

ERROR ALERT! **Example 2** Students may write an incorrect number for the length of the large rectangle. **Remediation:** Tell students the dashed lines seperate the figures into shapes whose areas are easy to find. Have students use the information given to write the length of each side of the two rectangles and the length of the dashed side of the triangle.

The area of a parallelogram is *the same as* the area of a rectangle with the same dimensions. The area of a triangle is *half* the area of a parallelogram with the same base length and height.

AREAS OF PARALLELOGRAMS AND TRIANGLES

Area of a parallelogram = base length × height = bh

Area of a triangle = $\frac{1}{2}$ × base length × height = $\frac{1}{2}bh$

■ EXAMPLE 1   *Real-World Problem Solving*

WHAT?
A nature conservancy is a group that buys land in order to preserve it in its natural state.

Conservation A nature conservancy plans to buy a triangular plot of land. The plot has a base length of 300 yards and a height of 100 yards. What is the plot area?

← Draw a diagram.

$A = \frac{1}{2}bh = \frac{1}{2} \times 300 \times 100$ ← Use the formula for the area of a triangle.
$= 15,000$

The area is 15,000 yd².

4. ■ *What If . . .* Suppose the base length of the triangular plot of land in Example 1 were doubled. Find the new area.
30,000 yd²

5. ✔*Try It Out* Find the area of a triangle with base 30 m and height 17.3 m. **259.5 m²**

Now you may assign Exercises 1–23.

Technology Options

Prentice Hall Technology

Software for Learners
• Math Blaster® Mystery*
• Interactive Student Tutorial, Chapter 9*

Teaching Resource Software
• Computer Item Generator 9-3
• Resource Pro™ Chapter 9*

Internet • For related mathematics activities, visit the Prentice Hall site at www.phschool.com/math

Available on CD-ROM only

Assignment Options for Exercises On Your Own

To provide flexible scheduling, this lesson can be split into parts.

▼**1 Core** 1–18, 21–23
Extension 19–20

▼**2 Core** 25–28
Extension 24

Use Mixed Review to maintain skills.

TACTILE LEARNING Give students a tangram. Ask them to find the area of different combinations of the shapes.

ASSESSMENT Have pairs of students draw a rectangle on grid paper. Ask students to divide the rectangle in half with a diagonal line. Have students first find the area of the rectangle and then find the area of each of the two triangles. Have pairs trade drawings and check answers.

3 Practice/Assess

EXERCISES *On Your Own*

VISUAL LEARNING **Exercises 1–6** Suggest that students draw pictures to represent each parallelogram. This will help students visualize the base and height measurements.

EXTENSION Ask students to work in pairs. Have each group draw several complex figures on grid paper. Have them draw dashed lines to seperate the figure into smaller shapes. Then have students find the area of each figure and show their work. Have the class choose several good examples to display in the room.

Exercise 13–18 Remind students to decide if each figure is a parallelogram or a triangle before they use an area formula.

▼2 *Areas of Complex Figures*

Sometimes it helps to split a figure into smaller polygons. Then you can find the area of each polygon and add.

■ **EXAMPLE 2**

Find the area of the figure below.

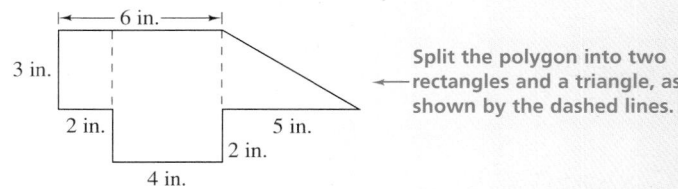

Split the polygon into two rectangles and a triangle, as shown by the dashed lines.

Area of smaller rectangle = $3 \times 2 = 6$ in.^{2}

Area of larger rectangle = $5 \times 4 = 20$ in.^{2}

Area of triangle = $\frac{1}{2}(5 \times 3) = \frac{1}{2} \times 15 = 7.5$ in.^{2}

Find the area of each of the polygons.

6 in.^{2} + 20 in.^{2} + 7.5 in.^{2} = 33.5 in.^{2} ← Add the three areas.

7. Sample: Draw a horizontal line extending the 5-in. side to the opposite 2-in. side.

6. ✔*Try It Out* Find the area of the figure at the right. **16 m²**

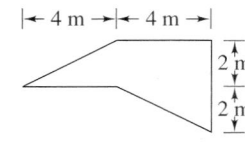

7. ⊞*Look Back* Show another way that you can split the figure in Example 2 to find the area. **See left.**

Now you may assign Exercises 24–28.

EXERCISES *On Your Own*

Find the area of each parallelogram.

1. $b = 4$ ft, $h = 9$ ft **36 ft²**   **2.** $b = 10$ in., $h = 7$ in. **70 in.²**   **3.** $b = 6$ km, $h = 8$ km **48 km²**

4. $b = 20$ yd, $h = 34$ yd **680 yd²**   **5.** $b = 2.4$ cm, $h = 4$ cm **9.6 cm²**   **6.** $b = 3.7$ m, $h = 6.3$ m **23.31 m²**

Find the area of each triangle.

7. $b = 12$ in., $h = 9$ in. **54 in.²**   **8.** $b = 5$ cm, $h = 10$ cm **25 cm²**   **9.** $b = 4$ yd, $h = 8$ yd **16 yd²**

10. $b = 14$ km, $h = 14$ km **98 km²**   **11.** $b = 3.5$ m, $h = 7$ m **12.25 m²**   **12.** $b = 5.3$ cm, $h = 6.5$ cm **17.225 cm²**

394

DIVERSITY and AUDITORY LEARNING
Exercise 20 Pair students who may have difficulty reading with strong readers. Suggest that students discuss words they find confusing.

Exercise 20 Give students grid paper. Have them draw an example for each statement. Ask students to label their examples and write explanations for each statement. It may help students to find the area for each figure to be sure an explanation is accurate.

CONNECTION TO GEOMETRY
Exercises 25–27 Encourage students to break figures into shapes they know how to find the area for. They may also be able to recombine the shapes to make the calculations easier.

REASONING Ask students to draw a triangle. Have them find the area. Ask them to change the length of one side. Then have them explain how changing the length of one side affects the area of the triangle.

WRAP UP

IDENTIFYING THE BIG IDEA Have students explain how to find the areas of parallelograms, triangles, and shapes that contain both figures.

JOURNAL Suggest that students draw a parallelogram and triangle with the same base and height measurements.

Find each area. Use units².

13.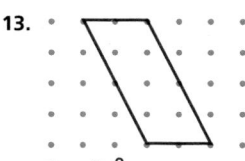

8 units²

14.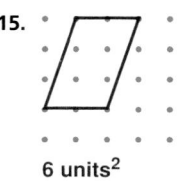

6 units²

15.

6 units²

16.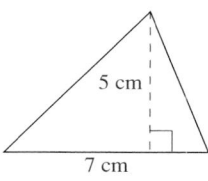

5 cm

7 cm

17.5 cm²

17.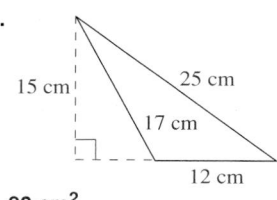

10 m

4 m 3 m 4 m

10 m

30 m²

18.

15 cm 25 cm

17 cm

12 cm

90 cm²

19. *Measurement* Use a centimeter ruler to measure the sides of the triangle at the right. Measure to the nearest millimeter. Then find its perimeter and its area.
Measures may vary: 156 mm; 837 mm²

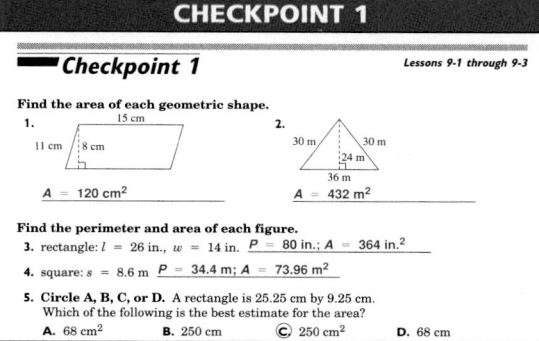

20. Choose A, B, C, or D. A right triangle and a rectangle have equal bases and equal heights. How do their perimeters compare? (*Hint:* Use *Guess and Test.*) **B**

A. The perimeter of the triangle is greater.
B. The perimeter of the rectangle is greater.
C. The perimeters are equal.
D. It is impossible to tell.

Find the area of each parallelogram. Use units².

21.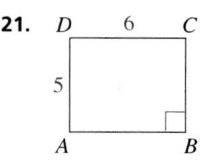

D 6 C

5

A B

30 units²

22.

D 6 C

5 4.3

A B

25.8 units²

23.

D 6 C

5 3.5

A B

21 units²

24. a. Copy the trapezoid onto paper. Split it into two triangles with 3 cm heights. Then find the area. **12 cm²**

b. *Writing* Explain how you can find the area of this trapezoid by splitting it into two triangles.
See margin.

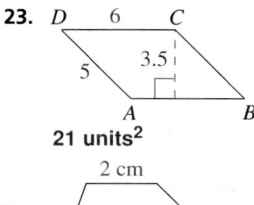

2 cm

3 cm

6 cm

CHECKPOINT 1

▬▬**Checkpoint 1**   *Lessons 9-1 through 9-3*

Find the area of each geometric shape.

1.

15 cm

11 cm 8 cm

A = 120 cm²

2.

30 m 30 m

24 m

36 m

A = 432 m²

Find the perimeter and area of each figure.

3. rectangle: *l* = 26 in., *w* = 14 in. *P* = 80 in.; *A* = 364 in.²

4. square: *s* = 8.6 m *P* = 34.4 m; *A* = 73.96 m²

5. Circle A, B, C, or D. A rectangle is 25.25 cm by 9.25 cm. Which of the following is the best estimate for the area?
A. 68 cm²   **B.** 250 cm   **C.** 250 cm²   **D.** 68 cm

pages 394–396   On Your Own

24b. Draw a diagonal connecting 2 vertices. Find the area of one triangle using the greater base and the altitude of the trapezoid. Find the area of the second triangle using the shorter base and the altitude of the trapezoid. The area of the trapezoid is the sum of the areas of the two triangles.

PRACTICE

Practice 9-3 Areas of Parallelograms and Triangles

Find the area of each figure.

1.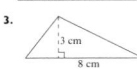

6 square units

2.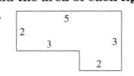

8 square units

3.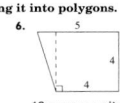

12 cm²

4.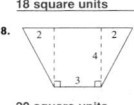

28 m²

Find the area of each figure by dividing it into polygons.

5.

12 square units

6.

18 square units

7.

14 square units

8.

20 square units

9. Draw and label a triangle and a parallelogram that each have an area of 20 square units.
Answers may vary. Sample drawings are shown.

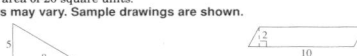

Tell whether each statement is *true* or *false*.

10. A parallelogram and triangle can have the same base and area. true
11. Two triangles that have the same base always have the same area. false
12. An obtuse triangle must have greater area than an acute triangle. false

In copymaster and workbook formats

RETEACHING

Reteaching 9-3 Areas of Parallelograms and Triangles

Parallelogram
To find the area of a parallelogram, multiply base times height.

$A = b \times h$

Find the area of the parallelogram.

$A = b \times h$
$= 3 \times 6$
$= 18 \text{ cm}^2$

The area is 18 cm².

Triangle
The area of the triangle is $\frac{1}{2}$ of base times height.

$A = \frac{1}{2}b \times h$

Find the area of the triangle.

$A = \frac{1}{2} \times b \times h$
$= \frac{1}{2} \times 3 \times 6$
$= 9 \text{ cm}^2$

The area is 9 cm².

Find the area of each parallelogram.

1. $b = 6$ ft, $h = 8$ ft
48 ft²

2. $b = 12$ in., $h = 9$ in.
108 in.²

3. $b = 6$ yd, $h = 12$ yd
72 yd²

4. $b = 2.8$ in., $h = 3.4$ in.
9.52 in.²

5. $b = 31$ yd, $h = 19$ yd
589 yd²

6. $b = 4.5$ m, $h = 4.5$ m
20.25 m²

Find the area of each triangle.

7. $b = 8$ cm, $h = 14$ cm
56 cm²

8. $b = 7$ in., $h = 18$ in.
63 in.²

9. $b = 11$ m, $h = 4.6$ m
25.3 m²

10. $b = 6.4$ ft, $h = 3.5$ ft
11.2 ft²

11. $b = 104$ in., $h = 55$ in.
2,860 in.²

12. $b = 5.9$ cm, $h = 4.2$ cm
12.39 cm²

13. $b = 1.7$ m, $h = 3.3$ m
2.805 m²

14. $b = 5.8$ yd, $h = 5.8$ yd
16.82 yd²

15. $b = 8.6$ in., $h = 0.8$ in.
3.44 in.²

ENRICHMENT

Minds on Math Transparency

9-3

Items at a garage sale were priced at $1, $2, and $5. Marty spent $21. He bought one more item for $2 than items for $1. He bought twice as many $2 items as $5 items. How many of each item did he buy?

three $1 items, four $2 items, two $5 items

See *Solution Key* for worked-out answers.

396

LESSON QUIZ

1. Find the area of a parallelogram with a base of 12.6 cm and height of 10.5 cm.
132.3 cm²

2. Find the area of the figure. 30 cm²

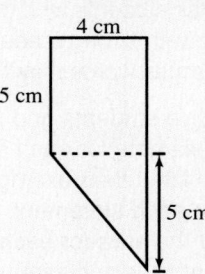

4 cm

5 cm

5 cm

Copy each figure on dot paper. Then find each area. Use units².

25.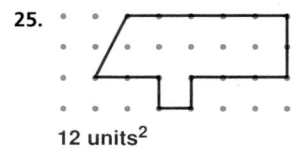

12 units²

26.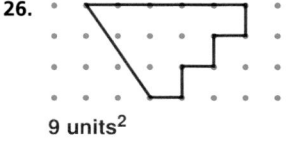

9 units²

27.

16 units²

28. Find the area of the figure at the right. 38 m²

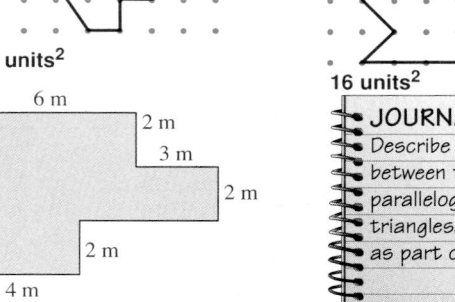

6 m
2 m
3 m
6 m
2 m
2 m
4 m

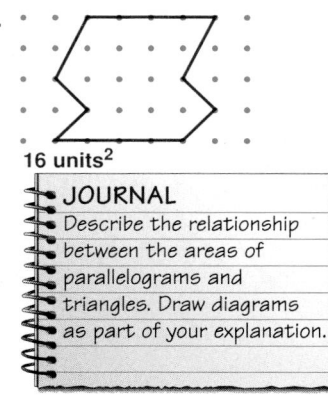

JOURNAL
Describe the relationship between the areas of parallelograms and triangles. Draw diagrams as part of your explanation.

Mixed Review

Find each product. *(Lesson 6-8)*

29. $3\frac{5}{8} \times \frac{1}{2}$ $1\frac{13}{16}$

30. $5\frac{3}{5} \times 3\frac{3}{4}$ 21

31. $2\frac{2}{3} \times 8\frac{3}{4}$ $23\frac{1}{3}$

32. $4\frac{1}{6} \times 1\frac{7}{8}$ $7\frac{13}{16}$

33. $12\frac{3}{5} \times 2\frac{1}{2}$ $31\frac{1}{2}$

Use a protractor to draw angles with the following measures. *(Lesson 8-2)* 34–39. Check students' work.

34. 32°
35. 173°
36. 92°
37. 104°
38. 12°
39. 45°

40. The club wants to buy 8 pizzas at $6.99 each and some juice. Kevin thinks that each of the 32 club members should pay $1.75. Barbara thinks they need to pay $2.00 each. Who do you think made a better estimate? Explain. *(Lesson 4-1)*
Barbara; Kevin would collect enough money for pizza, but not for pizza and juice.

✓ CHECKPOINT 1   Lessons 9-1 through 9-3

1. How much lace do you need to trim a 72 in. × 48 in. rectangular tablecloth?
240 in.

2. A rectangle is 35 in. long. Its width is 5 in. What are its perimeter and area?
80 in.; 175 in.²

Find the area of each figure.

3. rectangle: $\ell = 7$ in., $w = 12$ in. 84 in.²

4. square: $s = 8.5$ cm 72.25 cm²

5. parallelogram: $b = 13$ m, $h = 6$ m 78 m²

6. triangle: $b = 50$ ft, $h = 40$ ft 1,000 ft²

In Lesson 9-3, students learned how to find the areas of parallelograms, triangles, and complex figures. This toolbox allows students to explore forming and drawing tessellations.

ERROR ALERT! Students may not be able to determine how many figures they must sketch before they have shown that figures tessellate. **Remediation:** Have pairs of students continue the example tessellations.

One student can continue adding figures to Example 1 while the partner continues Example 2. Then discuss with the class how students realized each pattern could be continued indefinitely.

ASSESSMENT Exercises 1–4 Have students meet with a partner to compare results. Ask each pair of students to discuss which figures they can and cannot use to form a tessellation. Also have them consider why one of the figures (the circle in Exercise 3) cannot be made into a tessellation.

■ **ADDITIONAL PROBLEM**

Give students pattern blocks. Ask them to find as many different tessallation patterns as they can using the shapes.

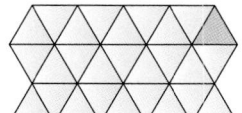

EXPLORATION

Tessellations

→ **After Lesson 9-3**

A *tessellation* is a repeated geometric design. It covers a plane with no gaps or overlaps. Brick walls and tiled floors are examples of tessellations.

■ **EXAMPLE 1**

Name the polygon used to form the tessellation below.

◄── Find the figure that repeats. It is a triangle.

The tessellation above is formed by a triangle.

You can use more than one type of polygon to form a tessellation.

■ **EXAMPLE 2**

Form a tessellation using the polygons at the right.

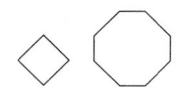

◄── Arrange the polygons with no gaps or overlaps.

1. yes

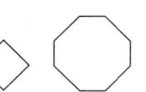

2. yes

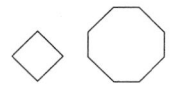

4. yes

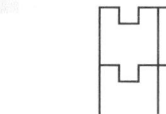

Trace each figure. Can you use it to form a tessellation? If so, sketch the tessellation.   1–2, 4. See above right.

1.

2.
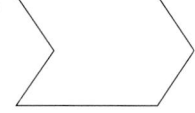

3.
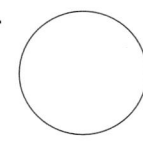

no

4.

5. *Open-ended* Use tiles, dot paper, or cutouts to create a tessellation from squares and equilateral triangles. **Check students' work.**

Materials/Manipulatives
• tiles
• cutouts
• dot paper

Resources

📦 **Teaching Resources**
Teaching Aids Masters 1, 2, 3, 7, 8, 9, 19

 **Transparencies**
1, 6, 9, 20, 21

Technology Options

Prentice Hall Technology

💾 💿 **Software for Learners**
• Hot Page™ 25*

*Available on CD-ROM only

1 Focus

CONNECTING TO PRIOR KNOWLEDGE Ask: *What is the perimeter of a rectangle that is 10 × 15 cm?* **50 cm** Have students find examples of perimeters for other objects. Ask students: *Since a circle does not have sides, can you find the perimeter of a circle?*

Explain. **Yes; you can measure the distance around the outer edge.**

2 Teach

THINK AND DISCUSS

VISUAL LEARNING Have students trace the red and blue lights with their fingertips as you review the difference between the words *circumference* and *diameter*.

CONNECTION TO TECHNOLOGY
Question 1a Students may want to record their table in a spreadsheet program. Consider using all student's data in a spreadsheet.

WRITING Question 1b Have students make a table showing the dimensions for each circle. Add a column for the result of $C \div d$. Then have them summarize the results.

Lesson Planning Options

Prerequisite Skills
- identifying parts of a circle (8-10)
- rounding (3-6)

Vocabulary/Symbols
circumference, pi (π)

Materials/Manipulatives
- calculator
- centimeter ruler
- string

Resources

 Student Edition

Skills Handbook, p. 535
Extra Practice, p. 530
Glossary/Study Guide

 Teaching Resources

Chapter Support File, Ch. 9
- Lesson Planner 9-4
- Practice 9-4, Reteaching 9-4
- Alternative Activity 9-4
- Answer Masters 9-4
Glossary, Spanish Resources

 Transparencies
Minds on Math 9-4

Warm Up

Write in order from least to greatest: 0.00602, 0.0062, 0.0620, 0.00600. **0.00600, 0.00602, 0.0062, 0.0620**

398

9-4 Gathering Data to Explore π

What You'll Learn

▼ To estimate π and the circumference of a circle

▼ To use π to find the circumference of a circle

...And Why

You can use the circumference of a circle to solve entertainment and sports problems.

Here's How

Look for questions that
- build understanding
✔ check understanding

QUICKreview

The distance across a circle (through its center) is the *diameter*. The *radius* is half the length of the diameter. For example, if the diameter is 10 in., the radius is 5 in.

1a. Check students' work. Answers will vary, but the $\frac{C}{d}$ column entries should all be close to 3.

b. Each ratio is about 3.

THINK AND DISCUSS

▼ *Estimating π and Circumference*

Suppose you design the circular stage shown below. How will the size of the stage affect the number of red and blue lights you need?

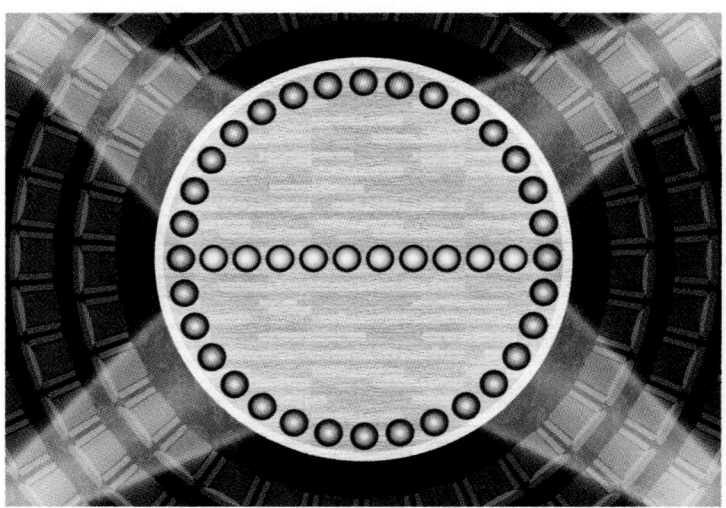

The distance around a circle is its **circumference.** You can use the relationship between the circumference and diameter of a circle to solve the stage problem.

1. a. First explore the ratio of the circumference of a circle to its diameter $\left(\frac{C}{d} = \blacksquare\right)$. Use a string and a centimeter ruler to measure the circumference and diameter of at least three different circles. Measure to the nearest tenth of a centimeter. Make a table with columns C, d, and $\frac{C}{d}$. Record your results.

   b. *Writing* What pattern do you see in the ratio $\frac{C}{d}$?

   c. *Analyze* How does the number of red lights you need compare to the number of blue lights? Does that change if the circle changes? **32 red lights : 10 blue lights; no, the relationship is the same when the circle changes size.**

FOR EXAMPLE

A theater in the round has a stage with a diameter of 55 ft. Find the circumference of the stage. Use a value of 3.14 for π. Round to the nearest whole unit. **173 ft**

KINESTHETIC LEARNING Question 4 Have students model this problem. Suggest students secure a string about 25 in. long to a piece of cardboard with a brad. Let the brad represent the center of the stage. Have another student hold the string at its end and move in a circle just as the drummer moves around the stage. Have students use a ruler to draw the diameter.

AEP DIVERSITY Ask students who have difficulty reading English to draw pictures for each problem to help understand each situation. Have them work with a partner to verify their understanding.

ASSESSMENT Question 8 Allow students to use a calculator. Remind students to use the correct formula for the given information. Have students exchange papers to check their understanding.

VISUAL LEARNING Have students write the formula for finding the circumference of a circle on an index card to place on their desk. Students may want to add the formula to any list they may have.

---

2. a. ✔ *Try It Out* Use your results from Question 1 to help estimate the circumference of the circle at the right. **about 12 cm**

   b. Find the square's perimeter. **16 cm**

   c. ⬛ *Think About It* Is the circumference of the circle less than or greater than the perimeter of the square? Does this make sense? Explain.

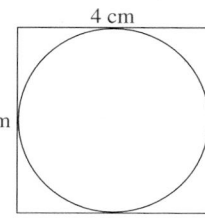
4 cm
4 cm

c. Reasoning may vary. Sample: Less; yes; the path following the circle is shorter than the path following the sides of the square.

You can use the relationship between the circumference and diameter of a circle to solve problems.

PROBLEM SOLVING HINT
Draw a diagram.

3. Suppose you design the circular stage to have an 83-ft diameter. The light bulbs are 1 ft apart. **about 249 ft**

   a. ✔ *Try It Out* Estimate the circumference of the stage.

   b. ⬛ *Explain* How did you find your estimate? **Multiply 83 by 3.**

   c. ⬛ *Draw a Conclusion* Will 200 red light bulbs be enough to go completely around the stage? Explain.
   No; the circumference is about 249 ft so the estimate is low.

4. Suppose the drummer sits 25 ft from the center of the stage.

   a. ⬛ *Spatial Reasoning* Draw a diagram that shows the drummer's path as the stage goes around once in one minute. **Check students' work.**

   b. What is the diameter of the circle made by the drummer's path? **50 ft**

   c. ⬛ *Analyze* Estimate the circumference of the circle made by the drummer's path in 1 minute. **about 150 ft**

   d. About how far does the drummer travel in 1 second?

   e. ⬛ *Draw a Conclusion* Write the speed at which the drummer travels on the stage as feet per second (ft/s). Will the drummer travel faster than 10 mi/h? **2.5 ft/s; no**

   d. **about 2.5 ft**

The ratio $\frac{C}{d}$ equals a number close to 3 that is called pi. The rounded value 3.14 is often used to represent the value of pi. We use the symbol π (read as "pi") to stand for this value.

QUICKreview

5,280 ft = 1 mi

5. ⬛ *Number Sense* Which point on the number line represents π? Explain. **Point *D*; its coordinate is close to 3.**

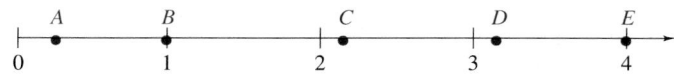

Now you may assign Exercises 1–5, 30.

Technology Options

Prentice Hall Technology

Software for Learners
- Math Blaster® Mystery*
- Interactive Student Tutorial, Chapter 9*

Teaching Resource Software
- Computer Item Generator 9-4
- Resource Pro™ Chapter 9*

Internet • For related mathematics activities, visit the Prentice Hall site at www.phschool.com/math

*Available on CD-ROM only

Assignment Options for Exercises On Your Own

To provide flexible scheduling, this lesson can be split into parts.

▼1 Core 1–5
   Extension 30

▼2 Core 6–15, 20–29
   Extension 16–19, 31

Use Mixed Review to maintain skills.

REASONING and KINESTHETIC LEARNING
Question 10a Have students place a red ribbon at one point on a bicycle tire. Ask a student to roll the bicycle slowly. Have another student use chalk to mark each point where the ribbon hits the sidewalk. Have students measure the distance between the chalk marks. Then have them compare the circumference of the tire to the distance between the chalk marks.

EXTENSION and TACTILE LEARNING Have students draw a circle with a compass. Have them estimate the circumference with pieces of uncooked spaghetti. Have students break the spaghetti and lay the straight noodles on the circle. Then have them move the noodles from the circle into a straight line. Have them decide how close their estimate will be and if it will be greater or less than the actual value. Then have them measure the diameter of the circle with a ruler and calculate the circumference. Have them compare the values and see if their prediction was correct.

CONNECTION TO TECHNOLOGY If you have block scheduling or extended class periods, you may wish to have students visit web sites devoted to π. Have students share examples of problems or puzzles they find that involve the use of π.

CONNECTING TO THE STUDENTS' WORLD Ask students for examples in their own lives of when they might need to know the circumference or diameter of a circle.
Answers may vary. Sample: measuring the size of a bicycle tire

❷ Using π to Find Circumference

You can use $\frac{C}{d} = \pi$ to find a circle's circumference C if you know its diameter d. Since $\frac{C}{d} = \pi$, $C = \pi d$.

CIRCUMFERENCE OF A CIRCLE
$C = \pi d$ (Circumference = pi × diameter)
$C = 2\pi r$ (Circumference = 2 × pi × radius)

6. ♣ *Explain* Why do you think $C = 2\pi r$ can also be used to find the circumference of a circle? **2r = d**

You can search the Internet for computer programs that calculate π to many decimal places. There are many Web sites devoted to π.

Computers can approximate the value of π to thousands of decimal places. You can use the value 3.14 to solve most problems. Also, many calculators have a π key.

7. ♣ *Calculator* Press the π key on your calculator. What is the result? **3.1415927; the number of digits displayed may vary.**

■ **EXAMPLE**   *Real-World Problem Solving*

Archery A regulation archery target has a circle with a 48-in. diameter. Find the circumference of a regulation target.

Estimate: $C = \pi d = \pi \times 48 \approx 3 \times 50 = 150$

Calculate: 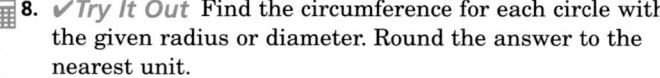 [π] [×] 48 [=] *150.7964474* ← Use a calculator. When necessary, round the answer to the nearest unit.

The circumference is about 151 in.

8. ✔ *Try It Out* Find the circumference for each circle with the given radius or diameter. Round the answer to the nearest unit.
a. $d = 1$ ft **3 ft**   b. $r = 13.5$ cm **85 cm**
c. $r = 22$ in. **138 in.**   d. $d = 30$ m **94 m**

9. ♣ *Think About It* The archery target at the left is a regulation one. Use the information in the Example. Estimate the length of the sides of the square around the target. **Sample: about 60 in.**

3 Practice/Assess

MENTAL MATH and ESTIMATION
Exercises 1–5 Ask students if their estimates for the circumference are greater or less than the actual circumference.
Estimated circumferences are less because 3 is less than 3.14.

ERROR ALERT! Exercises 6–15 Some students may incorrectly apply the formula $C = \pi d$ to find the circumference by substituting the value of r in place of d.
Remediation: Remind students that since the radius is half of the diameter, they need to use $C = 2\pi r$.

Exercises 6–15 Students may wish to compare the difference between using 3.14 and the π key on the calculator.

Exercises 16–25 Remind students they can use $d = \frac{C}{p}$ for their formula.

WRAP UP

IDENTIFYING THE BIG IDEA Ask students to explain how to find the circumference of a circle when they know the diameter or radius. Ask students to define π.

▽ **PROJECT LINK** Suggest students find the circumference or perimter of each shape they drew.

pages 398–401 **Think and Discuss**
10a. 69 in.; the tire rolls on the ground making one complete revolution between the two marks.
  b. Answers may vary. About 22 in.

You can use the circumference formula to find a circle's diameter if you know its circumference.

PROBLEM SOLVING HINT
Draw a diagram. Show the tire track and the point where the pebble makes a mark.

10. How good a detective are you? A pebble stuck in a bicycle's tire left a mark in the tire track every 69 in.
   a. *Reasoning* What is the circumference of the tire? How do you know? **See margin.**
   b. Estimate the diameter of the tire. **See margin.**
   ▦ c. *Calculator* Use the π key. Find the diameter of the tire. Round the answer to the nearest half inch. **22.0 in.**

Now you may assign Exercises 6–29, 31.

EXERCISES *On Your Own*

Estimate the circumference of a circle with the given radius or diameter. (*Hint:* To estimate, use 3 for π.)

1. $d = 5$ cm
   about 15 cm
2. $d = 11$ m
   about 33 m
3. $r = 1$ in.
   about 6 in.
4. $r = 3$ m
   about 18 m
5. $d = 40$ mi
   about 120 mi

▦ *Calculator* **Find the circumference of a circle with the given radius or diameter. Round the answer to the nearest unit.**

6. $d = 15$ ft
   47 ft
7. $d = 50$ m
   157 m
8. $r = 17$ in.
   107 in.
9. $r = 64$ m
   402 m
10. $d = 200$ ft
    628 ft

11. $d = 3.9$ m
    12 m
12. $r = 9.5$ in
    60 in.
13. $d = 17.5$ ft
    110 ft
14. $r = 0.39$ km
    2 km
15. $d = 3,183$ m
    9,995 m

16. **Choose A, B, C, or D.** If you double the radius of a circle, what happens to the circumference? **B**

   A. The circumference remains the same.
   B. The circumference is doubled.
   C. The circumference is tripled.
   D. The circumference is quadrupled.

17. Find the diameter and radius of a circle with a circumference of 62.8 mm. **20 mm; 10mm**

18. *Pets* A dog tied to a post gets exercise by running in a circle. One day the dog ran around the post 100 times with the 10-ft rope stretched tightly. (Assume that the rope did not wrap around the post.) Did the dog run at least 1 mi? **yes**

19. *Bicycles* A bicycle popular in the late 1800s had a large wheel in the front and a smaller wheel in the back. If the diameter of the large wheel was 3 ft, about how far would the bicycle travel as that wheel made one full turn? **Sample: about 9 ft**

401

PRACTICE

Practice 9-4 *Gathering Data to Explore Pi*

Use 3 for π to estimate the circumference of a circle with the given radius or diameter.
1. $d = 4$ in. <u>about 12 in.</u>   2. $d = 8$ cm <u>about 24 cm</u>
3. $r = 6$ m <u>about 36 m</u>   4. $r = 10$ ft <u>about 60 ft</u>
5. $r = 3$ in. <u>about 18 in.</u>   6. $d = 20$ cm <u>about 60 cm</u>

Use a calculator to find the circumference of a circle with the given radius or diameter. Round to the nearest unit.
7. $r = 18$ cm <u>113 cm</u>   8. $d = 44$ ft <u>138 ft</u>   9. $r = 28$ in. <u>176 in.</u>
10. $r = 24$ m <u>151 m</u>   11. $d = 34$ in. <u>107 in.</u>   12. $d = 42$ cm <u>132 cm</u>

Use a calculator to find the diameter of a circle with the given circumference. Round to the nearest unit.
13. $C = 128$ ft <u>41 ft</u>   14. $C = 36$ cm <u>11 cm</u>   15. $C = 200$ m <u>64 m</u>
16. $C = 85$ in. <u>27 in.</u>   17. $C = 57$ cm <u>18 cm</u>   18. $C = 132$ in. <u>42 in.</u>

Complete the table. Use a string and metric ruler to measure the circumference and the diameter of four different circular objects. Then check to see if the ratio $\frac{C}{d}$ = about 3.14.   Answers may vary. Check students' work.

	Object	Circumference, C	Diameter, d	$\frac{C}{d}$
19.				
20.				
21.				
22.				

23. Use the table you have just completed. What can you conclude about the ratio $\frac{C}{d}$?
$\frac{C}{d}$ is about 3.14.

In copymaster and workbook formats

RETEACHING

Reteaching 9-4 *Gathering Data to Explore Pi*

Circumference is the distance around a circle.
To find circumference:
    Multiply π times the diameter. $C = \pi d$
    Or multiply π times twice the radius. $C = 2\pi r$
To estimate quickly, use $\pi \approx 3$. To be more exact, use $\pi \approx 3.14$.

Estimate the circumference of the circle.
$C \approx 3d$
    $= 3 \times 8$
    $= 24$ cm
Find the circumference of the circle.
$C = \pi d$
    $\approx 3.14 \times 8$
    $= 25.12$ cm
The circumference is about 24 cm.
More precisely, it's 25.12 cm.

diameter = 8 cm
radius = 4 cm

Use 3 for π to estimate the circumference of a circle with the given radius or diameter.
1. 4 cm — <u>12 cm</u>   2. 9 in. — <u>27 in.</u>   3. 8 mi — <u>48 mi</u>
4. $r = 12$ in. <u>72 in.</u>   5. $d = 15$ yd <u>45 yd</u>   6. $d = 7$ m <u>21 m</u>
7. $d = 13$ ft <u>39 ft</u>   8. $r = 21$ yd <u>126 yd</u>   9. $r = 19$ cm <u>114 cm</u>

Find the circumference of a circle with the given radius or diameter. Round to the nearest unit.
10. 5 cm — <u>16 cm</u>   11. 23 in. — <u>72 in.</u>   12. 14 ft — <u>88 ft</u>
13. $r = 4.5$ cm <u>28 cm</u>   14. $d = 21.8$ cm <u>68 in.</u>   15. $r = 0.8$ m <u>5 m</u>

Reteaching

ENRICHMENT

Minds on Math Transparency
9-4

The diameter of a circle is tripled. How does this affect the area of the circle?

The area of the new circle is 9 times the area of the original circle.

See *Solution Key* for worked-out answers.

LESSON QUIZ

Find the circumference of the following circles. Use $\pi = 3.14$. Round the answer to the nearest whole unit.

1. a circle with a diameter of 114.5 cm
360 cm

2. a circle with a radius of 22.4 ft **141 ft**

3. Find the diameter of a circle that has a circumference of 4772.8 mm **1,520 mm**

Calculator **Find the diameter of a circle with the given circumference. Round the answer to the nearest tenth of a unit.**

20. 192 ft **61.1 ft**   21. 85 cm **27.1 cm**   22. 22.5 in. **7.2 in.**   23. 56 m **17.8 m**   24. 1,273 mm **405.4 mm**

25. 2 yd **0.64 yd**   26. 27.5 ft **8.8 ft**   27. 68.7 cm **21.9 cm**   28. 3.75 in. **1.2 in.**   29. 19.67 m **6.3 m**

Choose **For Exercises 30 and 31, use 3.14 for π or use the π key on a calculator.**

30. *Drafting* Suppose you want to draw a circle with a circumference of 10 cm. How wide should you set your compass (to the nearest 0.1 cm)? **1.6 cm**

31. *Cycling* The diameter of a bicycle's wheel is 28 in. About how many times does each wheel make a complete circle when the bicycle travels 1,000 ft? **about 11 times**

Mixed Review

Name each polygon. *(Lesson 8-5)*

32. **rectangle**   33. **octagon**   34. **acute triangle**   35. **pentagon**

Compare using <, >, =. *(Lesson 5-8)*

36. $\frac{5}{8}$ < $\frac{11}{16}$ 37. $\frac{7}{10}$ < $\frac{7}{8}$ 38. $\frac{121}{500}$ < $\frac{1}{2}$ 39. $\frac{9}{36}$ = $\frac{7}{28}$ 40. $\frac{5}{8}$ < $\frac{11}{12}$ 41. $\frac{2}{5}$ > $\frac{1}{4}$

42. *Choose a Strategy* At a gift shop, Nara bought twice as many cards as Ann. Ann bought 3 fewer cards than Jamil but three more than Kamala. Ann bought 8 cards. How many cards did each of the others buy? **Nara bought 16 cards, Jamil—11 cards, Kamala—5 cards.**

CHAPTER PROJECT

PROJECT LINK: DIAGRAMING

Draw a diagram of the two Web home pages you have chosen. Draw a rectangle, triangle, or circle around each block of text or graphic (photograph or artwork) on the page. Label each area as text, graphic, or white space. Save these diagrams for use later. **Check students' work.**

9-5 Teaching Notes

1 Focus

CONNECTING TO PRIOR KNOWLEDGE Ask students how to find the area of a rectangle and a triangle. Discuss how they might find the area of a circle. **Answers may vary. Sample: length × width, $\frac{1}{2}$ base × height; divide circle into other figures.**

2 Teach

Work Together

Have students work in groups of three to four. Remind students that congruent figures have the same size and shape. Be sure students are aware of what value to use for π.

ESTIMATION Question 2b Make sure that students' estimates are reasonable before they answer 2c.

REASONING Question 3 Ask students to compare their estimates. Have them explain what strategies they used.

THINK AND DISCUSS

Question 5 Have students discuss how close their estimate is to the actual area. Have them discuss whether they think the method used in Question 2 was a good method for estimating.

9-5 Area of a Circle

What You'll Learn

1 To find the area of a circle

2 To find combined areas of circles and polygons

...And Why

You can use the area of a circle to find areas on a basketball court.

Here's How

Look for questions that
▪ build understanding
✔ check understanding

Work Together

Exploring the Area of a Circle

Use a compass to draw a circle with radius 7 cm on centimeter graph paper. With a ruler, divide the circle into eight congruent wedges as shown.

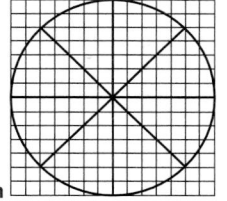

1. ▪*Geometry* About how many square centimeters are in the circle? What is the circumference of the circle? **about 152 cm²; 43.96 cm**

Cut out the circle and the eight wedges you drew. Rearrange the wedges into the figure shown below.

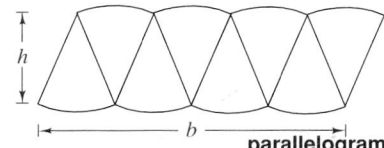

parallelogram

2. **a.** What quadrilateral is the new figure similar to?
   b. 22 cm; 7 cm **b.** ▪*Estimation* Estimate the base length b and height h.
   c. 154 cm² **c.** Use your answers to parts (a) and (b) to estimate the area of the new figure. (*Hint:* Use the formula $A = b \times h$.)
   d. How does the number of square centimeters in the uncut circle compare to the number of square centimeters in the new figure? **The estimates are about the same.**

THINK AND DISCUSS

▼ *Finding Area of a Circle*

You can use this formula to find the area A of a circle.

Area of a Circle

$$A = \pi \times r \times r = \pi r^2$$

Lesson Planning Options

Prerequisite Skills
- circle construction (precourse)
- metric units (3-8)

Materials/Manipulatives
- compass
- scissors
- centimeter graph paper
- straightedge
- calculator

Resources

 Student Edition

Skills Handbook, p. 540
Extra Practice, p. 530
Glossary/Study Guide

 Teaching Resources

Chapter Support File, Ch. 9
- Lesson Planner 9-5
- Practice 9-5, Reteaching 9-5
- Answer Masters 9-5
Teaching Aids Masters 1–3, 19
Glossary, Spanish Resources

 Transparencies
1, 9, 10, 18, 19, 94, Minds on Math 9-5

Warm Up

Lucy and Shay were both batting under 0.300. Lucy's average was 0.298. Shay's was one one-thousandth of a point higher than Lucy's. What was Shay's batting average? **0.299**

■ ADDITIONAL EXAMPLES

FOR EXAMPLE 1

Find the area of a circle with radius 10 cm. Round your answer to the nearest tenth of a unit. **314.2 cm²**

FOR EXAMPLE 2

The Pavilion plans to have a carpenter build a circular gazebo for wedding ceremonies on The Pavilion lawn. The size of the lawn is 60 ft by 30 ft. Find the area of the lawn around the gazebo. Use 3.14 for π. **about 1,093.5 ft²**

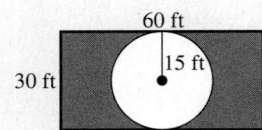

60 ft
15 ft
30 ft

ERROR ALERT! Example 2 Students may not understand why they need to multiply the width of the rectangle by $\frac{1}{2}$ to find the radius. **Remediation:** Ask students: *What is the diameter of the half circle?* **12** Remind students that the radius is $\frac{1}{2}$ the diameter.

CONNECTION TO GEOMETRY Suggest that half the class use the formula $C = \pi d$. Have the other half of the class use the formula $C = 2\pi r$. Have students discuss whether this makes a difference.

ASSESSMENT Have students work with a partner to write a description of the difference between the circumference and the area of a circle. Have students include equations for finding circumference and area. Ask pairs to provide examples and share answers with the class.

Technology Options

Prentice Hall Technology

 **Software for Learners**

- Hot Page™ 26*
- Math Blaster® Mystery*
- Interactive Student Tutorial, Chapter 9*

  Teaching Resource Software

- Computer Item Generator 9-5
- Resource Pro™ Chapter 9*

Internet • For related mathematics activities, visit the Prentice Hall site at www.phschool.com/math

*Available on CD-ROM only

Assignment Options for Exercises On Your Own

To provide flexible scheduling, this lesson can be split into parts.

1 Core 1–30, 34–51
Extension 31–33

2 Core 52–59
Extension 60

Use Mixed Review to maintain skills.

404

■ EXAMPLE 1

Calculator Find the area of a circle with radius 5 cm. Round your answer to the nearest tenth of a unit.

Estimate: $A = \pi r^2 \longrightarrow A \approx 3 \times 5^2 = 3 \times 25 = 75$

Use a calculator.

π ✕ 5 x² ▤ **78.539817** ◄—$A = \pi r^2$

The area is about 78.5 cm².

3. ✓Try It Out Find the area of a circle with the given radius or diameter. Round each answer to the nearest tenth of a unit.

a. $r = 7$ mi
153.9 mi²
b. $d = 16$ in.
201.0 in.²
c. $d = 10.5$ m
86.5 m²
d. $r = 5.5$ cm
95.0 cm²

4. a. *Calculator* Find the area of a circle with radius 7 cm.
b. How does this area compare to the number of square centimeters you counted for the circle in Question 1?

4a. about 153.9 cm²
  b. The estimate is close to the actual area.

Now you may assign Exercises 1–51.

2 Finding Areas of Circles and Polygons

You can find the area of a figure that contains polygons and circles.

■ EXAMPLE 2   *Real-World Problem Solving*

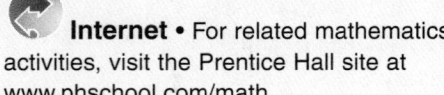

Basketball The shaded foul shot area at the right contains half a circle and a rectangle. Find the area of the shaded region.

Area of rectangle:

$\ell \times w = 19 \times 12 = 228$

Area of circle:

The radius is $\frac{1}{2}d$ or 6 ft.

$A = \pi r^2$

$A = 3.14 \times 6^2 = 3.14 \times 36 = 113.04$

$\text{area of rectangle} + \frac{1}{2}\left(\text{area of circle}\right) = 228 + \frac{1}{2}(113.04) = 284.52$

The area of the shaded region is 284.52 ft², or about $284\frac{1}{2}$ ft².

19 ft
12 ft

3 Practice/Assess

EXERCISES On Your Own

ERROR ALERT! Exercises 1–4 Some students may find the circumference instead of the area because they confuse the formulas. **Remediation:** Remind students the formula for the area is $A = \pi r^2$. Encourage students to come up with a mnemonic to help them remember this formula is for circle area.

Exercises 1–4 Caution students to check whether a figure shows a diameter or radius measurement before they find the area.

MENTAL MATH Exercises 5–9 Remind students to divide a diameter measurement mentally by 2 before they find the area.

ERROR ALERT! Exercises 11–27 When finding the area, some students may incorrectly square the *diameter*. **Remediation:** Remind students the formula for the Area of a circle is πr^2. Have them find all the circle radii for the exercises before using the formula. Ask: *How do you find the radius from the diameter?* **divide the diameter by 2.**

TACTILE LEARNING and WRITING Exercise 30 Suggest that students use compasses to draw and cut out two circles with the following dimensions: a radius of 10 in. and a diameter of 18 in. Have them place one circle on top of the other to compare areas. Ask: *How much larger is the larger circle?* **about 60 in.²**

5a. Find the area of the rectangle 47 ft × 50 ft. Find the area of the half circle by multiplying (22 × 22 × 3.14) ÷ 2. Subtract the area of the half circle from the shaded area.

b. 1,590.12 ft²

5. In the diagram at the right, the 3-point area of a basketball court is shaded.

   a. ♣*Explain* Describe how to find the area of the shaded region.

   b. ✓*Try It Out* Find the area. Use 3.14 for π.

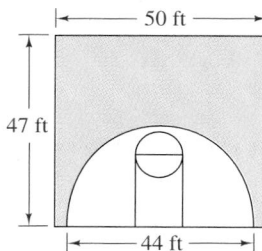

Now you may assign Exercises 52–60.

EXERCISES On Your Own

🖩 *Calculator* **Find the area of each circle. Round each answer to the nearest tenth of a unit.**

1.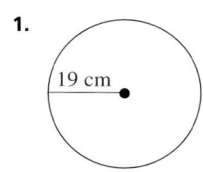

19 cm

1,133.5 cm²

2.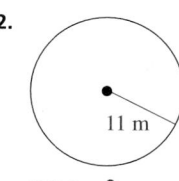

11 m

379.9 m²

3.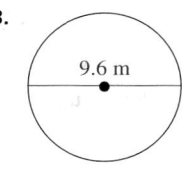

9.6 m

72.3 m²

4.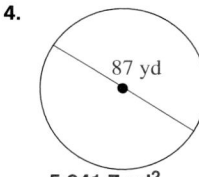

87 yd

5,941.7 yd²

Mental Math **Estimate the area of each circle with the given radius or diameter.** (*Hint:* To estimate, use 3 for π.)

5. $r = 2$ in. **6.** $d = 2$ m **7.** $r = 10$ cm **8.** $r = 5$ in. **9.** $d = 6$ mm **10.** $r = 20$ cm
  about 12 in.² about 3 m² about 300 cm² about 75 in.² about 27 mm² about 1,200 cm²

Find the area of each circle with the given radius or diameter. Round each answer to the nearest tenth of a unit.

11. $d = 20$ m **12.** $d = 9$ ft **13.** $d = 4$ yd **14.** $r = 6$ cm **15.** $r = 15$ in. **16.** $r = 1.3$ m
  314.2 m² 63.6 ft² 12.6 yd² 113.0 cm² 706.5 in.² 5.3 m²

17. $r = 3$ mm **18.** $r = 10$ ft **19.** $r = 4$ in. **20.** $d = 13$ m **21.** $d = 11$ ft **22.** $d = 2.4$ m
  28.3 mm² 314.0 ft² 50.2 in.² 132.7 m² 95.0 ft² 4.5 m²

23. $r = 4.4$ m **24.** $d = 2$ ft **25.** $r = 12$ ft **26.** $d = 10$ ft **27.** $r = 2.5$ m **28.** $d = 0.5$ m
  60.8 m² 3.1 ft² 452.2 ft² 78.5 ft² 19.6 m² 0.2 m²

29. *Communications* You can pick up the radio signal for station WAER FM 88 in Syracuse, New York, within a 45-mi radius of the station. What is the approximate area of the broadcast region? Use 3.14 for π. **6,358.5 mi²**

30. *Writing* Which is larger: a pan with a radius of 10 in. or a pan with a diameter of 18 in.? Explain. **A pan with a radius of 10 in.; if the diameter is 18 in., the radius is 9 in.**

DIVERSITY and EXTENSION

Exercises 31–33 You may wish to have students do a Web search or use the library to research other ways that Aztecs used math. Have students share their research results with the class.

Exercises 34–51 Caution students to make sure they use the radius to find the area of each circle. Remind them to divide the diameter by 2 before they solve.

Exercises 53 If students have difficulty, suggest they subtract the area of the smaller circle from the area of the larger circle.

Exercises 57–59 Estimate the areas by counting the squares. Check calculations with the estimate to make sure it is reasonable.

DIVERSITY Exercise 60 Some students may not know what hopscotch is. Have someone in class explain how to play. Consider letting students play at the end of the class period.

WRAP UP

IDENTIFYING THE BIG IDEA Ask students to explain how to find the area of a figure with both polygons and circles.

PROJECT LINK Provide students with centimeter rulers. Have students explain what formulas they used to find the text and graphic area on each page.

FOLLOW THE SUN

The Aztecs used their accurate knowledge of astronomy and mathematics to make a calendar called The Sun Stone. They carved the calendar on a circular stone 3.6 meters in diameter. The Aztecs began working on the calendar in 1427 and completed the work in 1479. The center circle of the stone shows the face of Tontiuh, the Aztec sun god. The 20 squares in the second ring name the 20 days of each Aztec month. There were 18 Aztec months.

31. Find the area of the Sun Stone. Use 3.14 for π.   **10.2 m²**

32. How long did it take the Aztecs to complete the calendar?   **52 years**

33. How many days were in the Aztec calendar?   **360 days**

▦ *Calculator* **Find the area of each circle with the given radius or diameter. Round each answer to the nearest tenth of a unit.**

34. $r = 9$ cm   **35.** $d = 7$ cm   **36.** $r = 25$ m   **37.** $d = 8$ ft   **38.** $d = 14$ in.   **39.** $r = 1$ mm
254.5 cm²   **38.5 cm²**   **1,963.5 m²**   **50.3 ft²**   **153.9 in.²**   **3.1 mm²**

40. $r = 7.5$ in.   **41.** $r = 18$ m   **42.** $d = 20$ ft   **43.** $d = 11$ in.   **44.** $r = 44$ cm   **45.** $d = 15$ ft
176.7 in.²   **1,017.9 m²**   **314.2 ft²**   **95.0 in.²**   **6,082.1 cm²**   **176.7 ft²**

46. $d = 4.5$ m   **47.** $d = 17$ in.   **48.** $r = 12$ in.   **49.** $r = 25$ in.   **50.** $d = 1.5$ m   **51.** $r = 0.5$ cm
15.9 m²   **227.0 in.²**   **452.4 in.²**   **1,963.5 in.²**   **1.8 m²**   **0.8 cm²**

▦ *Calculator* **Find the area of each shaded region. Round to the nearest unit.**

52.   **53.**   **54.**
3 m   16 cm
|← 10 m →| 10 m   4 m

74 m²   **66 m²**   **28 cm²**   8 cm

55.   **56.**
1 m   12 cm
1 m   6 cm   12 cm
1 m

19 m²   **31 cm²**

Find the area of the following figures. Round each answer to the nearest tenth of a unit.

1. A circle with a radius of 22.5 cm.
   1,589.6 cm²

2. Find the area of the shaded region.
   190.6 ft²

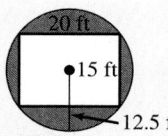

20 ft
15 ft
12.5 ft

PRACTICE

Practice 9-5 *Area of a Circle*

Use a calculator to find the area of a circle with the given radius or diameter. Round each answer to the nearest tenth.

1. $r = 12$ cm   452.4 cm²   2. $d = 15$ m   176.7 m²
3. $d = 9$ cm   63.6 cm²   4. $d = 14$ cm   153.9 cm²
5. $r = 22$ m   1,520.5 m²   6. $r = 28$ m   2,463.0 m²

Use a calculator to find the area of each circle. Round each answer to the nearest tenth.

7. 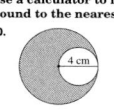 3 cm
8. 2.5 cm
9. 1.5 cm

28.3 cm²   19.6 cm²   7.1 cm²

Use a calculator to find the area of the shaded region. Round to the nearest unit.

10. 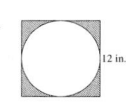 4 cm
11. 12 in.

38 cm²   31 in.²

Solve each problem. Round to the nearest square inch.

12. Find the area of an 8-in. diameter pizza.   50 in.²
13. Find the area of a 12-in. diameter pizza.   113 in.²
14. The cost of the 8-in. pizza is $7.00. The cost of the 12-in. pizza is $12.50.
    Which size pizza is the better buy?   12-in. pizza
    Explain.   Sample: The 8-in. pizza costs $.14 per square in., while the 12-in. pizza costs $.11 per square in.

In copymaster and workbook formats

📠 *Calculator* **Find the area of each figure. Use units². Round each answer to the nearest tenth of a unit.**

57.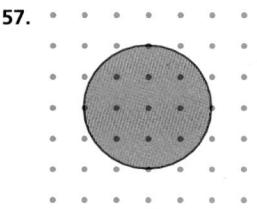
    12.6 units²

58.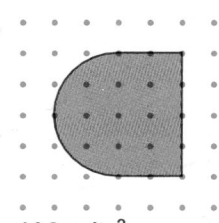
    14.1 units²

59.
    14.3 units²

60. *Games* Use the hopscotch drawing at the right.
    a. Suppose the sides of each square equal 2 ft. Find the area of the hopscotch drawing. **38.3 ft²**
    b. Suppose the sides of each square equal 1.5 ft. Find the area of the hopscotch drawing. **21.5 ft²**
    c. Compare the areas in parts (a) and (b). Which do you think would be easier to hop on without going outside the lines? Explain your reasoning. **Check students' work.**

```
    7  8
     6
    4  5
     3
     2
     1
```

RETEACHING

Reteaching 9-5 *Area of a Circle*

The formula for the area of a circle is:
   Area = π × radius × radius
   $A = \pi \times r \times r$
   $A = \pi r^2$
Find the area of the circle.

You can find the area of a circle when you know the diameter.
   radius = ½ diameter
Find the area of the circle.

 r = 4 m

$A = \pi r^2$
  ≈ 3.14 × 4²
  = 3.14 × 4 × 4
  = 3.14 × 16
  = 50.24 m²
The area is about 50.24 m².

d = 10 m

d = 10 m, so r = 5 m
$A = \pi r^2$
  ≈ 3.14 × 5²
  = 3.14 × 5 × 5
  = 3.14 × 25
  = 78.5 m²
The area is about 78.5 m².

Use a calculator to find the area of each circle. Round each answer to the nearest tenth.

1. 3 m   28.3 m²
2. 2 m   12.6 m²
3. 12 m   113.0 m²
4. $r = 8$ cm   201.0 cm²
5. $r = 13$ in.   530.7 in.²
6. $d = 14$ m   153.9 m²
7. $d = 24$ ft   452.2 ft²
8. $r = 5.2$ m   84.9 m²
9. $d = 13$ cm   132.7 cm²
10. $r = 9.6$ ft   289.4 ft²
11. $d = 29$ in.   660.2 in.²
12. $d = 23$ ft   415.3 ft²
13. $r = 2.5$ yd   19.6 yd²
14. $d = 48$ in.   1,808.6 in.²
15. $r = 19$ cm   1,133.5 cm²

Mixed Review

Classify each triangle with the given angle measures as *acute, right,* **or** *obtuse.* *(Lesson 8-4)*

61. 25°, 45°, 110°
    obtuse
62. 90°, 30°, 60°
    right
63. 80°, 50°, 50°
    acute
64. 60°, 70°, 50°
    acute

Estimate each amount. *(Lesson 7-8)*

65. 39% of 50
    20
66. 98% of 725
    711
67. 9% of 25
    2.5
68. 601% of 3
    18
69. 411% of 200
    822

70. *Choose a Strategy* Karim owns an office supply store. He sells a lap desk for two times his cost plus $4.25. The lap desk sells for $17.75. What is Karim's cost?   **$6.75**

CHAPTER PROJECT

PROJECT LINK: CALCULATING

For each home page you diagramed, calculate the total text or graphic area and the area of the home page screen. Write these areas as the ratio $\frac{\text{area with text or graphic}}{\text{area of home page screen}}$. Next, write this ratio as a percent. **Check students' work.**

ENRICHMENT

Minds on Math Transparency

9-5

The figure below has an area of 180 in.² and consists of 5 congruent squares. How can you rearrange the squares to make a figure with a perimeter of 60 in.?

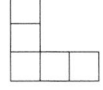

Answers may vary. Sample:

See *Solution Key* **for worked-out answers.**

1 Focus

CONNECTING TO PRIOR KNOWLEDGE Ask students to identify the number of sides for the following figures: triangle, rectangle, pentagon, hexagon, octagon. **3, 4, 5, 6, 8** Challenge students to name examples of three-dimensional figures they have seen that contain one of these shapes as one of their faces. **Answers may vary. Sample: a shoe box, the Pentagon building in Washington, D.C.**

2 Teach

THINK AND DISCUSS

AEP Show students a model of a cube while you discuss the meaning of these words: *parallel and congruent polygonal faces.* Have them point to faces that are congruent and parallel. Have students practice drawing a picture of a prism with parallel and congruent polygonal faces.

Example Ask students to define the following for a prism.

- a face **flat surface shaped like a polygon**
- bases **two parallel and congruent polygon faces**

Lesson Planning Options

Prerequisite Skills
- identifying regular geometric shapes (precourse)

Vocabulary/Symbols
three-dimensional figures, faces, prism, bases, edge, vertex, cube, pyramid, cylinder, cone, sphere, net

Materials/Manipulatives
- graph paper   • scissors
- tape

Resources

 Student Edition

Skills Handbook, p. 536
Extra Practice, p. 530
Glossary/Study Guide

Teaching Resources

Chapter Support File, Ch. 9
• Lesson Planner 9-6
• Practice 9-6, Reteaching 9-6
• Answer Masters 9-6
Teaching Aids Masters 1–3, 11–17
Glossary, Spanish Resources

 Transparencies
1, 9, Minds on Math 9-6

Warm Up
Describe the pattern:
18, 15.25, 12.5, 9.75, . . .
Start with 18. Subtract 2.75.

408

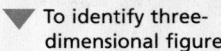

9-6 *Three-Dimensional Figures*

What You'll Learn

▼ To identify three-dimensional figures

...And Why

You can recognize three-dimensional figures in architecture.

Here's How

Look for questions that
  build understanding
✔ check understanding

THINK AND DISCUSS

Figures, such as those modeled by the Houston skyline buildings below, do not lie in a plane. These figures are called **three-dimensional figures.** The flat surfaces are called **faces.**

A **prism** is a three-dimensional figure with two parallel and congruent polygonal faces. In a prism, these faces are called **bases.** You name a prism by the shape of its bases. When you draw a prism, use dashed lines to show segments you cannot see.

■ **EXAMPLE**

Name the prism shown.

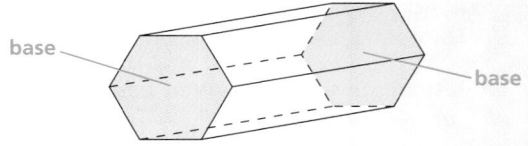

base   base

Each base is a hexagon. So the figure is a hexagonal prism.

1. ✔*Try It Out*
Name each prism.

a.

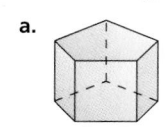

pentagonal prism

b.

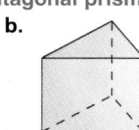

triangular prism

c.

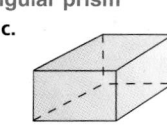

rectangular prism

■ **ADDITIONAL EXAMPLE**

Name the prism shown.
octagonal prism

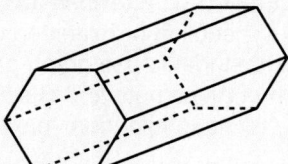

VISUAL LEARNING Have students try to make their own drawings of a cube. Discuss the use of *perspective* in drawing representations of 3-D figures on a 2-D surface. Have students label the parts of the cube. Have volunteers post their drawings in the room. Students may also add an explanation of *perspective* below the drawing.

CONNECTING TO THE STUDENTS' WORLD Have students give examples of cylinders, cones, or spheres that they have seen. Suggest that students bring examples from home.

TACTILE LEARNING Provide students with geosolids. Have them point to each vertex. Ask them to trace the sides of each face. Ask students to find how many faces a rectangular prism has. **6 faces** Make sure students understand that a *base* is also a *face.*

An **edge** is a segment where two faces meet. A **vertex** is a point where edges meet. A **cube** is a prism with six congruent faces.

2. How many faces, edges, and vertices are in the figure?
6 faces; 12 edges; 8 vertices
3. How many faces are "hidden from view" in this drawing?
3 faces

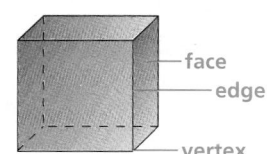

face
edge
vertex

A **pyramid** has one polygonal base. You name a pyramid by the shape of its base.

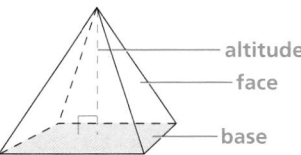

altitude
face
base

4. ✓*Try It Out* What name would you give each pyramid?

a.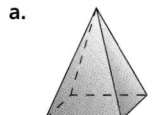
b.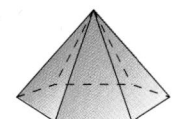
c.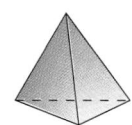

rectangular pyramid or square pyramid   **hexagonal pyramid**   **triangular pyramid**

5. ♣*Draw a Conclusion* What shape is any face of a pyramid that is not the base? **triangle**

Some three-dimensional figures do not have polygonal faces. A cylinder has two circular, parallel, and congruent bases. A cone has one circular base and one vertex. A sphere has no base.

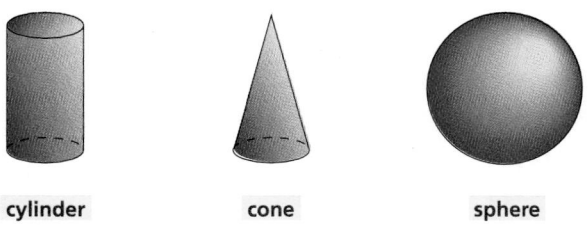

cylinder   **cone**   **sphere**

6. ♣*Analyze* How are a cylinder and a cone alike? How are they different?
A cylinder and a cone each have a circular base. The top of a cylinder is also a circle. The top of a cone is a point.

Technology Options

Prentice Hall Technology

 Software for Learners
• Hot Page™ 27*
• Math Blaster® Mystery*
• Interactive Student Tutorial, Chapter 9*

 Teaching Resource Software
• Computer Item Generator 9-6
• Resource Pro™ Chapter 9*

Internet • For related mathematics activities, visit the Prentice Hall site at www.phschool.com/math

*Available on CD-ROM only

Assignment Options for Exercises On Your Own

Core 1–12, 14–17, 22, 24
Extension 13, 18–21, 23, 25

Use Mixed Review to maintain skills.

Work Together

TACTILE LEARNING Provide students with graph paper and scissors. Ask students to predict what three-dimensional figure the net will form before they start working.

ASSESSMENT Ask students to name a prism that has two bases and three other faces. **triangular prism**

3 Practice/Assess

EXERCISES *On Your Own*

AEP **Exercises 1–4** If students need help, tell them that they can identify each prism by counting the number of sides of one base. Review with students who are developing English proficiency the names and number of sides of polygons.

Exercises 5–12 Give students grid paper to help them sketch figures. Accept drawings that are close approximations to the figures.

TACTILE LEARNING **Exercise 13** If you have block scheduling or extended class periods, have students use graph paper to create each of these nets and check their answers by trying to fold them into a cube.

Exercises 14–17 Suggest that students compare the figures in the photos with the figures on pages 408 and 409.

---

pages 410–412   On Your Own

5.

6.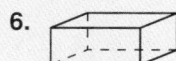

7.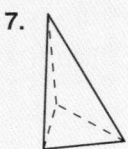

8.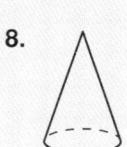

9.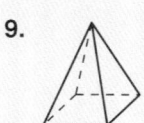

10.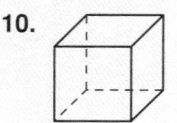

11.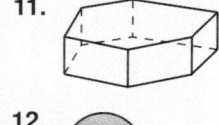

12.

8a.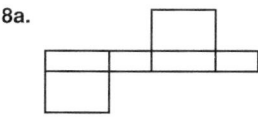

b.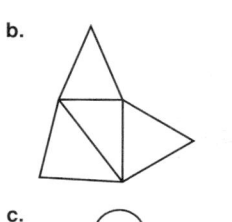

c.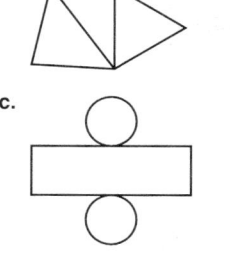

Work Together _____ *Making Three-Dimensional Figures*

Work with a partner. A **net** is a pattern that you cut out and fold to form a three-dimensional figure.

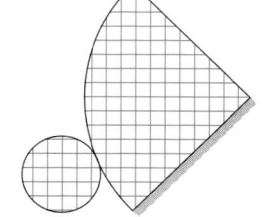

7. a. ⬛*Predict* Name the three-dimensional figure you can form from the net shown. **cone**

b. Copy the net onto centimeter graph paper. Cut, fold, and tape it to check your answer to part (a). **Check students' work.**

8. ⬛*Spatial Reasoning* Draw a net that will fold to form the figure given. Then cut, fold, and tape each net to check your answer. **8a–c. Samples are given at left.**

a. rectangular prism **b.** triangular pyramid **c.** cylinder

Now you may assign Exercises 1–25.

EXERCISES *On Your Own*

Name each prism.

1.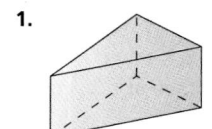
triangular prism

2.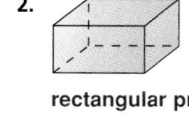
rectangular prism

3.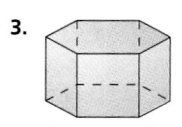
hexagonal prism

4.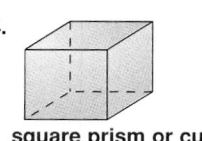
square prism or cube

Sketch each three-dimensional figure.   **5–12. See margin for samples.**

5. cylinder   **6.** rectangular prism   **7.** triangular pyramid **8.** cone

9. square pyramid   **10.** cube   **11.** hexagonal prism   **12.** sphere

13. *Spatial Reasoning* How many of the following nets could you fold to form a box without a top? Which nets are these? **4; C, F, G, H**

A.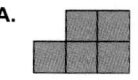

B.

C.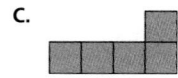

D.

E.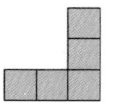

F.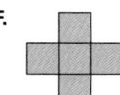

G.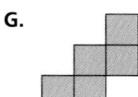

H.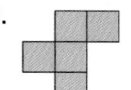

410

VISUAL LEARNING Exercises 18–21 Have students pick another three-dimensional prism and sketch a net they can fold to create this figure. Have students check their work by cutting out the net and making the prism.

ERROR ALERT! Exercise 22b Students may confuse the edges with the vertices.
Remediation: Review the difference between vertices and edges. Have students use a model prism to trace and count edges. Have them point to and count vertices.

WRITING Exercise 23 Some students may need to study the picture of a square pyramid on page 409 before they write.

TACTILE LEARNING Exercise 24 Have students answer the questions and then give them a number cube and a ruler to check their work.

AUDITORY LEARNING Exercise 25 Have pairs of students discuss which of the figures on page 411 are possible views of a cylinder. Ask volunteers to give explanations to the class.

WRAP UP

IDENTIFYING THE BIG IDEA Have students identify models or drawings of three-dimensional figures.

PROJECT LINK Encourage students to arrange text or pictures in the form of shapes to increase appeal and interest.

For each photo, identify the largest three-dimensional figure.

14.

pyramid

15.

rectangular prism

16.

cone

17.

sphere

Spatial Reasoning **Name the figure you can form from each net.**

18.

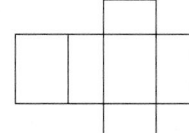

rectangular prism

19.

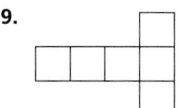

square prism or cube

20.

triangular pyramid

21.

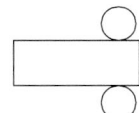

cylinder

22. a. Identify the figure at the right.
b. How many faces, edges, and vertices are in the figure?

22a. pentagonal pyramid
   b. 6 faces; 10 edges; 6 vertices

23. *Writing* Describe, in your own words, a square pyramid.   **Answers may vary. Sample: A square pyramid has a square base and four triangular faces.**

24. a. What shape is each face of a cube? square
b. How do the lengths of the edges of a cube compare?   All edges have the same length.

25. Choose A, B, C, or D. Which of the following is *not* a possible view of a cylinder? C

A.

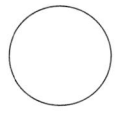

B.

C.

D.

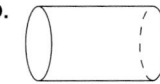

PRACTICE

Practice 9-6 *Three-Dimensional Figures*

Identify each three-dimensional figure.

1.
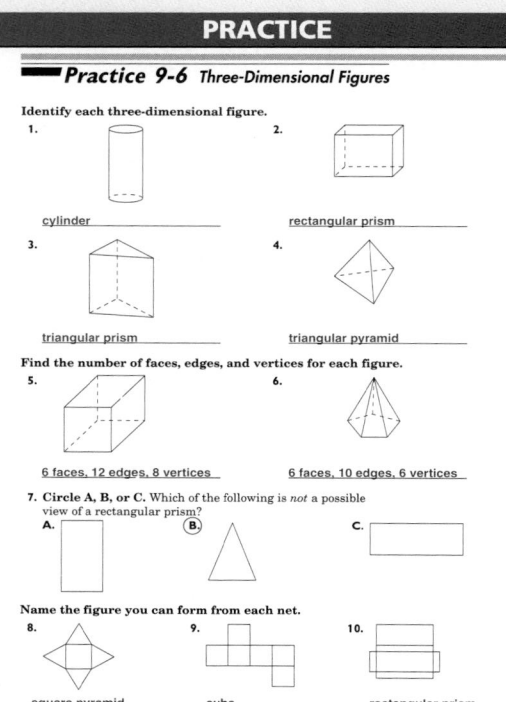
cylinder

2.
rectangular prism

3.
triangular prism

4.
triangular pyramid

Find the number of faces, edges, and vertices for each figure.

5.
6 faces, 12 edges, 8 vertices

6.
6 faces, 10 edges, 6 vertices

7. **Circle A, B, or C.** Which of the following is *not* a possible view of a rectangular prism?

A.   B.   C.

Name the figure you can form from each net.

8.
square pyramid

9.
cube

10.
rectangular prism

In copymaster and workbook formats

RETEACHING

Reteaching 9-6 *Three-Dimensional Figures*

Prisms and pyramids are three-dimensional figures. Their parts have special names.

• **Faces**—flat surface on a prism or pyramid

• **Edge**—segment where two faces meet

• **Vertex**—point where edges meet

Prisms and pyramids can be named by the shape of their bases.

Prism
• has two **bases** congruent and parallel to one another

6 faces
12 edges
8 vertices

The bases are rectangles. This prism is a **rectangular prism**.

Pyramid
• has one base; other faces are triangles

5 faces
8 edges
5 vertices

The base is a square. This pyramid is a **square pyramid**.

Name each figure. Give the number of faces, edges, and vertices for each.

1.
triangular prism; 5 faces, 9 edges, 6 vertices

2.
pentagonal pyramid; 6 faces, 10 edges, 6 vertices

3.
hexagonal pyramid; 7 faces, 12 edges, 7 vertices

4.
square pyramid; 5 faces, 8 edges, 5 vertices

Reteaching

ENRICHMENT

Minds on Math Transparency

9-6

Heather folded a square sheet of paper in half. Then she cut the sheet of paper along the fold. She told Wayne that the perimeter of each of the rectangles formed was 18 in. What was the area of Heather's original square sheet of paper?

36 in.²

See *Solution Key* for worked-out answers.

412

Math at Work

If you have block scheduling or extended class periods, you may wish to have students design a piece of furniture using a three-dimensional figures. Have them either draw the design or create it from paper prisms. Suggest they make their own prisms using nets. Have students look through magazines for inspiration if they have difficulty coming up with a design.

LESSON QUIZ

Name the following figures.

1. a prism with two bases, and 5 faces **pentagonal prism**

2. a soccer ball **sphere**

3. a three-dimensional figure with one circular base and one vertex **cone**

Mixed Review

Complete each sentence with *All, Some,* or *No.* *(Lesson 8-6)*

no

26. ■ trapezoids are parallelograms.

some

28. ■ rectangles are squares.

some

27. ■ rhombuses are rectangles.

all

29. ■ parallelograms are quadrilaterals

30. Make a cutout of the letter K. Trace around the letter K. Draw a black dot on the letter K. Then show two rotated images of the letter K. *(Lesson 8-11)* **Check students' work.**

31. Mr. Dawson, the gardener, increased his sale of rose bushes this year by 20%. By what fraction did he increase his sales? *(Lesson 7-7)* $\frac{1}{5}$

CHAPTER PROJECT

PROJECT LINK: DESIGNING

Design your own Web home page about yourself, your family, or your class. Neatly sketch the page. On a separate sheet, describe other Web pages to which your home page would be linked. **Check students' work.**

Math at Work

CARPENTER

If you like to work with your hands, you might find carpentry an interesting career. Carpenters use a wide array of tools such as power saws, planers, sanders, and lathes to shape raw wood into finished pieces. A good understanding of measurement and the ability to visualize in three dimensions are essential skills for a successful carpenter.

 Visit the Web site www.woodworking.com to learn more about what opportunities exist for a trained carpenter.

In Lesson 9-6, students learn how to identify three-dimensional figures. This toolbox allows students to explore visual thinking and models.

ERROR ALERT! Students may not be able make a model from the drawings.
Remediation: Have pairs of students practice modeling the example. One student can model the example for the partner,

explaining how many blocks are visible from each viewpoint. Then have the other partner describe the drawings. Have students compare their descriptions from the front, from the side, and from the top of the drawings. Then have each student make a model.

ASSESSMENT Exercise 1 Have students meet with a partner. Each pair of students should agree on different views of the blocks, and each pair should work together to model the blocks. Students can compare results.

■ **ADDITIONAL PROBLEM**

Have students meet with a partner to design their own model of blocks. Then have students make front, side, and top drawings. Have them trade drawings with another pair. Ask each pair to use the drawings to determine the number of blocks in the group. Have pairs share their findings.

Materials/Manipulatives
• blocks

Resources

Transparencies
9

EXPLORATION

Spatial Reasoning

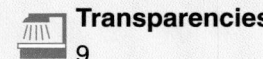
After Lesson 9-6

Stack 6 cubes as shown at the right. The number of cubes you can "see" depends on how you look at the stacks.

From the front, you see

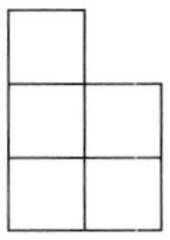

From the right side, you see

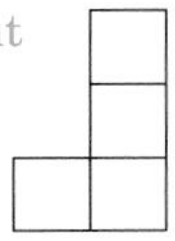

From the top, you see

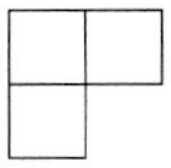

Front Right

■ **EXAMPLE**

Use the drawings below. How many cubes are in a possible model?

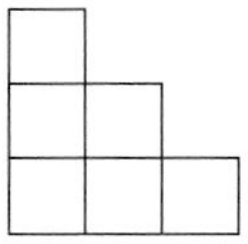

Front View 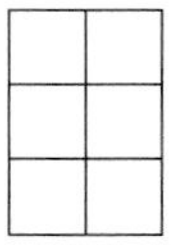   Right Side View 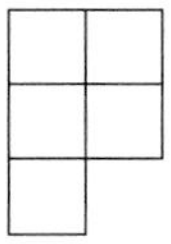   Top View

Use blocks to make a model that matches each view. Count the blocks.

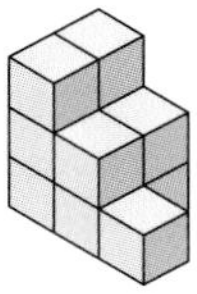

There are 11 blocks in this model although other models are possible.

Use blocks to create each group of blocks. Draw the front view, right side view, and top view of each group.
1–3. See above right.

1. 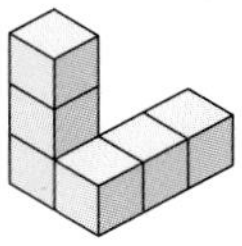   2.    3.

1. 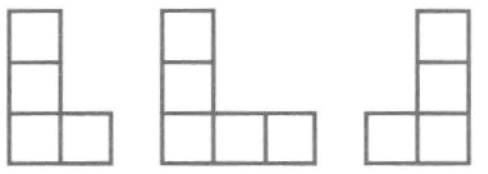
front   right   top

2. 
front   right   top

3. 
front   right   top

Use the drawings below. How many cubes may be in each group?

4. 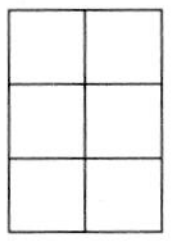
Front View 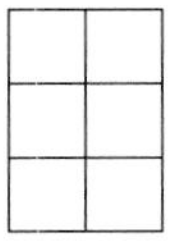   Right Side View 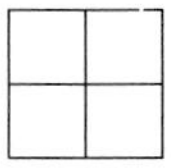   Top View
10, 11, or 12 cubes

5. 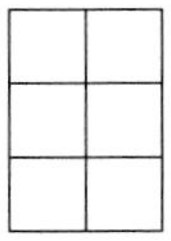
Front View 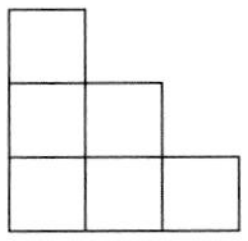   Right Side View 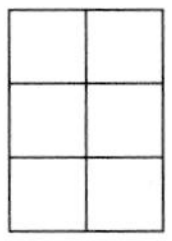   Top View
11 or 12 cubes

Math Toolbox 413

413

1 Focus

CONNECTING TO PRIOR KNOWLEDGE Ask students to recall how to find the surface area of a two-dimensional figure, such as a rectangle. *l* × *w* Then ask students to think of ways to use the same procedures to find the surface area of a rectangular prism.

2 Teach

Answers may vary. Sample: Find the area of each rectangular face and add.

THINK AND DISCUSS

DIVERSITY and TACTILE LEARNING
Students who are not visual learners may have difficulty understanding that a rectangular prism *has three pairs of*

congruent faces. Have students cut out each face of a cereal or juice box. Have them explain how to find the area of the faces they cut out.

ERROR ALERT! Example In problems such as these, students may confuse the dimensions of different face pairs.
Remediation: Suggest that students create a chart that lists the following face pairs: top and bottom; front and back; two sides. Have them record dimensions on the chart for each face pair.

Lesson Planning Options

Prerequisite Skills
- finding area of rectangles (9-2)
- multiplying decimals (4-5)

Vocabulary/Symbols
surface area (SA)

Materials/Manipulatives
- ruler or yardstick
- calculator

Resources

 Student Edition

Skills Handbook, p. 538
Extra Practice, p. 530
Glossary/Study Guide

 Teaching Resources

Chapter Support File, Ch. 9
- Lesson Planner 9-7
- Practice 9-7, Reteaching 9-7
- Alternative Activity 9-7
- Answer Masters 9-7
Teaching Aids Masters 1–3, 11–17
Glossary, Spanish Resources

 Transparencies

1, 9, 18, 95, Minds on Math 9-7

Warm Up

Nikki is twice as old as her sister Kellly. The sum of their ages is 24. How old are the sisters?
Nikki is 16; Kelly is 8.

9-7 Exploring Surface Area

What You'll Learn

▼ To find the surface area of a rectangular prism

...And Why

You often need to find surface area of ordinary things that need to be covered or painted, such as packages or rooms.

Here's How

Look for questions that
- build understanding
✔ check understanding

THINK AND DISCUSS

The **surface area** (SA) of a rectangular prism is the sum of the areas of all the faces. A rectangular prism has three pairs of congruent sides or faces.

$$\text{Area of top} = \text{Area of bottom}$$
$$\text{Area of front} = \text{Area of back}$$
$$\text{Area of left side} = \text{Area of right side}$$

SURFACE AREA OF A RECTANGULAR PRISM

SA of a rectangular prism $= 2(\ell \times w) + 2(\ell \times h) + 2(w \times h)$

■ **EXAMPLE**   *Real-World Problem Solving*

Package Design Package designers want to find the surface area of the juice box below. Multiply each area by 2 and find the sum.

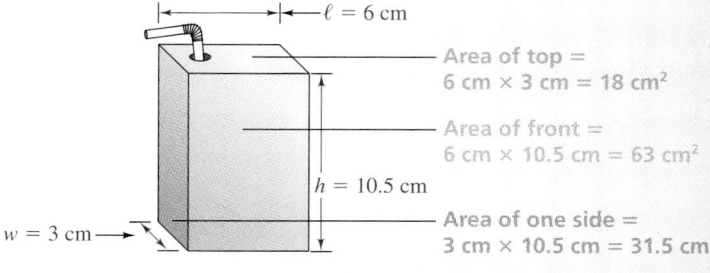

$\ell = 6$ cm

Area of top =
6 cm × 3 cm = 18 cm²

Area of front =
6 cm × 10.5 cm = 63 cm²

$h = 10.5$ cm

Area of one side =
3 cm × 10.5 cm = 31.5 cm²

$w = 3$ cm

Areas of top and bottom		Areas of front and back		Areas of other sides		Surface Area
$2(\ell \times w)$	+	$2(\ell \times h)$	+	$2(w \times h)$	=	▨
2(18)	+	2(63)	+	2(31.5)	=	▨
36	+	126	+	63	=	225

The surface area of the juice box is 225 cm².

■ **ADDITIONAL EXAMPLE**

Designers of cereal packages need to know the surface area of a cereal box to make a foil inner lining. Find the surface area of the cereal box.

247.5 in.²

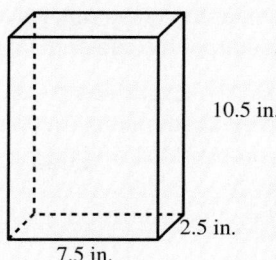

10.5 in.

2.5 in.

7.5 in.

Work Together

OPEN-ENDED Exercise 4 Suggest that pairs of students compare their prisms and their surface areas. Have students explain their methods.

ASSESSMENT Before students work the exercises, ask them the following: *Write a shortcut formula for finding the surface area of a cube 52 cm by 52 cm by 52 cm.*
Answers may vary. Sample:
6 × (52 × 52) = 16,224 cm²

1. ✓*Try It Out* Find the surface area of each prism.

a.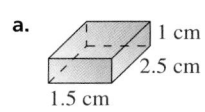
1 cm
2.5 cm
1.5 cm
15.5 cm²

b.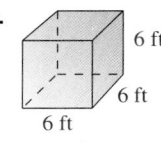
6 ft
6 ft
6 ft
216 ft²

c.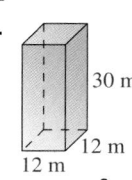
30 m
12 m
12 m
1,728 m²

2. ⚏*Think About It* How can you use a net to find the surface area of a rectangular prism? Explain. **Find the total area of the net; the net represents all the faces of the prism.**

3b. Find the area of a face, then multiply by 6; 96 in.².

3. a. What shape are the faces of the cube at right? **square**

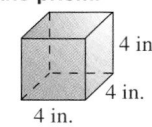
4 in.
4 in.
4 in.

b. ⚏*Reasoning* What shortcuts can you use to find the surface area of the prism shown?

c. How would the surface area of the cube change if the length of the sides were doubled?
The surface area quadruples.

Work Together

Finding Surface Area

Work with a partner to find the surface area of an object.
4a–d. Check students' work

4. a. ⚏*Open-ended* Select an object in your class that is a rectangular prism.

b. ⚏*Measurement* Measure the length, width, and height of the object.

c. Make a three-dimensional sketch of the object. Label the length, width, and height.

d. Find the surface area of the object.

Now you may assign Exercises 1–20.

EXERCISES *On Your Own*

Spatial Reasoning **Find the surface area of each figure.**
Each small cube measures 1 cm on a side.

1.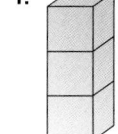
14 cm²

2.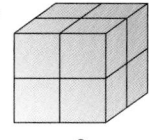
24 cm²

3.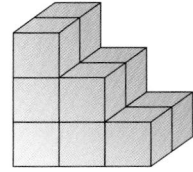
36 cm²

4.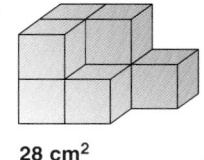
28 cm²

Technology Options

Prentice Hall Technology

💾 💿 **Software for Learners**
• Math Blaster® Mystery*
• Interactive Student Tutorial, Chapter 9

💾 💿 **Teaching Resource Software**
• Computer Item Generator 9-7
• Resource Pro™ Chapter 9*

🔗 **Internet** • For related mathematics activities, visit the Prentice Hall site at www.phschool.com/math

*Available on CD-ROM only

Assignment Options for Exercises On Your Own

Core 1–7, 9–16
Extension 8, 17–20

Use Mixed Review to maintain skills.

3 Practice/Assess

EXERCISES *On Your Own*

EXTENSION Exercises 1–4 Ask students how they can use the front, right, and top views of the figures to find the total surface area. **two times the area of each of these views will equal the total surface area** *Will this work for any three-dimensional figure?* **no; only figures made of cubes or rectangular prisms.**

Exercise 5 If you have block scheduling or extended class periods, you may wish to have students make the given net. Have students actually construct the rectangular prism.

MENTAL MATH Exercises 9–16 Have students who used mental math for a particular problem tell why they chose that strategy for the problem. Have students explain when they would not use mental math.

REASONING Exercise 21 Challenge students to write a rule for finding the area of one cube face if you know the surface area of a cube. **Answers may vary. Sample: Divide the surface area by 6.**

VISUAL LEARNING Exercise 22 Suggest that students use tracing paper to draw the parallelogram shown on page 417. Have them draw lines on the figure to explore ways to divide it into congruent parts.

416

Name the prism you can build from each net. Find the surface area of each prism.

5.
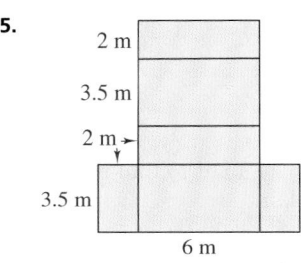
rectangular prism; 80 m²

6.
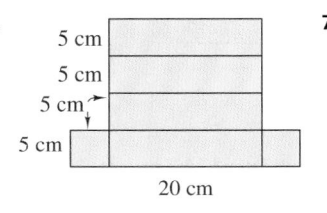
rectangular prism; 450 cm²

7.
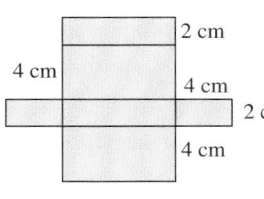
rectangular prism; 112 cm²

8. a. Draw a net that you could fold to form the rectangular prism at the right. **Check students' work.**
  b. Find the surface area of the prism. **319.5 cm²**

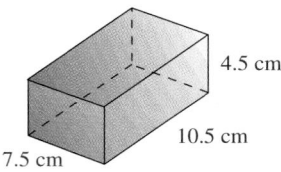

⊞ *Choose* **Use a calculator, paper and pencil, or mental math to find the surface area of each rectangular prism.**

9.
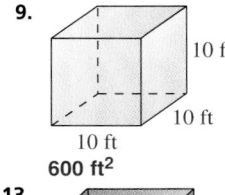
600 ft²

10.
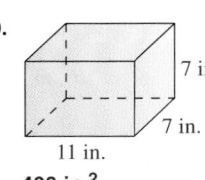
406 in.²

11.
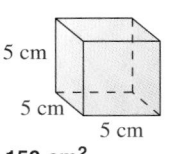
150 cm²

12.
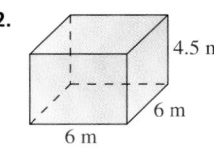
180 m²

13.
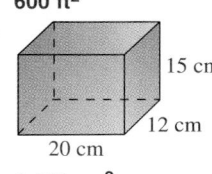
1,440 cm²

14.
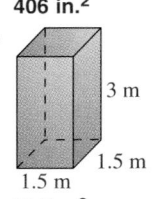
22.5 m²

15.
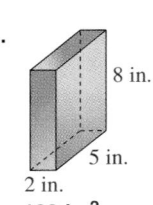
132 in.²

16.
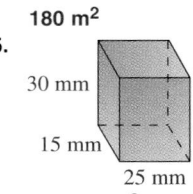
3,150 mm²

17. Choose A, B, or C. Which whole piece of wrapping paper below can *not* be used to wrap the box at the right? **B**

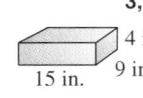

A.
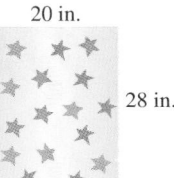

B.
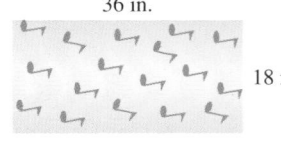

C.
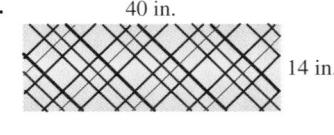

IDENTIFYING THE BIG IDEA Ask students to explain how to find the surface area of a rectangular prism.

JOURNAL You may wish to have students find the surface area of a cereal box using two different methods before they write.

LESSON QUIZ

Find the surface area of the rectangular prisms with the following dimensions.

1. a cube that is 8 in. by 8 in. by 8 in. **384 in.²**

2. a rectangular prism that is 35 ft wide, 12 ft high, and 10 ft long **1,780 ft²**

---

18. *Construction* You have been hired to paint the walls in the room shown below.

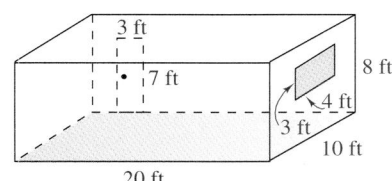

a. Find the area of the two walls that do not have doors or windows. **240 ft²**

b. Find the total area of the surface you will paint on the other two walls. (Assume that you will not paint the door or the window.) **207 ft²**

c. What is the surface area of the region you will paint? **447 ft²**

d. A gallon of paint covers about 400 ft². How many gallons do you need? **2 gal**

19. *Writing* Suppose you know the area of the top, front, and one side of a rectangular prism. How can you find its surface area? **Find the sum of the areas. Then double it.**

20. *Reasoning* The surface area of the cube shown at the right is 24 cm². What is the length of each edge? **2 cm**

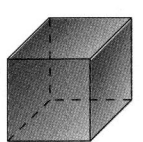

21. Answers may vary. Sample:

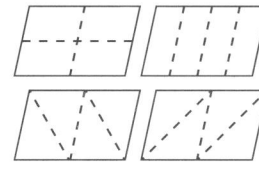

JOURNAL
Describe at least two different ways to find the surface area of a rectangular prism. Provide an example.

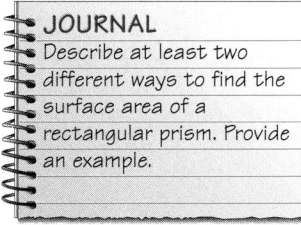

Mixed Review

21. Use the parallelogram at the right. Show four different ways in which the figure can be cut into congruent parts. *(Lesson 8-8)* **See above right.**

A scale model measures 3 cm × 5 cm. Find the dimensions of the actual object with the given scale. *(Lesson 7-5)*

22. 1 cm : 3 cm
9 cm × 15 cm

23. 4 cm : 6 m
4.5 m × 7.5 m

24. 1 cm : 0.5 m
1.5 m × 2.5 m

25. 1 mm : 1 km
30 km × 50 km

26. *Choose a Strategy* Ms. Spencer bought a rake for $9.00, a lawn mower for $250.00, and three garden hoses. She spent a total of $284.50. How much did she pay for each garden hose? **$8.50**

PRACTICE

Practice 9-7 *Exploring Surface Area*

Choose a calculator, paper and pencil, or mental math to find the surface area of the rectangular prism.

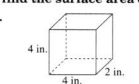
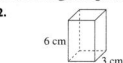
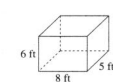

1. 4 in. 2 in. 4 in.   **64 in.²**
2. 6 cm 3 cm 5 cm   **126 cm²**
3. 6 ft 8 ft 5 ft   **236 ft²**

4. 5 cm 10 cm 6 cm   **280 cm²**
5. 5 in. 6 in. 2 in.   **104 in.²**
6. 4 yd 5.5 yd 2.5 yd   **91.5 yd²**

Find the surface area of the rectangular prism that has the given net.

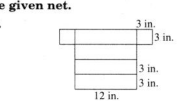
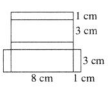

7. 3 in. 3 in. 3 in. 3 in. 12 in.   **162 in.²**

8. 1 cm 3 cm 3 cm 8 cm 1 cm   **70 cm²**

Draw or build a rectangular tower of centimeter cubes. Make the bottom layer 4 cm by 3 cm, and make 5 layers. Assume that you can view any face of the tower.

9. How many cubes have at least one side visible? **54 cubes**

10. How many cubes are hidden from view inside the tower? **6 cubes**

11. What is the surface area of the tower? **94 cm²**

In copymaster and workbook formats

RETEACHING

Reteaching 9-7 *Exploring Surface Area*

The **surface area** of a rectangular prism is the sum of the areas of the faces. You can use this formula to find surface area:

$$\text{Surface area} = \underset{\text{bottom}}{2(l \times w)} + \underset{\text{back}}{2(l \times h)} + \underset{\text{side}}{2(w \times h)}$$

top   front   side

Find the surface area.

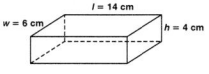

l = 14 cm, *w* = 6 cm, *h* = 4 cm

① Find the area of the top and bottom.
$A = 2(l \times w)$
$= 2(14 \times 6)$
$= 2(84)$
$= 168 \text{ cm}^2$

② Find the area of the front and back.
$A = 2(l \times h)$
$= 2(14 \times 4)$
$= 2(56)$
$= 112 \text{ cm}^2$

③ Find the area of both sides.
$A = 2(w \times h)$
$= 2(6 \times 4)$
$= 2(24)$
$= 48 \text{ cm}^2$

④ Add.
168
112
+ 48
328

The surface area is 328 cm².

Use a calculator, paper and pencil, or mental math to find the surface area of each rectangular prism.

1. 4 m 4 m 4 m   **96 m²**
2. 10 in. 1 in. 4 in.   **108 in.²**
3. 2 cm 2 cm 6 cm   **56 cm²**

4. 7 ft 5 ft 2 ft   **118 ft²**
5. 7 cm 4 cm 8 cm   **232 cm²**
6. 1.5 m 2.5 m 6 m   **55.5 m²**

ENRICHMENT

Minds on Math Transparency   9-7

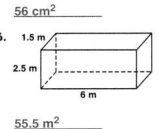

Terri's cube has a surface area of 6 cm². Each edge of Quinn's cube is twice as long as each edge of Terri's cube. What is the surface area of Quinn's cube?

24 cm²

See Solution Key for worked-out answers.

417

1 Focus

CONNECTING TO PRIOR KNOWLEDGE

Show students an empty tissue box. Have students find the surface area of the box. Ask students: *Which units of measurement would you use to measure the surface area of the box: linear or square? Explain.* **square units;** linear units measure one dimension, square units measure two dimensions

2 Teach

Work Together

AUDITORY LEARNING Have students discuss different ways to find the number of cubes that fit inside the empty tissue box. Encourage students to debate which method of finding the answer is most effective.

THINK AND DISCUSS

AEP Some students may need to review the words *length, width,* and *height.* Use a tissue box to model each dimension. Ask students to match each word with the following synonyms: tall or high, wide, and long. **height, width, length**

Lesson Planning Options

Prerequisite Skills

• multiplying decimals (4-4)

Vocabulary/Symbols

volume (V)

Materials/Manipulatives

• centimeter cubes
• empty box

Resources

 Student Edition

Skills Handbook, p. 540
Extra Practice, p. 530
Glossary/Study Guide

 Teaching Resources

Chapter Support File, Ch. 9
• Lesson Planner 9-8
• Practice 9-8, Reteaching 9-8
• Answer Masters 9-8
Teaching Aids Masters 1–3, 11–17
Glossary, Spanish Resources

 Transparencies

9, 18, 95, Minds on Math 9-8

Warm Up

Estimate each sum or difference.
8.31 + 3.96 **12**
5.038 − 4.21 **1**
39.51 + 26.97 + 59.94 **127**

418

ALGEBRA Connection

9-8 Volume of a Rectangular Prism

What You'll Learn

1 To find the volume of a rectangular prism

2 To find a missing dimension of a rectangular prism

...And Why

You can find the volume of everyday objects such as cereal boxes.

Here's How

Look for questions that
🔹 build understanding
✔ check understanding

3a. The product of length × width × height equals the number of cubes in a prism.

Work Together

Discovering Volume

Spatial Reasoning Work with a partner.
1a–b. Check students' work.
1. a. 🔹*Open-ended* Find the number of centimeter cubes that would fit inside a small box.
   b. 🔹*Summarize* Describe the method you used.

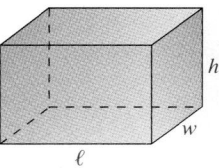

2. Next use the centimeter cubes to build rectangular prisms. Use the dimensions in the table. After you have built each prism, count how many cubes the prism contains. Copy and complete the table.
Check students' work for models.

3. a. *Patterns* Look at your completed table. How do the length, width, and height of a prism relate to the total number of cubes?
   b. Write a formula for finding the number of cubes within a rectangular prism. $\ell \times w \times h = V$

Length ℓ	Width w	Height h	Number of Cubes
3	4	2	24
5	6	4	120
8	1	3	24
4	4	4	64
6	3	6	108

THINK AND DISCUSS

1 *Finding Volume*

The **volume** of a three-dimensional figure is the number of cubic units needed to fill the space inside the figure.

Volume = length × width × height

$$V = \ell w h$$

ADDITIONAL EXAMPLES

FOR EXAMPLE 1

Find the volume of a packing box 24 cm wide, 40 cm long, and 28 cm tall. **26,880 cm³**

FOR EXAMPLE 2

The volume of a rectangular prism is 250 cm³. The length is 5 cm. The width is 10 cm. Find the missing dimension. **5 cm**

ERROR ALERT! Students may write volume units as a squared number instead of a cubed number. For example, they may write 299.88 cm² instead of 299.88 cm³.
Remediation: Remind students to write volume in cubic units because it measures *three* dimensions: length, width, and height. Area measures *two* dimensions: length and width.

ASSESSMENT Have small groups of students find the volume of rectangular prisms such as cereal boxes, number cubes, or juice boxes. On a piece of paper have students list the volume with the correct unit of measure, the length and the width of the object. Have groups trade papers to find the missing height measurements. Ask groups to check each other's answers.

REASONING Question 6 If students have trouble, remind them the area is the length times the width. Have them write the formula for calculating the volume then substitute the values they know into the equation.

Area measures two dimensions, *length* and *width*, in square units. Volume measures three dimensions, *length*, *width*, and *height*, in cubic units, such as cubic centimeters (cm³), cubic meters (m³), or cubic inches (in.³).

■ EXAMPLE 1   *Real-World Problem Solving*

Food Find the volume of the cereal box shown. Use the formula $V = \ell w h$.

$$V = \ell \times w \times h$$

$$V = 7.0 \times 4.2 \times 10.2 = 299.88$$

The volume is 299.88 cm³, or about 300 cm³.

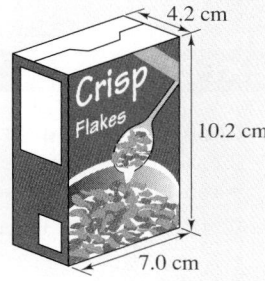

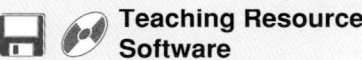

4. ✓*Try It Out* Find the volume of each rectangular prism with the given dimensions.
   a. $\ell = 8$ ft, $w = 7$ ft, $h = 10$ ft   **560 ft³**
   b. $\ell = 4$ cm, $w = 2.5$ cm, $h = 7$ cm   **70 cm³**

Now you may assign Exercises 1–22.

▼2 *Finding a Dimension*

If you know the volume and two dimensions of a prism, you can find the third dimension.

■ EXAMPLE 2

The volume of a rectangular prism is 105 in.³ The height of the prism is 5 in. The length is 7 in. Find the missing dimension.

$$V = \ell \times w \times h \quad \longleftarrow \text{Use the volume formula.}$$
$$105 = 7 \times w \times 5 \quad \longleftarrow \text{Substitute.}$$
$$105 = 35w$$
$$\frac{105}{35} = \frac{35w}{35} \quad \longleftarrow \text{Divide each side by 35.}$$
$$w = 3$$
Check: $105 = 7 \times 3 \times 5$ ✓

The missing dimension is the width. The width is 3 in.

Technology Options

Prentice Hall Technology

Software for Learners
- Math Blaster® Mystery*
- Interactive Student Tutorial, Chapter 9*

Teaching Resource Software
- Computer Item Generator 9-8
- Resource Pro™ Chapter 9*

Internet • For related mathematics activities, visit the Prentice Hall site at www.phschool.com/math

*Available on CD-ROM only

Assignment Options for Exercises On Your Own

To provide flexible scheduling, this lesson can be split into parts.

▼1 **Core** 1–12, 14–19
  Extension 13, 20–22

▼2 **Core** 23–28
  Extension 29–33

Use Mixed Review to maintain skills.

3 Practice/Assess

EXERCISES *On Your Own*

Exercise 1 Ask students: *What dimension changes if you remove the top level of cubes?* **height**

Exercise 8 After students complete this exercise ask them to use mental math to find the volume of the cube if it has a height of 10 cm instead of 5 cm. **250 cm³**

MENTAL MATH **Exercises 9–12** Have students discuss how they ordered the dimensions to make it easier to find the volume. Ask students to tell their strategies.

WRITING **Exercise 13** Help students understand that the length, height, and width of a cube are the *same* measure.

Exercises 14–19 Encourage students to use mental math when possible.

Exercise 20 Ask students: *What is the area of the water's surface?* **384 m²**

Exercise 21 Suggest that students use mental math to find the volume.

CONNECTION TO ALGEBRA **Exercises 23–28** Remind students to be careful to include the correct numbers when they substitute numbers for variables in the formula $V = l \times w \times h$.

5. ✓*Try It Out* Find the missing dimension for each prism.
   a. $V = 180$ cm³, $w = 4$ cm, $h = 9$ cm $l = 5$ **cm**
   b. $V = 168$ m³, $w = 2$ cm, $l = 7$ m $h = 12$ **m**
   c. $V = 336$ ft³, $l = 8, h = 6$ $w = 7$

6. ▪*Reasoning* The volume of a rectangular prism is 36 m³. The area of the base is 9 m². What is the height of the prism?
   4 m

Now you may assign Exercises 23–33.

EXERCISES *On Your Own*

1. **Choose A, B, C, or D.** Each cube of the rectangular prism at the right measures 1 cm on each side. If the top level of cubes is removed, what is the volume of the remaining prism? **A**

   A. 45 cm³   **B.** 60 cm³   **C.** 48 cm³   **D.** 40 cm³

   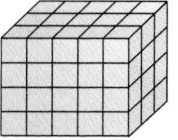

Find the volume of each rectangular prism.

2.
   2 in.
   2 in.
   10 in.
   40 in.³

3. 4 m
   3 m
   8 m
   96 cm³

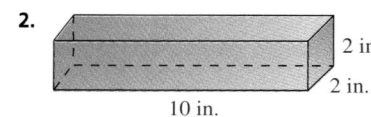

4. 6 ft
   3 ft   2 ft
   36 ft³

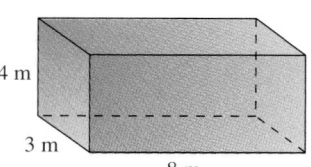
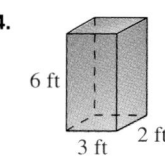

5. 4 cm
   2 cm
   6 cm
   48 cm³

6. 15 in.
   4 in.   10 in.
   600 in.³

7. 4.5 m
   3 m   2 m
   27 m³

8. 5 cm
   5 cm
   5 cm
   125 cm³

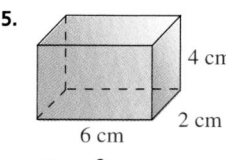
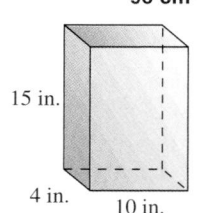
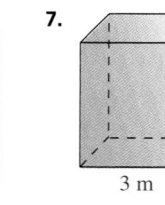
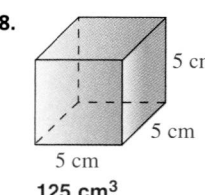

Mental Math **Find the volume of the rectangular prism with the given dimensions.**

9. $l = 6$ ft, $w = 1$ ft, $h = 7$ ft **42 ft³**

10. $l = 2$ in., $w = 6$ in., $h = 5$ in. **60 in.³**

11. $l = 10$ ft, $w = 4$ ft, $h = 8$ ft **320 ft³**

12. $l = 6$ yd, $w = 9$ yd, $h = 10$ yd **540 yd³**

13. *Writing* How could you write the formula for the volume of a cube in a different way than $V = lwh$? Explain.
    $V = s^3$; the three dimensions of a cube are the same.

Exercises 29–32 Have students keep a chart to help them organize the information. Make sure they understand that the order of the dimensions does not matter.

REASONING Exercise 33 Encourage students to use a variety of strategies such as drawing pictures or guess and test to find the answer. Have students share their strategies and answers with the class.

EXTENSION Have students draw several three-dimensional prisms. Ask students to label the faces, edges, and vertices. Then have students find the surface area and volume of each figure. Have students include their formulas and show their work. Ask students to write about their strategies for drawing the figures.

CONNECTION TO GEOMETRY Review with students the formulas for area and volume of different geometric shapes.

WRAP UP

IDENTIFYING THE BIG IDEA Ask students to explain how to find the volume of a rectangular prism.

Find the volume of each rectangular prism with the given dimensions.

14. $\ell = 5$ mm, $w = 4$ mm, $h = 9$ mm **180 mm³** **15.** $\ell = 14$ cm, $w = 7$ cm, $h = 2.5$ cm **245 cm³**

16. $\ell = 2.4$ m, $w = 3.1$ m, $h = 5.4$ m **40.176 m³** **17.** $\ell = 4$ mm, $w = 4$ mm, $h = 7$ mm **112 mm³**

18. $\ell = 1.5$ mm, $w = 1.5$ mm, $h = 4$ mm **9 mm³** **19.** $\ell = 5$ cm, $w = 8$ cm, $h = 11$ cm **440 cm³**

20. *Swimming Pools* A swimming pool is 24 m long and 16 m wide. The average depth of the water is 2.5 m.
   a. What is the volume of the water? **960 m³**
   b. *Measurement* Units of capacity such as liters (L) are used to measure the volume of liquids. A volume of 1 m³ is equivalent to 1,000 L. What is the capacity, in liters, of the swimming pool? **960,000 L**

21. Choose A, B, C, or D. A rectangular prism is 2 m long, 50 cm wide, and 1 m high. What is its volume? **C**
   A. 100 m³   **B.** 100 cm³   **C.** 1 m³   **D.** 10,000 cm³

22. *Draw a Conclusion* How do the volumes of these prisms compare? How do the surface areas compare? **The volumes are the same; the surface area of the 1st prism is greater.**

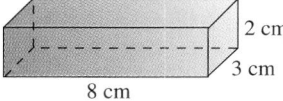
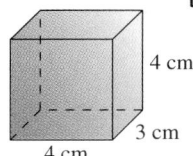

The volume and two dimensions of a rectangular prism are given. Find the third dimension.

23. $V = 154$ yd³, $h = 11$ yd, $w = 2$ yd **7 yd**   **24.** $V = 120$ cm³, $w = 4$ cm, $h = 6$ cm **5 cm**

25. $V = 108$ ft³, $\ell = 6$ ft, $w = 2$ ft **9 ft**   **26.** $V = 140$ ft³, $w = 4$ ft, $h = 7$ ft **5 ft**

27. $V = 180$ in.³, $w = 3$ in., $h = 12$ in. **5 in.**   **28.** $V = 256$ cm³, $\ell = 8$ cm, $w = 4$ cm **8 cm**

Number Sense **Find the whole-number dimensions of all possible prisms that have the given volume.** **29–32. See margin.**

29. $V = 32$ cm³   **30.** $V = 48$ cm³   **31.** $V = 54$ m³   **32.** $V = 24$ in.³

33. *Reasoning* A ton of coal fills a bin that is 3 ft by 4 ft by 4 ft. Find the dimensions of a bin that would hold 2 tons.
   Answers may vary. Sample: 3 ft × 4 ft × 8 ft

CHECKPOINT 2

■ *Checkpoint 2*   *Lessons 9-4 through 9-8*

Find the circumference and area of a circle with the given radius or diameter. Round each answer to the nearest tenth of a unit.

1. $r = 9$ in.   **2.** $r = 27$ m
   $C = 56.5$ in.; $A = 254.5$ in.² $C = 169.6$ m; $A = 2,290.2$ m²

3. $d = 12$ ft   **4.** $d = 8$ cm
   $C = 37.7$ ft; $A = 113.1$ ft² $C = 25.1$ cm; $A = 50.3$ cm²

Find the surface area and volume of each rectangular prism.

5. (5 cm, 4 cm, 8 cm)   **6.** (2 m, 4 m, 3 m)
   $SA = 184$ cm²; $V = 160$ cm³ $SA = 52$ m²; $V = 24$ m³

7. Identify the three-dimensional figure at the right.
   hexagonal prism

pages 420–421 On Your Own

   29. 1 cm × 1 cm × 32 cm, 1 cm × 2 cm × 16 cm, 1 cm × 4 cm × 8 cm, 2 cm × 2 cm × 8 cm, 2 cm × 4 cm × 4 cm

   30. 1 cm × 1 cm × 48 cm, 1 cm × 2 cm × 24 cm, 1 cm × 3 cm × 16 cm, 1 cm × 4 cm × 12 cm, 1 cm × 6 cm × 8 cm, 2 cm × 2 cm × 12 cm, 2 cm × 3 cm × 8 cm, 2 cm × 4 cm × 6 cm, 3 cm × 4 cm × 4 cm

   31. 1 m × 1 m × 54 m, 1 m × 2 m × 27 m, 1 m × 3 m × 18 m, 1 m × 6 m × 9 m, 2 m × 3 m × 9 m, 3 m × 3 m × 6 m

   32. 1 in. × 1 in. × 24 in., 1 in. × 2 in. × 12 in., 1 in. × 3 in. × 8 in., 1 in. × 4 in. × 6 in., 2 in. × 2 in. × 6 in., 2 in. × 3 in. × 4 in.

421

PRACTICE

Practice 9-8 Volume of a Rectangular Prism

Find the volume of each rectangular prism.

1.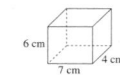
6 cm, 4 cm, 7 cm

2.
5 in., 5 in., 5 in.

3.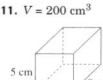
6 ft, 2 ft, 8 ft

168 cm³   125 in.³   96 ft³

4. $l = 6$ cm, $w = 5$ cm, $h = 12$ cm

360 cm³

5. $l = 13$ in., $w = 7$ in., $h = 9$ in.

819 in.³

The volume and two dimensions of a rectangular prism are given. Find the third dimension.

6. $V = 140$ ft³, $l = 5$ ft, $h = 7$ ft

w = 4 ft

7. $V = 255$ cm³, $w = 17$ cm, $h = 3$ cm

l = 5 cm

8. $V = 343$ in.³, $h = 7$ in., $l = 7$ in.

w = 7 in.

9. $V = 280$ yd³, $l = 14$ yd, $w = 4$ yd

h = 5 yd

Draw and label a rectangular prism with the given volume, using a set of whole-number dimensions. Answers may vary. Sample:

10. $V = 90$ cm³
10 cm, 9 cm, 1 cm

11. $V = 200$ cm³
5 cm, 8 cm, 5 cm

Solve each problem.

12. A fish aquarium measures 3 ft long, 2 ft wide, and 2 ft high. What is the volume of the aquarium?
12 ft³

13. A swimming pool is 25 ft wide, 60 ft long, and 7 ft deep. What is the volume of the pool? 10,500 ft³

In copymaster and workbook formats

RETEACHING

Reteaching 9-8 Volume of a Rectangular Prism

Volume is the number of cubic units needed to fill the space inside a three-dimensional figure. It is measured in cubic units.

Find the volume of the rectangular prism.

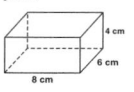
4 cm, 6 cm, 8 cm

Volume = length × width × height
$V = l \times w \times h$
$= 8 \times 6 \times 4$
$= 192$ cm³
The volume is 192 cm³.

If you know the volume and two dimensions of a rectangular prism, you can find the third dimension.

Find the missing dimension (length l).

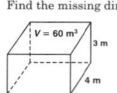
V = 60 m³, 3 m, 4 m

① Write the formula. $V = l \times w \times h$
② Substitute. $60 = l \times 4 \times 3$
   $60 = 12l$
③ Solve for l. $\frac{60}{12} = \frac{12l}{12}$
   $5 = l$

The length is 5 m.

Find the volume of each rectangular prism.

1.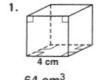
4 cm
64 cm³

2.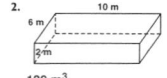
10 m, 6 m, 2 m
120 m³

3.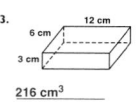
12 cm, 6 cm, 3 cm
216 cm³

Find the volume of the rectangular prism with the given dimensions.

4. $l = 6$ in., $w = 9$ in., $h = 3$ in.
162 in.³

5. $l = 3.5$ cm, $w = 1.5$ cm, $h = 7$ cm
36.75 cm³

6. $l = 16$ mm, $w = 18$ mm, $h = 2.5$ mm
720 mm³

7. $l = 5$ m, $w = 6.2$ m, $h = 3.9$ m
120.9 m³

The volume and two dimensions of a rectangular prism are given. Find the third dimension.

8. $V = 216$ m³, $l = 9$ m, $w = 8$ m
h = 3 m

9. $V = 168$ m³, $w = 12$ m, $h = 2$ m
l = 7 m

ENRICHMENT

Minds on Math Transparency

9-8

A rectangular pool has dimensions of 20 ft by 30 ft. There is a walkway that is 8 ft wide surrounding the pool. Find the area of the walkway.

1,056 ft²

See Solution Key for worked-out answers.

422

LESSON QUIZ

Find the volume of each rectangular prism with the given dimensions.

1. $l = 25$ cm, $w = 22.4$ cm, $h = 12.5$ cm
7,000 cm³

Given the volume and two dimensions, find the third dimension.

2. $w = 9.4$ m, $h = 16$ m, $V = 2556.8$ m³
$l = $ **17 m**

3. $V = 2,900$ cm³, $h = 10$, $w = 20$
$l = $ **14.5 cm**

4. $V = 1,080$ m³, $l = 15$ m, $w = 8$ m
$h = 9$ m

Mixed Review

Find the missing length in each circle. (*Lesson 8-10*)

34. $d = $ 26 cm, $r = 13$ cm

35. $d = 142$ ft, $r = $ 71 ft

36. $d = $ 74 m, $r = 37$ m

Find each quotient. (*Lesson 6-9*)

37. $3\frac{5}{8} \div \frac{1}{2}$ $7\frac{1}{4}$

38. $12 \div 3\frac{3}{4}$ $3\frac{1}{5}$

39. $16\frac{4}{5} \div \frac{3}{5}$ 28

40. $4\frac{1}{6} \div \frac{1}{3}$ $12\frac{1}{2}$

41. $2\frac{1}{4} \div \frac{1}{8}$ 18

42. *Gardening* Lahela has a rectangular vegetable garden with an area of 15 ft². If the width of the garden is $2\frac{1}{2}$ ft, what is the length of the garden? (*Lesson 9-2*)   **6 ft**

✓ CHECKPOINT 2

Lessons 9-4 through 9-8

Find the circumference of each circle. Round each answer to the nearest unit. Find the area of each circle. Round each answer to the nearest tenth of a unit.

1.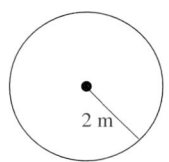
2 m

2.
13 in.

3.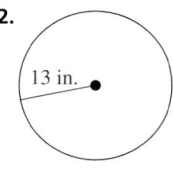
6 km

13 m; 12.6 m²   82 in.; 530.7 in.²   38 km; 113.0 km²

Identify each three-dimensional figure.

4.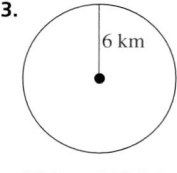
square prism

5.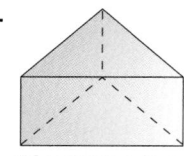
triangular prism

6.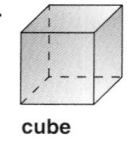
cube

7.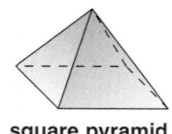
square pyramid

Find the surface area and volume of each figure.

8.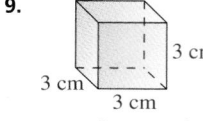
3 cm, 2 cm, 5 cm
62 cm²; 30 cm³

9.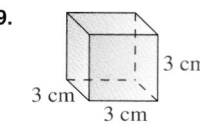
3 cm, 3 cm, 3 cm
54 cm²; 27 cm³

10.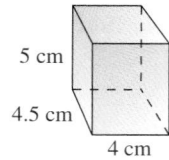
5 cm, 4.5 cm, 4 cm
121 cm²; 90 cm³

PROBLEM SOLVING PRACTICE ★★

This page provides problems for students to solve using their knowledge of rounding numbers, finding circumference, using ratios, finding perimeter, drawing reflections, evaluating similarity, using a scale drawing, and solving problems with area. Allow students to use any method they find helpful.

USING MANIPULATIVES Exercise 3
Students can use blocks or counters to model groups with the same ratio.

Exercises 4 and 6 Students may want to draw diagrams on dot paper to help them answer these questions.

COOPERATIVE GROUPS Exercise 8
Students can meet in small groups to answer the question. Have group members discuss the possible choices and agree on both an answer and the reason for the answer.

PROBLEM SOLVING PRACTICE ★★★★★

Choose the best answer.

1. An odometer on a car measured the distance between two cities as 163.9 miles. What is this distance rounded to the nearest ten? **A**

   A. 160 miles   B. 163 miles
   C. 164 miles   D. 170 miles

2. A circular mirror has a diameter of 12 inches. What is the circumference of the mirror rounded to the nearest inch? Use 3.14 for π. **G**

   F. 24 in.   G. 38 in.
   H. 113 in.   J. 452 in.

3. If the ratio of dogs to cats in a kennel is exactly 3 to 2, then the kennel could have — **C**

   A. 9 dogs and 4 cats
   B. 4 dogs and 6 cats
   C. 12 dogs and 8 cats
   D. 15 dogs and 8 cats

4. What is the perimeter of a rectangular pen that is 10 feet wide by 20 feet long? **G**

   F. 30 ft   G. 60 ft
   H. 200 ft   J. 400 ft

5. Look at the drawing of a fish below. Which drawing shows a reflection of the fish? **D**

   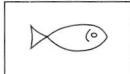

   A.    B.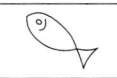

   C. 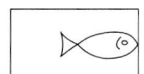   D.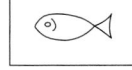

6. Suppose you are cutting out geometric shapes to make a collage. Which of the following figures are *always* similar? **H**

   F. two triangles
   G. two rectangles
   H. two squares
   J. two parallelograms

Please note that items 7 and 8 each have *five* answer choices.

7. Aldo made a scale drawing of his room. The room is 12 feet long by 9 feet wide. He used the scale 1 inch : 6 feet. Find the dimensions of the scale drawing. **D**

   A. 72 feet by 63 feet

   B. 72 inches by 63 inches

   C. 2 feet by $1\frac{1}{2}$ feet

   D. 2 inches by $1\frac{1}{2}$ inches

   E. Not Here

8. Sampson plans to carpet the patio around the pool. Which procedure should he use to find the shaded area? **G**

   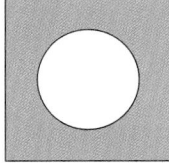

   F. Find the area of the square and add the area of the circle.
   G. Find the area of the square and subtract the area of the circle.
   H. Find the area of the square and subtract the circumference of the circle.
   J. Find the perimeter of the square and add the area of the circle.
   K. Find the perimeter of both figures.

1 Focus

CONNECTING TO PRIOR KNOWLEDGE Ask students to recall when they have seen a physical model to explain something. For example, a coach might draw a line in the dirt to explain a play for the football team. Ask students: *How do models help you solve*

problems? **Answers may vary. Sample: Models can help you visualize the answer.**

2 Teach

THINK AND DISCUSS

TACTILE LEARNING Suggest that students work in groups of three to four. Provide groups with at least 21 real pennies if possible.

DIVERSITY and AUDITORY LEARNING Ask strong readers in each group to read the sample problem and questions aloud to other members of the group. Suggest that students discuss each question before they write the answer.

ERROR ALERT! Some students may incorrectly think they need to find a surface area measurement for the Sample Problem. **Remediation:** Remind students that they need to find the number of pennies that will fill up the box.

Lesson Planning Options

Prerequisite Skills
• calculating volume (9-8)

Materials/Manipulatives
• centimeter ruler   • pennies

Resources

 Student Edition

Skills Handbook, p. 537
Extra Practice, p. 530
Glossary/Study Guide

 Teaching Resources

Chapter Support File, Ch. 9
• Lesson Planner 9-9
• Practice 9-9, Reteaching 9-9
• Answer Masters 9-9
Teaching Aids Masters 1–3, 19
Glossary, Spanish Resources

 Transparencies
1, 9, Minds on Math 9-9

Warm Up

Summer has $1.00 in change in her pocket. She has 9 silver coins and her largest coin is a quarter. What coins could she have? **1 quarter, 7 dimes, 1 nickel or 2 quarters, 3 dimes, 4 nickels**

424

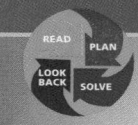

PROBLEM SOLVING STRATEGY

9-9 Make a Model

Problem Solving Strategies

Draw a Diagram
Guess and Test
Look for a Pattern
✔ Make a Model
Make a Table
Simulate a Problem
Solve a Simpler Problem
Too Much or Too Little
  Information
Use Logical Reasoning
Use Multiple Strategies
Work Backward

THINK AND DISCUSS

Sometimes words are not enough to help you visualize a problem. A physical model can help you solve problems. Architects and engineers make models to help solve problems.

SAMPLE PROBLEM...

Danica collects pennies. She keeps her pennies in a box. The dimensions of the inside of the box are 21 cm wide by 30 cm long by 21 cm high. About how many pennies will the box hold?

 READ
Read for understanding. Summarize the problem.

1. Think about the information you are given and what you are asked to find.   **a. the number of pennies the box holds**
  a. What does the problem ask you to find?
  b. Are you given all the information you need? What else do you need to know?   **No; you need to find the amount of space 1 penny takes up.**

PLAN
Decide on a strategy.

Making a model will help you solve the problem. If you have some pennies, you can model how many pennies are needed to form one layer that fits inside the bottom of the box. Make a model of the box by drawing a rectangle 21 cm wide and 30 cm long.

2. Reasoning may vary. Sample: No; you can find the number of pennies in a stack 3 cm high and multiply the result by 7.

2. You can stack pennies to find how many layers might fit in the box. Do you need to have a stack of pennies 21 cm high in order to find out how many layers will fit in the box? Why or why not? **See left.**

 SOLVE
Try the strategy.

3. Work with your group to make models you can measure.
  a. How many pennies can you fit in a row 21 cm long? **10 pennies**
  b. How many pennies will fit in a stack of pennies 21 cm high? **about 137 pennies**

4. a. How many pennies will fit in one layer? **150 pennies**
  b. About how many pennies will fit in the box? **about 20,550 pennies**

■ **ADDITIONAL PROBLEM**

Find how many unit cubes will fit in a rectangular box with the following dimensions: *l* = 8 cm, *w* = 3 cm, *h* = 2 cm. Each unit cube has a side length of 1 cm. **48 unit cubes** How many cubes make one layer? **24 unit cubes**

3 Practice/Assess

EXERCISES *On Your Own*

ASSESSMENT Have pairs of students write a volume problem in which they use a model to find the solution. Have pairs trade and solve problems. Check answers as a whole class.

CONNECTION TO GEOMETRY Exercise 5 Review geometry by asking students to find the perimeter of a game board.

CONNECTION TO GEOMETRY Exercise 9 If students need help suggest that they create a model on graph paper.

➤ **LOOK BACK**
Think about how you solved the problem.

Now you may assign Exercises 1–11.

EXERCISES *On Your Own*

Make a model to solve each problem.

1. *Coins* Lincoln's head is right-side-up on the penny on the left. If you roll the penny halfway around the other penny, will Lincoln's head be right-side-up, upside-down, or neither? **right-side-up**

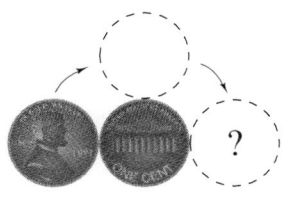

2. *Woodworking* It takes Clara 12 min to cut a log into 4 pieces. How long will it take her to cut a log that is the same size into 5 pieces? **16 min**

3. *Jobs* Chris works in a grocery store after school. He stacked grapefruit in the shape of a square pyramid. There was one grapefruit on the top level, four on the next level, and nine on the next level. If there were eight levels in all, how many grapefruit did Chris stack? **204 grapefruit**

Use any strategy to solve each problem. Show all your work.

4. *Gardening* Todd planted 60 seeds in his garden. Not all of the seeds grew into plants. Thirty more seeds grew into plants than did not grow at all. How many of the 60 seeds grew into plants? **45 seeds**

5. *Geometry* A square game board is 16 in. long and 16 in. wide. A square that measures 2 in. × 2 in. is cut from each corner of the board. What is the perimeter of the original game board? Of the new game board? **64 in.; 64 in.**

6. *Savings* Maria is saving her money to buy some basketball shoes that cost $72. She has $17 right now. Each week Maria earns $12 by mowing her neighbor's lawn. In how many weeks will she be able to buy the shoes? **5 weeks**

5. How reasonable is your final estimate for the number of pennies that will fit in the box? Explain. **See below.**

Think and Discuss
5. **Answers may vary. Sample: It's close but is probably a low estimate since there was a little extra space along the length and width of the box.**

Technology Options

Prentice Hall Technology

Software for Learners
• Math Blaster® Mystery*
• Interactive Student Tutorial, Chapter 9*

Teaching Resource Software
• Computer Item Generator 9-9
• Resource Pro™ Chapter 9*

Internet • For related mathematics activities, visit the Prentice Hall site at www.phschool.com/math

*Available on CD-ROM only

Assignment Options for Exercises On Your Own

Core 1–3, 5–7, 9–11
Extension 4, 8

Use Mixed Review to maintain skills.

Practice 9-9 *Problem-Solving Strategy: Make a Model*

Choose any strategy to solve each problem. Show all your work.

1. Circle the nets that you could fold to form a cube.

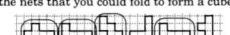

2. Find three numbers that continue the pattern.
   1, 3, 7, __13__, __21__, __31__

3. Describe two different ways to continue the pattern.
   2, 3, 5, ____, ____, ____
   2, 3, 5, ____, ____, ____
   Answers may vary.   Sample: 8, 12, 17 and 9, 17, 33

4. How many different rectangles can you form using 24 centimeter squares?
   4 rectangles: 1 by 24, 2 by 12, 3 by 8, 4 by 6

5. What is the area of the parallelogram at the right? Assume that each square represents 1 cm².
   20 cm²

6. **Circle A, B, or C.** Which piece of plastic wrap shown below can be used to cover the surface of the box shown? The piece can overlap, but cannot be cut.

   A. 12 / 16   ⓑ 16 / 20   C. 12 / 12

   [box: 4 4 4 / 4 4 4 / 12]

7. A farmer has 3 sons. The farmer decides to give each son the same amount of seeds and barrels. The farmer has 21 barrels: 7 are full of seeds, 7 are half-full, 7 are empty. You cannot move seeds from one barrel to another. How can the farmer divide the seed and barrels equally? Make a model to help solve.
   2 full, 3 half-full, 2 empty; 2 full, 3 half-full, 2 empty;
   3 full, 1 half-full, 3 empty

In copymaster and workbook formats

Reteaching 9-9 *Problem-Solving Strategy: Make a Model*

You want to build this box from a piece of cardboard that is 16 inches long and 12 inches wide. How can you cut the cardboard to make the box? How many square inches will be left over? Are there other ways to cut so that different amounts are left over?

Read   What information will help you solve the problem?
          You know the given dimensions of each face.

Plan   What kind of model can help you decide how to cut the cardboard?
          Mark 16-in. by 12-in. sheets of paper until you find a pattern.

Solve   Find a way to make all six faces. Then mark and cut the cardboard.

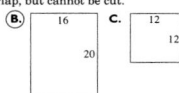   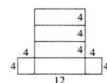

This arrangement does not make six faces. Don't cut the cardboard.   This arrangement works. 12 in.² are left over.

Look Back   Is there another way to cut the cardboard? *Try other arrangements.*

Make a model to solve Exercises 1 and 2.

1. You have a piece of cardboard that is 12 in. by 10 in. How can you cut the cardboard to build an open-topped cube with the greatest possible volume? Assume that each dimension is a whole number and each face must be only one piece.
   Cut 5 squares, each 4 in. by 4 in. The box will have a volume of 64 in³.

2. Meera collects nickels. She keeps them in a box. The dimensions of the inside of the box are 6½ in. by 2 in. by 3¼ in. About how many nickels can be stacked inside the box?
   1,024

3. How could you answer Exercise 2 without using a model?
   Find how many nickels fit in one layer (32) and how many fit in each stack (32), then multiply.

Minds on Math Transparency

9-9

I am a rectangle. My perimeter is 26 in. and my area is 36 in.². What are my dimensions?

9 in. by 4 in.

See *Solution Key* for worked-out answers.

426

IDENTIFYING THE BIG IDEA Ask students to explain how to use models to solve problems.

PORTFOLIO Share with students the criteria you use to assess their portfolio work. Share how you plan to use the results. Students need to understand how you use rubrics to assess their work, how each piece in the portfolio counts, and how portfolio scores affect their overall evaluation.

1. Chris stacked oranges in the shape of a triangular pyramid. There was one orange on the top level, three on the next level, and six on the next level. If there were five levels in all, how many oranges did Chris stack? **35 oranges**

2. How many different rectangular prisms with integer dimensions have a volume of 12 cm³? **4**

---

7. Jafar's birthday cake is cube shaped, with icing on the top and four sides. He cut it as shown at the right.
   a. How many cuts did Jafar make? **6 cuts**
   b. Into how many pieces did he cut the cake? **27 pieces**
   c. *Spatial Reasoning* How many of the pieces did not have any icing? **1 piece**

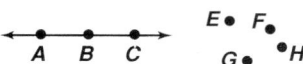

8a–b. **Answers may vary. Samples are given.**
8. a. *Patterns* Find three numbers that continue the pattern.
      1, 2, 4, ■, ■, ■ **8, 16, 32**
   b. Find another three numbers that continue the pattern in a different way. **7, 11, 16**

9. *Geometry* What are the whole-number dimensions of the rectangular prism with a volume of 12 cubic units and the greatest possible surface area? **1 × 1 × 12**

10. *Literature* The numbered pages in the book *Why Do Clocks Run Clockwise?* run from 1 to 251. How many of these page numbers contain at least one number 2? **90 pages**

11. Rachel wants to make a fenced rectangular area in her backyard for her dog Jesse. She has 36 m of fencing. What are the whole-number dimensions (in meters) of the different rectangular regions she can fence? **1 m × 17 m, 2 m × 16 m, 3 m × 15 m, 4 m × 14 m, 5 m × 13 m, 6 m × 12 m, 7 m × 11 m, 8 m × 10 m, 9 m × 9 m**

PORTFOLIO
Select one or two items from your work for this chapter.
• perimeter or area work
• drawings of three-dimensional figures
• problem-solving models
Explain why you have included each selection.

How many lines of symmetry does each figure have?
(Lesson 8-9)

12. [rectangle] 2 lines
13. [quadrilateral] no lines
14. [triangle] no lines
15. [ellipse] 2 lines

Write each statement as a percent. *(Lesson 7-6)*

16. 10 boys in a class of 25 **40%**
17. 7 silk scarves out of 21 **33⅓%**
18. 15 tables out of 50 **30%**

19. Draw three collinear points and four noncollinear points. *(Lesson 8-1)*

   A B C   E• F• / G• •H

20. *Choose a Strategy* A local bus picked up 3 passengers at its first stop. At every stop thereafter, it picked up 2 more passengers than at the previous stop. How many passengers got on at the fifth stop? **11 passengers**

PROJECT DAY You may wish to plan a project day on which students share their completed projects. Encourage students to explain their process as well as their product.

PROJECT NOTEBOOK Ask students to review their project work and bring their notebooks up to date.

SCORING RUBRIC

3 You produce two well-sketched diagrams of the Web pages you analyzed. You provide clear and accurate calculations of areas of useful information. You accurately calculate the percent of useful information on each page. You also provide your own well-thought-out home page design along with notes describing what you learned from analyzing Web pages.

2 You provide two diagrams of Web home pages. You correctly calculate the percent of useful information on at least one of these pages. You also provide your own home page design that shows what you learned from other Web pages.

1 You provide an incomplete sketch of two Web home pages. You omit areas of useful information or incorrectly calculate areas of useful information on each page. Your own home page design is incomplete.

0 You show little evidence that you analyzed several Web pages, and you do not design a home page.

FINISHING THE CHAPTER PROJECT

Home *on the* Web

Design a Home Page Project Links on pages 391, 402, 407, and 412 can help you work on the different parts of your project. Here is a checklist to help you gather together those parts.

- ✔ diagrams of two Web pages you evaluated
- ✔ calculations that show the measurement of areas on the home page
- ✔ calculations that show the percent of text and graphics on each page
- ✔ a sketch of the Web page you designed, with descriptions of its links to other Web pages

Prepare a presentation that explains what you learned from analyzing Web pages. Describe how you used what you learned to design your own home page. What factors other than space use affect the quality of a Web page?

Reflect and Revise

Exchange home pages with other students. Did the pages you and your classmates created use space better than the Web pages you studied? Make changes to improve your home page.

Web Extension

Prentice Hall's Internet site contains information you might find helpful as you complete your project. Visit www.phschool.com/mgm1/ch9 for some links and ideas related to the World Wide Web.

STUDENT SELF-ASSESSMENT SURVEY

Chapter 9 Student Self-Assessment Survey

1. Now that you have finished this chapter, think about what you have learned about measurement. Check each topic that you feel confident you understand.
   _____ estimate the area of a figure drawn on graph paper (9-1)
   _____ find perimeters and areas of rectangles and squares (9-2)
   _____ find areas of parallelograms and triangles (9-3)
   _____ find areas of complex figures (9-3)
   _____ find the circumference of a circle (9-4)
   _____ find the area of a circle (9-5)
   _____ find combined areas of circles and polygons (9-5)
   _____ identify three-dimensional figures such as pyramids and prisms (9-6)
   _____ find the surface area of rectangular prisms (9-7)
   _____ find volumes and dimensions of rectangular prisms (9-8)
   _____ make models to solve problems (9-9)

2. Before the Chapter Assessment, I need to review _____

3. **a.** Check one. In general, I thought this chapter was
   ___ a snap ___ easy ___ average ___ hard ___ a monster
   b. Why do you feel this way? _____

4. In this chapter, I did my best work on _____

5. In this chapter, I had trouble with _____

6. Check each one that applies. Now that I've spent some time working with the measurement of geometric figures, I think this kind of measurement is
   ___ important ___ boring ___ useful ___ fun
   ___ a waste of time ___ confusing ___ tricky ___ interesting

7. Did you use a calculator to explore the relationship between diameter and circumference? _____ If yes, did you find the calculator helpful? _____ Explain. _____

Vocabulary/Symbols

altitude, bases, circumference, cone, cube, cylinder, edge, faces, net, pi (π), prism, pyramid, sphere, square units, surface area (SA), three-dimensional figures, vertex, volume (V)

Materials/Manipulatives

• calculator
• dot paper

Resources

 Student Edition

Extra Practice, p. 530
Glossary/Study Guide

 **Teaching Resources**

Chapter Support file, Ch. 9
• Student Self-Assessment Survey,
Glossary, Spanish Resources
Tools for Studying Smarter

WRAP UP

Exercise 1 Remind students that the area of the figure is the number of squares enclosed by the figure.

Exercises 5–8 Remind students how to find the circumference and area of a circle given its radius or diameter. Point out that in Exercises 7 and 8, they have the diameter.

ASSESSMENT Exercises 16 and 17 Have students work with partners. For Exercise 16, partners may want to arrange squares of construction paper rather than draw pictures. For Exercise 17, have students make their own cubes from paper nets. Have them discuss what the problem says before acting it out.

9 WRAP UP

Perimeter and Area of Polygons   9-1, 9-2, 9-3

Perimeter is the distance around a figure.

Area is the number of square units inside a figure. The formula for area of a parallelogram is $A = bh$. The formula for area of a triangle is $A = \frac{1}{2}bh$.

1. Estimate the area of the figure. Assume each square represents 1 m². **about 19 m²**

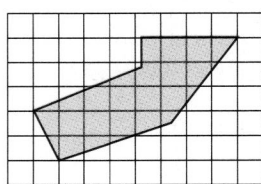

2. Find the area and perimeter of the parallelogram. **13.5 cm²; 22 cm**

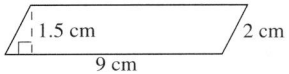

3. A rectangular yard has an area of 72 m². One side is 8 m long. How much fence do you need to enclose the entire yard? **34 m**

4. Find the area of a triangle with a base 12 cm and height 7.6 cm. **45.6 cm²**

Circumference and Area of Circles   9-4, 9-5

Use the symbol π to stand for the ratio $\frac{\text{circumference}}{\text{diameter}}$. The formula for the area of a circle is $A = \pi r^2$.

Find the circumference of each circle with the given radius or diameter. Round each answer to the nearest unit.

5. $r = 6$ in. **38 in.**
6. $r = 3.8$ m **24 m**
7. $d = 24.5$ cm **77 cm**
8. $d = 37.6$ ft **118 ft**

Calculator **Find the area of each circle. Round each answer to the nearest tenth of a unit.**

9.
5 in.
78.5 in.²

10.
13 m
530.7 m²

11.
4.7 m
69.4 m²

Remind students that the new mathematical terms in this chapter are defined in the Glossary/Study Guide in the back of the textbook.

Three-Dimensional Figures   9-6

Three-dimensional figures are figures such as boxes, cans, and buildings that do not lie in a plane. Most three-dimensional figures have flat, polygonal surfaces called **faces**. Where two faces meet, the resulting segment is called an **edge**. Each point where edges meet is a **vertex**.

A **prism** is a three-dimensional figure with two parallel and congruent polygonal faces, called **bases**. A prism is named for the shape of its base.

12. **a.** Identify the figure at the right.   **square pyramid**
    b. Find the number of faces, edges, and vertices.
    5 faces; 8 edges; 5 vertices

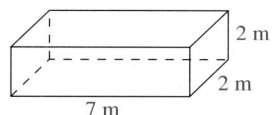

13. *Writing* Give a description of a rectangular prism.
    A rectangular prism has six rectangular faces, with two parallel bases that are rectangular.

Surface Area and Volume   9-7, 9-8

The **surface area** of a rectangular prism is the sum of the areas of all its faces.

The **volume** of a three-dimensional figure is the number of cubic units needed to fill the space inside the figure. The formula for the volume of a rectangular prism is $V = \ell wh$.

14. Find the surface area and the volume of the rectangular prism at the right.   **64 m²; 28 m³**

15. **Choose A, B, C, or D.** Which could not be the dimensions of a rectangular prism with a volume of 60 m³?   **B**

   A. 1 m by 1 m by 60 m   **B.** 4 m by 15 m by 2 m
   C. 3 m by 4 m by 5 m   **D.** 1 m by 6 m by 10 m

Problem Solving Strategies   9-9

Sometimes making a model can help you solve a problem.

16. You have 12 square tables. One person can sit on each side. You need to arrange the tables so that at least one side of each table is touching another table. How many people can you seat?   **26 people**

17. Suppose you have a heavy 3-ft wide cube with the letter K on top. If you flip the cube end over end in one straight line over a distance of 18 feet, where will the letter K end up? Draw a picture to show the path and final position of the letter K.
    Check students' work.

Chapter 9 Assessment • Form A

		Answers

1. Find the area of the figure. Assume each square represents 1 cm².

   1. **11 cm²**

2. Estimate the area of the figure. Assume each square represents 1 mi².

   2. **about 13 mi²**

3. Find the area of the rectangle.
   5 ft / 8 ft
   3. **40 ft²**

4. The width of a rectangle is 6 in. The perimeter is 28 in. Find the area.
   4. **48 in.²**

5. Find the area of a square with sides of 6 m.
   5. **36 m²**

6. Find the area of the figure shown.   3 cm / 2 cm / 6 cm / 6 cm
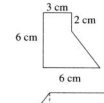
   6. **24 cm²**

7. Find the area of the parallelogram.   5 in. / 4 in. / 7 in.
   7. **28 in.²**

8. Find the circumference of a circle with a radius of 4 mi. Round to the nearest tenth.
   8. **25.1 mi**

9. Given a circumference of 21.98 ft, what is the diameter? Round to the nearest tenth.
   9. **7.0 ft**

10. Find the area of a circle with a diameter of 6 ft. Round to the nearest tenth.
   10. **28.3 ft²**

Chapter 9 Assessment • Form A (continued)

11. Find the area of the figure shown. Round to the nearest tenth.   7 cm / 3 cm / 4 cm / 3 cm
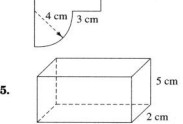
   11. **33.6 cm²**

Use the figure at the right for Exercises 12–15.   5 cm / 2 cm / 10 cm

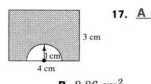

12. Identify the figure.   12. **rectangular prism**

13. Find the number of faces, edges, and vertices.   13. **6 faces, 12 edges, 8 vertices**

14. Find the surface area.   14. **160 cm²**

15. Find the volume.   15. **100 cm³**

16. The volume of a rectangular prism is 24 cm³. The length is 4 cm and the height is 2 cm. Find the surface area.   16. **52 cm²**

17. **Choose A, B, C, or D.** What is the area of the shaded region?   3 cm / 1 cm / 4 cm   17. **A**

   A. 10.43 cm²   **B.** 8.86 cm²
   C. 3.14 cm²   **D.** 12 cm²

Choose a Strategy

18. How many circles of 2 in. radius would fit inside a square with a side of 36 in.?   18. **81 circles**

Writing

19. How would you figure out the area of the shaded region in the figure shown?
    Find the area of the smaller circle and subtract it from the area of the larger circle.

429

Assessment

Chapter 9 Assessment • Form B

Choose the best answer. Circle A, B, C, or D.

1. What is the area of the figure shown? Assume each square represents 1 cm².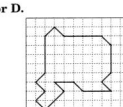

   Ⓐ 43.5 cm²   **B.** 46 cm²   **C.** 37 cm²   **D.** 40.5 cm²

2. Estimate the area of the figure. Assume each square represents 1 mi².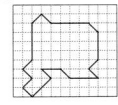

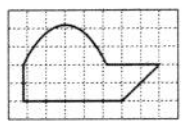

   A. about 10 mi²   **B.** about 15 mi²   Ⓒ about 18 mi²   **D.** about 22 mi²

3. What is the area of a square with sides of 5 ft?
   A. 10 ft²   **B.** 20 ft²   **C.** 125 ft²   Ⓓ 25 ft²

4. The length of a rectangle is 9 in. The area is 54 in.². What is the width?
   A. 45 in.   **B.** 30 in.   **C.** 9 in.   Ⓓ 6 in.

5. What is the area of the figure shown? 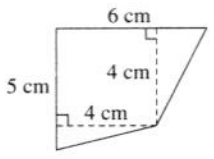
   A. 19 cm²   Ⓑ 22 cm²   **C.** 16 cm²   **D.** 28 cm²

6. What is the area of a parallelogram with base 9 in. and height 5 in.?
   Ⓐ 45 in.²   **B.** 67.5 in.²   **C.** 30 in.²   **D.** 54 in.²

7. A circle has a diameter of 6 ft. What is its circumference, rounded to the nearest tenth?
   A. 9.4 ft   **B.** 6 ft   Ⓒ 18.8 ft   **D.** 28.3 ft

8. Given that the circumference of a circle is 37 cm, what is the diameter, rounded to the nearest tenth?
   A. 7 cm   Ⓑ 11.8 cm   **C.** 30.7 cm   **D.** 232.4 cm

Chapter 9 Assessment • Form B (continued)

9. Find the area of a circle with a radius of 5 mi. Use 3.14 for π and round to the nearest tenth.
   A. 31.4 mi²   **B.** 15.7 mi²   Ⓒ 78.5 mi²   **D.** 314 mi²

10. Find the area of the figure at the right. Round to the nearest tenth.
    A. 18.3 cm²   Ⓑ 24.3 cm²   **C.** 30.6 cm²   **D.** 24.6 cm²

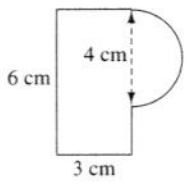

11. How many edges does the figure at the right have?
    A. 6 edges   **B.** 8 edges   Ⓒ 12 edges   **D.** 16 edges

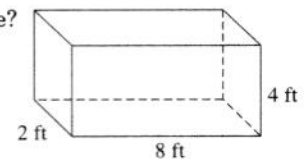

12. How many faces does the figure in Exercise 11 have?
    Ⓐ 6 faces   **B.** 8 faces   **C.** 12 faces   **D.** 16 faces

13. Find the surface area of the figure in Exercise 11.
    A. 64 ft²   **B.** 72 ft²   Ⓒ 112 ft²   **D.** 162 ft²

14. Find the volume of the figure in Exercise 11.
    A. 16 ft³   Ⓑ 64 ft³   **C.** 32 ft³   **D.** 128 ft³

15. The volume of a rectangular prism is 576 cm². The area of the base is 64 cm². Find the height.
    A. 3 cm   **B.** 8 cm   Ⓒ 9 cm   **D.** 512 cm

16. How would you find the area of the shaded region at the right?
    Ⓐ area of rectangle − area of circle
    B. area of rectangle + area of circle
    C. area of circle − area of rectangle
    D. area of circle + area of rectangle

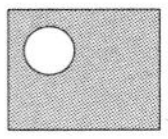

Choose a Strategy

17. How many triangles with the same dimensions as the triangle at the right could fit inside a square with 10-ft sides? 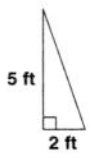
    A. 10 triangles   **B.** 15 triangles   Ⓒ 20 triangles   **D.** 30 triangles

---

 **Teaching Resources**

Chapter Support File, Ch. 9, and Spanish Resources

Teacher's Edition

See pp. 380C–D for Assessment Options.

Teaching Resource Software
- Computer Item Generator, Ch. 9

430

ASSESSMENT

ENHANCED MULTIPLE CHOICE QUESTIONS are more complex than traditional multiple choice questions, which assess only one skill. Enhanced multiple choice questions assess the processes that students use, as well as the end result. They are written so that students can use more than one strategy to solve the problem. Using multiple strategies is encouraged by the National Council of Teachers of Mathematics (NCTM). **Exercise 15** is an enhanced multiple choice question.

WRITING EXERCISES allow students to describe more fully their thinking and understanding of the concepts they've learned. **Exercise 8** is a writing exercise.

---

9 ASSESSMENT

1. Find the area of the figure below. Assume that each square represents 1 cm². **16 cm²**

   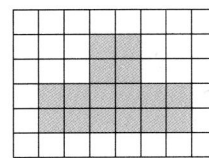

2. Find the area and perimeter of a square with sides 6 m. **36 m²; 24 m**

3. The perimeter of a rectangle is 32 ft. One dimension is 9 ft. Find the area. **63 ft²**

4. Find the area of the figure below. **126 m²**

   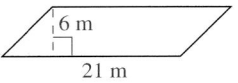
   6 m
   21 m

5. Find the area of a parallelogram with base 12 cm and height 7 cm. **84 cm²**

6. Find the area of a triangle with base 9.2 m and height 19.3 m. **88.78 m²**

7. Find the area of the triangle below. **12 yd²**

   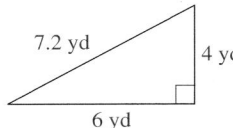
   7.2 yd   4 yd
   6 yd

8. *Writing* Which is larger: a pie plate with a radius of 5 in., or a pie plate with a diameter of 9 in.? Explain. **Pie plate with 5 in. radius; the diameter of 9 in. means a radius of 4.5 in.**

9. What is the surface area of a box with length 8 ft, width 5 ft, and height 4 ft? **112 ft²**

10. Find the circumference of a circle with the given radius or diameter. Round to the nearest unit.

    a. r = 10 km **63 km**   **b.** d = 12 cm **38 cm**
    c. d = 7.4 yd **23 yd**   **d.** r = 27 m **170 m**

11. **a.** Identify the figure at the right. **triangular prism**
    b. Find the number of faces, edges, and vertices. **5 faces; 9 edges; 6 vertices**

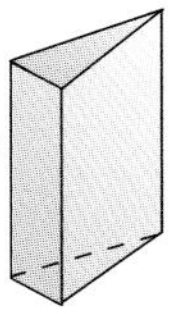

12. A rectangular prism is 17 m long, 3 m wide, and 5 m high. Find its volume. **255 m³**

13. The volume of a rectangular prism is 504 cm³. The area of the base is 72 cm². Find the height of the prism. **7 cm**

14. The volume and two dimensions of a rectangular prism are given. Find the third dimension. **a. 9 cm   b. 12 in.**
    a. V = 189 cm³, h = 7 cm, w = 3 cm
    b. V = 1,080 in.³, h = 15 in., w = 6 in.
    c. V = 360 ft³, h = 9 ft, w = 4 ft   **10 ft**

15. **Choose A, B, C, or D.** Which could be a net for a cube with an open top? **C**

    A. 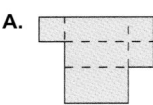   B.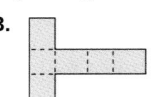

    C. 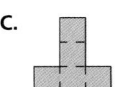   D.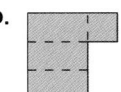

Item	Review Topic	Ch
1	Area of circles	9
2	Analyzing mean, median, and mode	1
3	Evaluating expressions	2
4	Volume of rectangular prisms	9
5	Estimating quotients of decimals	4

Item	Review Topic	Ch
6	Greatest common factor	5
7	Distributive property	4
8	Displaying data	1
9	Perimeter	9
10	Subtracting and adding fractions	6

9 CUMULATIVE REVIEW

Choose the best answer.

1. To the nearest tenth of a unit, what is the area of a circle with a 6-cm diameter? **B**

A. 12.0 cm^2 B. 28.3 cm^2
C. 36.0 cm^2 D. 113.4 cm^2

2. What is the median cost of peanut butter per serving? Use the table below. **C**

Peanut Butter Prices (3 tbsp serving)	
Sticky Stuff	22¢
Grandma's Choice	20¢
Shop Along	19¢
All Natural	22¢
Cityside	14¢
Nutty Taste	22¢

A. 20¢ B. 20.5¢
C. 21¢ D. 22¢

3. What do you do first to evaluate the expression $3.9 + 4.1 \times 16 - 6 \div 4.8$? **B**

A. Add 3.9 and 4.1.
B. Multiply 4.1 by 16.
C. Subtract 6 from 16.
D. Divide 6 by 4.8.

4. Find the volume of the open box made by folding the sides of the net below. **C**

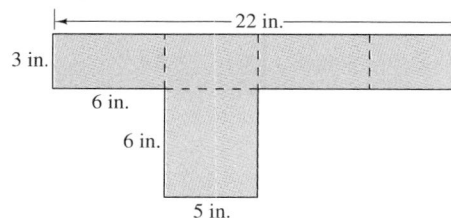

A. 14 in.^{3} B. 66 in.^{3}
C. 90 in.^{3} D. 165 in.^{3}

5. Which is a good estimate of the quotient $358.2 \div 0.67$? **C**

A. 50 B. 60
C. 500 D. 6,000

6. Which is the GCF of 20, 35, and 100? **B**

A. 5 B. 10 C. 100 D. 700

7. Which equation is *not* an example of the distributive property? **D**

A. $12(6.2) + 12(3.8) = 12(6.2 + 3.8)$
B. $0.75(8.869) + 0.25(8.869) = 1(8.869)$
C. $19.1(80) = 19.1(100) - 19.1(20)$
D. $8.1(1.9 + 3.5) = (8.1 + 1.9)(3.5)$

8. Which display would you use to show your height for each year since birth? **B**

A. line plot B. line graph
C. pictograph D. circle graph

9. Which statement is false? **D**

A. A nonrectangular parallelogram and a rectangle can have the same area.
B. A square is always a parallelogram.
C. You can divide a parallelogram into two congruent triangles.
D. Two rectangles with the same area always have the same perimeter.

10. The difference between two fractions is $2\frac{7}{12}$. Which fractions might have been used? **B**

A. $4\frac{1}{3}$ and $2\frac{11}{12}$
B. $4\frac{1}{4}$ and $1\frac{2}{3}$
C. $4\frac{2}{3}$ and $2\frac{11}{12}$
D. $4\frac{1}{2}$ and $1\frac{3}{4}$

CUMULATIVE REVIEW

Chapter 9 Cumulative Review

Choose the best answer. Circle A, B, C, or D.

1. Find the sum in simplest form.
$\frac{4}{12} + \frac{6}{12}$
A. $\frac{1}{6}$ B. $\frac{10}{24}$
C. $\frac{11}{12}$ D. $\frac{5}{6}$

2. Estimate the difference $3\frac{1}{3} - 1\frac{3}{8}$.
A. 1 B. $1\frac{1}{2}$
C. $2\frac{3}{4}$ D. 4

3. Adina has a 14-ft piece of rope and she wants to cut it into $3\frac{1}{2}$-ft lengths. How many $3\frac{1}{2}$-ft pieces can she make from the original rope?
A. 3 pieces B. 4 pieces
C. 5 pieces D. 49 pieces

4. Complete. 12 qt = ___ gal
A. 24 gal B. 8 gal
C. 3 gal D. 2 gal

5. Use mental math to find the value of y. $\frac{7}{18} = \frac{y}{36}$
A. 7 B. 14
C. 21 D. 28

6. What is 37 out of every 100 throws expressed as a percent?
A. 100% B. 74%
C. 37% D. 3.7%

7. How many lines of symmetry does a rectangle have?
A. 0 B. 1
C. 2 D. 4

8. Find the perimeter of an equilateral triangle whose sides are 16 cm.
A. 19 cm B. 32 cm
C. 48 cm D. 64 cm

9. Find the perimeter of a square with an area of 16 cm^2.
A. 8 cm B. 16 cm
C. 4 cm D. 12 cm

10. Find the perimeter of the figure below.
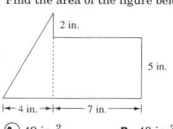
A. 38 ft B. 40 ft
C. 60 ft D. 75 ft

11. Find the area of the figure below.

A. 49 in.^{2} B. 43 in.^{2}
C. 18 in.^{2} D. 63 in.^{2}

12. The length of a bridge on a map is 3 in. The actual length of the bridge is 12 mi. What is the scale of the map?
A. 1 in. : 4 mi B. 1 in. : 8 mi
C. 1 in. : 12 mi D. 1 in. : 24 mi

Assessment

CUMULATIVE REVIEW

Chapter 9 Cumulative Review (continued)

13. What is the area of a circle whose radius is 3 m?
A. 9.42 m B. 18.84 m
C. 28.26 m D. 56.52 m

14. What is the complement of an angle whose measure is 32°?
A. 58° B. 90°
C. 148° D. 180°

15. What is the name given a polygon with 6 sides?
A. sixagon B. decagon
C. hexagon D. octagon

16. Which of the following is *not* a type of quadrilateral?
A. equilateral B. trapezoid
C. rhombus D. parallelogram

17. Find the area of the shaded region rounded to the nearest tenth.

A. 12.6 in.^{2} B. 100.5 in.^{2}
C. 113 in.^{2} D. 125.6 in.^{2}

18. Write $\frac{2}{5}$ as a percent and as a decimal.
A. 20%, 0.2 B. 25%, 0.25
C. 40%, 0.4 D. 52%, 0.52

19. What is 35% of 46?
A. 161 B. 156.4
C. 16.1 D. 16

20. Find the surface area of a rectangular prism with a volume of 60 cm^3 and a length of 5 cm and width of 4 cm.
A. 3 cm B. 47 cm^2
C. 94 cm^2 D. 104 cm^2

Use the spreadsheet below for Exercises 21–23.

	A	B	C	D	E
1	Day	Time Start	Time Stop	Hours Worked	Amount Earned
2	Sun.	3	6		
3	Wed.	6	8		
4	Fri.	6	10		
5	Sat.	7	11		
6			Totals		

21. Kelly baby-sits weekly and earns $3.75 an hour. The spreadsheet shows a typical weekly schedule for her. What is the formula for cell D4?
A. =B4−C4
B. =C4−B4
C. =B4+C4
D. =D2+D3

22. How much did Kelly earn on Saturday night?
A. $3.75 B. $7.50
C. $11.25 D. $15.00

23. What is the formula for cell E6?
A. =E2+E3+E4+E5
B. =A6+B6+C6+D6
C. =(C6−B6)×3.75
D. =4×D6

Resources

Teaching Resources

Chapter Support File, Ch. 9
• Cumulative Review

Teacher's Edition

See pp. 380C–D for Assessment Options.

10 Algebra: Integers and Graphing

CHAPTER OVERVIEW

To accommodate flexible scheduling, most lessons are divided into parts. Assignment Options are given in the Teacher's Edition for each lesson.

Pages 434–437	**Lesson 10-1** **Using a Number Line**
NCTM 1, 2, 3, 6, 9	**Part 1** Positive and Negative Numbers **Part 2** Comparing and Ordering Integers **Key terms:** positive, negative, integers, opposites

Pages 439–441	**Lesson 10-2** **Modeling Integers**
NCTM 2, 3, 7, 9	**Key term:** zero pair **Journal** ▼ **Project Link**

Pages 442–446	**Lesson 10-3** **Modeling Addition of Integers**
NCTM 2, 3, 4, 5, 6, 7, 9, 13	**Part 1** Adding Integers with Like Signs **Part 2** Adding Integers with Unlike Signs **Alternative Activity 10-3** ☑ **Checkpoint 1**

Pages 463–467	**Lesson 10-7** **Geometry: Graphing on the Coordinate Plane**
NCTM 1, 2, 3, 4, 5, 9, 12, 13	**Part 1** Graphing Points **Part 2** Naming Coordinates and Quadrants **Key terms:** coordinate plane, origin, *y*-axis, *x*-axis, coordinates, ordered pair, *x*-coordinate, *y*-coordinate, quadrants ☑ **Checkpoint 2**

Pages 468–472	**Lesson 10-8** **Data Analysis: Applying Integers and Graphs**
NCTM 1, 2, 3, 4, 5, 8, 12, 13	**Part 1** Finding Profit and Loss **Part 2** Making a Graph **Key terms:** balance, profit, loss **Math at Work**

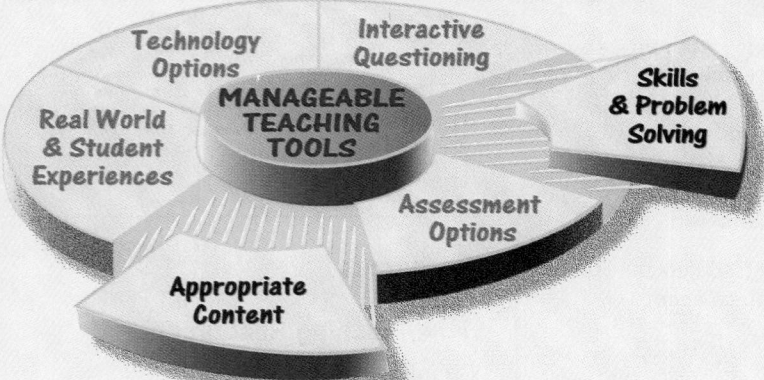

MANAGEABLE TEACHING TOOLS

Technology Options • Interactive Questioning • Skills & Problem Solving • Assessment Options • Appropriate Content • Real World & Student Experiences

Pacing Options

This chart suggests pacing only for the core lessons and their parts. It is provided merely as a possible guide. It will help you determine how much time you have in your schedule to cover other features, such as the Chapter Project, Math Toolboxes, Wrap Up, and Assessment.

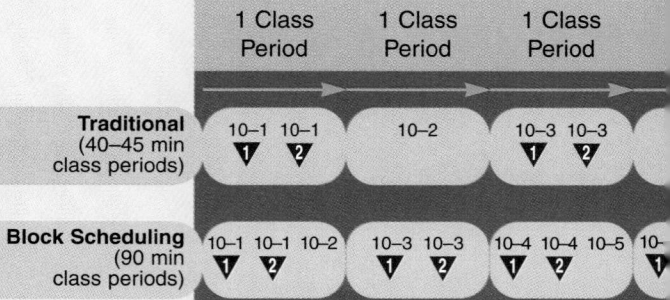

	1 Class Period	1 Class Period	1 Class Period
Traditional (40–45 min class periods)	10-1 ▼1 10-1 ▼2	10-2	10-3 ▼1 10-3 ▼2
Block Scheduling (90 min class periods)	10-1 ▼1 10-1 ▼2 10-2	10-3 ▼1 10-3 ▼2	10-4 ▼1 10-4 ▼2 10-5 10-

The Time of Your Life
Goals: Building a time line using ratios, measurements, scale drawings, and integers

**THEME:
HISTORY**

NCTM STANDARDS

1 Problem Solving
2 Communication
3 Reasoning
4 Mathematical Connections
5 Number and Number Relationships
6 Number Systems and Number Theory
7 Computation and Estimation
8 Patterns and Functions
9 Algebra
10 Statistics
11 Probability
12 Geometry
13 Measurement

Pages 448–452	**Lesson 10-4** **Modeling Subtraction of Integers**	Pages 454–456	**Lesson 10-5** **Problem Solving Strategy**	Pages 457–461	**Lesson 10-6** **Data Analysis:** **Graphing Functions**
NCTM 1, 2, 4, 5, 6, 9, 13	**Part 1** Modeling Subtraction of Integers **Part 2** Using Models to Solve Equations **Alternative Activity 10-4** ▼ **Project Link**	**NCTM** 1, 3, 4, 7, 10	**Use Multiple Strategies** **Journal**	**NCTM** 1, 2, 3, 4, 5, 6, 8, 9, 13	**Part 1** Making Function Tables **Part 2** Graphing Functions **Key terms:** function, function table, input, output **Alternative Activity 10-6** ▼ **Project Link**

Optional Materials and Manipulatives

calculator (10-1, 10-8)
algebra tiles (10-2, 10-3, 10-4)
paper bag (10-3)
green number cube (10-4)
red number cube (10-4)

rubber bands (10-7)
geoboards (10-7)
ruler (10-7, 10-8)
graph paper (10-7, 10-8)
computer (10-8)

spreadsheet software (10-8)
Optional calculator use is integrated throughout the course.

	1 Class Period	1 Class Period	1 Class Period	1 Class Period	1 Class Period	1 Class Period	1 Class Period	1 Class Period	1 Class Period	1 Class Period
	10–5	10–6 ▼1	10–6 ▼2	10–7 ▼1 10–7 ▼2	10–8 ▼1 10–8 ▼2					
10–8 ▼2										

MEETING INDIVIDUAL NEEDS

Accommodating Diverse Learning Styles

In your Teacher's Edition, you will find suggestions as to how you can help students complete mathematical tasks in Chapter 10 by meeting individual needs and supporting various learning styles. Here are some examples:

VISUAL LEARNING
using number lines to solve problems *(p. 442)*

TACTILE LEARNING
writing and acting out problems with play money *(p. 445)*

AUDITORY LEARNING
reading problems aloud to help students solve them *(p. 455)*

KINESTHETIC LEARNING
modeling negative integers with construction paper *(p. 448)*

EARLY FINISHERS
Performance-Based Project, MathBlaster® Mystery, Interdisciplinary Units

GIFTED AND TALENTED
creating a function table for basketball goals *(p. 458)*

DIVERSITY visually impaired students use tiles of different shapes instead of different colors *(p. 439)*

ACQUIRING ENGLISH PROFICIENCY (AEP)
naming opposites to understand the concept of opposite numbers *(p. 434)*

ASSESSING PROGRESS

A broad range of assessment tools are available to reach a variety of learners.

INFORMAL ASSESSMENT

Informal assessments provide day-to-day feedback to help give you a picture of conceptual understanding and skill development.

ONGOING ASSESSMENT is built into lesson instruction and the Teaching Notes of the Teacher's Edition.

In the Teacher's Edition
Lesson Quiz for every lesson

In the Student Edition
On Your Own, Mixed Review, Journal, Portfolio, Project Link, Chapter Wrap Up

Look for **Interactive Questions** within lessons that

- **BUILD UNDERSTANDING** with labels such as Analyze, Reasoning, Estimation, Writing, and Summarize
- ✔ **CHECK UNDERSTANDING** with the Try It Out label.

FORMAL ASSESSMENT

Formal assessment can occur before and after the chapter, as well as at natural breaking points in the chapter.

Checkpoints
Two forms of each self-assessment Checkpoints are available: one in the Student Edition and another in the Chapter Support File in the Teaching Resources box.
- Mid-Chapter Checkpoint 1, page 446
- End-of-Chapter Checkpoint 2, page 467

Chapter 10 Assessment, page 476.
Two alternative forms are available in the Chapter Support File. They may be used after a chapter has been completed, or as a pre-test and post-test comparison.

Cumulative Review, page 477.
Assesses skills and concepts in Chapters 1–10. An alternative form is available in Chapter Support File.

Computer Item Generator for Chapter 10
Customized tests can be generated for each lesson and for mid-chapter and end-of-chapter assessments, and for pre- and post-test comparisons of achievement.

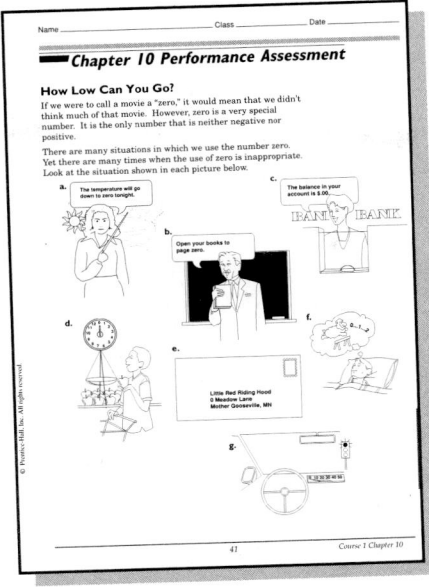

The Chapter Project in the student edition provides a real-world connection to the math context of the chapter. The Teacher's Edition contains a scoring rubric.

Another performance-based Chapter Project with a scoring rubric can be found in the Chapter Support File in the Teaching Resources Box.

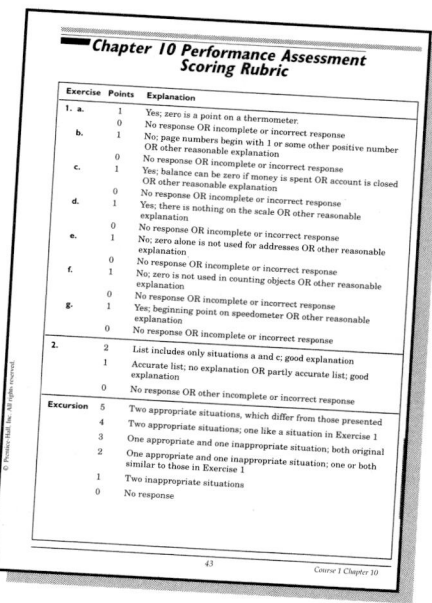

Correlation to Standardized Tests

Lesson		STANDARDIZED TEST ITEMS					
		CAT5	CTBS/5 Terra Nova	ITBS	MAT7	SAT9	Your Local Test
10-1	Using a Number Line		■				
10-2	Modeling Integers			■			
10-3	Modeling Addition of Integers	■	■	■	■	■	
10-4	Modeling Subtraction of Integers	■	■	■	■	■	
10-5	Problem Solving Strategy: Use Multiple Strategies			■	■	■	
10-6	Data Analysis: Graphing Functions	■	■			■	
10-7	Geometry: Graphing on the Coordinate Plane				■	■	
10-8	Data Analysis: Applying Integers and Graphs	■	■		■		

CAT5 California Achievement Test, 5th Edition
CTBS/5 Comprehensive Test of Basic Skills, 5th Edition

ITBS Iowa Test of Basic Skills, Form B
MAT 7 Metropolitan Achievement Test, 7th Edition

SAT9 Stanford Achievement Test, 9th Edition

432D

MAKING CONNECTIONS

Technology Options

Interactive Questioning

Real World & Student Experiences

MANAGEABLE TEACHING TOOLS

Skills & Problem Solving

Appropriate Content

Assessment Options

TEAM TEACHING WITH PRENTICE HALL MATERIALS

MIDDLE GRADES MATH INTERDISCIPLINARY UNITS	INTERDISCIPLINARY EXPLORATIONS	SCIENCE EXPLORER **L** Life Science **E** Earth Science **P** Physical Science
• **Sports: Activity 2** • **Space Exploration: Activity 8**	• *SOAP* p. 11 • *Mill Life in the 1840s* pp. 8 & 9	**E** Sec. 5-3 Layers of the Atmosphere (low temperatures) Sec 8-3 Mapping the Earth's Surface (longitude, latitude)

Lesson	Interdisciplinary Connections	Real World Connections	Math Integration
10-1	Football Geography	Golf Weather	Algebra
10-2	Algebra	Estimation	Algebra
10-3	Sports	Contests Office Mail Money Weather	Algebra Measurement
10-4	Algebra Geography	Weather Time Zones Student Council	Algebra Measurement
10-5	Biology	Contests Time Gardening Navigation Customer Service	Statistics Geometry
10-6	Football	Time Jobs Sales Mail-order	Algebra Geometry Measurement
10-7	Geography	Quilts Crafts Dogs	Algebra Geometry Measurement
10-8	Business	Accounting Technology Meteorology	Geometry Measurement

School to Home

MATERIALS:

2 number cubes or dice
2 pennies, nickels, dimes, or quarters
5 pairs of socks (each pair a different color or pattern)
paper bag
paper
pencil

English and Spanish versions are available in the Teacher's Communication Kit, Teacher's Resource box.

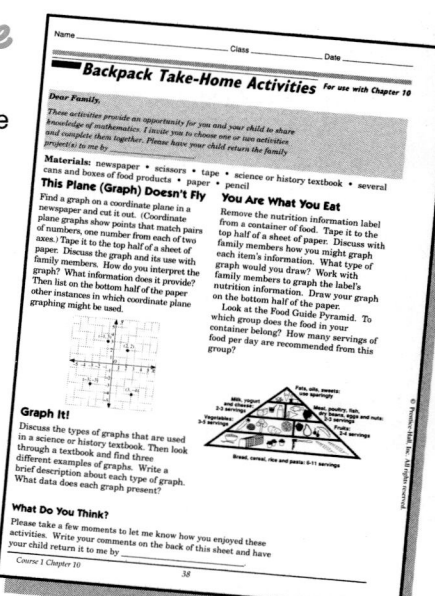

USING TECHNOLOGY TO ENHANCE INSTRUCTION

FOR THE STUDENT

Multimedia Math Hot Pages™

This interactive software and video package on CD-ROM integrates solid math content through a variety of media.

- Hot Page™ 28 (10-1)
- Hot Page™ 29 (10-7)
- Hot Page™ 30 (10-8)

Math Labs

This software, available on both diskette and CD-ROM, includes on-screen Math Lab activities. Students use linkable, interactive tools to explore math concepts.

- Math Lab: Modeling Integers (10-2)

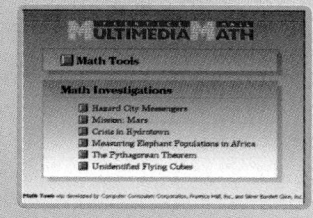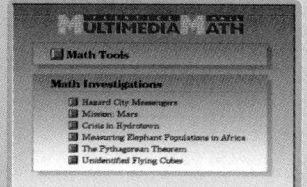

Multimedia Math Investigations

These in-depth interactive activities on CD-ROM develop real-world applications of mathematics. They allow students the opportunity to reinforce key concepts.

- Mission: Mars

Interactive Student Tutorial

Available on CD-ROM, this test preparation program contains self-tests with questions in standardized test format. Software includes electronic versions of the text lessons and the Math Tools and Math Labs.

MathBlaster® Mystery

This award-winning, interactive software program on CD-ROM can be used to maintain skills or to accommodate early finishers.

- Level: Earn 2 coins; Pay 6 coins
- Mission Mode (all lessons)
- Kitchen Comparisons (10-3)
- Number Guesser (10-2, 10-5)
- Equation Maker (10-3, 10-6, 10-8)
- Word Problems (10-1, 10-7, Problem Solving Practice)

Internet Connection

For Students
Support for the Chapter Project
A career-oriented link for Math at Work feature

www.phschool.com/math

For teachers
Curriculum Support
Product Information
Regional Support Information

FOR THE TEACHER

Computer Item Generator

Available on both CD-ROM and diskette, this software generates customized practice sheets, quizzes, and tests. It generates an unlimited supply of questions with varying levels of difficulty.

The Resource Pro™

Available on CD-ROM, this software can be used to customize and plan lessons.

Technology Options

MANAGEABLE TEACHING TOOLS

- Interactive Questioning
- Skills & Problem Solving
- Assessment Options
- Appropriate Content
- Real World & Student Experiences

CONNECTING TO PRIOR LEARNING Ask students if they have ever seen a thermometer with positive and negative numbers. Ask: *What do the positive numbers and negative numbers represent?* **temperatures above and below zero** Ask students how they would make a time line showing the past, present, and future. **Answers may vary. Sample: The positive numbers can be the future, the negative numbers the past, and 0 the present.**

CULTURAL CONNECTIONS Many ancient civilizations developed advanced ways to keep track of time: calendars, astronomical charts, and special architectural designs. Discuss with students all the tools that they are familiar with which either measure or keep track of time. **Answers may vary. Sample: digital watch, cuckoo clock, calendar, hourglass, computer**

INTERDISCIPLINARY CONNECTIONS Ask: *Why might an archeologist use a time line?* **Answers may vary. Sample: to help determine which items belong to which time period**

ABOUT THE PROJECT The Chapter Project allows students to use their knowledge of integers and graphing to make a timeline showing the past, present, and future.

Internet • For information and activities related to the Chapter Project, visit the Prentice Hall site at www.phschool.com/mgm1/ch10

Algebra: Integers and Graphing

10

| **WHAT YOU WILL LEARN IN THIS CHAPTER** | • How to model addition and subtraction of integers | • How to graph functions | • How to create and use a coordinate system |

LAUNCHING THE CHAPTER PROJECT

Ask students:

• *Have you ever used a timeline? What did you use it for?*

• *What have the timelines that you have seen in books and encyclopedias been used for?*

• *What are the different parts of a timeline?*

PROJECT NOTEBOOK Encourage students to keep all project-related materials in a separate folder or notebook.

TRACKING THE PROJECT You may wish to have students read Finishing the Chapter Project on page 473 to help them get an overview of the project. Set benchmark deadlines for students to show you their work in progress.

The TIME *of* your life

CHAPTER PROJECT

THEME: HISTORY

Do you know an older person who has lived an interesting life? That person could probably tell you a lot of stories about his or her life, but you could tell stories about your life, too. You may not have lived as long, but there have been important times in your life, and there will be other important times in your future.

Draw a Time Line Your project will be to build a time line of your life—past and future. Think about time lines you have seen in your social studies classes. You will get a chance to apply math skills such as ratios, measurements, scale drawings, and integers.

Steps to help you complete the project:

p. 441   Project Link: *Calculating*
p. 452   Project Link: *Drawing*
p. 461   Project Link: *Graphing*
p. 473   *Finishing the Chapter Project*

• **How to use multiple strategies to solve problems**

SCORING RUBRIC

3 You correctly calculate a scale and apply it to your time line. You locate events in the past on the negative side, and you list events or changes you think might happen in your future on the positive side. Your time line is detailed, interesting, and attractive.

2 You correctly apply a scale to your time line, and you locate events on both the negative and positive sides. Your details are adequate, and your time line is readable.

1 Your scale is incorrect, your time line is unorganized, or you include two few details.

0 You do not create a time line.

1 Focus

CONNECTING TO PRIOR KNOWLEDGE Ask students: *Where have you seen examples of negative numbers? Why were they used?* **Answers may vary. Sample: temperatures; golf scores; to show that the numbers are less than zero**

Lesson Planning Options

Prerequisite Skills

• graphing whole numbers on a number line (precourse)
• comparing and ordering whole numbers (precourse)

Vocabulary/Symbols

positive, negative, integers, opposites

Materials/Manipulatives

• calculator

Resources

 Student Edition

Skills Handbook, p. 535
Extra Practice, p. 531
Glossary/Study Guide

 Teaching Resources

Chapter Support File, Ch. 10
• Lesson Planner 10-1
• Practice 10-1, Reteaching 10-1
• Answer Masters 10-1

Teaching Aids Masters 3, 26
Glossary, Spanish Resources

 Transparencies

15, 96, Minds on Math 10-1

Warm Up

If you tossed a coin 200 times, what is the mathematical probability of getting a head on the 143rd toss? $P(\text{head}) = \frac{1}{2}$

434

2 Teach

THINK AND DISCUSS

AEP Write *tall* and *short* on the board to discuss *opposites*. Ask for examples of opposites. Have students brainstorm examples of opposite numbers after you discuss Example 1.

VISUAL LEARNING Question 2 Have groups of students draw a number line from −5 to 5 on a sheet of butcher paper 6 ft long . Have students use a ruler to mark the numbers.

Example 1 Make sure students understand that 3 and +3 name the same positive integer. Tell students that they do not have to write a plus sign to show a positive number.

OPEN-ENDED Question 4 Remind students that integers that are opposites are the same distance from 0.

10-1 Using a Number Line

What You'll Learn

▼ To graph integers on a number line
▼ To compare and order integers

...And Why

You can use integers in sports such as football and golf.

Here's How

Look for questions that
▪ build understanding
✔ check understanding

QUICKreview

To graph a number on a number line, draw a point at that number.

1.
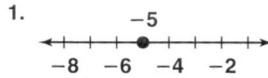

2.
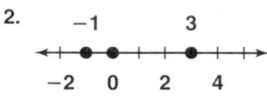

THINK AND DISCUSS

▼ Positive and Negative Numbers

Suppose you are playing football and your team moves 4 yd forward. You can say your new position is *positive* 4 yd, or +4 yd. If your team gets pushed back 3 yd, your new position is *negative* 3 yd, or −3 yd.

You can graph these numbers on a number line.

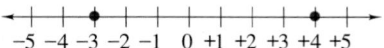

1. **✔Try It Out** Write negative 5 as a number. Then draw a number line and graph negative 5.
   −5; see below left for graph.
2. On the same number line, graph the numbers −1, 3, and 0.
   See below left.

The numbers . . . −3, −2, −1, 0, +1, +2, +3, . . . are **integers.**

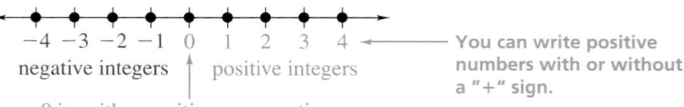

0 is neither positive nor negative.

Two numbers that are the same distance from 0 on a number line, but in different directions, are **opposites.**

■ EXAMPLE 1

Name the opposite of 3.

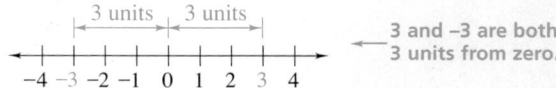

3 and −3 are both 3 units from zero.

The opposite of 3 is −3.

3. **✔Try It Out** Name the opposite of each integer.
   a. 4 **−4**   **b.** −6 **6**   **c.** 15 **−15** **d.** 8 **−8**   **e.** −120 **120**   **f.** 32 **−32**

REASONING **Question 9** Have students illustrate each answer with an example.

ASSESSMENT Ask students to list four numbers and their opposites. Then have students list three positive and three negative integers. Have students order these six integers from least to greatest.

■ ADDITIONAL EXAMPLES

FOR EXAMPLE 1

Name the opposite of 7. −7

FOR EXAMPLE 2

Max scored 4 under par. You scored 7 over par. Who has the lower score? **Max**

FOR EXAMPLE 3

A group of friends had the following golf scores: −1, 3, 0, 4, 2, and −4. Graph each score on the number line. Write the scores from least to greatest.

−4, −1, 0, 2, 3, 4

4. ▪ *Open-ended* Name two integers that are opposites. How far from 0 is each integer?
   Answers may vary. Sample: −10 and 10; 10 units away

5. **a.** What is the opposite of positive nine yards in football?
   b. Write the numbers from part (a) as integers. **9, −9**
   5a. negative 9 yards

▦ You can use the key to write the opposite of a number.

$$5 \; \boxed{\tfrac{+}{-}} \to -5 \qquad\qquad 5 \; \boxed{\tfrac{+}{-}} \; \boxed{\tfrac{+}{-}} \to 5$$

6. ✔*Try It Out* A calculator displays −12. Suppose you press the key. What will the calculator display? **12**
   7. The key changes the sign of the displayed number.

7. ▪ *Explain* Why do you think the key is called the "change-sign" key?

Now you may assign Exercises 1–21.

❷ *Comparing and Ordering Integers*

In golf, scores are related to an established number of strokes called *par*. A score of 1 *under* par can be represented as −1. A score of 3 *over* par can be represented as 3.

■ **EXAMPLE 2** *Real-World Problem Solving*

Golf Suppose your golf score is 1 under par (−1). Your friend's score is 5 under par (−5). Who has the lower score?

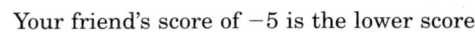

−5 is to the left of −1.
Therefore, −5 < −1 or −1 > −5.

Your friend's score of −5 is the lower score.

8. ✔*Try It Out* Use a number line to compare. Write < or >.
   a. 10 ■ 6 **>**
   b. −7 ■ 0 **<**
   c. 3 ■ −4 **>**
   d. −13 ■ −11 **<**

QUICK review

The values of numbers on a number line increase as you move from left to right.

Technology Options

Prentice Hall Technology

Software for Learners
- Hot Page™ 28*
- Math Blaster® Mystery*
- Interactive Student Tutorial, Chapter 10*

Teaching Resource Software
- Computer Item Generator 10-1
- Resource Pro™ Chapter 10*

Internet • For related mathematics activities, visit the Prentice Hall site at www.phschool.com/math

*Available on CD-ROM only

Assignment Options for Exercises On Your Own

To provide flexible scheduling, this lesson can be split into parts.

▼❶ **Core** 1–16, 19–21
   Extension 15–18

▼❷ **Core** 22–34
   Extension 35–39

Use Mixed Review to maintain skills.

3 Practice/Assess

Exercise 10 Tell students: *Write an integer to represent this situation: a coral reef is 98 ft below sea level.* −98

WRITING Exercise 18 Remind students to include examples with their descriptions.

CONNECTION TO METEOROLOGY Exercise 22 Have students use an almanac to record the highest and lowest temperature for selected states. Then have them list the temperatures from least to greatest.

If you have block scheduling or extended classes, you may want to have students find examples of temperatures for Antarctica. Ask them to compare and order the integers they find.

ERROR ALERT! Exercise 24 Students may think that −12 is greater than −9.
Remediation: Have students draw a number line. Ask students to graph −9 and −12. Ask: *Which number is the greatest distance away from 0?* −12 Tell students that negative numbers get *smaller* the farther away they are from zero.

---

pages 436–437   On Your Own

18. Answers may vary. Sample: Integers are all the numbers represented by points on a number line that are a whole number of units away from 0. For example, −3, −1, 0, 3, and 5 are integers. The numbers represented by points on the number line that are equidistant from 0 are opposites. −3 and 3 are opposites.

```
    −3            3
  ←─●─┼─┼─┼─┼─●─→
  −4  −2   0   2
```

35. −6, −5, −4, −3, −2, −1, 0, 1, 2
36. −5, −4, −3, −2, −1
37. −12, −11, −10, −9, −8, −7, −6
38. 0, 1
39. −8, −7, −6, −5, −4, −3, −2, −1

9. ⬝*Reasoning* Complete with *always*, *sometimes*, or *never*.
   a. 0 is ▪ greater than a negative integer. always
   b. 0 is ▪ greater than a positive integer. never
   c. A negative integer is ▪ less than another negative integer. sometimes

■ **EXAMPLE 3**   *Real-World Problem Solving*

Golf The table shows the scores of five golfers in a professional tournament. Order the scores from least to greatest.

Golfer	Score
Jonathan Lomas	2
Tiger Woods	0
Padraig Harrington	−4
Greg Norman	3
Shigeki Maruyama	−2

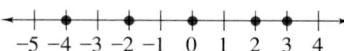

←─── Graph each score on a number line.

−4, −2, 0, 2, 3 ←── Write the scores from left to right.

In order from least to greatest, the scores are −4, −2, 0, 2, and 3.

10. ✔*Try It Out* Order from least to greatest: 7, −4, 11, 0, −8.
   −8, −4, 0, 7, 11

Now you may assign Exercises 22–39.

EXERCISES *On Your Own*

Name the integer that is represented by each point.

1. *M* 1
2. *N* −4
3. *P* 5
4. *Q* −6

5. Graph these integers on a number line: 6, −9, 7, −1, 0, 3.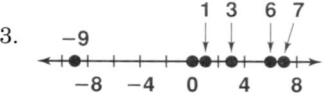

Write an integer to represent each situation.

6. earnings of $25 25
7. 14 degrees below zero −14
8. a debt of $100 −100

9. At 1,565 ft deep, the Carlsbad Caverns are the United States' deepest caves. −1,565
10. *Geography* Mt. Whitney in California has an elevation of 4,418 m. 4,418

Name the opposite of each integer.

11. 13 −13
12. −8 8
13. 150 −150
14. −212 212
15. −1 1
16. 3,999 −3,999

436

IDENTIFYING THE BIG IDEA Ask students to name opposites of numbers. Then have students explain how to compare and order integers by graphing them on a number line.

LESSON QUIZ

1. Name the opposite of 5. How far from zero is the integer? **−5; 5 units**

2. Order from least to greatest. **−32, 38, 0, 15, 7, −8 −32, −8, 0, 7, 15, 38**

3. Compare using <, >, or =. Sarah scored 2 below par and Rachel scored 3 below par. **−3 < −2**

---

17. Name three pairs of situations that are opposites. For example, walk up two stairs and walk down two stairs. **Check students' work.**

18. *Writing* Describe what integers and opposites are. Include number lines in your descriptions. **See margin p. 436.**

Calculator **Name the integer that results from each key sequence.**

19. 8 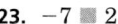 **−8**

20. 9 [+/-] [+/-] **9**

21. 6 [+/-] [+/-] [+/-] **−6**

22. *Weather* List the temperatures from least to greatest.

- Normal body temperature is about 37°C.
- An average winter day on the polar icecap is −25°C.
- The warmest day ever in Canada was 45°C.
- Water freezes at 0°C. Ski resorts can make artificial snow at this temperature.
- The coldest day ever in Alaska was −62°C.

22. −62°C, −25°C, 0°C, 37°C, 45°C

Compare. Write <, >, or =.

23. −7 ▓ 2 **<**

24. −12 ▓ −9 **<**

25. −17 ▓ −23 **>**

26. −4 ▓ 2 **<**

27. 0 ▓ −8 **>**

28. 1 ▓ −7 **>**

29. −12 ▓ −5 **<**

30. −3 ▓ −7 **>**

Order from least to greatest.

31. −2, 3, 4, −1   **−2, −1, 3, 4**

32. 3, −2, 0, −7   **−7, −2, 0, 3**

33. 4, −5, −2, 3, −1   **−5, −2, −1, 3, 4**

34. −10, 8, 0, −6, 5   **−10, −6, 0, 5, 8**

Open-ended **Name an integer between the given integers.**
35–39. Answers may vary. See margin p. 436 for all possible answers.

35. −7, 3

36. 0, −6

37. −5, −13

38. −1, 2

39. −9, 0

Mixed Review

Find the area of each circle. *(Lesson 9-5)*

40. r = 6 in. **about 113.10 in.²**

41. d = 24 mm **about 452.39 mm²**

42. r = 7 m **about 153.94 m²**

43. d = 11 in. **about 95.03 in.²**

44. r = 8.5 mm **about 226.98 mm²**

45. *Choose a Strategy* Tina has an appointment at 8:15 A.M. tomorrow. She wants to arrive at least 10 minutes early. It takes her one hour to get ready and 35 minutes to drive there. What time should Tina plan to get up? **6:30 A.M.**

Practice 10-1 *Using a Number Line*

1. Graph these integers on the number line: −4, 9, 1, −2, 3.
−10 −8 −6 −4 −2 0 2 4 6 8 10

Name the integer that is represented by each point.

2. J **−3**

3. K **4**

4. L **2**

5. M **−6**

M J N PL K
−6 −4 −2 0 2 4

Write an integer to represent each situation.

6. spent $23 **−23**

7. lost 12 yards **−12**

8. deposit of $58 **58**

Name the opposite of each integer.

9. 16 **−16**

10. −12 **12**

11. 100 **−100**

12. 75 **−75**

Compare. Write <, >, or =.

13. −5 [<] 8

14. 13 [>] −14

15. −11 [>] −19

Name an integer between the given integers. Answers will vary. Sample given.

16. −2, 9 **1**

17. 3, −12 **−6**

18. −7, −11 **−9**

Complete with an integer that makes the statement true. Samples are given.

19. −9 > **−12**

20. **7** > 3

21. 0 > **−5**

22. List the temperatures from least to greatest. **−25°F, −3°F, 32°F, 34°F, 78°F**

- The temperature was 25°F below zero.
- The pool temperature was 78°F.
- Water freezes at 32°F.
- The low temperature in December is −3°F.
- The temperature in the refrigerator was 34°F.

Think of the days of a week as integers. Let today be 0, and let days in the past be negative and days in the future be positive.

23. If today is Tuesday, what integer stands for last Sunday? **−2**

24. If today is Wednesday, what integer stands for next Saturday? **3**

25. If today is Friday, what integer stands for last Saturday? **−6**

26. If today is Monday, what integer stands for next Monday? **7**

In copymaster and workbook formats

Reteaching 10-1 *Using a Number Line*

The numbers . . . −3, −2, −1, 0, +1, +2, +3 . . . are **integers.** We see them on a number line.

−10 −9 −8 −7 −6 −5 −4 −3 −2 −1 0 1 2 3 4 5 6 7 8 9 10
−4 ———— 0 ———— 4

Opposite integers, like −4 and 4, are the same distance from 0. For two integers on a number line, the greater integer is farther to the right.

Compare −2 and 1.

① Locate −2 and 1 on the number line. −5 −4 −3 −2 −1 0 1 2 3 4 5

② Find that 1 is farther to the right.

③ Write 1 > −2 (1 is greater than −2), or −2 < 1 (−2 is less than 1.)

Name the opposite of each integer.

1. 7 **−7**

2. −212 **212**

3. 49 **−49**

4. 1,991 **−1,991**

5. −78 **78**

6. 16 **−16**

Compare. Write <, >, or =.

7. 6 [>] 3

8. 2 [<] 8

9. −2 [<] 2

10. 9 [>] −9

11. 0 [<] 5

12. −9 [<] −5

13. 0 [<] 10

14. −5 [<] −2

15. 7 [>] −9

16. −5 [<] −1

17. 6 [>] −6

18. −12 [<] 0

19. 8 [>] −3

20. −1 [>] −2

21. −5 [<] 4

22. −3 [<] −2

Order from least to greatest.

23. 6, −3, 1, −1 **−3, −1, 1, 6**

24. −5, 7, 0, −9 **−9, −5, 0, 7**

25. 2, −1, −3, 4 **−3, −1, 2, 4**

26. −6, 13, −8, −1 **−8, −6, −1, 13**

27. −2, −10, 5, −5 **−10, −5, −2, 5**

28. 11, −3, −7, 0 **−7, −3, 0, 11**

Minds on Math Transparency

10-1

Henry, Curtis, and Crista guessed the number of buttons in a jar. Henry guessed 113 buttons, Curtis guessed 119 buttons, and Crista guessed 120 buttons. One of the guesses was correct, one missed by 6, and one missed by 1. Who guessed the correct number of buttons?

Curtis

See *Solution Key* for worked-out answers.

In Lesson 10-1, students learned how to graph integers on a number line and how to compare and order integers. This toolbox shows students how to use a number line to show inequalities and absolute values.

ERROR ALERT! Students may confuse the open dot and closed dot in graphing. **Remediation:** Have students remember that when the dot is open, the number is not contained. When the dot is closed, the number is contained. Also tell students that when there is no line under the < or >, the dot is open.

ASSESSMENT Exercises 1–5 Have students compare their graph for each exercise with that of a partner. Have students explain why they used an open or closed dot for each inequality.

After Lesson 10-1

■ ADDITIONAL PROBLEMS

Find the absolute value of each number.
1. 9 9
2. −1 1
3. 23 23
4. −100 100

Resources

Teaching Resources

Teaching Aids Master 26

Transparencies
15, 18

page 438   Math Toolbox

1.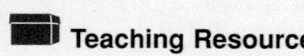
   -2 0 2 4

2.
   -2 0 2 4

3.
   -2 0 2 4

4.
   -4 -2 0 2

5.
   -4 -2 0 2

438

MATH TOOLBOX EXPLORATION

Inequalities and Absolute Values

You can use a number line to show *inequalities* and *absolute values*.

Karen bikes more than 2 mi but less than 3 mi. Frank bikes 3 mi or more. These distances can be described as *inequalities*.

You can write an inequality as a statement that compares two expressions.

Symbols
$<$ means *is less than*.
$\leq$ means *is less than or is equal to*.
$>$ means *is greater than*.
$\geq$ means *is greater than or is equal to*.

■ EXAMPLE 1

Write and graph the distances biked by Karen and Frank.

$$2 < d < 3 \qquad\qquad d \geq 3 \qquad \longleftarrow \text{Let } d = \text{distance.}$$

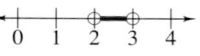 

An *open* dot means the number *is not* included.   A *closed* dot means the number *is* included.

The *absolute value* of a number is its distance, in either direction, from zero on a number line. Since direction does not matter, there are no negative absolute values.

The symbol for absolute value is a vertical rule before and after a number. For example: $|-10|$

■ EXAMPLE 2

Find $|-2|$.

2 units from 0

-4 -3 -2 -1 0 1 2 3 4 $\longleftarrow$ −2 is *two* units away from zero.

Therefore, $|-2| = 2$.

Graph each inequality.   1–5. See margin.

1. $x > 3$ 2. $x \leq 3$ 3. $x < 0$ 4. $x \geq -1$ 5. $x < -2$

Find each value.

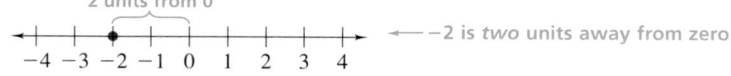

6. $|-4|$ 4   7. $|17|$ 17   8. $|-65|$ 65   9. $|0|$ 0   10. $|-2|$ 2   11. $|180|$ 18

Teaching Notes

1 Focus

CONNECTING TO PRIOR KNOWLEDGE Ask students: *How can you model a positive 5? A negative 5?* **Answers may vary. Sample: Use base ten blocks; use different colored blocks.**

2 Teach

THINK AND DISCUSS

DIVERSITY Provide visually impaired students with tiles of different shapes. Have students use large tiles for yellow tiles and small tiles for red tiles.

Question 5 Ask students: *How can you tell if a pair of tiles is a zero pair?* **Zero pairs have the same number of red and yellow tiles.**

ERROR ALERT! Question 9 Students may try to form zero pairs by using two tiles of the same color. **Remediation:** Remind students that this is not a subtraction problem. The tiles need to cancel each other out. Zero pairs are pairs of opposites, which together equal zero.

ASSESSMENT and TACTILE LEARNING Have groups of students use tiles to model the following integers in different ways: -3, 7, 2, and 10. **Answers may vary. Check students' work.**

10-2 Modeling Integers

What You'll Learn

▼ To use models to represent positive integers, negative integers, and zero

...And Why

Modeling will help you add and subtract integers.

Here's How

Look for questions that
- build understanding
- ✔ check understanding

4a.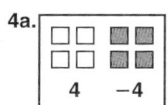

b.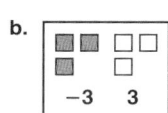

c.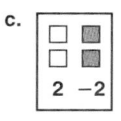

d.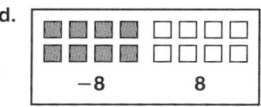

THINK AND DISCUSS

You can use colored tiles to model integers. Yellow tiles represent positive integers. Red tiles represent negative integers.

$$\square \rightarrow 1 \qquad \blacksquare \rightarrow -1$$
$$\square\square\square \rightarrow 3$$
$$\blacksquare\blacksquare\blacksquare\blacksquare \rightarrow -4$$

1. 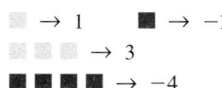 *Modeling* What integer is represented by each set of tiles?
   a. $\blacksquare\blacksquare$ -2
   b. $\square\square\square\square\square\square\square$ 7
   c. $\square\square\square\square\square$ 5
   d. $\blacksquare\blacksquare\blacksquare\blacksquare\blacksquare$ -5

2. Which integers in Question 1 are opposites? **5 and -5**

3. *Draw a Conclusion* What do you notice about the sets of tiles that represent a number and its opposite?
   The number of tiles in each set is the same.

4. ✔*Try It Out* Use tiles to model each integer and its opposite.
   a. 4   b. -3 c. 2   d. -8

Suppose you earned $1 and then spent $1. Then ▨ represents the $1 that you earned, and ■ represents the $1 that you spent. You have *no more or less* money than before.

These tiles are a *zero pair*. ⟶  represent 0, or
$$\square + \blacksquare = 0.$$

5. *What If . . .* Suppose you have seven positive tiles. How many negative tiles do you need to represent zero? **7**

6. Suppose you have ten negative tiles. How many positive tiles do you need to represent zero? **10**

7. Suppose you have four positive tiles and two negative tiles. How many tiles of each color do you need to represent zero?
   2 red tiles and no yellow tiles

Lesson Planning Options

Prerequisite Skills
- modeling whole numbers (precourse)

Vocabulary/Symbols
zero pair

Materials/Manipulatives
- algebra tiles

Resources

📖 **Student Edition**
Skills Handbook, p. 536
Extra Practice, p. 531
Glossary/Study Guide

Teaching Resources
Chapter Support File, Ch. 10
- Lesson Planner 10-2
- Practice 10-2, Reteaching 10-2
- Answer Masters 10-2
Teaching Aids Masters 2, 26, 27
Glossary, Spanish Resources

Transparencies
15, Minds on Math 10-2

Warm Up

 Mr. Vega spent $64.75 for five light fixtures and $12.50 for four light switches. Each light fixture cost the same amount. How much did each light fixture cost? **$12.95**

WRITING **Question 9d** Ask students how many ways they have represented zero so far. Then ask them how many more ways they think are possible.

■ **ADDITIONAL EXAMPLE**

What integer is represented by 7 yellow tiles and 8 red tiles? −1

3 Practice/Assess

EXERCISES *On Your Own*

Exercise 23 Suggest that students use tiles to model the combinations before they begin writing.

REASONING **Exercise 24** Give students yellow and red crayons and grid paper. Have them work in groups to explore the different integers they can show.

ESTIMATION **Exercise 36** Remind students that they are estimating to make sure they have enough money. Have students discuss why they should round up or down for different situations.

WRAP UP

IDENTIFYING THE BIG IDEA Ask students how to show negative and positive integers with models. Have them explain how to model zero pairs with tiles.

Technology Options

Prentice Hall Technology

 Software for Learners
• Math Lab: Modeling Integers
• Math Blaster® Mystery*
• Interactive Student Tutorial, Chapter 10*

 Teaching Resource Software
• Computer Item Generator 10-2
• Resource Pro™ Chapter 10*

Internet • For related mathematics activities, visit the Prentice Hall site at www.phschool.com/math

*Available on CD-ROM only

Assignment Options for Exercises On Your Own

    Core 1–23
    Extension 24

Use Mixed Review to maintain skills.

440

You can use pairs of tiles that represent zero to write integers when you have tiles of both colors together.

■ **EXAMPLE**

Write the integer that is represented by ■ ■ ■ ■ ■ □ □ .

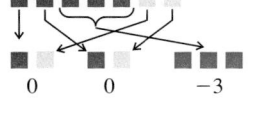

   0   0   −3   Group the pairs of tiles that represent zero. Then remove them.

■ ■ ■ ■ ■ □ □ = −3   Write the integer that the remaining tiles represent.

8. ✔*Try It Out* Write the integer that is represented by the tiles.

  a. ■ ■ ■ ■ □   **b.** ■ ■ ■ □ □ −4   **c.** ■ ■ ■ □ □ 6
    −1   ■ ■

9. **a.** What integer is represented by ■ ■ □ □ □ □ ? 2
   b. What integer is represented by □ □ □ □ ■ ■ ■ ? 2
   c. How do the answers to parts (a) and (b) compare?
   d. ⬩*Writing* How many ways are there to represent an integer with tiles? Explain.

9c. They are equal.
9d. An infinite number of ways; if you add equal numbers of red and yellow tiles, the number does not change.

Now you may assign Exercises 1–24.

EXERCISES *On Your Own*

Modeling **Model each integer and its opposite.** 1–6. See back of book.

  1. −2   **2.** 6   **3.** −4   **4.** 1   **5.** −5   **6.** 9

Write the integer that is represented by each set of tiles.

  7. ■ ■ □ 2   **8.** ■ ■ ■ □ 5   **9.** ■ ■ ■ □ −2   **10.** ■ ■ □ 3
    ■ ■

  11. □ □ □ □ 4   **12.** ■ ■ ■ −2   **13.** ■ −4   **14.** ■ ■ ■ −3

15. *Writing* Explain how you can use tiles to represent integers. Include examples and diagrams. See back of book.

▽ PROJECT LINK Have students explain their reasons for choosing their scales.

JOURNAL Have students include drawings of models to support their statements about integers.

LESSON QUIZ

1. What integer is represented by 3 yellow tiles and 9 red tiles? −6

2. Model −8 and its opposite. What integer does this model represent? Use 8 red tiles, 8 yellow tiles; 0.

Modeling **Model each integer in two ways.**
16–21. Answers may vary. See back of book for examples.

16. 1 **17.** −7 **18.** 0 **19.** −1 **20.** 5 **21.** −3

22. Choose A, B, C, or D. Which of the integers modeled is *not* equal to the others? A

A. ■□ ■ **B.** □ **C.** □ ■ □ **D.** ■ ■ □□□

23. *Modeling* Write the integer that is represented by each combination.
  a. 3 negative tiles and 7 positive tiles 4
  b. 12 negative tiles and 8 positive tiles −4
  c. 15 negative tiles and 9 positive tiles −6

24a.
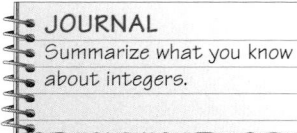
□□□□□□ 6   □■■■■ −2
□□□□□■ 4   □■■■■■ −4
□□□□■■ 2   ■■■■■■ −6
□□□■■■ 0

24. *Reasoning* Suppose you have 6 uncolored tiles, a yellow crayon, and a red crayon.
  a. Show all the different ways you can color the tiles so that when placed together they represent various integers.
  b. List all the integers that the tiles could represent.
  a. See above right.   b. −6, −4, −2, 0, 2, 4, 6

> **JOURNAL**
> Summarize what you know about integers.

Mixed Review

Find each sum or difference. *(Lessons 6-4 and 6-5)*

25. $8\frac{1}{3} + 2\frac{1}{6}$ $10\frac{1}{2}$ **26.** $15\frac{6}{9} - 13\frac{5}{12}$ $2\frac{1}{4}$ **27.** $6\frac{5}{12} + 12\frac{5}{8}$ $19\frac{1}{24}$ **28.** $23\frac{2}{3} - 4\frac{1}{2}$ $19\frac{1}{6}$ **29.** $26 - 4\frac{1}{9}$ $21\frac{8}{9}$

Evaluate each expression for $a = 2$ and $b = 4$. *(Lesson 2-4)*

30. $a + a$ 4   **31.** $72 \div b$ 18   **32.** $2ab$ 16   **33.** $a \times 0$ 0   **34.** $2a - b$ 0   **35.** $a + b \div 6$ $2\frac{2}{3}$

36. *Estimation* Suppose you want to buy 2 sets of pencils that cost $3.75 each and some markers that cost $2.31. The total sales tax is $.30. You have a ten-dollar bill. Do you have enough money? Explain. *(Lesson 3-7)*
No; the total with tax is greater than $10.

CHAPTER PROJECT

PROJECT LINK: CALCULATING

Plan a time line about 3 ft long. It should show a lifetime of about 80 yr. Use what you learned about ratios and scale drawings in Chapter 7 to choose a scale for your time line. What distance will you use between the one-year marks?

Check students' work.

PRACTICE

━━ *Practice 10-2* Modeling Integers

Write the integer that is represented by each set of tiles. Unshaded tiles represent positive integers and shaded tiles represent negative integers.

1. −7   2. 4   3. −3
4. 1   5. 6   6. −5
7. 0   8. −6   9. −5

Shade the tiles to represent each integer in two ways. Use unshaded tiles for positive integers and shaded tiles for negative integers. Answers will vary. Samples given.

10. −4   11. 5   12. 7
13. −8   14. 2   15. −9

Shade the tiles to represent the given integer.

16. 4   17. −3
18. −6   19. 0

20. Draw models of all possible integers that can be represented using 4 tiles.
4   2   0   −2   −4

In copymaster and workbook formats

RETEACHING

━━ *Reteaching 10-2* Modeling Integers

Sets of marbles can be used to model integers.

In this set, there are two more gray (negative) marbles than there are white (positive) marbles. This set represents −2.

In this set there is one more white marble than there are gray marbles. This set represents 1.

Write the integer that is represented by each set of marbles.

1. 3   2. −1
3. 1   4. 0
5. −3   6. −6
7. 2   8. 7
9. 6   10. −3
11. −3   12. −2

ENRICHMENT

Minds on Math Transparency

10-2

I am a four-digit multiple of 9. My first two digits are the same and my last two digits are 58. What number am I?

7,758

See *Solution Key* for worked-out answers.

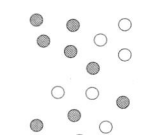

1 Focus

CONNECTING TO PRIOR KNOWLEDGE Ask students: *Suppose you are playing football and your team gains 5 yd, loses 7 yd, and then gains 9 yd. How do you find the number of yards gained or lost on the three plays?* **Answers may vary. Sample: Use a number line to add the gains and subtract the losses.**

Lesson Planning Options

Prerequisite Skills
• adding and subtracting whole numbers (precourse)
• modeling integers (10-2)

Materials/Manipulatives
• algebra tiles   • paper bag

Resources

 Student Edition

Skills Handbook, p. 538
Extra Practice, p. 531
Glossary/Study Guide

 Teaching Resources

Chapter Support File, Ch. 10
• Lesson Planner 10-3
• Practice 10-3, Reteaching 10-3
• Alternative Activity 10-3
• Answer Masters 10-3
Teaching Aids Masters 2, 26, 27
Glossary, Spanish Resources

 Transparencies

15, Minds on Math 10-3

Warm Up

Draw a triangle and place a dot directly above the midpoint of one of the sides. Then connect each vertex to that point. What three-dimensional figure have you drawn? **triangular pyramid**

442

2 Teach

THINK AND DISCUSS

VISUAL LEARNING and ALTERNATIVE METHOD Have students draw a number line to graph the jumps in each of Toadstool's rounds. Have students use the number lines to solve the questions about his jumps.

EXTENSION **Question 2** Let a student demonstrate how tiles can be used to find the sum of $3 + 4 + 2 + 1$.

REASONING **Question 3** Have students use a number line to show the reasoning for their answers.

Example 1 Ask students to think of another real-world example for adding two negative numbers. **Answers may vary. Sample: two plays in football where yards are lost**

REASONING **Question 5b** Challenge students use a number line to explain why this is true.

10-3 Modeling Addition of Integers

What You'll Learn
1 To use models to add integers with like signs
2 To use models to add integers with unlike signs

...And Why
You can add integers to keep score in contests.

Here's How
Look for questions that
🔹 build understanding
✔ check understanding

 The United States record for a jumping frog is 21 ft $5\frac{3}{4}$ in. total for 3 jumps. It happened at the Calaveras Jumping Jubilee in California.

Source: *The Guinness Book of Records*

THINK AND DISCUSS

1 Adding Integers with Like Signs

Toadstool the Frog is a contestant in the Frogville Double Jump. Each frog gets two jumps. A frog's total score is the sum of the distances of the two jumps. When a frog jumps in the wrong direction, the distance is recorded as a negative number. The chart shows Toadstool's practice jumps.

Toadstool's Practice Jumps

Round	1st Jump	2nd Jump	Total
1	3 ft	7 ft	▦
2	−5 ft	−2 ft	▦
3	6 ft	−4 ft	▦
4	−7 ft	3 ft	▦
5	4 ft	−4 ft	▦

You can use tiles to model Toadstool's jumps. To find the sum for his first round, write this number sentence.

$$3 \quad + \quad 7 \quad = \quad ▦$$

1. Complete the number sentence above. How many total feet did Toadstool jump in his first round? **10**

2. Show how tiles can be used to find the sum $5 + 4$.
See above left.

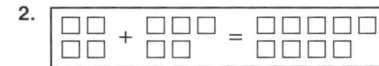
2.

3. 🔹*Reasoning* Complete the sentence: Adding two positive integers always results in a ▦ integer. **positive**

■ EXAMPLE 1

Find the sum of Toadstool's jumps in his second round.

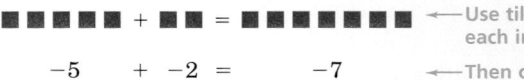 ←— Use tiles to model each integer.

$$-5 \quad + \quad -2 \quad = \quad -7$$ ←— Then count the tiles.

Toadstool jumped a total of −7 ft.

ASSESSMENT Ask students: *Will the sum of 25 + (−33) be negative or positive? Why?* The sum will be negative because 33 is greater than 25. The sum of the two integers has the same sign as the greater number.

■ **ADDITIONAL EXAMPLES**

FOR EXAMPLE 1
Use tiles to find the sum: −3 + −5. −8

FOR EXAMPLE 2
Use tiles to find the sum: −7 + 5. −2

AEP Make sure students understand the phrases *unlike signs* and *like signs*.

Show students examples of like and unlike signs. Remind students that *like* signs are the *same*. *Unlike* signs are *different*.

Work Together

ERROR ALERT! Students may write an incorrect sign with their scores. **Remediation:** Have students write a math sentence on a separate piece of paper to determine their

integer for each round. For example, if they draw 3 yellow tiles and one red tile, have them write 3 + (−1) = 2.

AUDITORY LEARNING and **DIVERSITY** Have students work in pairs. Ask partners to tell visually-impaired or color-blind students the color of tiles they remove from the bag.

WHERE? The largest frog in the world was found in Cameroon in Africa. It was 14.5 in. long and weighed 8 lb 1 oz. The world's smallest frog species lives in Cuba. An adult of this species is less than $\frac{1}{2}$ in. long.

Source: *The Guinness Book of Records*

4. ✔*Try It Out* Use tiles to find each sum.
   a. −8 + (−1)
      −9
   b. −3 + (−6)
      −9
   c. −12 + (−9)
      −21

5. a. What do you notice about the sign of the sum of two negative integers? **The sum is negative.**
   b. ▪*Reasoning* Complete: Adding two negative integers always results in a ■ integer. **negative**

Now you may assign Exercises 1–5, 11–13, 17–18, 23, 32–34.

▼2 Adding Integers with Unlike Signs

You can also use models to add integers that have unlike signs.

■ **EXAMPLE 2**

Use the table on page 442. What is the sum of Toadstool's two jumps in his third round?

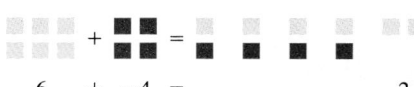

Model with tiles. Combine tiles to make zero pairs. Write the integer that the remaining tiles represent.

6 + −4 = 2

The sum is 2 ft.

7. The sign of the sum is the same as the sign of the number represented by the greater number of tiles.

6. ✔*Try It Out* Use tiles to find each sum.
   a. −5 + 9 4
   b. −8 + 3 −5
   c. 7 + (−7) 0

7. ▪*Draw a Conclusion* What do you notice about the sign of the sum of a positive integer and a negative integer? **See above left.**

ADDING INTEGERS

To add two integers with *like* signs, *add* the numbers without considering their signs. The sum of the integers has the same sign as the two integers.

To find the sum of two integers with *unlike* signs, *find the difference* between the two numbers without considering their signs. The sum of the two integers has the *same sign as the greater number*.

Technology Options

Prentice Hall Technology

 **Software for Learners**
- Math Blaster® Mystery*
- Interactive Student Tutorial, Chapter 10*

 Teaching Resource Software
- Computer Item Generator 10-3
- Resource Pro™ Chapter 10*

Internet • For related mathematics activities, visit the Prentice Hall site at www.phschool.com/math

*Available on CD-ROM only

Assignment Options for Exercises On Your Own

To provide flexible scheduling, this lesson can be split into parts.

▼1 **Core** 1–5, 11–13, 17, 18, 23
   Extension 32–34

▼2 **Core** 6–10, 14–16, 19–22, 24–31, 39–43, 45–48
   Extension 35–37, 44

Use Mixed Review to maintain skills.

3 Practice/Assess

EXERCISES *On Your Own*

ERROR ALERT! Questions 1–10 Students may model the sum correctly but write the incorrect sign for the answer. **Remediation:** Have students compare the color of the tiles that remain with the sign of the answer.

Exercises 11–16 Remind students that yellow tiles represent positive integers and red tiles represent negative integers.

MENTAL MATH Questions 17–21 Remind students that they do not have to find the sum. They only have to tell if the sum is positive or negative.

Exercises 22–27 Encourage students to use each method at least once. Have students explain which method they prefer and why.

OPEN–ENDED Exercises 32–34 Have students state a rule for doing each type of problem. In Exercise 32, for example, make sure that students find the difference between the two numbers. The sum of the two numbers has the sign of the greater number.

Exercises 35–37 Remind students that greater numbers are to the right on a number line and lesser numbers are to the left.

---

pages 444–446   On Your Own

38. **Answers may vary. Sample: Place yellow tiles for each score over par and red tiles for each score under par. After 18 holes subtract the number of red tiles from the number of yellow tiles.**

---

8. ⚏*Explain* What is the sum of a number and its opposite? Give examples to justify your answer.
   $0; 8 + (-8) = 0, (-2) + 2 = 0$

Work Together
Adding Integers

Work with a partner. Place 10 red and 10 yellow algebra tiles in a paper bag. Make a score card like the sample at the right.

9–13. **Check students' work.**

9. Remove 1 tile from the bag. Write the integer that the tile represents. Replace the tile.

10. Now your partner removes 1 tile, writes the integer, and replaces the tile.

Tiles	Player A	Player B
1	1	−1
2	2	−2
3	−1	3
4	4	2
5	▨	▨
6	▨	▨
7	▨	▨
8	▨	▨
Total	▨	▨

11. Continue removing tiles and writing integers. During each round, increase the number of tiles you remove by 1. For example, remove two tiles in the second round, three tiles in the third round, and so on.

12. At the end of 8 rounds, find your score. Cross out any zeros. Model the remaining integers with tiles. Your score is the sum of these integers.

13. ⚏*Analyze* Compare your scores. Who had the greater score?

Now you may assign Exercises 6–10, 14–16, 19–22, 24–31, 35–48.

EXERCISES *On Your Own*

Use tiles to find each sum.

1. $1 + 5$ 6
2. $-2 + (-6)$ −8
3. $0 + (-9)$ −9
4. $4 + 3$ 7
5. $-9 + (-5)$ −14
6. $-11 + 4$ −7
7. $10 + (-10)$ 0
8. $-1 + 4$ 3
9. $3 + (-8)$ −5
10. $-6 + 2$ −4

Write a numerical expression for each model. Find the sum.

11. ▦▦ + ▦
    ▦▦   ▦
    $-4 + (-2) = -6$

12. ▨▨▨ + ▨▨
    ▨▨▨   ▨
    $5 + 3 = 8$

13. ▦▦ + ▦▦▦▦
         ▦▦▦▦
    $-2 + (-8) = -10$

14. ▨▨ + ▦▦
    ▨▨   ▦▦
    $3 + (-4) = -1$

15. ▦ + ▨▨▨
    ▦   ▨▨▨
    $-2 + 6 = 4$

16. ▦▦▦ + ▨▨
    ▦▦▦   ▨
    $-6 + 5 = -1$

444

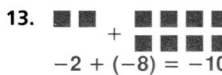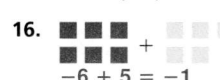

WRITING **Exercise 38** Ask students to include a list of scores with negative and positive integers. Have them explain how they might use tiles to model these scores.

TACTILE LEARNING **Exercise 40** If you have block scheduling or extended classes, ask students to work in groups. Have them write a story problem that involves positive and negative amounts of money. Have groups trade and solve problems. Let students use play money.

Exercise 44 Caution students to pay close attention to signs when they add the integers.

MENTAL MATH **Exercises 45–48** Ask students to name the opposites. Then have students list the remaining integers. **45.** −4 and 4; 7 + (−2); **46.** −3 and 3; 6 + (−8); **47.** 8 and −8, −9 and 9; none; **48.** −7 and 7; 5 + (−1) + (−7)

CONNECTION TO ALGEBRA **Exercises 49–53** You can use cross products to find the value of *n*.

Exercises 54–58 Make sure students remember that the first number goes inside the division house.

Mental Math **State whether the sum is positive or negative.**

17. 16 + 14
positive

18. −16 + (−14)
negative

19. −16 + 18
positive

20. 16 + −15
positive

21. 16 + −18
negative

Choose **Use tiles, paper and pencil, or mental math to find each sum.**

22. 9 + (−4) 5

23. −8 + (−7) −15

24. −15 + 6 −9

25. −11 + 11 0

26. 0 + (−8) −8

27. −6 + 11 5

28. 7 + (−11) −4

29. 12 + (−5) 7

30. 8 + (−4) 4

31. 5 + (−5) 0

Open-ended **Write an addition exercise involving a positive integer and a negative integer with each of the following types of sums.**
32–34. Answers may vary. Samples are given.

32. negative
6 + (−9)

33. zero
3 + (−3)

34. positive
6 + (−3)

Compare. Write <, >, or =.

35. −7 + (−3) ▧ 7 + 3
<

36. 5 + (−5) ▧ −1 + 1
=

37. −2 + 8 ▧ −8 + 2
>

38. *Writing* Explain how you could use tiles to model the score of a golfer as she plays 18 holes.
See margin p. 444.

39. *Office Mail* The mailroom of a large company is on the 15th floor. A mail clerk delivers mail by first going up 5 floors in the elevator. Next he goes down 3 floors. Then he goes down 4 floors. Where is he in relation to the mailroom?
2 floors down

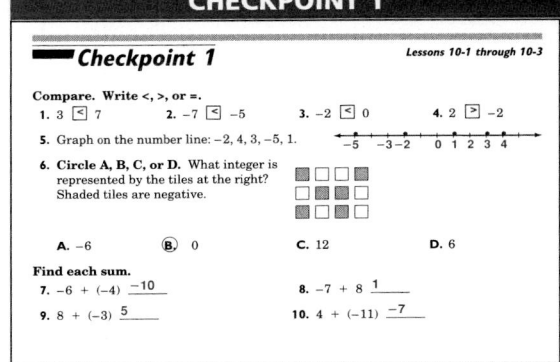

40. *Money* Suppose you earned $12 on Saturday running errands. On Monday, you spent $8. On Friday, you earned $7 baby-sitting. How much money did you have then? $11

41. *Sports* A football team gained 6 yd on one play. On the next play, the team lost 11 yd. Write the total gain or loss of yards as an integer. −5

42. *Weather* At 7:30 A.M. on January 22, 1943, the temperature was −4°F in Spearfish, South Dakota. At 7:32 A.M., the temperature had risen an amazing 49 degrees! What was the temperature then? 45°F

43. Use the table on page 444. After 4 rounds, did Player A or Player B have the greater score? Explain. Check students' work.

CHECKPOINT 1

Checkpoint 1   Lessons 10-1 through 10-3

Compare. Write <, >, or =.

1. 3 ▣< 7   **2.** −7 ▣< −5   **3.** −2 ▣< 0   **4.** 2 ▣> −2

5. Graph on the number line: −2, 4, 3, −5, 1.
−5 −3 −2   0 1 2 3 4

6. Circle **A, B, C, or D.** What integer is represented by the tiles at the right? Shaded tiles are negative.

A. −6   **B.** 0   **C.** 12   **D.** 6

Find each sum.

7. −6 + (−4) −10

8. −7 + 8 1

9. 8 + (−3) 5

10. 4 + (−11) −7

---

page 446   Checkpoint 1

8.
6   −6

9.
−5   5

10.
−2   2

11.
8   −8

12.
−3   3

13.
4   −4

Practice 10-3 *Modeling Addition of Integers*

Write a numerical expression for each model. Find the sum. Unshaded tiles represent positive integers and shaded tiles represent negative integers.

1. −3 + 5; 2   2. −4 + (−5); −9   3. −5 + 2; −3

Choose paper and pencil or mental math to find each sum.

4. −2 + (−8) −10   5. 8 + (−4) 4   6. −6 + 3 −3
7. 6 + (−4) 2   8. −1 + 7 6   9. −8 + 3 −5
10. −2 + (−6) −8   11. 6 + (−9) −3   12. −5 + (−7) −12
13. −4 + (−7) −11   14. 4 + (−7) −3   15. −4 + 7 3

Compare. Write <, >, or =.

16. −5 + (−6) < 6 + (−5)   17. −8 + 10 < −3 + 6
18. −4 + (−9) = −8 + (−5)   19. 20 + (−12) > −12 + (−4)

Solve.

20. Bill has overdrawn his account by $15. There is a $10 service charge for an overdrawn account. If he deposits $60, what is his new balance? $35

21. Jody deposited $65 into her savings account. The next day, she withdrew $24. How much of her deposit remains in the account? $41

22. The outside temperature at noon was 9°F. The temperature dropped 15 degrees during the afternoon. What was the new temperature? −6° F

23. The temperature was 10° below zero and dropped 24 degrees. What is the new temperature? −34° F

24. The high school football team lost 4 yd on one play and gained 9 yd on the next play. What is the total change in yards? 5 yd

25. Philip earned $5 for shoveling snow, $2 for running errands, and received $8 allowance. He spent $6 at the movies and $3 for baseball cards. How much money does he have left? $6

In copymaster and workbook formats

RETEACHING

Reteaching 10-3 *Modeling Addition of Integers*

You can add integers on a number line.

Add 4 + 3.
Move 4 units right and 3 units right.

4 + 3 = 7

Add 5 + −3.
Move 5 units right and 3 units left.

5 + −3 = 2

Add −3 + −2.
Move 3 units left and 2 units left.

−3 + −2 = −5

Add −4 + 1.
Move 4 units left and 1 unit right.

−4 + 1 = −3

Choose a number line, paper and pencil, or mental math to find each sum.

1. 3 + 2 5   2. 6 + 4 10   3. −4 + −1 −5
4. −4 + −8 −12   5. 4 + −1 3   6. −6 + 8 2
7. −7 + 3 −4   8. −5 + 8 3   9. 3 + 5 8
10. −3 + −5 −8   11. 3 + −5 −2   12. −3 + 5 2
13. −6 + −4 −10   14. 7 + −2 5   15. −1 + −6 −7
16. 9 + −2 7   17. −6 + −6 −12   18. 13 + 3 16
19. −14 + −5 −19   20. 5 + −12 −7   21. −9 + 9 0
22. 18 + −18 0   23. 0 + −4 −4   24. 6 + 0 6
25. 15 + −15 0   26. −12 + 0 −12   27. −9 + 10 1
28. 12 + −11 1   29. −12 + 11 −1   30. 2 + −10 −8

ENRICHMENT

Minds on Math Transparency

10-3

Change one of the operational symbols in the expression below so that the value of the expression is multiplied by 4.

81 − 12 − 13 − 14 − 15 − 17

81 − 12 − 13 − 14 + 15 − 17

See *Solution Key* for worked-out answers.

IDENTIFYING THE BIG IDEA Ask students to explain how to use models to add integers with negative and positive signs.

LESSON QUIZ
Use mental math, tiles, or paper and pencil to find each sum.

1. −25 + 9 −16
2. 35 + (−15) 20
3. 19 + 52 71
4. −42 + (−64) −106

---

44. Copy the Magic Integer Square. Arrange the integers −4, −3, −2, −1, 0, 1, 2, 3, 4 so they add up to zero in all eight directions (vertically, horizontally, and diagonally).

Magic Integer Square

?	?	?
−1	4	−3
?	?	?
−2	0	2
?	?	?
3	−4	1

Mental Math **Group opposites to get a sum of 0. Add the remaining integers.**

45. −4 + 7 + 4 + (−2) 5   46. 6 + (−3) + (−8) + 3 −2
47. 8 + (−9) + (−8) + 9 0   48. −7 + 5 + (−1) + 7 + (−7) −3

Mixed Review

Find the value of *n*. *(Lesson 7-3)*

49. $\frac{4}{6} = \frac{n}{9}$ 6   50. $\frac{22}{25} = \frac{n}{200}$ 176   51. $\frac{3}{7} = \frac{21}{n}$ 49   52. $\frac{9}{27} = \frac{n}{42}$ 14   53. $\frac{9}{10} = \frac{27}{n}$ 30

Find each quotient. *(Lessons 4-8 and 4-9)*

54. 10.2 ÷ 3   55. 8.45 ÷ 0.25   56. 37.1 ÷ 14   57. 128.31 ÷ 1.3   58. 0.125 ÷ 0.025
    3.4   33.8   2.65   98.7   5

59. Kay bought a case of shampoo. She sold 11 bottles to Sabrina and still had 25 bottles left. How many bottles were in the case? *(Lesson 2-6)* 36 bottles

---

✓ CHECKPOINT 1   *Lessons 10-1 through 10-3*

Compare. Write <, >, or =.

1. 2 < 5   2. −4 > −8   3. −3 < 0   4. 6 > −6   5. −11 < −10

6. Graph on a number line: 2, −5, 3, 1, −7, −2.

7. What integer is represented by ■ ■ ■ ☐ ☐ ☐ ? 1

Use tiles to represent each integer and its opposite.
8–13. See margin p. 445.

8. 6   9. −5   10. −2   11. 8   12. −3   13. 4

Find each sum.

14. −2 + (−3)   15. 7 + (−5)   16. −9 + 9   17. −1 + (−11)   18. −3 + 6
    −5   2   0   −12   3

PROBLEM SOLVING PRACTICE ★★

This page provides problems for students to solve using their knowledge of rounding decimals, using exponential notation, measuring, using translations and symmetry, and graphing data. Allow students to use any method they find helpful.

Exercises 3 and 4 Students can write an equation for each exercise using the rate of conversion from one unit of measurement to the other.

Exercise 5 Students may want to use tracing paper.

PROBLEM SOLVING PRACTICE

Choose the best answer.

1. A digital scale measured the weight of a baby as 7.819 pounds. What is the weight rounded to the nearest tenth of a pound? **B**

   A. 7 pounds
   B. 7.8 pounds
   C. 7.9 pounds
   D. 8 pounds

2. On a test, Alexis was asked to write $2 \times 2 \times 2 \times 5 \times 5$ in exponential notation. Which should she have written? **H**

   F. $8^3 \times 25^2$
   G. $3 \times 2 \times 5 \times 2$
   H. $2^3 \times 5^2$
   J. $3^2 \times 2^5$

3. The width of a doorway is 95 cm. What is the width in meters? **A**

   A. 0.95 m
   B. 9.5 m
   C. 950 m
   D. 9,500 m

4. Billy buys 80 ounces of fudge. How many pounds of fudge is this? **F**

   F. 5 lb
   G. $6\frac{2}{3}$ lb
   H. 8 lb
   J. 10 lb

5. Look at the drawing of a sailboat.

   Which drawing shows a translation of the sailboat? **D**

   A.
   B.
   C.
   D.

6. Which point is located at (4, 2)? **H**

   F. point M
   G. point N
   H. point P
   J. point Q

   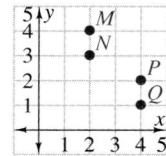

Please note that Exercises 7 and 8 each have *five* answer choices.

7. Four flag styles are available. Each flag is made up of 8 triangles. The cost of the flag depends on the types of triangles used. Red silk triangles cost $9.50 each. White cotton triangles cost $4.50 each. **D**

   Suppose you pick a flag that has both horizontal line symmetry and vertical line symmetry. How much would the flag cost?

   A. $41
   B. $46
   C. $51
   D. $56
   E. Not Here

8. The graph shows the results of a survey in which 200 people named their favorite dessert. How many people preferred ice cream? **J**

   Favorite Dessert

   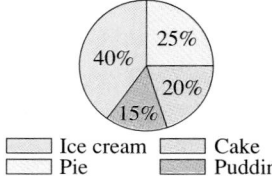

   F. 8
   G. 40
   H. 50
   J. 80
   K. Not Here

1 Focus

CONNECTING TO PRIOR KNOWLEDGE
Write $-4 + 11$ on the board. Ask students: *How can you use subtraction to find the sum of -4 and 11?* **Answers may vary. Sample: Subtract 4 from 11 to get 7.**

Lesson Planning Options

Prerequisite Skills
- modeling integers (10-2)
- adding integers (10-3)

Materials/Manipulatives
- algebra tiles
- green number cube
- red number cube

Resources

 Student Edition

Skills Handbook, p. 539
Extra Practice, p. 531
Glossary/Study Guide

 Teaching Resources

Chapter Support File, Ch. 10
- Lesson Planner 10-4
- Practice 10-4, Reteaching 10-4
- Alternative Activity 10-4
- Answer Masters 10-4
Teaching Aids Masters 2, 26, 27
Glossary, Spanish Resources

 Transparencies
15, Minds on Math 10-4

Warm Up

Harold spent $6.99 on a CD and twice that amount on a book. He has $9.03 left. How much did he have before making the purchases? **$30**

448

2 Teach

THINK AND DISCUSS

KINESTHETIC LEARNING Ask students to model $-8 - (-6)$. Have 8 students stand at the front of the room. Give each student a red piece of construction paper to represent a negative number. Ask 6 of the 8 students to sit down on the floor to represent the negative amount being removed from the starting negative integer. Ask: *What is $-8 - (-6)$?* **-2**

AEP Make sure students understand the mathematical meaning of the words *positive* and *negative*. Remind students that positive numbers are greater than zero, and negative numbers are less than zero.

Example 3 Some students may have difficulty in determining how many zero pairs to add to solve the problem. For example, 9 tiles need to be taken away. Adding 4 zero pairs to 5 positive tiles gives 9 positive tiles. The 4 positive tiles included in the zero pairs make up the 9 positive tiles needed.

10-4 Modeling Subtraction of Integers

What You'll Learn
1 To model the subtraction of integers
2 To use models to solve equations with integers

...And Why
You can subtract integers to solve problems involving weather.

Here's How
Look for questions that
- build understanding
- ✔ check understanding

THINK AND DISCUSS

1 Modeling Subtraction of Integers

You can use tiles to subtract integers.

■ EXAMPLE 1

Use tiles to find $-8 - (-6)$.

← Start with 8 negative tiles.

← Take away 6 negative tiles.

← Two negative tiles remain.

$-8 - (-6) = -2$

1. ✔**Try It Out** Use tiles to find each difference.
   a. $12 - 4$ → **8**
   b. $-10 - (-3)$ → **-7**
   c. $-15 - (-9)$ → **-6**

You may need to add zero pairs to subtract.

■ EXAMPLE 2

Use tiles to subtract $4 - (-3)$.

 Start with 4 positive tiles.
← There are not enough negative tiles to take 3 negative tiles away.

 ← Add 3 zero pairs.

 ← Take away 3 negative tiles. There are 7 positive tiles left.

$4 - (-3) = 7$
a–b. See above left.

2a. 0; the value of each zero pair is 0.
   b. No; adding 0 does not affect the value of a number.

2. a. What is the total value of the 3 zero pairs? Explain.
   b. Did adding 3 zero pairs affect the value of 4? Explain.

Now you may assign Exercises 1–14, 20–29, 36–40.

■ ADDITIONAL EXAMPLES

FOR EXAMPLE 1
Use tiles to find $-7 - (-3)$. -4

FOR EXAMPLE 2
Use tiles to subtract $7 - (-2)$. 9

FOR EXAMPLE 3
The high temperature at 3:00 P.M.was 6°C. The temperature dropped 7°C by midnight. What was the temperature at midnight? -1°C

Work Together

Demonstrate several rounds of the game with the whole class before students play.

ASSESSMENT Have students in each pair write an equation for their partner to solve. Then have pairs of students write four expressions subtracting negative integers. Ask them to model the expressions with tiles. Have pairs trade problems to check each other's work.

3 Practice/Assess

EXERCISES *On Your Own*

If you have block scheduling or extended class periods, you may want to have students use algebra software to practice subtracting integers.

ERROR ALERT! Exercise 5 Some students may not understand how many zero pairs to add. **Remediation:** Remind students to start

---

The Mount Washington Observatory in New Hampshire records weather conditions at the top of the highest peak in the northeastern United States. The temperature on the peak ranges from –47°F to 72°F (–44°C to 22°C). You can get today's weather report from Mount Washington at the Web site www.mountwashington.org.

4b. Answers may vary. Sample: Subtracting a number gives the same result as adding its opposite.

2 *Using Models to Solve Equations*

You can use tiles to solve equations with integers.

■ EXAMPLE 3 *Real-World Problem Solving*

Weather Between dawn and noon, the temperature rose 9 degrees Celsius. At noon it was 5°C. What was the temperature at dawn? Let t = temperature at dawn.

Words •	Temperature at dawn	plus	Rise in temperature	equals	Temperature at noon
Equation •	t	$+$	9	$=$	5

$t + 9 = 5$ ←— Solve for t.

$t = 5 - 9$ ←— Subtract 9 from each side.

 ←— Use tiles to subtract $5 - 9$. Start with 5 positive tiles.

 ←— There are not enough positive tiles to take 9 away. Add 4 zero pairs.

 ←— Take away 9 positive tiles. There are 4 negative tiles left.

$5 - 9 = -4$

So $t = -4$. The temperature at dawn was -4°C.

3. ✓Try It Out Solve each equation.
   a. $x + 4 = 2$ -2 **b.** $p + 8 = 3$ -5 **c.** $y + 7 = 1$ -6

4. a. Find $5 + (-9)$. Compare your answer to Example 3. -4
   b. ▪*Draw a Conclusion* Does your comparison suggest a rule for subtracting integers? Explain. **See left.**

SUBTRACTING INTEGERS

You can subtract an integer by *adding its opposite*.
Examples:

$10 - 6 = 10 + (-6) = 4$ $6 - 10 = 6 + (-10) = -4$

$10 - (-6) = 10 + 6 = 16$ $6 - (-10) = 6 + 10 = 16$

Technology Options

Prentice Hall Technology

Software for Learners
• Math Blaster® Mystery*
• Interactive Student Tutorial, Chapter 10*

Teaching Resource Software
• Computer Item Generator 10-4
• Resource Pro™ Chapter 10*

Internet • For related mathematics activities, visit the Prentice Hall site at www.phschool.com/math

Available on CD-ROM only

Assignment Options for Exercises On Your Own

To provide flexible scheduling, this lesson can be split into parts.

▼**1** Core 1–14, 20–29
   Extension 36–40

▼**2** Core 15–19, 30–35
   Extension 44–48

Use Mixed Review to maintain skills.

with 7 positive tiles. Ask students: *How many more tiles do you need to add to 7 so you can take away 12?* **5** *How many zero pairs do you need to add?* **5** The 5 positive tiles included in the zero pairs add the 5 positive tiles needed to make 12.

WRITING Exercise 14 Suggest that students include the following types of tiles for examples: positive − negative, negative − positive, and negative − negative.

CONNECTION TO ALGEBRA Exercise 15 Remind students to add an opposite or subtract the same integer from each side of the equation. For example, have them subtract 11 or add −11 to each side of the equation.

VISUAL LEARNING Exercises 20–29 Allow students to draw models to find each difference.

Exercises 30–35 Have students graph sums and differences on a number line to compare values. Challenge students to use reasoning when they can.

CONNECTION TO ECONOMICS Have students research financial reports of negative and positive numbers. If possible, have students show examples of operations with negative numbers and the use of parentheses for reporting negative numbers.

450

Need Help? For practice in subtracting whole numbers, see Skills Handbook page 539.

5. ✔Try It Out Find each difference.
  a. $12 - 19$ **−7**   **b.** $-10 - 5$ **−15**   **c.** $-5 - (-11)$ **6**

Work Together
Subtracting Integers

Play the Great Integer Game! You will need yellow and red tiles, a green number cube, and a red number cube.

- Work in groups. Each player starts with 3 positive and 3 negative tiles. Put the remaining tiles in the game pile.

- Roll the cubes. Subtract the number on the red cube from the number on the green cube. Take the resulting number of tiles away from your tiles and place them in the game pile.

- If you don't have enough tiles to put in the game pile, take zero pairs from the game pile in order to make your number.

- The winner is the first person to run out of tiles.

6. As you play, each person should complete a recording sheet. **Check students' work.**

Tiles at start of turn	Your Roll Green − Red	Taking away tiles	Tiles at end of turn

Now you may assign Exercises 15–19, 30–35, 41–48.

EXERCISES *On Your Own*

Write a numerical expression for each model. Find the difference.

1. $-1 - 2 = -3$ **2.** $3 - (-2) = 5$ **3.** 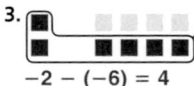 $-2 - (-6) = 4$

Modeling **Use tiles to find each difference.**

4. $14 - 8$ **6**   **5.** $7 - 12$ **−5**   **6.** $-8 - 4$ **−12**   **7.** $-1 - (-5)$ **4**   **8.** $4 - (-6)$ **10**

9. $9 - 5$ **4**   **10.** $-2 - 7$ **−9**   **11.** $6 - 9$ **−3**   **12.** $-3 - 3$ **−6**   **13.** $5 - (-1)$ **6**

450 Chapter 10 Algebra: Integers and Graphing

Exercises 41–43 A number line may help students see the patterns.

OPEN–ENDED Exercise 44 Ask students if they can use a positive number in one box and a negative number in the other to solve the problem. **No, the numbers must be the same.**

WRAP UP

IDENTIFYING THE BIG IDEA Ask students to explain how to model subtraction of negative integers. Have them describe how to use models to solve equations with positive and negative integers.

PROJECT LINK Encourage students to recall important events to list on the negative side of the timeline. Suggest that students include hopes of things to come and predictions about future events on the positive side.

14. *Writing* Describe how to use tiles to subtract integers. Include examples with both positive and negative integers.
See margin.

Algebra **Solve each equation.**

15. $b + 11 = -2$ 16. $7 + a = 4$ 17. $t - 20 = -5$ 18. $12 + b = -1$ 19. $x + 8 = 0$
  -13 -3 15 -13 -8

Choose **Use tiles, pencil and paper, or mental math to find each difference.**

20. $1 - 6$ -5 21. $-13 - 8$ -21 22. $-4 - (-15)$ 11 23. $-5 - 3$ -8 24. $-12 - 17$
                                                                                          -29

25. $-3 - (-7)$ 26. $-1 - 6$ 27. $-6 - (-6)$ 28. $11 - 15$ 29. $0 - 10$
   4 -7 0 -4 -10

Compare. Write <, >, or =.

30. $12 + (-3)$ ▧ $12 - 3$ 31. $-1 - 5$ ▧ $-5 - 1$ 32. $6 - 11$ ▧ $11 - 6$
    $=$ $=$ $<$

33. $-9 + 7$ ▧ $7 - 9$ 34. $-4 - (-9)$ ▧ $-4 + 9$ 35. $8 - (-8)$ ▧ $-8 + 8$
    $=$ $=$ $>$

Geography **The map shows the time zones for North America. The numbers indicate the time (in hours) compared to the time at the starting zone.**

36. Complete with *add* or *subtract*: For each zone you travel west, you ▧ 1 h. For each zone you travel east, you ▧ 1 h.
    subtract; add

37. It is midnight on New Year's Eve at Times Square in New York City. What time is it in Los Angeles? **9 P.M., New Year's Eve**

38. It is 2:30 P.M. in the starting zone. What is the time in Denver?   **7:30 A.M.**

39. It is 8:15 A.M. in San Francisco. What time is it in Dallas?   **10:15 A.M.**

40. *Research* Find the names of the various time zones on the map above.   **Check students' work.**

pages 450–452   On Your Own

14. **Answers may vary. Sample: Take away the number of tiles that represent the number being subtracted. If there are not enough tiles of the right color to take away, add zero pairs until you have enough tiles. Then take away the right number of tiles.**

PRACTICE

▬ Practice 10-4 *Modeling Subtraction of Integers*

Write a numerical expression for each model. Find the difference.

1. $-7 - (-4)$; -3 2. 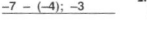 $6 - (-2)$; 8

3. $4 - 6$; -2 4. 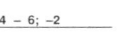 $-5 - (-6)$; 1

Choose paper and pencil or mental math to find each difference.

5. $2 - 5$ $\underline{-3}$ 6. $-5 - 2$ $\underline{-7}$ 7. $-6 - 3$ $\underline{-9}$

8. $10 - (-3)$ $\underline{13}$ 9. $-9 - (-2)$ $\underline{-7}$ 10. $0 - (-5)$ $\underline{5}$

11. $-12 - (-3)$ $\underline{-9}$ 12. $8 - 13$ $\underline{-5}$ 13. $11 - (-6)$ $\underline{17}$

Compare. Write <, >, or =.

14. $5 - 12$ $\boxed{<}$ $5 - (-12)$ 15. $8 - (-5)$ $\boxed{>}$ $-8 - 5$

16. $9 - (-4)$ $\boxed{=}$ $4 - (-9)$ 17. $-12 - 12$ $\boxed{<}$ $12 - (-12)$

Solve each equation.

18. $t + 15 = 10$ $\underline{-5}$ 19. $8 + c = 3$ $\underline{-5}$ 20. $x - 12 = -3$ $\underline{9}$ 21. $s + 6 = 1$ $\underline{-5}$

Solve.

22. The temperature was 48°F and dropped 15° in two hours. What was the temperature after the change? $\underline{33°F}$

23. The temperature at midnight is –5°C and is expected to drop 12° by sunrise. What is the expected temperature at sunrise? $\underline{-17°C}$

24. Catherine has $400 in her checking account. Her utility bills total $600. How much more money does she need to pay the utility bills? $\underline{\$200}$

25. On the first play, the football team lost 6 yd. On the second play, the team lost 5 yd. What was their total change in yards? $\underline{-11\ yd}$

26. Use the thermometer to find the final reading at 1 P.M. $\underline{-7°C}$

10 A.M.	reading of 5°C
11 A.M.	drops 5°C
12 noon	drops 3°C
1 P.M.	drops 4°C

In copymaster and workbook formats

RETEACHING

▬ Reteaching 10-4 *Modeling Subtraction of Integers*

To subtract an integer, add the opposite.

Subtract $5 - 8$.
Add the opposite: $5 + (-8)$

$5 - 8 = -3$

Subtract $2 - (-4)$.
Add the opposite: $2 + 4$

$2 - (-4) = 6$

Choose a number line, paper and pencil or mental math to find each difference.

1. $3 - (-6)$ $\underline{9}$ 2. $2 - (-4)$ $\underline{6}$ 3. $-1 - 2$ $\underline{-3}$

4. $-3 - (-5)$ $\underline{2}$ 5. $-8 - (-3)$ $\underline{-5}$ 6. $4 - (-4)$ $\underline{8}$

7. $-8 - 2$ $\underline{-10}$ 8. $8 - (-2)$ $\underline{10}$ 9. $-8 - (-2)$ $\underline{-6}$

10. $-7 - 4$ $\underline{-11}$ 11. $-10 - 2$ $\underline{-12}$ 12. $-5 - (-5)$ $\underline{0}$

13. $-5 - 6$ $\underline{-11}$ 14. $9 - (-3)$ $\underline{12}$ 15. $-11 - (-6)$ $\underline{-5}$

16. $15 - (-4)$ $\underline{19}$ 17. $-12 - 3$ $\underline{-15}$ 18. $21 - (-7)$ $\underline{28}$

19. $3 - (-12)$ $\underline{15}$ 20. $-2 - 10$ $\underline{-12}$ 21. $-13 - 13$ $\underline{-26}$

22. $5 - (-5)$ $\underline{10}$ 23. $18 - (-10)$ $\underline{28}$ 24. $-7 - (-13)$ $\underline{6}$

25. $14 - 16$ $\underline{-2}$ 26. $3 - 15$ $\underline{-12}$ 27. $-6 - (-9)$ $\underline{3}$

28. $-12 - 6$ $\underline{-18}$ 29. $15 - (-9)$ $\underline{24}$ 30. $7 - 19$ $\underline{-12}$

Compare. Write <, >, or =.

31. $6 - 2$ $\boxed{>}$ $-2 - 6$ 32. $3 + (-1)$ $\boxed{=}$ $-5 + 7$ 33. $4 - 7$ $\boxed{<}$ $8 - (-5)$

34. $12 - (-9)$ $\boxed{>}$ $0 - 3$ 35. $-10 - 2$ $\boxed{<}$ $-5 - (-4)$ 36. $-7 - 9$ $\boxed{<}$ $-1 - (-6)$

ENRICHMENT

◢ Minds on Math Transparency

10-4

Tomorrow will not be Monday or Friday. Today is not Tuesday or Wednesday. Yesterday was not Thursday or Sunday. What day was yesterday?

Friday

See *Solution Key* for worked-out answers.

452

LESSON QUIZ

1. Compare. Write $<$, $>$, or $=$.
   $-9 - (-8)$ ■ $-9 + (-8)$ $>$

2. Solve the equation $x - 8 = -14$. -6

Use tiles, mental math, or paper and pencil to solve.

3. $12 - (-2)$ 14

4. $-8 - (-11)$ 3

Patterns **Find the next three integers in each pattern.**

41. $12, 7, 2, -3,$ ■, ■, ■ $-8, -13, -18$

42. $19, 13, 7, 1,$ ■, ■, ■ $-5, -11, -17$

43. $-12, -9, -6, -3,$ ■, ■, ■ $0, 3, 6$

Open-ended **Use positive and negative integers to write two different subtraction sentences for each exercise.**

44–47. Answers may vary. Samples are given.

44. ■ $-$ ■ $= 0$ $5, 5; -5, -5$

45. ■ $-$ ■ $= 8$ $3, -11; 12, 4$

46. ■ $-$ ■ $= -5$ $3, 8; -1, 4$

47. ■ $- 3 =$ ■ $10, 7; -7, -10$

48. **a.** Find $-3 + (-3) + (-3) + (-3)$. -12
    b. Write part (a) as a multiplication sentence. $-3 \times 4 = -12$
    c. How could you write your answer to part (b) as a division sentence? $-12 \div 4 = -3$

Mixed Review

Use the graph for Exercises 49–52. *(Lesson 1-5)*

49. How many candidates were there? 5

50. What percent of the votes did Bianca get? 29%

51. Who got the fewest votes? Valli

52. Can you tell by looking at the graph how many students voted for George? no

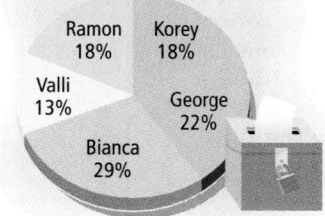

Student Council Election Results

Ramon 18% Korey 18% Valli 13% George 22% Bianca 29%

Write each decimal as a fraction or mixed number in simplest form. *(Lesson 5-9)*

53. 1.6 $1\frac{3}{5}$ 54. 0.375 $\frac{3}{8}$ 55. 0.09 $\frac{9}{100}$ 56. 0.57 $\frac{57}{100}$ 57. 2.125 $2\frac{1}{8}$ 58. 0.72 $\frac{18}{25}$

59. *Choose a Strategy* A teacher surveyed 48 sixth-grade students. She found that 18 had read *Mariel of Redwall*, 20 had read *Mossflower*, and 11 had read both books. How many students had not read either book? 21 students

CHAPTER PROJECT

PROJECT LINK: DRAWING

Draw your time line on a sheet of paper about 3 ft long. Use marks of different lengths to show the one-year, five-year, and ten-year divisions. Label the current year "0" so that your past lies on the negative side of the time line and your future lies on the positive side.   Check students' work.

MATH TOOLBOX

In Lesson 10-4, students learned to model the subtraction of integers and to solve equations with integers using models. This toolbox shows students how to use algebra tiles to solve two-step equations.

ERROR ALERT! Students may confuse the different kinds of algebra tiles and what they represent. **Remediation:** Tell students the algebra tile's area is the value it represents.

The length of the small square represents one unit, so its area is 1 unit^2. The x-bar is one unit wide and an unknown value x long, so its area is x units^2. The red tiles represent negative values. Suggest students write a key on their paper to help them remember.

ASSESSMENT **Exercises 1 and 2** Pair students. Have one partner solve the equation in Exercise 1 using algebra tiles while the other partner observes. The observing students should only give suggestions or feedback when prompted by their partner. Have partners change roles for Exercise 2.

■ **ADDITIONAL PROBLEMS**

Use algebra tiles to solve each equation.
1. $4x + 8 = 12$ **1**
2. $3x - 6 = -9$ **−1**
3. $2x + 10 = -4$ **−7**

Materials/Manipulatives
• algebra tiles

Resources

■ **Teaching Resources**
Teaching Aids Masters 2, 27

Transparencies
13

EXPLORATION

Solving Two-Step Equations

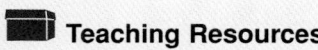
After Lesson 10-4

A *two-step equation* is an equation with two operations. You can use algebra tiles to solve two-step equations. Use the same methods you used to solve one-step equations.

■ **EXAMPLE**

Solve $2x - 1 = -7$.

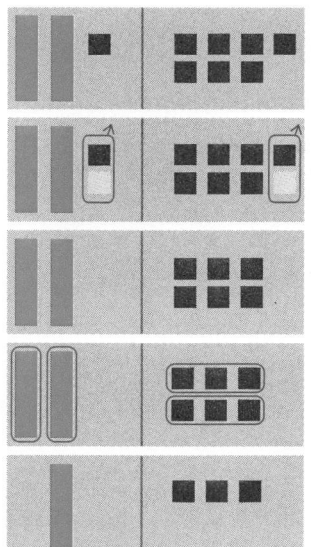

Model the equation. Notice that $2x - 1$ is shown as $2x + (-1)$.

Make zero pairs to get the x-tiles alone on one side of the equation.

Simplify each side. You now have a one-step equation, $2x = -6$.

Divide each side of the equation into 2 equal parts.

Find the solution.

The solution to $2x - 1 = -7$ is -3.

Use algebra tiles to solve each equation.

1. $2x + 3 = 5$ **1**
2. $3x - 4 = 2$ **2**
3. $2x - 4 = 4$ **4**
4. $4x + 3 = -5$ **−2**
5. $5x - 6 = 4$ **2**

6. $4x - 1 = 3$ **1**
7. $3x + 5 = -1$ **−2**
8. $2x + 7 = -1$ **−4**
9. $2x - 1 = -7$ **−3**
10. $3x - 6 = 3$ **3**

11. $5x - 2 = -7$ **−1**
12. $2x - 1 = 5$ **3**
13. $4x - 9 = -1$ **2**
14. $6x + 3 = -3$ **−1**
15. $2x + 4 = 4$ **0**

16. *Writing* Explain why $2x - 1$ can be written as $2x + (-1)$. **Answers may vary. Sample: Subtracting an integer is the same as adding its opposite.**

453

1 Focus

CONNECTING TO PRIOR KNOWLEDGE
Have students name and describe problem-solving strategies they have used. Review the following strategies: Make a Table, Use Logical Reasoning, Solve a Simpler Problem, Too Much or Too Little Information, Look for a Pattern, Make a Model, Work Backward, Draw a Diagram, Guess and Test, and Simulate a Problem.

2 Teach

THINK AND DISCUSS

KINESTHETIC LEARNING Model the scoring field for the flying ring contest in your classroom. Group students in teams of five. Give each one paper clip or one "o"-shaped cereal ring to toss. Record each team's score in a table. Compare these scores to those in the sample problem.

ERROR ALERT! Question 4 Students may think that you can only get one of each possible score. **Remediation:** Draw a sample flying ring contest field on paper and have a student toss five paper clips on the paper. Show students that you can get a score more than once.

ASSESSMENT Have students consider the possible scores for five throws in the flying ring contest. Have them list all possibilities. **3,**

Lesson Planning Options

Prerequisite Skills
• using Guess and Test (3-4)

Resources

 Student Edition

Skills Handbook, pp. 538, 539
Extra Practice, p. 531
Glossary/Study Guide

 Teaching Resources

Chapter Support File, Ch. 10
• Lesson Planner 10-5
• Practice 10-5, Reteaching 10-5
• Answer Masters 10-5
Glossary, Spanish Resources

 Transparencies
Minds on Math 10-5

Warm Up

One out of every 15 students in Hill Country Middle School chooses to study Japanese. If the school has 900 students, how many students are studying Japanese? **60**

454

10-5 *Use Multiple Strategies*

Problem Solving Strategies

Draw a Diagram
Guess and Test
Look for a Pattern
Make a Model
Make a Table
Simulate a Problem
Solve a Simpler Problem
Too Much or Too Little
  Information
Use Logical Reasoning
✔ Use Multiple Strategies
Work Backward

THINK AND DISCUSS

Sometimes you need to use more than one strategy to solve a problem.

SAMPLE PROBLEM..

Malcolm finished first in the flying ring contest held at his school's playing field. The field had scoring zones worth 1, 3, 5, 7, and 9 points. All five of Malcolm's throws landed in a scoring zone. Which of these total scores could be Malcolm's total score? **4 24 37 47**

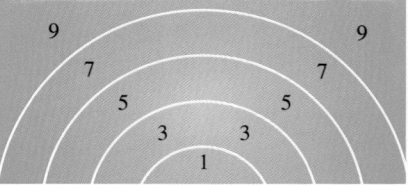

Throwing • Spot

....

READ

Read for understanding.
Summarize the problem.

1. How many times did Malcolm throw the ring? **5 times**

2. What scores were possible on each throw? **0, 1, 3, 5, 7, or 9**

3. Was 0 a possible score for one of Malcolm's throws? **no**

 PLAN

Decide on a strategy.

Use *Logical Reasoning* and *Look for a Pattern* to eliminate some of the scores in the list above. Then *Guess and Test* possible throw combinations.

5, 7, 9, 11, 13, 15, 17, 19, 21, 23, 25, 27 Ask: *What strategies did you use?* **Answers may vary. Sample: Make a Table and Look for a Pattern**

■ ADDITIONAL PROBLEM

Sheila types 6 pages in an hour. Jamal types 6 pages in 20 min. Jamal and Sheila begin typing at noon. If they type without any breaks, at what time will Jamal have typed 100 pages more than Sheila? **8:20 P.M.**

3 Practice/Assess

EXERCISES *On Your Own*

DIVERSITY and AUDITORY LEARNING Read the exercises aloud so students who have difficulty reading will have an easier time solving them. Suggest that students note on their papers the important information in each exercise.

Exercise 1 Ask students: *In how many hours will an accurate clock show the same time as it shows right now?* **12 h**

EXTENSION and CONNECTION TO STATISTICS Exercise 4 Have groups of students design similar problems using their classmates as a sample population.

CONNECTION TO CUSTOMER SERVICE Exercise 6 Tell students not to consider coins or $2 bills. Have them find the answer for common paper money only.

 SOLVE
Try the strategy.

The only possible scores for a throw were 1, 3, 5, 7, or 9 points. Think logically about the possible total scores for 5 throws.

4. What was the highest total score Malcolm could get? **45**

5. What was the lowest total score he could get? **5**

6. Which two scores in the list can you now eliminate? **4 and 47**

Now you can *Look for a Pattern* to find if Malcolm could get the remaining scores of 24 or 37. Notice that all the possible scores for a single throw are *odd* numbers. Look for a pattern in the sums of odd numbers.

7. Is the sum of two odd numbers odd or even? **even**

8. Is the sum of three odd numbers odd or even? **odd**

9. Is the sum of four odd numbers odd or even? **even**

10. Is the sum of five odd numbers odd or even? **odd**

Now that you know what kind of number results from adding five odd numbers, can you eliminate one of the two remaining totals?

11. Which score was not possible? Why?
24; a sum of five odd numbers must be odd. 24 is even.

13. Answers may vary. Any odd number from 5 to 45 is a possible answer; each score is an odd number 1, 3, 5, 7, or 9, so the sum must also be odd.

 LOOK BACK
Think about how you solved the problem.

12. Which was the only possible total score? *Guess and Test* to confirm your answer. **37**

13. What are two other possible total scores that Malcolm could have thrown? Explain. **See above left.**

Now you may assign Exercises 1–8.

EXERCISES *On Your Own*

Use one or more strategies to solve each problem. Show all your work.

1. *Time* The old town clock loses 10 minutes every 2 days. On May 1 the clock showed the correct time. If the clock continues to lose time at the rate noted, on what date will the clock again show the correct time? **September 22**

2. *Gardening* A gardener wants to fence in the greatest possible area using 200 ft of fencing. Find the best length and width for the garden. **50 ft; 50 ft**

Technology Options

Prentice Hall Technology

  Software for Learners
- Math Blaster® Mystery*
- Interactive Student Tutorial, Chapter 10*

  Teaching Resource Software
- Computer Item Generator 10-5
- Resource Pro™ Chapter 10*

Internet • For related mathematics activities, visit the Prentice Hall site at www.phschool.com/math

Available on CD-ROM only

Assignment Options for Exercises On Your Own

Core 1–7
Extension 8

Use Mixed Review to maintain skills.

PRACTICE

Practice 10-5 *Problem-Solving Strategy: Use Multiple Strategies*

Use one or more strategies to solve each problem. Show all your work.

1. The stick-on digits 0, 1, 2, 3, 4, 5, 6, 7, 8, and 9 can be bought at hardware stores. You need to label 100 lockers from 1 to 100 with the stick-on digits. Which digit will be used the least number of times? the most?   **0; 1**

2. A commuter train passes through the station every half hour from 6 A.M. through 7 P.M. How many trains pass through the station each day?   **27 trains**

3. Marika is older than Will and younger than Jean. Marika is younger than Kisha. Jean is older than Ty and younger than Megan. Ty is older than Marika. Who is the youngest?   **Will**

4. Seven schools will play each of the other schools once in a soccer tournament. How many games need to be played?
   21 games

5. Arrange the digits 0, 1, 2, 3, 4, 5, 6, 7, 8, and 9 to form two five-digit numbers so that the difference is as large as possible.

   9 8 7 6 5
   − 0 1 2 3 4
   9 7 5 3 1

6. Weekend admission charges at the zoo are $3.50 for adults, $1.50 for seniors, and $2.00 for children (5–12 years old). Children under 5 are admitted free. The parking fee is $3.00. What is the total cost for a group of four adults, two seniors, and children with ages 3, 4, 5, 6, 7, 8, 9, 10, 11, and 12 that came in three cars?   **$42.00**

7. Al went shopping and spent half his money and $5 more at a gift shop. At the food store, he spent half his remaining money and $5 more. He had only $2.50 left. How much money did Al have when he went into the gift shop?
   $40

8. The last Friday of last month was the 26th day of the month. What day of the week was the first day of last month?
   Monday

9. How many calls will be made among six people if each person needs to talk to each of the other people one time?
   15 calls

In copymaster and workbook formats

RETEACHING

Reteaching 10-5 *Problem-Solving Strategy: Use Multiple Strategies*

A restaurant has triangular and square tables that can seat one person on a side. The sides of the tables are all the same length so that they can be placed together to make larger tables. Is it possible to make one long table using square tables with a triangular table at each end in order to seat exactly 11 people?

Read   What does the problem ask you to find? *You need to find whether 11 people can be seated without any empty places at a long table made of squares and two triangles.*

Plan   Which strategies will help you solve the problem? *You can draw diagrams of the tables. Then you can make a chart to see whether it is possible to seat exactly 11 people.*

Solve   Draw diagrams:

1 square table and 2 triangular tables   2 square tables and 2 triangular tables   3 square tables and 2 triangular tables

Now make a chart to show what happens as more square tables are added.

Square Tables	Places
1	6
2	8
3	10
4	12

The chart shows that it is not possible to sit 11 people without empty places.

Look Back   Does my answer make sense? *Think about the pattern in the chart. There will always be only an even number of places.*

Use one or more strategies to solve each problem.

1. How many square tables are needed to make one long table for 18 people using a triangular table at each end?
   7 square tables

2. How many people can be seated using 16 square tables and 2 triangular tables?
   36 people

3. How can 11 people be seated at a long table with no empty seats?
   Use 4 square and 1 triangular table.

4. How many can be seated at a large table made from 4 square tables?
   Answers will vary. Sample: 8.

ENRICHMENT

Minds on Math Transparency

10-5

Mrs. Brown, Mrs. Black, and Mrs. Green have brown, black, and green raincoats. "None of our coats matches our names," says Mrs. Green. "You're right!" says the lady in the brown coat. Who has which coat?

Mrs. Green : black coat;
Mrs. Black : brown coat;
Mrs. Brown : green coat

See *Solution Key* for worked-out answers.

456

WRAP UP

IDENTIFYING THE BIG IDEA Ask students to explain how to use multiple strategies to solve problems.

JOURNAL Suggest that students list the strategies they used for each exercise. They may also want to look back at other problem-solving lessons. Have them use this information as examples in their journal entry.

LESSON QUIZ

1. Find the sum of all the odd numbers from 1 to 99.   **2,500**

2. The dart board has score zones of 0, 5, 15, 25, and 35. How many ways can you score 50 points with 4 throws?   **5**

3. *Navigation* Suppose you launched a raft on the Ohio River at Pittsburgh, Pennsylvania. Your raft drifted at a steady 3 miles per hour for 9 hours less than exactly 2 weeks. When your raft landed at Cairo, Illinois, you had traveled the entire length of the Ohio River. How long is the river?
   981 mi

4. *Statistics* There are 48 members of the band. Of these, 10 are left-handed and 19 wear eyeglasses. There are 27 members who are *not* left-handed and who do *not* wear eyeglasses. How many left-handed members wear eyeglasses?
   8 band members

5. *Weather* A pilot left Helena, Montana. The thermometer outside her plane showed a temperature rise of 100 degrees on her way to Houston, Texas. She then went on to Marshall, Minnesota, where she saw a 71-degree drop. When she reached Portland, Maine, the temperature was 12 degrees, a full 14 degrees warmer than Marshall. What was the temperature in Helena that morning?   **−31°F**

6. *Customer Service* Suppose a customer would like no more than 6 one-dollar bills in change. In how many different ways can you give change from a $100 bill for a $79 purchase?
   6 different ways

7. *Biology* Suppose the average blink of an eye takes $\frac{1}{5}$ of a second, and you blink 25 times per minute. You traveled at an average speed of 50 miles per hour for 12 hours. How many miles would you have traveled with your eyes closed?
   50 miles

8. *Geometry* Suppose you have a 4-cm stick and an 8-cm stick. You want to use a third stick to form a triangle. What whole-number lengths (in centimeters) can you use?
   5 cm, 6 cm, 7 cm, 8 cm, 9 cm, 10 cm, 11 cm

JOURNAL
Which problem solving strategies have you found most useful? Give examples to explain your answer.

Mixed Review

9–13. Answers may vary. Samples are given.

Estimate using rounding or compatible numbers. *(Lesson 4-1)*

9. $90.88 \div 14.2$
   6

10. 6.7×4.1
    28

11. 26.50×4
    108

12. $1.03 \div 0.3$
    3

13. 7.6×5.1
    40

Complete. *(Lesson 6-10)*

14. 3 gal = ▓ pt
    24

15. 6 lb = ▓ oz
    96

16. 11 ft = ▓ in.
    132

17. 12 yd = ▓ ft
    36

18. 3 T = ▓ lb
    6,000

19. *Choose a Strategy* Two numbers have a sum of 34 and a product of 273. What are the two numbers?   **21 and 13**

1 Focus

CONNECTING TO PRIOR KNOWLEDGE
Draw this table on the board. Ask students to look for patterns. **Answers may vary. Sample: The numbers in the second column are the numbers from the first column multiplied by 2.**

Input	Output
1	2
2	4
3	6
4	8
5	10

2 Teach

THINK AND DISCUSS

DIVERSITY Students from other countries may call soccer or rugby "football." Encourage students to share how aspects of these games are similar to and different from American football. Ask students explain a field goal.

DATA ANALYSIS Connection

10-6 Graphing Functions

What You'll Learn

▼ To make a function table
▼ To graph functions

...And Why

You can use functions to solve problems involving sports, time, and wages.

Here's How

Look for questions that
⊟ build understanding
✔ check understanding

THINK AND DISCUSS

▼ Making Function Tables

Sometimes one set of data depends on another. This kind of relationship is called a **function.**

In football, for example, the number of points scored by field goals is a function of the number of field goals kicked. The table shows the points scored for different numbers of field goals.

Input (Field Goals)	Output (Points)
1	3
2	6
3	9
4	12
5	▪

A table like the one above is called a **function table.** It shows the *input* and the *output* of the function. The input is the number of field goals and the output is the number of points.

1. **a.** You can describe the relationship between field goals and points as *number of field goals* × 3 = *number of points*. What is the output for an input of 5 field goals? **15 points**
   b. How many field goals would be needed to score 21 points? **7 field goals**

■ **EXAMPLE 1**   *Real-World Problem Solving*

You can describe the relationship between hours and minutes as *number of hours* × 60 = *number of minutes*. Each hour equals 60 minutes. Make a function table for minutes as a function of hours.

Multiply each input by 60 to get each output.

Input (hours)	Output (minutes)
1	60
2	120
3	180
4	240
5	300

Lesson Planning Options

Prerequisite Skills

- making tables (1-2)
- writing variable expressions (2-5)

Vocabulary/Symbols

function, function table, input, output

Resources

📖 **Student Edition**

Skills Handbook, p. 540
Extra Practice, p. 531
Glossary/Study Guide

🗂 **Teaching Resources**

Chapter Support File, Ch. 10
- Lesson Planner 10-6
- Practice 10-6, Reteaching 10-6
- Alternative Activity 10-6
- Answer Masters 10-6
Teaching Aids Masters 1, 2, 4, 19
Glossary, Spanish Resources

📽 **Transparencies**
1–3, 9, Minds on Math 10-6

Warm Up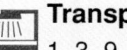

Write each number that makes these number sentences true.
(6 × 7) − ▪ = 35 **7**
23 − ▪ = 23 **0**
9 + ▪ = 21 **12**
8 × ▪ = 56 **7**

457

OPEN-ENDED Question 3b Suggest that students look at advertisements for music stores to help them make realistic estimations of the cost of the CDs and CD player.

CONNECTION TO PATTERNS Have students predict the wages for 5 h and 7 h of work. **$25; $35**

■ **ADDITIONAL EXAMPLES**

FOR EXAMPLE 1

Make a function table for days as a function of weeks.

Input (weeks)	Output (days)
1	7
2	14
3	21
4	28
5	35

FOR EXAMPLE 2

Suppose you earn $6 an hour. Graph the function. Then use the graph to find the wages you would earn for 7 hours of work. **Check students' work. $42**

ASSESSMENT Ask students to graph the field goal function. Draw the correct graph on the board so students can check their work. Ask: *How many field goals would you need to make to score at least 20 points?* **7** Have students discuss how they found their answers.

Technology Options

Prentice Hall Technology

  Software for Learners
- Math Blaster® Mystery*
- Interactive Student Tutorial, Chapter 10*

  Teaching Resource Software
- Computer Item Generator 10-6
- Resource Pro™ Chapter 10*

Internet • For related mathematics activities, visit the Prentice Hall site at www.phschool.com/math

Available on CD-ROM only

Assignment Options for Exercises On Your Own

To provide flexible scheduling, this lesson can be split into parts.

▼**Core** 1–7
Extension 11

▼**Core** 8–10, 14
Extension 15, 16

Use Mixed Review to maintain skills.

2. ✔ *Try It Out* Each day equals 24 hours. Make a function table for hours as a function of days. **See left.**

Now you may assign Exercises 1–7, 11.

2.

Input (days)	Output (hours)
1	24
2	48
3	72
4	96
5	120

5.

Input (touchdowns)	Output (points)
1	6
2	12
3	18
4	24
5	30

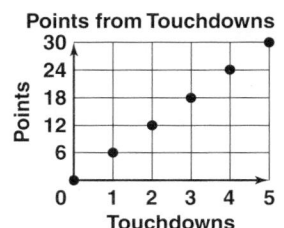

Points from Touchdowns

❷ Graphing Functions

You can graph the input and output of a function. You can extend the graph to find other values of the function.

■ **EXAMPLE 2** *Real-World Problem Solving*

Jobs Wages are a function of the number of hours you work. Suppose you earn $5 per hour. Graph the function. Then use the graph to find the wages you would earn for 6 hours.

Input (hours)	1	2	3	4
Output (dollars)	5	10	15	20

←— Make a table.

Draw the points and a line.

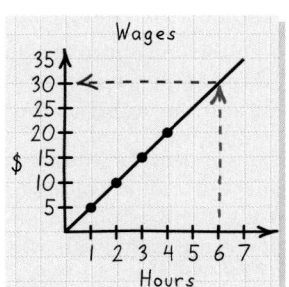

Mark the point on the line that represents 6 hours.

Through this point, draw a horizontal line that intersects the vertical axis.

You would earn $30 for 6 hours.

3. a. ▪*Patterns* Does the result $30 for 6 hours of work fit the pattern in the table? Explain. **Yes; output is 5 × input.**
   b. ▪*Open-ended* Use the graph above. Estimate how many hours you would need to work to purchase a CD player and 3 CDs. Explain your estimation.
   Check students' work.

4. ▪*Algebra* Let *h* stand for the number of hours worked. Write a variable expression that represents your wages in Example 2. **5h**

5. ✔ *Try It Out* Each touchdown in football scores 6 points. Make a function table and a graph to show points as a function of touchdowns. **See left.**

458

Work Together

ERROR ALERT! Question 6a Students may fail to include the $2 discount in their expression. **Remediation:** Suggest students carefully read the question, then restate it in their own words. Suggest that they use parentheses in their expressions. For example, they could write $(n \times 9) - 2$.

3 Practice/Assess

EXERCISES *On Your Own*

Exercises 1–3 If you have block scheduling or extended class periods, you may wish to have students graph the functions using a graphing calculator or spreadsheet program.

CONNECTION TO MEASUREMENT
Exercises 4–7 Have students make function tables for other measurement conversions such as cups as a function of pints.

WRITING Exercise 11 Draw the following table on the board. Ask several students for their age and the day of the month they were born. Sample:

Age	Day of the Month Born
11	3
10	7
11	15

Ask students: *Do the data in the second column of this table depend on the data in the first column?* **no** *Is this a function table?* **no**

Work Together

Graphing Functions

Work with a partner to copy and complete the table below.

6. Sporty Goods sells T-shirts for $9 each. There is no shipping charge. Better still, you have a coupon that gives you $2 off the total.

a. ⬛*Algebra* Let *n* stand for the number of T-shirts you order. Write an expression to represent the final price for T-shirts purchased at Sporty Goods. $9n - 2$

b. Make a prediction for the final price of 7 T-shirts. $61

c. Graph the data in the table to check your predictions.

Sporty Goods

Number of T-shirts	Final Price ($)
1	7
2	⬛
3	⬛
4	⬛

6c.

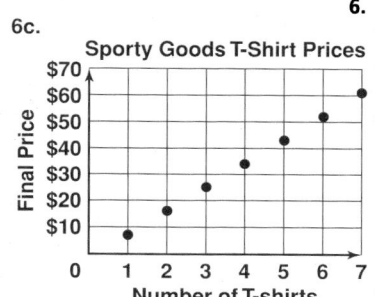

Sporty Goods T-Shirt Prices

Now you may assign Exercises 8–10, 12–16.

EXERCISES *On Your Own*

Complete each function table.

1.

Input	Output
1	4
2	8
3	12
4	⬛
5	⬛

16; 20

2.

Input	Output
3	5
4	6
5	7
6	⬛
7	⬛

8; 9

3.

Input	Output
10	30
15	45
20	60
25	⬛
30	⬛

75; 90

Measurement **Make a function table for each function.**
4–7. See margin.

4. feet as a function of yards

5. inches as a function of feet

6. months as a function of years

7. centimeters as a function of meters

Graph each function.
8–9. See margin.

8.

Hours	Wages
1 h	$7
2 h	$14
3 h	$21
4 h	$28

9.

Time	Distance
5 min	15 mi
6 min	18 mi
7 min	21 mi
8 min	24 mi

10. 10. See margin p. 460.

Correct Answers	Score
12 answers	60 points
13 answers	65 points
14 answers	70 points
15 answers	75 points

pages 459–461 On Your Own

4.

Input (yd)	Output (ft)
1	3
2	6
3	9
4	12
5	15

5.

Input (ft)	Output (in.)
1	12
2	24
3	36
4	48
5	60

6.

Input (yr)	Output (mo)
1	12
2	24
3	36
4	48
5	60

7.

Input (m)	Output (cm)
1	100
2	200
3	300
4	400
5	500

8.

Wages vs. Hours graph

9.

Distance vs. Time graph

Students will want to come up with other examples for their answers.

VISUAL LEARNING and CONNECTION TO GEOMETRY Exercise 14 To check their answers, have students sketch polygons with 6 and 7 sides and draw the diagonals.

EXTENSION Ask students to choose a number greater than 7. Then use the table in Exercise 14 to predict the number of triangles within a polygon with this number of sides. They can check their predictions by sketching.

TACTILE LEARNING and CONNECTION TO GEOMETRY Exercise 16 Have students divide their answer for the angle sum of a regular hexagon by 6. Tell them this is the measure of one angle. Then ask students to construct a hexagon with this angle measure using a protractor and a ruler. If they succeed, their answer is correct.

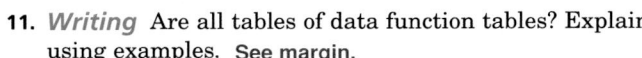

IDENTIFYING THE BIG IDEA Ask students to explain how to make a function table and how to graph functions.

PROJECT LINK Suggest that students make a two-column table with ages in the first column and events related to the age in the second column. The table will help them organize the information before they put it on their time line.

---

pages 459–461   On Your Own

10.

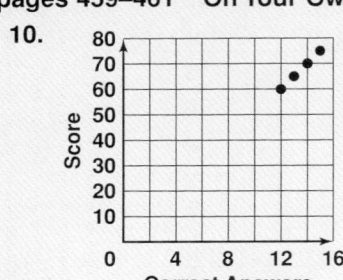

11. No; a table could describe a relation that is not a function. For example, a table listing an inventory of contents of boxes may not be a function.

Box label	Number of items
Books	12
Pencils	1,200
Books	27
Notebooks	84
Postcards	500

14.

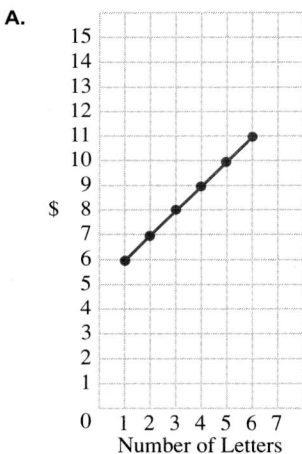

11. *Writing* Are all tables of data function tables? Explain using examples. **See margin.**

12. Use your graphs from Exercises 8–10.
  a. Find the wages for 6 hours. **$42**
  b. Find the distance for 11 minutes. **33 mi**
  c. Find the score for 18 correct answers. **90 points**

13. Choose A, B, or C. Three companies offer to sew your team name RANGERS on your uniforms. Pro Lettering charges $2 per letter. Uniforms-R-Us charges $1 per letter plus a fee of $5. Speedy Lettering charges a flat fee of $15. Which graph shows the fees of the company that would charge you least? (*Hint:* Each graph shows only the cost for 1 to 6 letters.) **A**

A.

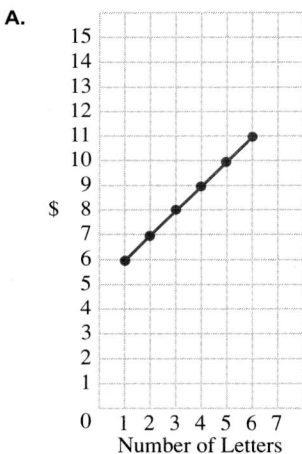

B.

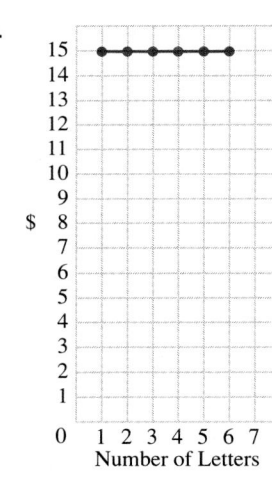

C.

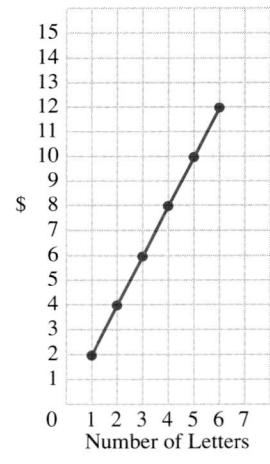

14. *Patterns* You can draw diagonals from one vertex inside a polygon to create triangles. As the number of sides of a polygon increases, the number of triangles you can make also increases. Complete the function table. Then graph the number of triangles within a polygon as a function of the number of sides. **See margin for graph.**

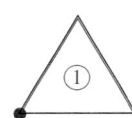 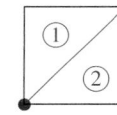 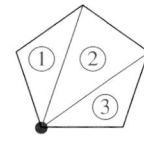 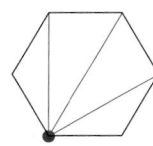

Number of Sides	Number of Triangles
3 sides	1
4 sides	2
5 sides	3
6 sides	▨ 4
7 sides	▨ 5

460

1. Make a function table to show the relationship between minutes and seconds.
Answers may vary. Sample:

Input (min)	Output(s)
2	120
3	180
4	240

2. Graph the function in Exercise 1.

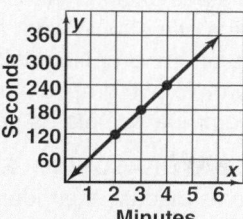

15. *Mail Order* Goalposters sells football kicking tees by mail for $3 each. There is a shipping charge of $5 no matter how many kicking tees you order.
   a. Complete the function table to show the final price for the purchase of two, three, and four tees.
   b. *Writing* Write a word equation that explains the cost of buying any number of football kicking tees by mail.
   The cost of tees is three times the number of tees plus five.

Goalposters

Number of Tees	Final Price ($)
1	8
2	▨ 11
3	▨ 14
4	▨ 17

16. *Geometry* The sum of the measures of the angles of a regular polygon is a function of the number of sides. Complete the function table. Then graph the function.
   See below right for graph.

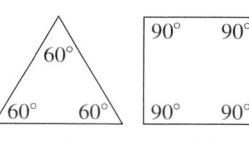 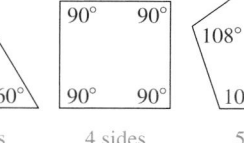 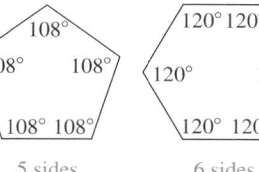

3 sides   4 sides   5 sides   6 sides

Regular Polygons

Number of Sides	Sum of Measures of Angles
3	180°
4	360°
5	540°
6	▨ 720°

Mixed Review

Find the area of each square given its perimeter. (*Lesson 9-2*)

17. 60 cm
225 cm²
18. 19.2 m
23.04 m²
19. 6.8 ft
2.89 ft²
20. 12 m
9 m²
21. $\frac{1}{2}$ ft
$\frac{1}{64}$ ft²
22. 36.4 cm
82.81 cm²

Find each percent. (*Lesson 7-10*)

23. 75% of 36
27
24. 200% of 14
28
25. 25.5% of 115
29.325
26. $33\frac{1}{3}$% of 21
7
27. $6\frac{1}{2}$% of 75
4.875
16.

28. *Choose a Strategy* Two student tickets and one adult ticket to a concert cost $19. One student ticket and three adult tickets cost $29.50. Find the cost of each kind of ticket.
   student ticket: $5.50; adult ticket: $8

Regular Polygons

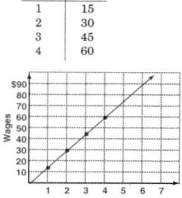

CHAPTER PROJECT
PROJECT LINK: GRAPHING
Make a list of entries for your time line. Include milestones such as learning to walk or crawl. Add events that have shaped who you are, such as making new friends, learning valuable lessons, or gaining new skills or confidence. Place these events on the negative side of your time line.

Check students' work.

PRACTICE

■ Practice 10-6 *Graphing Functions*

Complete each function table.

1.

Input	Output
1	5
2	10
3	15
4	20
5	25

2.

Input	Output
10	20
20	40
30	60
40	80
50	100

3.

Input	Output
3	6
4	7
5	8
6	9
7	10

Make a function table for each function. Samples are shown.

4. ounces as a function of pounds

Pounds	Ounces
1	16
2	32
3	48
4	64

5. pints as a function of cups

Cups	Pints
2	1
4	2
6	3
8	4

6. yards as a function of inches

Inches	Yards
36	1
72	2
108	3
144	4

Graph each function.

7.

Hours	Wages
1	15
2	30
3	45
4	60

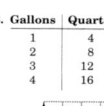

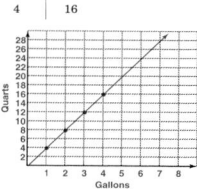

8.

Gallons	Quarts
1	4
2	8
3	12
4	16

9. Use your graphs from Exercises 7–8.
   a. Find the wages for 6 hours. **90**
   b. Find the number of quarts for 7 gallons. **28**

In copymaster and workbook formats

RETEACHING

■ Reteaching 10-6 *Graphing Functions*

A table or a graph can show how the input and output of a **function** are related.

Make a **function table** to show how number of feet is a function of number of yards.

Input (yards)	Output (feet)
1	3
2	6
3	9
4	12
5	15

The table shows that for every yard, there are 3 feet. You multiply the number of yards by 3 to find the number of feet.

Use the values in the table to draw a graph of the function.
① Locate the points from the table:
   (1, 3), (2, 6), (3, 9), (4, 12), (5, 15)
② Draw a line through the points.

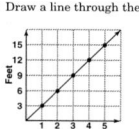

Complete each function table.

1.

Input	Output
1	4
2	5
3	6
4	7
5	8

2.

Input	Output
4	2
6	4
8	6
10	8
12	10

3.

Input	Output
2	10
3	15
4	20
5	25
6	30

Make a function table for each function. Then graph the function.

4. cups as a function of quarts

Quarts	Cups
1	4
2	8
3	12
4	16

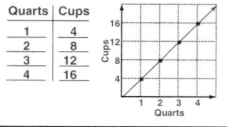

5. days as a function of weeks

Weeks	Days
1	7
2	14
3	21
4	28

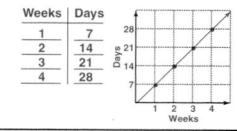

ENRICHMENT

Minds on Math Transparency

10-6

I am a fraction. My numerator is 3 less than my denominator. My reciprocal is 4 times my value. What fraction am I?

$\frac{3}{6}$

See Solution Key for worked-out answers.

In Lesson 10-6, students learned how to make a function table and to graph functions. This toolbox shows students how to graph equations on a graphing calculator.

ERROR ALERT! At first, students may be confused by the steps involved in graphing on a graphing calculator. **Remediation:** Pair students so that each student can work with a partner on the first four exercises. Students should use the steps given in the Example as their model. Each pair should work together to follow the steps on the graphing calculator and then make their own graphs individually. Partners can compare completed graphs.

ASSESSMENT and REASONING Exercise
18 Have students discuss their ideas in small groups. Students should give reasons for their ideas, and each group should reach a common conclusion.

Materials/Manipulatives

• graphing calculator
• graph paper

page 462   Math Toolbox

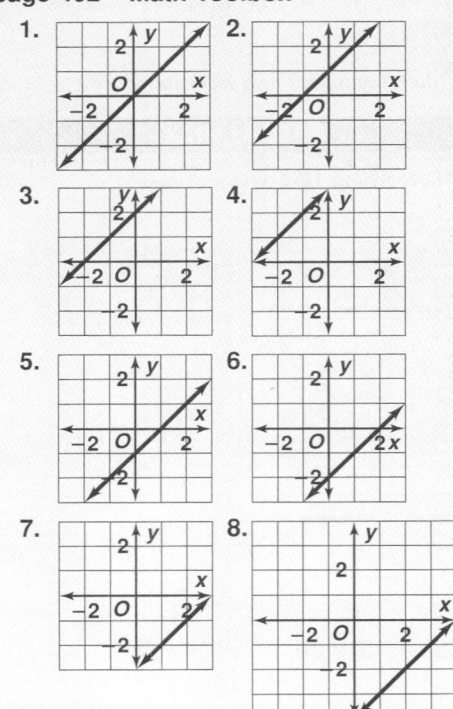

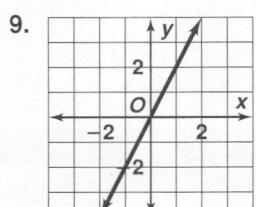

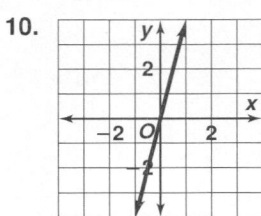

462

TECHNOLOGY

Using a Graphing Calculator

After Lesson 10-6

A graphing calculator makes it easy to graph equations.

Start by finding the **ON** key. Then find **CLEAR**. This key clears, or erases, the numbers on the calculator screen. **ENTER** is used to enter data and commands.

■ EXAMPLE

Use a graphing calculator to graph $y = x + 2$.

Press **Y=** . Your screen should look like the one at the right.

Press **X,T,θ** **+** **2** **ENTER** to enter the equation.

Press **ZOOM** and select **ZStandard** to view the graph in the standard viewing window. You can select other commands from the **ZOOM** menu to zoom in and out.

Press **GRAPH** to display the graph. If your graph does not look like the one at the right, ask for help.

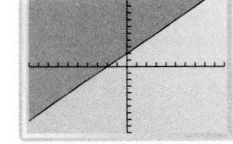

Use a graphing calculator to graph each equation. Sketch each graph on graph paper.

1–10. See margin.
11–16. See back of book.

1. $y = x$ **2.** $y = x + 1$ **3.** $y = x + 2$ **4.** $y = x + 3$

5. $y = x - 1$ **6.** $y = x - 2$ **7.** $y = x - 3$ **8.** $y = x - 4$

9. $y = 2x$ **10.** $y = 4x$ **11.** $y = 6x$ **12.** $y = 8x$

13. $y = 3x + 1$ **14.** $y = 5x - 2$ **15.** $y = 4x + 2$ **16.** $y = 2x - 4$

17. a. Look at your graphs for Exercises 1–4. What happens to the graph as the number that is added increases? **The graph shifts up.**

   b. Look at your graphs for Exercises 5–8. What happens when the number that is subtracted increases? **The graph shifts down.**

18. *Reasoning* Look at your graphs for Exercises 9–12. The number multiplied by x is called its *coefficient*. What happens to the graph as the coefficient changes? **The graph becomes steeper for larger coefficients and shallower for smaller ones.**

1 Focus

CONNECTING TO PRIOR KNOWLEDGE Ask students: *How do you locate a city or street using the index on a map?* **Answers may vary. Sample: The index gives you the coordinates of cities and streets.** Ask students to describe other grid systems.

2 Teach

Work Together

Remind students that they can use a grid system similar to those used on maps. Encourage them to ask specific questions about the length, width, and direction of the line segments in their partner's figure. Suggest students draw the figure on grid paper as they get the answers to their questions.

AEP To make sure students understand their partner's questions, have them repeat the questions in their own words.

THINK AND DISCUSS

ERROR ALERT! Question 7 Some students may not realize that quadrants are labeled in a counter-clockwise direction. Remind students that counter-clockwise means in the opposite direction to that of a clock.

GEOMETRY Connection

 **10-7**

Graphing on the Coordinate Plane

What You'll Learn

▼ To use a coordinate plane to graph points

▼ To name the coordinates of points and the quadrants of the coordinate plane

...And Why

The coordinate plane allows you to graph data so you can see trends and tendencies.

Here's How

Look for questions that
▪ build understanding
✓ check understanding

Work Together

Exploring Coordinates

Work with a partner. You need rubber bands and two geoboards. Agree on a system for locating points on the geoboard.

1. *Geometry* Create a figure on a geoboard with a rubber band. Don't let your partner see the figure you have created!

2. Your partner should ask questions about each line segment of your figure. Answer each question using your location system.

3. Your partner tries to guess the shape and to duplicate it on a geoboard. Compare your partner's version to your own.

4. ▪*Analyze* Switch roles and repeat the activity. Were the guesses accurate? Why or why not?
   1–4. **Check students' work.**

THINK AND DISCUSS

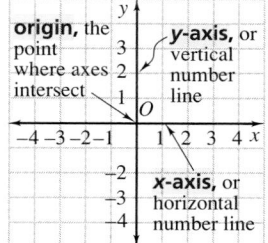

▼ *Graphing Points*

You can identify points by using a coordinate plane. The **coordinate plane** is formed by the intersection of two number lines.

```
origin, the                    y-axis, or
point                          vertical
where axes                     number
intersect                      line

    -4 -3 -2 -1   1  2  3  4  x

                   x-axis, or
                   horizontal
                   number line
```

Lesson Planning Options

Prerequisite Skills
- graphing integers on a number line (10-1)

Vocabulary/Symbols
coordinate plane, origin, *y*-axis, *x*-axis, coordinates, ordered pair, *x*-coordinate, *y*-coordinate, quadrants

Materials/Manipulatives
- rubber bands
- ruler
- geoboards
- graph paper

Resources

 Student Edition

Skills Handbook, p. 537
Extra Practice, p. 531
Glossary/Study Guide

 Teaching Resources

Chapter Support File, Ch. 10
- Lesson Planner 10-7
- Practice 10-7, Reteaching 10-7
- Answer Masters 10-7
Teaching Aids Masters 1, 2, 4, 19
Glossary, Spanish Resources

 **Transparencies**
1–3, 9, 97, Minds on Math 10-7

Warm Up

Solve the equation:
$-4 + y = 2.$ $y = 6$

REASONING Questions 8 and 9 Have students draw a coordinate plane and label *x*- and *y*-coordinates in each quadrant.

TACTILE LEARNING Example 1 Have students use an index finger to trace 3 units to the *right* of the origin on the *x*-axis. Then have students trace 2 units down from that point. The point is at (3, −2).

■ **ADDITIONAL EXAMPLES**

FOR EXAMPLE 1
Graph point *E* with coordinates (−2, 1).

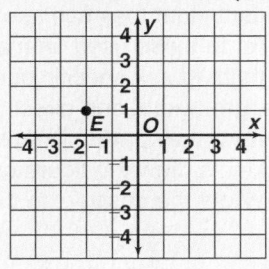

FOR EXAMPLE 2
Find the coordinates of point *R*. (3, −3)

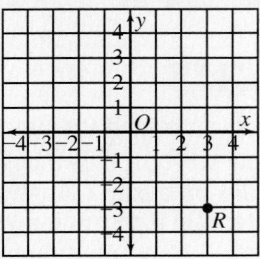

Technology Options

Prentice Hall Technology

  Software for Learners

- Hot Page™ 29*
- Math Blaster® Mystery*
- Interactive Student Tutorial, Chapter 10*

  Teaching Resource Software

- Computer Item Generator 10-7
- Resource Pro™ Chapter 10*

Internet • For related mathematics activities, visit the Prentice Hall site at www.phschool.com/math

*Available on CD-ROM only

Assignment Options for Exercises On Your Own

To provide flexible scheduling, this lesson can be split into parts.

▼**1 Core** 1–16
  Extension 18–20

▼**2 Core** 7–17, 21–30, 34
  Extension 31–33, 35–38

Use Mixed Review to maintain skills.

You can graph points on a coordinate plane. Each point has 2 *coordinates*, which form an **ordered pair.**

The *x-coordinate* tells how far to move left or right along the *x*-axis. $(-2, 4)$ The *y-coordinate* tells how far to move up or down along the *y*-axis.

The coordinates (0, 0) describe the origin. You move *left* from the origin to graph a negative *x*-coordinate. You move *down* from the origin to graph a negative *y*-coordinate.

■ **EXAMPLE 1**

Graph point *A* with coordinates (3, −2).

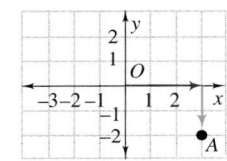

Move **3** units to the **right** from the origin.

Move **2** units **down** from the *x*-axis.

Draw a point and label it *A*.

5a–d.

5. ✔*Try It Out* Graph each point on a coordinate plane.
  a. $(-4, -4)$ **b.** $(-3, 1)$ **c.** $(1, -2)$ **d.** $(0, 5)$

Now you may assign Exercises 1–6, 18–20.

❷ *Naming Coordinates and Quadrants*

You can name the coordinates of points that are already graphed.

WHAT? A *scatter plot* is a graph of data from two different sets. The two sets of data are plotted as ordered pairs.

■ **EXAMPLE 2**   *Real-World Problem Solving*

Dogs Find the coordinates of point *B* on the scatter plot.

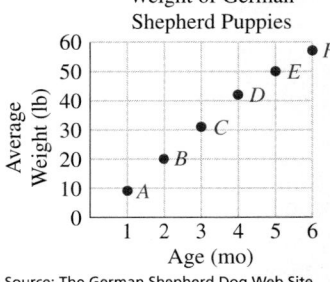

Start at the origin.

Move 2 units to the right. The first coordinate is 2.

Then move up from the *x*-axis. The second coordinate is 20.

The coordinates of point *B* are (2, 20).

ASSESSMENT Before students do Try It Out problems, have them work in pairs to write one coordinate pair for each quadrant of a coordinate plane. **Answers may vary. Sample: I: (2, 2); II: (−5, 4); III (−2, −2); IV (5, −6)**

EXTENSION Suggest students work in groups to create a map that shows their school and surrounding buildings. Some students may want to make a map of the neighborhood where they live. Have students make a grid system for each map.

3 Practice/Assess

EXERCISES *On Your Own*

ERROR ALERT! Some students may graph an *x*-coordinate on the *y*-axis or vice versa. For example, they may incorrectly graph G (−4, 1) as G (1, −4). **Remediation:** Remind students that the first coordinate is the *x*-coordinate, and the second coordinate is the *y*-coordinate. Tell students that *x* comes first in an ordered pair just as it comes first in

the alphabet. Ask students to think of the origin as a landmark at (0, 0) and to graph all points as a distance away from that landmark.

AUDITORY LEARNING Exercises 18 and 19 Suggest students work in pairs. One student reads out one pair of coordinates. The partner graphs them on a coordinate plane. Partners switch roles for the next pair.

b. quadrilateral or parallelogram

c. Parallelogram; the sides of the parallelogram are not congruent to each other and the angles are not congruent to each other.

6. ✔*Try It Out* Find the coordinates of points *C*, *D*, and *E* on the scatter plot. **(3, 31); (4, 42); (5, 50)**

The coordinate plane has four *quadrants*.

7. In which quadrant is the point *M*(−2, 5) located? **II**

8. ⬛*Reasoning* In which quadrants are the *x*-coordinates of the points positive numbers? **I and IV**

9. ⬛*Reasoning* In which quadrants are the *y*-coordinates of the points negative numbers? **III and IV**

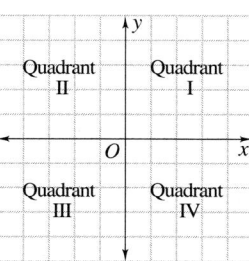

On Your Own
1–6.

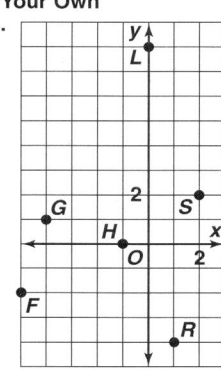

Now you may assign Exercises 7–17, 21–38.

EXERCISES *On Your Own*

Graph each labeled point on a coordinate plane. **See above.**

1. *G*(−4, 1)   2. *R*(1, −4)   3. *L*(0, 8)   4. *F*(−5, −2)   5. *S*(2, 2)   6. *H*(−1, 0)

Name the point with the given coordinates.

7. (1, 2)   8. (−2, −6)   9. (3, −3)   10. (0, −5)   11. (3, 0)
   A   *G*   *J*   *H*   *L*

Write the coordinates of each point.

12. *C*   13. *D*   14. *K*   15. *Q*   16. *N*
    (−6, 4)   (−5, 0)   (6, −4)   (0, 3)   (4, 6)

17. Point *M* is at (6, 4). Which point has opposite coordinates? **F**

18. a. Graph the points *M*(−5, −3), *N*(2, −4), and *P*(0, 1) on a coordinate plane. **See right.**
    b. *Geometry* Connect the points in order. What shape do you see? **triangle**

19. a. Graph the points *A*(4, 3), *B*(−1, 3), *C*(−4, 0), and *D*(1, 0).
    b. Connect the points in order. What shape do you see?
    c. *Geometry* What is the most specific name you can use to describe figure *ABCD*? Explain.

19a–c. See margin.

20. *Language* Why do you think the point where the *x*-axis and *y*-axis intersect is called the *origin*? **Answers may vary. Sample: *Origin* means *beginning*, and the origin is the point where the coordinate system begins.**

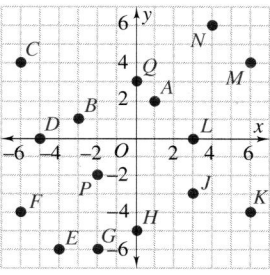

18a.

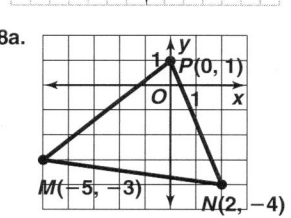

CONNECTION TO GEOGRAPHY Suggest that students choose four major cities to locate on a world map. Have students find the degrees of longitude and latitude for each city. Ask: *Which is similar to an x-coordinate, the latitude or longitude?* **the longitude** *Which is similar to a y-coordinate?* **the latitude**

RESEARCH **Exercise 32** Ask students to explain why they have to estimate the latitude and longitude of some locations. **The latitude and longitude have to be estimated when the location is not exactly on a grid line.**

WRITING and VISUAL LEARNING **Exercise 33** Ask students to make a map from a coordinate plane. Have them write directions to find a place on the map.

OPEN–ENDED **Exercise 35** Ask students how they could use coordinate points to describe patterns.

WRAP UP

IDENTIFYING THE BIG IDEA Ask students to explain how to graph points on a coordinate plane.

CHECKPOINT 2

Checkpoint 2   Lessons 10-4 through 10-7

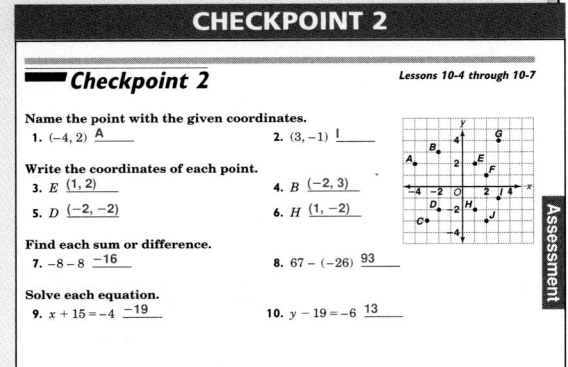

Name the point with the given coordinates.
1. (−4, 2) **A**
2. (3, −1) **I**

Write the coordinates of each point.
3. E **(1, 2)**
4. B **(−2, 3)**
5. D **(−2, −2)**
6. H **(1, −2)**

Find each sum or difference.
7. −8 − 8 **−16**
8. 67 − (−26) **93**

Solve each equation.
9. x + 15 = −4 **−19**
10. y − 19 = −6 **13**

Assessment

pages 465–467   On Your Own

33. **Answers may vary. Sample: Each uses coordinates to locate points; maps do not use negative coordinates.**

34. **(2, 0), (2, 1), (4, 1), (4, 0), (6, 2), (5, 2), (5, 4), (6, 4), (4, 6), (4, 5), (2, 5), (2, 6), (0, 4), (1, 4), (1, 2), (0, 2)**

Identify the quadrant in which each point lies.

21. (3, 2)   **I**
22. (−17, 2)   **II**
23. (−6, −40) **III**
24. (9, −11)   **IV**
25. (−1, 100) **II**
26. (38, 38)   **I**

27. **Choose A, B, C, or D.** Which point is in Quadrant IV? **B**
   A. (−2, 2)   B. (2, −2)   C. (−2, −2)   D. (2, 2)

28. In which quadrant are all coordinates positive? **I**

29. What are the signs for the x-coordinates and the y-coordinates for all the points in the second quadrant? **The x-coordinates are negative; the y-coordinates are positive.**

30. Three corners of a rectangle have coordinates (4, 2), (4, 7), and (−3, 2). Find the coordinates of the fourth corner. **(−3, 7)**

Where on Earth Are You?

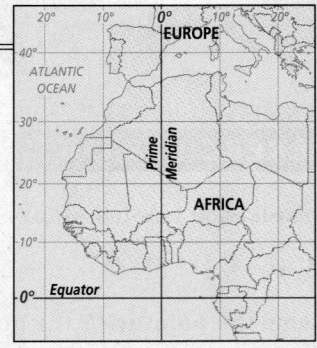

HOW CAN YOU TELL SOMEONE ELSE WHERE YOU ARE ON EARTH? Geographers have given Earth a coordinate system so that locations can be described easily. Imagine a coordinate plane wrapped around the planet. The equator is the "horizontal axis" and the prime meridian is the "vertical axis."

Distances on Earth's coordinate system are measured in *degrees*. Degrees north or south of the equator are called *degrees of latitude*. Degrees east or west of the prime meridian are called *degrees of longitude*.

31. Refer to the article above. On what continent is the location 30° N latitude, 20° E longitude? On what continent is 40° N latitude, 20° E longitude? **Africa; Europe**

32. *Research* Use a map to locate your town to the nearest degree of latitude and nearest degree of longitude. **Check students' work.**

33. *Writing* How are a map and the coordinate plane alike? How are they different? **See margin.**

Crafts **Some quilt makers use coordinate grids to plan their patterns before they stitch their quilts.**

34. The Monkey Wrench pattern shown at right is from an African American story quilt. Find the coordinates of the pattern points. **See margin.**

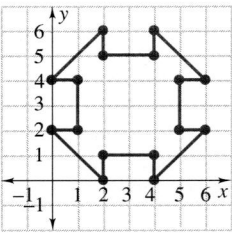

35. *Open-ended* Create your own quilt pattern. Draw the pattern on a grid and name the coordinates of the points. **Check students' work.**

466

1. Graph point *E* with the coordinates (0, −3).

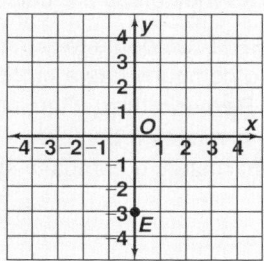

Write the coordinates of each point.

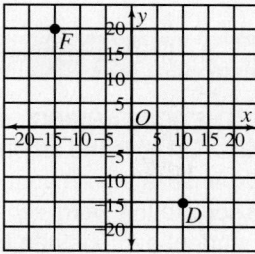

2. *D* (10, −15)

3. *F* (−15, 20)

Geography **Map makers use a coordinate system. On many maps, coordinates refer to a rectangular area of the map, instead of a specific point.**

36. What do the letters A−C identify? What do the numbers 1−7 identify? **See below right.**

37. What is located in section B3? **City Hall**

38. What are the coordinates of the school and its nearby playing fields? **C4, C5, and C6**

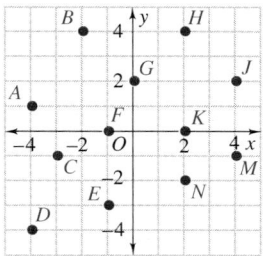

36. A–C identify the vertical location of each square on the map; 1–7 identify the horizontal location of each square.

Mixed Review

Classify the triangle with the given side lengths as scalene, isosceles, or equilateral. *(Lesson 8-4)*

39. 4 m, 4 m, 4m
equilateral

40. 2 ft, 8 ft, $8\frac{1}{2}$ ft
scalene

41. 7 m, 24m, 25m
scalene

42. 4 in., 3 in., 4 in.
isosceles

Evaluate each expression for $x = 8$. *(Lesson 2-4)*

43. $3x - 2$
22

44. x^2
64

45. $2x + 10$
26

46. $0.5x$
4

47. $12 \div x$
1.5

48. $4x$
32

49. Norma bought a bicycle for $126.90 at a store having a $\frac{1}{3}$-off sale. What was the bike's original price? *(Lessons 7-4 and 7-10)* **$190.35**

✓ CHECKPOINT 2

Lessons 10-4 through 10-7

Name the point with the given coordinates.

1. (−1, −3) **E**   **2.** (0, 2) **G**   **3.** (2, −2) **N**   **4.** (−4, 1) **A**

Write the coordinates of each point.

5. *J* (4, 2)   **6.** *M* (4, −1)   **7.** *B* (−2, 4)   **8.** *F* (−1, 0)

9. *D* (−4, −4)   **10.** *H* (2, 4)   **11.** *C* (−3, −1)   **12.** *K* (2, 0)

Find each sum or difference.

13. −10 − 10 −20

14. −215 + 343 128

15. 451 − (−134) 585

16. −1,035 − 961
−1,996

PRACTICE

Practice 10-7 *Graphing on the Coordinate Plane*

Name the point with the given coordinates.

1. (2, 3) B   **2.** (−4, 0) F
3. (−3, −5) I   **4.** (0, 6) H
5. (3, 5) L   **6.** (4, 0) K

Write the coordinates of each point.

7. *J* (3, −5)   **8.** *E* (0, 4)
9. *D* (3, 2)   **10.** *A* (6, 0)
11. *G* (−3, 2)   **12.** *C* (−2, 3)

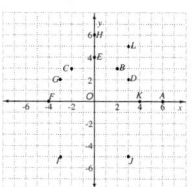

Identify the quadrant in which each point lies.

13. (8, −4) IV   **14.** (−4, 8) II   **15.** (4, 8) I
16. (−8, −4) III   **17.** (8, 4) I   **18.** (−4, −8) III

Use the coordinate plane below.

19. Graph four points on the coordinate plane so that when the points are connected in order, the shape is a rectangle. List the coordinates of the points.
Answers will vary. Sample shown.

20. Graph four points on the coordinate plane so that when the points are connected in order, the shape is a parallelogram that is not a rectangle. List the coordinates of the points.
Answers will vary. Sample shown.

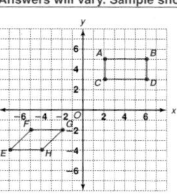

In copymaster and workbook formats

RETEACHING

Reteaching 10-7 *Graphing on the Coordinate Plane*

Graph (2, −4).
• 2 is the *x-coordinate*. It tells how far to move left or right from the origin.
• −4 is the *y-coordinate*. It tells how far to move up or down from the origin.

Find the coordinates of point *A*.
① Start at the origin.
② How far left or right? *3 left*
The *x-coordinate* is −3.
③ How far up or down? *5 up*
The *y-coordinate* is 5.
The coordinates of point *A* are (−3, 5).

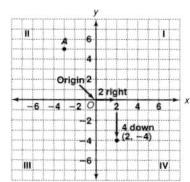

The **coordinate plane** has four **quadrants**, I, II, III, IV as shown above.

Graph each point on a coordinate plane.
Label the point with its letter.

1. *B* (1, 6)   **2.** *C* (−4, −3)
3. *D* (0, 5)   **4.** *E* (−2, 2)
5. *F* (−1, −5)   **6.** *G* (6, −4)
7. *H* (5, 5)   **8.** *J* (4, 0)
9. *K* (−4, −4)   **10.** *L* (2, −3)
11. *M* (−2, 0)   **12.** *N* (5, −1)
13. *P* (0, −3)   **14.** *Q* (−4, 0)

Write the coordinates of each point.

15. *R* (4, −1)   **16.** *S* (−3, 5)
17. *T* (0, 1)   **18.** *U* (−3, −2)

Identify the quadrant in which each point lies.

19. (−3, −7) III   **20.** (4, −4) IV   **21.** (−5, 19) II
22. (6, 23) I   **23.** (−9, −21) III   **24.** (−16, 8) II

ENRICHMENT

Minds on Math Transparency

10-7

Margie made corn muffins. Her family ate $\frac{1}{3}$ of them. She then gave $\frac{1}{4}$ of the remaining muffins to her neighbors and put the rest in the freezer. If she put 9 muffins in the freezer, how many muffins did she make?

18 muffins

See *Solution Key* for worked-out answers.

467

1 Focus

CONNECTING TO PRIOR KNOWLEDGE Ask students how they keep track of the money they receive and spend. Ask: *How do you think businesses keep track of their income and expenses? What kind of records do they need to keep?* Have students discuss their answers.

Lesson Planning Options

Prerequisite Skills
- adding integers (10-3)
- subtracting integers (10-4)

Vocabulary/Symbols
balance, profit, loss

Materials/Manipulatives
- calculator
- computer
- graph paper
- ruler
- spreadsheet software

Resources

 Student Edition

Teaching Resources

Chapter Support File, Ch. 10
- Lesson Planner 10-8
- Practice 10-8, Reteaching 10-8
- Answer Masters 10-8

Teaching Aids Masters 1, 2, 4, 19

Glossary, Spanish Resources

 Transparencies
1–3, 9, Minds on Math 10-8

Warm Up

Calculate the interest if you borrow $200 for 2 yr at a simple interest rate of 12% per year. **$48**

---

2 Teach

THINK AND DISCUSS

AEP **KINESTHETIC LEARNING** Help students remember that *income* is the amount of money coming in. *Expense* is the amount of money going out. Associate the word *expense* with exit. Have a student demonstrate by coming into the classroom while saying "income," then exiting while saying "expenses."

AUDITORY LEARNING **Question 1** Suggest that students say the numbers and operation signs aloud as they press the calculator keys.

ERROR ALERT! Students may incorrectly decide that a company has a profit when it has a loss. **Remediation:** Remind students that income is money a company receives, expenses are money a company spends.

DATA ANALYSIS Connection

10-8 Applying Integers and Graphs

What You'll Learn
1. To find profit and loss
2. To draw and interpret graphs involving integers

...And Why
You can use profit and loss and graphs to solve business problems.

Here's How
Look for questions that
- build understanding
- check understanding

THINK AND DISCUSS

1 Finding Profit and Loss

Businesses keep track of the money they receive (income) and the money they spend (expenses). The *balance* is the company's profit or loss.

To find the balance, add the income (positive numbers) and the expenses (negative numbers) together.

positive balance = *profit*   negative balance = *loss*

You can use a calculator and the key to find balances.

■ **EXAMPLE 1**   *Real-World Problem Solving*

Accounting Find Video Mania's profit or loss for February.

Add income to expenses.

12739 ➕ 9482 ± 🟰 *3257*

The balance is positive. So, there is a profit.

Income and Expenses for Video Mania		
Month	Income	Expenses
Jan.	$11,917	−$14,803
Feb.	$12,739	−$9,482
March	$11,775	−$10,954
April	$13,620	−$15,149

Video Mania had a profit of $3,257 for each month.
1a. $2,886 loss

1. ✔*Try It Out* Find the profit or loss for each month.
 a. January   **b.** March   **c.** April
                    $821 profit   **$1,529 loss**

Now you may assign Exercises 1–16, 25–28.

FOR EXAMPLE 1

Ashlie is in charge of the student store at her school. She calculates the expenses and income for the week on Fridays.

	Expenses	Income
Week 1	$120	$92
Week 2	$70	$108
Week 3	$125	$112
Week 4	$85	$128

Use the table to determine the profit or loss for each week. **−$28, loss; $38, profit; −$13, loss; $43, profit**

FOR EXAMPLE 2

Draw a line graph of the weekly balances for the student store.

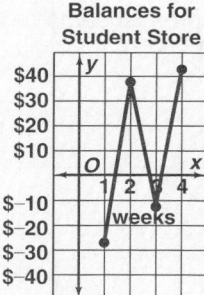
Balances for Student Store

2 *Making a Graph*

Businesses use line graphs to look at the trends of their monthly balances.

■ **EXAMPLE 2**   *Real-World Problem Solving*

Business Draw a line graph of the monthly profits and losses for Hobby & Toy Town.

Income and Expenses for Hobby & Toy Town			
Month	Profit/Loss	Month	Profit/Loss
January	−$1,917	July	$933
February	−$682	August	$1,110
March	$303	September	−$417
April	$781	October	−$824
May	−$150	November	$1,566
June	$250	December	$1,945

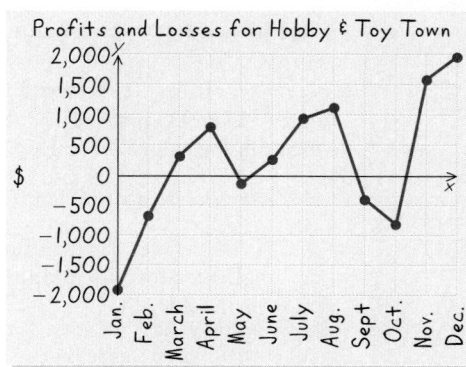

Profits and Losses for Hobby & Toy Town

 Put the dollar amounts on the vertical axis.

 Balances vary from −$1,917 to $1,945. Make a scale from −$2,000 to $2,000. Use intervals of 500.

Put the months on the horizontal axis.

Graph a point for each monthly balance. Connect the points.

2. **⁂***Analyze* In which months was there a profit?
   March, April, June, July, August, November, December
3. In which month did the greatest loss occur? **January**

4. In which month did Hobby & Toy Town come closest to breaking even? **May**

5. Which month's balance showed the greatest change from the previous month? **November**

Prentice Hall Technology

 Software for Learners
- Hot Page™ 30*
- Math Blaster® Mystery*
- Interactive Student Tutorial, Chapter 10*

 Teaching Resource Software
- Computer Item Generator 10-8
- Resource Pro™ Chapter 10*

Internet • For related mathematics activities, visit the Prentice Hall site at www.phschool.com/math

Available on CD-ROM only

Assignment Options for Exercises On Your Own

To provide flexible scheduling, this lesson can be split into parts.

▼**1** **Core** 1–16
   Extension 25–28

▼**2** **Core** 17–23
   Extension 24, 29

Use Mixed Review to maintain skills.

469

FOR EXAMPLE 3

Use a spreadsheet to find the student store's month-to-date profit or loss. Have them formulate the spreadsheet to calculate the month-to-date balance after each week.

	A	B	C	D	E
1	wk 1 bal	wk 2 bal	wk 3 bal	wk 4 bal	month-to-date bal
2	$28			−$28	
3	−$28	$38		$10	
4	−$28	$38	−$13		−$3
5	−$28	$38	−$13	$43	$40

ASSESSMENT Have students summarize how the student store is doing under Ashlie's management. **Answers may vary. Sample: Ashlie is doing a good job. The income increases each week, and the store is making money overall.**

3 Practice/Assess

EXERCISES *On Your Own*

CONNECTION TO BUSINESS If you have block scheduling or extended class periods, you may want to have students research or create business data. Then have them create a spreadsheet for their data.

You can use a spreadsheet program to find profit and loss.

■ **EXAMPLE 3** *Real-World Problem Solving*

▷*Technology* Use a spreadsheet and the data from Example 1 on page 468 to find Video Mania's year-to-date profit or loss for February.

The spreadsheet below calculates the year-to-date balances. Cell E3 shows the combined balances for the first two months, January and February.

	A	B	C	D	E
1	Month	Income	Expenses	Profit/Loss	Year-to-date Profit/Loss
2	January	$11,917	−$14,803	−$2,886	−$2,886
3	February	$12,739	−$9,482	$3,257	$371
4	March	$11,775	−$10,954	$821	$1,192
5	April	$13,620	−$15,149	−$1,529	−$337

Video Mania had a year-to-date profit of $371 for February.

6. ⚏*Think About It* To write the formula for cell E3, enter =E2+D3 into cell E3. How would you write the formula for cell E4? For E5? **= E3 + D4; = E4 + D5**

7. ✔*Try It Out* Copy and complete the spreadsheet above.
See above.

8. ⚏*Data Analysis* Draw a line graph that shows the year-to-date balances for Video Mania for January, February, March, and April. **See left.**

9. ⚏*Summarize* Describe the status of Video Mania, based on its balance for the first four months of the year.

9. Answers may vary. Sample: Video Mania is losing money.

8.

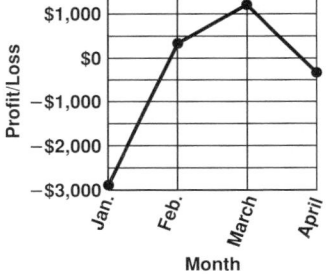

Video Mania Year-to-date Balances

Now you may assign Exercises 17–24, 29.

EXERCISES *On Your Own*

▦ *Calculator* **Use a calculator to find each sum or difference.**

1. −435 + 628 **193**   2. 581 − (−57) **638**   3. −321 − 789 **−1,110**   4. −2,044 − (−1,806) **−238**

5. −212 + 234 **22**   6. 246 − (−38) **284**   7. −459 − 659 **−1,118**   8. −3,265 − (−1,958) **−1,307**

470

ERROR ALERT! **Exercise 4** Students may write the difference as a positive number. **Remediation:** Review the rules for subtracting integers on page 449. Help students see that they can rewrite the problem as $-2044 + 1806$.

VISUAL LEARNING **Exercises 17–22** Some students may find it helpful to sketch a line graph of the data to determine the correct scale and interval for each data set.

WRITING **Exercise 29** Give students grid paper. Suggest that they include an example of each type of graph they describe.

WRAP UP

IDENTIFYING THE BIG IDEA Have students explain how to use income and expenses to determine whether a company makes a profit or loss. Have them explain how to draw and interpret graphs involving integers.

PORTFOLIO Share with students the criteria you will use to assess their work in portfolios, as well as how you plan to use the results. Students should understand how the rubrics are used to assess their work, how each piece in the portfolio counts, and how the scores they get in their portfolios will affect their overall evaluation.

pages 470–471 On Your Own

23b.

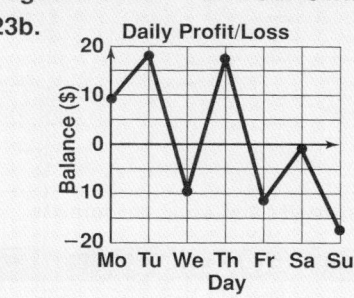

Choose Use a calculator, mental math, or paper and pencil.

9. $-12 + 5$ **−7**   **10.** $38 - 64$ **−26**   **11.** $29 - (-18)$ **47**   **12.** $-100 + 800$ **700**

13. $-245 + 245$ **0**   **14.** $1,434 + (-672)$ **762** **15.** $850 - 1,050$ **−200**   **16.** $-8,126 - (-134)$
−7,992

What scale and intervals would you use to graph each data set? 17–22. Answers may vary. Samples are given.

17. $-2, 3, 2, 4, -4, 1, -1, 3$
−5 to 5; by 1
18. $-34, 98, 12, -71, 53, -95$
−100 to 100; by 10
19. $4, 68, 50, 41, -13, -18, 27$
−20 to 70; by 10
20. $-20, 7, -9, 4, 18, 5, -1, 9$
−20 to 20; by 5
21. $-89, 89, 74, -22, 14, -45$
−90 to 90; by 15
22. $-32, -24, -14, -23, 0, 4, 16$
−35 to 20; by 5

23. a. Use the data at the right. Find the balance for each day. **$9; $18; −$9; $17; −$12; −$1; −$17**

  b. Draw a line graph to display the balances.
  See margin.

24. Choose A, B, C, or D. Which day should have the highest point on the graph for Exercise 23? **A**

  A. Tuesday   **B.** Thursday
  C. Saturday   **D.** Sunday

Day	Expenses	Income
Mon.	−$85	$94
Tues.	−$60	$78
Wed.	−$22	$13
Thurs.	−$73	$90
Fri.	−$49	$37
Sat.	−$16	$15
Sun.	−$36	$19

Computer Copy or use a spreadsheet like the one below.

	A	B	C	D	
1	Week	Income	Expenses	Profit/Loss	
2	2/1–2/7	$4,257	−$6,513	▪	−$2,256
3	2/8–2/14	$3,840	−$2,856	▪	$984
4	2/15–2/21	$4,109	−$3,915	▪	$194
5	2/22–2/28	$3,725	−$4,921	▪	−$1,196
6	Totals	▪	▪	▪	
		$15,931	−$18,205	−$2,274	

25. What formulas would you enter in cells D2 through D5?
= B2 + C2; = B3 + C3; = B4 + C4; = B5 + C5
26. What formula should be entered in cell B6? Explain.
= B2 + B3 + B4 + B5; the value in B6 is the total for the four
27. Enter the formulas to find the unknown values.
See table above.
28. What was the balance for the month? Was it a loss or profit? −$2,274; loss

29. *Writing* Describe two types of graphs you could use to show the data. Explain the advantages and disadvantages of each. Check students' work.

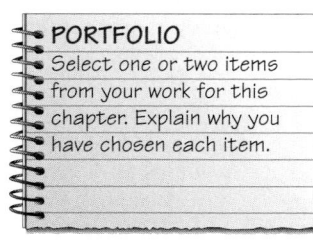

PORTFOLIO
Select one or two items from your work for this chapter. Explain why you have chosen each item.

PRACTICE

■Practice 10-8 *Applying Integers and Graphs*

What scale and intervals would you use on the vertical axis to graph each data set? Answers will vary. Sample given.

1. 5, –9, 18, –6, 12, 16 — scale from –10 to 20; intervals of 1
2. –13, 8, –10, 5, 9, 2 — scale from –15 to 10; intervals of 1
3. –45, 40, –16, –8, –26, 32 — scale from –50 to 50; intervals of 10
4. –10, –26, 18, 11, 3, –2 — scale from –30 to 20; intervals of 10

Choose a calculator, mental math, or paper and pencil.

5. –18 + 7 = **–11**
6. 16 – 37 = **–21**
7. 326 + (–326) = **0**
8. 43 – (–18) = **61**
9. 1,258 + (–271) = **987**
10. –73 + (–92) = **–165**

11. Find the closing balance for each day.

Day	Expenses	Income	Balance
Sunday	–$32	$45	$13
Monday	–$40	$50	$10
Tuesday	–$26	$40	$14
Wednesday	–$50	$45	–$5
Thursday	–$35	$30	–$5
Friday	–$70	$60	–$10
Saturday	–$53	$60	$7

12. Draw a line graph to display the balances in Exercise 11.

13. On which day did the greatest balance occur? **Tuesday**

14. On which day did the least balance occur? **Friday**

15. What was the total balance for the week? Was it a loss or profit? **$24; a profit**

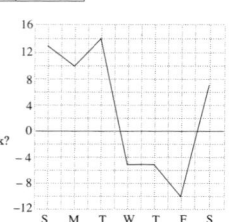

In copymaster and workbook formats

RETEACHING

■Reteaching 10-8 *Applying Integers and Graphs*

To find a **balance**, add the income (positive number) and the expenses (negative number). The sum is the balance.

Balance Sheet for Lunch Express		
Month	Income	Expenses
January	$1,095	$459
February	$1,468	$695
March	$1,773	$700
April	$602	$655

• To find the balance for February, add
  1,468 + (–695) = 773.
Lunch Express made a profit of $773.

• To find the balance for April, add
  602 + (–655) = –53.
Lunch Express had a loss of $53.

To look for a trend in the data, draw a line graph of the monthly balances.

• Balances range from –$53 to $1,073. Make the vertical scale from –$200 to $1,100. Use intervals of $100.

• Use the horizontal scale for the months.

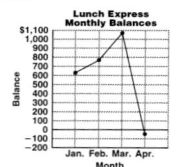

The trend was for increasing balances—until April.

Choose a calculator, mental math, or paper and pencil. Find each sum or difference.

1. –9 + 17 **8**
2. 51 – 83 **–32**
3. 42 – (–18) **60**
4. –77 + 92 **15**
5. –109 + 109 **0**
6. 28 – 431 **–403**
7. –156 + 429 **273**
8. 232 – (–97) **329**
9. –401 – 582 **–983**
10. 1,874 – (–1,892) **3,766**
11. 6,012 + (–3,933) **2,079**
12. –4,401 – (–1,560) **–2,841**

What scale and intervals would you use on the vertical axis to graph each data set? Sample given.

13. –21, –17, –4, 1, 3, 12, 24 — scale from –25 to 25; intervals of 5
14. –4, –1, 0, 2, 5, 7, 9 — scale from –10 to 10; intervals of 2
15. 48, –22, 15, 32, –39 — scale from –50 to 50; intervals of 10
16. –19, 5, –2, 39, 12, 24, –9 — scale from –20 to 40; intervals of 10

ENRICHMENT

■inds on Math Transparency

10-8

Jordan bought a CD for $5. He sold it for $10, and then bought it back for $15. Finally, he sold it for $20. Did Jordan make money, lose money, or break even? If he made money or lost money, how much did he make or lose?

Jordan made $10

See *Solution Key* for worked-out answers.

472

Math at Work

If you have block scheduling or extended class periods, have groups of students bring in local weather reports from a newspaper. They can use these reports to record daily high and low temperatures for a four-week period on a spreadsheet. Have each group write a spreadsheet formula to calculate the average daily temperature for each week. Then graph the averages they find.

LESSON QUIZ

Find the balance. Tell if it is a profit or loss.

1. Income: $545
   Expense: $650 **–$105; loss**

2. Income: $23
   Expense: $17 **$6; profit**

Mixed Review

Use prime factorization to find the GCF of each set of numbers. *(Lesson 5-3)*

30. 8, 12, 14 **2**
31. 2, 5, 10 **1**
32. 15, 25, 45 **5**
33. 9, 12, 18 **3**
34. 36, 45, 945 **9**

The volume and two dimensions of a rectangular prism are given. Find the third dimension. *(Lesson 9-8)*

35. $V = 48 \text{ m}^3$, $h = 3$ m, $\ell = 2$ m **8 m**
36. $V = 3,240 \text{ m}^3$, $h = 15$ m, $w = 8$ m **27 m**

37. *Choose a Strategy* Mercedes is a computer salesperson at RayState Computers. Her salary is $1,150 per month. In addition, she earns 12% of her monthly sales over $5,000.
   a. What did Mercedes earn in October if her computer sales totaled $11,640? **$1,946.80**
   b. The following amounts were subtracted from Mercedes's October earnings: 6.2% for Social Security, 18% for federal income tax, 4% for state income tax, and $40.35 for health insurance. What was the amount of Mercedes's paycheck? **$1,357.45**

Math at Work

METEOROLOGIST

If you enjoy studying earth science and working with computer models, consider a career as a meteorologist. Meteorologists apply mathematical relationships to create short- and long-range weather forecasts. They study air pressure, temperature, humidity, and wind velocity. In addition, meteorologists apply their knowledge of Earth's atmosphere to air pollution control, the study of global warming, and research about the ozone layer.

Visit the American Meteorological Society's Web site at www.ametsoc.org/AMS/amshomepage.cfm for more information.

FINISHING THE CHAPTER PROJECT

PROJECT DAY You may wish to plan a project day on which students share their completed projects. Encourage students to explain their process as well as their product.

PROJECT NOTEBOOK Ask students to review their project work and bring their notebooks up to date.

Have students review their methods for designing and constructing their timelines.

SCORING RUBRIC

3 You correctly calculate a scale and apply it to your time line. You locate events in the past on the negative side, and you list events or changes you think might happen in your future on the positive side. Your time line is detailed, interesting, and attractive.

2 You correctly apply a scale to your time line, and you locate events on both the negative and positive sides. Your details are adequate, and your time line is readable.

1 Your scale is incorrect, your time line is unorganized, or you include two few details.

0 You do not create a time line.

CHAPTER PROJECT

FINISHING THE CHAPTER PROJECT

The TIME of your life

Draw a Timeline Project Links on pages 441, 452, and 461 helped you complete the side of your time line that represents the past. Here is a checklist to help you gather together the parts of your project.

✔ an appropriate scale for a 3-ft time line

✔ a 3-ft time line labeled with appropriate divisions and 0

✔ past major events identified on your time line

Complete the time line for your future. List events or changes that you think will be important. What do you think will happen? What do you want to happen? Consider life changes such as getting married and having children. Consider education and career goals. Show your time line to your class. Explain why you chose the events you did. Add details to your time line to make it more attractive. Make the print bold enough to be readable. Add colors, and attach photographs, magazine pictures, or artwork.

Reflect and Revise

Review your time line with a classmate, friend, or family member. Did you choose an appropriate scale? Does your time line have enough details? Is it attractive? If necessary, make changes to improve your time line.

Web Extension

Prentice Hall's Internet site contains information you might find helpful as you complete your project. Visit www.phschool.com/mgm1/ch10 for some links and ideas related to history.

Internet Connection

Materials/Manipulatives

- photographs or pictures
- art materials
- ruler or yard stick

STUDENT SELF-ASSESSMENT SURVEY

Chapter 10 Student Self-Assessment Survey

1. Now that you have finished this chapter, think about what you have learned about integers and coordinate graphing. Check each topic that you feel confident you understand.
   _____ graph integers on a number line (10-1)
   _____ compare and order integers (10-1)
   _____ use models to represent integers (10-2)
   _____ add integers using models (10-3)
   _____ subtract integers using models (10-4)
   _____ solve equations using models (10-4)
   _____ use multiple strategies to solve problems (10-5)
   _____ make a function table (10-6)
   _____ graph functions (10-6)
   _____ graph points on a coordinate plane (10-7)
   _____ name the coordinates of points on a coordinate plane (10-7)
   _____ use a balance sheet to determine profit or loss (10-8)
   _____ draw and interpret graphs involving integers (10-8)

2. Before the Chapter Assessment, I need to review _____

3. a. Check one. In general, I thought this chapter was
   ____ a snap ____ easy ____ average ____ hard ____ a monster
   b. Why do you feel this way? _____

4. In this chapter, I did my best work on _____

5. In this chapter, I had trouble with _____

6. List three real-world situations in which people use negative integers. _____

7. Did you use a graphing calculator to graph equations? _____
   If so, did using the graphing calculator help you? _____
   Explain. _____

Vocabulary/Symbols

balance, coordinate plane, coordinates, function, function table, input, integers, loss, negative, opposites, ordered pair, origin, output, positive, profit, quadrants, x-axis, x-coordinate, y-axis, y-coordinate, zero pair

Materials/Manipulatives

• algebra tiles   • graph paper

Resources

 Student Edition

Extra Practice, p. 531
Glossary/Study Guide

 Teaching Resources

Chapter Support file, Ch. 10
• Student Self-Assessment Survey,
Glossary, Spanish Resources
Tools for Studying Smarter

474

WRAP UP

ASSESSMENT Have students work in pairs. Ask them to do each group of exercises and then check their partner's work. Have students list the types of errors they make. After they finish the exercises, discuss the lists with the class. Help students correct their mistakes.

Exercise 38 Encourage students to use the Make a Table, Draw a Diagram, and Guess and Test strategies to solve this problem.

Remind students that the new mathematical terms in this chapter are defined in the Glossary/Study Guide in the back of the book.

---

(10) WRAP UP

Integers and Opposites   10-1, 10-2

Opposites are two numbers that are the same distance from 0 on the number line, but in opposite directions. The set of **integers** is the set of whole numbers and their opposites.

To compare integers, think of the number line. The integer farther to the right is the greater integer.

1. What integer represents 7 degrees below zero? −7

2. Name the opposite of each integer.
   a. −7   b. 1   c. −8   d. −14   e. 89   f. −100
      7   −1   8   14   −89   100

3. Write three numbers that are between −4 and −5. Are these numbers integers? Explain. **See above right.**

4. *Writing* Explain how to order the following integers from least to greatest: 3, −1, −13, 5, 0. **See above.**

3. Answers may vary. Sample: −4.1, −4.55, −4.95; no; there are no integers between two consecutive integers.

4. Choose all the negative numbers. List them from greatest absolute value to least. Write 0. List the positive numbers from least to greatest: −13, −1, 0, 3, 5.

Compare using <, >, or =.

5. −9 ▧ −11   6. 4 ▧ −13   7. −21 ▧ 16   8. 0 ▧ 9   9. 6 ▧ 11
   >   >   <   <   <

Write the integer represented by each set of tiles.

10. ▧ −1   11. ▧ 3   12. ▧ 1   13. ▧ 2

Modeling Addition and Subtraction of Integers   10-3, 10-4

To add integers, model each integer with tiles. If possible, combine tiles to make zero pairs and remove as many zero pairs as possible. Write the integer that the remaining tiles represent.

To subtract integers, model the first integer with tiles. Take away the second number of tiles. (You may need to add zero pairs.) Write the integer that the remaining tiles represent.

Find the sum or difference.

14. $9 + (−4)$ 5   15. $−13 + 6$ −7   16. $1 − (−7)$ 8   17. $−2 − 8$ −10   18. $−3 − (−3)$ 0

19. $7 + (−5)$ 2   20. $−18 + 4$ −14   21. $3 − (−9)$ 12   22. $−5 − 5$ −10   23. $−4 − (−8)$ 4

Chapter 10 Assessment • Form A

Answers

1. Graph the numbers on the number line. $-5, 2, -2, -3, 4$

   1. 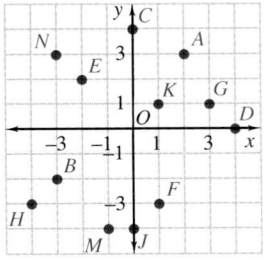 (number line with points at $-5, -3, -2, 0, 2, 4$)

2. Compare using $<$, $>$, or $=$. $4 \blacksquare -2$

   2. $\geq$

3. What number is represented by the tiles? A shaded tile is negative and an unshaded tile is positive.

   3. -1

4. Complete the function table.

Input	1	2	3	4	5
Output	4	8	12		

   4. 16, 20

5. Find the sum $-6 + 4$.

   5. -2

6. Compare the sums using $<$, $>$, or $=$.
   $-5 + 3 \blacksquare 5 + (-3)$

   6. $<$

7. Find the difference $8 - (-4)$.

   7. 12

8. Find the difference $-12 - (-15)$.

   8. 3

9. Find the difference $-6 - 8$.

   9. -14

10. Graph the points with given coordinates $A(-2, -3)$, $B(2, -3)$, and $C(4, 3)$.

    10. (graph)

11. What are the coordinates of the points on the graph?

    11. $P(-3, 2)$, $Q(-2, -3)$, $R(3, 4)$

Chapter 10 Assessment • Form A (continued)

12. In which quadrant is the point with coordinates $(10, -20)$?

    12. IV

13. Find the sum $15 + (-6)$.

    13. 9

Solve each equation.

14. $a + 9 = -3$

    14. -12

15. $12 + b = 8$

    15. -4

16. $c - 15 = -3$

    16. 12

17. In the first four months of their new home-based business, Jasmine and Koletta had the following balance sheet.

Month	Income	Expenses	Balance
1	$1,500	−250	1,250
2	500	−749	−249
3	650	−405	245
4	1,750	−650	1,100
Total			2,346

    Fill in the balances for each month and the total. Is their business profitable?

    17. yes

Choose A, B, C, or D.

18. Based on the balance sheet above, which months were profitable?
    A. 1, 2, 3 **B.** 1, 3 **C.** 2, 3 **D.** 1, 3, 4

    18. D

Choose a Strategy

19. A dart can score 1, 2, 3, 4, or 5 points. How many possible scores can you make if you throw 3 darts which all land on the dartboard?

    19. 13 scores

Writing

20. Describe ways in which a business could use a balance sheet to help it be more effective.

    Sample: A balance sheet could help a business determine which months are busiest and how many supplies to buy.

Making Function Tables and Graphing Functions 10-6

You can represent functions using a **function table** or a graph. Both methods show the function's *input* and *output*.

24. The cost of a 1-min telephone call is $.10. The cost of a 2-min call to the same place is $.20. A 3-min call is $.30.
    a. Make a function table and a graph for the data.
    b. *Writing* Explain how you could use the graph to find the cost of an 8-min call. **See back of book.**

    24a.
Input (min)	Output (dollars)
1	$.10
2	$.20
3	$.30

Graphing on the Coordinate Plane 10-7

The **coordinate plane** is formed by the intersection of the *x-axis* and the *y-axis*. Every point on the plane can be described by an **ordered pair** of numbers (x, y). These *coordinates* tell how far a point is from the **origin**, $(0, 0)$.

Name the point with the given coordinates.

25. $(0, 4)$ **C**   26. $(3, 1)$ **G**   27. $(-3, 3)$ **N**

28. $(2, 3)$ **A**   29. $(-4, -3)$ **H**   30. $(1, 1)$ **K**

Write the coordinates of each point.

31. B **$(-3, -2)$** 32. F **$(1, -3)$**   33. J **$(0, -4)$**

34. E **$(-2, 2)$**   35. D **$(4, 0)$**   36. M **$(-1, -4)$**

Problem Solving Strategies and Graphing Applications 10-5, 10-8

You can use multiple strategies to solve problems.

A *profit and loss* statement is a table of *income* and *expenses*. Income is listed as a positive number. Expenses are listed as negative numbers.

37. Find Royale Bakery's balance for each month. Graph the balances. Over four months, was there a profit or a loss? **$486; $2,000; −$266; $673; see back of book for graph.**

38. Two people live 36 mi apart. They leave their homes at 10:00 A.M., riding bicycles toward each other. The first person averages 8 mi/h, and the second person averages 10 mi/h. At what time will they meet? **12 noon**

Income and Expenses for Royale Bakery

Month	Income	Expenses
Jan.	$1,314	−$828
Feb.	$2,120	−$120
March	$1,019	−$1,285
April	$1,438	−$765

CHAPTER ASSESSMENT • FORM B

Chapter 10 Assessment • Form B

Choose the best answer. Circle A, B, C, or D.

1. Which is a graph of the points −3, 1, −1, and 3?
   A.
   B.
   C.
   D.

2. Which statement is *not* true?
   A. 4 < 6   B. −7 < −4   C. −3 > −2   D. −5 < 5

3. What number is represented by the tiles?
   A shaded tile is negative and an unshaded tile is positive.
   A. 1   B. −1   C. 9   D. −4

4. Order from least to greatest −5, 6, 1, −2.
   A. 1, −2, −5, 6   B. −2, 1, −5, 6   C. −5, −2, 1, 6   D. −2, −5, 1, 6

5. Find the sum −14 + −9.
   A. −23   B. −5   C. 5   D. 223

6. Find the sum −18 + 6.
   A. 12   B. −24   C. 24   D. −12

7. Which statement is true?
   A. −5 + 2 < −5 − 2   B. −6 + 4 < −4 + 6
   C. 8 − 3 = −8 + 3   D. −5 − 3 > −3 − 5

8. Find the difference 10 − (−2).
   A. 12   B. −12   C. 8   D. −8

9. Find the difference −6 − (−3).
   A. −9   B. 9   C. −3   D. 3

10. Find the difference −4 − 6.
    A. −2   B. 10   C. 2   D. −10

11. In which quadrant is point A with coordinates (35, 2)?
    A. I   B. II   C. III   D. IV

Assessment

CHAPTER ASSESSMENT • FORM B

Chapter 10 Assessment • Form B (continued)

12. Which is a graph of the points D(−3, −2), E(3, 2), and F(−1, 4)?
    A.   B.   C.   D.

13. What are the coordinates of the points of this graph?
    A. A(1, 2), B(3, −2), C(−1, −3)
    B. A(2, 1), B(−2, 3), C(−3, −1)
    C. A(2, 1), B(−2, 3), C(−1, −3)
    D. A(−2, −1), B(2, −3), C(3, 1)

14. Which numbers complete the function table?
    A. 11, 12, 13   B. 13, 16, 19
    C. 24, 27, 30   D. 19, 29, 48

Input	Output
5	8
6	9
7	10
8	?
9	?
10	?

15. Solve the equation 9 + x = −4.
    A. −13   B. −5   C. 5   D. 13

16. Solve the equation y + 12 = 5.
    A. 17   B. 7   C. −7   D. −17

17. Based on the balance sheet given, which months were profitable?
    A. Jan., Feb.   B. Mar., Apr.
    C. Jan., Mar.   D. Feb., Apr.

Month	Income	Expenses
Jan.	6,500	−7,000
Feb.	4,950	−6,350
March	7,450	−5,400
April	8,430	−4,350

Choose a Strategy

18. Tasha spent half her time at work writing reports, ⅛ of her time in meetings, ¼ of her time making telephone calls, and the remaining 1 h instructing a new trainee. How many hours did she spend at work on this day?
    A. 5 h   B. 7 h   C. 8 h   D. 10 h

Teaching Resources

Chapter Support File, Ch. 10, and Spanish Resources

Teacher's Edition

See pp. 432C–D for Assessment Options.

Teaching Resource Software

• Computer Item Generator, Ch. 10

476

ASSESSMENT

ENHANCED MULTIPLE CHOICE QUESTIONS are more complex than traditional multiple choice questions, which assess only one skill. Enhanced multiple choice questions assess the processes that students use, as well as the end results. They are written so that students can use more than one strategy to solve the problem. Using multiple strategies is encouraged by the National Council of

Teachers of Mathematics (NCTM). **Exercise 10** is an enhanced multiple choice question.

WRITING EXERCISES allow students to describe more fully their thinking and understanding of the concepts they have learned. **Exercise 14b** is a writing exercise.

10 ASSESSMENT

1. Compare. Write <, >, or =.
   a. 18 ■ −24 >
   b. −15 ■ −9 <
   c. 27 ■ −27 >
   d. −3 ■ −4 >

2. Write the integer that is represented by the tiles.
   a. 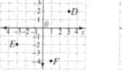 2
   b. −3

3. Use tiles to model each integer and its opposite. **See back of book.**
   a. −1   b. 6   c. −2   d. −9

4. Compare using <, >, or =.
   a. −13 + 4 ■ 13 + (−4) <
   b. 7 + (−8) + (−1) ■ 7 + (−9) =

5. The temperature was 4°F at midnight. By 6:00 A.M. the temperature had risen 22 degrees. What was the temperature at 6:00 A.M.?   **18°F**

6. Use tiles to find each sum or difference.
   a. −11 + (−4) **−15**   b. −12 − 4 **−16**
   c. 6 − (−3) **9**   d. −5 + 5 **0**

7. Solve d + 6 = −3. **−9**

8. a. Complete the function table below.

Input	Output
5	40
6	48
7	56
8	■ 64
9	■ 72

   b. Graph the function. **See back of book.**

9. Graph each point on a coordinate plane. **a–d.**
   a. A (1, 1)   b. B (2, 0) **See back of book.**
   c. C (−3, −2)   d. D (4, −1)

10. **Choose A, B, C, or D.** On a corrected math quiz, a student got −2 points on the first question, −1 on the second, −3 on the third, −2 on the fourth, and −1 on the fifth. A perfect score was 50 points. What was the student's score? **B**
    A. 50   B. 41   C. 32   D. 12

11. Suppose you bought 3 birthday cards for $1.50 each and 2 posters for $2.75 each. How much did you spend in all? **$10**

12. Use a calculator to find each sum or difference.   **680**
    a. −85 + 54 **−31**   b. −112 − (−792)
    c. 384 + (−556) **−172**   d. 3,077 − (−1,902) **4,979**

13. Identify the quadrant in which each point lies.
    a. (4, 2) **I**   b. (−6, −5) **III**
    c. (9, −15) **IV**   d. (−8, 3) **II**

14. Below is part of the profit and loss statement for Balloons Galore.

Month	Profit/Loss
January	−$985
February	$10,241
March	−$209
April	$17,239

   a. Find the total balance for the four months ending with April. **$26,286**
   b. *Writing* Did Balloons Galore have a profit or a loss during that time? Explain.
   Profit; ending balance is positive.

Item	Review Topic	Ch
1	Classifying quadrilaterals	8
2, 6	Geometry and measurement	9
3	Estimating percents	7
4	Using ratios	7
5	Comparing fractions	5
7	Evaluating expressions	2

Item	Review Topic	Ch
8	Writing and solving expressions	2
9	Scale drawings	7
10, 11	Graphing points on a coordinate plane	10

10 CUMULATIVE REVIEW

Choose the best answer.

1. Which statement is false? **C**

   A. A square is always a rectangle.
   B. Some rectangles are rhombuses.
   C. All quadrilaterals are parallelograms.
   D. Parallelograms can be divided into two congruent triangles.

2. Which could be a net for a rectangular prism? **C**

   A.
   B.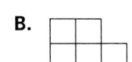
   C.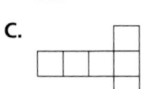
   D.

3. Find the best estimate for 43% of 87. **B**

   A. 50   B. 36
   C. 30   D. 25

4. Suppose you bought 9 apples, 6 oranges, 12 pears, and 8 plums. What was the ratio of the number of plums bought to the number of pears bought? **A**

   A. $\frac{2}{3}$ B. 9 to 12
   C. 12 : 8   D. 4 : 2

5. A hardware store sells window glass in thicknesses of $\frac{3}{16}$ inch, $\frac{5}{16}$ inch, and $\frac{7}{32}$ inch. A homeowner plans to install glass that is at least $\frac{1}{4}$ inch thick. Which thickness should the homeowner use? **C**

   A. $\frac{3}{16}$ inch

   B. $\frac{7}{32}$ inch

   C. $\frac{5}{16}$ inch

   D. either $\frac{7}{32}$ or $\frac{3}{16}$ inch

6. Find the perimeter of a square with sides 5 m. **B**

   A. 10 m   B. 20 m
   C. 25 m   D. 125 m

7. Evaluate the expression $b - a - 8$ when $a = -7$ and $b = -4$. **C**

   A. -19 B. -11
   C. -5 D. 11

8. Write the numerical expression that is represented by the set of tiles. Then find the sum. **B**

   A. $-5 + 7; 2$
   B. $5 + (-7); -2$
   C. $5 + 7; 12$
   D. $-5 + (-7); -12$

9. On a scale drawing, the scale shown is 1 in. represents 10 ft. The length of a room is 2.5 in. on the drawing. How long is the actual room? **D**

   A. 4 in.   B. 25 in.
   C. 4 ft   D. 25 ft

10. What is the correct ordered pair for point P? **D**

    A. $(-3, -2)$
    B. $(-2, -3)$
    C. $(3, -2)$
    D. $(-3, 2)$

11. Which ordered pair names the location of a reflected image of point P above? **D**

    A. $(2, 3)$ B. $(1, 1)$
    C. $(-1, -1)$ D. $(-3, -2)$

CUMULATIVE REVIEW

■ Chapter 10 Cumulative Review

Choose the best answer. Circle A, B, C, or D.

1. What is the area of the triangle shown?

   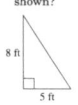

   A. 13 ft²   **B.** 20 ft²
   C. 30 ft²   D. 40 ft²

2. What is the circumference of a circle with a diameter of 3.2 m? Use 3.14 for π.

   A. 10.048 m   B. 3.14 m
   C. 3.2 m   D. 6.28 m

3. Find the area of the shaded region. Use 3.14 for π.

   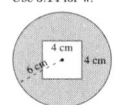

   A. 113.04 cm²   B. 16 cm²
   C. 97.04 cm²   D. 129.04 cm²

4. How many faces does a square prism have?

   A. 2 faces   B. 4 faces
   C. 6 faces   D. 8 faces

5. Find the surface area of the rectangular prism shown.

   A. 24 ft²   B. 40 ft²
   C. 70 ft²   **D.** 94 ft²

6. The bicyclist rode 3 mi in 20 min. Find the unit rate in mi/h.

   A. 6 mi/h   B. 1 mi/h
   C. 9 mi/h   D. 1.5 mi/h

7. Triangles ABC and XYZ are similar. Which of the following is true?

   A. $\frac{AB}{BC} = \frac{XY}{XZ}$ **B.** $\frac{AB}{XY} = \frac{BC}{YZ}$
   C. $\frac{BC}{YZ} = \frac{AC}{YZ}$ D. $\frac{BC}{YZ} = \frac{XZ}{AC}$

8. The distance you need to travel measures 4 in. on the map. The actual trip is 112 mi. What is the scale on the map?

   A. 1 in. : 4 mi
   B. 1 in. : 16 mi
   C. 1 in. : 22 mi
   D. 1 in. : 28 mi

CUMULATIVE REVIEW

Chapter 10 Cumulative Review (continued)

9. What is $\frac{2}{5}$ as a decimal and as a percent?

   A. 0.4, 40%   B. 0.2, 20%
   C. 0.4, 4%   D. 0.5, 50%

10. Find 44% of 95.

    A. 38   **B.** 41.8
    C. 4,180   D. 4.18

Use the figure below for Exercises 11–14.

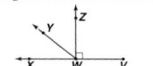

11. Which are all shown in the figure?

    A. $\overrightarrow{WV}, \overrightarrow{WZ}, \overrightarrow{WY}$ **B.** $\overrightarrow{WX}, \overrightarrow{WY}, \overrightarrow{WZ}$
    C. $\overrightarrow{WV}, \overrightarrow{XY}, \overrightarrow{WZ}$ D. $\overrightarrow{XY}, \overrightarrow{XZ}, \overrightarrow{VZ}$

12. Which is an acute angle in the figure?

    A. $\angle XWZ$ B. $\angle ZWV$
    C. $\angle XWV$ **D.** $\angle YWZ$

13. Which is a right angle in the figure?

    A. $\angle XWV$ B. $\angle WZV$
    C. $\angle ZWV$ D. $\angle ZWY$

14. Which angle is the complement of $\angle XWY$?

    A. $\angle YWZ$ B. $\angle YWX$
    C. $\angle ZWV$ D. $\angle XWZ$

15. Sharran gets her nails done every 5 days. Jessie gets her nails done every 4 days. Melissa gets her nails done every 8 days. All three got their nails done today. In how many days will all three of them again get their nails done on the same day?

    A. 24 days   B. 25 days
    C. 32 days   **D.** 40 days

16. Add $-6 + 3 + (-2)$.

    A. -3 B. 5
    C. -5 D. -11

17. Subtract $-13 - (-13)$.

    A. -26 **B.** 0
    C. 26   D. not here

18. In which quadrant of the coordinate plane is the point with coordinates $(-35, 200)$?

    A. I   **B.** II
    C. III   D. IV

19. Write $\frac{18}{4}$ as a decimal.

    A. 0.45   B. 0.5
    C. 4.05   **D.** 4.5

20. Of a class of 31 students, 12 are in the computer club. Seven of the students are in the newspaper club and 5 are in the Spanish club only. If 4 of the students in the computer club are also in the newspaper club, how many students do not belong to a club at all?

    A. 3   B. 10
    C. 11   D. 21

21. Suppose in a bag there are 8 red cards, 6 blue cards, 4 green cards, and 2 yellow cards. What is the ratio of the number of blue cards to the number of red cards?

    A. 3:2   **B.** 3:4
    C. 4:3   D. 3:20

22. Point $P(-1, 3)$ is reflected about the x-axis. Which is the ordered pair that names its reflected image?

    A. $(1, -3)$ B. $(1, 3)$
    C. $(-1, -3)$ D. $(-1, 1)$

Resources

▮ Teaching Resources

Chapter Support File, Ch. 10
• Cumulative Review

📖 Teacher's Edition

See pp. 432C–D for Assessment Options.

477

CHAPTER OVERVIEW

To accommodate flexible scheduling, most lessons are divided into parts. Assignment Options are given in the Teacher's Edition for each lesson.

Pages 480–484	**Lesson 11-1** Fair and Unfair Games
NCTM 1, 2, 3, 4, 5, 6, 11	**Part 1** Experimental Probability **Part 2** Possible Outcomes **Key terms:** fair, equally likely, experimental probability, possible outcomes

Pages 485–487	**Lesson 11-2** Problem Solving Strategy
NCTM 1, 2, 3, 4, 5, 10, 11, 13	**Simulate a Problem** **Key terms:** simulating, trial

Pages 488–491	**Lesson 11-3** Technology: Simulations and Random Numbers
NCTM 1, 2, 3, 4, 10, 11, 13	**Key term:** random numbers **Alternative Activity 11-3** ▼ Project Link

Pages 507–510	**Lesson 11-7** Exploring Arrangements
NCTM 1, 2, 3, 4, 5, 10, 11	**Part 1** Using a Tree Diagram or List **Part 2** Using the Counting Principle **Key terms:** permutation, factorial notation ☑ Checkpoint 2

Pages 512–516	**Lesson 11-8** Data Analysis: Making Predictions from Data
NCTM 1, 2, 3, 4, 5, 8, 10, 11, 13	**Part 1** Identifying Samples **Part 2** Making Predictions **Key terms:** population, sample, representative, random sample, convenience sampling, biased

Pacing Options

This chart suggests pacing only for the core lessons and their parts. It is provided merely as a possible guide. It will help you determine how much time you have in your schedule to cover other features, such as the Chapter Project, Math Toolboxes, Wrap Up, and Assessment.

	1 Class Period	1 Class Period	1 Class Period	1 P
Traditional (40–45 min class periods)	11–1 ▼1	11–1 ▼2	11–2	
Block Scheduling (90 min class periods)	11–1 ▼1 11–1 ▼2	11–2	11–3	11– ▼1

NCTM STANDARDS

1 Problem Solving	6 Number Systems and Number Theory	10 Statistics
2 Communication	7 Computation and Estimation	11 Probability
3 Reasoning	8 Patterns and Functions	12 Geometry
4 Mathematical Connections	9 Algebra	13 Measurement
5 Number and Number Relationships		

Pages 492–496	Lesson 11-4 Theoretical Probability	Pages 498–501	Lesson 11-5 Tree Diagrams and the Counting Principle	Pages 502–506	Lesson 11-6 Independent Events
NCTM 3, 4, 5, 10, 11, 13	**Part 1** Finding Theoretical Probability **Part 2** Types of Events **Key term:** theoretical probability **Alternative Activity** 11-4 **Journal** ▼ **Project Link** ✓ **Checkpoint 1**	**NCTM 1, 3, 4, 5, 10, 11, 12, 13**	**Part 1** Using a Tree Diagram **Part 2** Using the Counting Principle **Key terms:** tree diagram, counting principle	**NCTM 1, 3, 4, 5, 10, 11**	**Part 1** Exploring Independent Events **Part 2** Multiplying Probabilities **Key term:** independent **Alternative Activity** 11-6 **Journal** ▼ **Project Link** **Math at Work**

Optional Materials and Manipulatives

colored cubes (11-1, 11-6)
bag (11-1, 11-6)
blank spinners (11-2)
graphing calculator (11-3)

random number generator program (11-3)
computer (11-3)
large number of objects (approximately 400) with 2, 3, or 4 different colored objects (11-8)

Optional calculator use is integrated throughout the course.

---

ss d	1 Class Period	1 Class Period	1 Class Period	1 Class Period	1 Class Period	1 Class Period	1 Class Period	1 Class Period	1 Class Period	1 Class Period
-4 ▼2	11–5 ▼1	11–5 ▼2	11–6 ▼1	11–6 ▼2	11–7 ▼1	11–7 ▼2	11–8 ▼1	11–8 ▼2		
-5 ▼	11–6 ▼1 11–6 ▼2	11–7 ▼1 11–7 ▼2	11–8 ▼1 11–8 ▼2							

MEETING INDIVIDUAL NEEDS

Accommodating Diverse Learning Styles

In your Teacher's Edition, you will find suggestions as to how you can help students complete mathematical tasks in Chapter 11 by meeting individual needs and supporting various learning styles. Here are some examples:

VISUAL LEARNING
creating time lines to record events *(p. 486)*

TACTILE LEARNING
modeling problems using coins *(p. 498)*

AUDITORY LEARNING
relating probability terms to everyday language *(p. 503)*

KINESTHETIC LEARNING
acting out a combinations problem *(p. 507)*

EARLY FINISHERS
Performance-Based Project, MathBlaster® Mystery, Interdisciplinary Units

GIFTED AND TALENTED
researching uses of probability *(p. 481)*

DIVERSITY helping students develop their thinking *(p. 502)*

ACQUIRING ENGLISH PROFICIENCY (AEP)
reviewing language of probability *(p. 483)*

Interactive Questioning

Technology Options

Real World & Student Experiences

MANAGEABLE TEACHING TOOLS

Skills & Problem Solving

Appropriate Content

Assessment Options

ASSESSING PROGRESS

A broad range of assessment tools are available to reach a variety of learners.

INFORMAL ASSESSMENT

Informal assessments provide day-to-day feedback to help give you a picture of conceptual understanding and skill development.

ONGOING ASSESSMENT is built into lesson instruction and the Teaching Notes of the Teacher's Edition.

In the Teacher's Edition
Lesson Quiz for every lesson

In the Student Edition
On Your Own, Mixed Review, Journal, Portfolio, Project Link, Chapter Wrap Up

Look for **Interactive Questions** within lessons that

BUILD UNDERSTANDING with labels such as Analyze, Reasoning, Estimation, Writing, and Summarize

✔ **CHECK UNDERSTANDING** with the Try It Out label.

FORMAL ASSESSMENT

Formal assessment can occur before and after the chapter, as well as at natural breaking points in the chapter.

Checkpoints
Two forms of each self-assessment Checkpoints are available: one in the Student Edition and another in the Chapter Support File in the Teaching Resources box.
- Mid-Chapter Checkpoint 1, page 496
- End-of-Chapter Checkpoint 2, page 510

Chapter 11 Assessment, page 520.
Two alternative forms are available in the Chapter Support File. They may be used after a chapter has been completed, or as a pre-test and post-test comparison.

Cumulative Review, page 521.
Assesses skills and concepts in Chapters 1–11.
An alternative form is available in Chapter Support File.

Computer Item Generator for Chapter 11
Customized tests can be generated for each lesson and for mid-chapter and end-of-chapter assessments, and for pre- and post-test comparisons of achievement.

CHAPTER PROJECT

The Chapter Project in the student edition provides a real-world connection to the math context of the chapter. The Teacher's Edition contains a scoring rubric.

Another performance-based Chapter Project with a scoring rubric can be found in the Chapter Support File in the Teaching Resources Box.

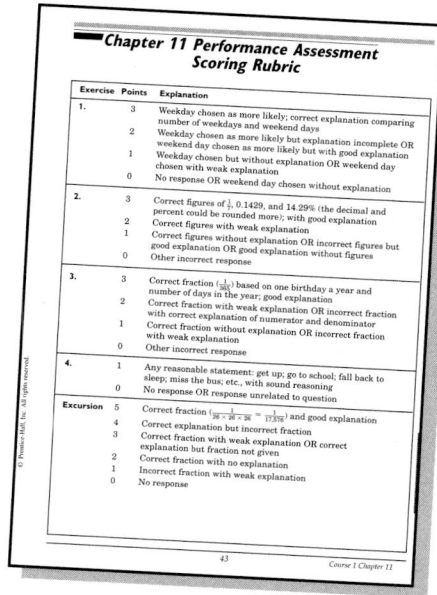

Correlation to Standardized Tests

Lesson		CAT5	CTBS/5 Terra Nova	ITBS	MAT7	SAT9	Your Local Test
	STANDARDIZED TEST ITEMS						
11-1	Fair and Unfair Games	■	■	■	■	■	
11-2	Problem Solving Strategy: Simulate a Problem	■	■	■	■	■	
11-3	Technology: Simulations and Random Numbers	■	■	■	■	■	
11-4	Theoretical Probability	■	■	■	■	■	
11-5	Tree Diagrams and Counting Principle	■	■	■	■	■	
11-6	Independent Events	■	■	■	■	■	
11-7	Exploring Arrangements	■	■	■	■	■	
11-8	Data Analysis Connection: Making Predictions from Data	■	■	■	■	■	

CAT5 California Achievement Test, 5th Edition
CTBS/5 Comprehensive Test of Basic Skills, 5th Edition

ITBS Iowa Test of Basic Skills, Form B
MAT 7 Metropolitan Achievement Test, 7th Edition

SAT9 Stanford Achievement Test, 9th Edition

MAKING CONNECTIONS

TEAM TEACHING WITH PRENTICE HALL MATERIALS

MIDDLE GRADES MATH INTERDISCIPLINARY UNITS	INTERDISCIPLINARY EXPLORATIONS	SCIENCE EXPLORER L Life Science E Earth Science P Physical Science
• **The Great Outdoors: Activities 4 & 6**	• *Sleuth's Supper* p. 41	**P** Lab p. 290 Half-Life of a Sugar Cube

Lesson	Interdisciplinary Connections	Real World Connections	Math Integration
11-1	Probability	Games	Statistics Probability
11-2	Music Sports	Movie Theaters Restaurants Games Collecting	Statistics Probability Measurement
11-3	Probability	Movie Theaters Technology	Statistics Probability Measurement
11-4	Science	Prize Drawing Surveys Raffles	Statistics Probability Measurement
11-5	Photography	Food Cars Menu Planning Games Travel	Statistics Probability Geometry Measurement
11-6	Biology Science	Games	Statistics Probability
11-7	Sports Track and Field Chorus Literature	Fitness Games	Statistics Probability
11-8	Health	Tourism Quality Control Surveys Natural Resources	Statistics Probability Measurement

School to Home

MATERIALS:

newspaper

scissors

tape

science or history textbook

several cans and boxes of food products

paper

pencil

English and Spanish versions are available in the Teacher's Communication Kit, Teacher's Resource box.

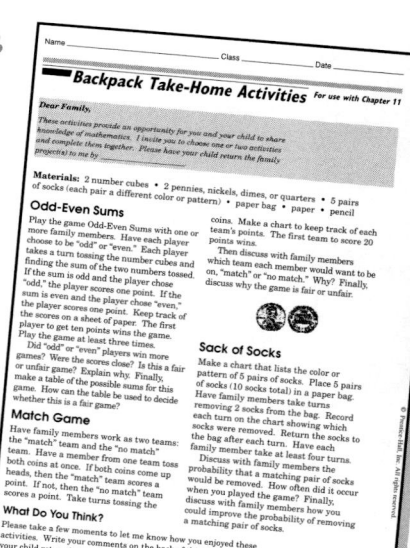

USING TECHNOLOGY TO ENHANCE INSTRUCTION

FOR THE STUDENT

Multimedia Math Hot Pages™
This interactive software and video package on CD-ROM integrates solid math content through a variety of media.

- Hot Page™ 31 (11-1)
- Hot Page™ 32 (11-2)
- Hot Page™ 33 (11-5)
- Hot Page™ 34 (11-8)

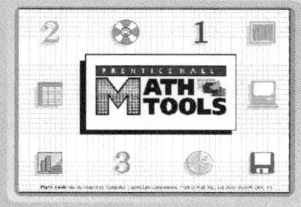

Math Labs
This software, available on both diskette and CD-ROM, includes on-screen Math Lab activities. Students use linkable, interactive tools to explore math concepts.

- Math Lab: Experimental Probability and Simulations (11-2)

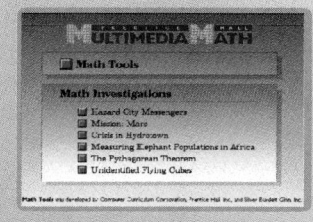

Multimedia Math Investigations
These in-depth interactive activities on CD-ROM develop real-world applications of mathematics. They allow students the opportunity to reinforce key concepts.

- Hazard City Messengers
- Measuring Elephant Populations in Africa

Interactive Student Tutorial
Available on CD-ROM, this test preparation program contains self-tests with questions in standardized test format. Software includes electronic versions of the text lessons and the Math Tools and Math Labs.

MathBlaster® Mystery
This award-winning, interactive software program on CD-ROM can be used to maintain skills or to accommodate early finishers.

- Level: Earn 2 coins; Pay 6 coins
- Mission Mode (all lessons)
- Kitchen Comparisons (11-5, 11-7)
- Number Guesser (11-1, 11-3, 11-8)
- Equation Maker (11-4, 11-6)
- Word Problems (11-2, Problem Solving Practice)

Internet Connection

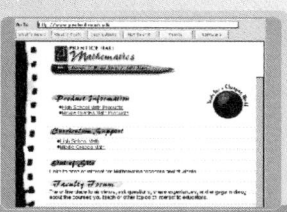

For Students
Support for the Chapter Project
A career-oriented link for Math at Work feature

www.phschool.com/math

For teachers
Curriculum Support
Product Information
Regional Support Information

FOR THE TEACHER

Computer Item Generator
Available on both CD-ROM and diskette, this software generates customized practice sheets, quizzes, and tests. It generates an unlimited supply of questions with varying levels of difficulty.

The Resource Pro™
Available on CD-ROM, this software can be used to customize and plan lessons.

Technology Options

MANAGEABLE TEACHING TOOLS

- Interactive Questioning
- Skills & Problem Solving
- Assessment Options
- Appropriate Content
- Real World & Student Experiences

CONNECTING TO PRIOR LEARNING Ask students if they have ever played a game that they thought was not fair. Then ask students to describe a *fair* game. **Answers may vary. Sample: one in which all players have an equal chance of winning** Then have students give examples that fit their definitions of fair.

CULTURAL CONNECTIONS Have students discuss the Olympic games. Brainstorm names of countries that participate in the games. Challenge students to find information in the library or on the Internet about rules athletes have to follow. Have students discuss why these rules exist. Have students discuss if exceptions to rules are fair.

INTERDISCIPLINARY CONNECTIONS Ask students: *What do you think happens when a professional sports team is accused of unfairness?* **Answers may vary. Sample: There is an investigation to see if any rules were broken.**

ABOUT THE PROJECT The Chapter Project challenges students to use their knowledge of gathering data and finding probability to design a three-outcome device.

Internet • For information and activities related to the Chapter Project, visit the Prentice Hall site at www.phschool.com/mgm1/ch11

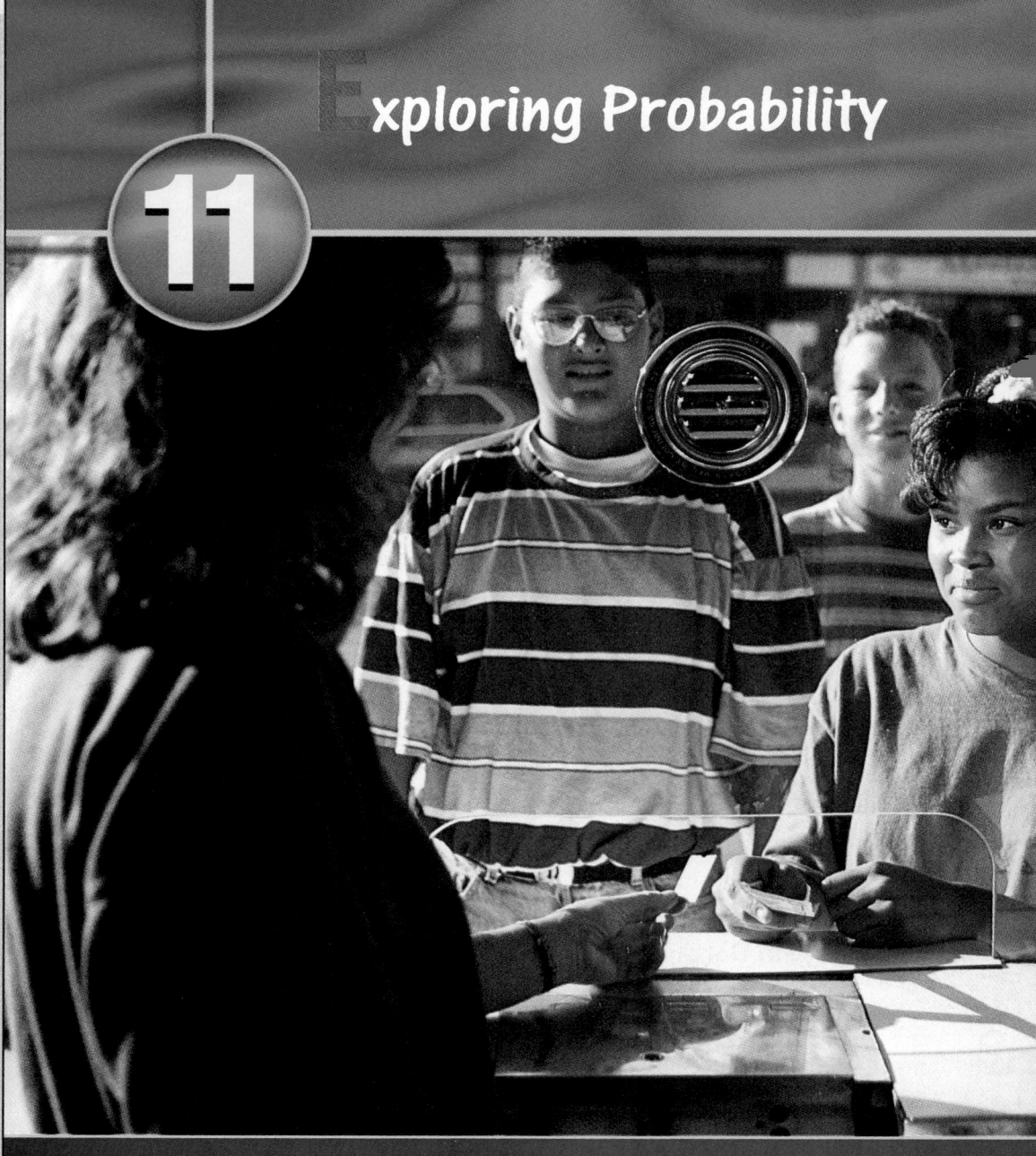

exploring Probability

11

WHAT YOU WILL LEARN IN THIS CHAPTER
- How to identify fair and unfair games
- How to find experimental and theoretical probabilities
- How to use probability to make predictions

Ask students:

- *Have you ever used a system to generate outcomes? Describe the system.*

- *How can a system be equally fair to three different outcomes?*

- *How do you think you would go about designing such a system?*

PROJECT NOTEBOOK Encourage students to keep all project-related materials in a separate folder or notebook.

TRACKING THE PROJECT You may wish to have students read Finishing the Chapter Project on page 517 to help them get an overview of the project. Set benchmark deadlines for students to show you their work in progress.

CHAPTER PROJECT

THEME: STATISTICS

NOW PLAYING

Suppose you and a friend have to choose among three movies, and you can't make up your mind. Should you flip a coin? You'd probably agree that assigning "heads" to one movie, "tails" to the second, and "lands on edge" to the third would not give the third movie much of a chance. What should you do?

Design a Three-Choice System Your project will be to design a device or system that is equally fair to three different outcomes. You will test your system to make sure each outcome can be expected one third of the time in a large number of trials.

Steps to help you complete the project:

p. 491 Project Link: *Simulating*
p. 496 Project Link: *Designing*
p. 506 Project Link: *Analyzing*
p. 517 *Finishing the Chapter Project*

- How to use simulations to solve problems

PROBLEM SOLVING

SCORING RUBRIC

3 You design two three-outcome systems, one based on random numbers and another based on a three-dimensional shape. You collect data from each system, and you find the experimental probabilities of the different outcomes. You collect additional data for one of your systems, and you prepare a presentation explaining your tests and calculations. You prove that your chosen system works for choosing among three equally likely outcomes.

2 You collect an adequate amount of data from the two systems you designed. You choose one system and collect additional data. You find the experimental probabilities of the three possible outcomes for both systems.

1 You complete only one three-outcome system. You collect data and attempt to find the experimental probabilities of the three possible outcomes.

0 You do not devise a three-outcome system, you do not collect an adequate amount of data, or you do not find the required experimental probabilities.

479

1 Focus

CONNECTING TO PRIOR KNOWLEDGE Ask students if they have ever played checkers. Have students describe some of the rules for play. Ask students: *Do you think checkers is a fair game? Why or why not?* **Answers may vary. Sample: Yes, because each player**

begins with the same number of checkers and has the same chance to win.

2 Teach

THINK AND DISCUSS

TACTILE LEARNING Provide each pair of students with blocks of two colors and a paper bag. Before students begin, have them sketch a table in which to record the results. Remind students to replace the cube after each draw.

Question 1 Ask students to explain why they think the game is fair or unfair.

Question 2 Decide who will draw the cubes. Have the other partner record the data. Have students save their data from Game 3 for future lessons.

Example 1 Tell students that the probability $\frac{2}{5}$ means that A will most likely win the game 2 out of 5 times.

Lesson Planning Options

Prerequisite Skills
• working with ratios (7-1)

Vocabulary/Symbols
fair, equally likely, experimental probability, possible outcomes

Materials/Manipulatives
• colored cubes   • bag

Resources

 Student Edition

Skills Handbook, p. 535
Extra Practice, p. 532
Glossary/Study Guide

 Teaching Resources

Chapter Support File, Ch. 11
• Lesson Planner 11-1
• Practice 11-1, Reteaching 11-1
• Answer Masters 11-1
Teaching Aids Masters 1, 2
Glossary, Spanish Resources

 Transparencies
1, 19, 98, Minds on Math 11-1

Warm Up

Stacy paid $12.00 for 15 juice bars at a fair. How much did each cost? **$.80**

11-1 **Fair and Unfair Games**

What You'll Learn

1 To find experimental probability

2 To find possible outcomes

...And Why

You can use experimental probability to determine whether games and contests are fair.

Here's How

Look for questions that
⊞ build understanding
✔ check understanding

THINK AND DISCUSS

1 *Experimental Probability*

A game is **fair** if each player has the same chance of winning. Players are *equally likely* to win in a fair game.

Play these three games with a partner. For each game, place the given numbers of colored cubes in a bag. Then draw cubes without looking. Answer Question 1 before each game. Answer Questions 2 and 3 after each game.

Game 1	Game 2	Game 3
1 red and 1 blue	2 red and 2 blue	3 red and 1 blue
Draw 1 cube.	Draw 1 cube. Then draw a second cube.	Draw 1 cube. Then draw a second cube.
Red: A wins.	Same color: A wins.	Same color: A wins.
Blue: B wins.	Two colors: B wins.	Two colors: B wins.

1. **Answers may vary. Sample: Games 1 and 3 seem fair, Game 2 seems unfair.**

1. ⊞ *Think About It* Before playing, decide whether the game seems fair or unfair. Which player seems more likely to win? **See below left.**

2. ⊞ *Data Collection* Play the game 20 times. Record your results in a table like the one below. For more data, combine your results with the results of two other groups. **Check students' work.**

	Your Group	3 Groups Combined
Number of times A won	▪	▪
Number of times B won	▪	▪
Number of games played	20	60

3. ⊞ *Draw a Conclusion* Does the game seem fair or unfair now? Explain. **Check students' work.**

480

AUDITORY LEARNING **Question 5** Tell students that you can read *Probability(A wins)* *as the probability that A will win is . . .*

■ ADDITIONAL EXAMPLES

FOR EXAMPLE 1

In 24 rounds of Game 3, player A won 14 times and player B won 10 times. What is the experimental probability that A wins? $\frac{7}{12}$

FOR EXAMPLE 2

A dime and a penny are tossed in a coin game. If a toss shows *two heads* or *two tails*, Player A wins. If a toss shows heads and tails, Player B wins. Show the possible outcomes of the game. Is it a fair game? **TT, TH, HT, HH; fair**

KINESTHETIC LEARNING Students may simulate the Game 2 and Game 3. Have one student for each cube stand and hold up a piece of paper with the color written on it. Have these students face each other in a circle. Blindfold another student and have this student act as a spinner, turning with one arm out. Another student, with his or her back turned says stop. Whoever the blindfolded person is pointing at is "picked" and leaves the circle. The "spinner" turns again to represent the second draw.

EXTENSION Explain that probability is utilized in fields such as weather prediction and farming. Have students find other fields that use probability. Ask students to report on the number of fields they find and how they would

You can write a ratio to show the fraction of games that a player wins. This ratio is the **experimental probability** of winning.

> ### EXPERIMENTAL PROBABILITY
>
> $\text{Probability(A wins)} = \frac{\text{number of games A won}}{\text{total number of games played}}$
>
> $\text{Probability(B wins)} = \frac{\text{number of games B won}}{\text{total number of games played}}$

■ EXAMPLE 1

In 20 rounds of Game 2, Player A won 8 and Player B won 12. What is the experimental probability that A wins?

$\text{Probability(A wins)} = \frac{8}{20}$ ← **number of games A won**
← **total number of games played**
$= \frac{2}{5}$

The probability that A wins is $\frac{2}{5}$.

4. ✓*Try It Out* In Example 1, what is the experimental probability that B wins? $\frac{3}{5}$

5. ⠿*Analyze* In one class the Game 2 results were $\text{Probability(A wins)} = \frac{70}{200}$ and $\text{Probability(B wins)} = \frac{130}{200}$. The Game 3 results were $\text{Probability(A wins)} = \frac{96}{200}$ and $\text{Probability(B wins)} = \frac{104}{200}$. What do these results suggest about the fairness of each of the games?
5. **Game 3 seems more fair than Game 2.**

6. **See left.**

6. ⠿*Reasoning* If you play the games tomorrow, will the experimental probabilities be the same as today? Explain.

Now you may assign Exercises 1–4, 8, 10–11, 14.

2 *Possible Outcomes*

You can decide if a game is fair or unfair by finding the *possible outcomes*. Then compare the possible outcomes to the game rules.

HISTORY The Mandan people who lived along the Missouri River played a game by tossing decorated bone disks in a basket. The score depended on which sides of the disks landed facing up.

6. **No; the actual results of the games need not be the same.**

7. ⠿*Look Back* In Game 1, the 2 possible outcomes are red and blue. Are they equally likely to occur? How do you know?
Yes; you have 1 possible outcome of red and 1 possible outcome of blue.

8. ⠿*What If . . .* Imagine a game in which all the cubes in the bag are the same color. How many possible outcomes would there be? **1**

Technology **O**ptions

Prentice Hall Technology

Software for Learners
• Hot Page™ 31*
• Math Blaster® Mystery*
• Interactive Student Tutorial, Chapter 11*

Teaching Resource Software
• Computer Item Generator 11-1
• Resource Pro™ Chapter 11*

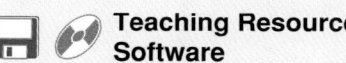

Internet • For related mathematics activities, visit the Prentice Hall site at www.phschool.com/math

Available on CD-ROM only

Assignment Options for Exercises On Your Own

To provide flexible scheduling, this lesson can be split into parts.

▼ **Core** 1–4, 8, 11
Extension 10, 14

▼ **Core** 5–7, 9, 12
Extension 13

Use Mixed Review to maintain skills.

ASSESSMENT Ask students to explain what makes a game fair or unfair. Have students tell which player they would like to be—Player A or Player B. Ask students to explain their choice.

3 Practice/Assess

EXERCISES *On Your Own*

ERROR ALERT! Exercise 1 Some students

may think that *past draws* affect the *next one* and may, therefore, answer *red*.

Remediation: Point out that at the start of each draw, there is an *equal* chance of drawing a red or a blue cube. This is because the same number of red and blue cubes are in the bag each time.

OPEN-ENDED Exercise 10 Allow students to work in groups of 2–3. Then have groups exchange their games with another group. Groups can find the experimental probabilities of the games. Have students explain whether

they think the games are fair or unfair.

You can make an organized list to find all the possible outcomes. Some outcomes are identical. For Game 2, drawing Red 1, Red 2 is the same as Red 2, Red 1. You can cross out duplicate outcomes.

Red 1, Red 2	~~Red 2, Red 1~~	~~Blue 1, Red 1~~	~~Blue 2, Red 1~~
Red 1, Blue 1	Red 2, Blue 1	~~Blue 1, Red 2~~	~~Blue 2, Red 2~~
Red 1, Blue 2	Red 2, Blue 2	Blue 1, Blue 2	~~Blue 2, Blue 2~~

There are 12 possible outcomes in all.

Here's another way to find possible outcomes for Game 2. This method eliminates duplicate outcomes.

■ **EXAMPLE 2**

Draw a diagram of the possible outcomes of Game 2. List the possible outcomes for picking two cubes at a time.

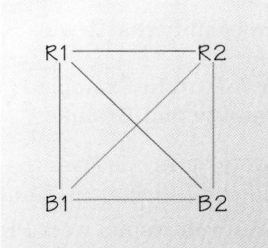

First red cube = **R1**
Second red cube = **R2**
First blue cube = **B1**
Second blue cube = **B2**

Each line represents a possible draw of 2 cubes.

The six possible outcomes are: R1 R2, R1 B2, R1 B1, B1 R2, B1 B2, and B2 R2.

10b. Check students' work; the game is likely to be fair if the experimental probabilities are about the same, unfair if they are very different.

11a.

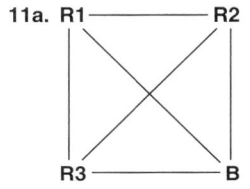

R1 R2, R1 R3, R2 R3,
R1 B, R2 B, R3 B

9. Recall that A wins Game 2 if the cubes are the same color, and B wins if they are different. How many outcomes of Game 2 give Player A a win? How many give Player B a win? Are A and B equally likely to win?   **2, 4; no**

10. a. ♣*Explain* Is Game 2 fair or unfair?   **unfair**
   b. ♣*Modeling* Find the experimental probabilities of winning Game 2 for Player A and Player B. How are these results related to your answer to Question 10(a)?   **See left.**

11. a. ✔*Try It Out* Draw a diagram for Game 3. List the possible outcomes.   **See left.**
   b. Is Game 3 fair or unfair? Explain.
   Fair; each player is equally likely to win.

Now you may assign Exercises 5–7, 9, 12–13.

Challenge them to change each unfair game into a fair game.

CULTURAL CONNECTION The game of dreidel, played during the Jewish holiday of Chanukah, includes probability. Each player places a counter in the center of the table and takes a turn spinning a four-sided top, called a dreidel. Depending on the letter that lands face up, the player will take either all the counters, half the counters, put in a counter, or do nothing.

AEP Review some of the language of probability. Write the words *equally likely* and *event* for the class and have students discuss the meanings. Some students may need to review the difference between *experimental* and *theoretical* probability. Discuss the theoretical probability of tossing a coin and getting heads as $\frac{1}{2}$. Then ask students to discuss the difference in probability if a coin is actually tossed.

Exercise 13 Remind students that a prime number has exactly two factors: one and itself.

CONNECTING TO THE STUDENTS' WORLD Have students name some real-life situations that involve probabilities that might be interpreted as fair of unfair. Ask them to explain their reasoning. **Answers may vary. Sample: name for a team being randomly chosen from a list, fair game**

EXERCISES *On Your Own*

1. Ki-Jana and Dwayne played Game 1. The first 3 cubes drawn were blue. Is the fourth cube more likely to be red or blue?
equally likely to be red or blue

2. The table at the right shows the scores of two players. Find Probability(A wins) and Probability(B wins). $\frac{9}{20}, \frac{11}{20}$

Game Results	
A wins	⊞⊞ IIII
B wins	⊞⊞ ⊞⊞ I
Times played	⊞⊞ ⊞⊞ ⊞⊞ ⊞⊞

3. Suppose Probability(A wins) = Probability(B wins). What can you say about the fairness of the game? **probably fair**

4. Si and Karen played a fair game. Karen won 7 times and Si won 13 times. How can this happen if the game is fair?
Answers may vary. Sample: Just because the game is fair, this does not imply the scores will be the same.

List all the possible outcomes for each game.

5. Place 1 red, 1 blue, and 1 yellow cube in a bag. Draw 2 cubes. **RB, RY, BY**

6. Place 1 green and 3 yellow cubes in a bag. Draw 2 cubes. **GY, YY**

7. Spin a spinner with sections labeled 1–4. Then flip a coin. **1H, 1T, 2H, 2T, 3H, 3T, 4H, 4T**

8. **Choose A, B, or C.** You and your friend want to play a game, but your only number cube is chipped. To try to make a fair game, you toss the cube 100 times and record the results.

Number	1	2	3	4	5	6
Times rolled	4	10	21	7	23	35

Which of the following games seems fair? Explain. **B; the experimental probabilities are about the same.**
A. You win if you roll a 6, and your friend wins if she rolls a 4.
B. If the number is even, you win. If it is odd, your friend wins.
C. If the number is 1, 2, or 3, you win. If it is 4, 5, or 6, your friend wins.

9a–b. Check students' work.
9. a. *Data Collection* Toss 2 coins at least 25 times. If you toss 2 heads or 2 tails, Player A wins. If you toss 1 head and 1 tail, Player B wins. Record your results in a table.
   b. Does the game seem fair or unfair? Explain.
   c. *Reasoning* Consider all possible outcomes for the game. Is the game fair? Support your answer without using your recorded data. **Yes; the outcomes are equally likely.**

10. *Open-ended* Design one game that is fair and one that is unfair. Use coins, number cubes, spinners, or colored cubes.
Check students' work.

■Practice 11-1 *Fair and Unfair Games*

Mirga and José played a game and completed the table below.

Mirga wins	ℍℍ ℍℍ ℍℍ ℍℍ ℍℍ I
José wins	ℍℍ I
Times played	ℍℍ ℍℍ ℍℍ ℍℍ ℍℍ ℍℍ II

1. Find Probability(Mirga wins) and Probability(José wins).
   Probability(Mirga wins) $\frac{26}{32}$; Probability(José wins) $\frac{6}{32}$

2. Do you think the game is fair? Explain.
   Answers may vary. Sample: No; if it is a game of skill, Mirga may be more skilled.

Andy and Bryan are playing a game in which Andy wins if the sum of the numbers on 2 number cubes is even, and Bryan wins if the sum of the numbers is odd.

3. Complete the grid at the right.

+	1	2	3	4	5	6
1	2	3	4	5	6	7
2	3	4	5	6	7	8
3	4	5	6	7	8	9
4	5	6	7	8	9	10
5	6	7	8	9	10	11
6	7	8	9	10	11	12

4. What sum appears most often?
   7

5. How many outcomes are even numbers?
   18

6. How many outcomes are odd numbers?
   18

7. Is the game they are playing fair or unfair? **fair**

8. Nick and Pat are playing a game with a black and white spinner like the one at the right. Nick wins if the spinner stops on black, and Pat wins if it stops on white. Is the game fair or unfair? Explain.
   Unfair; there is a larger area of black than white.
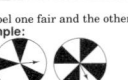

9. Draw two spinners. Make and label one fair and the other unfair. **Answers may vary. Sample:**

Unfair Fair

In copymaster and workbook formats

■Reteaching 11-1 *Fair and Unfair Games*

A game is **fair** when all players have an equal chance of winning. To decide whether a game is fair:

① Make a list of all the possible outcomes of the game.

② Determine whether each player has the same number of ways to win.

The Spinner Game
Spin a spinner with equal-size sections numbered 1–8. Player A wins on a multiple of 2 or 3. Player B wins on any other number. Is this game fair?

① Possible outcomes: 1, 2, 3, 4, 5, 6, 7, 8.

② Player A wins with a 2, 3, 4, 6, and 8. Player B wins with a 1, 5, 7.

The game is not fair.

You can use the results of playing a game to find the **experimental probability** of each player winning.

Two players played a game 25 times. Player A won 15 times and player B won 10 times.

$$\text{Probability(A wins)} = \frac{\text{number of times A won}}{\text{total games played}}$$
$$= \frac{15}{25}$$
$$= \frac{3}{5}$$

$$\text{Probability(B wins)} = \frac{\text{number of times B won}}{\text{total games played}}$$
$$= \frac{10}{25}$$
$$= \frac{2}{5}$$

For Exercises 1–3, list all possible outcomes for each game.

1. Toss a nickel and a quarter.
   HQ HN, HQ TN, TQ HN, TQ TN

2. Toss a coin and spin a spinner labeled 1–4.
   H1, H2, H3, H4, T1, T2, T3, T4

3. Toss a coin and roll a number cube.
   H1, H2, H3, H4, H5, H6, T1, T2, T3, T4, T5, T6

The line plot shows the results of rolling a number cube 20 times. Find the experimental probability.

4. Probability(6) $\frac{5}{20}$ or $\frac{1}{4}$

5. Probability(less than 4) $\frac{9}{20}$

6. Probability(greater than 3) $\frac{11}{20}$

7. Probability(even number) $\frac{12}{20}$ or $\frac{3}{5}$

8. Probability(prime number) $\frac{7}{20}$

■inds on Math Transparency

11-1

Write the numbers 1 through 12 in the magic star, using each number only once, so that the sum of numbers at the six points of the star and in each of the six rows is 26.

Answers may vary. Sample is shown.

See *Solution Key* for worked-out answers.

WRAP UP

IDENTIFYING THE BIG IDEA Ask students to explain how to determine whether a game is fair or unfair. Then have students describe how to find experimental probability.

LESSON QUIZ

Place 1 red, 1 blue, 1 green, and 1 yellow cube in a bag. Draw 2 cubes.

1. List all the possible outcomes for the game. What is the experimental probability of drawing a red and a green cube? **RB, RG, RY, BG, BY, GY; $\frac{1}{6}$**

Use the following information for Exercises 11–13.

Leroy rolled 2 number cubes and found the sum. He played the game many times and recorded the sums in the line plot below.

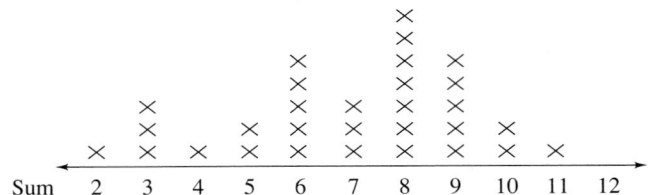

11. Find each experimental probability.
   a. Probability(3) $\frac{1}{10}$ b. Probability(8) $\frac{7}{30}$ c. Probability(12) 0
   d. Probability(5) $\frac{1}{15}$ e. Probability(2) $\frac{1}{30}$ f. Probability(1) 0

12. Complete a grid like the one at the right to show all possible outcomes. Which sum appears most likely? How does this compare to Leroy's results? **See right.**

	1	2	3	4	5	6
1	2	3	4	5	6	7
2	3	4	5	6	7	8
3	4	5	6	7	8	9
4	5	6	7	8	9	10
5	6	7	8	9	10	11
6	7	8	9	10	11	12

7 seems most likely; the answers are different.

13. Leroy said to Tim, "If the sum of the 2 number cubes is prime, you win. If the sum is not prime, I win." Use your grid from Exercise 12. Is this game fair or unfair? Explain. **Unfair; only 15 of the 36 outcomes are prime.**

Sums of Two Number Cubes

	1	2	3	4	5	6
1	2	3	4			
2	3	4				
3	4					
4	5					
5						
6						

14. *Writing* Elan and Litisha played a game 10 times and decided it was unfair. Jaime and Marek played the same game 50 times and decided it was fair. Who do you think is correct? Why? **Jaime and Marek; they played the game 40 more times.**

Mixed Review

Find the area of each parallelogram. *(Lesson 9-1)*

15. $b = 15$ in., $h = 10$ in.
    150 in.^{2}

16. $b = 28$ cm, $h = 21$ cm
    588 in.^{2}

17. $b = 16$ mm, $h = 42$ mm
    672 in.^{2}

Compare. Write <, >, or =. *(Lesson 10-1)*

18. $-7 \overset{>}{■} -9$ 19. $2 \overset{>}{■} -2$ 20. $25 \overset{>}{■} -50$ 21. $0 \overset{>}{■} -8$ 22. $6 ■ 0$ 23. $-11 \overset{<}{■} 13$

24. Find all the numbers less than 100 that have the prime factors 2, 5, and 7. *(Lesson 5-1)* **70**

Extra Practice, Lesson 11-1, page 532

1 Focus

CONNECTING TO PRIOR KNOWLEDGE
Ask students why a team of astronauts would practice situations that may occur in space. **Answers may vary. Sample: to know what to do if the real situation arises**
Tell students the term *simulation* means to model a situation.

2 Teach

THINK AND DISCUSS

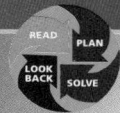 **Question 4** Review the meaning of the words *dependent* and *independent*.

TACTILE LEARNING Have students write and simulate their problems using models such as blank spinners and blank number cubes.

ASSESSMENT When students have completed Exercises 1–3, have pairs work together to write a paragraph describing how to use simulation to model problems.

EXTENSION and CONNECTION TO DESIGN Have students report on safety designs for automobiles. Have students explain the use of crash dummies in safety testing.

PROBLEM SOLVING STRATEGY

11-2 Simulate a Problem

Problem Solving Strategies

Draw a Diagram
Guess and Test
Look for a Pattern
Make a Model
Make a Table
✔ Simulate a Problem
Solve a Simpler Problem
Too Much or Too Little Information
Use Logical Reasoning
Use Multiple Strategies
Work Backward

THINK AND DISCUSS

You can solve many probability problems by *simulating* them. Make a model and collect data from the model. Then use the data to solve the problem.

SAMPLE PROBLEM........

Each day, Sam delivers Mr. Hay's newspaper sometime between 6:30 A.M. and 7:30 A.M. Mr. Hay leaves for work between 7:00 A.M. and 8:00 A.M. What is the probability that he gets his paper before he leaves for work?

 **READ**
Read for understanding. Summarize the problem.

1. Will Mr. Hay get the newspaper before he leaves for work if Sam delivers it before 7:00 A.M.? After 7:00 A.M.?
   yes; sometimes

2. Sam is equally likely to deliver Mr. Hay's paper at any time between 6:30 A.M. and 7:30 A.M. How much of the time does he deliver Mr. Hay's paper before 7:00 A.M.? After 7:00 A.M.? $\frac{1}{2}, \frac{1}{2}$

3. Mr. Hay is equally likely to leave for work at any time between 7:00 A.M. and 8:00 A.M. How much of the time does he leave before 7:30 A.M.? After 7:30 A.M.? $\frac{1}{2}, \frac{1}{2}$

4. Two times are important: the time at which Sam delivers the paper and the time at which Mr. Hay leaves for work. Do these times depend on each other, or are they independent?
   No, they are independent.

 PLAN
Decide on a strategy.

You can't collect data on Sam and Mr. Hay. Instead, simulate the situation with a model. You can draw colored cubes, toss coins, spin spinners, or roll number cubes.

Lesson Planning Options

Prerequisite Skills
• using experimental probability (11-1)

Vocabulary/Symbols
simulating, trial

Materials/Manipulatives
• blank spinners

Resources

Student Edition
Skills Handbook, p. 536
Extra Practice, p. 532
Glossary/Study Guide

Teaching Resources
Chapter Support File, Ch. 11
• Lesson Planner 11-2
• Practice 11-2, Reteaching 11-2
• Answer Masters 11-2
Teaching Aids Master 10
Glossary, Spanish Resources

Transparencies
19, Minds on Math 11-2

Warm Up
At the Grand Towers Youth Camp, 6 children stay in a cabin. If 140 children come to the camp, how many cabins are needed? **24**

VISUAL LEARNING **Question 6** Students can create a time line to record the times for each trial. They can make a time line for 6:30 to 8:00 A.M. They can mark a *P* on the time the paper arrives and an *L* to show the time Mr. Hay leaves for work. When students are spinning the spinners, suggest that they record the spins to the nearest quarter hour for each trial. For example: 6:30, 6:45, 7:00, and 7:15.

■ **ADDITIONAL PROBLEM**

Yan runs a restaurant. His favorite customer leaves the restaurant each night between 8:00 and 9:00 P.M. His next best customer comes to the restaurant every night between 8:45 and 9:45. What is the probability that these customers will dine in the restaurant at the same time? **Answers may vary. Sample:** $\frac{1}{16}$

3 Practice/Assess

EXERCISES *On Your Own*

ERROR ALERT! Exercise 2 Some students may have difficulty simulating the problem because it differs from the Sample Problem. **Remediation:** Tell students they can still use spinners to solve the problem. Have them designate 75% of each circle as a free throw and the other 25% as a miss.

Technology Options

Prentice Hall Technology

  Software for Learners
- Math Lab: Experimental Probability and Simulations
- Hot Page™ 32*
- Math Blaster® Mystery*
- Interactive Student Tutorial, Chapter 11*

Teaching Resource Software
- Computer Item Generator 11-2
- Resource Pro™ Chapter 11*

Internet • For related mathematics activities, visit the Prentice Hall site at www.phschool.com/math

*Available on CD-ROM only

Assignment Options for Exercises On Your Own
Core 1–7, 9
Extension 8
Use Mixed Review to maintain skills.

486

5. a. The spinner at the right models the times at which Sam delivers the paper. Make your own version of this spinner. **Check students' work.**

b. Make another spinner that models the times at which Mr. Hay leaves for work.

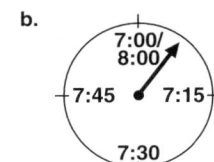

Sam's Delivery Times

Spinning each spinner once simulates what may happen on any given day. Each time you simulate the problem, you complete one **trial.**

 SOLVE
Try the strategy.

6. Simulate the problem. Make a table like the one below. Perform at least 20 trials. Spin both spinners for each trial. Record the time Sam delivers the newspaper and the time Mr. Hay leaves for work. **Check students' work.**

Trial	Time Sam Delivers	Time Mr. Hay Leaves	Did Mr. Hay Get a Paper?
1	6:45 A.M.	7:15 A.M.	Yes
2	7:21 A.M.	7:00 A.M.	No

7. Use the data in your table to find the experimental probability that Mr. Hay will get his newspaper before he leaves for work. This probability is the *number of times he gets his paper* divided by *the number of delivery days*.

7–8. Check students' work.

 **LOOK BACK**
Think about how you solved the problem.

8. ▲*Summarize* Based on your experiment, about how often might Mr. Hay expect to get his paper before leaving for work?

Now you may assign Exercises 1–9.

EXERCISES *On Your Own*

Simulate and solve each problem. Show all your work.

1. *Music* Suppose you practice piano for 15 minutes each weekday between 4:00 P.M. and 5:00 P.M. Your father gets home from work between 4:30 P.M. and 5:30 P.M. Find the experimental probability that your father gets home during your practice.

1–2. Check students' work.

2. *Sports* A professional basketball player makes 75% of his free throws. Find the experimental probability that he will make two free throws in a row.

TACTILE LEARNING Exercises 7–9 Have students use a checkerboard, newspaper ad, and a meter stick to help them solve the problems.

WRAP UP

IDENTIFYING THE BIG IDEA Ask students to describe how to simulate a problem in order to solve it.

LESSON QUIZ

Ms. Martin arrives at work between the hours of 7:15 and 8:00 A.M. Ms. Melon arrives at work between 7:30 and 8:15 A.M.

1. What is the probability that Ms. Martin will arrive at work earlier than Ms. Melon. **Answers may vary. Sample: $\frac{6}{9}$**

2. What model would you use to simulate this problem? **Answers may vary. Sample: a timeline**

3. *Collecting* Suppose each box of cereal contains a coupon for one of four collectible figures. Each box of cereal costs $3.50. About how much will it cost for you to get all four coupons? **Check students' work.**

Use any strategy to solve each problem. Show all your work.

4. *Statistics* How many people do you need to gather to be sure that at least two of them have birthdays in the same month? Explain your reasoning. **13; each of the first 12 could have birthdays in different months.**

5. *Movie Theaters* A survey reports that 73% of moviegoers buy a container of popcorn at the theater. A theater pays 45¢ for a container of popcorn and sells it for $1.50. What profit can the theater expect on a day when it has 1,000 customers? **$766.50**

6. *Restaurants* A restaurant has 25 of each sticker: soup, sandwich, salad, and drink. A sticker is put on each menu. Each time you visit the restaurant, you receive a menu. The item listed on the sticker is free. How many times will you need to visit the restaurant to get every free item? **Check students' work.**

7. *Games* An 8-by-8 checkerboard is missing two opposite corners. One domino covers two squares of the board. Can you exactly cover the entire surface with dominoes? **no**

8. *Writing* Suppose you want to order a new bedroom carpet. Write down all the information you would need to find out before you leave for the carpet store. **Check students' work.**

9. *Biology* Jumping spiders can jump 40 times their body length. About how far in centimeters might a 15-mm spider jump? **60 cm**

Mixed Review

Use tiles to find each sum. *(Lesson 10-3)*

10. $12 + (-3)$ **9**
11. $-8 + (-3)$ **−11**
12. $7 + (-7)$ **0**
13. $-49 + 69$ **20**
14. $-2 + (-1)$ **−3**
15. $4 + (-17)$ **−13**

Find the area of each triangle. *(Lesson 9-3)*

16. $b = 16$ m, $h = 11$ m **88 m²**
17. $b = 7.7$ cm, $h = 6.6$ cm **25.41 cm²**
18. $b = 19$ in., $h = 8\frac{1}{2}$ in. **$80\frac{3}{4}$ in.²**

19. *Choose a Strategy* Susan and Deepa made a total of 33 pairs of gloves. Deepa made twice as many pairs as Susan. How many pairs did each girl make? **Susan: 11 pairs, Deepa: 22 pairs**

PRACTICE

Practice 11-2 *Problem-Solving Strategy: Simulate a Problem*

Simulate and solve each problem. Show all your work.

1. Marty makes 60% of his free throws.
   a. What is the probability that he will make two free throws in a row? Draw a spinner to represent his free throw percent. Use the circle at the right. **About 36% of pairs of spins should be successes (2 free throws made).**

   Sample: (60%, 40%)
   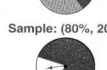

   b. Marty practices and can now make 80% of his free throws. Draw a spinner to represent his free throw percent. Use the circle at the right.

   Sample: (80%, 20%)
   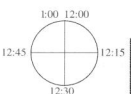

2. Mail is delivered between 12:00 P.M. and 1:00 P.M. every day to Joe's house. Joe comes home for lunch at 11:30 A.M. for 45 min. What is the probability that the mail will arrive during Joe's lunch break? Draw a spinner to represent the times that the mail is delivered. **$\frac{1}{4}$**

   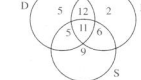

Use any strategy to solve each problem. Show all your work.

3. You have several coins that total 38 cents. You have the same number of pennies as nickels. How many coins do you have? **8 coins: 2 dimes, 3 nickels, and 3 pennies**

A group of 50 middle school students were surveyed about their after school activities. There were 33 students who take dance lessons, 31 students who take music lessons, and 31 students who play organized sports. There are 11 who do all three activities. Of these 50 students, 5 students only take dance and play sports, 6 students only take music and play sports, and 12 students only take dance and music.

4. How many take only dance lessons? **5**
5. How many take only music lessons? **2**
6. How many only play sports? **9**

7. There were 10 people at a party. At the end of the party, each person shook hands with each of the others. How many hand shakes were there in all? **45 handshakes**

In copymaster and workbook formats

RETEACHING

Reteaching 11-2 *Problem-Solving Strategy: Simulate a Problem*

Imagine that you have six different-color pairs of loose socks in a drawer. You reach into the drawer without looking and take out two socks. What is the probability you will pick a matched pair?

Read   How many socks are in the drawer? *12* How many different colors are there? *6* What are the possible results of picking two socks? *You can pick two socks of the same color or two socks of different colors.* What are you trying to find? *The probability of picking two socks of the same color.*

Plan   You can simulate the problem by making a spinner like the one at the right. Each number stands for one of the six colors. Spin the spinner twice to find the colors of the two socks. Record whether the colors are the same or different.

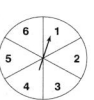

Solve   Repeat the simulation many times. Divide the number of times the colors were the same by the total number of simulations to find the experimental probability of getting a matched pair.

Look Back   What other methods could you use to simulate the problem? *Randomly pick two cards from six matched pairs of cards.*

Simulate and solve each problem. Show all your work.

1. You have four pairs of different-color loose socks in a drawer. You pick 2 socks without looking. What is the probability that you will get a matched pair? **about $\frac{1}{4}$**

2. You have 5 different-color pens and 2 different-color pencils in your pocket. You pick a pen and a pencil without looking. What is the probability that you will pick the red pen and red pencil? **about $\frac{1}{10}$**

3. Each day a restaurant offers a special sandwich made with one of three different meats and one of three different cheeses. Your favorite is salami with American cheese. What is the probability that your favorite is the special of the day? **about $\frac{1}{9}$**

4. In the refrigerator, you have 3 different juices in bottles and 4 different sodas in cans. Your favorites are the orange juice and the ginger ale. If you pick a juice and a soda without looking, what is the probability that you get both your favorites? **about $\frac{1}{12}$**

ENRICHMENT

Minds on Math Transparency

11-2

How many squares are in a 5 by 5 square grid?

55 squares

See *Solution Key* for worked-out answers.

Teaching Notes

1 Focus

CONNECTING TO PRIOR KNOWLEDGE Have students recall how they used cubes or spinners to simulate random events in order to solve problems. Then ask students: *What do you think the term random numbers means?* **Answers may vary. Sample: drawings numbers by chance**

Lesson Planning Options

Prerequisite Skills
- using experimental probability (11-1)
- working with percents (7-8)

Vocabulary/Symbols
random numbers

Materials/Manipulatives
- graphing calculator   • computer
- random number generator program

Resources

 Student Edition

Skills Handbook, p. 536
Extra Practice, p. 532
Glossary/Study Guide

 Teaching Resources

Chapter Support File, Ch. 11
- Lesson Planner 11-3
- Practice 11-3, Reteaching 11-3
- Alternative Activity 11-3
- Answer Masters 11-3
Teaching Aids Master 10
Glossary, Spanish Resources

Transparencies
99, Minds on Math 11-3

Warm Up

How many weeks are in 231 days? **33**

488

2 Teach

THINK AND DISCUSS

Explain to students that the two random number tables on page 488 contain the same numbers. The second table is in groups of three.

VISUAL LEARNING Organizing random number tables into different groups can reduce confusion. Having different groups also makes it easier to decode the numbers.

DIVERSITY Take care during the discussion of probability to avoid references to gambling or risk-taking. Emphasize probability as playing games. Encourage students to see the games as *experiments.*

ALTERNATIVE METHOD If a computer or graphing calculator is not available, students can find copies of random number tables in math or reference books.

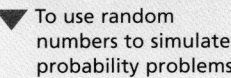 **Simulations and Random Numbers**

What You'll Learn

▼ To use random numbers to simulate probability problems

...And Why

You can use random numbers to find experimental probability quickly.

Here's How

Look for questions that
⚫ build understanding
✔ check understanding

THINK AND DISCUSS

It can take a lot of time to simulate a problem by spinning a spinner or flipping a coin. A quicker way is to use *random numbers.* This list shows how a computer printed out the digits 1 and 2 at random. Because the list is random, both digits are equally likely to occur.

List of Random 1's and 2's								
2	1	1	2	1	2	1	2	2
2	1	1	2	2	1	2	1	2
1	1	1	1	1	2	1	2	1
2	1	2	1	2	2	2	1	2
2	2	2	1	2	1	1	1	1
2	1	2	1	2	2	2	2	1
1	1	2	1	2	1	1	2	2
1	1	1	1	2	2	2	1	2

1. **a.** ⚫*Modeling* Suppose the number 1 represents a coin toss landing heads. Use the table above. Out of 72 trials, how many times might a coin land on heads? **36**
   b. Suppose the number 2 represents a coin toss landing tails. How many times might a coin land on tails? **36**

■ EXAMPLE

Modeling Use the random number table above. Find the experimental probability of tossing a coin three times and getting three heads in a row.

2 1 1	2 1 2	1 2 2	Make groups of 3 to
2 1 1	2 2 1	2 1 2	simulate 3 tosses.
1 1 1	1 1 2	1 2 1	
2 1 2	1 2 2	2 1 2	Let 1 represent heads, and
2 2 2	1 2 1	1 1 1	look for groups of 111.
2 1 2	1 2 2	2 2 1	
1 1 2	1 2 1	1 2 2	3 groups out of 24 show
1 1 1	1 2 2	2 1 2	3 heads in a row.

$$\text{Probability(3 heads)} = \frac{\text{number of groups of 3 heads}}{\text{total number of groups}}$$
$$= \frac{3}{24} = \frac{1}{8}$$

The experimental probability of tossing three heads in a row is $\frac{1}{8}$.

Question 2 To help avoid errors, have students copy the random number tables on lined or graph paper.

Questions 3 and 4 If technology is not available, give students photocopies of 500-digit (1's and 2's) tables before class.

■ **ADDITIONAL EXAMPLE**

FOR EXAMPLE

Look at the table on page 488 to answer the following: Find the experimental probability of tossing tails, heads, then tails. $\frac{6}{24}$ or $\frac{1}{4}$

Work Together

REASONING   Question 5d Ask students if they think that for the same number of tosses, the results for Probability(Tails) will be the same. **The probability of tossing heads or tails are equally likely.**

ERROR ALERT! Students may lose track of their tallies as they figure experimental probabilities. **Remediation:** Have students circle the probabilities they have checked on the random number tables as they look for the various combinations.

CONNECTING TO THE STUDENTS' WORLD Students may be interested to know that random number generation is used in some computer games to determine how far a player will move, or in situations involving chance.

2. Copy the random number table on page 488.
   a. ✔*Try It Out* Find the experimental probability of tossing two tails in a row.   **Answers may vary. Sample:** $\frac{1}{6}$
   b. ⊹*Think About It* Find the experimental probability of tossing heads, then tails, then heads, then tails.
   Answers may vary. Sample: $\frac{2}{9}$

You can use a graphing calculator or a random number generator program on a computer to generate random numbers.

 3. ⊹*Technology* Generate and print at least 500 random 1's and 2's. Model four coin tosses.   **a–b. Check students' work.**
   a. Find the number of times 3 heads were tossed, followed by heads again (1111). Write Probability(3 heads, then heads).
   b. Find the number of times 3 heads were tossed, followed by tails (1112). Write Probability(3 heads, then tails).

4. ⊹*Reasoning* Suppose a 500-digit random number table represents 125 groups of 4 coin tosses. About how many groups out of 125 would you expect to consist of 4 heads? Explain.
Check students' work. The answer should match the probability in Question 3(a).

Work Together 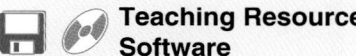 *Using Random Numbers*

Technology Work with a partner to find the experimental probability of tossing heads. Use any section of your 500-digit random number table from Question 3.

a–c. Check students' work.
5. a. Copy and complete the table below. Simulate tossing a coin 10 times. Then simulate 50 tosses, and so on.

Number of Tosses	Number of Heads	Number of Tails	Probability(Heads) = Number of Heads / Number of Tosses
10	▩	▩	▩
50	▩	▩	▩
100	▩	▩	▩
200	▩	▩	▩
500	▩	▩	▩

d. **Answers may vary. Sample: The probability is likely to be closer to $\frac{1}{2}$.**
   b. Make a line graph to show what happens to Probability(heads) as the number of tosses increases.
   c. ⊹*Writing* Describe any trends or patterns in the graph.
   d. ⊹*Reasoning* What do you think will happen to Probability(heads) if you simulate another 1,000 tosses?

Now you may assign Exercises 1–13.

Technology Options

Prentice Hall Technology

💾 📀 **Software for Learners**
- Math Blaster® Mystery*
- Interactive Student Tutorial, Chapter 11*

💾 📀 **Teaching Resource Software**
- Computer Item Generator 11-3
- Resource Pro™ Chapter 11*

Internet • For related mathematics activities, visit the Prentice Hall site at www.phschool.com/math

Available on CD-ROM only

Assignment Options for Exercises On Your Own
> **Core** 1–10, 12
> **Extension** 11, 13

Use Mixed Review to maintain skills.

3 Practice/Assess

EXERCISES *On Your Own*

WRITING **Exercise 11** Encourage students to use drawings or models to illustrate their explanations of simulations.

WRAP UP

IDENTIFYING THE BIG IDEA Ask students to explain how to use random numbers to simulate probability problems.

▷ **PROJECT LINK** Students should choose one method to conduct their trials. Have students save their tables for use later in the chapter.

EXERCISES *On Your Own*

Choose **Use technology or the random number table on page 488. Find the experimental probability of each set of coin tosses.** 1–4. Answers may vary. Samples are given.

1. the probability of getting two heads in a row $\frac{1}{6}$

2. the probability of getting two heads, then tails $\frac{1}{12}$

3. the probability of getting two tails, then heads $\frac{1}{12}$

4. the probability of getting three tails in a row $\frac{1}{24}$

5. *Reasoning* Do you think your answers to Exercises 1–4 will be different if you use a different random number table? Why or why not? **Yes; the answers are affected by the order of the numbers.**

Describe a way to use random numbers to find each probability. 6–9. Answers may vary. Samples are given.

6. You toss four coins and get four heads.
   Look for groups of four 1's.

7. On a spinner divided into two equal sections of different colors, you spin the same color five times in a row.
   Look for groups of five 2's.

8. You roll a number cube and get a prime number.
   Use numbers 1–6 and count 2's, 3's, and 5's.

9. *Modeling* A theater prints one digit 0–9 on each ticket. If you collect every digit, you get a free ticket. How many movies will you see before you get a free ticket? Use the random digits at the right to simulate this problem. **22**

10. **Choose A, B, or C.** The forecast calls for a 50% chance of rain for each of the next three days. Which method will *not* work to find the probability of three days of rain? **C**

    A. Toss a coin. Let heads be "rain" and tails be "no rain."
    B. Use a computer to list random digits 0–9. Let 0–4 be "rain" and let 5–9 be "no rain."
    C. Spin a spinner with three equal sections: one day of rain, two days of rain, and three days of rain.

11. *Writing* A basketball player makes 50% of her free throws. Explain how to use a simulation to find the experimental probability that she makes 7 of 10 free throws.

List of Random Numbers, 0–9
5 8 2 0 3 2 1 9
8 4 5 6 0 3 2 1
6 6 1 9 8 7 2 3
0 4 7 2 8 2 2 7
0 1 3 6 3 9 3 9
0 2 6 5 8 3 1 0
8 8 6 8 4 2 9 7
5 0 1 8 2 3 9 5

11. **Answers may vary. Sample: Form groups of ten from a list of random numbers 1 and 2. Let 1 be "makes free throw." Find the ratio of the number of groups with seven 1's to the total number of groups.**

490

LESSON QUIZ

How likely is a sum of 7 when you roll two number cubes? Use the list for a simulation. Use two digits at a time.

1	6	3	5	2	4	2
6	3	2	3	4	5	1
2	3	4	6	2	5	4
5	6	1	1	1	4	2

1. number of sums of 7   4

2. number of times the cubes were rolled   14

3. Probability(sums of 7) $\frac{2}{7}$

12. *Modeling* A game involves tossing three coins. If you get exactly two heads or two tails, you win. Otherwise, your opponent wins. Use a simulation to decide whether the game is fair or unfair. **Check students' work for simulation.**
The game is unfair.

13. a. *Modeling* How likely are "doubles" when you roll two number cubes? Use the list at the right to do a simulation. Use two digits at a time. Complete the table below.

List of Random Numbers, 1–6							
2	3	4	1	6	3	2	4
1	1	2	5	3	4	5	2
4	3	5	1	4	2	6	3
5	2	3	2	4	3	4	6
4	4	2	4	1	2	3	3
6	2	3	1	3	2	6	4
5	5	4	3	6	3	1	1
4	1	3	4	2	4	5	3
1	4	1	5	2	6	2	2

Number of Doubles	▨	6
Number of Times the Number Cubes Were Rolled	▨	36
Probability(Doubles)	▨	$\frac{1}{6}$

a. Answers may vary. Samples are given.

b. Now find the probability by listing all possible outcomes. How does your answer compare to the answer you got using a simulation? $\frac{1}{6}$; **check students' work.**

Mixed Review

Find the circumference and area of each circle. Round to the nearest unit. *(Lesson 9-5)*

14. $r = 7$ cm
44 cm; 154 cm^2

15. $d = 19$ m
60 m; 284 m^2

16. $r = 2.6$ m
16 m; 21 m^2

17. $d = 37$ mm
116 mm; 1,075 mm^2

18. $d = 11$ cm
35 cm; 95 cm^2

Use tiles to find the difference. *(Lesson 10-4)*

19. $-9 - 11$
-20

20. $4 - (-5)$
9

21. $-14 - (-3)$
-11

22. $-19 - 34$
-53

23. $-21 - (-7)$
-14

24. *Choose a Strategy* For the student meeting, 75% came on time. Of the students who came late, 50% were no more than ten minutes late. Four students were more than ten minutes late. How many students came to the meeting?   **32 students**

CHAPTER PROJECT

PROJECT LINK: SIMULATING

Design a method of choosing among three different movies. Use a computer, a list of random digits, a spinner, or number cubes to simulate the situation. Test your method for 100 trials and record your data in a table. Use the data to find the experimental probability of each outcome.

Check students' work.

PRACTICE

Practice 11-3 *Simulations and Random Numbers*

Use this list of random numbers for Exercises 1–4 to simulate tosses of two number cubes.

62 31 32 64 55 43 63 11 41 34 24 51 14 15 26 32 22 41 26 31
23 41 63 24 11 25 34 52 22 51 42 63 52 32 43 41 11 24 12 33

1. Are you more likely to get two different digits or the same two digits?
two different digits.

2. Find the number of pairs with different digits.
33 pairs

3. Find the number of times the cubes were tossed.
40 times

4. Find Probability(different digits).
$\frac{33}{40}$

5. Complete the table. Show the possible two-digit numbers formed when two number cubes are tossed.

	1	2	3	4	5	6
1	11	12	13	14	15	16
2	21	22	23	24	25	26
3	31	32	33	34	35	36
4	41	42	43	44	45	46
5	51	52	53	54	55	56
6	61	62	63	64	65	66

6. How many numbers with two different digits were possible in Exercise 5?   **30**

7. How many possible numbers are there?   **36**

8. Find Probability (numbers with different digits) as a percent.
83$\frac{1}{3}$%

Use this list of random numbers for Exercise 9.

1 1 2 1 1 1 2 1 2 1 1 1 1 2 2 2 1 1 1 1 2 2 1 2 2
1 2 2 2 1 1 1 1 2 1 1 2 2 1 2 1 1 2 2 2 2 1 1 2
2 2 2 2 2 1 1 1 1 1 1 2 1 2 2 1 2 2 1 2 1 2 1

9. Suppose 1 represents a coin toss landing heads. How many times would a coin land heads in the first 50 trials?
28 times

In copymaster and workbook formats

RETEACHING

Reteaching 11-3 *Simulations and Random Numbers*

A table of *random numbers* is one in which each number has an equal chance of being listed. Many simulations can be done using a table of random numbers. The table below lists 70 random numbers from 1–6.

List of Random Numbers, 1–6
4 2 1 2 3 4 1 5 6 1 3 1 5 4 2 1 3 5 2 2 4 6 3 3 4 2 1 3 1 2 1 4 2 1 4
4 3 3 1 3 6 2 2 3 4 1 1 3 6 2 3 6 2 4 4 5 1 5 1 4 2 3 5 6 3 3 4 1 5 1

Because the listed numbers are 1–6, you can use the table to simulate tossing a number cube.

4 2 1 2 3 4 1 5 6   For example, the first four numbers could represent tosses of 4, 2, 1, and 2.

4 2 1 2 3 4 1 5 6 3 1   The first five pairs could represent five rolls of two cubes: 4, 2; 1, 2; 3, 4; 1, 5; and 6, 1.

You can also use the table to simulate tossing a coin. Think of even numbers as heads and odd numbers as tails on a coin toss. For example, the first ten digits represent tossing two coins five times.

4, 2→H, H   1, 2→T, H   3, 4→T, H   1, 5→T, T   6, 1→H, T

Use the table of random numbers above to find each experimental probability. **Answers may vary. Samples are given.**

1. Toss three coins and get three heads.
$P = \frac{2}{23}$

2. Toss three coins and get either three heads or three tails.
$P = \frac{6}{23}$

3. Toss four coins and get two heads and two tails.
$P = \frac{6}{17}$

4. Roll two number cubes and get two twos.
$P = \frac{13}{34}$

5. Roll two number cubes and get different numbers.
$P = \frac{29}{35}$

6. Roll three number cubes and get two odd numbers and one even number.
$P = \frac{8}{35}$

ENRICHMENT

Minds on Math Transparency

11-3

The ratio of females to males in the computer club is 6 to 5. If four females and six males miss a meeting, the ratio is 10 to 7. How many students are in the computer club?

44 students

See *Solution Key* for worked-out answers.

491

1 Focus

CONNECTING TO PRIOR KNOWLEDGE
Write the words *probably* and *theoretical* for the class. Ask students to define the words. **Answers may vary. Sample: most likely to occur; hypothetical, supposed** Tell students they will be learning about theoretical probability.

Lesson Planning Options

Prerequisite Skills
• working with percents, fractions, and decimals (7-8)

Vocabulary/Symbols
theoretical probability

Resources

 Student Edition
Skills Handbook, p. 541
Extra Practice, p. 532
Glossary/Study Guide

 Teaching Resources
Chapter Support File, Ch. 11
• Lesson Planner 11-4
• Practice 11-4, Reteaching 11-4
• Alternative Activity 11-4
• Answer Masters 11-4
Teaching Aids Master 10
Glossary, Spanish Resources

 Transparencies
19, Minds on Math 11-4

Warm Up
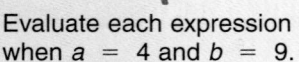
Evaluate each expression when $a = 4$ and $b = 9$.
1. $(4 + b) - a$ **9**
2. $(b + a) \cdot 6$ **78**
3. $(a \cdot b) + (a + b)$ **49**

492

2 Teach

Work Together

AEP Some students may not be familiar with the new terms associated with probability. Write the following words, one each on an index card: *outcome, event, improbable, likely, favorable, certain,* and *impossible.* Discuss the definitions as they appear in the lessons.

THINK AND DISCUSS

Example Ask students: *Where did the 5 in the denominator come from?* **There are a total of 5 marbles in the bag.** *Do you expect the probability for yellow to be higher or lower than* $\frac{2}{5}$? **lower** *Why?* **There are fewer yellow marbles than red marbles.**

 **11-4**

Theoretical Probability

What You'll Learn

▼ To find the theoretical probability of an event
▼ To define types of events

...And Why

You can use theoretical probability to predict the expected outcome of events.

Here's How

Look for questions that
▪ build understanding
✔ check understanding

Work Together   *Exploring Theoretical Probability*

Work with a partner. Look back at Game 3 on page 480. It involves 3 red cubes and 1 blue cube in a bag.

1. ▪ *Explain* Suppose you draw 1 cube from the bag. Which are you more likely to pick, red or blue? How do you know? **Red; there are more red than blue.**

2. ▪ *What If . . .* Suppose you draw 1 cube from the bag, and then put it back. If you do this many times, what fraction of the outcomes would you expect to be red? What fraction would you expect to be blue? **3; 1**

3. ▪ *Reasoning* Are all 4 cubes equally likely to be drawn? **yes**

THINK AND DISCUSS

▼ Finding Theoretical Probability

You can find experimental probability by doing simulations. You can find **theoretical probability** without a simulation. When all outcomes are equally likely, the theoretical probability of an event is the ratio below.

$$\text{Probability(event)} = \frac{\text{number of favorable outcomes}}{\text{number of possible outcomes}}$$

You can write this ratio as a fraction, a decimal, or a percent.

▪ **EXAMPLE**

Suppose you draw one marble from the bag at the left. What is the probability that you draw a red marble?

$$\text{Probability(red)} = \frac{\text{number of favorable outcomes}}{\text{number of possible outcomes}}$$
$$= \frac{\text{red marbles}}{\text{all marbles}}$$
$$= \frac{2}{5}$$
$$\text{Probability(red)} = \frac{2}{5} = 0.4 = 40\%$$

FOR EXAMPLE

A bag contains 2 red cubes, 3 blue cubes, and 5 white cubes.

a. How many possible outcomes are there?
   10

b. How many outcomes are favorable for blue? **3**

c. Find Probability(white). Write it as a fraction, as a decimal, and as a percent.
   $\frac{5}{10}$ or $\frac{1}{2}$, 0.5, 50%

ERROR ALERT! **Question 5** Students may not write the ratio with the correct number of possible outcomes. For example, they may write the probability of choosing a blue cube as $\frac{1}{3}$. **Remediation:** Point out that the first step in determining theoretical probability is to *consider all of the possible outcomes*. The denominator of the ratio will be the total number of possible outcomes, 4. The numerator will be the number of *events possible that you would like to happen*. For example, Question 5b asks for the number of events possible or favorable for red cubes

being drawn, 3. The probability is
 $\frac{\text{number of favorable outcomes}}{\text{number of possible outcomes}} = \frac{3 \text{ red}}{4 \text{ possible}}$.

VISUAL LEARNING Have students copy the chart of event types onto note cards. Encourage them to decorate the chart with colored pencils or markers.

---

4. ⁂*Reasoning* Look at the bag of marbles.
   a. How many yellow marbles should you add to the bag to make Probability(yellow) equal Probability(red)? **1 marble**
   b. After you add yellow marbles to the bag, what is the probability of drawing yellow? Drawing red? $\frac{1}{3}, \frac{1}{3}$

5. ✔*Try It Out* A bag contains 3 red cubes and 1 blue cube. Suppose you draw one cube.
   a. Are all cubes equally likely to be drawn? **yes**
   b. How many possible outcomes are there? How many outcomes are favorable for red? **4 outcomes; 3 outcomes**
   c. Find Probability(red). Write it as a fraction, as a decimal, and as a percent. $\frac{3}{4}$; 0.75; 75%

6. Answers may vary. Sample: *Favorable* is the outcome you want to occur.

6. ⁂*Explain* Look at the formula for theoretical probability on page 492. What does the word *favorable* mean?

Now you may assign Exercises 1–22.

▼**2** *Types of Events*

When the probability of an event is 1, the event is *certain* to happen. When the probability of an event is 0, the event is *impossible*. Events with probabilities between 0 and 1 are *possible*. Possible events can be likely or unlikely.

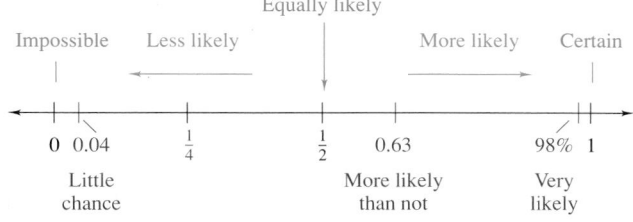

7a–c. Answers may vary. Samples are given.

7a. drawing a blue cube from a bag containing 5 blue cubes

   b. drawing a green cube from a bag containing 5 blue cubes

   c. drawing a blue cube from a bag containing 5 blue and 5 red cubes

7. ⁂*Think About It* Name an example of each type of event.
   a. certain   **b.** impossible   **c.** possible

8. ✔*Try It Out* Find the probability of each example you gave. Write each probability as a fraction, a decimal, and a percent.
   Answers may vary. Sample: 1, 1.0, 100%; 0, 0, 0%; $\frac{1}{2}$, 0.5, 50%

9. Suppose you roll a number cube once.
   a. List all the possible outcomes. **1, 2, 3, 4, 5, 6**
   b. What is the theoretical probability of rolling an odd number? $\frac{1}{2}$
   c. ⁂*Go a Step Further* Find the sum Probability(odd) + Probability(not odd). What does this sum represent?
   1; all possibilities

Now you may assign Exercises 23–33.

Technology Options

Prentice Hall Technology

 Software for Learners
- Math Blaster® Mystery*
- Interactive Student Tutorial, Chapter 11*

Teaching Resource Software
- Computer Item Generator 11-4
- Resource Pro™ Chapter 11*

Internet • For related mathematics activities, visit the Prentice Hall site at www.phschool.com/math

*Available on CD-ROM only

Assignment Options for Exercises On Your Own

To provide flexible scheduling, this lesson can be split into parts.

▼**1** **Core** 1–19
   Extension 20–22

▼**2** **Core** 23–32
   Extension 33

Use Mixed Review to maintain skills.

EXTENSION and CONNECTION TO SCIENCE
Tell students that scientists use theoretical probability in the science of genetics. For example, one parent may carry a gene for blue and brown eyes, and the other parent may carry a gene for blue and brown eyes. Scientists use theoretical probability to determine the likelihood of each possible eye color. In this case, the offspring has a $\frac{1}{4}$ chance of having blue eyes. Ask students to research the use of Punnett squares to determine genetic probabilities.

3 Practice/Assess

EXERCISES *On Your Own*

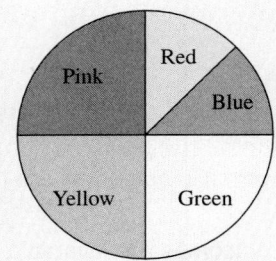

Exercise 7 Ask students to find the theoretical probability for blue or pink for the sections on the spinner shown. **Blue:** $\frac{1}{8}$; **Pink:** $\frac{1}{4}$; **Pink or Blue:** $\frac{3}{8}$

EXERCISES *On Your Own*

Find the theoretical probability for one roll of a number cube. Write each as a fraction, a decimal, and a percent.

1. Probability(4) $\frac{1}{6}$; $0.1\overline{6}$; 16%
2. Probability(9) 0; 0; 0%
3. Probability(not 5) $\frac{5}{6}$; $0.8\overline{3}$; 83%

4. Probability(1 or 3 or 6) $\frac{1}{2}$; 0.5; 50%
5. Probability(2 or 5) $\frac{1}{3}$; $0.\overline{3}$; 33%
6. Probability(even or odd) $\frac{6}{6}$; 1.0; 100%

Find the theoretical probability of each event.

7. A spinner has equal sections of red, blue, pink, green, and yellow. You spin blue or pink. $\frac{2}{5}$

8. You toss two coins. Both tosses are heads. $\frac{1}{4}$

9. The sum of the numbers rolled on two number cubes is 7. $\frac{1}{6}$

10. Find the theoretical probabilities of spinning red and spinning blue for the spinner at the right. $\frac{1}{3}$; $\frac{2}{3}$

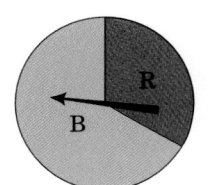

11. *Prize Drawing* Suppose your teacher writes the name of each student in your class on a card. To select a winner, your teacher draws one card from a box. Use your class data to find Probability(you win). Find Probability(you do not win). **Check students' work. The sum of probabilities must be 1.**

12. *Raffles* One thousand raffle tickets are sold. Suppose you buy two of them. One winning ticket is drawn.
    a. What is the probability that you will win? $\frac{1}{500}$
    b. What is the probability that you will not win? $\frac{499}{500}$

Ten cards are numbered 1–10. Find the theoretical probability of each event below. Write each as a fraction, a decimal, and a percent.

13. Probability(6) $\frac{1}{10}$; 0.1; 10%
14. Probability(even number) $\frac{1}{2}$; 0.5; 50%
15. Probability(odd number) $\frac{1}{2}$; 0.5; 50%

16. Probability(not 6) $\frac{9}{10}$; 0.9; 90%
17. Probability(1 or 2 or 3) $\frac{3}{10}$; 0.3; 30%
18. Probability(1 through 10) $\frac{10}{10}$; 1.0; 100%

19. A bag contains only red and green cubes. You select one cube without looking. Probability(red) $= \frac{3}{8}$.
    a. Find Probability(green). $\frac{5}{8}$
    b. How many of each color cube might the bag contain?
    c. Draw a spinner you could use to simulate this problem.
    b. **Answers may vary. Sample: 3 red and 5 green cubes**

c. **Answers may vary. Sample:**

WRITING **Exercise 21** Ask students who choose opposing points of view to compare their rationales.

OPEN-ENDED **Exercise 22** Allow students to work in pairs. Students can take turns spinning and recording the data.

ASSESSMENT Provide pairs of students two number cubes. Have them pick three different possible sums. Ask them to use the two cubes to find the theoretical probability for each sum.

WRAP UP

IDENTIFYING THE BIG IDEA Ask students how to determine the theoretical probability of an event.

JOURNAL Ask students to provide examples that illustrate their explanations. They may use drawings or diagrams.

PROJECT LINK Students who are visual learners may enjoy creating net patterns of their three-dimensional shapes. Students can use random number charts, spinners, or number cubes in their trials. Make sure students save their results for Lesson 6.

20. *Reasoning* Suppose you toss an *icosahedron*, a solid with 20 faces. All outcomes are equally likely. Each face is colored red, blue, yellow, or green. You know that Probability(yellow) = Probability(blue) = Probability(green) = Probability(red). How many faces are colored red? **5 faces**

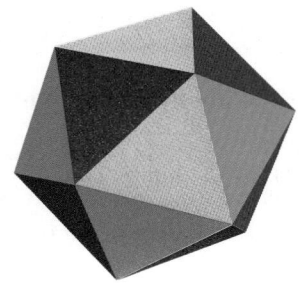

21. *Writing* Does it make more sense to you to think of probability as a fraction, a decimal, or a percent? Explain. **Check students' work.**

22. **a.** *Open-ended* Make a spinner with Probability(A) = 50%, Probability(B) = 10%, Probability(C) = 0%, and Probability(D) = 40%. **a–b. Check students' work.**

   b. Use a simulation to find the experimental probabilities of spinning the different letters. Then compare the experimental probabilities to the theoretical probabilities.

Use the letters at the right. Write the theoretical probability of each event as a fraction. Copy the number line and show where each probability lies.

$$A, B, C, D, E, F, G, H, I, J$$

23. Probability(H) $\frac{1}{10}$ 24. Probability(A or B) $\frac{1}{5}$

25. Probability(M) **0**   26. Probability(vowel) $\frac{3}{10}$

27. Probability(consonant) $\frac{7}{10}$ 28. Probability(A through J) **1**

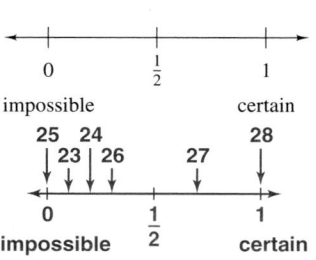

Classify each event as *certain, likely, unlikely,* or *impossible.*

29. You spin a wheel numbered 1–30 and land on a multiple of 2, 3, or 5. **likely**

30. You roll three number cubes. Their sum is 19. **impossible**

31. You roll five number cubes. Their sum is at least 5. **certain**

32. A meteorite lands in your schoolyard. **unlikely**

33. Order the following events from most likely to least likely.
   A. The sun rises tomorrow.
   B. You have a homework assignment tonight.
   C. The next coin you toss comes up heads.
   D. It snows somewhere in your state this week.
   E. You live to be 195 years old.
   F. You make a basket next time you play basketball.
   Check students' work.

JOURNAL
Summarize the difference between theoretical probability and experimental probability.

CHECKPOINT 1

■ *Checkpoint 1*   *Lessons 11-1 through 11-4*

One card is chosen at random from six cards labeled E, F, G, H, I, and J. Find the theoretical probability of each event. Write as a fraction, a decimal, and a percent.

1. Probability(H)
   $\frac{1}{6}$, 0.1$\overline{6}$, 16.6%

2. Probability(vowel)
   $\frac{2}{6}$ or $\frac{1}{3}$, 0.$\overline{3}$, 33.$\overline{3}$%

3. Probability(F or G)
   $\frac{1}{3}$, 0.$\overline{3}$, 33.$\overline{3}$%

4. Probability(*not* E)
   $\frac{5}{6}$, 0.8$\overline{3}$, 83.$\overline{3}$%

5. Circle A, B, C, or D. Which event is most likely?
   A. an even number when you roll a number cube
   B. odd number when you randomly choose a number 1–25
   C. an odd number when you roll a number cube
   D. "heads" when you toss a coin

Practice 11-4 *Theoretical Probability*

A number cube is rolled once. Find each probability. Write as a fraction, decimal, and percent.

1. Probability(even) $\frac{1}{2}$, 0.5, 50%
2. Probability(*not* 3) $\frac{5}{6}$, 0.8$\overline{3}$, 83$\frac{1}{3}$%
3. Probability(1, 3, or 5) $\frac{1}{2}$, 0.5, 50%
4. Probability(0) 0, 0.0, 0%
5. Probability(1 or 6) $\frac{1}{3}$, 0.3$\overline{3}$, 33$\frac{1}{3}$%
6. Probability(less than 7) 1, 1.00, 100%

Use the spinner at the right.

7. Find Probability(white) as a fraction, decimal, and percent.
$\frac{2}{5}$, 0.40, 40%

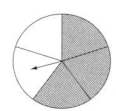

8. Find Probability(shaded) as a fraction, decimal, and percent.
$\frac{3}{5}$, 0.60, 60%

The fund-raising committee sold 500 raffle tickets. Tyrone bought three tickets. There will be one winning ticket.

9. What is the probability that Tyrone will win? $\frac{3}{500}$

10. What is the probability that Tyrone will not win? $\frac{497}{500}$

A box contains blue marbles and yellow marbles. One marble is to be drawn. Probability(yellow) = $\frac{5}{12}$.

11. What is Probability(blue)? $\frac{7}{12}$

12. **Choose A, B, or C.** Which spinner could you use to simulate the problem? A

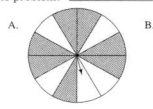 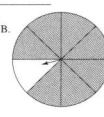 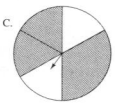

A.   B.   C.

13. If the box contains 24 marbles, how many of each color are there?
10 yellow and 14 blue

In copymaster and workbook formats

Reteaching 11-4 *Theoretical Probability*

For an event in which each outcome is equally likely to occur, the **theoretical probability** is the following ratio.

Probability(event) = $\frac{\text{number of favorable outcomes}}{\text{number of possible outcomes}}$

Find the probability of choosing the red chip if the chips are placed in a bag and mixed.

(Red) (Blue) (Blue) (Blue) (Blue)

$P(\text{red}) = \frac{\text{number of favorable outcomes}}{\text{number of possible outcomes}} = \frac{1}{5}$

The probability of choosing the red chip is $\frac{1}{5}$.

An event can be *impossible, certain,* or *possible but uncertain.*

- If an event is impossible, its probability is 0. The probability of the sun rising in the west is 0.
- If an event is possible, its probability is between 0 and 1. The probability that you will have homework tonight is between 0 and 1.
- If an event is certain, its probability is 1. If today is Tuesday, the probability that tomorrow is Wednesday is 1.

Find the probability of each event.

1. You pick a vowel from the letters in the word *event.* $P = \frac{2}{5}$
2. You pick a weekend day from days of the week. $P = \frac{2}{7}$
3. You pick a month that begins with the letter J. $P = \frac{1}{4}$
4. A spinner is labeled 1–6. You spin 1 or 5. $P = \frac{2}{6}$
5. You pick an odd number from 75 to 100. $P = \frac{1}{2}$
6. You pick a word with four letters from this sentence. $P = \frac{3}{5}$
7. You have a birthday on February 30. $P = 0$
8. Two number cubes are tossed. You toss a sum of 5. $P = \frac{1}{9}$

Classify the following events as *impossible, certain,* or *possible but uncertain.*

9. You toss three heads in a row with a coin. possible but uncertain
10. It rains the day of your school outing. possible but uncertain
11. You get a sum of 13 on two rolls of a number cube. impossible

Minds on Math Transparency

11-4

Karol is decorating a cube with 7 colors of paint. She paints 2 dots of each color on each side of the cube. How many dots does she paint on the cube?

84 dots

See *Solution Key* for worked-out answers.

LESSON QUIZ

Find the theoretical probability for each of the following on a spinner with five equal sections labeled 1–5. Write the probability as a fraction, a decimal, and a percent.

1. Probability(5) $\frac{1}{5}$; 0.20; 20%
2. Probability(odd) $\frac{3}{5}$; 0.60; 60%
3. Probability(3 or 5) $\frac{2}{5}$; 0.40; 40%

Classify each event as certain, likely, unlikely, or impossible.

4. You draw a number less than 75 from a bag containing 100 cards numbered from 1–100. **likely**
5. You roll three number cubes numbered 1–6. Their sum is 1. **impossible**
6. You roll two number cubes numbered 1–6. Their sum is a prime or a composite number. **certain**

Mixed Review

Find the perimeter and area of each square or rectangle.
(Lesson 9-2)

34. $s = 54$ mm
216 mm; 2,916 mm^2
35. $\ell = 17.5$ m, $w = 8$
51 m; 140 m^2
36. $\ell = 4$ m, $w = 3.2$ m
14.4 m; 12.8 m^2
37. $s = 4\frac{1}{2}$ in.
18 in.; 20.25 in.^{2}

Model each integer in two ways. *(Lesson 10-2)*

38. -7 39. 15   40. -4 41. -9 42. 11   43. -21
38–43. Check students' work for models.

44. *Survey* Jennifer surveyed all 28 members of her home economics class about their favorite food. In the survey, 75% of the students chose pizza. How many students did not choose pizza? *(Lesson 7-9)* **7 students**

✓ CHECKPOINT 1

Lessons 11-1 through 11-4

1. Five cards are numbered 1–5. Find the theoretical probability of each event. Write as a fraction, a decimal, and a percent.
   a. Probability(3) b. Probability(odd number) c. Probability(2 or 3)
   $\frac{1}{5}$; 0.2; 20% $\frac{3}{5}$; 0.6; 60% $\frac{2}{5}$; 0.4; 40%
2. Lei-Li and Earline played a game and completed the table at the right.
   a. Find the experimental probability that Earline wins. $\frac{7}{15}$
   b. Find the experimental probability that Lei-Li wins. $\frac{8}{15}$
   c. Is the game fair? Explain. **Probably yes; the experimental probabilities of winning are fairly close.**

Game Results	
Earline wins	14
Lei-Li wins	16
Times played	30

3. **Choose A, B, C, or D.** Which event is most likely? **B**
   A. "tails" when you toss a coin
   B. "consonant" when you randomly choose a letter A–Z
   C. "9" in a list with the digits 0–9
   D. "not 3" when you roll a number cube

CHAPTER PROJECT

PROJECT LINK: DESIGNING

Design a three-dimensional shape that would result in three equally likely outcomes. (Look back at Lesson 9-6 if necessary.) How would you use the shape so that a fair situation results? Test this method for 100 trials and record your data. Use the data to find the experimental probability of each outcome.

Check students' work.

In Lesson 11-4, students learned how to find the theoretical probability of an event and to define types of events. This toolbox allows students to explore how to find the complement of an event.

ERROR ALERT! Example Students may have trouble grasping the concept of the *complement of an event.* **Remediation:**

Point out to students that the probability of the event occurring and the probability of the complement occurring include *all the possible outcomes.* Show students that by adding the probability of the event to the complement the sum is 1. For example, Probability(star) + Probability(not star) = 1.

ASSESSMENT Exercises 1, 3, and 5 Have students compare probabilities. Have students work together to find the complement to the events. Share the students' results with the class.

■ **ADDITIONAL PROBLEMS**

A bowl contains 5 red counters, 4 white counters, and 3 blue counters. You select one counter without looking. Find each probability.
1. Probability(not red) $\frac{7}{12}$
2. Probability(not blue) $\frac{9}{12}$ or $\frac{3}{4}$

Resources

Transparencies
19

EXPLORATION

Complement of an Event

 After Lesson 11-4

The *complement of an event* includes all ways that the event *cannot* happen. Suppose you draw one of the marbles at the right without looking. The complement of picking a marble that has a star on it is picking a marble that does *not* have a star on it. If the probability of an event is Probability(event), then the complement of the event is Probability(*not* event).

■ EXAMPLE

Find Probability(star). Then find the probability of the complement of that event.

Probability(star) = $\dfrac{3}{5}$ ◀— favorable outcomes (marbles that have a star)
◀— all possible outcomes (total number of marbles)

Probability(not star) = $\dfrac{2}{5}$ ◀— favorable outcomes (marbles that do not have a star)
◀— all possible outcomes (total number of marbles)

Suppose you toss a number cube. Find each probability.

1. Probability(3) $\frac{1}{6}$
2. Probability(not 3) $\frac{5}{6}$
3. Probability(3 or 6) $\frac{1}{3}$
4. Probability(not 3 or 6) $\frac{2}{3}$
5. Probability(1, 2, 3, or 4) $\frac{2}{3}$
6. Probability(not 1, 2, 3, or 4) $\frac{1}{3}$

Suppose you draw one of the marbles shown at the right without looking. Find each probability.

7. Probability(plain white marble) $\frac{3}{10}$
8. Probability(not plain white marble) $\frac{7}{10}$
9. Probability(plain black marble) $\frac{2}{5}$
10. Probability(not plain black marble) $\frac{3}{5}$
11. Probability(happy face marble) $\frac{1}{5}$
12. Probability(not happy face marble) $\frac{4}{5}$
13. Probability(star marble) $\frac{1}{10}$
14. Probability(not star marble) $\frac{9}{10}$

15. *Writing* Look at the results of Exercises 7–14.
    a. Find the sum Probability(event) + Probability(not event). **1**
    b. Is this statement true or false?
       Probability(not event) = 1 − Probability(event) **true**
    c. If Probability(event) is $\frac{5}{8}$, what is Probability(not event)? $\frac{3}{8}$

1 Focus

CONNECTING TO PRIOR KNOWLEDGE
Ask students to recall how to determine the number of possible outcomes for the roll of two number cubes. **Answers may vary. Sample: Use a chart to list all of the possible numbers you can roll.** Then show students a tree diagram of all the possibilities

Lesson Planning Options

Prerequisite Skills

• simplifying fractions (precourse)
• multiplying whole numbers (precourse)

Vocabulary/Symbols

tree diagram, counting principle

Resources

 Student Edition

Skills Handbook, p. 540
Extra Practice, p. 532
Glossary/Study Guide

 Teaching Resources

Chapter Support File, Ch. 11
• Lesson Planner 11-5
• Practice 11-5, Reteaching 11-5
• Answer Masters 11-5
Glossary, Spanish Resources

 Transparencies
19, Minds on Math 11-5

Warm Up

Grace is tying carnations into bunches of one dozen. If she has 336 carnations, how many bunches can she make? Will she have any carnations left over? Explain. **28 bunches; none left over; 336 is divisible by 12.**

if they roll a one on the first cube. Draw branches for the numbers 1–6 to show the possibilities for the second number cube.

2 Teach

THINK AND DISCUSS

Example 1 Point out that only one of each combination applies. Tell students that the order of the letters is important. For example, PY is not the same as YP.

TACTILE LEARNING Question 2 Allow students to model the exercise using three different types of coins.

ERROR ALERT! Some students may not be sure of the number of branches to draw for a tree diagram. **Remediation:** Point out that in a tree diagram, each possible decision requires a branch. Tell students the number of branches means the *number of choices possible* for each decision.

11-5 ## Tree Diagrams and the Counting Principle

What You'll Learn

▼ To use tree diagrams to find possible outcomes and probabilities

▼ To use the counting principle to find possible outcomes and probabilities

...And Why

Tree diagrams and the counting principle can help you make choices in everyday life.

Here's How

Look for questions that
🔹 build understanding
✔ check understanding

THINK AND DISCUSS

▼ *Using a Tree Diagram*

Suppose you want to choose among three after-school activities. You can choose the photography club, the yearbook club, or the computer club for a ten-week period. After ten weeks, you choose again for the next ten weeks. You can choose the same activity.

1. How many choices do you have for the first activity? **3 choices**

A **tree diagram** displays all possible choices. Each branch shows one choice. Use a tree diagram when all outcomes are equally likely to occur and when an event has two or more stages.

■ **EXAMPLE 1**   *Real-World Problem Solving*

Draw a tree diagram for the after-school activities. How many different ways can you choose?

Use P for the photography club, Y for the yearbook club, and C for the computer club.

First Activity	Second Activity	Possible Choices
P	P	PP
	Y	PY
	C	PC
Y	P	YP
	Y	YY
	C	YC
C	P	CP
	Y	CY
	C	CC

There are 9 different ways to choose activities.

2. ✔*Try It Out* Draw a tree diagram that shows all possible outcomes when you toss 3 coins. **See margin p. 500.**

■ ADDITIONAL EXAMPLES

FOR EXAMPLE 1
Draw a tree diagram that shows the possible outcomes for painting a house when the sides can be yellow, gray, or tan and the shutters can be black or white.

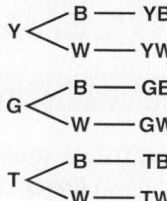

FOR EXAMPLE 2
Find the probability of choosing music during the second period if there is a choice of basketball as a fourth activity. $\frac{4}{16} = \frac{1}{4}$

FOR EXAMPLE 3
Sandwiches are prepared for a school field trip. Each sandwich has one of the following fillings: avocado, cheese, turkey, ham, or chicken salad. Each sandwich is made with either white or rye bread. Use the counting principle to find the number of different kinds of sandwiches that can possibly be made.
5 × 2 = 10 different sandwiches

You can use a tree diagram to find the probability of an event.

■ **EXAMPLE 2**

Use the tree diagram in Example 1. Suppose you choose randomly. What is the probability you choose the computer club for the second period?

$$\text{Probability} = \frac{\text{number of favorable outcomes}}{\text{number of possible outcomes}}$$

$$= \frac{3}{9} \quad \longleftarrow \text{There are 3 favorable outcomes:} \\ \text{PC, YC, and CC.}$$

$$= \frac{1}{3}$$

Probability(computer club in second period) $= \frac{1}{3}$

3. **Reasoning** Is there a relationship between the number of first- and second-period activities and the number of possible choices? If so, what is it?

3. The number of possible choices is the product of the number of first-period activities and the number of second-period activities.

4. **Yes; multiply the number of choices at each stage.**

4. **Analyze** Do you see a way to count all possible outcomes without using a tree diagram or a grid? Explain.

Now you may assign Exercises 1–4.

▼ *Using the Counting Principle*

Another way to find the number of possible outcomes is to use *the counting principle*.

THE COUNTING PRINCIPLE

The number of outcomes for an event with two or more distinct stages is the product of the number of outcomes at each stage.

■ **EXAMPLE 3** *Real-World Problem Solving*

Food Suppose you want to buy a pizza. The menu is at the left. Thick and thin crusts cost the same. You have enough money for only one topping. How many different types of pizza can you buy?

Use the counting principle.

Topping (6 choices)	Crust (2 choices)	Types of pizza
6	× 2	= 12

You can buy 12 different types of pizza.

Pizza Palace

Toppings	Crusts
mushrooms	thick
onions	thin
pepperoni	
sausage	
peppers	
extra cheese	

Technology Options

Prentice Hall Technology

Software for Learners
- Hot Page™ 33*
- Math Blaster® Mystery*
- Interactive Student Tutorial, Chapter 11*

Teaching Resource Software
- Computer Item Generator 11-5
- Resource Pro™ Chapter 11*

Internet • For related mathematics activities, visit the Prentice Hall site at www.phschool.com/math

*Available on CD-ROM only

Assignment Options for Exercises On Your Own

To provide flexible scheduling, this lesson can be split into parts.

▼ **Core** 1–3
   Extension 4

▼ **Core** 5–8
   Extension 9

Use Mixed Review to maintain skills.

Suppose one of each type of sandwich is made. What is the probability of getting a turkey sandwich? $\frac{2}{10}$ or $\frac{1}{5}$

ASSESSMENT Ask students to write their own definition of the counting principle. Ask them to provide an example with their definitions.

DIVERSITY and VISUAL LEARNING Ask students to discuss why they might choose a tree diagram over another model to solve a problem.

3 Practice/Assess

EXERCISES *On Your Own*

DIVERSITY and WRITING Exercise 4 Some students may still need help interpreting tree diagrams. Let students work in pairs to write a problem.

Exercises 5–8 Have students use either tree diagrams or the counting principle to solve each problem. Ask students to explain their reasons for choosing their methods.

IDENTIFYING THE BIG IDEA Ask students how to use tree diagrams and the counting principle to find possible outcomes and probabilities.

---

pages 498–500   Think and Discuss

2.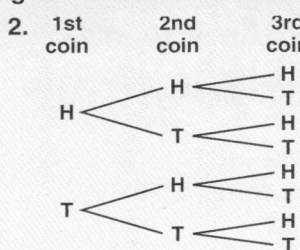

pages 500–501   On Your Own

1.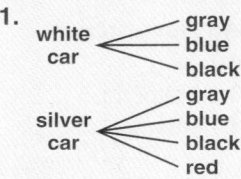

2. small cube, small pyramid, small cone, small cylinder, small triangular prism, large cube, large pyramid, large cone, large cylinder, large triangular prism

8a. 36 outcomes

b. Answers may vary. Sample: It is quicker.

c. $\frac{1}{36}$

page 501   Mixed Review

10. 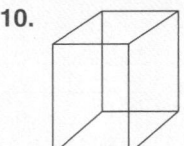   11.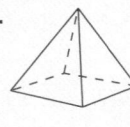

12.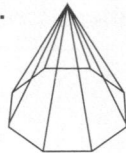

500

---

5. ✔*Try It Out* Suppose Pizza Palace decides to offer one more topping. Now how many types of pizza can you buy?   **14 types**

6. ⬛*Visual Thinking* What information do you get with a tree diagram that you do not get with the counting principle?
Answers may vary. Sample: a list of possible outcomes

You can also use the counting principle to find the probability of an event.

■ EXAMPLE 4

Use the menu from Example 3. Suppose you choose a pizza at random. What is the probability that you choose a mushroom pizza with a thin crust?

Number of possible outcomes = $6 \times 2 = 12$ ⟵ Use the counting principle.

$$\text{Probability} = \frac{\text{number of favorable outcomes}}{\text{number of possible outcomes}}$$

$$= \frac{1}{12}$$

Probability(mushroom, thin crust) = $\frac{1}{12}$

7. ✔*Try It Out* Find the probability of randomly choosing each type of pizza.
   a. a thick crust $\frac{1}{2}$ b. a pepperoni pizza $\frac{1}{6}$

Now you may assign Exercises 5–9.

EXERCISES *On Your Own*

1. *Cars* A white car comes with a gray, blue, or black interior. A silver car also has the option of a red interior. Draw a tree diagram showing all possible color combinations. How many are there? **See margin for diagram; 7.**

2. Small and large blocks in a set come in five shapes: cube, pyramid, cone, cylinder, and triangular prism. List all the different types of blocks in the set. **See margin.**

3. A spinner has equal sections of red, blue, and green. Use a tree diagram to find the probability of no more than one result of red in two spins. $\frac{8}{9}$

4. *Writing* Write a problem that can be solved using the tree diagram at the right. Solve your problem.
Check students' work.

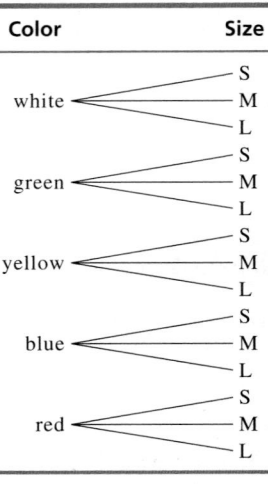

Color	Size
white	S / M / L
green	S / M / L
yellow	S / M / L
blue	S / M / L
red	S / M / L

LESSON QUIZ

1. A new line of mountain bikes comes in three models: the Jetstar, the Road Hawk, and the Eagle. Each bike comes in two colors—black or red. Use a tree diagram to find all the possible combinations.

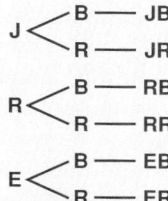

```
      B —— JB
J  <
      R —— JR

      B —— RB
R  <
      R —— RR

      B —— EB
E  <
      R —— ER
```

2. Use the counting principle to find the number of choices for each bike if handle bars come in steel or chrome. **12**

---

5. *Menu Planning* A cafeteria always serves the same three main courses and three desserts. Each day, you choose a combination of one main course and one dessert. How many meals can you eat before you repeat a combination? **9 days**

6. *Games* To play a game, you spin a $\frac{1}{12}$ spinner and take a card. The spinner has sections that tell you to move 1, 2, 3, or 4 spaces. The cards read Free Turn, Lose a Turn, or No Change. Find the probability that you move 3 spaces and lose a turn.
8a–c. See margin p. 500.

7. *Travel* Four airlines fly nonstop from Baltimore to Columbus. Five airlines fly nonstop from Columbus to Seattle. How many different pairs of airlines can you use to fly from Baltimore to Seattle through Columbus? **20 pairs**

8. a. Suppose you roll two number cubes. Use the counting principle to find the number of possible outcomes.
   b. Why is using the counting principle easier than drawing a tree diagram?
   c. Find the probability of rolling two 5's.

9. *Consumer Issues* The table below gives some of the choices available when you buy a computer. Suppose you choose one keyboard, one monitor, and one printer.

Keyboards	Monitors	Printers
Standard $50	Color 15-in. $369	Inkjet $149
Extended $90	Color 17-in. $699	Color Inkjet $369
Adjustable $130	Color 19-in. $1,399	Laser $819

a. How many outcomes are possible? **27 outcomes**   b. **12 outcomes**
b. You want a monitor larger than 15 in., but you do not want an adjustable keyboard. How many outcomes are left?
c. Which combination costs the least? Which combination costs the most? What is the range of costs? **standard keyboard with 15-in. monitor and inkjet printer; adjustable keyboard with 19-in. monitor and laser printer; $568–$2,348**

Mixed Review

Sketch each three-dimensional figure. *(Lesson 9-6)* **10–12. See margin p. 500.**

10. square prism   11. rectangular pyramid   12. octagonal pyramid

Make a function table for each function. *(Lesson 10-6)*

13. meters as a function of kilometers
$f(x) = 1,000x$

14. hours as a function of days
$f(x) = 24x$

15. *Choose a Strategy* Randy delivers 270 newspapers during a seven-day week. He delivers twice as many on the weekend as on the weekdays. How many newspapers does he deliver on the weekend? **180 newspapers**

■ *Practice 11-5* Tree Diagrams and the Counting Principle

Each shape in a set of attribute blocks comes in two sizes (small and large), three colors (yellow, red, and blue), and two thicknesses (thick and thin).

1. Use a tree diagram and list all the different blocks for each shape. Check students' diagrams.

Size	Color	Thickness	Size	Color	Thickness
small	yellow	thick/thin	large	yellow	thick/thin
	red	thick/thin		red	thick/thin
	blue	thick/thin		blue	thick/thin

2. How many outcomes are possible?   **12**

3. Find Probability(red)   **$\frac{1}{3}$**

4. How many outcomes will be blue and thin? **2**

5. How many outcomes will be large? **6**

6. Show how you could use the counting principle to find the number of outcomes.   **2 · 3 · 2 = 12**

7. Suppose a medium size is also available. What is the new total outcomes? **18**

Each day Jake makes his lunch for school. Today he can choose from white, rye, or wheat bread. He can choose turkey, cheese, or ham slices.

8. Draw a tree diagram to show all possible sandwiches. Check students' diagrams.

Bread	Slices	Bread	Slices	Bread	Slices
white	turkey/cheese/ham	rye	turkey/cheese/ham	wheat	turkey/cheese/ham

9. How many sandwich choices would he have if lettuce were an option? **18 sandwiches**

Marguerite has socks in 4 different colors (red, blue, white, and black) and shoes in 3 different colors (blue, white, and black).

10. What is the probability that she will choose white socks and white shoes? **$\frac{1}{12}$**

11. What is the probability that she will choose matching socks and shoes? **$\frac{3}{12}$ or $\frac{1}{4}$**

In copymaster and workbook formats

■ *Reteaching 11-5* Tree Diagrams and the Counting Principle

Your choices for your new car are an exterior color of white, blue, or black, and an interior of fabric or leather.

A **tree diagram** shows all possible choices. Each branch shows one choice.

```
white < fabric / leather
blue  < fabric / leather
black < fabric / leather
```

You can use the *counting principle* to find the total number of choices.

When there are m choices for one decision and n choices for another decision, then there are $m \times n$ choices for the two decisions.

The tree diagram shows 6 choices. Choosing your car at random, the probability of picking a white car with leather interior is

$P(\text{white, leather}) = \frac{1}{6}$.

Exterior choices		Interior choices		Total
3	×	2	=	6

There are 6 possible choices for your car.

Make a tree diagram. Then tell how many possible choices there are. Check students' diagrams.

1. Marva can have a small, medium, or large salad. She can have Italian, French, or Russian dressing on it. **9 choices**

2. Students can use a spiral notebook, a loose-leaf binder, or a folder, and white, yellow, blue, or tan paper. **12 choices**

3. Tyron can have a corn tortilla or a flour tortilla. He can put either beans, beef, chicken, cheese, or grilled vegetables in it. **10 choices**

Use the counting principle to solve each problem.

4. There are 4 kinds of fruit, 2 kinds of cereal, and 2 kinds of milk. How many ways can a bowl of cereal, fruit, and milk be chosen? **16 ways**

5. There are 4 choices for skis, 2 choices for bindings, and 5 choices for boots. How many ways can skis, bindings, and boots be chosen? **40 ways**

6. There are 3 pairs of jeans, 2 vests, and 5 shirts. How many ways can jeans, a vest, and a shirt be chosen? **30 ways**

7. There are 10 ice cream flavors, 4 syrups, and 5 toppings. How many ways can one flavor, one syrup, and one topping be chosen? **200 ways**

Minds on Math Transparency

11-5

Find the next four numbers in the pattern.

$-1, 2, -2, 1, -3,$ ___, ___, ___, ___

$0, -4, -1, -5$

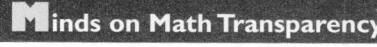

See *Solution Key* for worked-out answers.

501

1 Focus

CONNECTING TO PRIOR KNOWLEDGE Ask students: *I tossed a coin two times. It landed heads up both times. On the third toss, is it more likely that the coin will land heads up or tails?* **Answers may vary. Sample: Each side has the same chance.** *Why doesn't the fact that the coin came up heads two times*

make it more likely the coin will be tails the next time? **Answers may vary. Sample: Each coin toss is a separate event.**

2 Teach

THINK AND DISCUSS

Question 2 It may be necessary to combine the results for several games to detect a pattern in the experimental data.

DIVERSITY Lessons in this chapter ask students to think about thinking. Students' thinking moves from the concrete operations stage to the formal operations stage. In formal operations, students see a concept as part of a larger system. Some students progress at different rates. Sometimes this progression in thinking does not ever occur or it occurs at a later time in their development. Allow students to continue to use manipulatives, but encourage students to also write more formal mathematical expressions.

Lesson Planning Options

Prerequisite Skills
• multiplying fractions (6-7)

Vocabulary/Symbols
independent

Materials/Manipulatives
• colored cubes   • bag

Resources

 Student Edition

Skills Handbook, p. 540
Extra Practice, p. 532
Glossary/Study Guide

 Teaching Resources

Chapter Support File, Ch. 11
• Lesson Planner 11-6
• Practice 11-6, Reteaching 11-6
• Alternative Activity 11-6
• Answer Masters 11-6
Teaching Aids Master 10
Glossary, Spanish Resources

 Transparencies
19, Minds on Math 11-6

Warm Up

Sixteen teams play in a tournament. Each team plays until it loses. How many games must be played to determine the winner?
15 games

11-6 **Independent Events**

What You'll Learn

1️⃣ To identify independent events

2️⃣ To use multiplication to find probabilities of independent events

...And Why

The probability of independent events is a factor in many games.

Here's How

Look for questions that
⚓ build understanding
✔ check understanding

THINK AND DISCUSS

1️⃣ *Exploring Independent Events*

Look again at Game 3 on page 480.

1. ⚓*Look Back* Recall your results for Game 3. Is Game 3 fair or unfair? If you need to, play the game again or draw a diagram to consider all possible outcomes. **fair**

2. ⚓*Data Analysis* Change Game 3 to Game 3A, described below. Play Game 3A with a partner at least 20 times. To get more data, combine your results with the results of two other groups. Do you think Game 3A is fair or unfair? Explain. **unfair**

Game 3A

Place 3 red cubes and 1 blue cube in a bag. Draw a cube from the bag without looking. Record the color, put the cube back into the bag, and draw a second cube. If the 2 cubes are the same color, Player A wins. If not, Player B wins.

The tree diagram at the right shows 16 possible outcomes.

3. Is the tree diagram for Game 3, Game 3A, or both games? **Game 3A**

4. ⚓*Analyze* Use the tree diagram to decide whether this game is fair or unfair. **unfair**

5. In Game 3A, are all 4 cubes equally likely to be drawn on the first draw? On the second draw? Does the second cube drawn depend on the first cube drawn? **yes; yes; no**

6. Yes; the number of possible outcomes for the second cube is lower because the first cube is not available as an outcome.

6. In Game 3, does the second cube drawn depend on the first cube drawn? Why or why not?

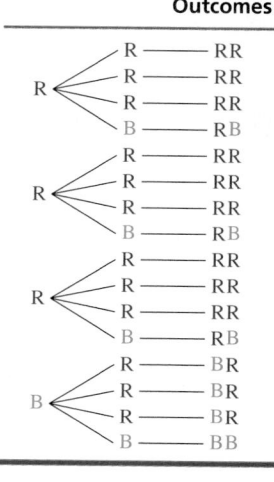

Outcomes

R — RR
R — RR
R — RR
B — RB
R — RR
R — RR
R — RR
B — RB
R — RR
R — RR
R — RR
B — RB
R — BR
R — BR
R — BR
B — BB

502

■ **ADDITIONAL EXAMPLE**

FOR EXAMPLE

There are six cubes in a bag. Four cubes are red and two cubes are blue. You draw a cube and put it back in the bag. This process is repeated two more times. Find the probability that you draw red cubes all three times.
$\frac{2}{3} \times \frac{2}{3} \times \frac{2}{3} = \frac{8}{27}$

Question 9 Encourage students to name events that do not involve games, such as getting tickets to two popular music concerts.

ERROR ALERT! Question 10 Students may not understand the difference between multiplying probabilities and using the counting principle. **Remediation:** Tell students that if events are *independent*, you find the probability that both events or all events will occur *by multiplying the probabilities together that you want to occur.*
Probability(blue) × Probability (blue) =

$\frac{1}{4} \times \frac{1}{4} = \frac{1}{16}$. Remind students that you use the counting principle to find all the possibilities that can occur: $4 \times 4 = 16$. (Have students look back at Example 3 on page 499.)

VISUAL LEARNING Question 11 Have students draw a tree diagram to verify the probabilities.

AEP **AUDITORY LEARNING** Ask students to relate the word *independent* to familiar vocabulary. Have them find the word *depend* within the word *independent*. Point out that

When the outcome of one event does not depend on the outcome of another event, the events are **independent.**

7. Which game has independent events, Game 3 or Game 3A?
3A

8. ✔ *Try It Out* Are the two events independent? Why or why not?
   a. It snows in Washington, D.C. A new President of the United States is inaugurated.
   b. A card is drawn from a deck and is not replaced. Another card is drawn from the deck.
   c. Your team scores the most points. Your team wins.
   d. At a soccer game, a coin is tossed and comes up heads. At the next game, the coin comes up tails.
   e. You take a dish from the kitchen cabinet. The dish falls and breaks.
   a–e. See left.

…ident John F. Kennedy was inaugurated on January 20, 1961.

8a. Yes; the outcome of one event does not depend on the outcome of the other.
b. No; the outcome of the second event depends on the outcome of the first.
c. No; winning depends on the number of points scored.
d. Yes; the outcome of one event does not depend on the outcome of the other.
e. No; the outcome of the second event depends on the outcome of the first.

9. ⊞ *Think About It* List some events that are independent and some that are not. Think of events that are not already described in this chapter. **Check students' work.**

Now you may assign Exercises 1–10.

▼2 *Multiplying Probabilities*

When events are independent, you can find the probability that both or all of them occur by multiplying the probabilities.

Probability(A and B) = Probability(A) × Probability(B)

■ **EXAMPLE**

For Game 3A, find Probability(both red).

Since the draws are independent, multiply their probabilities.
Probability(both red) = Probability(red) × Probability(red)

$$= \quad \frac{3}{4} \quad \times \quad \frac{3}{4}$$
$$= \quad \frac{9}{16}$$

10. ✔ *Try It Out* Use multiplication to find Probability(both blue). $\frac{1}{16}$

Technology Options

Prentice Hall Technology

💾 💿 **Software for Learners**
• Math Blaster® Mystery*
• Interactive Student Tutorial, Chapter 11*

💾 💿 **Teaching Resource Software**
• Computer Item Generator 11-6
• Resource Pro™ Chapter 11*

🌐 **Internet** • For related mathematics activities, visit the Prentice Hall site at www.phschool.com/math

*Available on CD-ROM only

Assignment Options for Exercises On Your Own

To provide flexible scheduling, this lesson can be split into parts.

▼1 **Core** 1–6, 9, 10
   Extension 7, 8

▼2 **Core** 11–20
   Extension 21, 22

Use Mixed Review to maintain skills.

depend means to rely on something else. The prefix *in* means *not* or *no*. So the meaning of the word *independent* is to *not depend* or *not rely* on something.

EXTENSION and CONNECTION TO SCIENCE
The study of genetics deals with the probability that certain traits will appear in an offspring. Have students find out if the probabilities of having a certain hair or eye color are independent events. Ask them to support their findings with examples.

ASSESSMENT A spinner has equal sections that are green, red, yellow, and blue. Players spin the spinner once and toss a coin. What is the probability that the outcome will be green and heads? Ask pairs of students to solve this problem and determine if the events are independent. Then ask them to write an explanation of how to determine all possible outcomes. $\frac{1}{4} \times \frac{1}{2} = \frac{1}{8}$; **independent; multiply 4 times 2.**

3 Practice/Assess

EXTENSION Exercises 12–17 Students may be interested in conducting experimental trials to see if this data matches the theoretical probabilities. Ask students to analyze their results and explain any large differences between the experiments and the theoretical probabilities.

$\frac{1}{2} \times \frac{1}{2} \times \frac{1}{2} = \frac{1}{8}$ **11.** ⚓ *Go a Step Further* Use multiplication to find the probability of tossing 3 tails in a row. Complete: Probability(tails, tails, tails) = Probability(tails) × Probability(tails) × Probability(tails) = ▓ × ▓ × ▓ = ▓.

12. *Clothes* Mei-Ling has 3 sweaters: pink, white, and blue. She has 2 pairs of jeans: white and blue. She has 5 pairs of socks: 3 white, 1 blue, and 1 pink. She randomly selects 1 sweater, 1 pair of jeans, and 1 pair of socks. What is the probability that all are blue?

a. Use the counting principle to find the number of possible outcomes. Then find the probability. **30; $\frac{1}{30}$**

b. Use multiplication to find the probability. $\frac{1}{3} \times \frac{1}{2} \times \frac{1}{5} = \frac{1}{30}$

c. They are equal; check students' work for reasoning.

c. Compare your answers for parts (a) and (b). Which method do you prefer for finding the probability? Why?

d. Explain why you might not want to use a tree diagram to find this probability. **Answers may vary. Sample: tree diagram would be huge.**

Now you may assign Exercises 11–22.

EXERCISES *On Your Own*

Decide whether the events are independent. Explain your answer.

1. You take a coin from your pocket. Then you take another coin from your pocket. **Dependent; the second outcome depends on the first.**

2. It snows one night. The next day you go sledding. **Dependent; you can go sledding only if there is snow.**

3. A card is drawn from a deck and replaced. Another card is drawn from the deck.

3–5. Independent; the second outcome does not depend on the first.

4. You reach into your drawer and take a pencil. At the same time, you take a pen.

5. The local basketball team wins the league championship. That same year, the local baseball team also wins its league championship.

6. Choose A, B, or C. Which events are *not* independent? **B**

A. Your computer randomly lists a 1 and then a 2.

B. You draw a blue card from a deck of colored cards. Then you draw a red card.

C. You roll a number cube twice and get 6 both times.

504

IDENTIFYING THE BIG IDEA Ask students to describe independent events. Have them explain how to determine the probability of two independent events both happening.

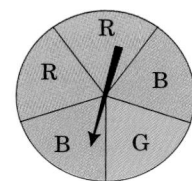 **PROJECT LINK** Ask students to compare and contrast the two methods that they used. Then have them write a general statement that explains why they prefer one method over the other.

Math at Work

If you have block scheduling or extended class periods, consider having students bring board games to class. Have small groups choose one board game. Have them determine whether events occurring in the games are independent.

LESSON QUIZ

Decide whether the events are independent. Explain your answer.

1. You are allowed two foul shots in a basketball game. You make the first shot, but miss the second. **independent; one does not depend on the other**

2. You are caught holding in a game of football. Your team is then penalized 10 yd. **not independent; one event affects the other event.**

7. *Writing* Use your own words to explain to a friend what independent events are. Give some examples. **Check students' work.**

8. *Biology* Assume "boy" and "girl" are equally likely outcomes for a baby. Is having two babies of the same sex as likely as having two babies of different sexes? Use a tree diagram to show your solution. **Yes; see margin for diagram.**

Use the spinner for Exercises 9–11. It is spun twice.

9. Are the two spins independent events? Explain.
Yes; the outcome of the second spin does not depend on the first.

10. Draw a tree diagram to show all possible outcomes. Find the probability that the two spins are the same color. **See margin for diagram;** $\frac{9}{25}$.

11. Use multiplication to find the probability that the first spin is blue and the second spin is red. $\frac{4}{25}$

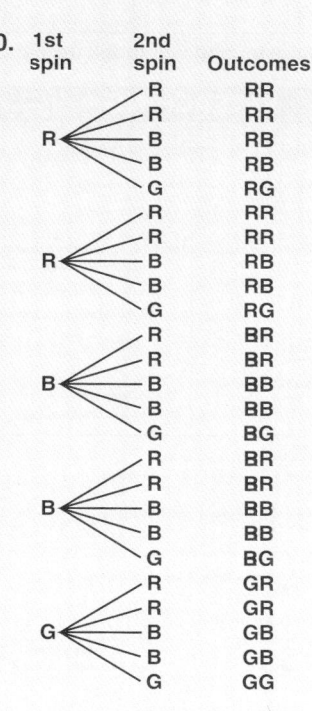

You roll a number cube, and you spin a spinner that is half red and half yellow. Find the probability of each result.

12. any number and red $\frac{1}{2}$

13. any odd number and red $\frac{1}{4}$

14. the number 1 and yellow $\frac{1}{12}$

15. a number less than 3 and either color $\frac{1}{3}$

16. a number less than 7 and either color 1

17. a number greater than 6 and either color 0

Use the two boxes at the right for Exercises 18–20. Box 1 contains 4 cards. Box 2 contains 5 cards.

18. A card is drawn from Box 1. Find Probability(M). $\frac{1}{4}$

19. A card is drawn from Box 1. Then a card is drawn from Box 2. Find Probability(ME). $\frac{1}{10}$

Box 1

20. A card is drawn from Box 1 and put back. Then another card is drawn. Find Probability(HA). $\frac{1}{16}$

Box 2

21. In a game you toss a coin and roll two number cubes. How many possible outcomes are there for each of the following?
   a. one coin **2 outcomes**   b. one cube **6 outcomes**
   c. one coin and one cube **12 outcomes**   d. the game **72 outcomes**

22. *Biology* Assume "boy" and "girl" are equally likely outcomes for a baby. What is the probability of having five girls in a row? Show your solution in at least two different ways. $\frac{1}{32}$; **check students' work for reasoning.**

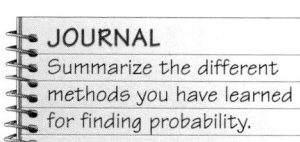

JOURNAL
Summarize the different methods you have learned for finding probability.

pages 504–506   On Your Own

8.
1st baby	2nd baby
Boy	Boy
	Girl
Girl	Boy
	Girl

10.
1st spin	2nd spin	Outcomes
R	R	RR
	R	RR
	B	RB
	B	RB
	G	RG
R	R	RR
	R	RR
	B	RB
	B	RB
	G	RG
B	R	BR
	R	BR
	B	BB
	B	BB
	G	BG
B	R	BR
	R	BR
	B	BB
	B	BB
	G	BG
G	R	GR
	R	GR
	B	GB
	B	GB
	G	GG

Practice 11-6 Independent Events

Use the spinner at the right for Exercises 1–5. It is spun twice.

1. Use multiplication to find the probability that the first spin is white and the second spin is black. $\frac{1}{4} \times \frac{1}{2} = \frac{1}{8}$

2. Draw a tree diagram to show all possible outcomes. **Check students' diagrams.**

```
      R—RR        R—WR        R—BR        R—BR
R <   W—RW    W < W—WW    B < W—BW    B < W—BW
      B—RB        B—WB        B—BB        B—BB
      B—RB        B—WB        B—BB        B—BB
```

3. Find the probability that the two spins are different colors. $\frac{5}{8}$

4. Find the probability that the two spins are the same color. $\frac{3}{8}$

5. Are the spins independent events? Explain **Yes; the second spin does not depend on the first.**

6. Assume a number cube is rolled. Find Probability(4). $\frac{1}{6}$

7. The number cube is rolled again. Find Probability(4). $\frac{1}{6}$

8. Find the probability of rolling 5 two times in a row. $\frac{1}{36}$

9. Find the probability of rolling two 4's in a row. $\frac{1}{36}$

A coin is tossed four times.

10. Find Probability(HTHT). $\frac{1}{16}$

Suppose each letter of your name is printed on a separate card. Samples for "Linda Carpenter".

11. One card is drawn from a container holding first-name letters. Find Probability(first letter of your first name).
$\frac{1}{5}$

12. One card is drawn from a container holding last-name letters. Find Probability(first letter of your last name).
$\frac{1}{9}$

13. One card is drawn from each container. Find Probability(your initials).
$\frac{1}{45}$

In copymaster and workbook formats

RETEACHING

Reteaching 11-6 Independent Events

Events are **independent** when the occurrence of one event does not affect the other event. If two events are independent, the probability that both will occur is the product of their probabilities.

A chip is drawn from the bag, its color noted, and put back into the bag. Then another chip is drawn. Are the two events independent?

The events are independent because the color of the first chip drawn does not affect the color of the next chip drawn.

Find the probability that a red chip will be drawn, followed by a blue chip.
• Probability of drawing a red chip is $\frac{2}{5}$.
• Probability of drawing blue chip is $\frac{1}{5}$.

Probability(red) × Probability(blue)
$= \frac{2}{5} \times \frac{1}{5}$
$= \frac{2}{25}$

The probability of drawing a red chip followed by a blue chip is $\frac{2}{25}$.

Are the events independent? Write yes or no.

1. You get a B on the first math test and a B on the second math test. **no**

2. It rains on the first day of November. It snows on the first day of December. **yes**

3. You get three 4's on three rolls of a number cube. **yes**

4. A light bulb burns out in your kitchen. A light bulb burns out in your flashlight. **yes**

Find the probability for each situation.

5. A letter is chosen from each word: BABY GIRL. Find Probability (Y and R). $\frac{1}{16}$

6. A letter is chosen from each word: BABY BOY. Find Probability (B and B). $\frac{1}{6}$

A number cube is rolled and a coin is tossed. Find the probability of each event.

7. the number 6 and tails $\frac{1}{12}$

8. an even number and heads $\frac{1}{4}$

9. a number less than 1 and heads 0

10. an odd number and tails $\frac{1}{4}$

ENRICHMENT

Minds on Math Transparency

11-6

I am an integer. When you add −1 to me, the sum is the opposite of the difference when you subtract −5 from me. What integer am I?

−2

See Solution Key for worked-out answers.

You roll a number cube numbered 1–6 and toss a coin. Find the probability of each result.

3. the numbers 1 or 6 and heads $\frac{1}{6}$

4. an even number and heads $\frac{1}{4}$

5. a number greater than 1 and tails $\frac{5}{12}$

Mixed Review

Calculator Find the diameter of a circle with the given circumference. Round to the nearest unit. *(Lesson 9-4)*

23. 112.3 cm **36 cm**
24. 19.5 m **6 m**
25. 265.6 mm **85 mm**
26. 131.7 in. **42 in.**
27. 160 ft **51 ft**
28. 178 km **51 km**

Give the measures of the complement and the supplement for each angle. *(Lesson 8-3)*

29. 27° **63°, 153°**
30. 58° **32°, 122°**
31. 62° **28°, 118°**
32. 73° **17°, 107°**
33. 87° **3°, 93°**
34. 14° **76°, 166°**

35. *Choose a Strategy* Mr. Oblas is ordering wrapping paper. He can order ten 12 in.-by-12 in. sheets for $2.95 each or a roll that measures 30 in. by $2\frac{1}{2}$ ft for the same price. Which is the better buy? **12-in. × 12-in. sheets**

CHAPTER PROJECT

PROJECT LINK: ANALYZING

Compare the experimental method you used on page 496 with the one you used on page 491. Which method do you prefer? Using your preferred method, conduct and record 150 more trials. Then compare the experimental probability of each event to its theoretical probability. Do you think you made the right decision? Explain. **Check students' work.**

Math at Work

BOARD GAME DESIGNER

A career as a board game designer could be just right for you if you love games. Game design requires an eye for color and a creative mind. It also calls for mathematical skills. Many games involve the use of spinners or number cubes. That's where probability comes in. Data analysis is used to evaluate marketing information about a game.

Visit the Game Designers Guide at www.public.iastate.edu/~shad/ EnvGames/ resource.shtml for information.

1 Focus

CONNECTING TO PRIOR KNOWLEDGE Ask students to recall the use of a tree diagram to find possible outcomes for an event. Have students brainstorm to find for what situations it would be helpful to have an organized list of possible different *combinations* or *arrangements* of items. **Answers may vary. Sample: seating arrangements**

2 Teach

Work Together

KINESTHETIC LEARNING Question 2 It is important for students to act out this activity. Have one student in each group record the possibilities.

AEP VISUAL LEARNING Provide flash cards with the following words written on them: *prediction, different, arrangement*. Have students work in pairs to write a definition on the back of each flash card. As each term comes up in the lesson, discuss its meaning. Then have students try to repeat the definitions to each other.

11-7 Exploring Arrangements

What You'll Learn

▼ To use a tree diagram or a list to find number of arrangements

▼ To use the counting principle to find number of arrangements

...And Why

You can use arrangements to solve problems involving hobbies and sports.

Here's How

Look for questions that
🔹 build understanding
✔ check understanding

Work Together

Exploring Order

Work in groups of four.

1. 🔹*Predict* In how many different ways do you think you can arrange your group members in a line? **24 ways**

2. 🔹*Data Collection* Form a line of your group members. Then form as many different lines as you can. How many could you form? **24 ways**

3. 🔹*Modeling* Simulate the problem. Represent each member with an object, such as a pencil or a book. Arrange the objects in as many different lines as you can. Do you get the same result as in Question 2? **yes**

4. 🔹*Modeling* Represent each group member with a letter or number. Make an organized list of all possible arrangements.
   a. How many arrangements are in your list? **24 arrangements**
   b. Compare this number with your prediction and your answers to Questions 2 and 3. **Check students' work.**

THINK AND DISCUSS

▼ *Using a Tree Diagram or List*

You can use a tree diagram or an organized list to count possible arrangements. An arrangement in a particular order is called a **permutation.**

5. The tree diagram shows the arrangements of the numbers 1, 2, and 3.
   a. Draw a tree diagram that shows all possible arrangements of the numbers 1, 2, 3, and 4. **See back of book.**
   b. How many permutations of 1, 2, 3, and 4 are there? **24 permutations**

			Outcomes
1	2 — 3	— 123	
	3 — 2	— 132	
2	1 — 3	— 213	
	3 — 1	— 231	
3	1 — 2	— 312	
	2 — 1	— 321	

Lesson Planning Options

Prerequisite Skills
• working with tree diagrams (11-5)

Vocabulary/Symbols
permutation, factorial notation

Resources

 Student Edition

Skills Handbook, p. 540
Extra Practice, p. 532
Glossary/Study Guide

 Teaching Resources

Chapter Support File, Ch. 11
• Lesson Planner 11-7
• Practice 11-7, Reteaching 11-7
• Answer Masters 11-7
Teaching Aids Masters 1, 2
Glossary, Spanish Resources

 Transparencies
1, 19, Minds on Math 11-7

Warm Up

In a group of six people, each person shakes hands once with each of the other people in the group. How many handshakes are exchanged? **15**

Question 4 Ask students: *Are all arrangements accounted for in your list? Have you repeated any arrangement? Is there a better strategy?*

■ **ADDITIONAL EXAMPLES**

FOR EXAMPLE 1

In how many different orders can 5 bells be rung? **120**

FOR EXAMPLE 2

You are in a competition with 9 other students. In how many different orders can all of you finish? Give your answer in factorial notation and as a number. **10!; 3,628,800**

ERROR ALERT! Question 8 Students may not understand this application of the counting principle. **Remediation:** Tell students to examine the possible choices for each stage.

a. There are four possible bells that can be rung at first.

b. After the first bell is rung, there are three bells *left* that could be rung.

c. Then there are two bells left.

d. Then there is one bell left.

Have students model the example using counters.

Example 2 Review the meaning of the word *factor*.

Technology Options

Prentice Hall Technology

  Software for Learners
• Math Blaster® Mystery*
• Interactive Student Tutorial, Chapter 11*

Teaching Resource Software
• Computer Item Generator 11-7
• Resource Pro™ Chapter 11*

Internet • For related mathematics activities, visit the Prentice Hall site at www.phschool.com/math

*Available on CD-ROM only

Assignment Options for Exercises On Your Own

To provide flexible scheduling, this lesson can be split into parts.

▼ **Core** 1–5
   Extension 8

▼ **Core** 6, 7, 9–14
   Extension 15, 16

Use Mixed Review to maintain skills.

---

6. ⬛*Think About It* To count the number of permutations of A, B, C, and D, Veronica started to make the list at the right. Complete the list. Would you organize the list this way? Explain.

Veronica's List
ABCD BCDA CDAB ⋯
ABDC
ACBD
⋮

See back of book for list; check students' work for reasoning.

Answers may vary. Sample: list; yes

7. ⬛*Choose* Which method do you prefer, drawing a tree diagram or making a list? Do they give the same results?

Now you may assign Exercises 1–5, 8.

▶ *Using the Counting Principle*

You can also use the counting principle to find permutations.

■ **EXAMPLE 1** *Real-World Problem Solving*

Music In how many different orders can 4 bells be rung?

Find the product of the number of outcomes at each stage.

First bell rung	Second bell rung	Third bell rung	Fourth bell rung
4	× 3	× 2	× 1 = 24

There are 24 different ways to ring the bells.

 On special occasions, church-bell ringers *ring the changes*. That means they ring the bells in every possible permutation.

8. ⬛*Reasoning* Why are there four choices for the first bell to be rung, but only three choices for the second? **One bell has already been chosen.**

9. ⬛*Think About It* When might using the counting principle be most practical? What disadvantage does this method have that an ordered list does not? **When the number of options is large; you cannot see all the outcomes.**

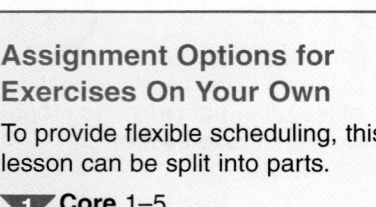

ASSESSMENT Ask pairs of students to write a definition of the term *permutation*. Have them describe why using the counting principle to find a permutation is, in some cases, more practical than using a tree diagram.

3 Practice/Assess

EXERCISES *On Your Own*

Exercises 1–2 Students can check their

results using the counting principle.

OPEN-ENDED Exercise 8 Students with long first names may want to use calculators to solve.

CONNECTION TO LITERATURE Exercise 15 In the 1950s, C.S. Lewis wrote *The Chronicles of Narnia* which included *The Lion, The Witch, and the Wardrobe*, and *Prince Caspian*.

EXTENSION Exercise 16 Ask students to figure out how long it would take Flora to ring

all of the numbers if it took 15 s for each try.

5,040 × 15 s = 75,600 s or 21 h

WRAP UP

IDENTIFYING THE BIG IDEA Ask students how they can use a tree diagram and the counting principle to find the number of arrangements of a given number of items.

LESSON QUIZ

1. In how many different ways can you

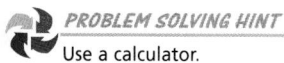
PROBLEM SOLVING HINT
Use a calculator.

10. ✔*Try It Out* A bell-ringing club wants to ring the changes of 6 bells. In how many different orders can 6 bells be rung?
720 ways

In Example 1, there are $4 \times 3 \times 2 \times 1$ permutations. Instead of writing out the multiplications, you can use **factorial notation.** Write 4!, which is read "4 factorial." Most calculators have a factorial key.

■ **EXAMPLE 2** *Real-World Problem Solving*

🔲 *Track and Field* Suppose you are in the finals of the 50-meter dash with 7 other students. In how many different orders can all of you finish?

8 ⚀ *40320* ◀── Use a calculator.

There are 40,320 different ways for the race to end!

11. ✔*Try It Out* Suppose one student has to drop out of the 50-meter race. Now how many ways are there for the race to end? Give your answer in factorial notation and as a number.
7! or 5,040 ways

Now you may assign Exercises 6–7, 9–16.

EXERCISES *On Your Own*

1. Mai lists the arrangements of the letters in her name as follows: MAI, IAM, IMA, MIA, and AMI. Has she left out any arrangements? If so, which? **yes; AIM**

2. Make an organized list of all possible arrangements of the letters in the word STOP. How many are English words?
See margin for list; 3 words.

3. *Sports* It's better to have the first turn in a bobsled competition, because the bobsled track slows with use. Draw a tree diagram to show all the possible arrangements of bobsled teams from Germany, Switzerland, and Italy.
See margin.

red — white / blue
white — red / blue
blue — red / white

4. *Writing* Write a problem that can be solved by using the tree diagram at the right. Solve the problem another way.
Check students' work.

5. *Chorus* The school chorus will sing five songs at an assembly. In how many different orders can the songs be sung?
120 orders

6. *Radio* A radio disc jockey has ten songs to play in the next hour. In how many different ways can he arrange the songs?
3,628,800 ways

7. *Games* Many newspapers feature scrambled word games. In how many ways can you scramble the letters in the word RANDOM? **720 ways**

8. *Open-ended* How many permutations are there of the letters in your first name? State the method you used to find the answer, and explain why you chose it.
Check students' work.

CHECKPOINT 2

■ *Checkpoint 2*   *Lessons 11-5 through 11-7*

1. A box contains the six cards shown at the right. A card is picked at random and replaced. Another card is picked. What is the probability that two Y's are picked? _¼_

2. Using the digits 2 through 7, how many different 6-digit numbers can be made without repeating a digit in a number? _720_

3. Eight children enter a foot race. In how many different ways can the runners finish the race? Assume there are no ties. _40,320 ways_

4. The school is planning to sell T-shirts. There will be a choice of 3 colors, 4 sizes, and 3 styles. Use the counting principle to find the number of possible choices. _36_

5. The cafeteria menu each day includes choices of 3 entrees, 3 beverages, 2 soups, and 3 desserts. What is the number of possible combinations for choosing one of each? _54_

pages 509–510   On Your Own

2.
SING	ISNG	NSIG	GINS
SIGN	ISGN	NSGI	GISN
SNIG	IGSN	NGSI	GSIN
SNGI	IGNS	NGIS	GSNI
SGNI	INGS	NIGS	GNSI
SGIN	INSG	NISG	GNIS

3.

page 510   Checkpoint 2

1a.

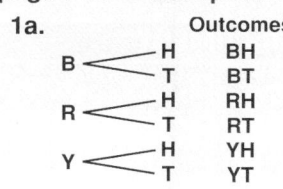

509

Practice 11-7 Exploring Arrangements

1. Make an organized list of how Ali, Ben, and Chou can sit in a row one behind another.

Ali	Ali	Ben	Ben	Chou	Chou
Ben	Chou	Ali	Chou	Ali	Ben
Chou	Ben	Chou	Ali	Ben	Ali

2. Make an organized list of all possible arrangements of the letters in the word BITE. How many of the arrangements are English words? one; bite

BITE	ITEB	TEBI	EBIT
BIET	ITBE	TEIB	EBTI
BTIE	IBTE	TBIE	EITB
BTEI	IBET	TBEI	EIBT
BETI	IETB	TIEB	ETIB
BEIT	IEBT	TIBE	ETBI

3. Mrs. Schoup has three errands to do on her way home from work.

a. Draw a tree diagram to show all the different arrangements of going to the post office, the library, and the gas station. Check students' diagrams.

P⟨ L–G – PLG / G–L – PGL   L⟨ P–G –LPG / G–P –LGP   G⟨ P–L – GPL / L–P –GLP

b. How many different ways can Ms. Schoup organize her errands? 6 ways

4. Vince has homework in math, science, language, and reading. How many different ways can he do his homework? 24

5. The spring program will feature songs from five grade levels. How many different ways can these grade levels be arranged? 120

6. How many different ways can six posters be displayed side-by-side? 720

7. Amy can scramble the letters in her name and make two more words. How many different ways can the letters in her name be scrambled into nonwords? 3

8. How many different ways can you scramble the letters in your first name? Answers will vary. Sample: Casi, 24 ways

Use a calculator to find each value.

9. 6!   10. 9!   11. 5! + 5   12. 11!
720   362,880   125   39,916,800

In copymaster and workbook formats

Reteaching 11-7 Exploring Arrangements

An arrangement of items in a particular order is a **permutation**.

Find the number of permutations for lining up Leah, Brian, and Ahmad for a photograph. You can use these different methods.

- Draw a tree diagram.

Leah⟨ Brian—Ahmad / Ahmad—Brian
Brian⟨ Leah—Ahmad / Ahmad—Leah
Ahmad⟨ Leah—Brian / Brian—Leah

- Use the counting principle.

In how many ways can the first person be chosen? 3 ways

In how many ways can the middle person be chosen? 2 ways

In how many ways can the remaining person be chosen? 1 way

3 × 2 × 1 = 6

(The multiplication expression 3 × 2 × 1 can also be written as 3!. Read "3!" as "3 factorial.")

- Make an organized list.
  Leah, Brian, Ahmad
  Leah, Ahmad, Brian
  Brian, Leah, Ahmad
  Brian, Ahmad, Leah
  Ahmad, Leah, Brian
  Ahmad, Brian, Leah

There are 6 permutations of Leah, Brian, and Ahmad.

Use a tree diagram, a list, or the counting principle to find each total. You may want to use a calculator.

1. In how many ways can the letters of the word EATS be arranged? 24 ways

2. In how many ways can 6 desks be arranged across the front of a classroom? 720 ways

3. A basketball team has 5 starting players. In how many ways can their names be announced before the game? 120 ways

4. In how many ways can 8 songs on a CD be played if you use the shuffle feature on your CD player? 40,320 ways

5. Three students are waiting for the cafeteria to open. In how many ways can they enter the food line? 6 ways

6. For how many consecutive baseball games can the manager use a different batting order for 9 players? 362,880 games

Find the value.

7. 7! 5,040   8. 4! 24   9. 5! 120   10. 6! 720

Minds on Math Transparency

11-7

In a barnyard full of cows and chickens, there are 30 more legs than heads. If the ratio of cows to chickens is 4 to 3, how many cows are in the barnyard?

8 cows

See Solution Key for worked-out answers.

---

arrange the letters in the word PART? 24 ways

2. Three athletes, A, B, and C are competing in a diving competition. Draw a tree diagram to show all the possible arrangements of the order in which they will dive.

A⟨ BC — ABC / CB — ACB
B⟨ AC — BAC / CA — BCA
C⟨ AB — CAB / BA — CBA

3. What is the probability that diver B will go second? $\frac{1}{3}$

Use a calculator to find each value.

9. 6!   10. 10!   11. 8!   12. 7!   13. 13!   14. 4! + 4
720   3,628,800   40,320   5,040   6,227,020,800   28

15. *Literature* A library receives a new seven-volume set of *The Chronicles of Narnia* by C. S. Lewis.

a. In how many ways can the books be arranged in a row?

b. The seven books are placed in a random order on a shelf. What is the probability that the books are in the correct order from left to right? $\frac{1}{5,040}$

a. 5,040 ways

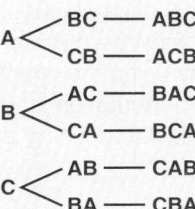

16. *Reasoning* Lola tells Ana that her phone number includes one of each digit from 3 through 9. Ana decides to try each possible number until she reaches Lola. If Ana is as unlucky as possible, how many tries will it take to reach Lola? 5,040 tries

Mixed Review

Find the surface area of each rectangular prism. *(Lesson 9-7)*

17. $\ell = 8$ m, $w = 10$ m, $h = 7$ m 412 m²

18. $\ell = 6.4$ m, $w = 5.2$ m, $h = 2.1$ m 115.28 m²

Graph each point on a coordinate plane. Label it with its letter. *(Lesson 10-7)* 19–24. See back of book.

19. $A(2, -2)$ 20. $B(-2, 2)$ 21. $C(-3, -5)$ 22. $D(2, 4)$ 23. $E(-3, 0)$ 24. $F(0, -5)$

25. *Fitness* Kay exercises $\frac{1}{6}$ h the first day, $\frac{1}{4}$ h the second day, and $\frac{1}{3}$ h the third day. If she continues this pattern, how long will Kay exercise on the fifth day? *(Lesson 2-2)* 1 h

---

✓ CHECKPOINT 2   Lessons 11-5 through 11-7

1. A blue, red, or yellow chip is selected, and a coin is tossed.

a. Draw a tree diagram to show all possible outcomes. See margin p. 509.

b. Find Probability(yellow, then tails). $\frac{1}{6}$

2. When ordering the luncheon special, you can choose from 3 entrees, 2 soups, and 2 desserts. Use the counting principle to find the number of possible combinations. 12 meals

3. A bag contains 3 green cubes and 4 red cubes. A cube is drawn and replaced. Another cube is drawn. What is the probability that 2 red cubes are drawn? $\frac{16}{49}$

4. In how many different ways can 6 students be lined up shoulder-to-shoulder for a photograph? 720 ways

PROBLEM SOLVING PRACTICE ★★

This page provides problems for students to solve using their knowledge of probability, predictions, combinations, scale, and reading tables of data. Allow students to use any method they find helpful.

Exercise 2 Encourage students to think of the probability of each event separately. Then students can think of the probability of both events happening together.

Exercises 3, 8, and 10 Have students show the ratios and proportions they used to find the answers.

Exercise 5 Point out to students that their scale drawings must fit on 8½ in. by 11 in. sheet of paper.

Exercise 9 Remind students to simplify the probability before searching for the correct response.

PROBLEM SOLVING PRACTICE ★★★★★

Choose the best answer.

1. Suppose you pick one letter at random from the word MATHEMATICS. What is the probability that the letter will be a vowel? **A**

   A. $\frac{4}{11}$ B. $\frac{1}{2}$ C. $\frac{4}{7}$ D. $\frac{7}{11}$

2. Suppose you roll a number cube and toss a coin. What is the probability that the number cube will show 6 and the coin will show heads? **J**

   F. $\frac{1}{2}$ G. $\frac{1}{6}$ H. $\frac{1}{8}$ J. $\frac{1}{12}$

3. In playing a game, Tosha won 8 times, Pete won 7 times, and Maurice won 10 times. Based on this information, how many times would you expect Maurice to win if they play the game 100 more times? **D**

   A. 10   B. 15   C. 25   D. 40

4. How many different 4-letter "words" can be formed by using the letters *L, O, V,* and *E* if each letter is used only once and the words do not have to make sense?   **H**

   F. 12   G. 16   H. 24   J. 256

5. You want to draw a map of your neighborhood on a piece of paper that is 8½ in. by 11 in. What scale should be used to map an area 1,000 yd by 750 yd? **D**

   A. 1 in. = 75 yd   B. 1 in. = 80 yd
   C. 1 in. = 85 yd   D. 1 in. = 95 yd

6. What is the volume of a rectangular prism 2 m long, 35 cm wide, and 0.4 m high? **J**

   F. 280 m³   G. 28 m³
   H. 2.8 m³   J. 0.28 m³

7. At an ice cream shop you have a choice of 14 flavors of ice cream and 6 choices of topping. Suppose you order a sundae made with 2 scoops of different flavors and 1 topping. How many different sundaes could be ordered?   **C**

   A. 33   B. 34   C. 1,092   D. 1,176

8. At a restaurant last night, 8 people ordered steaks, 10 ordered seafood, 18 ordered chicken, and 14 ordered pasta. From this information, how many people out of 100 would you expect to order pasta?

   F. 28   G. 50   H. 280   J. 450 **F**

Please note that items 9 and 10 each have *five* answer choices.

9. Use the data below. If one person from the survey is picked at random, what is the probability that the person will prefer news? **B**

   Favorite Television Program

Type of Program	Number of People
Situation comedy	13
Sports	16
Drama	11
News	10

   A. $\frac{1}{10}$ B. $\frac{1}{5}$ C. $\frac{1}{4}$
   D. $\frac{4}{5}$ E. Not Here

10. A store recorded the following video rentals for one night: comedy, 32; drama, 20; science fiction, 14; horror, 26; other, 8. If the owner has 500 videos for rent, how many would you expect to be comedies? **H**

    F. 68   G. 100   H. 160
    J. 320   K. Not Here

1 Focus

CONNECTING TO PRIOR KNOWLEDGE Ask students if they have ever heard the term *Gallup poll*. Explain that many national and state polls sample public opinion on various topics. They publish the results in newspapers or magazines. Ask students how they think the pollsters obtain the information. **Answers may vary. Sample: written questionnaires, telephone surveys**

2 Teach

THINK AND DISCUSS

AEP **ERROR ALERT!** Students may not understand the terms *population* and *sample*.

Remediation: Ask students to give their own everyday definitions of the two terms. Explain that a *sample* is *part of a population*, much like a *part* is *part of a whole*.

Question 6 Ask students to give examples of biased survey results. **Answers may vary. Sample: You want a sample of all people over age 21 and you survey only people 21–30 years old.**

Lesson Planning Options

Prerequisite Skills
- solving proportions (7-3)

Vocabulary/Symbols
population, sample, representative, random sample, convenience sampling, biased

Materials/Manipulatives
- about 400 objects that are 2, 3, or 4 different colors

Resources

 Student Edition

Skills Handbook, p. 541
Extra Practice, p. 532
Glossary/Study Guide

 Teaching Resources

Chapter Support File, Ch. 11
- Lesson Planner 11-8
- Practice 11-8, Reteaching 11-8
- Answer Masters 11-8

Teaching Aids Masters 1, 2
Glossary, Spanish Resources

 Transparencies
1, 19, Minds on Math 11-8

Warm Up

At an amusement park, deluxe hamburgers cost $2.75 each. How many can Antria buy with a $20 bill? How much change will she receive? **7 hamburgers; $.75 change**

512

11-8 Making Predictions from Data

What You'll Learn

▼ To identify samples from a given population

▼ To make predictions about a population based on a sample

...And Why

Sampling methods let you draw conclusions about elections, natural resources, and manufacturing quality control.

Here's How

Look for questions that
- build understanding
- ✔ check understanding

THINK AND DISCUSS

▼ *Identifying Samples*

Tourism A survey was sent to over 8,000 adults in the United States. Only about 2,000 people responded. The survey asked "Have you ever visited the White House?" and "Have you ever visited Disneyland or Disney World?" Here are the results.

Site	Yes	No
White House	60%	40%
Disneyland or Disney World	70%	30%

Source: *The First Really Important Survey of American Habits*

1. **Data Analysis** According to the data, have more adults visited the White House or Disneyland/Disney World? **Disneyland or Disney World**

2. Of 2,000 people who responded, how many have visited the White House? **1,200 people**

3. What is the probability that a person who responded to the survey visited the White House? Disneyland or Disney World? **60%; 70%**

A **population** is a group about which you want information. A **sample** is a part of the population you use to make predictions about the population.

ADDITIONAL EXAMPLE

FOR EXAMPLE

A random sample shows that 6 wallets out of 400 are defective. Predict how many wallets out of 15,000 will be defective. **225 wallets**

 **Work Together**

TACTILE LEARNING Have students work in groups. Provide objects such as marbles, cubes, or beans in different colors. If there are not enough objects for each group, have students make their populations from colored squares on a sheet of graph paper. Limit each group's population to fewer than 400 items.

Have groups assemble their populations. Challenge groups to draw up a plan for taking their sample. Ask students to evaluate the samples of each group.

AEP Point out that surveys tell us whether it is *more likely* that a person may have done something or believes something. They cannot predict for certain what an individual thinks. Make sure students understand that surveys reveal a great deal of information but there is much they *do not* tell us.

To predict accurately, a sample must be *representative* of the population. In a **random sample,** choosing any population member is equally likely. A random sample is usually representative.

4. **Look Back** For the survey on page 512, what is the population? What is the sample?
adults in the U.S.; 2,000 people who responded

5a. No; the sample was not random.

5. **a.** ✔*Try It Out* Do you think the sample was representative of all people in the United States? Explain.

b. Answers may vary. Sample: The sample favors people who respond on their own, so it is not representative.

b. About one fourth of those questioned returned their surveys. Why is this a problem?

There are several methods of conducting a survey. You could do it at just one location, such as a grocery store. This method is known as *convenience sampling*, because the method is convenient for the one taking the survey. A sample is **biased** if it is not random and may therefore give results that are not representative of the population.

Reasoning may vary. Sample: yes; the sample would be biased toward people who live near Disney World.

6. **Think About It** Suppose the city of Orlando, Florida, (home of Disney World), asks people on the street the question "Have you ever visited Disney World?" Do you think the results would be biased? Why or why not?

Now you may assign Exercises 1–11.

 Making Predictions

You can use a random sample to make predictions about a larger population. Write a proportion using the random sample and the population. Then solve for the unknown.

■ EXAMPLE *Real-World Problem Solving*

Quality Control From 15,000 pairs of sports shoes, a manufacturer takes a random sample of 300 pairs. The sample has 4 defective pairs. Predict the total number of defective pairs.

Write a proportion.

$$\text{defective pairs in sample} \to \frac{4}{300} = \frac{n}{15{,}000} \leftarrow \begin{array}{l}\text{defective pairs} \\ \text{in population}\end{array}$$
$$\text{pairs in sample} \to \qquad\qquad \leftarrow \text{pairs in population}$$

$$300n = 4 \times 15{,}000 \quad \leftarrow \text{Solve.}$$

$$n = 200$$

The company can predict that 200 pairs are defective.

Technology Options

Prentice Hall Technology

Software for Learners
- Hot Page™ 34*
- Math Blaster® Mystery*
- Interactive Student Tutorial, Chapter 11*

Teaching Resource Software
- Computer Item Generator 11-8
- Resource Pro™ Chapter 11*

Internet • For related mathematics activities, visit the Prentice Hall site at www.phschool.com/math

Available on CD-ROM only

Assignment Options for Exercises On Your Own

To provide flexible scheduling, this lesson can be split into parts.

1 Core 1–7, 9–11
Extension 8

2 Core 12–17
Extension 18

Use Mixed Review to maintain skills.

3 Practice/Assess

EXERCISES *On Your Own*

Exercises 3–5 For those examples that are not representative, ask students to provide suggestions as to how to make the sampling unbiased.

ALTERNATE METHOD Exercises 5–9 If computers are available, students can use software that explores sampling.

RESEARCH Exercise 18 Provide back issues of local papers or magazines. If you have block scheduling or extended class periods, you may want to allow class time for students to conduct their research using microfilm resources in your school or public library.

EXTENSION Challenge students to find examples of polls used in famous elections. For example they may want to research the 1948 presidential election between Truman and Dewey. Have them find out as much as

---

7. ⸬*What If . . .* Suppose the sample in the Example had contained only 20 pairs of shoes. Would you expect the prediction to be more or less accurate? Explain.
Less accurate; a smaller sample is less likely to be representative.

8. ⸬*Go a Step Further* Find the probability that a pair of shoes in the Example is defective. $\frac{1}{75}$

9. ✔*Try It Out* A later sample shows 4 pairs of 500 are defective. Predict how many of 20,000 pairs are defective.
160 pairs

Work Together _____ *Using Random Samples*

Work in teams to experiment with random samples. Take turns being Team 1 and Team 2. Then answer the questions.

Team 1: Create a population of objects (such as marbles, cubes, or beans) that differ only in color. Use 2, 3, or 4 colors. Record the number of objects of each color. Tell Team 2 only the size of your population and the number of colors you used.

Team 2: Take a random sample of the population. From it, predict the distribution of colors in the population. For example, if the population contains 400 white or red cubes, you might predict that there are 100 white cubes and 300 red cubes.

10. ⸬*Explain* How did you make sure that the samples were random? **10–12. Check students' work.**

11. ⸬*Data Collection* How many objects did you use for a sample? Why?

12. ⸬*Data Analysis* How well did your sample represent the population? Explain.

Now you may assign Exercises 12–18.

EXERCISES *On Your Own*

In a survey, 1,580 parents were asked which trait they ranked as most desirable in their children. The table shows the results.

1. Which trait was considered most desirable? **honesty**

2. Of the 1,580 parents surveyed, about how many ranked "good judgment" as the most desirable trait? **about 284 parents**

Trait	% Ranked as Most Desirable
Honest	36%
Good judgment	18%
Obeys parents	16%

Source: *Statistical Handbook on the American Family*

they can about the polling methods used. Have them include comments on how polling has changed through the years.

ASSESSMENT Have students answer the following and explain their reasoning. *You have taken a sample of 100 beans from a population of 400 and obtained these results: 35 kidney, 17 pinto, and 48 lima. Based on this sample, what is your prediction for the entire population for each type of bean?* **About 140 kidney, 68 pinto, and 192 lima; set up proportions to solve.**

WRAP UP

IDENTIFYING THE BIG IDEA Ask students: *What is a random sample? How can you use it to make predictions about a population?*

PORTFOLIO Share with students the criteria you use to assess their work in portfolios, as will as how you plan to use the results. Students should understand how the rubrics are used to assess their work, how each piece in the portfolio counts, and how the scores they get in their portfolios affect their overall evaluation.

Is each sample described in Exercises 3–6 random? Is it representative? Explain.

3. A company wants the opinions of sixth graders in a town. They place the name of every sixth grader in town in a revolving bin and draw 30 names.
   Yes; probably; a random sample is usually representative.

4. To find the national cost of a two-bedroom apartment, 100 New Yorkers who live in two-bedroom apartments are polled.
   No; no; the sample is biased toward New Yorkers.

5. To determine the most popular car in your city, you survey the cars in the high school parking lot. **No; no; the sample is biased toward high school students and teachers.**

6. To taste a bowl of soup, you take a spoonful.
   Yes; probably; all parts of the soup are equally likely to be spooned.

7. *Writing* Why would you take a random sample instead of counting or surveying the whole population? **Answers may vary. Sample: The whole population is usually too large.**

8. *Reasoning* Can you have a sample that is representative but not random? Can you have a sample that is random but not representative? Explain using examples.

8. **Yes; Sample: You deliberately select 1 red cube and 1 blue cube from a bag that contains 5 red cubes and 5 blue cubes; yes; Sample: Without looking, you select 1 red cube and 1 blue cube from a bag that contains 1 red cube and 9 blue cubes.**

9. *Health* Suppose 6 of the 22 students in your mathematics class are out with the flu. Is this a good sample to use to predict how many of 484 students in the school have the flu? Why or why not? **No; they were all in close contact with each other.**

The survey below appeared in a magazine sold all over the United States. Use it for Exercises 10 and 11.

WHAT DO YOU THINK?

Call the number below to give your opinion. Each call costs 75¢. Use only a touch-tone phone. Press 1 for YES. Press 3 for NO. After you answer the questions, enter your age. This opinion poll lasts only until midnight Eastern Standard Time on Tuesday May 15. This magazine will publish the results in a future issue.

10. Identify the population and sample for this survey.
    magazine readers, callers

11. Give at least three reasons why the survey data will not be representative of the population. **Answers may vary. Sample: The survey is biased toward magazine readers, people willing to pay 75¢, and people with touch-tone phones.**

Practice 11-8 *Making Predictions from Data*

Answer each question in a complete sentence in your own words. Answers may vary. Samples are given.

1. What is a population? A population is a group of people or other objects about which you want information.

2. What is a sample? A sample is the part of the population you use to make predictions about the population.

3. When is a sample random? In a random sample, each member of the population has the same chance of being in the sample.

4. Why must a sample be representative of the whole population? In order to make accurate predictions, the sample must be representative of the whole population.

For Exercises 5–7, state whether the sample is random. Explain.

5. To provide better service to the town, the library plans to increase its hours of operation. For a two-week period, it is surveying each patron who checks out books. The sample is not random. Only those people with library cards and who checked out books during the two weeks were surveyed.

6. A permanent traffic signal is being considered at a certain intersection. An electronic counter records the times and numbers of vehicles from 6:00 A.M. to 9:00 P.M. for one week. The sample is random if the week selected is typical for an entire year.

7. A book publisher wants to know the opinions of 12-year-olds in a school district. The name of each 12-year-old is placed in a bin and 20 names are chosen. The sample is random. Each 12-year-old has the same chance of being in the sample.

In copymaster and workbook formats

RETEACHING

Reteaching 11-8 *Making Predictions from Data*

Sometimes you cannot survey an entire **population**. Instead, you survey a **sample**—a part of the population that can be used to make predictions about the entire population.

A city has 5,000 sixth graders. To estimate the number of sixth graders who ride bicycles to school, a random sample was used. Of the 200 sixth graders chosen, 40 said they ride bicycles to school. Predict the number of sixth graders out of 5,000 who ride bicycles to school.

① Write a proportion. $\frac{40}{200} = \frac{n}{5,000}$

② Solve.
$200 \times n = 40 \times 5,000$
$200n = 200,000$
$n = \frac{200,000}{200}$
$n = 1,000$

The sample suggests that 1,000 sixth graders ride bikes to school.

Identify the sample size. Then make a prediction for the population.

1. How many in a class of 100 students prefer chocolate ice cream to other flavors? Of 10 students asked, 6 prefer chocolate.
Sample size 10
Prediction for population 60

2. How many of the 1,900 joggers seen at the park like to run at 6 A.M.? Of 190 joggers asked, 35 like to run at 6 A.M.
Sample size 190
Prediction for population 350

3. Of 600 first graders in the school district, 109 were not yet reading. How many first graders out of the 180,000 in the entire state were not yet reading?
Sample size 600
Prediction for population 32,700

4. Out of 300 families, 150 read the morning newspaper. There are 2,400 families in town. How many read the morning newspaper?
Sample size 300
Prediction for population 1,200

5. How many in a town of 500 students walk to school? Of 100 students asked, 32 walked to school.
Sample size 100
Prediction for population 160

6. Out of 150 families, 16 drive SUVs. How many of the 4,500 families in the county drive SUVs?
Sample size 150
Prediction for population 480

ENRICHMENT

Minds on Math Transparency

11-8

Someone once said "Sisters and brothers have I none, but that man's father is my father's son." Explain how this can be true.

"That man" is the son of the speaker or the speaker is "that man's father."

See *Solution Key* for worked-out answers.

LESSON QUIZ

Is each sample they described random? Is it representative? Explain.

1. A pollster wants the opinions of 15 year olds across the nation. They survey 100 teens from California, Texas, and Idaho who subscribe to Teen's Now magazine.
Random: No, only a certain population subscribes to the magazine; Representative: No, there are not enough states polled and there are not enough teens polled in the sample.

Out of a group of 35,000 of each item, predict how many will have the given flaw.

2. Of 500 pairs of sneakers, 15 have fabric flaws. **1,050**

3. Of 70 cases of grapefruit, 4 cases have spoiled fruit. **2,000**

Exercises 12–15 describe random samples. Out of a group of 24,000 of each item, predict how many have the given quality or flaw.

12. Of 400 grapefruit, 52 are "premium." **3,120 grapefruit**

13. Of 250 computer chips, 2 are defective. **192 computer chips**

14. Of 160 eggs, 96 are Grade AA. **14,400 eggs**

15. Of 75 pairs of jeans, 7 have fabric or stitching flaws. **2,240 pairs of jeans**

16. Use the data from Exercise 15.
   a. Find the probability that a pair of jeans randomly chosen has fabric or stitching flaws. $\frac{7}{75}$
   b. Does it matter whether you use 75 pairs of jeans or 24,000 pairs of jeans to find the probability in 16(a)? Explain. **No; they are equivalent.**

17. *Natural Resources* Random samples of crushed ore from part of a gold mine show 2 ounces of gold in 17 tons of ore. How much gold would you expect from 120,000 tons of ore? **about 14,118 oz**

18. *Research* Find a newspaper or magazine article that includes survey data. Write and send a letter to the editor, asking about the sample, the population, and the survey methods. **Check students' work.**

PORTFOLIO
Select one or two items from your work for this chapter. For example:
• your best work
• a tree diagram
• a journal entry
Explain why you have chosen each item.

Mixed Review

Find the volume of a rectangular prism with the given dimensions. *(Lesson 9-8)*

19. $\ell = 15$ cm, $w = 10$ cm, $h = 2$ cm **300 cm³**

20. $\ell = 12$ cm, $w = 15$ cm, $h = 8$ cm **1,440 cm³**

21. $\ell = 6.4$ cm, $w = 5$ cm, $h = 5$ cm **160 cm³**

22. $\ell = 9.1$ cm, $w = 4.2$ cm, $h = 6.5$ cm **248.43 cm³**

Choose **Use a calculator, mental math, or paper and pencil.** *(Lesson 10-8)*

23. $-52 - 12$ **−64**

24. $-1,423 + 3,256$ **1,833**

25. $-320 - (-523)$ **203**

26. $85 - 987$ **−902**

27. *Measurement* Catherine lives $1\frac{1}{4}$ mi from the park. Sharon lives $1\frac{1}{2}$ mi from the park. How much farther is Sharon's trip to and from the park than Catherine's? *(Lesson 6-5)* **$\frac{1}{2}$ mi**

Extra Practice, Lesson 11-8, page 532

PROJECT DAY You may wish to plan a project day on which students share their completed projects. Encourage students to explain their process as well as their product.

PROJECT NOTEBOOK Ask students to review their project work and bring their notebooks up to date.

SCORING RUBRIC

3 You design two three-outcome systems, one based on random numbers and another based on a three-dimensional shape. You collect data from each system, and you find the experimental probabilities of the different outcomes. You collect additional data for one of your systems, and you prepare a presentation explaining your tests and calculations. You prove that your chosen system works for choosing among three equally likely outcomes.

2 You collect an adequate amount of data from the two systems you designed. You choose one system and collect additional data. You find the experimental probabilities of the three possible outcomes for both systems.

1 You complete only one three-outcome system. You collect data and attempt to find the experimental probabilities of the three possible outcomes.

0 You do not devise a three-outcome system, you do not collect an adequate amount of data, or you do not find the required experimental probabilities.

FINISHING THE CHAPTER PROJECT

CHAPTER PROJECT

Design a Three-Choice System The Project Links on pages 491, 496, and 506 should help you complete your project. This checklist will help you gather together the parts of your project.

✔ your table of data from using a computer, random digits, a spinner, or number cubes

✔ your table of data from using a three-dimensional object

✔ one of the tables above with data from additional trials

Pretend that you want to sell your three-outcome system and that your classmates are your clients. They will base their decision to "buy" or "not buy" your system on the strength of your test procedures, data, and explanations. Prepare a presentation that demonstrates or explains your system. Prove that it works using your test data and calculations.

Reflect and Revise
Give a practice presentation to a friend or family member. Is your data believable and clearly presented? Are your calculations accurate? Is your chosen system the best choice? If necessary, make changes to improve your system and your presentation.

Web Extension

Prentice Hall's Internet site contains information you might find helpful as you complete your project. Visit www.phschool.com/mgm1/ch11 for some links and ideas related to statistics.

STUDENT SELF-ASSESSMENT SURVEY

Chapter 11 Student Self-Assessment Survey

1. Now that you have finished this chapter, think about what you have learned about probability. Check each topic that you feel confident you understand.
   _____ find experimental probability (11-1)
   _____ find possible outcomes to tell whether a game is fair (11-1)
   _____ use simulation to solve problems (11-2)
   _____ use random numbers to simulate probability problems (11-3)
   _____ find the theoretical probability of an event (11-4)
   _____ use tree diagrams and the counting principle (11-5)
   _____ identify independent events (11-6)
   _____ find the probability of independent events by multiplication (11-6)
   _____ find number of arrangements of items (11-7)
   _____ make predictions about a population based on a sample (11-8)

2. Before the Chapter Assessment, I need to review _____

3. a. Check one. In general, I thought this chapter was
      ____ a snap ____ easy ____ average ____ hard ____ a monster
   b. Why do you feel this way? _____

4. In this chapter, I did my best work on _____

5. In this chapter, I had trouble with _____

6. Check each one that applies. Now that I've spent some time studying probability, I think it is
   ___important ___boring ___useful ___fun
   ___a waste of time ___confusing ___tricky ___interesting

7. Describe a situation in your everyday life in which it is helpful to know something about probability. _____

8. Did you like working with simulations? ___ Explain. _____

Vocabulary/Symbols

biased, convenience sampling, equally likely, experimental probability, factorial notation, fair, independent, permutation, population, possible outcomes, random numbers, random sample, representative, sample, simulating, theoretical probability, tree diagram, trials

Materials/Manipulatives

- number cubes

Resources

Teaching Resources

Chapter Support File, Ch. 11
- Student Self-Assessment Survey
Glossary, Spanish Resources
Tools for Studying Smarter

WRAP UP

ASSESSMENT **Exercises 1–4** Have students work in pairs. Each pair of students should then meet with another pair and compare answers. Tell students they should be able to give reasons for their answers. If students have difficulty with a particular problem, encourage them to go back through the lessons to find similar problems they have solved.

Exercises 7 and 8 Students can compare diagrams in small groups. Group members can describe their strategies. Have the group discuss the advantages and disadvantages of different methods of solving the problems.

Exercises 10 and 11 Tell students to also name the strategy they used and explain their reasons for using that strategy.

Remind students that the new mathematical terms in this chapter are defined in the Glossary/Study Guide in the back of the book.

---

11 WRAP UP

Fair and Unfair Games   11-1

A game is **fair** if each player has the same chance of winning. One way to decide if a game is fair or unfair is to consider all the possible outcomes of the game.

You can also play the game many times to determine if it is fair. **Experimental probability** is a ratio that shows the fraction of times that a player wins a game (or that any given event occurs).

1. Players take turns tossing two number cubes. If the sum of the numbers on the two cubes is even, Player A scores a point. If the sum is odd, Player B scores a point.
   a. List all possible outcomes of rolling two cubes.
   b. *Writing* Is the game fair or unfair? Explain.
   Fair; the number of even sums equals the number of odd sums

1a.
	1	2	3	4	5	6
1	2	3	4	5	6	7
2	3	4	5	6	7	8
3	4	5	6	7	8	9
4	5	6	7	8	9	10
5	6	7	8	9	10	11
6	7	8	9	10	11	12

2. Results of a game are shown below.

A wins	|||
B wins	⊩⊩ ||
Times played	⊩⊩ ⊩⊩

   a. Find Probability(A wins) and Probability(B wins). $\frac{3}{10}, \frac{7}{10}$
   b. Does the game seem fair or unfair? Explain.
   Probably unfair; one player seems more likely to win.

Simulations and Experiments   11-2, 11-3

You can represent many probability situations with a model. You can **simulate** an experiment with a model or a list of random digits like the one at the right.

List of Random Digits, 1–6
23	41	63	24	11	25	34	52	22
51	42	63	52	32	43	41	11	24
12	33	62	31	32	64	55	43	63
11	41	34	24	51	14	15	26	32

3. How likely are consecutive numbers when you toss two number cubes? Use the list of random digits at the right to simulate this problem. $\frac{1}{4}$

4. You walk Spot for 20 minutes each weekday any time between 5:00 P.M. and 6:00 P.M. Your mother returns from work any time between 5:30 P.M. and 6:30 P.M. Explain how to use a spinner, number cubes, or random digits to find the experimental probability that your mother will return during your walk.   **Check students' work.**

Chapter 11 Assessment • Form A

Answers

1. York has a bag with 5 blue marbles and 3 red marbles. He wants to play a game with you where a marble is pulled from the bag: blue, he wins; red you win. Is this game fair or unfair?

1. **unfair**

2. The list of random numbers simulates tossing a coin. Use three digits at a time from the list to find the experimental probabilities indicated in the chart.

List of Random Digits 1–2

1 1 2 1 2 1 2 2 2 1 1 2 1 1 2 1 2
1 1 1 2 2 1 2 1 1 1 1 2 1 2 2 2 1

	Experimental Probability
P(third toss is the same as the first toss)	$\frac{6}{11}$
P(third toss is the same as the second toss)	$\frac{2}{11}$
P(third toss is different than the first two tosses)	$\frac{5}{11}$

3. Karen has a bag with 6 red, 3 blue, and 2 green blocks. What is the theoretical probability of drawing a red block from the bag?

3. $\frac{6}{11}$

4. Find Probability(*not* green) in Exercise 3.

4. $\frac{9}{11}$

5. For lunch there is a choice of turkey, chicken salad, or vegetarian sandwich makings on a choice of wheat or white bread. How many different choices of sandwiches are there?

5. **6 sandwiches**

6. Given the color wheel, find the theoretical probability of first spinning red and then spinning green.

6. $\frac{1}{9}$

7. You toss a coin twice. What is the theoretical probability that if the first toss is heads the second toss will be heads?

7. $\frac{1}{2}$

8. In how many different ways can you arrange the letters A, B, and C?

8. **6**

CHAPTER ASSESSMENT • FORM A

Chapter 11 Assessment • Form A (continued)

9. There are 5 students who want to see the counselor one-on-one. In how many different ways can the counselor arrange a schedule to see all 5 students?

9. **120 ways**

10. Your class is holding a raffle for a pair of in-line skates. You buy 6 tickets. Just before the drawing, you find out that a total of 120 tickets were sold. What is the theoretical probability of your winning?

10. $\frac{1}{20}$

Choose A, B, C, or D

11. Which events are independent? You have a drawer with 3 blue socks and 2 red socks.
   A. You pick one red, then pick another sock.
   B. You pick one blue, replace it, then pick another sock.
   C. You pick two socks, then pick one more.
   D. You pick one blue, then pick another sock.

11. **B**

Choose a Strategy

12. You ride your bike to school most mornings arriving between 7:45 A.M. and 8:15 A.M. Your favorite teacher arrives between 7:30 A.M. and 8:00 A.M. How would you figure out the probability of the teacher arriving before you?
   A. use guess and test
   B. simulate the problem
   C. look for a pattern
   D. work backward

12. **B**

Writing

13. There is a population of 600 rabbits on the farm. Some rabbits are all gray, some are all brown, and some are a mixture of gray and brown. You catch 15 rabbits: 5 are gray, 2 are brown, and the rest are the mixture. What prediction can you make about the population of the rabbits?

Answers may vary. Sample: 200 rabbits are gray, 80 are brown, and 320 are a mixture.

Theoretical Probability 11-4

You can describe the **theoretical probability** of an event as the ratio of the number of favorable outcomes to the number of possible outcomes.

5. A bag contains the letters of the word CIVILIZATION. Find each probability.
   a. selecting the letter I $\frac{2}{11}$
   b. selecting the letter R **0**
   c. selecting a vowel $\frac{4}{11}$

6. Give an example of a certain event and an impossible event. What are their probabilities? **Check students' work; 1, 0.**

Tree Diagrams, Counting Principle, and Independent Events 11-5, 11-6

You can use a **tree diagram** or the **counting principle** to find the number of possible outcomes. You can find the probability that more than one **independent event** will occur by **multiplying probabilities.**

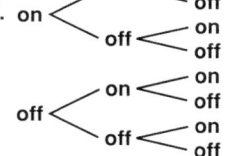

7. Three on/off switches are set at random. Make a tree diagram and find the probability that at least two are set to "off." $\frac{1}{2}$

8. A company makes 5 car models. Each comes in 6 colors, 4 interior styles, and with automatic or standard transmission. Harold wants one of each kind of car for his lot. How many cars must he order? **240 cars**

9. Find the theoretical probability that the first spin of the spinner at the right is yellow and the second spin is green. $\frac{15}{64}$

Arrangements and Making Predictions 11-7, 11-8

You can find the number of arrangements, or **permutations**, of a set of objects by making a list, drawing a tree diagram, using the counting principle, or simulating the problem.

A sample is *random* if each member of a population has an equal chance of being in the sample.

10. Zalika will play 5 songs for her piano recital. In how many ways can Zalika order the songs? **120 ways**

11. To find the favorite sport of boys in your school, you survey all boys on the soccer team. Is the sample random? Explain.
No; the population members are not equally likely to be chosen.

Chapter 11 Assessment • Form B

Choose the best answer. Circle A, B, C, or D.

1. You and Chris play a game with 5 black cubes and 2 white cubes. If a black cube is pulled from the box, Chris receives a point. If the cube is white, you get a point. The cube is replaced each time. Chris wins the game by 15 points. Which of the following is most reasonable?
   A. You decide the game is fair, and you are just unlucky.
   B. You decide the game is unfair.
   C. You decide the game is fair, and Chris just has better luck.
   D. You decide the game is fair and ask Chris to play.

2. Use the chart to find the experimental probability that B wins.

A wins	JHT JHT I
B wins	JHT JHT IIII

   A. $\frac{11}{25}$ B. $\frac{11}{14}$ C. $\frac{14}{11}$ **D.** $\frac{14}{25}$

3. Suppose the number 3 represents a coin toss landing heads and the number 4 represents tails. How would you complete the table below based upon the random number chart?

   3 3 4 3 4 4 4 3 4 3 3 4 3 3 3 3 4
   4 3 4 3 4 4 3 3 4 4 4 3 4 3 3 3 4 3

1	Number of 3's	
2	Number of 4's	
3	Number of trials	

   A. 9, 8, 17   B. 18, 16, 18   **C.** 18, 16, 34   D. 16, 18, 24

4. Marina has a bag of 15 red, 8 blue, and 3 green marbles. What is the theoretical probability of drawing a blue marble from the bag?
   A. $\frac{3}{26}$ B. $\frac{11}{26}$ C. $\frac{15}{26}$ **D.** $\frac{4}{13}$

5. What color is most likely to be spun?
   A. green   **B.** red
   C. blue   D. yellow

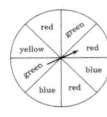

6. There is a choice of roast beef, sliced turkey, or pastrami on either wheat, sourdough, or white bread for lunch. Use the counting principle to find the number of possible sandwiches.
   A. 3 sandwiches   B. 6 sandwiches   **C.** 9 sandwiches   D. 12 sandwiches

Chapter 11 Assessment • Form B (continued)

7. Jon has 7 cubes in his bag: 3 blue, 2 red, 1 white, and 1 black. He draws a cube, puts it back in the bag, and then draws again. What is Probability(red and black)?
   A. $\frac{2}{49}$ B. $\frac{2}{7}$ C. $\frac{3}{7}$ D. $\frac{4}{49}$

8. You toss a number cube twice. The first toss is a 5. What is the probability that the second toss will be a 5?
   A. $\frac{1}{36}$ **B.** $\frac{1}{6}$ C. $\frac{1}{12}$ D. $\frac{1}{3}$

9. How many ways can you arrange the letters in the word MOUSE?
   A. 2 ways   B. 25 ways   C. 60 ways   **D.** 120 ways

10. There are 6 chairs in the front row at the puppet show. How many different ways can 6 people sit in those 6 chairs?
    A. 36 ways   B. 120 ways   **C.** 720 ways   D. 1,000 ways

11. Your class is holding a raffle for a new bicycle. You bought 11 tickets. Just before the drawing, the announcement was made that 330 tickets had been sold. What is the probability of your winning?
    A. $\frac{1}{30}$ B. $\frac{1}{10}$ C. $\frac{11}{165}$ D. $\frac{5}{165}$

12. You have four pairs of pants in your closet. Which events are not independent?
    A. You pick a pair of socks, and then you pick a pair of pants.
    B. You pick one pair of pants, and then pick another pair.
    C. You pick a pair of socks, and you pick out a shirt.
    D. You pick one pair of pants, and you pick out a shirt.

Choose a Strategy

13. You ride your bike home from school arriving between 3:30 P.M. and 4:00 P.M. Your mom gets home between 3:45 P.M. and 4:30 P.M. How would you figure out the probability of your arriving home before your mom?
    A. use guess and test
    B. simulate the problem
    C. look for a pattern
    D. work backward

 **Teaching Resources**

Chapter Support File, Ch. 11, and Spanish Resources

 Teacher's Edition

See pp. 478C–D for Assessment Options.

  Teaching Resource Software
• Computer Item Generator, Ch. 11

520

ASSESSMENT

ENHANCED MULTIPLE CHOICE QUESTIONS are more complex than traditional multiple choice questions, which assess only one skill. Enhanced multiple choice questions assess the processes that students use, as well as the end results. They are written so that students can use more than one strategy to solve the problem. Using multiple strategies is encouraged by the National Council of Teachers of Mathematics (NCTM). **Exercise 4** is an enhanced multiple choice question.

OPEN-ENDED PROBLEMS allow for more than one solution. Students must construct their own responses instead of choosing from possible answers. The student responses will help you determine the depth of their understanding and any possible areas of difficulty. **Exercise 11** is an open-ended problem.

WRITING EXERCISES allow students to describe more fully their thinking and understanding of the concepts they've learned. **Exercise 1c** is a writing exercise.

---

11 ASSESSMENT

1. Sal and Matt played a game. The results are below.

Game Results	
Sal Wins	7
Matt wins	13
Times Played	20

   a. Find the experimental probability that Sal wins. $\frac{7}{20}$
   b. Find the experimental probability that Matt wins. $\frac{13}{20}$
   c. *Writing* Does this game seem fair? Explain.
      No; one player seems more likely to win.

2. A number cube is rolled twice. What is the theoretical probability of getting a 2 on the first roll and a 5 on the second roll? $\frac{1}{36}$

3. Use the counting principle to find the number of possible outcomes.
   a. selecting a meal from 5 entrees, 4 soups, and 3 desserts   **60 outcomes**
   b. tossing a coin four times   **16 outcomes**
   c. selecting groups of three letters for a monogram   **17,576 outcomes**

4. **Choose A, B, C, or D.** The probability of a *certain* event is ■. **B**
   A. 0   B. 1   C. $\frac{1}{2}$ D. $\frac{1}{4}$

5a. **independent**
5. Determine if the events are independent.
   a. Two number cubes are thrown. One shows a 3. The other shows a 1.
   b. You choose a red marble from a bag containing red and yellow marbles. You do not put the marble back. You choose again and get another red marble.   **dependent**

6. The spinner below is spun three times.

   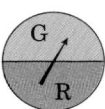

   a. Make a tree diagram to show all possible outcomes.   **See back of book.**
   b. Find Probability(green, red, green). $\frac{1}{8}$
   c. Find Probability(all red). $\frac{1}{8}$

7. A bag contains blue and green chips. The probability of drawing a blue chip is $\frac{5}{12}$.
   a. Find Probability(green). $\frac{7}{12}$
   b. Draw a spinner you could use to simulate this problem.
      See back of book.

8. Find the theoretical probability that a digit selected at random from the number 216,394 is a multiple of 3. $\frac{1}{2}$

9. A number cube with 12 faces numbered 1–12 is rolled. All outcomes are equally likely. Find each theoretical probability.
   a. Probability(even number) $\frac{1}{2}$
   b. Probability(13)   **0**
   c. Probability(7 or 8) $\frac{1}{6}$
   d. Probability(number less than 10) $\frac{3}{4}$

10. Suppose you tossed a coin 20 times with these results: 12 heads, 8 tails. Use this data to find the experimental probability of getting heads. $\frac{3}{5}$

11. Suppose you read in the newspaper that the probability of rain is 10%. Write this probability two other ways and describe it using words.   **0.1, $\frac{1}{10}$; Answers may vary.**
    Sample: There is a one-in-ten chance that it will rain.

12. What is the theoretical probability of getting two 6's when you roll two number cubes?
    $\frac{1}{36}$

Item	Review Topic	Ch
1	Patterns	2
2, 4	Probability	11
3	Solving proportions	7
5	Adding fractions	6
6	Identifying triangles	8
7	Solving equations with decimals	4

Item	Review Topic	Ch
8	Estimating perimeter	9
9	Circumference and area	9
10	Tools of geometry	8
11	Ordering fractions and decimals	5
12	Adding mixed numbers	6

11 CUMULATIVE REVIEW

Choose the best answer.

1. Find the next two terms in the number pattern 2, 6, 12, 20, . . . **B**

A. 28, 36 B. 30, 42 C. 24, 32 D. 32, 44

2. You and a friend play the game "Rock, paper, scissors." Each of you puts your hand behind your back and then brings it forward in one of the three shapes. What is the probability that you both show "paper"? **D**

A. $\frac{1}{2}$ B. $\frac{1}{3}$ C. $\frac{1}{6}$ D. $\frac{1}{9}$

3. What is the value of m if $\frac{2m}{21} = \frac{8}{35}$? **D**

A. 12 B. 7 C. $\frac{13}{5}$ D. 2.4

4. Which event is least likely to occur? **C**

A. You roll a number cube once and get a 6.

B. You toss a coin twice and get two heads.

C. A single digit produced by a random digit generator is 4.

D. One of the next 7 days is Saturday.

5. Which value of d will make the sum $\frac{8}{1} + \frac{3}{d}$ greatest? **A**

A. 4 B. 5 C. 6 D. 7

6. What is the *best* name for the triangle below? **B**

A. acute B. obtuse
C. scalene D. right

7. Solve the equation $0.2x = 46$. **D**

A. 2.3 B. 9.2 C. 23 D. 230

8. Without measuring, choose the best estimate for the perimeter of the triangle shown in Exercise 6. **B**

A. 7 mm B. 7 cm C. 7 m D. 7 km

9. Find the circumference and area of a circle with a diameter of 4.6 m. Round to the nearest tenth. **C**

A. $C = 16.6$ m, $A = 124.4$ m^2
B. $C = 28.9$ m, $A = 66.4$ m^2
C. $C = 14.4$ m, $A = 16.6$ m^2
D. $C = 4.6$ m, $A = 5.29$ m^2

10. Look at the button.

Which drawing shows a rotation of the button? **B**

A.   B.

C.  D.

11. Which of the following is given in increasing order? **B**

A. $\frac{1}{2}, \frac{3}{4}, \frac{2}{3}, 0.8, \frac{9}{10}$

B. $0.5, \frac{2}{3}, 0.75, \frac{4}{5}, 0.9$

C. $\frac{1}{3}, \frac{1}{2}, 0.67, 0.9, \frac{4}{5}$

D. $\frac{1}{4}, 0.3, \frac{8}{5}, 0.5, \frac{2}{3}$

12. Find the sum of $6\frac{3}{4}$ and $2\frac{4}{5}$. **D**

A. $8\frac{11}{20}$ B. $8\frac{7}{9}$ C. $9\frac{1}{20}$ D. $9\frac{11}{20}$

CUMULATIVE REVIEW

Chapter 11 Cumulative Review

Choose the best answer. Circle A, B, C, or D.

1. What are the next three numbers in this pattern? 2, 8, 14, 20, . . .

Ⓐ 26, 32, 38 B. 30, 44, 56
C. 26, 38, 48 D. 31, 37, 44

Use the figure below for Exercises 2–5.

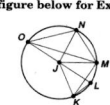

2. Which names a diameter of circle J?

A. $\overline{NJ}$ Ⓑ $\overline{OL}$
C. $\overline{KM}$ D. $\overline{OM}$

3. Which are both chords of circle J?

Ⓐ $\overline{KL}, \overline{ON}$ B. $\overline{KJ}, \overline{JN}$
C. $\overline{ON}, \overline{OJ}$ D. $\overline{MJ}, \overline{MN}$

4. If the length of $\overline{MJ}$ is 4 cm, how long is the diameter of circle J?

A. 2 cm B. 4 cm
Ⓒ 8 cm D. 16 cm

5. Which is *not* a central angle of circle J?

A. $\angle OJN$ B. $\angle NJK$
C. $\angle NJM$ Ⓓ $\angle LKJ$

6. Which of the following words has a line of symmetry?

A. RICE B. HUB
Ⓒ MOM D. DARK

7. What is the area of a square with sides of 7 m?

A. 14 m^2 B. 28 m^2
C. 42 m^2 Ⓓ 49 m^2

8. Find the area of the figure below. Use $\pi = 3.14$. Round to the nearest tenth.

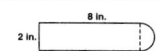

Ⓐ 17.6 in.^{2} B. 19.1 in.^{2}
C. 25.6 in.^{2} D. 28.5 in.^{2}

9. Which statement is true?

Ⓐ $13 < 31$ B. $-9 > 3$
C. $-8 > -1$ D. $-14 > 14$

10. Find the difference $12 - (-3)$.

Ⓐ 15 B. -15
C. 9 D. -9

11. Which numbers complete the function table?

Time	Distance
4 min	16 mi
6 min	24 mi
8 min	
10 min	
12 min	

A. 28 mi, 32 mi, 36 mi
B. 30 mi, 36 mi, 42 mi
Ⓒ 32 mi, 40 mi, 48 mi
D. 40 mi, 56 mi, 72 mi

CUMULATIVE REVIEW

Chapter 11 Cumulative Review (continued)

12. What is the best name for the triangle shown?

A. isosceles, acute
B. scalene, acute
Ⓒ scalene, obtuse
D. isosceles, obtuse

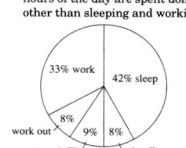

13. A winter coat is on sale for 80% of the original price of $55.89. Estimate the sale price of the coat to the nearest dollar.

Ⓐ $45 B. $48
C. $40 D. $47

14. Use the circle graph below. How many hours of the day are spent doing things other than sleeping and working?

33% work 42% sleep
8%
work out 9% 8%
watch TV miscellaneous

A. 4 h Ⓑ 6 h
C. 8 h D. 10 h

15. A bag contains 16 marbles: 3 red, 5 green, 4 blue, 3 yellow, and 1 clear. Find Probability(green) as a fraction, a decimal, and a percent.

A. $\frac{11}{16}$, 0.6875, 68.75%
Ⓑ $\frac{5}{16}$, 0.3125, 31.25%
C. $\frac{1}{4}$, 0.25, 25%
D. $\frac{5}{16}$, 3.125, 31.25%

16. For dinner the restaurant's menu lists 3 meats, 2 potatoes, 2 salads, and 3 desserts. How many different combinations of one meat, potato, salad, and dessert are there?

A. 12 combinations
B. 18 combinations
Ⓒ 36 combinations
D. 45 combinations

17. How many different ways can you arrange the letters in the word MATH?

A. 6 ways B. 54 ways
Ⓒ 24 ways D. 30 ways

18. There are 300 color pegs in a bag. You take out 35 pegs. You find that 15 are white, 6 are green, and the rest are blue. What is *not* a prediction about the rest of the pegs in the bag?

Ⓐ The rest of the pegs are white or blue.
B. There are about the same number of blue as white pegs.
C. There are about half the number of green pegs as blue.
D. There are more than twice as many white pegs as green ones.

19. Solve the equation $0.3y = 51$.

A. 0.17 B. 1.7
C. 17 Ⓓ 170

Resources

Teaching Resources

Chapter Support File, Ch. 11
• Cumulative Review

Teacher's Edition

See pp. 478C–D for Assessment Options.

521

End-of-Course Skills Assessment

A broad range of assessment tools are available to reach a variety of learners.
Options for Formal and Informal Assessment appear on the **Assessing
Progress** pages that precede each chapter.

Computer Item Generator

With the Computer Item Generator, you can
customize assessment tests and create customized practice worksheets.

Standardized Test Preparation

You may wish to take advantage of the
Standardized Test Preparation component that
is available on the Computer Item Generator
and the Resource Pro™ CD-ROM. With this
component, you can generate tests to help
students prepare for these standardized tests:

CATS California Achievement Test,
5th Edition
ITBS Iowa Test of Basic Skills, Form B
MAT 7 Metropolitan Achievement Test,
7th Edition
SAT9 Stanford Achievement Test, 9th Edition
CTBS/5 (Terra Nova) Comprehensive Test of
Basic Skills, 5th Edition

End-of-Course Assessment

The End-of-Course Assessment is available in the *Cumulative
Assessment* booklet in the Teaching Resources.

Structure The End-of-Course Assessment is a four-page, multiple
choice test. The test assesses student progress on the skills and
concepts covered in Chapters 1–11 of *Prentice Hall Middle Grades
Math* program. The test contains 3–5 test items from each chapter.

Scoring Usually 75 percent correct should demonstrate that the
student has sufficient mastery of the content to be considered
successful in this program. However, you may wish to set your
own criteria.

Progress and Remediation Chart To assist you in assessing the
skill level of your students, a Progress and Remediation Chart
appears with the End-of-Course Assessment. This chart identifies the
skills and concepts
assessed, student
achievement on the
assessment test, and
suggests where
remediation help, if
necessary, will be found
within the *Prentice Hall
Middle Grades Math*
program.

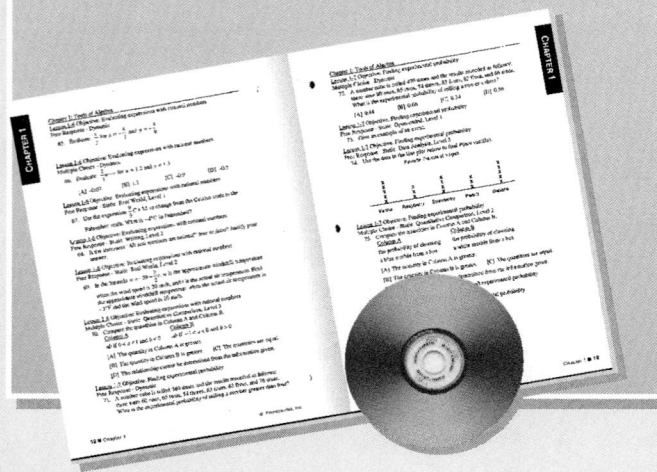

End-of-Course Assessment

Choose the best answer. Circle A, B, C, or D.

1. Which is *not* a line plot of this data?

Color	Frequency
purple	III
blue	IIII I
red	II
green	IIII

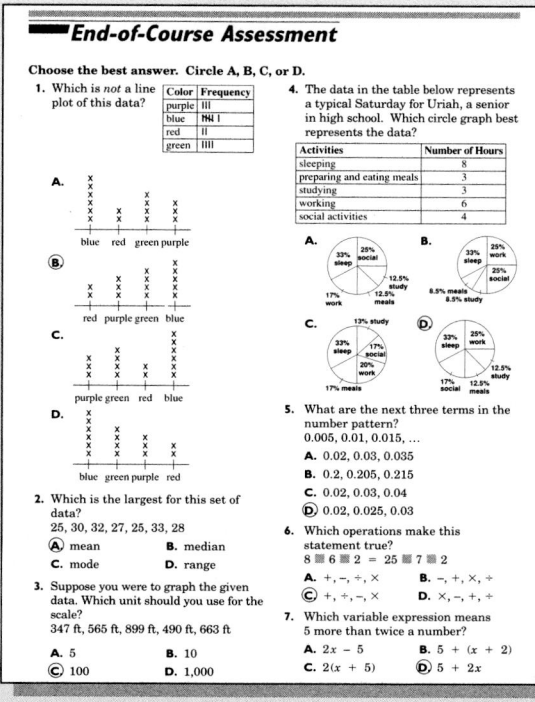

A.
blue   red   green   purple

(B)
red   purple   green   blue

C.
purple   green   red   blue

D.
blue   green   purple   red

2. Which is the largest for this set of data?
25, 30, 32, 27, 25, 33, 28
   (A) mean
   B. median
   C. mode
   D. range

3. Suppose you were to graph the given data. Which unit should you use for the scale?
347 ft, 565 ft, 899 ft, 490 ft, 663 ft
   A. 5
   (C) 100
   B. 10
   D. 1,000

4. The data in the table below represents a typical Saturday for Uriah, a senior in high school. Which circle graph best represents the data?

Activities	Number of Hours
sleeping	8
preparing and eating meals	3
studying	3
working	6
social activities	4

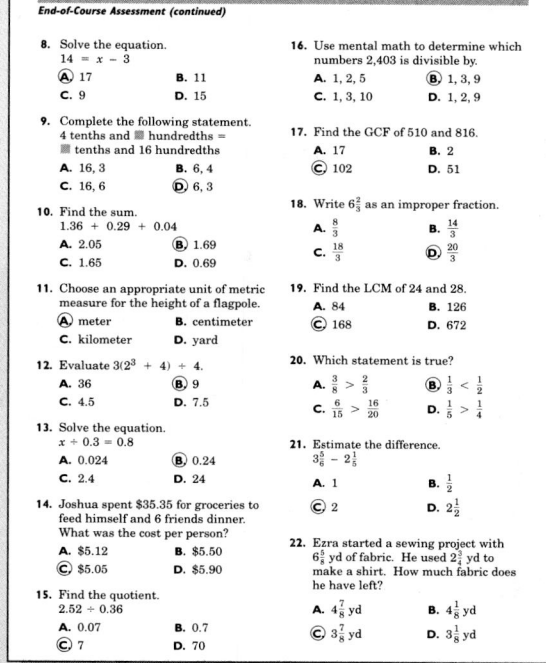

A. 33% sleep, 25% social, 12.5% study, 12.5% meals, 17% work

B. 33% sleep, 25% work, 25% social, 8.5% meals, 8.5% study

C. 33% sleep, 13% study, 17% social, 20% work, 17% meals

(D) 33% sleep, 25% work, 12.5% study, 12.5% meals, 17% social

5. What are the next three terms in the number pattern?
0.005, 0.01, 0.015, …
   A. 0.02, 0.03, 0.035
   B. 0.2, 0.205, 0.215
   C. 0.02, 0.03, 0.04
   (D) 0.02, 0.025, 0.03

6. Which operations make this statement true?
$8 \blacksquare 6 \blacksquare 2 = 25 \blacksquare 7 \blacksquare 2$
   A. $+, -, \div, \times$
   B. $-, +, \times, \div$
   (C) $+, \div, -, \times$
   D. $\times, -, +, \div$

7. Which variable expression means 5 more than twice a number?
   A. $2x - 5$
   B. $5 + (x + 2)$
   C. $2(x + 5)$
   (D) $5 + 2x$

End-of-Course Assessment (continued)

8. Solve the equation.
$14 = x - 3$
   (A) 17
   B. 11
   C. 9
   D. 15

9. Complete the following statement.
4 tenths and $\blacksquare$ hundredths = $\blacksquare$ tenths and 16 hundredths
   A. 16, 3
   B. 6, 4
   C. 16, 6
   (B) 6, 3

10. Find the sum.
$1.36 + 0.29 + 0.04$
   A. 2.05
   (B) 1.69
   C. 1.65
   D. 0.69

11. Choose an appropriate unit of metric measure for the height of a flagpole.
   (A) meter
   B. centimeter
   C. kilometer
   D. yard

12. Evaluate $3(2^3 + 4) + 4$.
   A. 36
   (B) 9
   C. 4.5
   D. 7.5

13. Solve the equation.
$x \div 0.3 = 0.8$
   A. 0.024
   (B) 0.24
   C. 2.4
   D. 24

14. Joshua spent $35.35 for groceries to feed himself and 6 friends dinner. What was the cost per person?
   A. $5.12
   B. $5.50
   (C) $5.05
   D. $5.90

15. Find the quotient.
$2.52 \div 0.36$
   A. 0.07
   B. 0.7
   (C) 7
   D. 70

16. Use mental math to determine which numbers 2,403 is divisible by.
   A. 1, 2, 5
   (B) 1, 3, 9
   C. 1, 3, 10
   D. 1, 2, 9

17. Find the GCF of 510 and 816.
   A. 17
   B. 2
   (C) 102
   D. 51

18. Write $6\frac{2}{3}$ as an improper fraction.
   A. $\frac{8}{3}$
   B. $\frac{14}{3}$
   C. $\frac{18}{3}$
   (D) $\frac{20}{3}$

19. Find the LCM of 24 and 28.
   A. 84
   B. 126
   (C) 168
   D. 672

20. Which statement is true?
   A. $\frac{3}{8} > \frac{2}{3}$
   (B) $\frac{1}{3} < \frac{1}{2}$
   C. $\frac{6}{15} > \frac{16}{20}$
   D. $\frac{1}{5} > \frac{1}{4}$

21. Estimate the difference.
$3\frac{5}{6} - 2\frac{1}{5}$
   A. 1
   B. $\frac{1}{2}$
   (C) 2
   D. $2\frac{1}{2}$

22. Ezra started a sewing project with $6\frac{5}{8}$ yd of fabric. He used $2\frac{3}{4}$ yd to make a shirt. How much fabric does he have left?
   A. $4\frac{7}{8}$ yd
   B. $4\frac{1}{8}$ yd
   (C) $3\frac{7}{8}$ yd
   D. $3\frac{1}{8}$ yd

End-of-Course Assessment (continued)

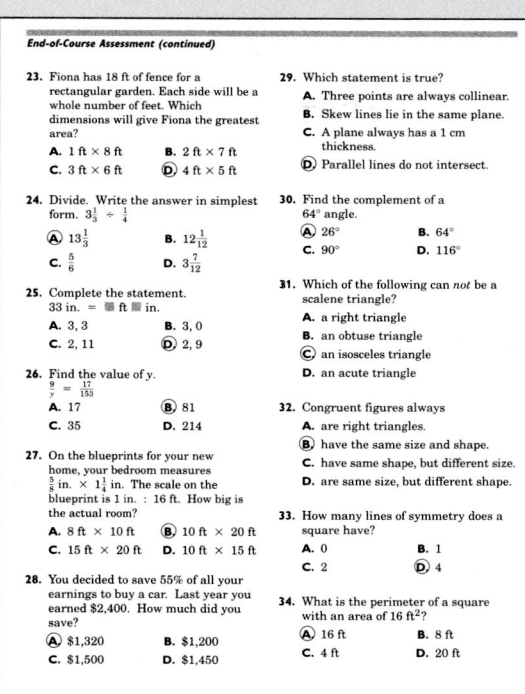

23. Fiona has 18 ft of fence for a rectangular garden. Each side will be a whole number of feet. Which dimensions will give Fiona the greatest area?
   A. 1 ft × 8 ft
   B. 2 ft × 7 ft
   C. 3 ft × 6 ft
   (D) 4 ft × 5 ft

24. Divide. Write the answer in simplest form. $3\frac{1}{3} \div \frac{1}{4}$
   (A) $13\frac{1}{3}$
   B. $12\frac{1}{12}$
   C. $\frac{5}{6}$
   D. $3\frac{7}{12}$

25. Complete the statement.
33 in. = $\blacksquare$ ft $\blacksquare$ in.
   A. 3, 3
   B. 3, 0
   C. 2, 11
   (D) 2, 9

26. Find the value of y.
$\frac{9}{y} = \frac{17}{153}$
   A. 17
   (B) 81
   C. 35
   D. 214

27. On the blueprints for your new home, your bedroom measures $\frac{5}{8}$ in. × $1\frac{1}{4}$ in. The scale on the blueprint is 1 in. : 16 ft. How big is the actual room?
   A. 8 ft × 10 ft
   (B) 10 ft × 20 ft
   C. 15 ft × 20 ft
   D. 10 ft × 15 ft

28. You decided to save 55% of all your earnings to buy a car. Last year you earned $2,400. How much did you save?
   (A) $1,320
   B. $1,200
   C. $1,500
   D. $1,450

29. Which statement is true?
   A. Three points are always collinear.
   B. Skew lines lie in the same plane.
   C. A plane always has a 1 cm thickness.
   (D) Parallel lines do not intersect.

30. Find the complement of a $64°$ angle.
   (A) $26°$
   B. $64°$
   C. $90°$
   D. $116°$

31. Which of the following can *not* be a scalene triangle?
   A. a right triangle
   B. an obtuse triangle
   (C) an isosceles triangle
   D. an acute triangle

32. Congruent figures always
   A. are right triangles.
   (B) have the same size and shape.
   C. have same shape, but different size.
   D. are same size, but different shape.

33. How many lines of symmetry does a square have?
   A. 0
   B. 1
   C. 2
   (D) 4

34. What is the perimeter of a square with an area of 16 ft^2?
   (A) 16 ft
   B. 8 ft
   C. 4 ft
   D. 20 ft

End-of-Course Assessment (continued)

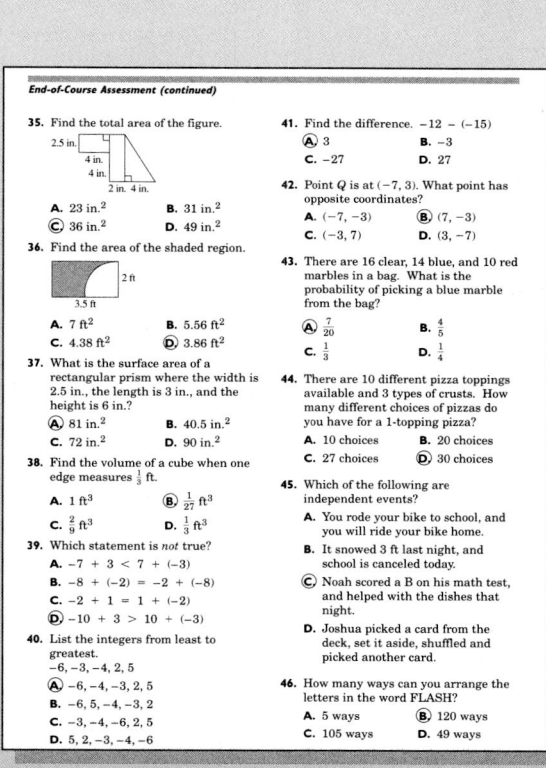

35. Find the total area of the figure.
2.5 in., 4 in., 4 in., 2 in., 4 in.
   A. 23 in.^{2}
   B. 31 in.^{2}
   (C) 36 in.^{2}
   D. 49 in.^{2}

36. Find the area of the shaded region.
2 ft, 3.5 ft
   A. 7 ft^2
   B. 5.56 ft^2
   C. 4.38 ft^2
   (D) 3.86 ft^2

37. What is the surface area of a rectangular prism where the width is 2.5 in., the length is 3 in., and the height is 6 in.?
   (A) 81 in.^{2}
   B. 40.5 in.^{2}
   C. 72 in.^{2}
   D. 90 in.^{2}

38. Find the volume of a cube when one edge measures $\frac{1}{3}$ ft.
   A. 1 ft^3
   (B) $\frac{1}{27}$ ft^3
   C. $\frac{2}{9}$ ft^3
   D. $\frac{1}{3}$ ft^3

39. Which statement is *not* true?
   A. $-7 + 3 < 7 + (-3)$
   B. $-8 + (-2) = -2 + (-8)$
   C. $-2 + 1 = 1 + (-2)$
   (D) $-10 + 3 > 10 + (-3)$

40. List the integers from least to greatest.
$-6, -3, -4, 2, 5$
   (A) $-6, -4, -3, 2, 5$
   B. $-6, 5, -4, -3, 2$
   C. $-3, -4, -6, 2, 5$
   D. $5, 2, -3, -4, -6$

41. Find the difference. $-12 - (-15)$
   (A) 3
   B. -3
   C. -27
   D. 27

42. Point Q is at $(-7, 3)$. What point has opposite coordinates?
   A. $(-7, -3)$
   (B) $(7, -3)$
   C. $(-3, 7)$
   D. $(3, -7)$

43. There are 16 clear, 14 blue, and 10 red marbles in a bag. What is the probability of picking a blue marble from the bag?
   (A) $\frac{7}{20}$
   B. $\frac{4}{5}$
   C. $\frac{1}{3}$
   D. $\frac{1}{4}$

44. There are 10 different pizza toppings available and 3 types of crusts. How many different choices of pizzas do you have for a 1-topping pizza?
   A. 10 choices
   B. 20 choices
   C. 27 choices
   (D) 30 choices

45. Which of the following are independent events?
   A. You rode your bike to school, and you will ride your bike home.
   B. It snowed 3 ft last night, and school is canceled today.
   (C) Noah scored a B on his math test, and helped with the dishes that night.
   D. Joshua picked a card from the deck, set it aside, shuffled and picked another card.

46. How many ways can you arrange the letters in the word FLASH?
   A. 5 ways
   (B) 120 ways
   C. 105 ways
   D. 49 ways

CHAPTER 1

1. Books Read
Each Month | Frequency

Books Read Each Month	Frequency
4	4
3	2
2	3
1	3

Books Read Each Month

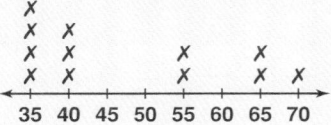

2. Words
per Minute | Frequency

Words per Minute	Frequency
70	1
65	2
55	2
40	3
35	4

Words per Minute

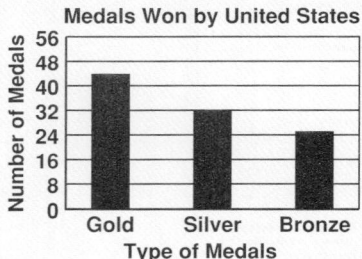

7b.

Medals Won by United States

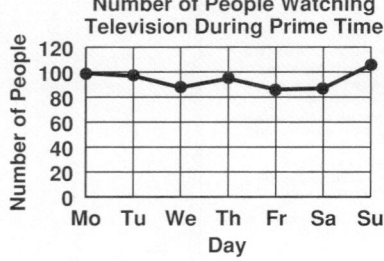

10a.

Number of People Watching
Television During Prime Time

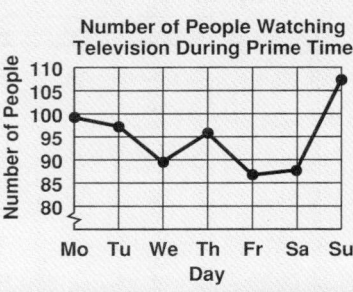

b.

Number of People Watching
Television During Prime Time

[line graph with days Mo Tu We Th Fr Sa Su, Number of People 80–110]

Make a frequency table and a line plot for each set of data. ■ LESSON 1-1
Then find the range.

1. books read each month: 3, 1, 4, 2,
4, 1, 3, 2, 4, 4, 2, 1 **See margin.**

2. words per minute: 65, 35, 40, 35, 55, 65,
40, 40, 55, 35, 35, 70 **See margin.**

Find the mean, median, and mode. ■ LESSON 1-3

3. 23, 26, 22, 25, 22, 28, 22, 10, 11
21; 23; 22

4. 102, 202, 102, 302, 102, 402, 102, 402, 201
13; 201; 102

The spreadsheet below shows the number of medals the ■ LESSONS 1-4, 1-6
United States earned during the 1996 Summer Olympics.
Use the data in the spreadsheet for Exercises 5–7.

	A	B	C	D	E
1	Country	Gold	Silver	Bronze	Total
2	United States	44	32	25	▨

5. What is the value in C2? What does this number mean? **32; United States won 32 silver medals**

6. Write the formula for cell E2. **B2 + C2 + D2**

7. **a.** Would you use a bar graph or a line graph to display the
data in the spreadsheet? Explain your choice. **Answers may vary. Sample: Bar Graph.**
b. Graph the data. **See margin.**

Choose the most appropriate type of graph to display ■ LESSON 1-5
each set of data. Explain your reasoning.

8. amount of rainfall in Costa Rica
each month for 1 year **line graph**

9. number of students from each grade
who play soccer **bar graph**

10. Use the data in the table at the right
to draw two different line graphs.
a. In the first line graph, mark 0 to 120
in units of 20. **See margin.**
b. In the second line graph, mark 80 to
110 in units of 5. **See margin.**
c. How does the change in scale affect
each representation?
Check students' work.

Number of People
Watching Television
During Prime Time
(in millions) ■ LESSON 1-7

Monday	99.2
Tuesday	97.2
Wednesday	89.7
Thursday	95.9
Friday	86.7
Saturday	87.8
Sunday	107.2

522

CHAPTER 2

Extra Practice

Find the next three terms in each number pattern. Write a rule to describe each number pattern.

■ LESSON 2-1

1. 1, 4, 16, 64, . . .
81, 100, 121; square numbers

2. 0, 3, 6, 9, . . .
12, 15, 18; add 3

3. 1, 3, 5, 7, . . .
9, 11, 13; add 2

4. 2, 6, 18, 54, . . .
162, 486, 1,458; multiply by 3

5. 7, 11, 15, 19, . . .
23, 27, 31; add 4

6. 80, 74, 68, 62, . . .
56, 50, 44; add 4

Choose **Use a calculator, paper and pencil, or mental math to find the value of the expression.**

■ LESSON 2-3

7. $2 + 6 \times 3 + 1$ 21

8. $6(5 + 5)$ 60

9. $(14 + 44) \div 2$ 29

10. $4(1 + 4)$ 20

11. $3 + 64 \div 4 - 10$ 9

12. $7 \times 8 \div 2$ 28

13. $50 \div (25 - 15)$ 5

14. $144 + 56 \div 4$ 158

Mental Math **Evaluate each expression.**

■ LESSON 2-4

15. $7x$ for $x = 7$ 49

16. $n - 7$ for $n = 16$ 9

17. $3b - 24$ for $b = 8$ 0

18. $22 - 2n$ for $n = 5$ 12

19. $a + 30$ for $a = 170$ 200

20. $4c + 6$ for $c = 11$ 50

21. $2b + 7$ for $b = 3$ 13

22. $14 - x$ for $x = 5$ 9

23. $10n - 3$ for $n = 7$ 67

Write a variable expression for each word phrase.

■ LESSON 2-5

24. one less than b $b - 1$

25. twice as many p $2p$

26. four greater than b $b + 4$

27. three more than x $x + 3$

28. three times k $3k$

29. half of n $\frac{n}{2}$

Choose **Use algebra tiles, mental math, or paper and pencil to solve each equation.**

■ LESSON 2-6

30. $4 + b = 77$ 73

31. $20 = y + 1$ 19

32. $27 + a = 163$ 136

33. $c - 35 = 75$ 110

34. $b - 11 = 36$ 47

35. $x + 17 = 45$ 28

36. $25 = p - 42$ 67

37. $t - 10 = 24$ 34

38. $302 = h + 5$ 297

Choose **Use algebra tiles, mental math, or a calculator to solve each equation.**

■ LESSON 2-7

39. $3n = 21$ 7

40. $62 = 2b$ 31

41. $a \div 3 = 3$ 9

42. $b \div 5 = 25$ 125

43. $178 = 10d$ 17.8

44. $b \div 7 = 7$ 49

45. $48 = 3c$ 16

46. $15t = 600$ 40

47. $40 = k \div 5$ 200

Extra Practice

Write each decimal in words. ■ LESSON 3-1

1. 0.8
eight tenths

2. 0.35
thirty-five hundredths

3. 0.12
twelve hundredths

4. 0.045
forty-five thousandths

5. 0.07
seven hundredths

6. 0.17
seventeen hundredths

Write each number in standard form. ■ LESSON 3-2

7. three thousand forty
3,040

8. fifty-seven hundredths
0.57

9. sixty-six and seven
hundredths **66.07**

10. one hundred forty-two thousandths
0.142

11. two hundred twenty-two thousandths
0.222

Find the value of the digit 9 in each number.

12. 0.9
tenths

13. 1.009
thousandths

14. 52.39
hundredths

15. 0.4829
ten-thousandths

16. 351.09
hundredths

Use >, =, or < to complete each statement. ■ LESSON 3-3

17. 1.11 ■ 1.09 **>**

18. 0.2357 ■ 0.23 **>**

19. 11.521 ■ 11.53 **<**

20. 13.10 ■ 13.1 **=**

Use models to find each sum or difference. ■ LESSON 3-5

21. 0.8 + 1.5 **2.3**

22. 1.2 − 0.62 **5.58**

23. 2.01 + 0.67 **2.68**

24. 1.41 − 0.61 **0.8**

Round each number to the underlined place. ■ LESSON 3-6

25. 0.1̲7
0.2

26. 4.55̲638
4.556

27. 3356.7̲76
3,356.8

28. 0.0005̲43
0.0005

29. 14.53̲42
14.534

30. 0.4̲5332
0.5

Find each sum or difference. ■ LESSON 3-7

31. 1.14 + 9.3 **10.43**

32. 9 − 3.5 **5.5**

33. 4.11 − 2.621 **1.489**

34. 3.541 + 1.333 **4.874**

35. Measure each side of the triangle in
millimeters and centimeters.
**Measurements may vary. Sample: 11 mm,
15 mm, 23 mm; 1.1 cm, 1.5 cm, 2.3 cm** ■ LESSON 3-8

36. What metric unit would you use to measure each item? ■ LESSON 3-9

   a. mass of a book
kilograms

   b. mass of a pencil
grams

   c. amount of water in a pool
kiloliters

Find the elapsed time between each pair of times. ■ LESSON 3-10

37. 3:45 P.M. and 5:15 P.M.
1 h 30 min

38. 8:10 P.M. and 11:55 P.M.
3 h 45 min

39. 11:45 A.M. and 6:23 P.M.
6 h 38 min

40. 4:05 A.M. and 4:10 P.M.
12 h 5 min

41. 3:25 P.M. and 5:02 P.M.
1 h 37 min

42. 8:10 A.M. and 11:55 A.M.
3 h 33 min

524

Extra Practice

Estimation **Round to the nearest whole number to estimate the product or quotient.**   ■ LESSON 4-1

1. 3.7×6.8 **28**   **2.** 4.8×3.2 **15**   **3.** 11.69×4.1 **48**   **4.** 5.3×6.9 **35**

5. $30.2 \div 4.9$ **150**   **6.** $21.49 \div 3.16$ **7**   **7.** $12.28 \div 5.59$ **2**   **8.** $120.4 \div 2.89$ **40**

Simplify each expression.   ■ LESSON 4-2

9. $7 + 5^2 \times 6 \div 3$ **57**   **10.** $5^4 \times 3 + 5$ **1,880**   **11.** $6^3 \div 2 + 5 \times 3$ **123**   **12.** $8 \times 8 \times 8$ **512**

13. $(3^2 \times 5) \times (6 \div 2)$ **135**   **14.** $3^3 \times (7 + 5)$ **324**   **15.** $8^3 \div (1.25 + 0.75)$ **256**   **16.** $5 \times 5 \times 5 \times 5$ **625**

Use the distributive property to rewrite and simplify each expression.   ■ LESSON 4-3

17. 7×78
$(7 \times 70) + (7 \times 8) = 546$

18. $3 \times (10 + 5)$
$(3 \times 10) + (3 \times 5) = 45$

19. 6×66
$(6 \times 60) + (6 \times 6) = 396$

20. $4 \times (50 - 5)$
$(4 \times 50) - (4 \times 5) = 180$

Modeling **Model each product.**   ■ LESSON 4-4
21–24. Check students' work for models.

21. 2×0.7 **1.4**   **22.** 1.5×0.2 **0.3**   **23.** 4×0.5 **2**   **24.** 1.4×0.6 **0.84**

Find each product.   ■ LESSON 4-5

25. 1.2
  $\times\ 9$
  91.8

26. 0.33
  $\times\ 15$
  4.95

27. 3.5
  $\times\ 0.4$
  1.4

28. 0.96
  $\times\ 0.15$
  0.144

29. 0.55
  $\times\ 2.8$
  1.54

30. 6.15
  $\times\ 2.4$
  14.76

Modeling **Model each quotient.**   ■ LESSON 4-6
31–34. Check students' work for models.

31. $0.6 \div 0.3$ **2**   **32.** $1.5 \div 0.3$ **5**   **33.** $0.24 \div 0.06$ **4**   **34.** $1.8 \div 0.09$ **20**

Find each quotient.   ■ LESSON 4-7

35. $6.72 \div 4$ **1.68**   **36.** $6\overline{)105}$ **17.5**   **37.** $7\overline{)64.5}$ **9.2**   **38.** $21.12 \div 4$ **5.28**

Find each quotient. Estimate first.   ■ LESSON 4-8

39. $28 \div 0.5$ **56**   **40.** $12.25 \div 0.25$ **49**   **41.** $0.6\overline{)0.307}$ **0.51**   **42.** $0.25\overline{)54.72}$ **218.88**

Mental Math **Complete each statement.**   ■ LESSON 4-10

43. $35\ \text{mm} = \blacksquare\ \text{cm}$ **3.5**   **44.** $10.8\ \text{km} = \blacksquare\ \text{m}$ **10,800**   **45.** $\blacksquare\ \text{L} = 2,400\ \text{mL}$ **2.4**   **46.** $1,008\ \text{g} = \blacksquare\ \text{kg}$ **1.008**

19.

20.

21.

22.

23.

24.

Mental Math **Decide whether each number is divisible by 2, 3, 5, 9, or 10.** ■ LESSON 5-1

1. 324
2, 3, 9

2. 2,685
3, 5

3. 540
2, 3, 5, 9, 10

4. 114
2, 3

5. 31
none

6. 981
3, 9

Tell whether each number is prime or composite. ■ LESSON 5-2

7. 24
composite

8. 49
composite

9. 7
prime

10. 81
composite

11. 37
prime

12. 29
prime

Find the GCF for each set of numbers. ■ LESSON 5-3

13. 10, 30 10 **14.** 15, 18 3 **15.** 25, 35 5 **16.** 28, 36 4 **17.** 45, 72 9 **18.** 8, 12, 20 4

Modeling **Model each fraction.** 19–24. See margin. ■ LESSON 5-4

19. $\frac{3}{5}$ **20.** $\frac{1}{10}$ **21.** $\frac{4}{4}$ **22.** $\frac{5}{12}$ **23.** $\frac{4}{6}$ **24.** $\frac{7}{12}$

Simplify each fraction. ■ LESSON 5-5

25. $\frac{6}{60}$ $\frac{1}{10}$ **26.** $\frac{30}{35}$ $\frac{6}{7}$ **27.** $\frac{27}{36}$ $\frac{3}{4}$ **28.** $\frac{40}{50}$ $\frac{4}{5}$ **29.** $\frac{32}{48}$ $\frac{2}{3}$ **30.** $\frac{42}{70}$ $\frac{3}{5}$

Write each improper fraction as a mixed number. ■ LESSON 5-6

31. $\frac{25}{7}$ $3\frac{4}{7}$ **32.** $\frac{39}{12}$ $3\frac{1}{4}$ **33.** $\frac{12}{5}$ $2\frac{2}{5}$ **34.** $\frac{10}{7}$ $1\frac{3}{7}$ **35.** $\frac{7}{2}$ $3\frac{1}{2}$ **36.** $\frac{100}{16}$ $6\frac{1}{4}$

Write each mixed number as an improper fraction. ■ LESSON 5-6

37. $1\frac{7}{8}$ $\frac{15}{8}$ **38.** $2\frac{3}{5}$ $\frac{13}{5}$ **39.** $11\frac{1}{9}$ $\frac{100}{9}$ **40.** $5\frac{6}{8}$ $\frac{46}{8}$ **41.** $10\frac{1}{8}$ $\frac{81}{8}$ **42.** $3\frac{2}{25}$ $\frac{77}{25}$

Find the LCM for each set of numbers. ■ LESSON 5-7

43. 4, 8 8 **44.** 6, 14 42 **45.** 15, 25 75 **46.** 20, 36 130 **47.** 3, 4, 12 12 **48.** 8, 10, 15 120

Compare using <, >, or =. ■ LESSON 5-8

49. $\frac{1}{2}$ ■ $\frac{2}{3}$ < **50.** $\frac{3}{8}$ ■ $\frac{2}{6}$ > **51.** $\frac{8}{24}$ ■ $\frac{4}{12}$ = **52.** $1\frac{1}{5}$ ■ $1\frac{1}{4}$ < **53.** $\frac{3}{10}$ ■ $\frac{1}{3}$ < **54.** $\frac{5}{6}$ ■ $\frac{7}{9}$ >

Order each set of numbers from least to greatest.

55. $\frac{4}{7}, \frac{4}{5}, \frac{4}{9}$
$\frac{4}{9}, \frac{4}{7}, \frac{4}{5}$

56. $\frac{6}{16}, \frac{7}{16}, \frac{5}{16}$
$\frac{5}{16}, \frac{6}{16}, \frac{7}{16}$

57. $\frac{2}{3}, \frac{5}{6}, \frac{7}{12}$
$\frac{7}{12}, \frac{2}{3}, \frac{5}{6}$

58. $\frac{3}{4}, \frac{4}{6}, \frac{7}{9}$
$\frac{4}{6}, \frac{3}{4}, \frac{7}{9}$

59. $2\frac{3}{4}, 2\frac{1}{8}, 2\frac{1}{2}$
$2\frac{1}{8}, 2\frac{1}{2}, 2\frac{3}{4}$

60. $\frac{3}{8}, \frac{3}{5}, \frac{9}{20}$
$\frac{3}{8}, \frac{9}{20}, \frac{3}{5}$

Write each fraction as a decimal. ■ LESSON 5-9

61. $\frac{2}{3}$ $0.\overline{6}$ **62.** $\frac{3}{4}$ 0.75 **63.** $\frac{2}{5}$ 0.4 **64.** $\frac{1}{4}$ 0.25 **65.** $\frac{1}{2}$ 0.5 **66.** $\frac{3}{5}$ 0.6

61–66. Check students' work for equivalent fractions.

Extra Practice

Estimate each sum or difference.　　　　　■ LESSON 6-1

1. $\frac{1}{2} + \frac{1}{8}$　$\frac{1}{2}$
2. $\frac{5}{6} - \frac{1}{2}$　$\frac{1}{2}$
3. $12\frac{3}{4} - 7\frac{4}{9}$　6
4. $5\frac{7}{9} + 9\frac{3}{5}$　16

Find each sum or difference.　　　　　■ LESSON 6-2

5. $\frac{5}{8} + \frac{1}{8}$　$\frac{3}{4}$
6. $\frac{4}{5} - \frac{2}{5}$　$\frac{2}{5}$
7. $\frac{11}{12} + \frac{5}{12}$　$1\frac{1}{3}$
8. $\frac{7}{8} - \frac{3}{8}$　$\frac{1}{2}$

Find each sum or difference.　　　　　■ LESSON 6-3

9. $\frac{5}{6} + \frac{2}{3}$　$1\frac{1}{2}$
10. $\frac{7}{8} - \frac{3}{4}$　$\frac{1}{8}$
11. $\frac{3}{5} + \frac{5}{8}$　$1\frac{9}{40}$
12. $\frac{3}{8} - \frac{1}{12}$　$\frac{7}{24}$

Find each sum.　　　　　■ LESSON 6-4

13. $6\frac{2}{3} + 1\frac{1}{2}$　$8\frac{1}{6}$
14. $3\frac{2}{3} + 3\frac{1}{2}$　$7\frac{1}{6}$
15. $7\frac{5}{6} + 9\frac{3}{4}$　$17\frac{7}{12}$
16. $5\frac{7}{8} + 1\frac{3}{4}$　$7\frac{5}{8}$

Find each difference.　　　　　■ LESSON 6-5

17. $7\frac{3}{8} - 1\frac{2}{3}$　$5\frac{17}{24}$
18. $11\frac{1}{6} - 2\frac{3}{4}$　$8\frac{5}{12}$
19. $7\frac{5}{6} - 2\frac{1}{10}$　$5\frac{11}{15}$
20. $4\frac{2}{3} - 4\frac{1}{8}$　$\frac{13}{24}$

Find each product.　　　　　■ LESSON 6-7

21. $\frac{1}{2}$ of $\frac{2}{3}$　$\frac{1}{3}$
22. $\frac{1}{4} \times \frac{5}{6}$　$\frac{5}{24}$
23. $\frac{1}{3}$ of $\frac{1}{5}$　$\frac{1}{15}$
24. $\frac{7}{8} \times \frac{3}{4}$　$\frac{21}{32}$
25. $\frac{1}{2} \times 4\frac{1}{4}$　$2\frac{1}{8}$
26. $\frac{1}{20} \times 100$　5
27. $\frac{8}{7} \times 21$　24
28. $\frac{7}{6} \times 42$　49

Find each product.　　　　　■ LESSON 6-8

29. $7\frac{1}{2} \times 2\frac{2}{3}$　20
30. $4\frac{1}{2} \times 3\frac{5}{6}$　$17\frac{1}{4}$
31. $6\frac{1}{3} \times 7\frac{1}{5}$　$45\frac{3}{5}$
32. $5\frac{7}{8} \times 2\frac{1}{2}$　$14\frac{11}{16}$
33. $8\frac{1}{3} \times 6\frac{1}{4}$　$52\frac{1}{12}$
34. $12\frac{1}{4} \times 6\frac{2}{3}$　$81\frac{2}{3}$
35. $10\frac{4}{5} \times 11\frac{1}{3}$　$122\frac{2}{5}$
36. $4\frac{5}{6} \times 2\frac{2}{3}$　$12\frac{8}{9}$

Find each quotient.　　　　　■ LESSON 6-9

37. $2 \div \frac{4}{5}$　2.5
38. $\frac{2}{3} \div \frac{2}{5}$　$1\frac{2}{3}$
39. $2\frac{1}{4} \div \frac{2}{3}$　$3\frac{3}{8}$
40. $4\frac{1}{2} \div 3\frac{1}{3}$　$1\frac{7}{20}$
41. $6\frac{2}{5} \div \frac{2}{25}$　80
42. $5\frac{2}{3} \div 1\frac{1}{2}$　$3\frac{7}{9}$
43. $7\frac{1}{3} \div 3\frac{1}{3}$　$2\frac{1}{5}$
44. $12\frac{1}{2} \div 3\frac{3}{4}$　$3\frac{1}{3}$

Complete each statement.　　　　　■ LESSON 6-10

45. 4 ft = ■ yd　12
46. 48 oz = ■ lb　3
47. 32 qt = ■ gal　8
48. 8,000 lb = ■ T　4

49. 10 lb = ■ oz　160
50. ■ ft = 60 in.　5
51. 64 c = ■ pt　32
52. 9 mi = ■ ft　47,520

53. $5\frac{1}{4}$ ft = ■ yd　$1\frac{3}{4}$
54. $6\frac{3}{4}$ mi = ■ yd　11,880
55. $6\frac{1}{2}$ qt = ■ pt　13
56. $4\frac{1}{2}$ gal = ■ qt　18

22.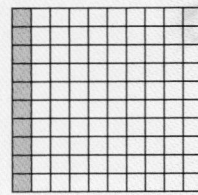

23.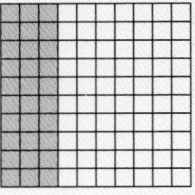

24.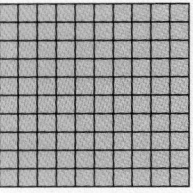

25.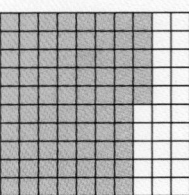

26.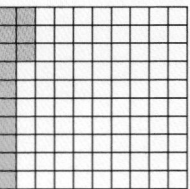

27.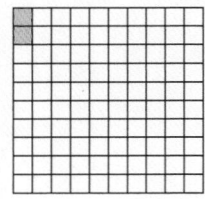

49.  **50.**

51.  **52.**

Write a ratio in three ways for each statement.   ■ LESSON 7-1

1. Mix 2 parts berries with 3 parts cream.
2 to 3, 2 : 3, $\frac{2}{3}$

2. Combine 1 cup water to 2 cups broth.
1 to 2, 1 : 2, $\frac{1}{2}$

Write in simplest form.   ■ LESSON 7-2

3. 30 to 60 1 to 2   4. 5 : 15 1 : 3   5. 13 to 52 1 to 4   6. 7 : 77 1 : 11   7. 18 : 72 1 : 4

Find the value of *n*.   ■ LESSON 7-3

8. $\frac{n}{30} = \frac{3}{15}$ 6   9. $\frac{64}{n} = \frac{5}{10}$ 128   10. $\frac{13}{3} = \frac{n}{6}$ 26   11. $\frac{5}{225} = \frac{2}{n}$ 90   12. $\frac{9}{12} = \frac{12}{n}$ 16

13. $\frac{n}{50} = \frac{3}{75}$ 2   14. $\frac{18}{n} = \frac{3}{10}$ 60   15. $\frac{51}{17} = \frac{n}{3}$ 9   16. $\frac{2}{16} = \frac{n}{24}$ 3   17. $\frac{3}{45} = \frac{4}{n}$ 60

A scale model measures 2 cm × 5 cm. Find the dimensions   ■ LESSON 7-5
of the actual object with the given scale.

18. 1 cm : 10 km
20 km × 50 km

19. 1 cm : 3 cm
6 cm × 15 cm

20. 1 cm : 4.5 m
9 m × 22.5 m

21. 1 mm : 1 km
20 km × 50 km

Modeling **Model each percent using a 10 × 10 square grid.**   ■ LESSON 7-6
22–27. See margin.

22. 10%   23. 30%   24. 100%   25. 75%   26. 13%   27. 2%

Write each fraction or decimal as a percent.   ■ LESSON 7-7

28. 0.77 77%   29. $\frac{10}{25}$ 40%   30. 0.06 6%   31. 0.9 90%   32. $\frac{13}{50}$ 26%   33. $\frac{18}{60}$ 30%

Write each percent as a decimal and then as a fraction in
simplest form.

34. 42%
0.42, $\frac{21}{50}$

35. 96%
0.96, $\frac{24}{25}$

36. 80%
0.8, $\frac{4}{5}$

37. 1%
0.01, $\frac{1}{100}$

38. 87%
0.87, $\frac{87}{100}$

39. 88%
0.88, $\frac{22}{25}$

Estimation **Estimate each amount.**   ■ LESSON 7-8

40. 50% of 168
80

41. 60% of 75
42

42. 75% of 34
24

43. 10% of 171
17

44. 15% of 55
9

Find each percent.   ■ LESSON 7-9

45. 20% of 80 16   46. 15% of $17.50 $2.63   47. 50% of 86 43   48. 90% of 100 90

Sketch a circle graph with the percentages given.   ■ LESSON 7-10
49–52. See margin.

49. 30%, 20%, 50%   50. 29%, 71%   51. 33%, 41%, 22%, 4%   52. 15%, 85%

21.

4.5 cm [rectangle] 12 cm

6 cm [rectangle] 16 cm

Extra Practice

Use the figure at the right for Exercises 1–9.
Name each of the following. 1–4. **Answers may vary. Sample given.** ■ **LESSON 8-1**

1. 3 acute angles
∠*AHG*, ∠*BHC*, ∠*BHD*

2. 4 obtuse angles
∠*AHC*, ∠*AHD*, ∠*GHE*, ∠*GHC*

3. 3 noncollinear points
A, B, E

4. 6 rays
$\overrightarrow{AE}$, $\overrightarrow{HB}$, $\overrightarrow{GH}$, $\overrightarrow{HG}$, $\overrightarrow{FH}$, $\overrightarrow{HD}$

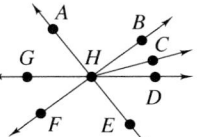

Use a protractor to find the measure of each angle. ■ **LESSONS 8-2, 8-3**

5. ∠*BHF* **180°**   **6.** ∠*FHC* **158°**   **7.** ∠*FHG* **37°**   **8.** ∠*CHD* **15°**   **9.** ∠*AHC* **72°**

10. Draw and measure an acute ∠*Z*. Find the measure of the angle
that is complementary to ∠*Z*. **Check students' work.**

Classify the triangle with the given side lengths as scalene, ■ **LESSON 8-4**
isosceles, or equilateral.

11. 7 cm, 9 cm, 7 cm **isosceles** **12.** 3 m, 3 m, 3 m **equilateral**   **13.** 18 in., 16 in., 5 in. **scalene**

Classify the triangle with the given angle measures as
acute, obtuse, or *right.*

14. 2°, 176°, 2° **obtuse**   **15.** 30°, 60°, 90° **right**   **16.** 45°, 65°, 70° **acute**

Complete each statement with *All, Some,* or *No.*   ■ **LESSONS 8-5, 8-6**

17. ■ triangles have three sides.
all

18. ■ quadrilaterals have two congruent sides.
some

19. ■ circles are polygons. **no**

20. ■ rectangles are squares. **some**

21. Draw two rectangles that are similar to one with length   ■ **LESSON 8-8**
8 cm and width 3 cm. **See margin.**

22. Find the number of lines of symmetry
in the octagon at the right. **2**   ■ **LESSON 8-9**

Find the unknown length in each circle.   ■ **LESSON 8-10**

23. *r* = 24 in.; *d* = ■   **24.** *d* = 70 ft; *r* = ■   **25.** *d* = 3 m; *r* = ■   **26.** *r* = 65 cm; *d* = ■
   48 in.   **35 ft**   **1.5 m**   **30 cm**

27. *Writing* Explain what is meant by the terms *translation,*   ■ **LESSON 8-11**
reflection, and *rotation.* **Check students' work.**

13.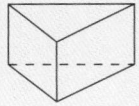

14.

15.

16.

Extra Practice

The area of each square is 1 cm². Estimate the area of each figure. Estimates may vary for Ex. 2–3.　　■ LESSON 9-1

1. 16 cm²　　**2.** 18 cm²　　**3.** 15 cm²

Find the area of each figure.　　■ LESSON 9-2, 9-3

4. 52.25 ft²
9.5 ft
5.5 ft

5. 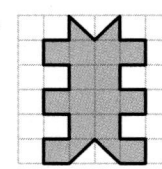 4 m　5 m　12 m²
6 m

6.  18 cm　144 cm²
10 cm　8 cm

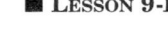 Find the circumference of a circle with the given radius or diameter. Round the answer to the nearest unit.　　■ LESSON 9-4

7. $d = 26$ yd
82 yd

8. $d = 10.6$ ft
33 ft

9. $r = 30$ in.
188 in.

10. $r = 11$ cm
69 cm

11. $d = 8.5$ m
27 m

12. Find the area for each circle noted in Exercises 7–11. Round each answer to the nearest tenth of a unit.　　■ LESSON 9-5
530.7 yd² , 88.2 ft² , 2,826 in.² , 379.9 cm² , 56.7 m²

Sketch each three-dimensional figure. See margin.　　■ LESSON 9-6

13. triangular prism　　**14.** hexagonal prism　　**15.** cylinder　　**16.** cone

Find the surface area of each rectangular prism.　　■ LESSON 9-7

17. 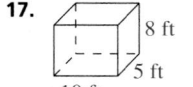 340 ft²
8 ft
5 ft
10 ft

18. 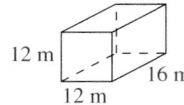 1,056 m²
12 m
12 m　16 m

19. 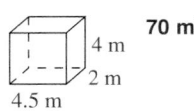 70 m²
4 m
2 m
4.5 m

Find the volume of the rectangular prism with the given dimensions.　　■ LESSON 9-8

20. $\ell = 5$ ft, $w = 3$ ft, $h = 4$ ft　60 ft³

21. $\ell = 2$ in., $w = 6$ in., $h = 2$ in.　24 in.³

22. $\ell = 7$ m, $w = 8$ m, $h = 10$ m　560 m³

23. $\ell = 22$ cm, $w = 14$ cm, $h = 4$ cm　1,232 cm³

CHAPTER 10

22.

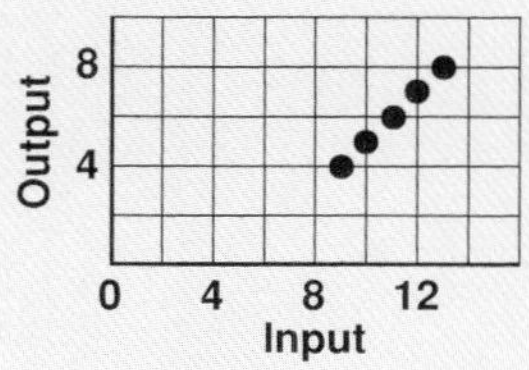

23.

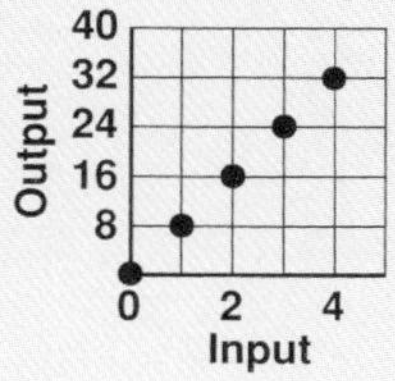

24.

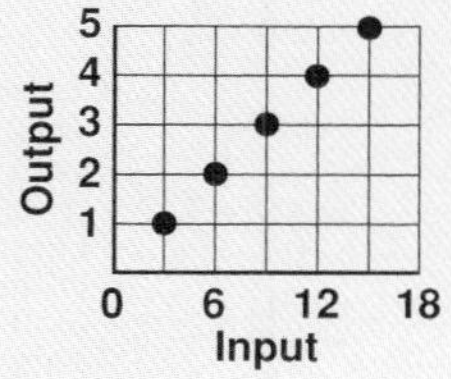

CHAPTER 10 Extra Practice

Compare using <, >, =. ■ LESSON 10-1

1. −3 ■ −1 <
2. 5 ■ 7 <
3. −5 ■ −7 >
4. −6 ■ 0 <
5. −3 − 1 ■ −3 + (−1) =
6. 4 − 8 ■ 8 − 4 <
7. −5 − (−2) ■ −5 − 2 >

Modeling **Model each integer in two ways.** ■ LESSON 10-2

8–13. Check students' work for models.

8. 3
9. −2
10. 0
11. −4
12. 6
13. −5

Find each sum or difference. ■ LESSONS 10-3, 10-4

14. −14 + 28 14
15. 31 − (−52) 83
16. −72 + (−53) −125
17. −83 − (−3) −80
18. 19 − (−18) 37
19. −101 + 121 20
20. 65 + (−5) 60
21. −217 − (−217) 0

Graph each function. 22–24. See margin. ■ LESSON 10-6

22.

Input	Output
9	4
10	5
11	6
12	7
13	8

23.

Input	Output
1	0
1	8
2	16
3	24
4	32

24.

Input	Output
3	1
6	2
9	3
12	4
15	5

Use the graph at the right for Exercises 25–36. Name the coordinates of each point. ■ LESSON 10-7

25. *A* (2, 3)
26. *B* (3, −3)
27. *C* (−3, −1)
28. *D* (−3, 3)
29. *E* (−1, −1)

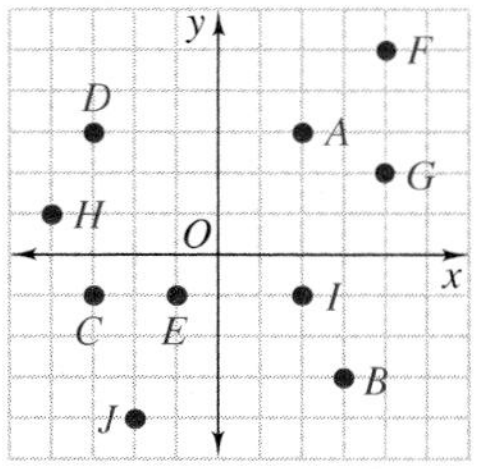

Name the point with the given coordinates.

30. (4, 2) G
31. (4, 5) F
32. (2, −1) I
33. (−4, 1) H
34. (−3, 3) D
35. (−2, 4) J
36. In which quadrant are points *C*, *E*, and *J*? quadrant III
37. On graph paper, graph the points *L*(−3, 2), *M*(5, −4), and *N*(0, 5). See right.

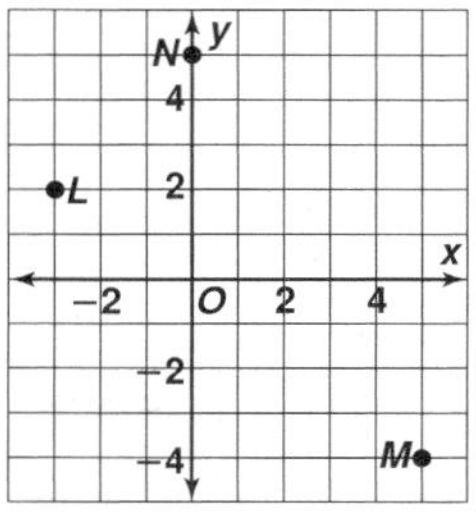

What scale and intervals would you use to graph the data set given? 38–39. Check students' work. ■ LESSON 10-8

38. 0, −35, 25, 15, −17, 5, −4.1
39. −12, 0, 12, −7, −6, 3, −8, 6

4.

Fillings	Breads	Toppings

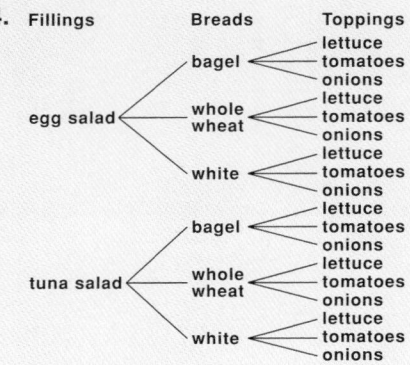

---

1. Harvey rolls a number cube. If he rolls an even number, he wins. If he rolls an odd number, his sister wins. Is this a fair game? Explain. **Fair game; the chances of rolling even (2, 4, 6) or odd (1, 3, 5) are equally likely.** ■ LESSON 11-1

2. Suppose you take a four-question true–false test. You guess all the answers. What is the probability that you will guess three correct answers? Use a simulation to solve the problem. **Check students' work.** ■ LESSON 11-3

3. Use the number 3,486,335,206 to find each theoretical probability. Write each probability as a percent and a fraction. ■ LESSON 11-4
   a. probability that a digit selected at random is a 3 **30%, $\frac{3}{10}$**
   b. probability that a digit selected at random is a 2 **10%, $\frac{1}{10}$**

4. Make a tree diagram to show all possible sandwich combinations. Assume you choose one from each category. **See margin.** ■ LESSON 11-5

Sandwiches

Fillings:	Egg Salad, Tuna Salad
Breads:	Bagel, Whole Wheat, White
Toppings:	Lettuce, Tomatoes, Onions

5. Suppose you flip a coin and roll a number cube. Find the theoretical probability of each result. ■ LESSON 11-6
   a. the number 6 and heads $\frac{1}{12}$ **b.** any even numbers and tails $\frac{1}{4}$

6. How many possible arrangements are there for the letters in the word TYPE? **24 arrangements** ■ LESSON 11-7

⊞ *Calculator* **Use a calculator to find each value.**

7. 5! **120**   **8.** 11! **39,916,800** **9.** 2! **2**   **10.** 9! **362,880**   **11.** 3! **6**

12. 4! **24**   **13.** 8! **40,320**   **14.** 6! **720**   **15.** 7! **5,040**   **16.** 10! **3,628,800**

Is each sample random? Representative? ■ LESSON 11-8

17. A school district wants to find out which fruits to sell in its school cafeterias. They survey all the students in one school. **representative**

18. A teacher wants to know the opinions of all her students on the upcoming elections. She places each student's name in a box and draws 15 names. **random**

Tables

TABLE 1 *Measures*

Metric	United States Customary

Metric

Length

10 millimeters (mm) = 1 centimeter (cm)

100 cm = 1 meter (m)

1,000 m = 1 kilometer (k)

Area

100 square millimeters (mm^2) = 1 square centimeter (cm^2)

10,000 cm^2 = 1 square meter (m^2)

Volume

1,000 cubic millimeters (mm^3) = 1 cubic centimeter (cm^3)

1,000,000 cm^3 = 1 cubic meter (m^3)

Mass

1,000 milligrams (mg) = 1 gram (g)

1,000 g = 1 kilogram (kg)

Capacity

1,000 milliliters (mL) = 1 liter (L)

1,000 L = 1 kiloliter (kL)

United States Customary

Length

12 inches (in.) = 1 foot (ft)

3 feet = 1 yard (yd)

36 in. = 1 yd

5,280 ft = 1 mile (mi)

1,760 yd = 1 mi

Area

144 square inches ($in.^2$) = 1 square foot (ft^2)

9 ft^2 = 1 square yard (yd^2)

4,840 yd^2 = 1 acre

3,077,600 yd^2 = 1 square mile (mi^2)

Volume

1,728 cubic inches ($in.^3$) = 1 cubic foot (ft^3)

27 ft^3 = 1 cubic yard (yd^3)

Weight

16 ounces (oz) = 1 pound (lb)

2,000 lb = 1 ton (T)

Capacity

8 fluid ounces (fl oz) = 1 cup (c)

2 c = 1 pint (pt)

2 pt = 1 quart (qt)

4 qt = 1 gallon (gal)

Time

1 minute (min) = 60 seconds (s)

1 hour (h) = 60 min = 3,600 s

1 day (d) = 24 h = 1,440 min

1 year (yr) ≈ 52 wk ≈ 365 d

TABLE 2 *Formulas*

Circles

area: $A = \pi r^2$

circumference: $C = \pi d$ or $C = 2\pi r$

diameter: $d = 2r$

radius: $r = \frac{d}{2}$

Area

parallelogram: $A = base \times height$
$A = b \times h$

rectangle: $A = length \times width$
$A = l \times w$

square: $A = side \times side$
$A = s \times s$
$A = s^2$

triangle: $A = \frac{1}{2}base \times height$
$A = \frac{1}{2}b \times h$

Perimeter

rectangle: $P = l + w + l + w$
$P = 2l + 2w$ or
$P = 2(l + w)$

square: $P = s + s + s + s$
$P = 4s$

Volume

rectangular prism:

$V = length \times width \times height$
$V = lwh$

Surface Area

rectangular prism:

$SA = 2(l \times w) + 2(l \times h) + 2(w + h)$

Simple Interest

amount deposited $\times$ interest rate $\times$ number of years = simple interest

Probability

Probability (Event) $= \frac{\text{number of favorable outcomes}}{\text{number of possible outcomes}}$

Probability (A and B) =
    Probability (A) $\times$ Probability (B)

TABLE 3 *Symbols*

$>$	is greater than	$\overline{AB}$	segment AB	$\lvert 5 \rvert$	absolute value of 5
$<$	is less than	$\overrightarrow{AB}$	ray AB	7^3	seven to the power of three
$=$	is equal to	$\overleftrightarrow{AB}$	line AB		
$\neq$	is not equal to	$\angle ABC$	angle ABC	$30°$	degrees
$\leq$	is less than or equal to	∟	right angle ($90°\angle$)	10%	percent
		mi/h	miles per hour	unit^2	square unit
$\geq$	is greater than or equal to	mi/gal	miles per gallon	π	pi; ≈ 3.14
		$+8$	positive 8	$a : b$	ratio of a to b
$\approx$	is approximately equal to	-8	negative 8		

534

Place Value of Whole Numbers

The digits in a whole number are grouped into periods. A period has 3 digits, and each period has a name. Each digit in a whole number has both a place and a value.

Billions Period			Millions Period			Thousands Period			Ones Period		
Hundred billions	Ten billions	Billions	Hundred millions	Ten millions	Millions	Hundred thousands	Ten thousands	Thousands	Hundreds	Tens	Ones
9	5	1	6	3	7	0	4	1	1	8	2

The digit 5 is in the ten billions place. So, its value is 5 ten billion, or 50 billion.

■ **EXAMPLE**

a. In what place is the digit 7?
   millions

b. What is the value of the digit 7?
   7 million

EXERCISES *On Your Own*

Use the chart above. Write the place of each digit.

1. the digit 3 ten millions

2. the digit 4 ten thousands

3. the digit 6 hundred millions

4. the digit 8 tens

5. the digit 9 hundred billions

6. the digit 0 hundred thousands

Use the chart above. Write the value of each digit.

7. the digit 3 3 ten million

8. the digit 4 4 ten thousand

9. the digit 6 6 hundred million

10. the digit 8 8 ten

11. the digit 9 9 hundred billion

12. the digit 0
0 hundred thousand

Write the value of the digit 6 in each number.

13. 633
6 hundred

14. 761,523
6 ten thousand

15. 163,500,000
6 hundred thousand

16. 165,417
6 ten thousand

17. 265
6 ten

18. 4,396
6 one

19. 618,920
6 hundred thousand

20. 204,602
6 hundred

21. 162,450,000,000
6 ten billion

22. 7,682
6 hundred

23. 358,026,113
6 thousand

24. 76,030,100
6 million

25. 642,379
6 hundred thousand

26. 16,403
6 thousand

27. 45,060
6 ten

28. 401,601,001
6 hundred thousand

Reading and Writing Whole Numbers

To read a number, you read the number in each period followed by its period name (except for the ones period).

Billions Period			Millions Period			Thousands Period			Ones Period		
Hundred billions	Ten billions	Billions	Hundred millions	Ten millions	Millions	Hundred thousands	Ten thousands	Thousands	Hundreds	Tens	Ones
6	0	7	3	2	4	0	7	0	2	3	4

607 billion, 324 million, 70 thousand, 234

To write a number in standard form, use commas to show the periods. Add zeros if you need to so that each period has 3 digits.

607,324,070,234

■ EXAMPLE

Write each number in standard form.

a. 21 million, 4 thousand, 37

21,004,037

b. 125 billion, 2 million

125,002,000,000

EXERCISES *On Your Own*

Complete each statement.

1. 7,360,900 = ▓ million, ▓ thousand, ▓
  7 360 900

2. 92,170,000,000 = ▓ billion, ▓ million
  92 170

3. 67,013,005 = ▓ million, ▓ thousand, ▓
  67 13 5

4. 85,000,400 = ▓ million, ▓
  85 400

Write each number in standard form.

5. 232 billion, 753 thousand
232,000,753,000

6. 65 million, 2 thousand, 42
65,002,042

7. 321 thousand, 29
321,029

8. 38 billion, 37 thousand, 90
38,000,037,090

9. 322 million, 135
322,000,135

10. 430 million, 15 thousand, 6
430,015,006

11. 5 billion, 4 million, 12 thousand
5,004,012,000

12. 5 billion, 32 million, 269 thousand
5,032,269,000

536

Comparing and Ordering Whole Numbers

The numbers on a number line are in order from least to greatest. So, a number line can be used to compare numbers.

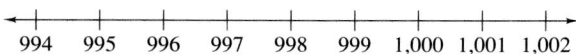

994   995   996   997   998   999   1,000 1,001 1,002

■ EXAMPLE

Use > or < to compare the numbers.

a. 995 ▓ 998

995 is to the left of 998.

995 < 998

b. 1,001 ▓ 999

1,001 is to the right of 999.

1,001 > 999

c. 12,875 ▓ 12,675

Compare the digits starting with the highest place values.

1 = 1, 2 = 2, 8 > 6, so 12,875 > 12,675

d. 84,662 ▓ 840,667

The number on the left has fewer digits, so it is less.

84,662 < 840,667

EXERCISES *On Your Own*

Use > or < to compare the numbers.

1. 366 ▓ 36 **>**   **2.** 54,001 ▓ 54,901 **<**   **3.** 8,801 ▓ 810 **>**   **4.** 84,123 ▓ 9,996 **>**

5. 29,286 ▓ 29,826 **<**   **6.** 129,631 ▓ 142,832 **<** **7.** 31,010 ▓ 30,101 **<**   **8.** 4,328 ▓ 4,238 **>**

9. 98,410 ▓ 98,140 **>**   **10.** 40,000 ▓ 300,009 **<**   **11.** 611,401 ▓ 611,701 **<**

12. 478,296 ▓ 478,269 **>**   **13.** 1,801,342 ▓ 801,142 **>**   **14.** 27,248,315 ▓ 27,283,718 **<**

Write the numbers in order from least to greatest.

15. 1,367; 1,437; 1,747; 1,374
     1,367; 1,374; 1,437; 1,747

16. 20,403; 20,304; 23,404; 23,040
     20,304; 20,403; 23,040; 23,404

17. 9,897; 9,987; 9,789
     9,789; 9,897; 9,987

18. 54,172; 51,472; 57,142; 51,572
     51,472; 51,572; 54,172; 57,142

19. 17,444; 18,242; 17,671; 17,414
     17,414; 17,444; 17,671; 18,242

20. 7,910; 7,890; 7,901
     7,890; 7,901; 9,701

Use > or < to make each sentence true.

21. 60,789 ▓ 60,798 ▓ 62,532 **<   <**

22. 24,861 ▓ 18,000 ▓ 42,501 **>   <**

23. 42,101 ▓ 42,077 ▓ 41,963 **>   <**

24. 10,455 ▓ 11,900 ▓ 11,483 **<   >**

Adding Whole Numbers

When you add, line up the digits in the correct columns. You may need to regroup from one column to the next.

■ EXAMPLE 1

Add 463 + 58.

Step 1	Step 2	Step 3
$\overset{1}{}$ 463	$\overset{11}{}$ 463	$\overset{11}{}$ 463
+ 58	+ 58	+ 58
1	21	521

■ EXAMPLE 2

Find each sum.

a. 962 + 120

$$\begin{array}{r} 962 \\ + 120 \\ \hline 1,082 \end{array}$$

b. 25 + 9 + 143

$$\begin{array}{r} \overset{1}{2}5 \\ 9 \\ + 143 \\ \hline 177 \end{array}$$

c. 3,887 + 1,201

$$\begin{array}{r} \overset{1}{3},887 \\ + 1,201 \\ \hline 5,088 \end{array}$$

EXERCISES *On Your Own*

Add.

1.	45	2.	56	3.	25	4.	43	5.	66	6.	87
	+ 31		+ 80		+ 16		+ 29		+ 78		+ 35
	76		136		41		72		144		122

7.	81	8.	406	9.	207	10.	480	11.	217	12.	675
	+ 312		+ 123		+ 72		+ 365		+ 347		+ 329
	393		529		279		845		564		1,004

13.	2,051	14.	786	15.	5,227	16.	3,104	17.	5,337	18.	4,282
	+ 843		+ 4,109		+ 1,527		+ 2,698		+ 1,812		+ 7,518
	2,894		4,895		6,754		5,802		7,149		11,800

19. 78 + 56 134   **20.** 35 + 96 131   **21.** 105 + 71 176   **22.** 29 + 342 371   **23.** 654 + 103 757

24. 286 + 42 328   **25.** 55 + 77 132   **26.** 242 + 83 325   **27.** 32 + 68 100   **28.** 108 + 13 121

29. 589 + 318 907   **30.** 642 + 975 1,617   **31.** 2,308 + 451 2,759   **32.** 976 + 4,035 5,011

33. 8,228 + 1,024 9,252   **34.** 5,417 + 2,391 7,808   **35.** 6,470 + 9,828 16,298   **36.** 7,121 + 5,359 12,840

538

Subtracting Whole Numbers

When you subtract, line up the digits in the correct columns. Begin by subtracting the ones. Regroup if the bottom digit is greater than the top digit.

■ EXAMPLE 1

Subtract 725 − 86.

Step 1

$$\begin{array}{r} \scriptstyle 115 \\ 72\cancel{5} \\ -\ 86 \\ \hline 9 \end{array}$$

Step 2

$$\begin{array}{r} \scriptstyle 11 \\ \scriptstyle 6\cancel{1}\,15 \\ 72\cancel{5} \\ -\ 86 \\ \hline 39 \end{array}$$

Step 3

$$\begin{array}{r} \scriptstyle 11 \\ \scriptstyle 6\cancel{1}\,15 \\ 72\cancel{5} \\ -\ 86 \\ \hline 639 \end{array}$$

■ EXAMPLE 2

Find each difference.

a. 96 − 27

$$\begin{array}{r} \scriptstyle 8\,16 \\ 9\cancel{6} \\ -\ 27 \\ \hline 69 \end{array}$$

b. 625 − 273

$$\begin{array}{r} \scriptstyle 5\,12 \\ 6\cancel{2}5 \\ -\ 273 \\ \hline 352 \end{array}$$

c. 3,127 − 1,648

$$\begin{array}{r} \scriptstyle 10\,11 \\ \scriptstyle 2\ \cancel{0}\cancel{1}\ 17 \\ 3,12\cancel{7} \\ -\ 1,648 \\ \hline 1,479 \end{array}$$

EXERCISES *On Your Own*

Subtract.

1. 81 − 37 44	**2.** 59 − 23 36	**3.** 41 − 19 22	**4.** 83 − 25 58	**5.** 99 − 78 21	**6.** 87 − 31 56
7. 781 − 312 469	**8.** 619 − 83 536	**9.** 247 − 72 175	**10.** 881 − 391 490	**11.** 517 − 287 230	**12.** 973 − 529 444
13. 7,411 − 583 6,828	**14.** 3,789 − 809 2,980	**15.** 6,227 − 1,127 5,100	**16.** 4,178 − 2,098 2,080	**17.** 5,337 − 1,812 3,525	**18.** 8,282 − 4,118 4,164

19. 78 − 19 59   **20.** 231 − 99 132   **21.** 534 − 71 463   **22.** 629 − 382 247   **23.** 918 − 133 785

24. 827 − 125 702   **25.** 517 − 291 226   **26.** 973 − 228 745   **27.** 721 − 119 602   **28.** 522 − 146 376

29. 642 − 223 419   **30.** 427 − 193 234   **31.** 444 − 345 99   **32.** 988 − 489 499   **33.** 601 − 425 176

Multiplying Whole Numbers by One-Digit Numbers

When you multiply by a one-digit number, multiply the one-digit
number by each digit in the other number.

■ **EXAMPLE 1**

Multiply 294 × 7.

Step 1: Multiply 7 by the ones digit.

$$\begin{array}{r} \overset{2}{2}9\overset{}{4} \\ \times \quad 7 \\ \hline 8 \end{array}$$

Step 2: Multiply 7 by the tens digit.

$$\begin{array}{r} \overset{6\,2}{2}94 \\ \times \quad 7 \\ \hline 58 \end{array}$$

Step 3: Multiply 7 by the hundreds digit.

$$\begin{array}{r} \overset{6\,2}{2}94 \\ \times \quad 7 \\ \hline 2{,}058 \end{array}$$

■ **EXAMPLE 2**

Find each product.

a. 681 × 4

$$\begin{array}{r} 681 \\ \times \quad 4 \\ \hline 2{,}724 \end{array}$$

b. 402 × 9

$$\begin{array}{r} 402 \\ \times \quad 9 \\ \hline 3{,}618 \end{array}$$

c. 7 × 96

$$\begin{array}{r} 96 \\ \times \quad 7 \\ \hline 672 \end{array}$$

EXERCISES *On Your Own*

Multiply.

1. $\begin{array}{r}81\\\times\ 3\\\hline 243\end{array}$	**2.** $\begin{array}{r}47\\\times\ 2\\\hline 94\end{array}$	**3.** $\begin{array}{r}58\\\times\ 6\\\hline 348\end{array}$	**4.** $\begin{array}{r}37\\\times\ 5\\\hline 185\end{array}$	**5.** $\begin{array}{r}76\\\times\ 4\\\hline 304\end{array}$	**6.** $\begin{array}{r}39\\\times\ 3\\\hline 117\end{array}$
7. $\begin{array}{r}678\\\times\ 5\\\hline 3{,}390\end{array}$	**8.** $\begin{array}{r}412\\\times\ 7\\\hline 2{,}884\end{array}$	**9.** $\begin{array}{r}326\\\times\ 4\\\hline 1{,}304\end{array}$	**10.** $\begin{array}{r}228\\\times\ 9\\\hline 2{,}052\end{array}$	**11.** $\begin{array}{r}864\\\times\ 5\\\hline 4{,}320\end{array}$	**12.** $\begin{array}{r}717\\\times\ 3\\\hline 2{,}151\end{array}$
13. $\begin{array}{r}25\\\times\ 6\\\hline 1{,}150\end{array}$	**14.** $\begin{array}{r}87\\\times\ 3\\\hline 2{,}697\end{array}$	**15.** $\begin{array}{r}62\\\times\ 8\\\hline 496\end{array}$	**16.** $\begin{array}{r}312\\\times\ 3\\\hline 936\end{array}$	**17.** $\begin{array}{r}456\\\times\ 7\\\hline 3{,}192\end{array}$	**18.** $\begin{array}{r}915\\\times\ 2\\\hline 1{,}830\end{array}$

19. 7 × 45 315 **20.** 62 × 3 186 **21.** 213 × 4 852 **22.** 8 × 177 1,416 **23.** 673 × 9 6,057

24. 5 × 41 205 **25.** 3 × 82 246 **26.** 94 × 6 564 **27.** 63 × 4 252 **28.** 58 × 3 174

29. 4 × 76 304 **30.** 32 × 3 96 **31.** 371 × 8 3,038 **32.** 562 × 1 562 **33.** 946 × 7 6,622

34. 8 × 111 888 **35.** 443 × 5 2,215 **36.** 199 × 2 398 **37.** 138 × 3 414 **38.** 224 × 8 1,792

One-Digit Divisors

$6\overline{)466}$ and $466 \div 6$ are two ways of writing the same division problem. In the problem, 466 is the dividend and 6 is the divisor. The answer is a quotient with a remainder.

■ **EXAMPLE 1**

Find $6\overline{)466}$.

Step 1

$$
\begin{array}{r}
7 \\
6\overline{)466} \\
-42 \\
\hline
4
\end{array}
$$

Step 2

$$
\begin{array}{r}
77 \\
6\overline{)466} \\
-42 \\
\hline
46 \\
-42 \\
\hline
\end{array}
$$

Step 3

$$
\begin{array}{r}
77\,\text{R}4 \\
6\overline{)466} \\
-42 \\
\hline
46 \\
-42 \\
\hline
4
\end{array}
$$

■ **EXAMPLE 2**

Find each quotient.

a. $568 \div 5$

$$
\begin{array}{r}
113\,\text{R}3 \\
5\overline{)568} \\
-5 \\
\hline
06 \\
-5 \\
\hline
18 \\
-15 \\
\hline
3
\end{array}
$$

b. $232 \div 8$

$$
\begin{array}{r}
29 \\
8\overline{)232} \\
-16 \\
\hline
72 \\
-72 \\
\hline
0
\end{array}
$$

Be careful to place the first digit of the quotient over the correct digit in the dividend.

EXERCISES *On Your Own*

Divide.

1. $7\overline{)29}$ 4 R1
2. $3\overline{)20}$ 6 R2
3. $2\overline{)11}$ 5 R1
4. $8\overline{)70}$ 8 R6
5. $4\overline{)18}$ 4 R2

6. $9\overline{)659}$ 73 R2
7. $7\overline{)96}$ 13 R5
8. $9\overline{)347}$ 38 R5
9. $4\overline{)82}$ 20 R2
10. $8\overline{)232}$ 29

11. $89 \div 7$ 12 R5
12. $90 \div 8$ 11 R2
13. $66 \div 4$ 16 R2
14. $68 \div 6$ 11 R2
15. $95 \div 5$ 19

16. $359 \div 3$ 119 R2
17. $941 \div 9$ 104 R5
18. $148 \div 5$ 29 R3
19. $929 \div 8$ 116 R1
20. $735 \div 6$ 122 R3

21. $965 \div 5$ 193
22. $845 \div 4$ 211 R1
23. $294 \div 7$ 42
24. $487 \div 6$ 81 R1
25. $532 \div 4$ 134

Zeros in Quotients

When you divide, after you bring down a digit you must write a digit in the quotient. In this example, the second digit in the quotient is zero.

■ EXAMPLE 1

Find $8\overline{)3,208}$.

Step 1

$$
\begin{array}{r}
4 \\
8\overline{)3208} \\
-32 \\
\hline
0
\end{array}
$$

Step 2

$$
\begin{array}{r}
40 \\
8\overline{)3208} \\
-32 \\
\hline
00
\end{array}
$$

Step 3

$$
\begin{array}{r}
401 \\
8\overline{)3208} \\
-32 \\
\hline
008 \\
-\ 8 \\
\hline
0
\end{array}
$$

■ EXAMPLE 2

Find each quotient.

a. $423 \div 7$

$$
\begin{array}{r}
60\,R3 \\
7\overline{)423} \\
-42 \\
\hline
03 \\
-\ 0 \\
\hline
3
\end{array}
$$

b. $1,158 \div 23$

$$
\begin{array}{r}
50\,R8 \\
23\overline{)1158} \\
-115 \\
\hline
08 \\
-\ 0 \\
\hline
8
\end{array}
$$

c. $7,211 \div 9$

$$
\begin{array}{r}
801\,R2 \\
9\overline{)7211} \\
-72 \\
\hline
01 \\
-\ 0 \\
\hline
11 \\
-\ 9 \\
\hline
2
\end{array}
$$

EXERCISES *On Your Own*

Divide.

1. $7\overline{)212}$ 30 R2

2. $9\overline{)367}$ 40 R7

3. $3\overline{)271}$ 90 R1

4. $8\overline{)485}$ 60 R5

5. $6\overline{)483}$ 80 R3

6. $34\overline{)1,371}$ 40 R11

7. $19\overline{)1,335}$ 70 R5

8. $62\overline{)1,881}$ 70 R21

9. $54\overline{)1,094}$ 20 R14

10. $41\overline{)3,710}$ 90 R20

11. $282 \div 4$ 70 R2

12. $143 \div 7$ 20 R3

13. $181 \div 3$ 60 R1

14. $400 \div 8$ 50

15. $365 \div 9$ 40 R5

16. $1,008 \div 5$ 201 R3

17. $3,018 \div 6$ 503

18. $4,939 \div 7$ 705 R4

19. $1,682 \div 4$ 420 R2

20. $3,647 \div 6$ 607 R5

21. $2,488 \div 31$ 80 R8

22. $3,372 \div 67$ 50 R22

23. $1,937 \div 48$ 40 R17

24. $4,165 \div 59$ 70 R35

25. $1,686 \div 82$ 20 R 46

Dividing by Multiples of 10

You can use patterns to divide by a multiple of ten. The divisor is a multiple of ten when it ends in zero, such as 10, 100, or 1,000. To find the quotient, move the decimal point of the dividend to the left as many places as the number of zeros in the divisor.

■ EXAMPLE 1

Find each quotient.

Step 1: Count the number of zeros in the divisor.

Step 2: Move the decimal point in the dividend that many places to the left.

a. $46 \div 10$	$=$	4.6	← 1 place to the left
b. $46 \div 100$	$=$	0.46	← 2 places to the left
c. $46 \div 1,000$	$=$	0.046	← 3 places to the left

■ EXAMPLE 2

Find each quotient.

a. $78 \div 100$

$78 \div 100 = 0.78$

b. $29.5 \div 1,000$

$29.5 \div 1,000 = 0.0295$

c. $453 \div 10$

$453 \div 10 = 45.3$

EXERCISES *On Your Own*

Find each quotient.

1. $25 \div 10$ 2.5

2. $467 \div 1,000$ 0.467

3. $890 \div 10$ 89

4. $4.3 \div 100$ 0.043

5. $10.8 \div 100$ 0.108

6. $70 \div 10$ 7

7. $0.014 \div 100$ 0.00014

8. $12.2 \div 10$ 1.22

9. $1.4 \div 1,000$ 0.0014

10. $36.1 \div 1,000$ 0.0361

11. $40.5 \div 10$ 4.05

12. $309 \div 100$ 3.09

13. $8 \div 10$ 0.8

14. $455 \div 100$ 4.55

15. $6,890 \div 100$ 68.9

16. $90.5 \div 10$ 9.05

17. $0.09 \div 100$ 0.0009

18. $0.085 \div 10$ 0.0085

19. $66.6 \div 100$ 0.666

20. $4 \div 1,000$ 0.004

Use mental math to find each quotient.

21. $360 \div 30$ 12

22. $420 \div 20$ 21

23. $1,400 \div 70$ 20

24. $500 \div 50$ 10

25. $8,000 \div 200$ 40

26. $60 \div 30$ 2

27. $2,000 \div 20$ 100

28. $900 \div 300$ 3

Reading Thermometer Scales

The thermometer at the right shows temperature in degrees Celsius (°C) and degrees Fahrenheit (°F).

■ EXAMPLE 1

How do you read point *A* on the Celsius thermometer below?

Each 1-degree interval is divided into 10 smaller intervals of 0.1 degree each. The reading at point *A* is 36.2°C.

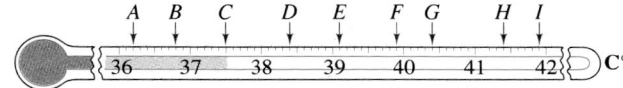

■ EXAMPLE 2

How do you read point *V* on the Fahrenheit thermometer below?

Each 1-degree interval is divided into 5 smaller intervals. Since 10 ÷ 5 = 2, each smaller interval represents 0.2 degree. Count by 0.2, beginning with 98.0. The reading at point *V* is 98.6°F.

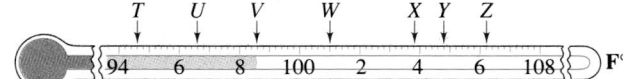

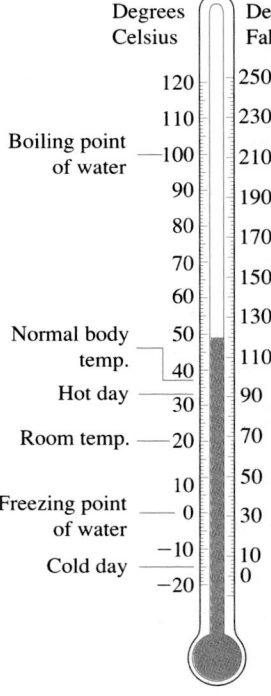

EXERCISES *On Your Own*

Use the thermometers above to write the temperature reading for each point. Tell whether the reading is in degrees Celsius (°C) or degrees Fahrenheit (°F).

1. *B* 36.8° C **2.** *C* 37.5° C **3.** *D* 38.4° C **4.** *T* 94.6° F **5.** *U* 96.6° F **6.** *Z* 106.2° F

Use the thermometers above to name the point that relates to each temperature reading.

7. 40.4°C G **8.** 41.9°C I **9.** 39.9°C F **10.** 104.8°F Y **11.** 101°F W **12.** 103.8°F X

544

Roman Numerals

The ancient Romans used letters to represent numerals. The table below shows the value of each Roman numeral.

I	V	X	L	C	D	M
1	5	10	50	100	500	1,000

Here are the Roman numerals from 1 to 10.

1	2	3	4	5	6	7	8	9	10
I	II	III	IV	V	VI	VII	VIII	IX	X

Roman numerals are read in groups from left to right.

If the value of the second numeral is the same as or less than the first numeral, add the values. The Roman numerals II, III, VI, VII, and VIII are examples in which you use addition.

If the value of the second numeral is greater than the first numeral, subtract the values. The Roman numerals IV and IX are examples in which you use subtraction.

■ EXAMPLE

Find the value of each Roman numeral.

a. LD

$500 - 50$

450

b. MXXVI

$1,000 + 10 + 10 + 5 + 1$

1,026

c. XCIV

$(100 - 10) + (5 - 1)$

$90 + 4 = 94$

EXERCISES *On Your Own*

Find the value of each Roman numeral.

1. XI 11

2. DIII 503

3. VC 45

4. CMX 910

5. XXIX 29

6. DLIX 559

7. MLVI 1,056

8. LX 60

9. LDIV 454

10. DCV 605

Write each number as a Roman numeral.

11. 15 XV

12. 45 VC

13. 1,632 MDCXXXII

14. 222 CCXXII

15. 159 CLIX

16. 67 LXVII

17. 92 XCII

18. 403 CDIII

19. 2,490 MMXD

20. 64 LXIV

Examples

A

Absolute value (p. 438)   The absolute value of a number is its distance, in either direction, from zero on a number line.

$|-10| = 10$

Acute angle (p. 333)   An acute angle is any angle that measures less than 90°.
Example: The measure of ∠1 is between 0° and 90°.

Acute triangle (p. 340)   A triangle that contains all acute angles is an acute triangle.
Example: The measures of ∠1, ∠2, and ∠3 are each less than 90°.

Altitude (p. 392)   See *Triangle*.

Angle (p. 331)   An angle is made up of two rays with a common endpoint.

Angle bisector (p. 336)   An angle bisector is a ray that divides an angle into two congruent angles.
Example: $\overrightarrow{BD}$ bisects ∠ABC.

Area (p. 143)   The number of square units inside a figure is the area.
Example: $\ell = 6$ ft, and $w = 4$ ft, so the area is 24 ft².

Each square equals 1 ft².

Associative Property of Addition (p. 74)   Changing the grouping of the addends does not change the sum.

$16 + (4 + 8) = (16 + 4) + 8$

Associative Property of Multiplication (p. 74)   Changing the grouping of the factors does not change the product.

$(7 \times 5) \times 2 = 7 \times (5 \times 2)$

Examples

B

Bar graph (p. 22)   A bar graph compares amounts.
Example: This bar graph represents class sizes for grades 6, 7, and 8.

Base (p. 139)   When a number is written in exponential form, the number that is used as a factor is the base.

$5^4 = 5 \times 5 \times 5 \times 5$

base

Bases (p. 408)   See *Cone, Cube, Cylinder, Prism, Pyramid, Triangle*.

Box-and-whisker plot (p. 32)   A box-and-whisker plot shows how data are distributed. This type of plot also identifies high, low, and median values.

C

Capacity (p. 119)   Capacity is a measure of the amount of space an object or a liquid occupies.

A juice bottle has a capacity of about 1 L.

Central angle (p. 365)   A central angle is an angle with its vertex at the center of the circle.
Example: In circle O, ∠AOB is a central angle.

Chord (p. 364)   A chord is a segment with endpoints on a circle.
Example: $\overline{BC}$ is a chord of circle O.

Circle (p. 364)   A circle is the set of points in a plane that are all the same distance from a given point, called the *center*.

Examples

Circle graph (pp. 23, 315)   A circle graph is a graph of data where the circle represents the whole. Each wedge in the circle graph represents a part of the whole.
Example: The circle graph represents the different types of plays William Shakespeare wrote.

Plays by William Shakespeare
Histories 26%
Tragedies 26%
Romances 13%
Comedies 35%

Circumference (p. 398)   Circumference is the distance around a circle. You calculate the circumference of a circle by multiplying the diameter by pi, or π, $(C = \pi \times d)$. Pi is approximately equal to 3.14.
Example: The circumference of a circle with a diameter of 10 cm is approximately 31.4 cm.

10 cm   about 31.4 cm

Collinear (p. 327)   If a line can be drawn through a set of points, the points are collinear.
Example: Points B, C, R, and S are collinear.

Common factor (p. 189)   Factors that are the same for two or more numbers are common factors.

4 is a common factor of 8 and 20.

Common multiples (p. 206)   Multiples that are shared by two or more numbers are common multiples.

12 is a common multiple of 4 and 6.

Commutative Property of Addition (p. 74)   Changing the order of the addends does not change the sum.

$7 + 8 = 8 + 7$

Commutative Property of Multiplication (p. 74)   Changing the order of the factors does not change the product.

$9 \times 5 = 5 \times 9$

Compass (p. 364)   A compass is a tool that is used to draw circles or parts of circles called arcs.

Compatible numbers (p. 134)   Compatible numbers are numbers close in value to the numbers you want to multiply or divide. Estimating products or quotients is easier when you use compatible numbers. Compatible numbers are easy to multiply or divide mentally.
Example: To estimate the quotient $151 \div 14.6$, use the compatible numbers 150 and 15.

$151 \approx 150$
$14.6 \approx 15$
$150 \div 15 = 10$, so
$151 \div 14.6 \approx 10$

Examples

Complement of an event (p. 497)   The complement of an event is all the ways that the event cannot happen.

For a toss of a coin, the complement of tossing heads is tossing tails.

Complementary angles (p. 337)   Two angles are complementary if the sum of their measures is 90°.
Example: ∠A and ∠B are complementary.

Composite number (p. 185)   A number that has more than two factors is called a composite number.

24 is a composite number that has 1, 2, 3, 4, 6, 8, 12, and 24 as factors.

Cone (p. 409)   A cone is a three-dimensional figure with one circular base and one vertex.

vertex
base

Congruent angles (p. 338)   Congruent angles are angles that have the same measure.
Example: The measures of ∠C and ∠B are each 60°, so ∠C is congruent to ∠B.

Congruent figures (p. 356)   Figures that have the same size and shape are congruent.
Example: $\overline{AB}$ is congruent to $\overline{QS}$, $\overline{CB}$ is congruent to $\overline{RS}$, and $\overline{AC}$ is congruent to $\overline{QR}$.
∠A is congruent to ∠Q, ∠C is congruent to ∠R, and ∠B is congruent to ∠S. Triangles ABC and QSR are congruent.

Congruent segments (p. 341)   Congruent segments are segments that have the same length.
Example: $\overline{AB}$ is congruent to $\overline{WX}$.

Coordinate plane (p. 463)   A coordinate plane is formed by the intersection of a horizontal number line, called the x-axis, and a vertical number line, called the y-axis.

Coordinates (p. 464) Each point on the coordinate plane is identified by a unique ordered pair of numbers called its coordinates. The first coordinate tells you how to move from the origin along the x-axis. The second coordinate tells you how to move from the origin along the y-axis.

Example: The ordered pair $(-2, 1)$ describes the point that is two units to the left of the origin and one unit above the x-axis.

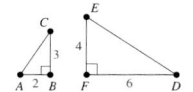

Corresponding parts of polygons (p. 357) The matching parts of similar figures are called corresponding parts.

Example: $\overline{AB}$ and $\overline{EF}$ are corresponding segments.
$\overline{AC}$ and $\overline{ED}$ are corresponding segments.
$\overline{BC}$ and $\overline{FD}$ are corresponding segments.

Counting principle (p. 499) The number of outcomes for an event with two or more distinct stages is the product of the number of outcomes at each stage.

Suppose you flip a coin and roll a number cube. The total number of possible outcomes is $2 \times 6 = 12$.

Cross products (p. 285) The cross products of the proportion $\frac{a}{b} = \frac{c}{d}$ are $a \times d$ and $b \times c$.

The cross products of the proportion $\frac{2}{15} = \frac{6}{45}$ are 2×45 and 15×6.

Cube (p. 409) A cube is a rectangular prism with six congruent faces. Each face is a base of the cube.

Customary system (p. 256) The customary system of measurement uses units of inches, feet, yards, cups, pints, quarts, ounces, and pounds.

Cylinder (p. 409) A cylinder is a three-dimensional figure with two circular, parallel, and congruent bases.

D

Database (p. 138) A database is an electronic spreadsheet. The information can be organized and reorganized for a variety of purposes.

Decagon (p. 345) A decagon is a polygon with ten sides.

Degree (°) (p. 331) Angles are measured in units called degrees.

Example: The measure of $\angle A$ is $45°$.

Diagonal (p. 347) A diagonal of a polygon is a segment that connects two vertices that are not next to each other.

Example: $\overline{AC}$ is a diagonal of quadrilateral $ABCD$.

Diameter (p. 364) A diameter is a segment that passes through the center of a circle and has both endpoints on the circle.

Example: $\overline{RS}$ is a diameter of circle O.

Distributive Property (p. 144) If a, b, and c are any numbers, then
$a(b + c) = ab + ac$ and
$a(b - c) = ab - ac$.

$6(4 + 2) = 6(4) + 6(2)$
$6(4 - 2) = 6(4) - 6(2)$

Divisible (p. 182) One number is divisible by another number if the remainder is zero.

15 and 20 are both divisible by 5, because $15 \div 5 = 3$ R0 and $20 \div 5 = 4$ R0.

E

Edge (p. 409) An edge is a segment where two faces of a three-dimensional figure meet.

edges

Elapsed time (p. 124) The time between two events is called elapsed time.

The elapsed time between 8:10 A.M. and 8:45 A.M. is 35 min.

Glossary/Study Guide

Equal ratios (p. 281) Ratios that make the same comparison or describe the same rate are equal ratios.

$\frac{2}{3}, \frac{4}{6},$ and $\frac{24}{36}$ are equal ratios.

Equation (p. 338) A mathematical sentence that contains an equal sign, =, is an equation.

$2(6 + 17) = 46$

Equilateral triangle (p. 340) An equilateral triangle is a triangle with three congruent sides.

Example: $\overline{SL}$ is congruent to $\overline{LW}$ and $\overline{LW}$ is congruent to $\overline{WS}$.

Equivalent (p. 85) Numbers or values that represent the same amount are equivalent.

$0.7 = 0.70, \frac{1}{10} = 0.1,$ and 2 pt = 1 qt.

Equivalent fractions (p. 197) Fractions that have the same simplest form are equivalent fractions.

$\frac{1}{2}$ and $\frac{25}{50}$ are equivalent fractions because they have the same simplest form of $\frac{1}{2}$.

Evaluate an expression (p. 58) To evaluate an expression, replace each variable with a number. Then follow the order of operations.

To evaluate the expression $3x + 2$ for $x = 4$, substitute 4 for x.
$3x + 2 = 3(4) + 2 = 14$

Even number (p. 182) An even number is a nonzero whole number that is divisible by 2.

$2, 4, 6, 8, \ldots$

Expanded form (p. 89) Expanded form shows the place and value of each digit.

0.85 can be written in expanded form as $0.8 + 0.05$.

Experimental probability (p. 481) Experimental probability is used to describe how likely an event is, based on collected data.

Probability (A wins) =
$\frac{\text{number of games A won}}{\text{total number of games played}}$

Exponent (p. 139) An exponent tells you how many times a number, or base, is used as a factor.

exponent
$3^4 = 3 \times 3 \times 3 \times 3$

Exterior angle (p. 338) Angles 1, 2, 7, and 8 are outside the parallel lines. These are exterior angles.

F

Face (p. 408) A flat surface on a three-dimensional figure is called a face.

face

Factor (p. 185) One number is a factor of another if it divides that number with no remainder.

1, 2, 3, 4, 6, 9, 12, 18, and 36 are factors of 36.

Factor tree (p. 186) A factor tree is used to find a number's prime factors.

Example: The prime factors of 78 are 2, 3, and 13.

Fair game (p. 480) A game is fair if each player has the same chance of winning.

Predicting whether a coin will land "heads" or "tails" is a game where each player has the same chance of winning, so it is a fair game.

Formula (p. 19) A formula is a statement of a mathematical relationship.

$A = \ell \times w$
or
=A1+B1+C1 (spreadsheet formula)

Fraction model (p. 193) A fraction model shows a fraction's numerator and denominator as shaded parts and total parts.

 is a fraction model of $\frac{2}{3}$.

Frequency table (p. 4) A frequency table lists items together with the number of times, or frequency with which, they occur.

Household Telephones

Phones	Tally	Frequency
1	卌 |||	8
2	卌		6
3						4

Front-end estimation (p. 105) To use front-end estimation to estimate sums, first add the front-end digits. Then adjust by estimating the sum of the remaining digits. Add the two values.

Example: $3.09 + 2.99 \approx \$6$

Estimate $\$3.09 + \$2.99$.

3.09	$\$3.09$	$\$5$
$+ \$2.99$ ⇒	$\$2.99$ ⇒	$\$1$
$\$5$	$\$1$	$\$6$

Function (p. 457) A function is a relationship in which each member of one set is paired with exactly one member of another set.

Number of Nickels	Value in Cents
0	0
1	5
2	10
3	15

Function table (p. 457) A function table shows the input and the output values of a function

The table above is a function table.

Glossary/Study Guide

Glossary/Study Guide

G

Gram (g) (p. 118) A gram is the standard unit of mass in the metric system.

A paper clip has a mass of about 1 g.

Greatest common factor (GCF) (p. 189) The greatest common factor of two or more numbers is the greatest number that is a factor of all the numbers.

12 and 30 have a GCF of 6.

H

Height (p. 392) The height, or altitude, of a parallelogram or triangle is the length of a perpendicular segment from a vertex to the line containing the base.

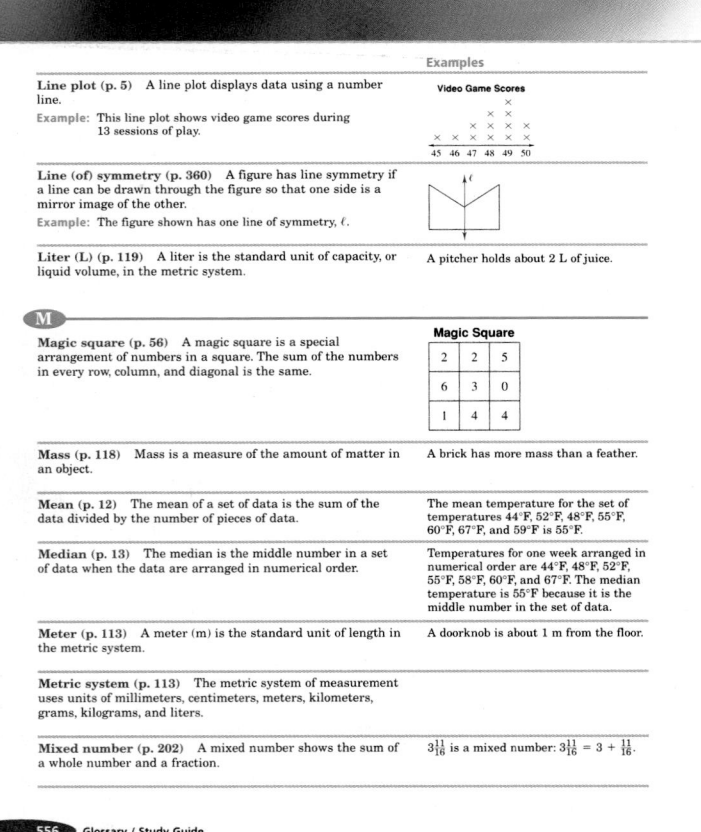

Hexagon (p. 345) A hexagon is a polygon with six sides.

Horizontal (p. 327) A horizontal line is parallel to the horizon.
Example: $\overleftrightarrow{BC}$ is a horizontal line.

I

Identity Property of Addition (p. 74) The sum of zero and any number a is a.

$0 + 121 = 121$

Identity Property of Multiplication (p. 74) The product of 1 and any number a is a.

$1 \times 75 = 75$

Image (p. 370) A point, line, or figure that is moved to a new position is the image of the original point, line, or figure.
Example: Shape B is an image of Shape A.

Shape A   Shape B

Improper fraction (p. 202) A fraction whose numerator is greater than or equal to its denominator is called an improper fraction.

$\frac{73}{16}$ and $\frac{12}{12}$ are improper fractions.

Independent events (p. 503) Two events are independent if the outcome of one event has no effect on the outcome of the other.

Rolling a number cube and tossing a coin are independent events.

Inequality (p. 438) An inequality is a statement comparing expressions that are not equal.

$2 < d < 3$ means that d is greater than 2 and less than 3.

Integers (p. 434) Integers are the set of whole numbers and their opposites.

$\dots -3, -2, -1, 0, 1, 2, 3, \dots$ are integers.

Interior angles (p. 338) Angles 3, 4, 5, and 6 are inside the parallel lines. They are interior angles.

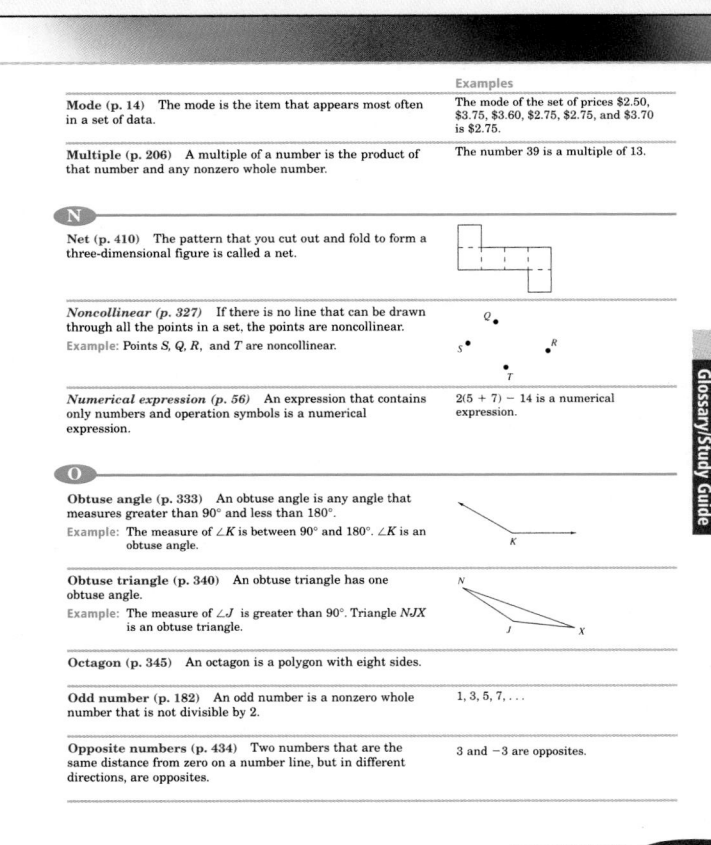

Isosceles triangle (p. 340) An isosceles triangle is a triangle with at least two congruent sides.
Example: $\overline{LM}$ is congruent to $\overline{LB}$. Triangle LMB is isosceles.

L

Least common denominator (LCD) (p. 209) The least common denominator of two or more fractions is the least common multiple of their denominators.

The LCD of the fractions $\frac{3}{8}$ and $\frac{7}{10}$ is 40.

Least common multiple (LCM) (p. 206) The least number that is a common multiple of two or more numbers is the least common multiple.

The LCM of 15 and 6 is 30.

Line (p. 326) A line continues without end in opposite directions.

Line graph (p. 23) A line graph shows how an amount changes over time.

Time Spent Watching Television

Line of reflection (p. 371) See *Reflection*.

Line plot (p. 5) A line plot displays data using a number line.
Example: This line plot shows video game scores during 13 sessions of play.

Video Game Scores

Line (of) symmetry (p. 360) A figure has line symmetry if a line can be drawn through the figure so that one side is a mirror image of the other.
Example: The figure shown has one line of symmetry, ℓ.

Liter (L) (p. 119) A liter is the standard unit of capacity, or liquid volume, in the metric system.

A pitcher holds about 2 L of juice.

M

Magic square (p. 56) A magic square is a special arrangement of numbers in a square. The sum of the numbers in every row, column, and diagonal is the same.

Magic Square

2	2	5
6	3	0
1	4	4

Mass (p. 118) Mass is a measure of the amount of matter in an object.

A brick has more mass than a feather.

Mean (p. 12) The mean of a set of data is the sum of the data divided by the number of pieces of data.

The mean temperature for the set of temperatures 44°F, 52°F, 48°F, 55°F, 60°F, 67°F, and 59°F is 55°F.

Median (p. 13) The median is the middle number in a set of data when the data are arranged in numerical order.

Temperatures for one week arranged in numerical order are 44°F, 48°F, 52°F, 55°F, 58°F, 60°F, and 67°F. The median temperature is 55°F because it is the middle number in the set of data.

Meter (p. 113) A meter (m) is the standard unit of length in the metric system.

A doorknob is about 1 m from the floor.

Metric system (p. 113) The metric system of measurement uses units of millimeters, centimeters, meters, kilometers, grams, kilograms, and liters.

Mixed number (p. 202) A mixed number shows the sum of a whole number and a fraction.

$3\frac{11}{16}$ is a mixed number: $3\frac{11}{16} = 3 + \frac{11}{16}$.

Mode (p. 14) The mode is the item that appears most often in a set of data.

The mode of the set of prices $2.50, $3.75, $3.60, $2.75, $2.75, and $3.70 is $2.75.

Multiple (p. 206) A multiple of a number is the product of that number and any nonzero whole number.

The number 39 is a multiple of 13.

N

Net (p. 410) The pattern that you cut out and fold to form a three-dimensional figure is called a net.

Noncollinear (p. 327) If there is no line that can be drawn through all the points in a set, the points are noncollinear.
Example: Points S, Q, R, and T are noncollinear.

Numerical expression (p. 56) An expression that contains only numbers and operation symbols is a numerical expression.

$2(5 + 7) - 14$ is a numerical expression.

O

Obtuse angle (p. 333) An obtuse angle is any angle that measures greater than 90° and less than 180°.
Example: The measure of $\angle K$ is between 90° and 180°. $\angle K$ is an obtuse angle.

Obtuse triangle (p. 340) An obtuse triangle has one obtuse angle.
Example: The measure of $\angle J$ is greater than 90°. Triangle NJX is an obtuse triangle.

Octagon (p. 345) An octagon is a polygon with eight sides.

Odd number (p. 182) An odd number is a nonzero whole number that is not divisible by 2.

$1, 3, 5, 7, \dots$

Opposite numbers (p. 434) Two numbers that are the same distance from zero on a number line, but in different directions, are opposites.

3 and -3 are opposites.

T548

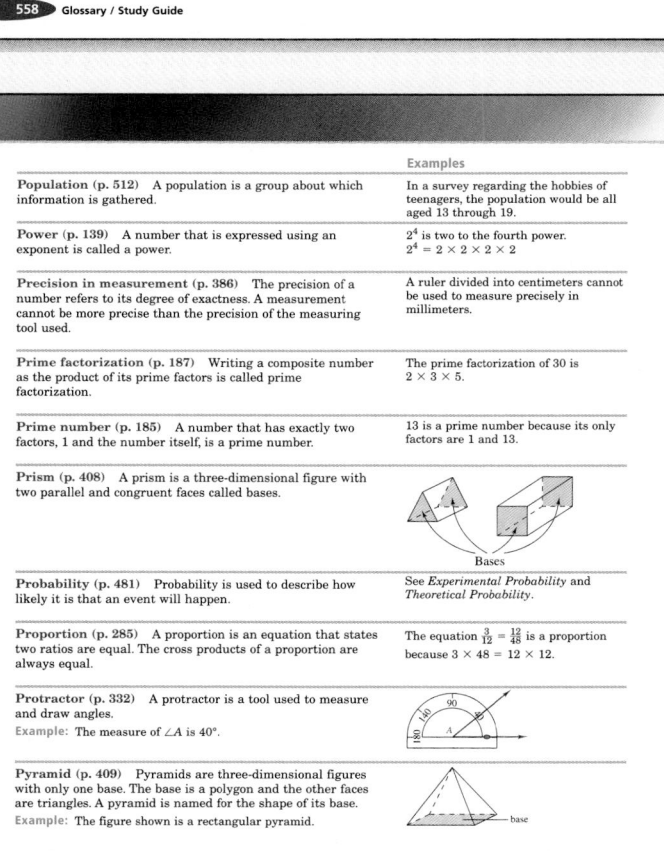
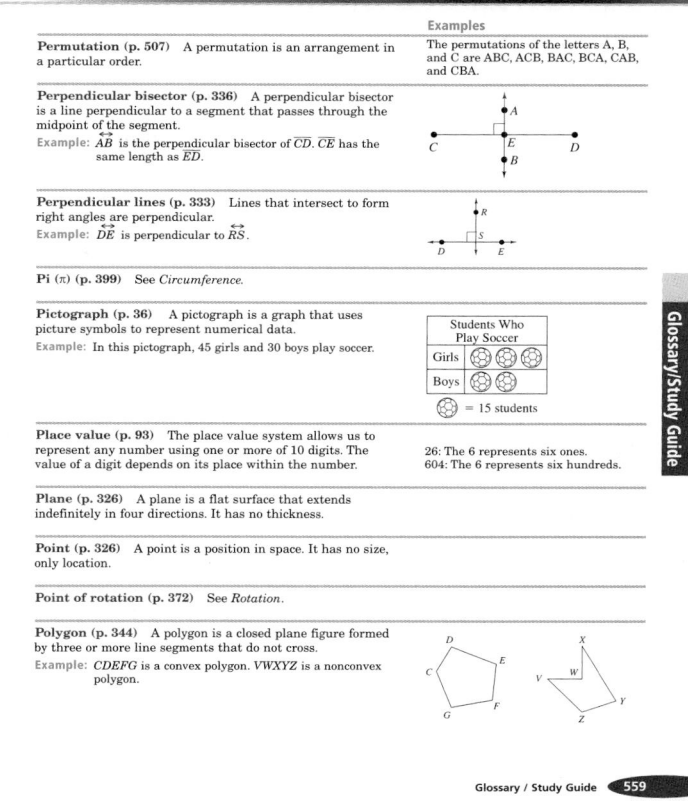
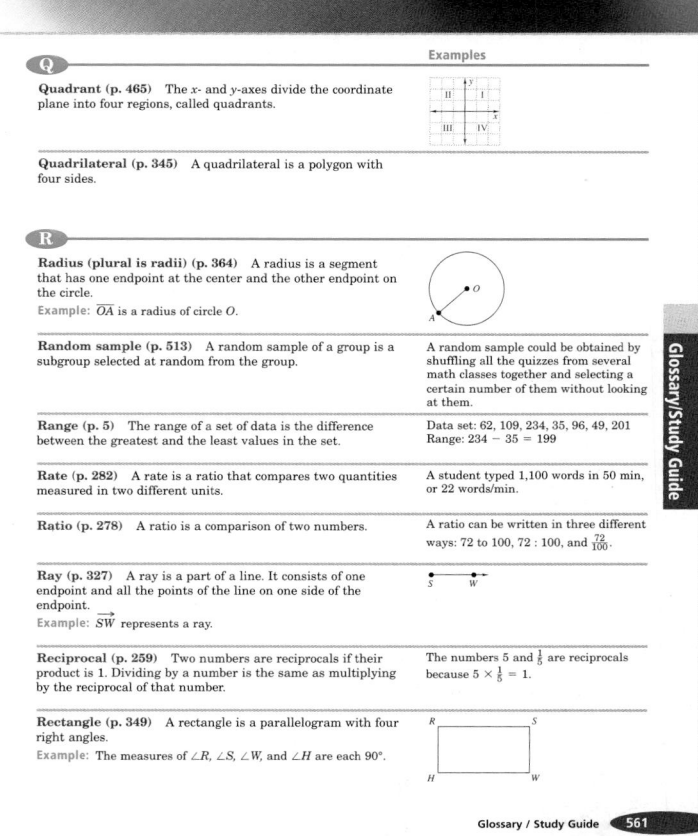

Examples

Order of operations (pp. 51, 140)
1. Do all operations within parentheses.
2. Do all work with exponents.
3. Multiply and divide in order from left to right.
4. Add and subtract in order from left to right.

$2^3(7 - 4) = 2^3(3) = 8 \cdot 3 = 24$

Ordered pair (p. 464) An ordered pair is a pair of numbers that describe the location of a point on a coordinate plane. The first value is the *x*-coordinate and the second value is the *y*-coordinate.
Example: The *x*-coordinate of the point $(-2, 1)$ is -2; the *y*-coordinate is 1.

Origin (p. 464) The origin is the point of intersection of the *x*- and *y*-axes on a coordinate plane.
Example: The ordered pair that describes the origin is $(0, 0)$.

P

Parallel lines (p. 327) Parallel lines are lines in the same plane that do not intersect.
Example: $\overleftrightarrow{EF}$ is parallel to $\overleftrightarrow{HI}$.

Parallel segments (p. 327) Parallel segments lie in parallel lines.
Example: $\overline{JK}$ is parallel to $\overline{LM}$.

Parallelogram (p. 349) A parallelogram is a quadrilateral with both pairs of opposite sides parallel.
Example: $\overline{KV}$ is parallel to $\overline{AD}$ and $\overline{AK}$ is parallel to $\overline{DV}$.

Pentagon (p. 345) A pentagon is a polygon with five sides.

Percent (%) (p. 297) A percent is a ratio that compares a number to 100.

The ratio 50 to 100 is a percent because 50 is compared to 100. $\frac{50}{100} = 50\%$

Perimeter (p. 387) The perimeter of a figure is the distance around it.
Example: The perimeter of rectangle *ABCD* =
2 ft + 4 ft + 2 ft + 4 ft = 12 ft.

Examples

Permutation (p. 507) A permutation is an arrangement in a particular order.

The permutations of the letters A, B, and C are ABC, ACB, BAC, BCA, CAB, and CBA.

Perpendicular bisector (p. 336) A perpendicular bisector is a line perpendicular to a segment that passes through the midpoint of the segment.
Example: $\overleftrightarrow{AB}$ is the perpendicular bisector of $\overline{CD}$. $\overline{CE}$ has the same length as $\overline{ED}$.

Perpendicular lines (p. 333) Lines that intersect to form right angles are perpendicular.
Example: $\overleftrightarrow{DE}$ is perpendicular to $\overleftrightarrow{RS}$.

Pi (π) (p. 399) See *Circumference*.

Pictograph (p. 36) A pictograph is a graph that uses picture symbols to represent numerical data.
Example: In this pictograph, 45 girls and 30 boys play soccer.

Students Who Play Soccer
Girls
Boys
= 15 students

Place value (p. 93) The place value system allows us to represent any number using one or more of 10 digits. The value of a digit depends on its place within the number.

26: The 6 represents six ones.
604: The 6 represents six hundreds.

Plane (p. 326) A plane is a flat surface that extends indefinitely in four directions. It has no thickness.

Point (p. 326) A point is a position in space. It has no size, only location.

Point of rotation (p. 372) See *Rotation*.

Polygon (p. 344) A polygon is a closed plane figure formed by three or more line segments that do not cross.
Example: *CDEFG* is a convex polygon. *VWXYZ* is a nonconvex polygon.

Examples

Population (p. 512) A population is a group about which information is gathered.

In a survey regarding the hobbies of teenagers, the population would be all aged 13 through 19.

Power (p. 139) A number that is expressed using an exponent is called a power.

2^4 is two to the fourth power.
$2^4 = 2 \times 2 \times 2 \times 2$

Precision in measurement (p. 386) The precision of a number refers to its degree of exactness. A measurement cannot be more precise than the precision of the measuring tool used.

A ruler divided into centimeters cannot be used to measure precisely in millimeters.

Prime factorization (p. 187) Writing a composite number as the product of its prime factors is called prime factorization.

The prime factorization of 30 is $2 \times 3 \times 5$.

Prime number (p. 185) A number that has exactly two factors, 1 and the number itself, is a prime number.

13 is a prime number because its only factors are 1 and 13.

Prism (p. 408) A prism is a three-dimensional figure with two parallel and congruent faces called bases.

Bases

Probability (p. 481) Probability is used to describe how likely it is that an event will happen.

See *Experimental Probability* and *Theoretical Probability*.

Proportion (p. 285) A proportion is an equation that states two ratios are equal. The cross products of a proportion are always equal.

The equation $\frac{3}{12} = \frac{12}{48}$ is a proportion because $3 \times 48 = 12 \times 12$.

Protractor (p. 332) A protractor is a tool used to measure and draw angles.
Example: The measure of $\angle A$ is 40°.

Pyramid (p. 409) Pyramids are three-dimensional figures with only one base. The base is a polygon and the other faces are triangles. A pyramid is named for the shape of its base.
Example: The figure shown is a rectangular pyramid.

base

Examples

Q

Quadrant (p. 465) The *x*- and *y*-axes divide the coordinate plane into four regions, called quadrants.

Quadrilateral (p. 345) A quadrilateral is a polygon with four sides.

R

Radius (plural is radii) (p. 364) A radius is a segment that has one endpoint at the center and the other endpoint on the circle.
Example: $\overline{OA}$ is a radius of circle *O*.

Random sample (p. 513) A random sample of a group is a subgroup selected at random from the group.

A random sample could be obtained by shuffling all the quizzes from several math classes together and selecting a certain number of them without looking at them.

Range (p. 5) The range of a set of data is the difference between the greatest and the least values in the set.

Data set: 62, 109, 234, 35, 96, 49, 201
Range: $234 - 35 = 199$

Rate (p. 282) A rate is a ratio that compares two quantities measured in two different units.

A student typed 1,100 words in 50 min, or 22 words/min.

Ratio (p. 278) A ratio is a comparison of two numbers.

A ratio can be written in three different ways: 72 to 100, 72 : 100, and $\frac{72}{100}$.

Ray (p. 327) A ray is a part of a line. It consists of one endpoint and all the points of the line on one side of the endpoint.
Example: $\overrightarrow{SW}$ represents a ray.

Reciprocal (p. 259) Two numbers are reciprocals if their product is 1. Dividing by a number is the same as multiplying by the reciprocal of that number.

The numbers 5 and $\frac{1}{5}$ are reciprocals because $5 \times \frac{1}{5} = 1$.

Rectangle (p. 349) A rectangle is a parallelogram with four right angles.
Example: The measures of $\angle R$, $\angle S$, $\angle W$, and $\angle H$ are each 90°.

Reflection (p. 371) A reflection flips a figure across a line.

Example: Shape B is a reflection of Shape A. $\overleftrightarrow{XY}$ is the line of reflection.

Repeating decimal (p. 215) A decimal whose digits repeat without end is a repeating decimal. A bar indicates the digits that repeat.

$0.6666\ldots$ or $0.\overline{6}$

Representative sample (p. 513) A representative sample of a group is a subgroup that has the same characteristics as the larger group.

A representative sample of last week's math quizzes would include quizzes from each of several math classes.

Rhombus (p. 349) A rhombus is a parallelogram with four congruent sides.

Right angle (p. 333) A right angle is an angle with a measure of 90°.

Example: The measure of $\angle D$ is 90°.

Right triangle (p. 340) A right triangle is a triangle with a right angle.

Example: The measure of $\angle B$ is 90°. Triangle ABC is a right triangle.

Rotation (p. 372) A rotation turns, or rotates, a shape.

Example: Shape B is a rotation of Shape A.

S

Sample (p. 512) A sample of a group is a smaller subgroup selected from within the group.

Your English teacher might read one or two poems from the poems written by your class.

Scale (p. 292) A scale is a ratio that compares a length on a model to the actual length of the real object.

A map may have a scale where 1 in. represents 50 mi.

Scalene triangle (p. 340) A scalene triangle is a triangle with no congruent sides.

Scatter plot (p. 464) A scatter plot is a graph of data from two different sets. The two sets of data are plotted as ordered pairs, or points.

Example: This scatter plot shows amounts spent on advertising compared to product sales.

Scientific notation (p. 156) A number is expressed in scientific notation when it is written as the product of two factors. The first is a number greater than or equal to 1 and less than 10, and the second is a power of 10.

309,000,000 is written as 3.09×10^8 in scientific notation.

Second (p. 123) A second (s) is the standard unit of time. 60 s = 1 min

Segment (p. 326) A segment is part of a line. It consists of two points and all the points on the line that are between the two points.

Example: $\overline{CB}$ is a segment.

Sides (p. 331) See *Angle*.

Similar (p. 296) Figures that have the same shape are similar.

Example: Triangle ABC is similar to triangle RTS.

Simplest form of a fraction (p. 198) A fraction is in simplest form when the only common factor of the numerator and denominator is 1.

The fraction $\frac{3}{7}$ is in simplest form because the common factor of 3 and 7 is 1.

Simulation (p. 485) A simulation is a model of a real-world situation.

A baseball team has equal chances of winning or losing the next game. You can toss a coin to simulate the outcome.

Skew lines (p. 328) Skew lines are lines that lie in different nonparallel planes. They are neither parallel nor intersecting.

Example: $\overleftrightarrow{AB}$ and $\overleftrightarrow{CD}$ are skew lines.

Solution of an equation (p. 66) The solution of an equation is the value of the variable that makes the equation true.

4 is the solution of $x + 5 = 9$.

Solve (p. 66) To solve an equation you replace a variable with a number that makes the equation true.

To solve the equation $x + 2 = 5$, subtract 2 from both sides.
$x = 3$

Sphere (p. 409) A sphere is the set of points in space that are the same distance from a given point called the center.

Spreadsheet (p. 18, 138) A spreadsheet is a tool used for organizing and analyzing data using a computer. Spreadsheets are arranged in rows and columns. A *cell* is the box on a spreadsheet where a row and a column meet. The names of the row and column determine the name of the cell. A cell may contain data values, labels, or formulas.

Example: In the spreadsheet shown, column C and row 2 meet at the shaded box, cell C2. The value in cell C2 is 2.75.

	A	B	C	D
1	0.50	0.70	0.60	0.50
2	1.50	0.50	2.75	2.50

Square (p. 350) A square is a rectangle with four congruent sides.

Standard form of a number (p. 88) To write a number in standard form, use commas to separate periods and add zeros so that each period has 3 digits.

230 thousand, 8 in standard form is 230,008.

Stem-and-leaf plot (p. 32) A stem-and-leaf plot displays a set of data to show the frequencies of values.

Example: This stem-and-leaf plot shows recorded times in a race. The stem represents the number of seconds. The leaves represent tenths of a second.

stem	leaves
27	7
28	568
29	69
30	8

27 | 7 means 27.7

Straight angle (p. 333) An angle that measures 180° is called a straight angle.

Example: The measure of $\angle TPL$ is 180°.

Straightedge (p. 327) A straightedge is a tool used to draw lines, rays, and segments. It is similar to a ruler, but does not have marks to indicate measure.

A ruler, if you ignore the markings, can be used as a straightedge.

Supplementary angles (p. 337) Two angles are supplementary if the sum of their measures is 180°.

Example: $\angle 1$ and $\angle 2$ are supplementary angles.

Surface area of a prism (p. 414) The surface area of a prism is the sum of the areas of the faces.

Example: Surface area $= 2(3 \times 5) + 2(3 \times 4) + 2(4 \times 5) = 94$

Symmetry (p. 360) A figure has symmetry when one side of the figure is the mirror image of the other side.

See *Line of Symmetry*.

T

Term (p. 44) A term is a part of a variable expression or a number sequence.

The expression $2x + 12$ has two terms, $2x$ and 12. The number sequence 38, 34, 32 has three terms.

Terminating decimal (p. 215) A terminating decimal is a decimal that stops, or terminates.

Both 0.6 and 0.7265 are terminating decimals.

T550

Examples

Tessellation (p. 397)   A tessellation is a repeated geometric design that covers a plane with no gaps and no overlaps.

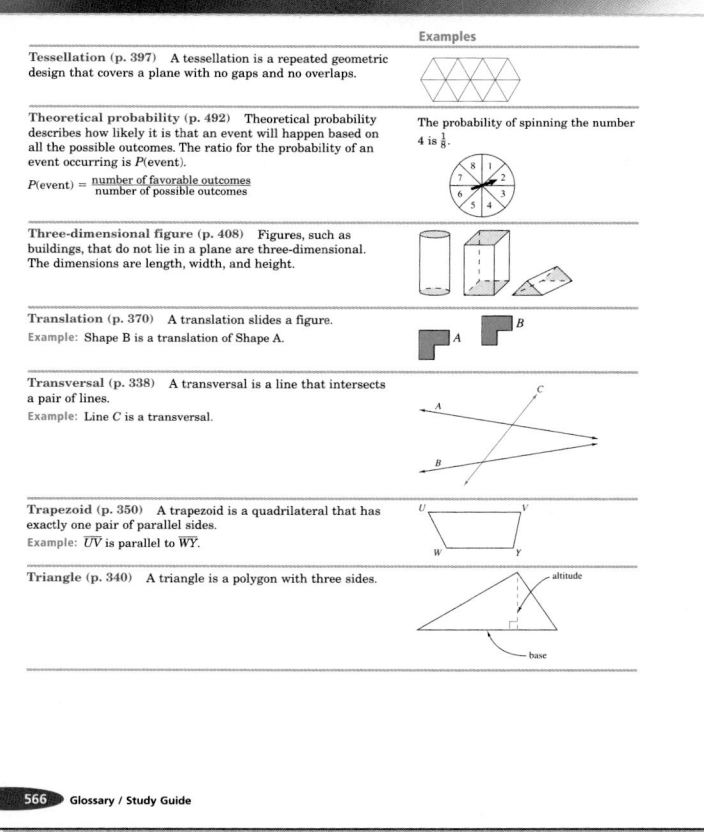

Theoretical probability (p. 492)   Theoretical probability describes how likely it is that an event will happen based on all the possible outcomes. The ratio for the probability of an event occurring is P(event).

P(event) = $\frac{\text{number of favorable outcomes}}{\text{number of possible outcomes}}$

The probability of spinning the number 4 is $\frac{1}{8}$.

Three-dimensional figure (p. 408)   Figures, such as buildings, that do not lie in a plane are three-dimensional. The dimensions are length, width, and height.

Translation (p. 370)   A translation slides a figure.
Example: Shape B is a translation of Shape A.

Transversal (p. 338)   A transversal is a line that intersects a pair of lines.
Example: Line C is a transversal.

Trapezoid (p. 350)   A trapezoid is a quadrilateral that has exactly one pair of parallel sides.
Example: $\overline{UV}$ is parallel to $\overline{WY}$.

Triangle (p. 340)   A triangle is a polygon with three sides.

altitude

base

Examples

Tree diagram (p. 498)   A tree diagram displays all the possible outcomes of an event.
Example: There are 4 possible outcomes for tossing 2 coins: HH, HT, TH, TT.

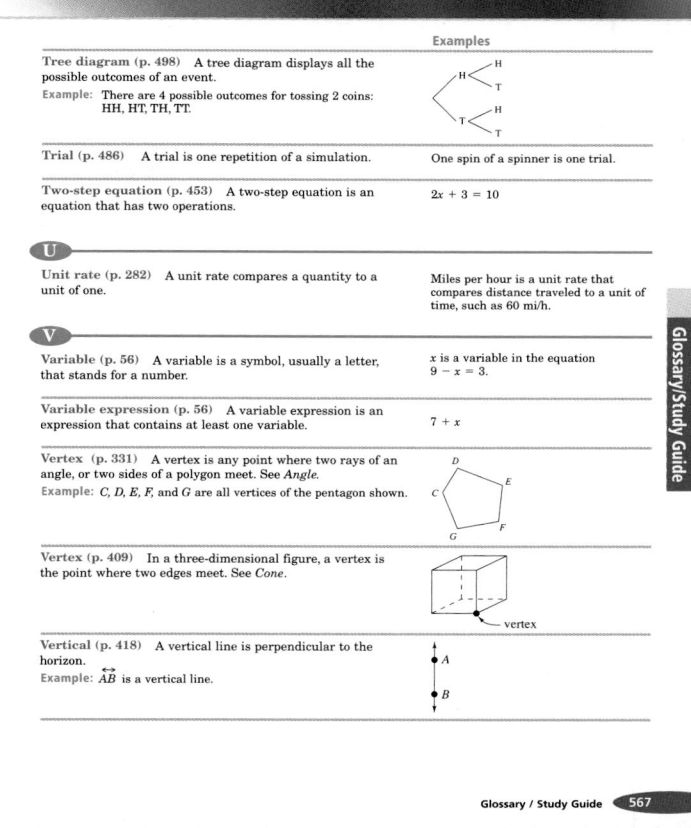

Trial (p. 486)   A trial is one repetition of a simulation.

One spin of a spinner is one trial.

Two-step equation (p. 453)   A two-step equation is an equation that has two operations.

$2x + 3 = 10$

U

Unit rate (p. 282)   A unit rate compares a quantity to a unit of one.

Miles per hour is a unit rate that compares distance traveled to a unit of time, such as 60 mi/h.

V

Variable (p. 56)   A variable is a symbol, usually a letter, that stands for a number.

x is a variable in the equation $9 - x = 3$.

Variable expression (p. 56)   A variable expression is an expression that contains at least one variable.

$7 + x$

Vertex (p. 331)   A vertex is any point where two rays of an angle, or two sides of a polygon meet. See *Angle*.
Example: C, D, E, F, and G are all vertices of the pentagon shown.

Vertex (p. 409)   In a three-dimensional figure, a vertex is the point where two edges meet. See *Cone*.

vertex

Vertical (p. 418)   A vertical line is perpendicular to the horizon.
Example: $\overleftrightarrow{AB}$ is a vertical line.

Examples

Volume (p. 259)   The volume of a three-dimensional figure is the number of cubic units needed to fill the space inside the figure.
Example: The volume of the rectangular prism is 36 in.^{3}.

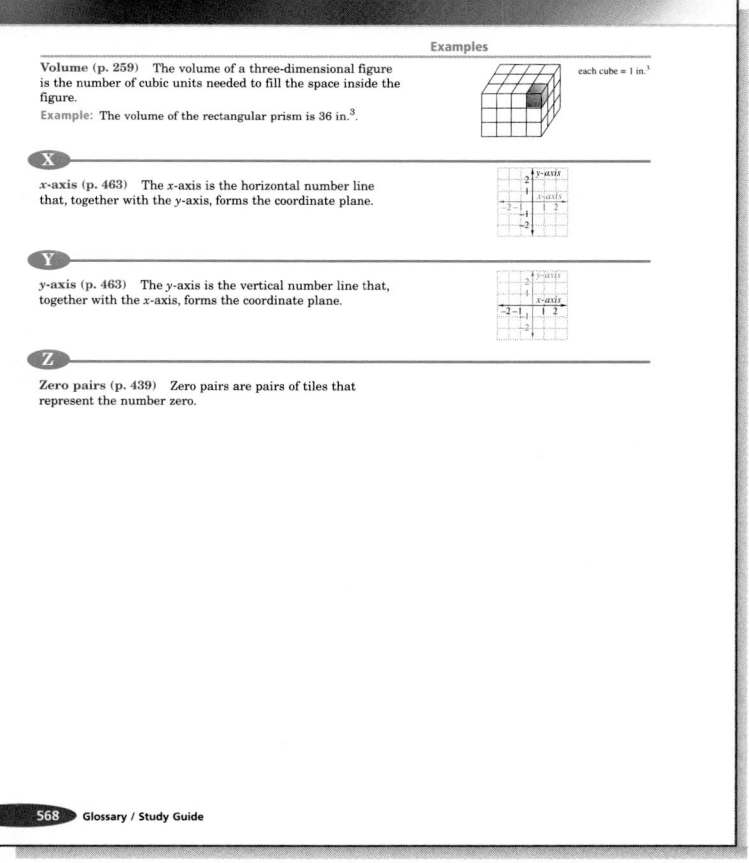

each cube = 1 in.^{3}

X

x-axis (p. 463)   The x-axis is the horizontal number line that, together with the y-axis, forms the coordinate plane.

Y

y-axis (p. 463)   The y-axis is the vertical number line that, together with the x-axis, forms the coordinate plane.

Z

Zero pairs (p. 439)   Zero pairs are pairs of tiles that represent the number zero.

T551

TOOLS FOR PROBLEM SOLVING

The Four Step Approach   page xxii

ON YOUR OWN **1.** 6 **3.** $205

Using Strategies   page xxv

ON YOUR OWN **1.** 72 in., 80 in. **3.** 64 calls

Working Together   page xxvii

ON YOUR OWN **3.** yes; no

Preparing for Standardized Tests   page xxix

ON YOUR OWN **1.** B **3.** C

CHAPTER 1

Lesson 1-1   pages 4–7

ON YOUR OWN

1a.

Letter	Tally	Frequency
a	|||	3
e			1
i	|||	3
o	||||		6
u		0

3.

Cost	Frequency
$122	3
$125	3
$135	1
$138	1

9. Test Scores
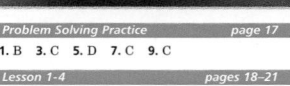

11. Speeds of Runners (mi/h) **13.** 5 **15.** 4 **17.** grades on a science test **19.** 13 students

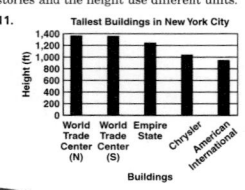

21a. Birth States of U.S. Presidents
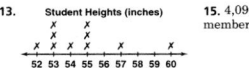

MIXED REVIEW **25.** 1,139 **27.** 18,629 **29.** 9,818 **31.** 2 pennies, 1 nickel, 2 dimes, 1 quarter

Lesson 1-2   pages 8–10

ON YOUR OWN **1.** 13 ways **3.** 16 race cars and 12 tugboats **5.** 45, 40, 35, 30, 25, 20, 15 **7.** 1:10 P.M. **9.** 2 links **11.** 6 outfits

MIXED REVIEW

13. Student Heights (inches) **15.** 4,096 members

Toolbox   page 11

1. 30 R2 **3.** 93 R1 **5.** 80 R3 **7.** 503 **9.** 429 R2 **11.** 50 R22 **13.** 34 R21 **15.** 98 R20 **17.** 51 **19.** 25 **21.** Round the dividend and the divisor to two numbers that are easy to divide mentally.

Lesson 1-3   pages 12–16

ON YOUR OWN **1.** 10 **3.** 2 **5.** 19 **7.** 22 **9.** 40 **11.** player's scoring in basketball games: 15, 12, 9, 15, 32, 21, 23, 19, 22 **13a.** 12.5; 12 **15.** 19 **17.** 51 **19.** 810 **21.** 17 **23.** 2 **25.** 0 and 1 **27.** 9 and 12 **29.** 31 **31.** no mode **33.** C **35.** Median; 114 affects the mean too much. **37.** Mode; the data are not numeric.

MIXED REVIEW **39.** 1,488 **41.** 31 **43.** 77

CHECKPOINT **1.** 20 **2.** 20 **3.** 15

4.

Grams of Fat	Frequency
0	8
1	9
2	5
3	3

Problem Solving Practice   page 17

1. B **3.** C **5.** D **7.** C **9.** C

Lesson 1-4   pages 18–21

ON YOUR OWN **1.** column C **3.** F2 **5.** E4 **7.** D6 **9.** = B2 + C2 + D2; = B3 + C3 + D3; = B4 + C4 + D4; = B5 + C5 + D5; = B6 + C6 + D6 **11.** Multiply the mean in cell F3 by 3. Then subtract the values in B3 and C3. **13.** No; you could use the formulas for the mean directly in column F. **15.** 5 **17.** 3 **19.** 6 **21.** Subtract B2 from C2. **23.** Multiply the value in D6 by 6, or add E2, E3, E4, and E5. **25.** Subtract B5 from C5. **27.** = C2 – B2; = C3 – B3; = C4 – B4; = C5 – B5; = D2 + D3 + D4 + D5; = D6 / 4; = D2 * 6; = D3 * 6; = D4 * 6; = D5 * 6; = D6 * 6; = D7 * 6; **29a.** $72 **b.** E6

MIXED REVIEW **31.** 17 **33.** 11

Lesson 1-5   pages 22–26

ON YOUR OWN **1.** ME; RI **3.** Maine has about 3 times as much land as Vermont. **7.** 1983–1986 and 1992–1994 **9a.** 650 balloons **b.** 850 balloons **11.** No; the wedge for 4 teachers is much larger than the wedge for 1 teacher. **13.** Line graph; the graph shows change in time. **15.** Line graph; the graph shows change in time. **17.** The longer the bar, the more money it represents.

MIXED REVIEW **19.** 155; 155; 155 **21.** 21 and 22

Lesson 1-6   pages 27–31

ON YOUR OWN **1.** 1,000 or 5,000; a graph with smaller units would either be too large or too difficult to read. **3.** 5,000; a graph with smaller units would either be too large or too difficult to read. **5.** 5; a graph with larger units would not show enough detail. **7.** C **9.** No; the number of stories and the height use different units.

11. Tallest Buildings in New York City

21. The bars have unequal width. **23.** The horizontal gridlines are unevenly spaced.

25a. U.S. Population (per square mile)

b. U.S. Population (per square mile)

MIXED REVIEW

27. **29.**

31. **33.** bar graph

CHECKPOINT **1.** C

2. Student's Mean Test Scores **3.** Army **4.** 239 medals

Toolbox   page 32

1. 47 min **3b.** 43 min; 35 min **5.** 49; 27 **7.** The data above the median are spread out more than the data below the median.

Lesson 1-7   pages 33–36

ON YOUR OWN **7.** ii; the gap in the scale makes B's margin appear much greater. **9.** i; the wider bar directs attention to candidate A.

11. Money Pledged During a National Telethon **13.** Use the broken line or zig-zag symbol to represent a gap in the scale.

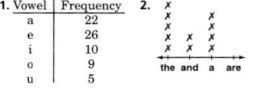

MIXED REVIEW **17.** 120 **19.** 1,211 **21.** 1,000 **23.** 10 **25.** 1,000,000

27.

Snowiest Cities	
Albany, NY	❊ ❊ ❊ ⌇
Boston, MA	❊ ❊
Juneau, AK	❊ ❊ ❊ ❊ ❊
Omaha, NE	❊ ⌇
Key: ❊ = 20 in.	

Wrap Up   pages 38–39

1.

Vowel	Frequency
a	22
e	26
i	10
o	9
u	5

2.

the and a are

3. 6 **4.** 18 **5.** 10 **6.** 9 ways **7.** 12 ways **8.** 3 quarters **9.** 45; 49 **10.** 6; 7 **11.** 16; 15 **12.** M **13.** 18 **14.** 8 **15.** B2 and B3 **16.** $65 **17.** = B2 + C2 + D2 **18.** $940

19. Ticket Prices

20. Vowels in the Paragraph
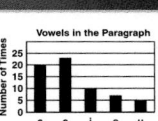

21. Line graph; the graph shows change over time. **22.** Circle graph; the data are parts of a whole. **23.** The bars have unequal width. **24.** The range of the vertical scale is too great. The graph appears flat. **25.** The gap in scale makes it appear that toaster C sold much better.

Cumulative Review   page 41

1. A **3.** C **5.** C **7.** C **9.** B

CHAPTER 2

Lesson 2-1   pages 44–47

ON YOUR OWN

1a. 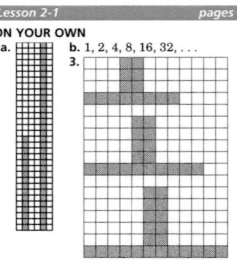 **b.** 1, 2, 4, 8, 16, 32, … **3.**

5. 12, 14, 16 **7.** 26, 32, 38 **9.** 37, 43, 49 **11.** 4, 2, 1 **13.** 125, 150, 175 **17.** 486; 1,458; 4,374; start with 6 and multiply by 3 repeatedly. **19.** 42, 52, 62; start with 2 and add 10 repeatedly. **21.** 60, 45, 30; start with 120 and subtract 15 repeatedly. **23.** 103, 97, 91; start with 127 and subtract 6 repeatedly. **25.** 18, 6, 2; start with 1,458 and divide by 3 repeatedly.

MIXED REVIEW

27.

Ages	Frequency
8	1
9	3
10	1
11	1
12	1
13	1
15	2
16	1
20	1

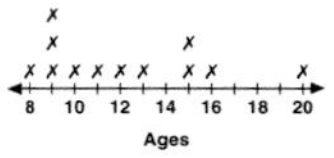
8 10 12 14 16 18 20
Ages

29. 12.25; 11.5; 9

31.

x	$x + 6$
1	7
4	10
7	13
10	16
14	20

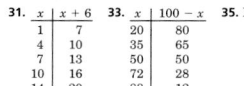

33.

x	$100 - x$
20	80
35	65
50	50
72	28
88	12

35. D

MIXED REVIEW **39.** 256; 1,024; 4,096 **41.** 27, 9, 3 **43.** 95 people

Lesson 2-2 *pages 48–50*

ON YOUR OWN **1.** 66 handshakes **3.** 5 h **5.** 35 cars **7.** pages 24 and 25

MIXED REVIEW **9.** 15 ways **11.** 20 **13.** 429

Lesson 2-3 *pages 51–54*

ON YOUR OWN **1.** × **3.** × **5.** − **7.** 12 **9.** 13 **11.** 60 **13.** 20 **15.** 2 **17.** 210 **21a.** i. 45; ii. 29; iii. 29 **23.** > **25.** = **27.** < **29.** $(12 + 6) \div 2 - 1 = 8$ **31.** $(1 + 2) \times (15 - 4) = 33$ **33.** $14 - (3 - 2) \times 3 = 11$ **35.** 5 **37.** 8 **39.** 26 **41.** 15 **43.** 2 **45.** −; ×; ×

MIXED REVIEW **49.** 176 lockers

CHECKPOINT **1.** 34 **2.** 11 **3.** 2 **4.** 5,625; 28,125; 140,625 **5.** 34, 29, 24 **6.** 28, 35, 42

Problem Solving Practice *page 55*

1. C **3.** D **5.** D **7.** C **9.** D

Lesson 2-4 *pages 56–60*

ON YOUR OWN

5. 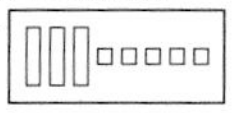

7. 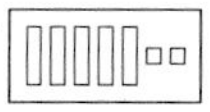

11. 20 **13.** 56 **15.** 4 **17.** 8 **19.** 193 **21.** 3 **23.** 18 **25.** 50 **27.** 46 **29.** 2,100

Lesson 2-5 *pages 61–64*

ON YOUR OWN **11.** + **13.** + **15.** × **17.** − **19.** ÷ **21.** B **23.** $k - 34$ **25.** $50 + d$ **27.** $7 + b$ **29.** $h \times 150$ or $150h$ **31.** $s - 8$ **33.** $h + 2$ **35.** $r + s$ **37a.** $45t$ **b.** $\frac{3}{4}t$ **41.** $a + 3$ **43.** $p \div 2$

MIXED REVIEW **45.** 1992

Toolbox *page 65*

1. 632 **3.** 346 **5.** 4,170 **7.** 335 **9.** 355 **11.** 365 **13.** 71 **15.** 41 **17.** 6,212 **19.** 1,005 **21.** 4,361 **23.** 5,492

Lesson 2-6 *pages 66–70*

ON YOUR OWN **1.** true **3.** true **5.** C **7.** yes **9.** yes **11.** no **13.** no **17.** 3 **19.** 2 **21.** 0 **23.** 5 **25.** 9 **27.** 3 **29.** 8 **31.** 16 **33.** 76 **35.** 21 **37.** 129 **39.** 6 **41.** 9 **43.** 54 days **45.** 2,174 **47.** 46,851 **49.** 17,165

MIXED REVIEW **53.** about 88 million people **55.** 0

CHECKPOINT **1.** 33 **2.** 8 **3.** 6 **4.** 33 **5.** 63 **6.** $12 + y$ **7.** $b + 5$ **8.** $6w$ **9.** $20 - r$ **10.** 50 **11.** 385 **12.** 2 **13.** 9 **14.** D

Toolbox *page 71*

1. 16,536 **3.** 18,120 **5.** 48,480 **7.** 1,150 **9.** 5,456 **11.** 2,697 **13.** 1,404 **15.** 67,837 **17.** 3,128 **19.** 31,540 **21.** 15,040 **23.** 35,002 **25.** 17,856 **27.** 20,200 **29.** 30,350 **31.** 10,400 **33.** 20,860 **35.** 18,000 **37.** 7,661 **39a.** i. 15,000; ii. 1,500; iii. 1,500; iv. 1,500; v. 15,000

Lesson 2-7 *pages 72–76*

ON YOUR OWN

1. 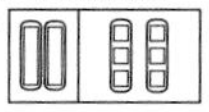

3. 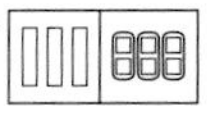

5. no **7.** yes **9.** no **11.** 7 **13.** 8 **15.** 2 **17.** 5 **21.** 125 **23.** 4 **25.** 200 **27.** 42 **29.** 165 **31.** 15 **33.** 5 **35.** 108 **37.** 100,000 **39.** B **41.** 83 **43.** 18,564,595 **45.** 18,036,201 **47.** C **49.** 34 ft

MIXED REVIEW

51.

Number of CDs	Cost ($)
1	18.37
2	34.36
3	50.35
4	66.34
5	82.33

53. February and March

Wrap Up *pages 78–79*

1. 162; 486; 1,458 **2.** 55, 67, 79 **3.** 35, 25, 15 **4.** 112, 224, 448 **5.** 5, 12, 19, 26, 33 **6.** 39 cents **7.** 46 **8.** 49 **9.** 37 **10.** 4 **11.** 15 **12.** 240 **13.** 13 **14.** 2 **15.** < **16.** > **17.** 8 **18.** 49 **19.** 42 **20.** 6 **21.** 27 **22.** 18 **23.** $x - 5$ **24.** $y \div p$ **25.** $20 + b$ **26.** $h \times 4$ or $4h$ **27.** $2t$ **28.** 5 **29.** 433 **30.** 5,640 **31.** 128 **32.** 56 **33.** 23 **34.** 8 **35.** 5 **36.** D

Cumulative Review *page 81*

1. D **3.** D **5.** C **7.** B **9.** A

CHAPTER 3

Lesson 3-1 *pages 84–87*

ON YOUR OWN **1.** 0.8 **3.** 0.75

5. 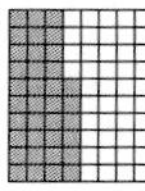

7. 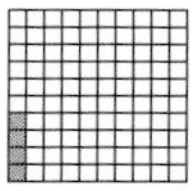

11. two tenths **13.** forty hundredths **15.** thirty hundredths **17.** 0.40 **19.** 0.5 **21.** 0.31 **23.** 0.12 **25.** 20 **27.** 80 **29.** 40 **35.** about 0.94

MIXED REVIEW **37.** 4,250 lb **39.** 153 **41.** 190 **43.** < **45.** =

Lesson 3-2 *pages 88–91*

ON YOUR OWN **1.** 3; 460; 800 **3.** two hundred five **5.** six thousand, seven hundred forty-five **7.** forty-five million, six hundred fifty-four thousand, three hundred thirty-two **9.** 4,600 **11.** 478,027 **13.** 213,000,125 **15.** 6,023,158,000 **17.** 300,020 **19.** four tenths **21.** four hundred-thousandths **23.** four ones **25.** four ten-thousandths **27.** four hundreds **29.** three hundred fifty-two and three tenths **31.** eleven and two thousand, eight hundred fifty-nine ten-thousandths **33.** six hundred fifty-seven hundred-thousandths **35.** 2.00004 **37.** 42.3794 **39.** $.8 **41.** $.49 **43.** As you move left to right, the value decreases by a factor of 10. **45a.** i. $.006; ii. $.207; iii. $.053; iv. $.328 **b.** 1 cent; 21 cents; 5 cents; 33 cents **47.** 4.7 pt/d **49.** 0.001 s **51.** 0.17 mi/h

MIXED REVIEW **53.** 4,527,982; 3,201,455; 3,097,854; 2,852,238; 2,684,387; 978,897

Lesson 3-3 *pages 92–95*

ON YOUR OWN

1. 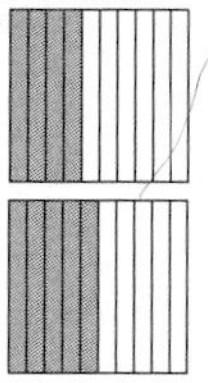

The shaded area for 0.4 is less than the shaded area for 0.5, so 0.4 < 0.5.

3. 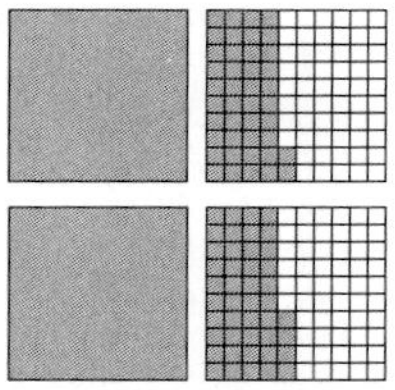

The shaded area for 1.42 is less than the shaded area for 1.44, so 1.42 < 1.44.

5. The shaded area for 0.2 is greater than the shaded area for 0.02, so 0.2 > 0.02. **7.** > **9.** > **11.** < **13.** > **15.** < **17.** =

19. 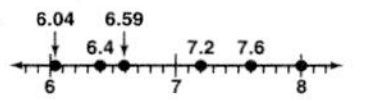
6.04
6.59
6.4
7.2
7.6
6
7
8

21. C **23.** 4.28, 4.37, 8.7, 11.09, and 11.4 light-years

25. Check students' work.

MIXED REVIEW **27.** 5 **29.** 11 **31.** 7,079 **33.** 65

CHECKPOINT **1.** nine tenths **2.** one hundredth **3.** seventy-three hundredths **4.** sixty hundredths **5.** fifty-six hundredths **6.** ninety-nine hundredths **7.** 0.3 **8.** 0.02 **9.** 0.92 **10.** 0.36 **11.** 6 tenths **12.** 7 hundredths **13.** 8 ones **14.** 3 thousandths **15.** 6 tenths **16.** 1 hundredth **17.** = **18.** > **19.** > **20.** < **21.** < **22.** = **23.** > **24.** <

Lesson 3-4 *pages 96–98*

ON YOUR OWN **1.** 43 tickets **3.** 80 adult tickets **5.** $1,309 **7.** 19 quarters **9.** 243 passengers

MIXED REVIEW **11.** nine hundred seventy-three million, four hundred thirty thousand, six hundred twenty-four **13.** sixteen billion, seven hundred sixty-five million, eight hundred three thousand, five hundred seventy-eight **15.** 20 **17.** 22 **19.** 10,880 ft

Lesson 3-5 *pages 99–102*

ON YOUR OWN **1.** 1.3 **3.** 1 **5.** 0.7 **7.** 0.31 **9.** six; sixteen **11.** five; fifteen **13.** 0.9 + 0.5 **15.** 0.72 + 0.48 **19.** 4.88 **21.** 11.07 **23.** 0.44 **25.** 6.51 **27.** 4.24 **29.** 6.27 **31.** 3.55

MIXED REVIEW **35.** 5.13 **37.** 0.00006 **39.** 332 **41.** 600 **43.** 20

Toolbox *page 103*

1. 70 **3.** 4,440 **5.** 3,550 **7.** 300 **9.** 1,100 **11.** 6,400 **13.** 13,700 **15.** 6,100 **17.** 16,000 **19.** 89,000 **21.** 16,000 **23.** 164,000 **25.** 102,000 **27.** After rounding to the nearest thousand, decide if you should round up or down to the nearest ten thousand.

Lesson 3-6 *pages 104–107*

ON YOUR OWN **1.** 2.64; 2.6 **3.** 0.74; 0.7 **5.** 23.45; 23.5 **7.** 0.69; 0.7 **9.** 4.06; 4.1 **11.** 491.30; 491.3 **15.** 0.402 **17.** 0.01 **19.** 0.6 **21.** $7 **23.** $15 **25.** $7 **27.** $4 **29.** Higher; each number is rounded up. Yes; the actual answer is 21.112. **33.** B **35.** $14 **37.** $58 **39.** $14

MIXED REVIEW **41.** 26, 37, 50; start with 2, then add 3, then continue by adding a number 2 greater than the one added before it. **43.** 625; 3,125; 15,625; start with 1, then multiply by 5 repeatedly. **45.** 30 **47.** 18 **49.** 3

Lesson 3-7 *pages 108–111*

ON YOUR OWN **1.** 4; 4 **3.** 9; 8.771 **5.** 13; 13.025 **7.** 13.5; 13.21 **9.** 5; 5.1 **11.** 9.5; 9.461 **13.** yes **15.** C **17.** 2; 1.7 **19.** 1; 1.16 **21.** 0.7; 0.674 **23.** 5; 5.11 **25.** 8; 7.79 **27a.** 1; the total amount of energy produced **b.** 0.66; yes; 0.5 is half of 1 and 0.66 > 0.5. **c.** gas and firewood/charcoal

d. 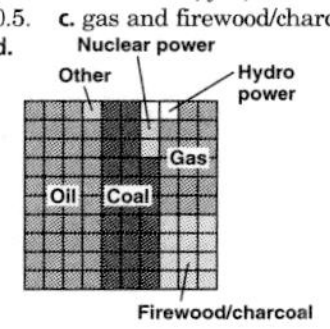
Nuclear power
Other
Hydro power
Gas
Oil
Coal
Firewood/charcoal

29. 0 **31.** 9.01 **33.** 5.866 **35.** 22.412 **37a.** $67.45 **b.** $6.95 **c.** $80.90

MIXED REVIEW **39.** 40 **41.** 25 **43.** 9.004, 9.04, 90.4, 900.4 **45.** $70

Toolbox *page 112*

1. The amount in cell F3, $75.47, is the difference between the balance on 11/14, in B3, $173.47, and the withdrawal on 11/14, in C3. **3.** F2 and B3, F3 and B4; the ending balance after one transaction is the initial balance for the next transaction.

Lesson 3-8 *pages 113–117*

ON YOUR OWN **1.** 28 mm; 2.8 cm **3.** 92 mm; 9.2 cm **5c.** 16 cm **7a.** 136 mm **b.** 11 cm **9.** 18 m **11a.** 3.3 cm, 4.8 cm, 6.7 cm **b.** 14.8 cm **13.** km **15.** m **17.** cm **19.** cm **21.** m **23.** yes **25.** yes

MIXED REVIEW **29.** > **31.** = **35.** 12 packages

CHECKPOINT **1.** 7; 7.32 **2.** 8; 8.26 **3.** 18; 18.19 **4.** 29; 29.2 **5.** 1,354; 1,354.356 **6.** 12.04 **7.** 2 **8.** 9.066 **9.** 53.9 **10.** 0.44 **11.** 23.57 **12.** A **13.** 105 mm; 10.5 cm

Lesson 3-9 *pages 118–121*

ON YOUR OWN **1.** g **3.** mg **5.** g **7.** g **9.** g **11.** L **13.** L **15.** L **17.** L **19.** capacity **21.** mass **23.** mass **25.** mass **27.** mass

29. capacity **37.** False; mL is not a unit of mass. **39.** true **41.** true

MIXED REVIEW **45.** $58 **47.** $6 **49.** six hundred thirty-eight thousand, nine hundred seventy **51.** two and forty-three hundredths **53.** one thousand three and two hundred eighty-nine thousandths **55.** $56.25

Problem Solving Practice *page 122*

1. C **3.** C **5.** D **7.** F

Lesson 3-10 *pages 123–126*

ON YOUR OWN **1.** 90 min **3.** 179 min **5.** 615 min **7.** 372 min **9.** 2 h 27 min **11.** 5 h 46 min **13.** 2 h 59 min **15.** 4 h 5 min **17.** 12 h 34 min **19.** 13 h 33 min **21a.** 12:15 P.M. **c.** yes; 1:15 P.M. **d.** 12:50 P.M. **23a.** 3 h **b.** 45 min

c.

Time	Activity
11:00 A.M.	Friends arrive, play outside
12:00 noon	Clown show
12:45 P.M.	Lunch
1:30 P.M.	Open presents
2:30 P.M.	Friends leave

25. The Beast **27.** 6:00 P.M.

MIXED REVIEW **29.** 60 times **31.** 9 thousand **33.** 9 hundred thousand **35.** 9 thousandths

Wrap Up *pages 128–129*

1. 50 **2.** 200 **3.** 310 **4.** 90 **5.** 33 **6.** C **7.** > **8.** > **9.** > **10.** > **11.** 14, 14.02, 14.1, 14.18, 14.2 **12.** 11 small feeders **13.** 0.7 **14.** 0.23 **15.** 0.931 **16.** 53.624 **17.** 357.48 **18.** $14 **19.** 59 **20.** 2 **21.** 624 **22.** km **23.** kg **24.** L **25.** Each prefix describes how different units are related to each other. The units of length, mass, and capacity measure different kinds of quantities. **26.** yes; 8:15 P.M.

Cumulative Review *page 131*

1. B **3.** B **5.** A **7.** B **9.** B

CHAPTER 4

Lesson 4-1 *pages 134–137*

ON YOUR OWN **1.** 45 **3.** 12 **5.** 36 **7.** 2 **9.** 93

MIXED REVIEW **51.** 50 mi/h

53.

Q	1	1	1	0	0	0	0	0
D	2	1	0	4	3	2	1	0
N	0	2	4	1	3	5	7	9

Toolbox *page 138*

1. 5 records

Lesson 4-2 *pages 139–142*

ON YOUR OWN **1.** 4, 5 **3.** 6, 3 **5.** 8, 1 **7.** 6^3; 6, 3 **9.** 8^4; 8, 4 **11.** $1{,}500^3$; 1,500, 3 **13.** 625 **15.** 343 **17.** 4,096 **19.** 5 **21.** 1 **23.** 2^3 **25a.** 10,000; 10^5, 100,000 **b.** The number of zeros is the same as the exponent. **c.** 1,000,000; 10,000,000; 100,000,000 **d.** 1, 0.1, 0.01 **27.** When written using exponents, the sequence is $1^3, 2^3, 3^3, 4^3, 5^3, 6^3, \ldots$ **29.** 25 **31.** 2,187 **33.** 10,000,000,000 **35.** 19 **37.** 112 **39.** 147 **41.** 41 **43.** 82

MIXED REVIEW **45.** 10.725 **47.** 19.61 **49.** 178.17 **51.** 20 **53.** 40 **55.** Yes; the total cost is only $3.87.

Lesson 4-3 *pages 143–147*

ON YOUR OWN **1.** 15 in.^{2}, 24 in.^{2}, 40 in.^{2} **5.** $(4 \times 5) + (4 \times 5)$; 40 units^2 **9a.** 20 in.^{2}, 864 in.^{2} **b.** 52 in.^{2}

11. 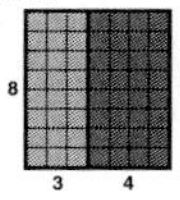
8
3
4

13. 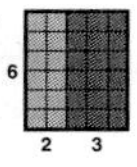
6
2
3

15. 6, 2 **17.** 8, 3 **19.** 13, 8, 7 **23.** $4 \times (6 + 3)$; 36 **25.** $(12 \times 4) + (12 \times 10)$; 168 **27.** $13 \times (6 + 4)$; 130 **29.** $(11 \times 50) - (11 \times 4)$; 506 **31.** $6 \times (22 - 18)$; 24 **33.** 132 **35.** 1,260

MIXED REVIEW **37.** 405; 1,215; 3,645 **39.** 400; 800; 1,600

41. 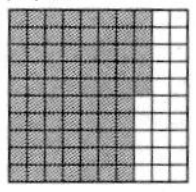

43. 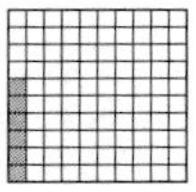

47. 7 h 57 min

CHECKPOINT **1.** 18 **2.** 52 **3.** 60 **4.** 1,000 **9.** 128 **10.** 468 **11.** 4 **12.** 14 **13.** C

Lesson 4-4 pages 148–150

ON YOUR OWN **1.** 0.6 **3.** 0.6 **5.** 4.0 **7.** 0.9 **9.** 1.8 **11.** 4.0 **13.** 2.4 **15.** 1.6 **17.** $0.6 \times 0.9 = 0.54$ **19.** $0.5 \times 0.5 = 0.25$ **21.** $1.5 \times 0.7 = 1.05$ **23.** 0.04 **25.** 0.26 **27.** 0.99 **29.** 0.72 **31.** 1.44

MIXED REVIEW **35.** 38 **37.** 2 **39.** 0.38 **41.** 3.95 **43.** 0.18

Lesson 4-5 pages 151–155

ON YOUR OWN **1.** 2.015 **3.** 261.5 **5.** 405.24 **7.** 3.434 **9.** 18.65 **11.** 149.28 **13.** 14.72 **15.** 17.100 **17.** 5 cm **19.** 17.1 **21.** 878.75 **23.** 213.78 **25.** 2.478 **27.** 0.124 **29.** 0.1152 **31.** 1.05 **33.** 0.616 **35.** 0.1485 **37.** 105 calories **41.** 0.015 **43.** 0.0945 **45.** 0.072 **47.** 0.010075 **49.** 0.708 **51.** 0.26 **53.** 820 **55.** 160 **57.** 0.00482 **59.** 100 **61.** 0.8 **65.** Each product involves multiplying the factors 3 and 4, but for 0.3×0.4, you must place a decimal point in the product. **67.** false; $3.5 \times 4.2 = 14.7 = 4.2 \times 3.5$

MIXED REVIEW **69.** 8 **71.** 15 **73.** 16 **75.** $<$ **77.** $>$

Toolbox page 156

1. 3.4×10^4 **3.** 6.54321987×10^8 **5.** 8×10^5 **7.** 9.415027392×10^9 **9.** 164,000 **11.** 823.4

Lesson 4-6 pages 157–159

ON YOUR OWN **1.** 0.8 **3.** 1.6 **5.** 0.05 **7.** 0.06 **9.** A **11.** 2 **13.** 4 **15.** 3 **17.** 3 **19.** 7 **21.** 3 **23.** 90 **25a.** 3 times greater. **b.** 8 times greater

MIXED REVIEW **27.** 3 **29.** 6 **31.** 32

Lesson 4-7 pages 160–162

ON YOUR OWN **1.** 68 **3.** 36.5 **5.** 2.5 **7.** \$6.60 **9.** 1.9 **11.** 3.45 **13.** 25.88 **15.** 1.36 **17.** D **19.** Sample: Write a number sentence $15 \times \square$ ¢ = 75¢, then guess numbers that multiply to make 75¢. **21.** \$2.07 **23.** 0.015 **25.** \$8.03 **27.** 2.44 **29.** 0.817 **31.** 44.3

MIXED REVIEW **37.** $=$ **39.** $>$

Lesson 4-8 pages 163–166

ON YOUR OWN **1.** 72.5 **3.** 850 **5.** 132 **7.** 0.05 **9.** 0.73 **11.** 0.21 **13.** 3.31 **15.** 12.5 **17.** 41.5 **19.** 13.9 **21.** 9 **23a.** 5.56 times greater **b.** 2.69 times greater **25.** 20.30 **27.** 0.21 **29.** 6.6 **31.** 0.02 **33.** 64 **35.** 99 **37.** 8.25 **39.** 4.40 **41.** 12.4 mi/gal

MIXED REVIEW **43.** $14 + x$ **45.** $\frac{p}{q}$ **47.** forty-five and nine hundred twenty-seven thousandths **49.** four hundred fifty-seven million, two hundred fifty-eight thousand, six hundred fifty-four **51.** fifty-four ten thousandths

CHECKPOINT **1.** 32.76 **2.** 1.9598 **3.** 16.4 **4.** 5.022 **5.** 24 oz **6.** 13 test tubes **7.** \$308.75

Problem Solving Practice page 167

1. A **3.** A **5.** C **7.** D **9.** C

Lesson 4-9 pages 168–170

ON YOUR OWN **1a.** \$10.95 **b.** cost for two tires **c.** 1.45 lb **d.** weight of two tires **3a.** 0.75 lb **b.** curtain cost and measurements **5.** either 12 blue and 13 red or 12 red and 13 blue **7.** 19.5 hands **9.** You need to know the number of stores. **11.** nine \$.79 cards and six \$1.19 cards

MIXED REVIEW **13.** 23 **15.** 2,580 **17.** 579,000 **19.** 8.1 **21.** 658.4 **23.** Jerry; \$.15 more

Lesson 4-10 pages 171–174

ON YOUR OWN **1.** 1,300 m **3.** 0.2 m **5.** 3.7 m **7.** 5 L **9.** 3.07 L **11.** 0.503 L **13.** 8,000 g **15.** 240 g **17.** 0.5 g **19.** A **21.** 0.86 **23.** 108 **25.** 2,100 **27.** 4.5 **29.** 1,200,000 **31.** 500,000 **35.** 299,792.458 km/s

MIXED REVIEW **41.** x divided by 5 **43.** 9 times a **45.** 42 more than two times c

Wrap Up pages 176–177

5. 16,384 **6.** 20 **7.** 28 **8.** 31 **9.** 0.12 **11.** 90 **12.** 30 **13.** 120 **14.** 80 **15.** 96 **16.** 236 **17.** 342 **18.** 29 **19.** $0.1 \times 0.3 = 0.03$ **20.** $0.5 \div 0.1 = 5$ **21.** 0.1286 **22.** 46.08 **23.** 0.75 **24.** 30 **25.** 6.64 **26.** 645 **27.** 0.6 **28.** 0.1125 **29.** Not possible; you need to know the number of students in the class. **30.** 153.5 cm **31.** 2,500 **32.** 57 **33.** 1.257 **34.** 8.09 **35.** 0.3 **36.** 15

CUMULATIVE REVIEW **1.** A **3.** D **5.** D **7.** C **9.** C **11.** D

CHAPTER 5

Lesson 5-1 pages 182–184

ON YOUR OWN **1.** yes **3.** no **5.** no **7.** yes **9.** yes **11.** yes **13.** 1, 3, 5 **15.** 1, 2, 3, 5, 10 **17.** 1, 2, 3, 9 **19.** 4 **21.** 7 **23.** 4 **27.** B **29a.** yes

MIXED REVIEW **31.** 3.96 **33.** 32,000 **35.** 0.5 **37.** 4.97 L

Lesson 5-2 pages 185–188

ON YOUR OWN **1.** 1, 2, 4, 8, 16

3. **5.**

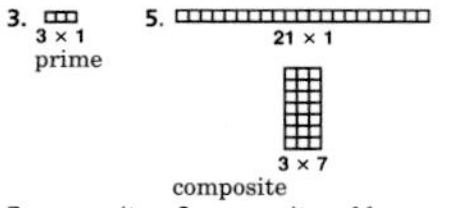
3 × 1
prime
21 × 1
3 × 7
composite

7. composite **9.** composite **11.** composite **13.** prime **15.** prime **17.** composite **19.** prime **21.** composite **23.** prime **25.** composite **27.** 3; 3; 3 **29.** 10; 3; 5; 2; 5 **31.** $3^2 \times 7$ **33.** $5^2 \times 11$ **35.** 2^5 **37.** $2 \times 3^2 \times 5$ **39.** $2^5 \times 5$ **41.** $3^2 \times 59$ **43.** 3, 5; 5, 7; 11, 13; 17, 19; 29, 31; 41, 43; 59, 61; 71, 73 **45.** 440,657

MIXED REVIEW **47.** 0.9 **49.** 6 **51.** 21 **53.** 436

Lesson 5-3 pages 189–191

ON YOUR OWN **1.** 7 **3.** 2 **5.** 3 **7.** 1 **9.** 5 **11.** 3 **13.** 2 **15.** 3 **17.** 6 **19.** 4 **21.** 1 **23.** 17 **25.** 1; each number has only two factors. The second factor is the number itself. Since the numbers are different, so are the second factors.

MIXED REVIEW **27.** 7 **29.** 76 **31.** 1.3 **33.** 1.46 **35.** 1.71 **37.** 2.05 **39.** 0.4518 **41.** 18 numbers

Problem Solving Practice page 192

1. C **3.** D **5.** C **7.** C

Lesson 5-4 pages 193–195

ON YOUR OWN **1.** $\frac{3}{4}$ **3.** $\frac{6}{6}$ **5.** $\frac{7}{12}$

7. 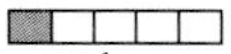 **9.** 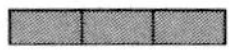

21. 1 **23.** $\frac{1}{2}$

MIXED REVIEW **27.** 2.5; 2.6 **29.** 22; 22.35 **31.** 65; 64.79

Toolbox page 196

5. $\frac{13}{16}$

Lesson 5-5 pages 197–200

ON YOUR OWN

1a. 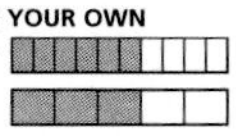

3. $\frac{2}{6}$; $\frac{1}{3}$; yes **5.** $\frac{5}{10}$; $\frac{3}{6}$; yes **7.** 5 **9.** 9 **11.** 8 **13.** 2 **15.** 30

29. The first engineer wrote the time in minutes, the second wrote it in hours.

31. no; $\frac{2}{3}$ **33.** yes **35.** no; $\frac{3}{11}$ **37.** yes **39.** no; $\frac{1}{3}$ **41.** no; $\frac{4}{5}$

MIXED REVIEW **45.** 1 **47.** $\frac{1}{2}$ **49.** $\frac{1}{2}$ **51.** 3.2 **53.** 5 **55.** flum

CHECKPOINT **1.** 1, 2, 3, 5, 10 **2.** 1, 3, 9 **3.** 1, 2, 3, 5, 10 **4.** 1, 2, 3, 5, 10 **5.** 1, 3, 5 **6.** $2^3 \times 5$ **7.** $3^2 \times 11$ **8.** $2^6 \times 3 \times 5$ **9.** 3^5 **10.** $2 \times 3 \times 5 \times 7 \times 11$ **11.** 8 **12.** 1 **13.** 3 **14.** 6 **15.** 150 **16.** $\frac{3}{4}$ **17.** $\frac{2}{3}$ **18.** $\frac{7}{9}$ **19.** $\frac{1}{6}$ **20.** $\frac{1}{2}$

Toolbox page 201

1. $\frac{6}{17}$ **3.** $\frac{6}{11}$ **5.** $\frac{4}{13}$ **7.** $\frac{4}{5}$ **9.** $\frac{2}{5}$ **11.** $\frac{3}{4}$ **13.** $\frac{7}{9}$ **15.** $\frac{5}{6}$ **17.** $\frac{23}{33}$ **19.** $\frac{7}{18}$

Lesson 5-6 pages 202–205

ON YOUR OWN **3.** $\frac{7}{5}$ **5.** $\frac{11}{4}$ **7.** $\frac{23}{8}$ **11.** $\frac{67}{10}$ **13.** $\frac{60}{7}$ **15.** $\frac{11}{4}$ in.; $2\frac{3}{4}$ in. **17.** $9\frac{1}{2}$ in., $5\frac{1}{2}$ in., $14\frac{1}{16}$ lb; $\frac{19}{2}$ in., $\frac{11}{2}$ in., $\frac{225}{16}$ lb **19.** $1\frac{6}{7}$ **21.** $3\frac{1}{12}$ **23.** $3\frac{1}{5}$ **25.** $2\frac{1}{4}$ **27.** $\frac{11}{9}$ **29.** $2\frac{3}{8}$ **31.** $2\frac{1}{6}$ **33.** $2\frac{7}{23}$ **35.** $4\frac{5}{8}$ **37.** $1\frac{4}{5}$

MIXED REVIEW **39.** 5:50 P.M. **41.** 73 **43.** 7

Lesson 5-7 pages 206–208

ON YOUR OWN **1.** 12 **3.** 30 **5.** 60 **7.** 60 **9.** 24 **11.** 24 **13a.** 40 **15.** D **17.** 72 **19.** 60 **21.** 300 **23.** 260 **25.** 56 **27.** 108 **29a.** i. 6; 36; 216; 216; ii. 5; 100; 500; 500; iii. 4; 168; 672; 672 **b.** The product of the GCF and the LCM is equal to the product of the numbers.

MIXED REVIEW **31.** 5.7 **33.** 5.176 **35.** $k - 28$ **37.** $12 + y$ **39.** 12 people

Lesson 5-8 pages 209–212

ON YOUR OWN **1.** $>$ **3.** $=$ **5.** $<$ **7.** $>$ **9.** Timothy **11.** B **13.** $\frac{2}{7}, \frac{2}{5}, \frac{2}{3}$ **15.** $1\frac{2}{3}, 1\frac{3}{4}, 1\frac{5}{6}$ **17.** $2\frac{5}{6}, 2\frac{8}{9}, 2\frac{17}{18}$ **19.** $\frac{1}{3}, \frac{7}{15}, \frac{7}{12}$ **21.** $\frac{5}{7}, \frac{3}{4}, \frac{11}{14}$ **23.** $\frac{8}{15}, \frac{23}{40}, \frac{7}{12}, \frac{19}{30}$

MIXED REVIEW **27.** 253 min **29.** 499 min **31.** 156 min **33.** 31.713 **35.** 8.9 **37.** The collector made \$7.

Lesson 5-9 pages 213–217

ON YOUR OWN **1.** $\frac{3}{10}$ **3.** $2\frac{5}{8}$ **5.** $5\frac{1}{2}$ **7.** $1\frac{31}{50}$ **9.** $\frac{7}{100}$ **11.** $\frac{8}{125}$ **13.** $\frac{1}{125}$ **15.** $\frac{29}{200}$ **17.** $\frac{113}{200}$ **19.** $\frac{3}{2{,}000}$ **21.** $\frac{11}{20}$ **25.** 0.18 **27.** $0.8\overline{3}$ **29.** 0.875 **31.** 10.75 **33.** 0.35 **35.** $0.\overline{54}$ **37.** 0.56 **39.** 4.7 **41.** $0.208\overline{3}$ **43.** $3.\overline{36}$ **45.** \$10.625 **47a.** 0.34, $0.\overline{3}$, 0.32, $0.34\overline{6}$ **b.** $\frac{8}{25}, \frac{1}{3}, \frac{17}{50}, \frac{26}{75}$

MIXED REVIEW **49.** 3.5 **51.** 8.2 **53.** 6.3 **55.** No; the numbers in the last column are declining, but not at a constant rate.

CHECKPOINT **1.** 96 **2.** 504 **3.** 360 **4.** 140 **5.** 0.4 **6.** 0.07 **7.** 0.375 **8.** $0.\overline{6}$ **9.** $5.\overline{5}$ **10.** $\frac{13}{25}$ **11.** $\frac{1}{25}$ **12.** $\frac{3}{4}$ **13.** $15\frac{1}{40}$ **14.** $1\frac{3}{8}$ **15.** D

Lesson 5-10 pages 218–220

ON YOUR OWN **1.** 11 **3.** 90 cards **5.** Saturday **7.** after 1 h 54 min **9.** 13 people **11.** \$8 **13.** 12 dimes and 3 nickels

MIXED REVIEW **21.** 18,000 **23.** 0.85

Wrap Up pages 222–223

1. 1, 3 **2.** 1, 2 **3.** 1, 3, 9 **4.** 1, 3, 5, 9 **5.** 1, 2 **6.** 1, 2, 5, 10 **7.** B **8.** $2^3 \times 3^2$ **9.** $2^3 \times 3 \times 5$ **10.** 3×11 **11.** $2^4 \times 5$ **12.** $2 \times 3^2 \times 13$ **13.** $3 \times 5 \times 23$ **14.** 20; 280 **15.** 1; 924 **16.** 3; 72 **17.** 5; 75 **18.** 6; 1,260 **19.** 2; 240 **20.** $\frac{1}{2}$ **21.** 1 **22.** 0 **23.** 0 **24.** $\frac{1}{2}$ **25.** $\frac{1}{2}$ **28.** $\frac{1}{2}$ **29.** $\frac{3}{5}$ **30.** $\frac{8}{9}$ **31.** $\frac{3}{8}$ **32.** $\frac{2}{7}$ **33.** $\frac{19}{4}$ **34.** $4\frac{2}{5}$ **35.** $8\frac{1}{7}$ **36.** $\frac{19}{8}$ **37.** $2\frac{1}{2}$ **38.** $\frac{57}{11}$ **39.** $\frac{35}{36}, 1\frac{3}{4}, 1\frac{7}{9}, 1\frac{5}{6}$ **40.** $\frac{1}{25}$ **41.** $3\frac{7}{8}$ **42.** $2\frac{7}{50}$ **43.** 0.425 **44.** $0.\overline{8}$ **45.** $0.\overline{54}$ **46.** \$39

Cumulative Review page 225

1. A **3.** C **5.** C **7.** C **9.** D

CHAPTER 6

Lesson 6-1 pages 228–231

ON YOUR OWN **1.** $\frac{1}{2}$ **3.** $1\frac{1}{2}$ **5.** $1\frac{1}{2}$ **7.** $1\frac{1}{2}$ **9.** 1 **11.** $1\frac{1}{2}$ **13.** $1\frac{1}{2}$ **15.** 2 **17.** $3\frac{1}{2}$ in. **19.** 9 **21.** 12 **23.** 1 **25.** 4 **27.** 31 **29.** 21 **31.** 2 **33.** \$15.00 **35.** 24 ft

MIXED REVIEW **37.** $\frac{3}{4}$ **39.** $\frac{3}{14}$ **41.** $\frac{24}{25}$

43. Ages of First Cousins **45.** \$21

Ages	Frequency
5–9	4
10–14	4
15–19	3
20–25	1

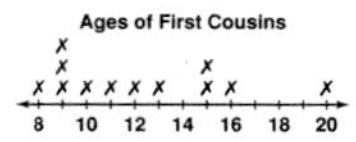
Ages of First Cousins
8
10
12
14
16
18
20

Lesson 6-2 pages 232–235

ON YOUR OWN **1.** $\frac{1}{3} + \frac{1}{2} = \frac{5}{6}$ **3.** $\frac{3}{12} + \frac{4}{12} = \frac{7}{12}$ **5.** 1 **7.** $\frac{1}{2}$ **9.** $\frac{5}{6}$ **11.** 1 **13.** $\frac{3}{4}$ **15.** $\frac{71}{100}$ **17.** $\frac{7}{10}$ **19.** $\frac{9}{10} - \frac{7}{10} = \frac{2}{10}$ **21.** $\frac{5}{8} - \frac{3}{8} = \frac{2}{8}$ **23.** no; $\frac{1}{3}$ **25.** yes **27a.** Subtract. **b.** $\frac{1}{8}$ in. **29.** $\frac{2}{5}$ **31.** $\frac{1}{4}$ **33.** $\frac{1}{3}$ **35.** $\frac{1}{4}$ **37.** $\frac{1}{5}$ **39.** $\frac{1}{2}$ **41.** $\frac{7}{8}$ **43a.** $\frac{1}{2}$ T **b.** $\frac{1}{4}$ c

MIXED REVIEW **47.** 6^4 **49.** 5.8^5 **51.** 5 **53.** 9 **55.** Jan: \$2.00; Leah: \$3.25

Lesson 6-3 pages 236–240

ON YOUR OWN **1.** $\frac{2}{3} - \frac{5}{12} = \frac{1}{4}$ **3.** $\frac{2}{5} + \frac{1}{2} = \frac{9}{10}$

5. 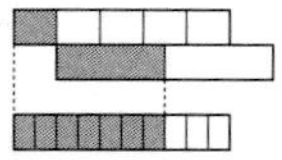

7. 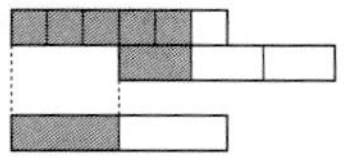

9. $\frac{3}{10}$ **11.** $\frac{7}{10}$ **13.** $\frac{1}{2}$ **15.** $\frac{11}{12}$ **17.** $\frac{1}{5}$ **19.** less **21.** less **23.** $1\frac{5}{12}$ yd **25.** $\frac{11}{15}$ **27.** $\frac{3}{10}$ **29.** $\frac{29}{30}$ **31.** $1\frac{7}{40}$ **33.** $\frac{1}{3}$ **35.** $1\frac{1}{4}$ **37.** $\frac{1}{4}$ **39.** $1\frac{7}{36}$ **41.** $\frac{9}{20}$ **43.** $\frac{1}{40}$ **45.** Belize, Panama, Costa Rica, Nicaragua, Honduras, El Salvador, Guatemala **47.** El Salvador **49.** $\frac{3}{10}$ **51.** $1\frac{5}{12}$ **53.** $1\frac{1}{4}$ **55.** $1\frac{3}{8}$ **57.** $\frac{9}{10}$ **59.** no

MIXED REVIEW **61.** line graph **63.** Saturday

CHECKPOINT **1.** 1 **2.** 0 **3.** 10 **4.** 18 **5.** 2 **6.** $\frac{1}{4} + \frac{1}{4} = \frac{2}{4}$ or $\frac{1}{2}$ **7.** $\frac{7}{10} - \frac{3}{10} = \frac{4}{10}$ or $\frac{2}{5}$ **8.** $\frac{1}{3} - \frac{1}{6} = \frac{1}{6}$ **9.** $\frac{3}{5}$ **10.** $\frac{1}{3}$ **11.** $\frac{1}{2}$ **12.** $\frac{3}{8}$ **13.** $\frac{1}{2}$ **14.** $\frac{1}{10}$

Lesson 6-4 pages 241–244

ON YOUR OWN **1.** $1\frac{1}{6}$ **3.** $15\frac{1}{3}$ **5.** 9 **7.** $5\frac{1}{6}$ **9.** $13\frac{7}{16}$ **11.** $7\frac{3}{4}$ **13.** $13\frac{15}{16}$ **15.** $56\frac{11}{15}$ **17.** $8\frac{17}{20}$ **19.** $13\frac{7}{12}$ **23.** 5 **25.** 13 **29.** $5\frac{7}{8}$ **31.** $5\frac{1}{2}$ **33.** $3\frac{1}{8}$ **35.** $9\frac{2}{15}$ **37.** $30\frac{3}{10}$ **39.** $44\frac{13}{20}$ **41.** $12\frac{3}{10}$ **43a.** $7\frac{5}{8}$ ft **b.** Add **45.** $24\frac{1}{5}$ **47.** $27\frac{2}{3}$ **49.** $4\frac{1}{3}$ **51.** $31\frac{11}{12}$ **53.** $24\frac{1}{3}$ **55.** $10\frac{1}{4}$ **57.** $171\frac{1}{3}$ **59.** $36\frac{17}{24}$ **61.** $5\frac{1}{8}$ **63.** D **65.** \$77.50

MIXED REVIEW **67.** 2,574 **69.** 380 **71.** 369 **73.** 972; 2,916; 8,748

Toolbox page 245

1. $\frac{7}{20}$ **3.** $\frac{7}{10}$ **5.** $\frac{13}{24}$ **7.** $\frac{7}{90}$ **9.** $\frac{7}{45}$ **11.** $13\frac{1}{2}$ **13.** $4\frac{7}{18}$ **15.** $8\frac{11}{12}$ **17.** $8\frac{1}{12}$ **19.** $10\frac{4}{5}$

Lesson 6-5 pages 246–249

ON YOUR OWN **1.** 4 **3.** $1\frac{1}{3}$ **5.** $2\frac{1}{2}$ **7.** $1\frac{1}{16}$ **9.** $10\frac{1}{16}$ **11.** $8\frac{1}{8}$ **13.** $4\frac{11}{20}$ **15.** $25\frac{1}{10}$ **17.** $1\frac{5}{8}$ **19.** $3\frac{8}{15}$ **21.** $16\frac{5}{6}$ **23.** $\frac{9}{16}$ **25.** $7\frac{11}{16}$ **27.** $2\frac{1}{6}$ **29.** $7\frac{5}{6}$ **33.** $3\frac{1}{2}, 2\frac{1}{3}$

35.

Spruce Tree	Length of Cone (in.)
Black	$\frac{7}{8}$
Red	$1\frac{1}{4}$
White	$1\frac{5}{8}$
Norway	$5\frac{1}{2}$

37. black and red, red and white **39.** 2 ft $5\frac{3}{4}$ in. **41.** $9\frac{1}{4}$ **43.** $10\frac{11}{16}$ **45.** $9\frac{3}{10}$ **47.** $4\frac{1}{4}$ **49.** $14\frac{7}{8}$ **51.** $12\frac{1}{4}$ **53a.** $2\frac{3}{4}$ in. **b.** Subtraction

MIXED REVIEW **55.** $\frac{12}{25}$ **57.** 0.12 **59.** 0.84 **61.** 9,300,000 **63.** 5.62 **65.** 0.133

Lesson 6-6 pages 250–252

ON YOUR OWN **1.** 1 ft by 11 ft, 2 ft by 10 ft, 3 ft by 9 ft, 4 ft by 8 ft, 5 ft by 7 ft, 6 ft by 6 ft; 6 ft by 6 ft **3.** 39 in. **5.** 19 boxes **7.** 8 different sandwiches **9.** 8:45 A.M.

MIXED REVIEW

11.

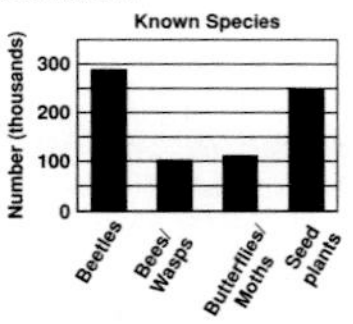
Known Species
Number (thousands)
300
200
100
0
Beetles
Bees/
Wasps
Butterflies/
Moths
Seed
plants

13. price for one box of juice

Lesson 6-7 pages 253–256

ON YOUR OWN **1.** $\frac{1}{2} \times \frac{1}{2} = \frac{1}{4}$ **3.** $\frac{2}{3} \times \frac{2}{3} = \frac{4}{9}$

5. 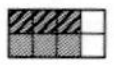 **7.** 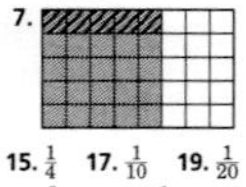

9. C **13.** $\frac{2}{5}$ **15.** $\frac{1}{4}$ **17.** $\frac{1}{10}$ **19.** $\frac{1}{20}$ **21.** $\frac{9}{20}$ **23.** $10\frac{5}{6}$ **25.** $27\frac{9}{10}$ **27.** $10\frac{2}{3}$ **29.** $17\frac{1}{4}$ **31.** $27\frac{1}{2}$ **33.** $\frac{1}{8}$

MIXED REVIEW **35.** prime **37.** composite **39.** prime **41.** 3 tenths **43.** 3 thousandths **45.** 3 ten-thousandths

Problem Solving Practice page 257

1. B **3.** B **5.** B **7.** B **9.** D

Lesson 6-8 pages 258–261

ON YOUR OWN **1.** 4 **3.** 80 **5.** 18 **7.** 54 **9.** about 150 in.^{2} **11.** $33\frac{3}{4}$ **13.** $49\frac{5}{6}$ **15.** $13\frac{7}{8}$ **17.** $2\frac{4}{5}$ **19.** 6 **21.** $9\frac{5}{6}$ **23.** 20 **25.** $17\frac{1}{4}$ **27.** $4\frac{3}{8}$ **29.** 3 in. by 3 in. **31.** $13\frac{1}{2}$ in.

MIXED REVIEW **33.** 30 **35.** 360 **37.** 1,260 **39.** 0.191 **41.** 0.0367 **43.** \$3.00

CHECKPOINT 1. $10\frac{7}{8}$ 2. $5\frac{3}{16}$ 3. $28\frac{1}{2}$ 4. $4\frac{9}{10}$
5. $8\frac{4}{15}$ 6. $10\frac{1}{4}$ 7. $23\frac{5}{9}$ 8. $9\frac{5}{16}$ 9. $13\frac{17}{24}$ 10. C
11. $\frac{1}{12}$ 12. 15 13. $2\frac{1}{4}$ 14. $10\frac{1}{8}$ 15. $11\frac{1}{3}$

17a.
8 ft × 8 ft	8 ft × 10 ft
4 ft × 18 ft	

b. bathroom: 8 ft by 10 ft; office: 8 ft by 8 ft **c.** bathroom: 80 ft²; office: 64 ft²; hallway: $72\frac{2}{3}$; total area: 216 ft²

18. $\frac{1}{2}$ 19. $\frac{1}{12}$ 20. $8\frac{1}{8}$ 21. $\frac{19}{20}$ 22. 11 23. $7\frac{3}{3}$
24. 40 25. 6 26. $20\frac{1}{6}$ yd

Cumulative Review page 275
1. A 3. C 5. D 7. D 9. C 11. B

CHAPTER 7

Lesson 7-1 pages 276–280
ON YOUR OWN 1. 3 : 1 3. 1 : 2
11. 1 to 2, 1 : 2, $\frac{1}{2}$ 13. 14 to 12, 14 : 12, $\frac{14}{12}$
15. 35 to 24, 35 : 24, $\frac{35}{24}$ 17. 24 to 11, 24 : 11, $\frac{24}{11}$
19. 24 to 70, 24 : 70, $\frac{24}{70}$ 25. 5 : 7
MIXED REVIEW 33. 106.2 35. 17.78 43. about 12.2 homes; about 146 homes

Lesson 7-2 pages 281–284
ON YOUR OWN 13. $\frac{2}{5}$ 15. $\frac{21}{25}$ 17. $\frac{7}{2}$ 19. $\frac{6}{1}$
21. $\frac{4}{5}$ 23. $\frac{9}{2}$ 27. 2 : 3 29. 2 : 5 31. 3 : 4 33. 3
35. 5 37. 33 pages/h 39. 4 mi/h 41. \$3 per toy
43. 2.5 mi/practice
MIXED REVIEW 45. 165 47. 48 49. 7

LESSON 7-3 pages 285–288
ON YOUR OWN 1. yes 3. no 5. yes 7. yes
9. no 11. 36 = 36 13. $\frac{2}{5} = \frac{6}{15}, \frac{5}{2} = \frac{15}{6}, \frac{2}{6} = \frac{5}{15}, \frac{6}{2} = \frac{15}{5}$ 15. 84 17. 27
19. 35 21. 63 23. 60
25. 1 27. 27 29. 0.375 31. 108 in. 33. $2\frac{1}{2}$ h
MIXED REVIEW 37. $\frac{1}{8}$ 39. $\frac{11}{32}$ 41. $\frac{3}{20}$
43. 180 45. 4 47. yes; 7 cm taller

CHECKPOINT 7. \$.89 per taco 8. \$.35 per battery
9. 12 10. 18 11. 8 12. 15 13. 78 14. C

Lesson 6-9 page 262–265
ON YOUR OWN
1. 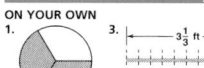 3. $\overleftarrow{\qquad 3\frac{1}{3} \text{ ft} \qquad}$
0 1 2 3
5. $\frac{1}{3}$ 7. 5 9. $\frac{6}{17}$ 11. 15 13. 35 15. 36
17. 6 pieces 19. 20 21. 36 23. 49 25. $\frac{5}{9}$
27. $1\frac{1}{4}$ 29. $7\frac{3}{4}$ 31. $3\frac{3}{8}$ 33. $\frac{22}{25}$ 35. $\frac{2}{5}$ 37. $34\frac{1}{2}$
39. 16 servings 41. 24 pieces 43a. 10 **b.** divide
MIXED REVIEW 45. 50 47. 3 49. 2,400
51. Taro is the pharmacist, Alma is the stock broker, and Wanell is the teacher.

Toolbox page 266
1. pounds 3. gallons 5. ounces or cups

Lesson 6-10 pages 267–270
ON YOUR OWN 1. 27 3. 4 5. 96 7. 16
9. $2\frac{1}{12}$ 11. 5 13. $1\frac{1}{2}$ 15. 34 17. $10\frac{1}{2}$ 19. 66
21a. division **b.** multiplication **c.** multiplication
23. 6,665$\frac{1}{8}$ in. 25. 4 c 27. 3 yd 2 ft 29. 7 lb 15 oz
31. No; if each person eats 3 oz per serving, together they should eat 18 oz, or $1\frac{1}{8}$ lb.
33. No; $3\frac{1}{8}$ ft are needed. 35a. 45,000,000 gal
b. about 3,000 T 37. = 39. < 41. = 43. >
45. < 47. =
MIXED REVIEW 49. 0.0072 51. $9\frac{4}{5}$ 53. $8\frac{1}{6}$
55. $\frac{53}{60}$ 57. 2 dimes and 1 nickel

Wrap Up pages 272–273
1. $\frac{1}{2}$ 2. $1\frac{1}{3}$ 3. 5 4. 6 5. $\frac{1}{5} + \frac{1}{2} = \frac{7}{10}$
6. $\frac{5}{6} - \frac{1}{3} = \frac{1}{2}$ 7. $\frac{7}{9}$ 8. $\frac{1}{2}$ 9. $1\frac{1}{12}$ 10. $\frac{3}{10}$ 11. $\frac{1}{40}$
12. 6 13. $3\frac{13}{14}$ 14. $5\frac{7}{24}$ 15. $4\frac{4}{15}$ 16. $4\frac{23}{36}$

Lesson 7-4 pages 289–291
ON YOUR OWN 1a. 2 times; 120 times
b. 1,051,200 times; find the number of hours in 1 yr. Then multiply it by 120. 3. 63,072,000 times
5. \$91.25; \$912.50 7. no
MIXED REVIEW 9. 60 11. 20.58 13. 34 15. 4
17. 0.18 19. 0.48 21. 1.65 23. 8 birds;
2 squirrels

Lesson 7-5 pages 292–295
ON YOUR OWN 1. 1 in. to 4 ft 3. 1 ft to 25 ft
11. 400 km 13. 70 km 15. 1.25 cm 17. 40 cm
19. 10 m × 35 m 21. 2 m × 7 m 23. 12 m × 42 m
25. 20 km × 70 km 29. 0.24 in. 31. 0.135 in.
33. 6 cm 35. 36 in. 37a. 4×12 **b.** The height remained the same, but the length doubled.
MIXED REVIEW 39. 11.43 41. 1.5 45. 6:58 A.M.

Toolbox page 296
1. 12 ft 3. $7\frac{1}{2}$ ft

Lesson 7-6 pages 297–299
ON YOUR OWN
1. 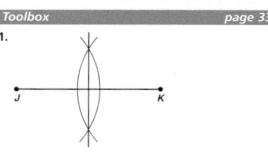 3.

7a. 46%; 32% **b.** Subtract both results from 100%.
c. 22% 9. 97% of the days last summer were sunny. 11. 85% of the answers are correct.
15. 48% 17. 33% 19. 25%
MIXED REVIEW 21. $1\frac{7}{30}$ 23. $1\frac{1}{2}$ 25. $6\frac{11}{20}$ 27. $5\frac{1}{4}$
29. $28\frac{33}{40}$ 31. $7\frac{9}{10}$

Lesson 7-7 pages 300–303
ON YOUR OWN
1. 3.

7. 0.15; $\frac{7}{20}$ 9. 0.88; $\frac{22}{25}$ 11. 0.5; $\frac{1}{2}$ 13. 0.07; $\frac{7}{100}$

---

15. 0.625; $\frac{5}{8}$ 17. 0.274; $\frac{137}{500}$ 19. 0.42; $\frac{21}{50}$
21. 0.17; $\frac{17}{100}$ 23. 0.44; $\frac{11}{25}$ 25. $\frac{4}{5}$, 0.8; $\frac{1}{5}$, 0.2
27. 23% 31. 95% 33. 14% 35. 70% 37. 3%
39. 11% 41. 100% 43. 99% 45. 1% 47. 40%
49. Move the decimal point two places to the right and append the % sign. 51a. 25%; 34%; 44%; 55%; 69%; 77%
b.

Percent of High School Students Who Graduated
53. 26.7%
55. 26.7%
57. 14.3%
59. 56.7%
61. 13.3%
63. 85.7%
MIXED REVIEW 65. > 67. < 69. -7 71. \$105

Problem Solving Practice page 304
1. C 3. B 5. D 7. C 9. D

Lesson 7-8 pages 305–312
ON YOUR OWN 1. \$64 3. \$26 5. 36 7. 13
9. 13 11. 3 13a. \$11.90 **b.** \$91 15. \$16.20
17a. 80% **c.** No; \$22 < \$24 or \$25.60. 19. 45
21. 10 23. 5 25. 480 27. 87 29. 30 31. 20
33. 20 41. Double the 10% tip to get the 20% tip. Add half the 10% tip to the 10% tip to get the 15% tip.
MIXED REVIEW 43. $2\frac{5}{9}$ 45. $\frac{230}{261}$ 47. $1\frac{16}{99}$ 49. 4
51. 15 53. 7 55. 64 teams

Lesson 7-9 pages 309–313
ON YOUR OWN 1. 9.6 3. 64.8 5. 28 7. 4.3
9. 11 11. 65.34 13. 30.6 15. 72.6 17. 50.05
19. 8.64 21. 190 girls 23. 5 girls
25. 647 children and teenagers 27. 112 A's
29. 42 T's 31. 36 33. 48 35. 510 37. 48
39. 16 41a. 39 people 43. 21 games 45. \$200
MIXED REVIEW 47. 0.05693 49. 3.6 51. 5
53. 11 55. \$10.50

CHECKPOINT
1. 2.

7. 75% 8. 45% 9. 67% 10. 60% 11. 95%
12. 7% 13. 7 14. 32 15. 24 16. 50 17. 30
18. 262.5 km 19. D

Lesson 7-10 pages 314–317
ON YOUR OWN
1. 3. 7.
9. 23. Reading for Pleasure
Don't know Too much About right Too little
25. 22% 25% 53%
MIXED REVIEW 31. 75 33. 228 35. 120
37. 136 39. 52

Toolbox page 318
1. Age of People Eating at Freddy's Fast Food
Over 50 Under 12 30–50 12–18 19–30
3. How Often Adults Need to Search for Keys
Once a Week Once a Day Never Once a Month Once a Year

Wrap Up pages 320–321
1. $\frac{1}{4}$ 2. $\frac{3}{7}$ 3. $\frac{3}{4}$ 4. $\frac{1}{4}$ 5. $\frac{1}{6}$ 6. $\frac{45}{100}$, 45 : 100,
45 to 100 7. \$1.99; \$1.88; package of 3 tapes
8. 21 9. 27 10. 3 11. 16 12. 3 13. 9 14. 21
15. 72 16. 0 17. 6 18. 3 m 19. 1 m 20. 24 ft
21. 1.5 m 22. 1,440 times 24. $\frac{6}{25}$; 0.24
25. 55%; $\frac{11}{20}$; 0.55 26. 12%; $\frac{3}{25}$; 0.12 27. 25%; $\frac{1}{4}$;
0.25 28. 40%; $\frac{2}{5}$; 0.40 29. 20%; $\frac{1}{5}$; 0.20
30. 0.65; $\frac{13}{20}$ 31. about \$72 32. C 33. 30
34. 4.37 35. 48 36. 23.5 37. \$.80
38. Ways We Get to School
Walk Car Bike Bus

Cumulative Review page 323
1. B 3. B 5. A 7. C 9. C 11. B

CHAPTER 8

Lesson 8-1 pages 326–330
ON YOUR OWN 1. d 3. c 7. A, B, C 11. $\overleftrightarrow{AC}$, $\overleftrightarrow{DE}$
13. A B C D E 15. not possible
17. $\overline{XY}$ and $\overline{WZ}$ 19. no parallel segments
21. never 23. always 25. never 27. never
MIXED REVIEW 37. 289 39. 192 41. 10 43. 11
45. 1 47. 60 singers

Lesson 8-2 pages 331–335
ON YOUR OWN 1. vertex: R; sides: $\overrightarrow{RQ}$ $\overrightarrow{RS}$
3. vertex: S; sides: $\overrightarrow{SD}$ $\overrightarrow{SE}$
5. $\angle KLM$, $\angle KLN$; $\angle MLN$; $\angle NLK$, $\angle NLM$
7. 19. 60°; 58° 21. 30°; 28°
23. 30°; 30° 25. obtuse
27. straight 29. acute
31a. T R S W **b.** 4 right angles 35. A
MIXED REVIEW 43. 9 45. 28 47. 2

Toolbox page 336
1.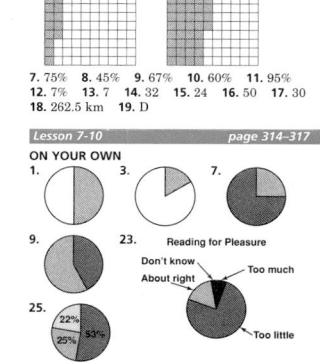
J K

Lesson 8-3 pages 337–339
ON YOUR OWN 1. sometimes 3. never 5. 64°
7. 90° 9. 85° 11. congruent: $\angle 2$ and $\angle 5$, $\angle 3$ and $\angle 7$, $\angle 4$ and $\angle 6$, $\angle 8$ and $\angle 9$, $\angle 10$ and $\angle 11$; complementary: $\angle 3$ and $\angle 8$, $\angle 3$ and $\angle 9$, $\angle 7$ and $\angle 8$, $\angle 7$ and $\angle 9$; supplementary: $\angle 4$ and $\angle 10$, $\angle 4$ and $\angle 11$, $\angle 6$ and $\angle 10$, $\angle 6$ and $\angle 11$
MIXED REVIEW 19. 30 21. 0.4 23. \$2,440

Lesson 8-4 pages 340–343
ON YOUR OWN 1. isosceles 3. scalene
5. isosceles 7. scalene 9. scalene 11. isosceles
13. right 15. right 17. acute 19. obtuse 21. e
23. b, d, f 25. a, b, c 27. acute, isosceles, equilateral; equilateral 29. Isosceles, isosceles, isosceles; isosceles triangles have two angles of equal measure. 31. right triangle, isosceles triangle; isosceles right triangle
33. 35.
MIXED REVIEW 43. 30 45. 63 47. < . =
51. <

Lesson 8-5 pages 344–348
ON YOUR OWN 1. not convex 3. not convex
5. convex 9. triangle 11. hexagon
13. quadrilateral 15. quadrilateral 17. Each is a polygon. 19a. 9 diagonals
MIXED REVIEW 21. $\frac{13}{20}$ 23. $51\frac{21}{32}$ 25. 18
27. 0.0006 29. 0.0044
CHECKPOINT 1. $\overleftrightarrow{KN}$, $\overleftrightarrow{LM}$ 8. $\angle LJN$
9. not possible 10. $\overleftrightarrow{LM}$, $\overleftrightarrow{PJ}$ 11. B 12. 10 sides
13. 8 sides 14. 4 sides 15. 6 sides

Lesson 8-6 pages 349–352
ON YOUR OWN 1a. i, ii, iii, v, vi, vii, viii, ix
b. i, v, vi, vii, viii, ix **c.** i, vii, viii **d.** i, v, vii
e. i, vii **f.** ii
3. 5. 11. No
13. All
15. No 17. All 19. Some
21. parallelogram, rectangle
23. parallelogram, rhombus
25a. They are congruent. **b.** isosceles
27. rectangle, square
MIXED REVIEW 31. 5 33. 27 35. $\frac{3}{2}$, or 1.5

Lesson 8-7 pages 353–355
ON YOUR OWN 1. 4 students 3. $9\frac{1}{2}$ in.
5a. 17 customers **b.** 4 customers
7. 6 combinations
MIXED REVIEW 9. 4; 800 11. 7; 8 13. 19.25
15. 4.65 17. 82°F

Lesson 8-8 pages 356–359
ON YOUR OWN 1. A, D 5. C 7. similar
9. congruent 11. 4 congruent triangles; 4 triangles are similar to the large triangle
13. A and E, C and D, I and L 15b. No; some rhombuses have four right angles and some do not.
c. Yes; all squares have four right angles and their sides are always proportional.
MIXED REVIEW 17. $6\frac{1}{3}$ 19. $15\frac{2}{3}$ 21. $3\frac{3}{5}$
23. 18% 25. 3 wore neither.

Lesson 8-9 pages 360–363
ON YOUR OWN 1. yes 3. yes 5. yes 7. no
9. none 11. too many to count
13. 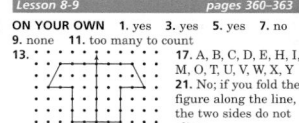 17. A, B, C, D, E, H, I, M, O, T, U, V, W, X, Y
21. No; if you fold the figure along the line, the two sides do not align.
23. No; if you fold the figure along the line, the two sides do not align.
MIXED REVIEW 25. 4,959.665 27. 462.2499
29. 0.00174 31. $\frac{1}{2}$ 33. $\frac{1}{2}$ 35. 5 games

CHAPTER 8 (continued)

Lesson 8-10 pages 364–367
ON YOUR OWN 1. $\overline{OR}, \overline{OS}, \overline{OT}$ 3. $\overline{ST}, \overline{RT}$
5. 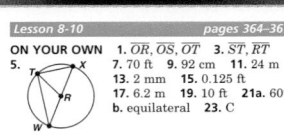 7. 70 ft 9. 92 cm 11. 24 m
13. 2 mm 15. 0.125 ft
17. 6.2 m 19. 10 ft 21a. 60°
b. equilateral 23. C

MIXED REVIEW 25. $2^2 \times 3 \times 5$ 27. $2^2 \times 5^3$
29. $2^3 \times 5 \times 31$ 31. 13 students
CHECKPOINT 1. A square is a parallelogram with four congruent sides and four right angles.
2a. 6 customers b. 21 customers 3a. A, B, E
b. A, B, D, E 4. A 5. 20 in. 6. 70 ft 7. 2.5 m
8. 92 cm

Toolbox page 368
3. The results are the same. 5. Their measures are the same.

Problem Solving Practice page 369
1. C 3. D 5. C 7. D 9. B

Lesson 8-11 pages 370–374
ON YOUR OWN
7. 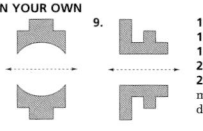 9. 13. translation
15. yes
17. yes 19. no
21. A, B, C, D, E
23. Both can be measured in degrees.

MIXED REVIEW 25. $7\frac{1}{3}$ 27. $5\frac{2}{5}$
29. seventy-three hundredths 31. three hundred eighty-six and nine hundred eight thousandths
33. four hundred seven thousand, six hundred eighty-three and seven hundredths
35. 28 handshakes

Wrap Up pages 376–377
1. 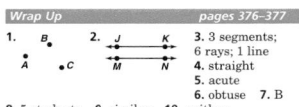 2. 3. 3 segments; 6 rays; 1 line
4. straight
5. acute
6. obtuse 7. B
8. 5 students 9. similar 10. neither
12. $\overline{OV}, \overline{OX}, \overline{OY}$ 13. $\overline{VX}$ 14. $\overline{VW}, \overline{VX}, \overline{WY}$

Cumulative Review page 379
1. C 3. B 5. D 7. B 9. C

CHAPTER 9

Lesson 9-1 pages 382–385
ON YOUR OWN 1. 8 cm² 3. 8 cm² 5. 20 in.²
7. 52 cm² 9. 36 cm²

MIXED REVIEW 15. $\frac{4}{5}$ 17. $1\frac{1}{8}$ 19. $1\frac{1}{12}$
21. 1 to 3; 1 : 3; $\frac{1}{3}$ 23. 1 to 2; 1 : 2; $\frac{1}{2}$ 25. 5 days

Toolbox page 386
1. $\frac{1}{8}$ in. 3. $\frac{1}{16}$ in. 5. $1\frac{5}{16}$ in.

Lesson 9-2 pages 387–391
ON YOUR OWN 1. 26 cm; 30 cm² 3. 26 ft; 36 ft² 5a. 180 ft b. 60 sections 7. 50 yd; 150 yd² 9. 38 yd; 84 yd² 11. 21.8 cm; 26.64 cm²
13. 7 cm; 3 cm² 15. 8 cm; 3.75 cm² 17. 7 ft; 28 ft²
19. 3 ft 21. 18 in.; 20.25 in.² 23. 84 mm; 441 mm²
25. 6 cm; 2.25 cm² 27. 400 ft; 10,000 ft²
29. 1 yd × 24 yd, 2 yd × 12 yd, 3 yd × 8 yd, 4 yd × 6 yd 33. 4 cm² 35. 144 in.² 37a. 16 in.²
b. The perimeter would be 8 in.; the area would be 4 in.².

MIXED REVIEW 39. 4 41. 1.3 43. 0.23

Lesson 9-3 pages 392–396
ON YOUR OWN 1. 36 ft² 3. 48 km² 5. 9.6 cm²
7. 54 in.² 9. 16 yd² 11. 12.25 m² 13. 8 units²
15. 6 units² 17. 30 m² 21. 30 units²
23. 21 units² 25. 12 units² 27. 16 units²
29. $1\frac{13}{16}$ 31. $23\frac{1}{3}$ 33. $31\frac{1}{2}$
CHECKPOINT 1. 240 in.² 2. 80 in.; 175 in.²
3. 84 in.² 4. 72.25 cm² 5. 78 m² 6. 1,000 ft²

Toolbox page 397
1. yes 3. no

Lesson 9-4 pages 398–402
ON YOUR OWN 1. about 15 cm 3. about 6 in.
7. about 120 mi 9. 157 m 9. 402 m 11. 12 m
13. 110 ft 15. 9,995 m 17. 20 mm; 10 mm
21. 27.1 cm 23. 17.8 m 25. 0.64 yd 27. 21.9 cm
29. 6.3 m 31. about 11 times

MIXED REVIEW 33. octagon 35. pentagon
37. < 39. = 41. >

Lesson 9-5 pages 403–407
ON YOUR OWN 1. 1,133.5 cm² 3. 72.3 m²
5. about 12 in.² 7. about 300 cm²
9. about 27 mm² 11. 314.2 m² 13. 12.6 yd²
15. 706.5 in.² 17. 28.3 mm² 19. 50.2 in.²
21. 95.0 ft² 23. 60.8 cm² 25. 452.2 ft²
27. 19.6 m² 29. 6,358.5 mi² 31. 10.2 m²
33. 360 days 35. 38.5 cm² 37. 50.3 ft²
39. 3.1 mm² 41. 1,017.9 m² 43. 95.0 in.²
45. 176.7 ft² 47. 227.0 in.² 49. 1,963.5 in.²
51. 0.8 cm² 53. 66 m² 55. 19 m²
57. 12.6 units² 59. 14.3 units²

MIXED REVIEW 61. obtuse 63. acute 65. 20
67. 2.5 69. 822

Lesson 9-6 pages 408–412
ON YOUR OWN 1. triangular prism
3. hexagonal prism 13. 4; C, F, G, H
15. rectangular prism 17. sphere
19. square prism or cube 21. cylinder 25. C
MIXED REVIEW 27. some 29. all

Toolbox page 413
1. 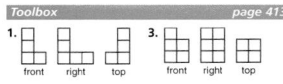 front right top 3. front right top
5. 11 or 12 cubes

Lesson 9-7 pages 414–417
ON YOUR OWN 1. 14 cm² 3. 36 cm²
5. rectangular prism; 80 cm² 7. rectangular prism;
112 cm² 9. 600 ft² 11. 150 cm² 13. 1,440 cm²
15. 132 in.² 17. B and C 19. Find the sum of the areas. Then double it.
MIXED REVIEW 23. 4.5 m × 7.5 m
25. 30 km × 50 km

Lesson 9-8 pages 418–422
ON YOUR OWN 1. A 3. 96 cm³ 5. 48 cm³
7. 27 m³ 9. 42 ft³ 11. 320 ft³ 13. $V = s^3$;
the three dimensions of a cube are the same.
15. 245 cm³ 17. 112 mm³ 19. 440 cm³ 21. C
23. 7 yd 25. 9 ft 27. 5 in.

29. 1 cm × 1 cm × 32 cm, 1 cm × 2 cm × 16 cm, 1 cm × 4 cm × 8 cm, 2 cm × 2 cm × 8 cm, 2 cm × 4 cm × 4 cm

MIXED REVIEW 35. 71 37. $7\frac{1}{4}$ 39. 28 41. 18
CHECKPOINT 1. 13 m; 12.6 m² 2. 82 in.;
530.7 in.² 3. 38 km; 113.0 km² 4. square prism
5. triangular prism 6. cube 7. square pyramid
8. 62 cm²; 30 cm³ 9. 54 cm²; 27 cm³
10. 121 cm²; 90 cm³

Problem Solving Practice page 423
1. A 3. C 5. D 7. D

Lesson 9-9 pages 424–426
ON YOUR OWN 1. right-side-up
3. 204 grapefruit 5. 64 in.; 64 in. 7a. 6 cuts
b. 27 pieces c. 1 piece 9. 1 × 1 × 12
11. 1 m × 17 m, 2 m × 16 m, 3 m × 15 m, 4 m × 14 m, 5 m × 13 m, 6 m × 12 m, 7 m × 11 m, 8 m × 10 m, 9 m × 9 m
MIXED REVIEW 13. no lines 15. 2 lines
17. $33\frac{1}{3}$%

Wrap Up pages 428–429
1. about 19 m² 2. 13.5 cm²; 22 cm 3. 34 m
4. 45.6 cm² 5. 38 in. 6. 24 m 7. 77 cm
8. 118 ft 9. 78.5 in.² 10. 530.7 m² 11. 69.4 m²
12a. square pyramid b. 5 faces; 8 edges; 5 vertices
13. A rectangular prism has six rectangular faces, with two parallel bases that are rectangular.
14. 64 m²; 28 m³ 15. B 16. 26 people

Cumulative Review page 431
1. B 3. B 5. C 7. D 9. D

CHAPTER 10

Lesson 10-1 pages 434–437
ON YOUR OWN 1. 3 5.
5. 7. -14 9. -1,565 13. -13 15. -150
15. 1 19. -8
21. -6 23. < 25. > 27. > 29. <
31. -2, -1, 3, 4 33. -5, -2, -1, 3, 4
MIXED REVIEW 41. about 452.39 mm²
43. about 95.03 in.² 45. 6:30 A.M.

Toolbox page 438
1. [number line] -2 0 2 4 3. [number line] -2 0 2 4
7. 17 9. 0 11. 180

Lesson 10-2 pages 439–441
ON YOUR OWN
1. 3. 7. 2 9. -2 11. 4
13. -4 23. 4; -4; -6
MIXED REVIEW 25. $10\frac{1}{2}$ 27. $19\frac{1}{24}$ 29. $21\frac{8}{9}$
31. 18 33. 0 35. $2\frac{3}{5}$

Lesson 10-3 pages 442–446
ON YOUR OWN 1. 6 3. -9 5. -14 7. 0
9. -5 11. -4 + (-2) = -6 13. -2 + (-8) = -10
15. -2 + 6 = 4 17. positive 19. positive
21. negative 23. -15 25. 0 27. 5 29. 7 31. 0
35. < 37. > 39. 2 floors down 41. -5 45. 5
47. 0
MIXED REVIEW 49. 6 51. 49 53. 30 55. 33.8
57. 98.7 59. 36 bottles
CHECKPOINT 1. < 2. > 3. < 4. > 5. <
6. [number line] -8 -6 -4 -2 0 2 7. 1
8. 14. -5
15. 2 16. 0
17. -12
18. 3

Problem Solving Practice page 447
1. B 3. A 5. D 7. D

Lesson 10-4 pages 448–452
ON YOUR OWN 1. -1 - 2 = -3 3. -2 - (-6) =
4 5. -5 7. 4 9. 4 11. -3 13. 6 15. -13
17. 15 19. -8 21. -21 23. -8 25. 4 27. 0
29. -10 31. = 33. = 35. > 37. 9 P.M., New Year's Eve 39. 10:15 A.M. 41. -8, -13, -18
43. 0, 3, 6
MIXED REVIEW 49. 5 51. Valli 53. $1\frac{3}{5}$ 55. $\frac{9}{100}$
57. $2\frac{1}{8}$ 59. 21 students

Toolbox page 453
1. 1 3. 4 5. 2 7. -2 9. -3 11. -1
13. 2 15. 0

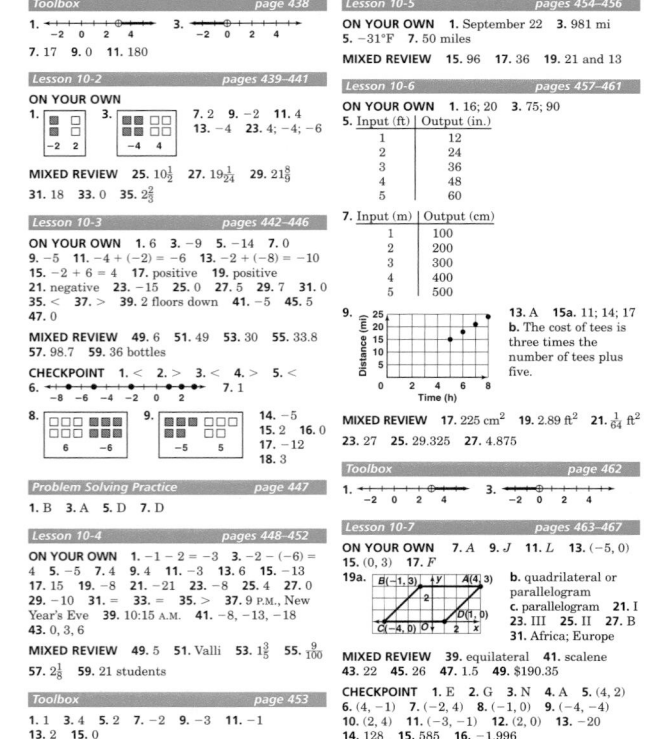

Lesson 10-5 pages 454–456
ON YOUR OWN 1. September 22 3. 981 mi
5. -31°F 7. 50 miles
MIXED REVIEW 15. 96 17. 36 19. 21 and 13

Lesson 10-6 pages 457–461
ON YOUR OWN 1. 16; 20 3. 75; 90
5.

Input (ft)	Output (in.)
1	12
2	24
3	36
4	48
5	60

7.

Input (m)	Output (cm)
1	100
2	200
3	300
4	400
5	500

9. 13. A 15a. 11; 14; 17
b. The cost of tees is three times the number of tees plus five.
MIXED REVIEW 17. 225 cm² 19. 2.89 ft² 21. $\frac{1}{64}$ ft²
23. 27 25. 29.325 27. 4.875

Toolbox page 462
1. [number line] -2 0 2 4 3. [number line] -2 0 2 4

Lesson 10-7 pages 463–467
ON YOUR OWN 7. A 9. J 11. L 13. (-5, 0)
15. (0, 3)
19a. [graph] B(-1, 3), A(4, 3), C(-4, 0), D(1, 0)
b. quadrilateral or parallelogram
c. parallelogram 21. I
23. III 25. II 27. B
31. Africa; Europe
MIXED REVIEW 39. equilateral 41. scalene
43. 22 45. 26 47. 1.5 49. $190.35
CHECKPOINT 1. E 2. G 3. N 4. A 5. (4, 2)
6. (4, -1) 7. (-2, 4) 8. (-1, 0) 9. (-4, -4)
10. (2, 4) 11. (-3, -1) 12. (2, 0) 13. -20
14. 128 15. 585 16. -1,996

Lesson 10-8 pages 468–472
ON YOUR OWN 1. 193 3. -1,110 5. 22
7. -1,118 9. -7 11. 47 13. 0 15. -200
23a. $9; $18; -$9; $17; -$12; -$1; -$17
b. 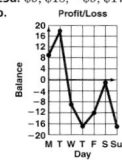 Profit/Loss
25. = B2 + C2; = B3 + C3; = B4 + C4; = B5 + C5 27. -$2,256; $984; $194; -$1,196; $15,931; -$18,205; -$2,274
MIXED REVIEW 31. 1 33. 3 35. 8 m
37a. $1,946.80 b. $1,357.45

Wrap Up pages 474–475
1. -7 2a. 7 b. -1 c. 8 d. 14 e. -89 f. 100
5. > 6. > 7. < 8. < 9. < 10. -1 11. 3
12. 1 13. 2 14. 5 15. -7 16. 8 17. -10
18. 0 19. 2 20. -14 21. 12 22. -10 23. 4
24a.

Input (min)	Output (dollars)
1	$.10
2	$.20
3	$.30

25. C 26. G 27. N
28. A 29. H 30. K
31. (-3, -2)
32. (1, -3)
33. (0, -4) 34. (-2, 2)
35. (4, 0) 36. (-1, -4)
b. 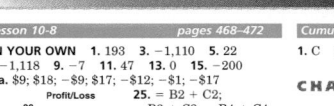 Cost of Telephone Calls
37. $486; $2,000; -$266; $673
38. 12 NOON
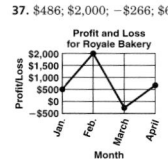 Profit and Loss for Royale Bakery

Cumulative Review page 477
1. C 3. B 5. C 7. C 9. D 11. D

CHAPTER 11

Lesson 11-1 pages 480–484
ON YOUR OWN 1. equally likely to be red or blue
3. probably fair 5. RB, RY, BY 7. 1H, 1T, 2H, 2T, 3H, 3T, 4H, 4T 9c. Yes; the outcomes are equally likely. 11a. $\frac{1}{10}$ b. $\frac{3}{10}$ c. 0 d. $\frac{1}{15}$ e. $\frac{1}{30}$
f. 0 13. Unfair; only 15 of the 36 outcomes are prime.
MIXED REVIEW 15. 150 in.² 17. 672 in.² 19. >
21. > 23. <

Lesson 11-2 pages 485–487
ON YOUR OWN 5. $766.50 7. no 9. 60 cm
MIXED REVIEW 11. -11 13. 20 15. -13
17. 25.41 cm² 19. Susan: 11 pairs, Deepa: 22 pairs

Lesson 11-3 pages 488–491
ON YOUR OWN 5. Yes, the answers are affected by the order of the numbers.
MIXED REVIEW 15. 60 m; 284 m² 17. 116 mm;
1,075 mm² 19. -20 21. -11 23. -14

Lesson 11-4 pages 492–496
ON YOUR OWN 1. $\frac{1}{6}$; 0.16; 16% 3. $\frac{5}{6}$; 0.8$\overline{3}$; 83%
5. $\frac{1}{3}$; 0.$\overline{3}$; 33% 7. $\frac{9}{11}$ 9. $\frac{1}{10}$; 0.1; 10%
15. $\frac{1}{2}$; 0.5; 50% 17. $\frac{3}{10}$; 0.3; 30% 19a. $\frac{5}{8}$ 23. $\frac{5}{8}$
25. 0 27. $\frac{7}{10}$ 29. likely 31. certain
MIXED REVIEW 35. 51 m; 140 m² 37. 18 in.;
20.25 in.²
CHECKPOINT 1a. $\frac{1}{5}$; 0.2; 20% b. $\frac{3}{5}$; 0.6; 60%
c. $\frac{2}{5}$; 0.4; 40% 2a. $\frac{7}{15}$ b. $\frac{8}{15}$ c. Probably yes; the experimental probabilities of winning are fairly close. 3. B

Toolbox page 497
1. $\frac{1}{6}$ 3. $\frac{1}{3}$ 5. $\frac{2}{3}$ 7. $\frac{7}{10}$ 9. $\frac{2}{5}$ 11. $1\frac{1}{6}$ 13. $\frac{1}{10}$
15a. 1 b. true c. $\frac{3}{8}$

Lesson 11-5 — pages 498–501

ON YOUR OWN
1. 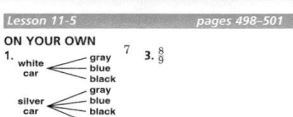 7 3. $\frac{8}{9}$

5. 9 days 7. 20 pairs 9a. 27 outcomes
b. 12 outcomes c. standard keyboard with 15-in. monitor and inkjet printer; adjustable keyboard with 19-in. monitor and laser printer; $568–$2,348

MIXED REVIEW
11.
13. $f(x) = 1,000x$
15. 180 newspapers

Lesson 11-6 — pages 502–506

ON YOUR OWN 1. Dependent; the second outcome depends on the first. 3. Independent; the second outcome does not depend on the first. 5. Independent; the second outcome does not depend on the first. 9. Yes; the outcome of the second spin does not depend on the first.

11. $\frac{4}{25}$ 13. $\frac{1}{4}$ 15. $\frac{1}{3}$ 17. 0 19. $\frac{1}{10}$

21a. 2 outcomes b. 6 outcomes c. 12 outcomes
d. 72 outcomes

MIXED REVIEW 23. 36 cm 25. 85 mm 27. 51 ft
29. 63°, 153° 31. 28°, 118° 33. 3°, 93°
35. 12-in. × 12-in. sheets

Lesson 11-7 — pages 507–510

ON YOUR OWN 1. yes; AIM
3. 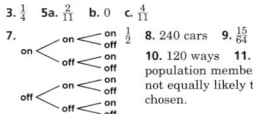 5. 120 orders
7. 720 ways 9. 720 ways
11. 40,320
13. 6,227,020,800
15a. 5,040 ways b. $\frac{1}{5,040}$

MIXED REVIEW 17. 412 m² 25. 1 h

CHECKPOINT
1a. 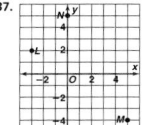 b. $\frac{1}{6}$ 2. 12 meals 3. $\frac{16}{49}$
4. 720 ways

Problem Solving Practice — page 511

1. A 3. D 5. D 7. C 9. B

Lesson 11-8 — pages 512–516

ON YOUR OWN 1. honesty 3. Yes; probably; a random sample is usually representative. 5. No; no; the sample is biased toward high school students and teachers. 7. Answers may vary. Sample: The whole population is usually too large. 9. No; they were all in close contact with each other. 13. 192 computer chips 15. 2,240 pairs of jeans 17. about 14,118 oz

MIXED REVIEW 19. 300 cm³ 21. 160 cm³
23. −64 25. 203 27. $\frac{1}{2}$ mi

Wrap Up — pages 518–519

1a.

	1	2	3	4	5	6
1	2	3	4	5	6	7
2	3	4	5	6	7	8
3	4	5	6	7	8	9
4	5	6	7	8	9	10
5	6	7	8	9	10	11
6	7	8	9	10	11	12

b. Fair; the number of even sums equals the number of odd sums. 2a. $\frac{3}{10}, \frac{7}{10}$ b. Probably unfair; one player seems more likely to win.

3. $\frac{1}{4}$ 5a. $\frac{2}{11}$ b. 0 c. $\frac{4}{11}$

7. on $\frac{1}{2}$ 8. 240 cars 9. $\frac{15}{64}$
10. 120 ways 11. No; the population members are not equally likely to be chosen.

Cumulative Review — page 521

1. B 3. D 5. A 7. D 9. C 11. B

EXTRA PRACTICE

CHAPTER 1
1.

Books Read Each Month	Frequency
4	4
3	2
2	3
1	3

Books Read Each Month

```
X   X   X
X   X   X
X   X   X
X   X   X
1   2   3   4
```

3. 21; 23; 22 5. 32; United States won 32 silver medals. 9. bar graph

CHAPTER 2 1. 81, 100, 121; square numbers
3. 9, 11, 13; add 2 5. 23, 27, 31; add 4 7. 21
9. 29 11. 9 13. 5 15. 49 17. 0 19. 200
21. 13 23. 67 25. 2p 27. x + 3 29. $\frac{6}{2}$ 31. 19
33. 110 35. 28 37. 34 39. 7 41. 9 43. 17.8
45. 16 47. 200

CHAPTER 3 1. eight tenths 3. twelve hundredths 5. seven hundredths 7. 3,040
9. 66.07 11. 0.222 13. thousandths
15. ten-thousandths 17. > 19. < 21. 2.3
23. 2.68 25. 0.2 27. 3,356.8 29. 14.534
31. 10.43 33. 1.489 35. 48 mm; 4.8 cm
37a. centimeters b. kilometers c. 1 h 30 min
39. 6 h 38 min 41. 1 h 37 min

CHAPTER 4 1. 28 3. 48 5. 150 7. 2 9. 57
11. 123 13. 135 15. 256 17. (7 × 70) + (7 × 8) = 546 19. (6 × 60) + (6 × 6) = 396 21. 1.4 23. 2
25. 91.8 27. 1.4 29. 1.54 31. 2 33. 4 35. 1.68
37. 9.2 39. 56 41. 0.51 43. 3.5 45. 2.4

CHAPTER 5 1. 2, 3, 9 3. 2, 3, 5, 9, 10 5. none
7. composite 9. prime 11. prime 13. 10 15. 5
17. 9

19.

21.

25. $\frac{1}{10}$ 27. $\frac{3}{4}$ 29. $\frac{2}{3}$ 31. $3\frac{4}{7}$ 33. $2\frac{2}{5}$ 35. $3\frac{1}{2}$
37. $\frac{15}{8}$ 39. $\frac{100}{9}$ 41. $\frac{81}{8}$ 43. 8 45. 75 47. 12
49. < 51. = 53. < 55. $\frac{4}{9}, \frac{4}{5}, \frac{4}{7}$ 57. $\frac{7}{12}, \frac{2}{3}, \frac{5}{6}$
59. $2\frac{1}{8}, 2\frac{1}{2}, 2\frac{3}{4}$ 61. $0.\overline{6}$ 63. 0.4 65. 0.5

CHAPTER 6 1. $\frac{1}{2}$ 3. 6 5. $\frac{3}{4}$ 7. $\frac{1}{2}$ 9. $1\frac{1}{2}$
11. $1\frac{9}{40}$ 13. $8\frac{1}{6}$ 15. $17\frac{7}{12}$ 17. $5\frac{17}{24}$ 19. $5\frac{11}{15}$

21. $\frac{1}{3}$ 23. $\frac{1}{15}$ 25. $2\frac{1}{6}$ 27. 24 29. 20 31. $45\frac{3}{5}$
33. $52\frac{1}{12}$ 35. $122\frac{5}{8}$ 37. 2.5 39. $3\frac{3}{8}$ 41. 80
43. $2\frac{1}{5}$ 45. 12 47. 8 49. 160 51. 32 53. $1\frac{3}{4}$
55. 13

CHAPTER 7 1. 2 to 3, 2 : 3, $\frac{2}{3}$ 3. 1 to 2 5. 1 to 4
7. 1 : 4 9. 128 11. 90 13. 2 15. 9 17. 60
19. 6 cm × 15 cm 21. 20 km × 50 km
23. 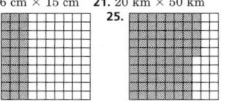 25.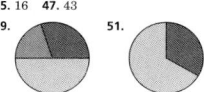

29. 40% 31. 90% 33. 30% 35. 0.96, $\frac{24}{25}$
37. 0.01, $\frac{1}{100}$ 39. 0.88, $\frac{22}{25}$ 41. 42 43. 17
45. 16 47. 43

49. 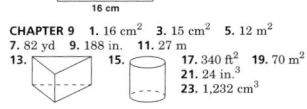 51.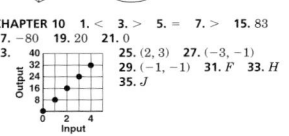

CHAPTER 8 1. 180° 7. 37° 9. 72° 11. isosceles
13. scalene 15. right 17. all 19. no
21.

4.5 cm
12 cm
23. 48 in. 25. 1.5 m

6 cm
16 cm

CHAPTER 9 1. 16 cm² 3. 15 cm² 5. 12 m²
7. 82 yd 9. 188 in. 11. 27 m
13. 15. 17. 340 ft² 19. 70 m²
21. 24 in.³
23. 1,232 cm³

CHAPTER 10 1. < 3. > 5. = 7. > 15. 83
17. −80 19. 20 21. 0
23.

25. (2, 3) 27. (−3, −1)
29. (−1, −1) 31. F 33. H
35. J

37.

CHAPTER 11 1. Fair game; the chances of rolling even (2, 4, 6) or odd (1, 3, 5) are equally likely.

3a. 30%, $\frac{3}{10}$ b. 10%, $\frac{1}{10}$ 5a. $\frac{1}{12}$ b. $\frac{1}{4}$ 7. 120
9. 2 11. 6 13. 40,320 15. 5,040
17. representative

SKILLS HANDBOOK

PAGE 535 1. ten millions 3. hundred millions
5. hundred billions 7. 3 ten million
9. 6 hundred million 11. 9 hundred billion
13. 6 hundred 15. 6 hundred thousand
17. 6 ten 19. 6 hundred thousand
21. 6 ten billion 23. 6 thousand
25. 6 hundred thousand 27. 6 ten

PAGE 536 1. 7; 360; 900 3. 67; 13; 5
5. 232,000,753,000 7. 321,029 9. 322,000,135
11. 5,004,012,000

PAGE 537 1. > 3. > 5. < 7. < 9. > 11. <
13. > 15. 1,367; 1,374; 1,437; 1,747 17. 9,789;

9,897; 9,987 19. 17,414; 17,444; 17,671; 18,242
21. < < 23. > <

PAGE 538 1. 76 3. 41 5. 144 7. 393 9. 279
11. 564 13. 2,894 15. 6,754 17. 7,149 19. 134
21. 176 23. 757 25. 132 27. 100 29. 907
31. 2,759 33. 9,252 35. 16,298

PAGE 539 1. 44 3. 22 5. 21 7. 469 9. 175
11. 230 13. 6,828 15. 5,100 17. 3,525 19. 59
21. 463 23. 785 25. 226 27. 602 29. 419
31. 99 33. 176

PAGE 540 1. 243 3. 348 5. 304 7. 3,390
9. 1,304 11. 4,320 13. 1,150 15. 496 17. 3,192
19. 315 21. 852 23. 6,057 25. 246 27. 252
29. 304 31. 3,038 33. 6,622 35. 2,215 37. 414

PAGE 541 1. 4 R1 3. 5 R1 5. 4 R2 7. 13 R5
9. 20 R2 11. 12 R5 13. 16 R2 15. 19 17. 104 R5
19. 116 R1 21. 193 23. 42 25. 134

PAGE 542 1. 30 R2 3. 90 R1 5. 80 R3 7. 70 R5
9. 20 R14 11. 70 R2 13. 60 R1 15. 40 R5
17. 503 19. 420 R2 21. 80 R8 23. 40 R17
25. 20 R46

PAGE 543 1. 2.5 3. 89 5. 0.108 7. 0.00014
9. 0.0014 11. 4.05 13. 0.8 15. 68.9 17. 0.0009
19. 0.666 21. 12 23. 20 25. 40 27. 100

PAGE 544 1. 36.8° C 3. 38.4° C 5. 96.6° F
7. G 9. F 11. W

PAGE 545 1. 11 3. 45 5. 29 7. 1,056 9. 454
11. XV 13. MDCXXXII 15. CLIX 17. XCII
19. MMXD

Additional Answers

CHAPTER 1

LESSON 1-1

pages 6–7   On Your Own

2.

Number of Letters	Frequency
2	2
3	12
4	3
5	3
6	3
7	2

9.

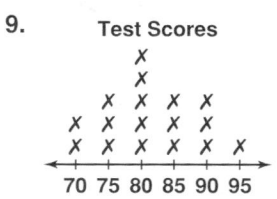

Test Scores

10.

Heights of Plants (inches)

11.

Speeds of Runners (mi/h)

12.

Shoe Sizes

21a.

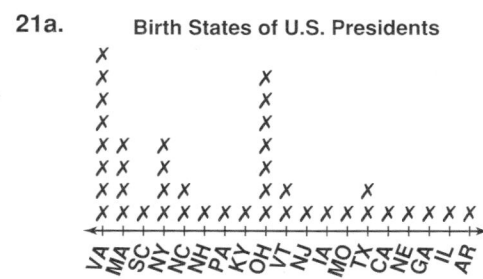

Birth States of U.S. Presidents

LESSON 1-2

pages 9–10   On Your Own

13.

Student Heights (inches)

LESSON 1-6

pages 29–31   On Your Own

8a.

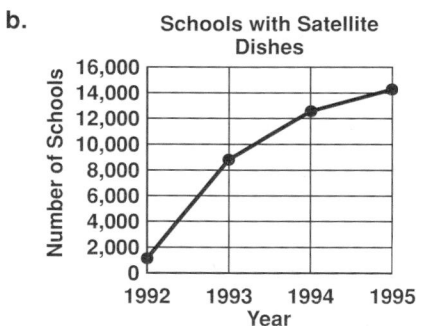

Schools with CD-ROMs

b.

Schools with Satellite Dishes

10.

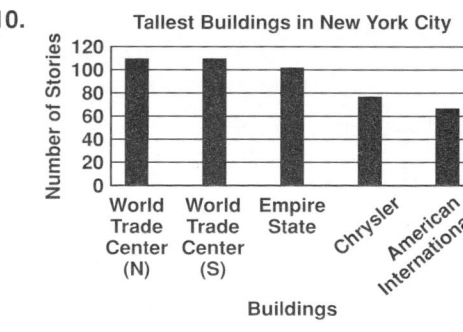

Tallest Buildings in New York City

11.

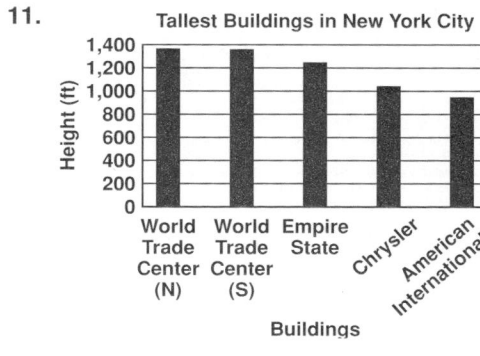

Tallest Buildings in New York City

24b.

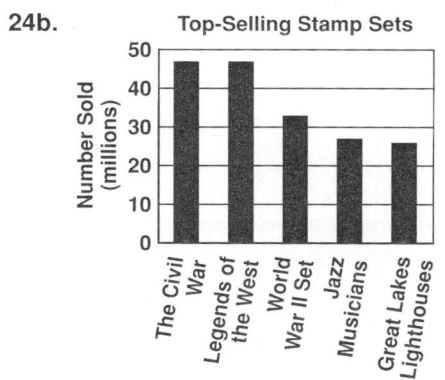

Top-Selling Stamp Sets

25a.

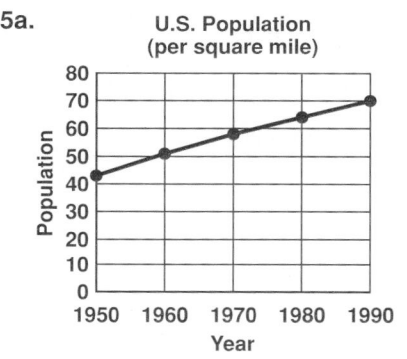

U.S. Population (per square mile)

b.

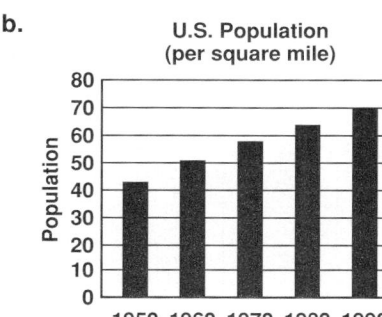
U.S. Population (per square mile)

26.
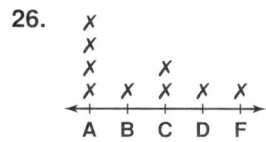
A B C D F

27.
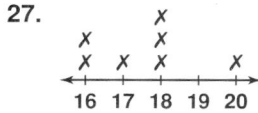
16 17 18 19 20

28.
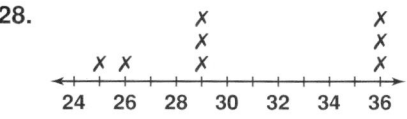
24 26 28 30 32 34 36

29.
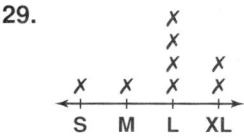
S M L XL

30.
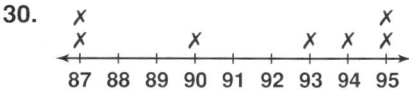
87 88 89 90 91 92 93 94 95

31.
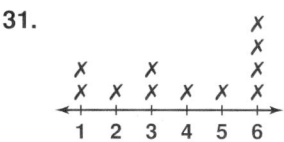
1 2 3 4 5 6

page 31   Checkpoint

2.
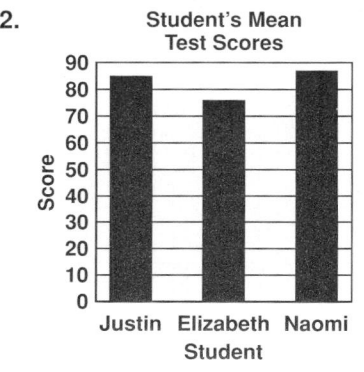
Student's Mean Test Scores

LESSON 1-7

pages 34–36   On Your Own

10.
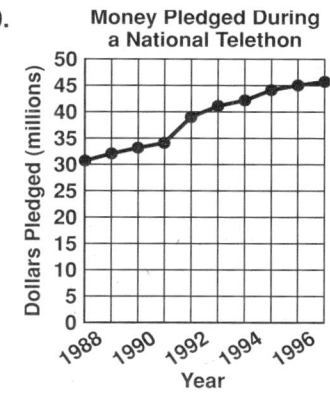
Money Pledged During a National Telethon

11.
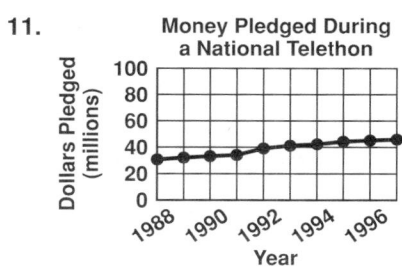
Money Pledged During a National Telethon

12. Use a gap in the scale to show that the amount increased greatly. Use a wide range and more horizontal space between data points to show that the amount increased little.

pages 38–39   Wrap Up

1.

Vowel	Frequency
a	22
e	26
i	10
o	9
u	5

2.
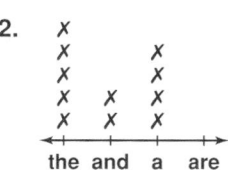
the and a are

19.
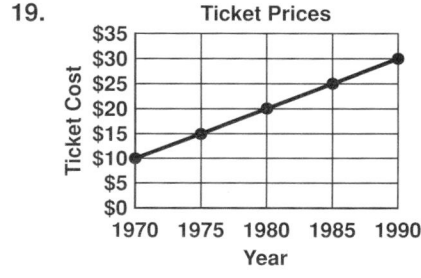
Ticket Prices

20.
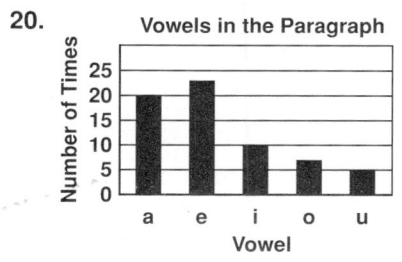
Vowels in the Paragraph

page 40   Assessment

1a.

People in Family	Frequency
1	3
2	3
3	5
4	2
5	1
6	1

b.
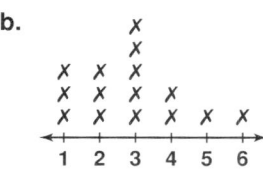
1 2 3 4 5 6

8a.
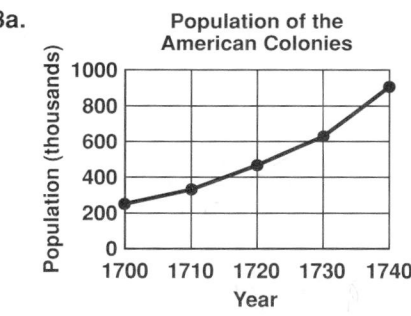
Population of the American Colonies

CHAPTER 2

LESSON 2-1

pages 44–45   Think and Discuss

1a.
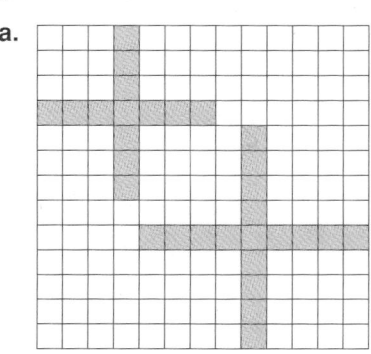

Additional Answers

c. The sixth design is a cross with 1 square at the center and 5 squares in each arm.

page 45   Work Together

5b. Start with 10 and add 5 repeatedly; start with 1.2 and add 0.6 repeatedly.

d.

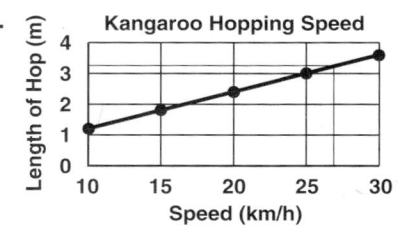

about 3.2 m

pages 46–47   On Your Own

4.

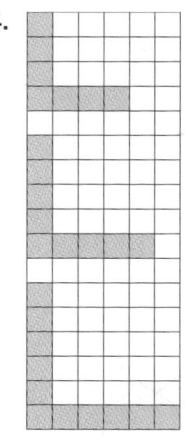

page 47   Mixed Review

27.

Ages	Frequency
8	1
9	3
10	1
11	1
12	1
13	1
15	2
16	1
20	1

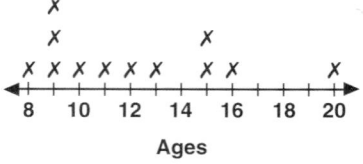

28.

Points	Frequency
8.1	1
8.4	2
8.5	3
8.6	1
8.8	1
9	2

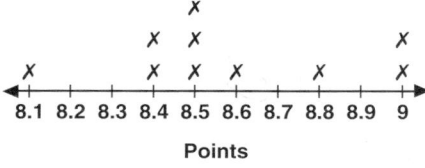

LESSON 2-7

page 80   Assessment

2. Start with 6 and add 4 repeatedly.

3. Start with 64 and divide by 2 repeatedly.

4. Start with 78 and subtract 9 repeatedly.

5. Start with 4 and multiply by 3 repeatedly.

CHAPTER 3

LESSON 3-1

pages 84–85   Think and Discuss

5.

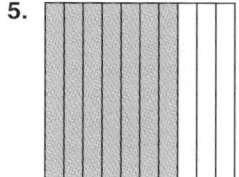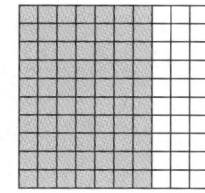

page 85   Work Together

10.

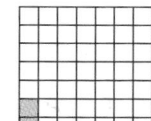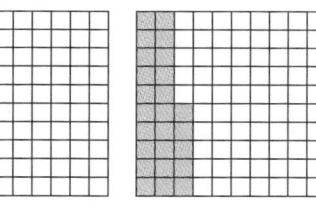

0.05; 0.25

LESSON 3-3

pages 92–93   Think and Discuss

1.

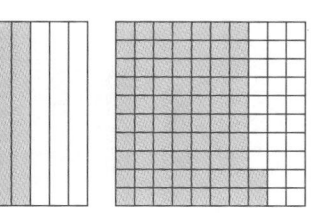

pages 94–95   On Your Own

1.

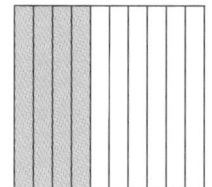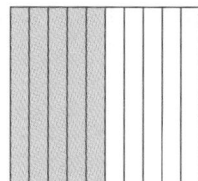

2.

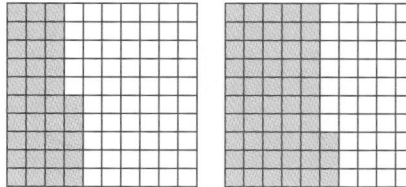

3.

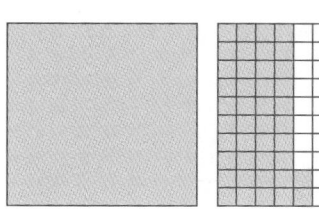

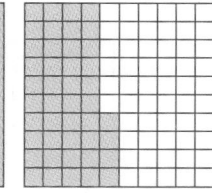

4.

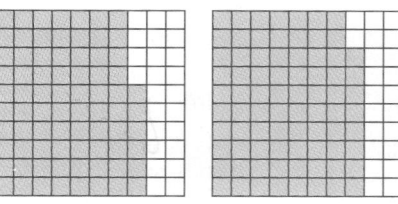

5.

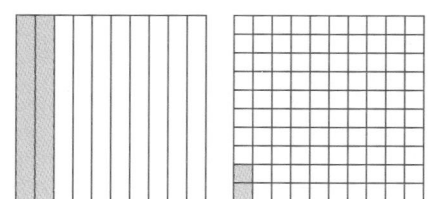

LESSON 3-5

page 99 Work Together

3.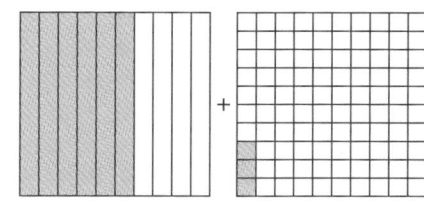

4.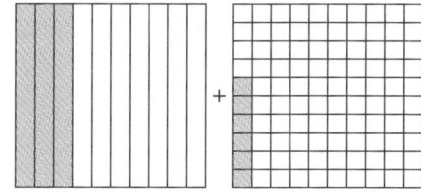

pages 99–100 Think and Discuss

6c.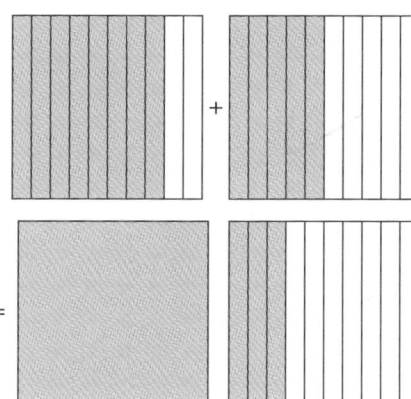

pages 101–102 On Your Own

33.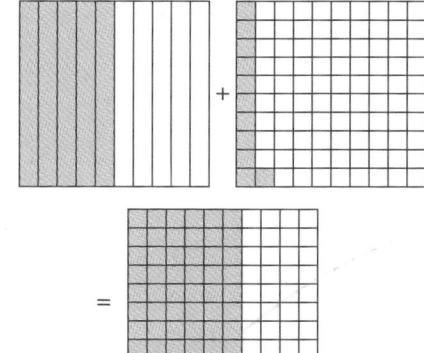

$$0.5 + 0.11 = 0.61$$

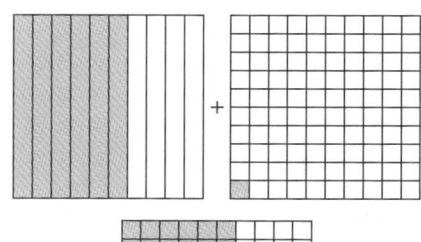

$$0.6 + 0.01 = 0.61$$

LESSON 3-10

page 123 Work Together

4. Clock 3
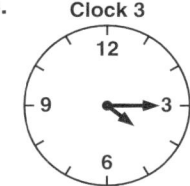

5. Clock 4

pages 123–125 Think and Discuss

6. 80 min; 4800 s; 1 h is 60 min, so 1 h 20 min = 60 min + 20 min. 1 min = 60 s, so 80 min = 80 × 60 s.

page 126 Mixed Review

30.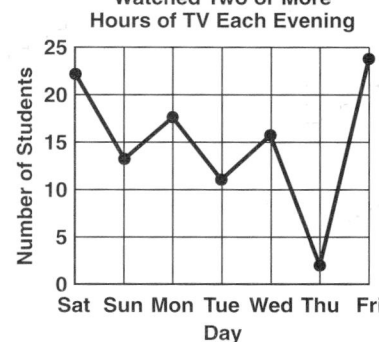

Number of Students Who Watched Two or More Hours of TV Each Evening

page 130 Assessment

1. One hundredth is equivalent to ten thousandths, so thirteen hundredths is equivalent to 13 × 10 = 130 thousandths.

6.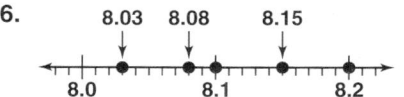

12.

Time	Activity
9:35 A.M.	Shower and dress
10:10 A.M.	Eat breakfast
10:35 A.M.	Do chores
12:15 P.M.	Get beach supplies
12:40 P.M.	Bike to party

CHAPTER 4

LESSON 4-4

pages 149–150 On Your Own

32. Answers may vary. Sample: Draw two squares with 10 rows and 10 columns each. Shade in red all the columns in the first square and two columns of the second square. Shade in blue four of the ten rows in both squares. Count the number of purple squares.

33.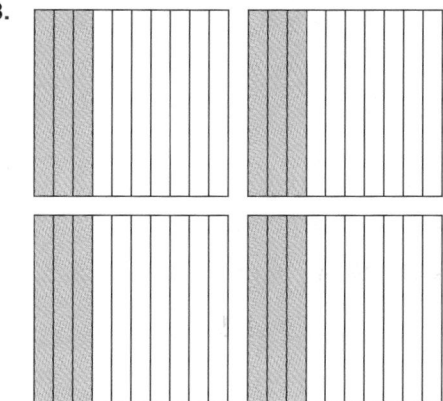

LESSON 4-6

pages 157–158 Think and Discuss

3a.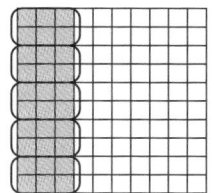

b.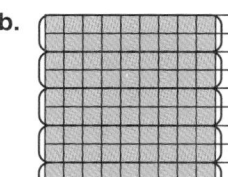

Additional Answers

c.

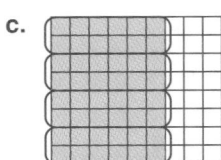

5.

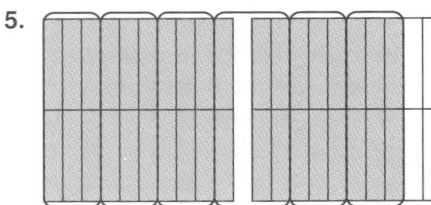

6.

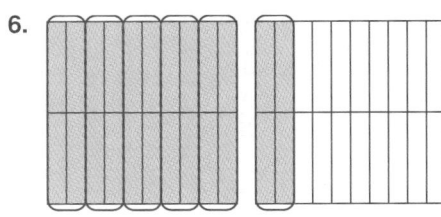

7.

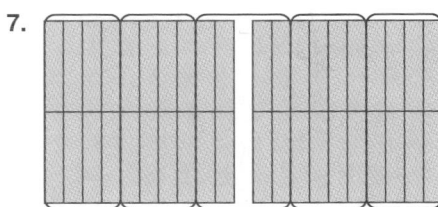

LESSON 4-7

pages 161–162   On Your Own

32. Check students' work. Sample: Measure 1 cm worth of pages; count pages; divide 1 cm by the number of pages.

33. Answers may vary. Sample: When dividing decimals, you must correctly place the decimal point in the quotient.

CHAPTER 5

LESSON 5-1

page 182   Work Together

1a. Answers may vary. Sample: One number is *divisible* by another if the first number can be divided by the second with no remainder.

c. Answers may vary. Sample: A number is divisible by 2 if its last digit is 0, 2, 4, 6, or 8.

pages 183–184   On Your Own

28. Answers may vary. Sample: Divide the two numbers on the calculator. If the result is an integer, then the first number is divisible by the second; mental math is easier to find divisibility by 2, 3, 5, 9, or 10.

29b. Answers may vary. Sample: To check if a decimal is divisible by 3 or 9, ignore the decimal point and check if the sum of the digits is divisible by 3 or 9. 1.05 is divisible by 3 but not 9, and 1 + 0 + 5 = 6 is divisible by 3 but not 9. 56.61 is divisible by 9, and 5 + 6 + 6 + 1 = 18 is divisible by 9.

LESSON 5-4

pages 193–194   Think and Discuss

2.

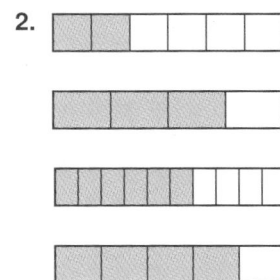

pages 194–195   On Your Own

7.
8.
9.
10.
11.
12.
13.
14.
15.
16.

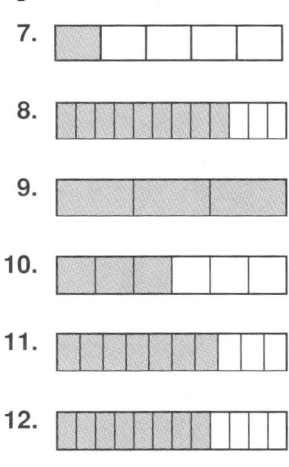

17.
18.

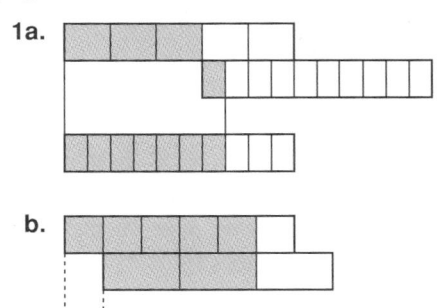

LESSON 5-10

pages 222–223   Wrap Up

26. The GCF is the product of all the prime factors the given numbers have in common. The LCM is the product of the highest power of each prime factor among all the given numbers. Examples may vary.

CHAPTER 6

LESSON 6-3

pages 236–237   Think and Discuss

1a.

b.

c.

d.

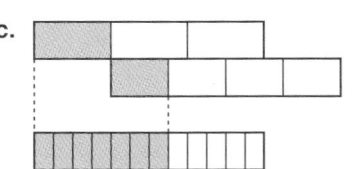

pages 238–239   On Your Own

12.

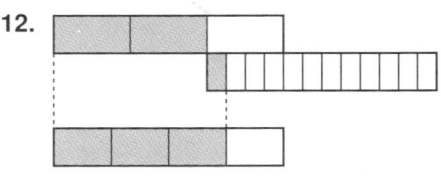

13.

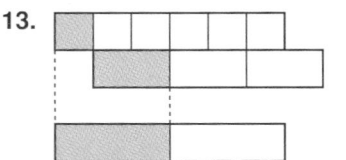

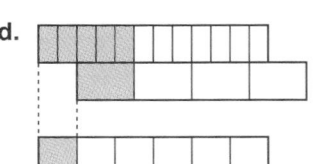

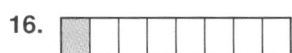

14.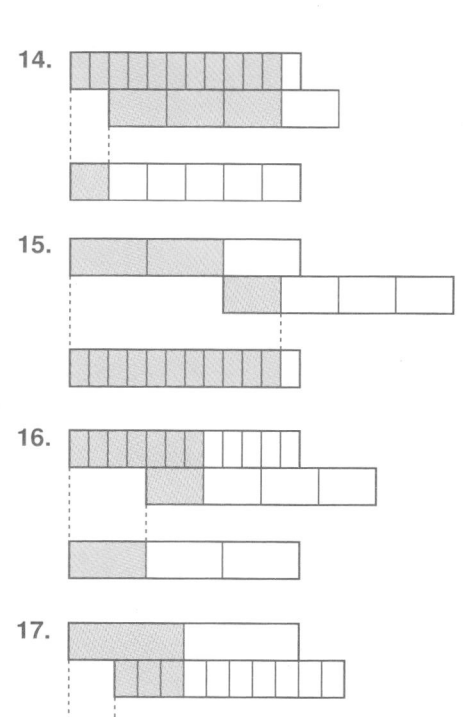

15.

16.

17.

LESSON 6-6

pages 251–252 On Your Own

4.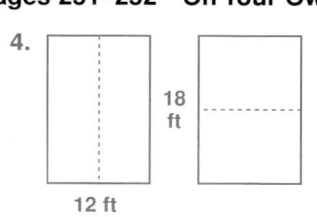

18
ft

12 ft

page 252 Mixed Review

11.

Known Species

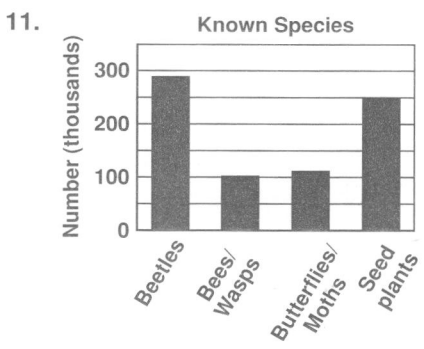

Number (thousands)

300

200

100

0

Beetles | Bees/Wasps | Butterflies/Moths | Seed plants

page 274 Assessment

2a.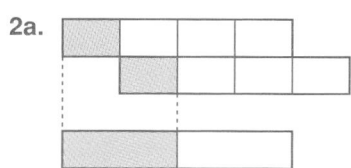

---

b.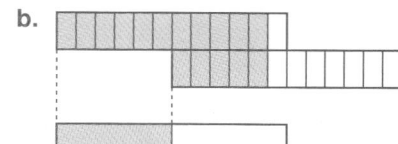

6. Add numbers with like denominators first: $3\frac{1}{4} + 5\frac{3}{4} = 9$ **and** $2\frac{2}{3} + 1\frac{1}{3} = 4.$ **Then add** $9 + 4.$ **The sum is 13.**

CHAPTER 7

LESSON 7-1

pages 278–279 Think and Discuss

5.

6.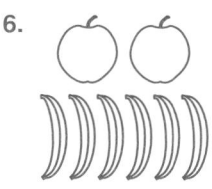

7.

8.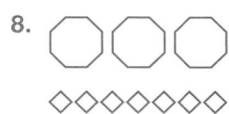

9.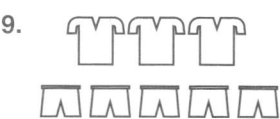

10.

22. For each 1 c of water use 2 c of vinegar to make pickles.

23. Each arrangement has 6 red roses and 1 white rose.

24. Jose always buys 2 bags of dog food and 3 bags of cat food for his pets.

25. Xing brought 3 apricots and 1 kiwi for lunch.

26. Replace every 10 pennies with 1 dime.

27. Mix 3 c of milk with 5 c of flour.

LESSON 7-6

pages 298–299 On Your Own

1.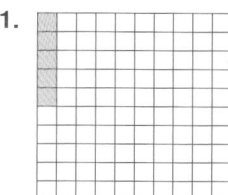

2.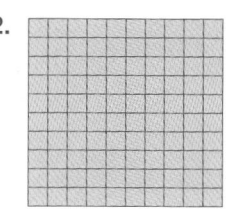

3.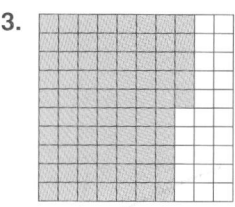

4.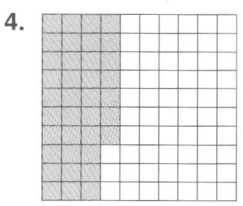

5.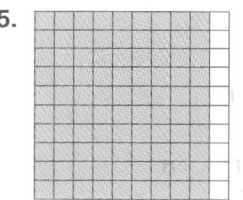

6.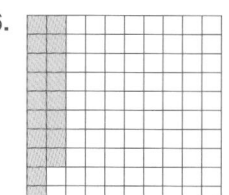

Additional Answers

LESSON 7-7

page 300   Work Together

1a–d.

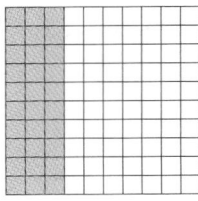

$30\% = \frac{3}{10} = 0.3$

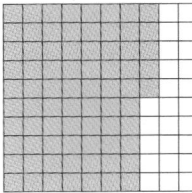

$75\% = \frac{3}{4} = 0.75$

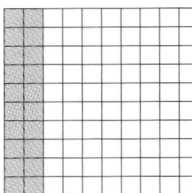

$20\% = \frac{1}{5} = 0.2$

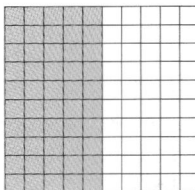

$50\% = \frac{1}{2} = 0.5$

pages 302–303   On Your Own

1.

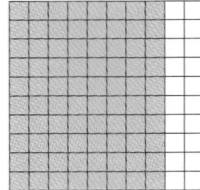

2.

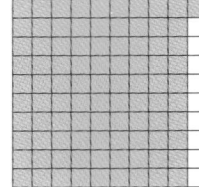

3.

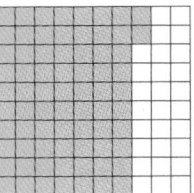

4.

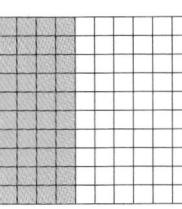

5.

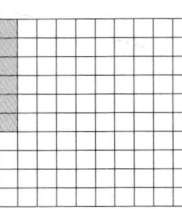

6.

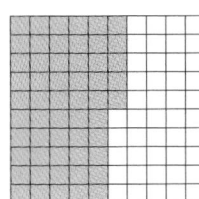

LESSON 7-10

pages 315–316 Think and Discuss

9.

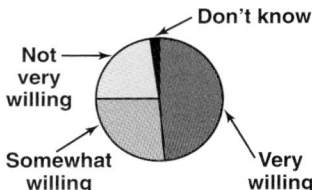

What Teen Drivers Will Do for Air Quality: Carpool More Often

pages 316–317   On Your Own

19.

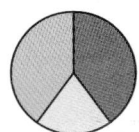

20.

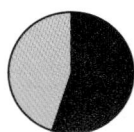

21.

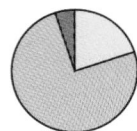

22.

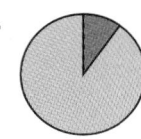

23.

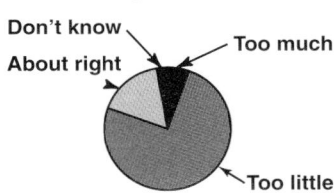

Reading for Pleasure

27.

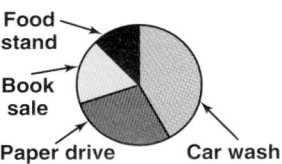

Money Raised from La Monte Middle School Fundraisers

28a. Estimates may vary slightly. Sample: toys—34%; health foods—3%; breakfast foods—23%; snacks and drinks—19%; fast foods—6%; other products—17%

b. toys—33.7%; health foods—2.8%; breakfast foods—22.5%; snacks and drinks—18.4%; fast foods—5.7%; other products—16.9%

30.

page 320–321   Wrap Up

38.

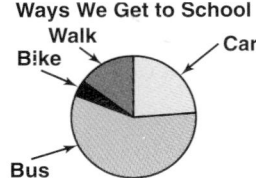

Ways We Get to School

page 322 Assessment

11a.
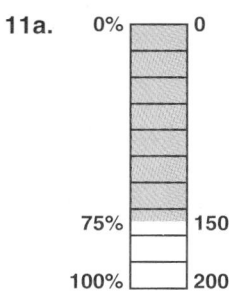

b.
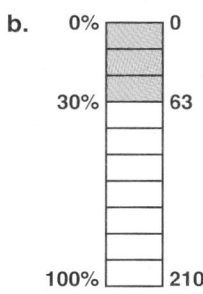

13. Favorite Types of Books
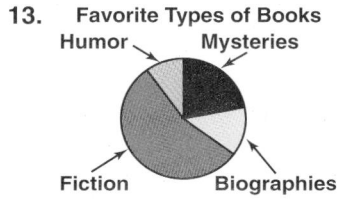

CHAPTER 8

LESSON 8-3

pages 338–339   On Your Own

11. $\angle 2$ and $\angle 5$, $\angle 3$ and $\angle 7$, $\angle 4$ and $\angle 6$, $\angle 8$ and $\angle 9$, $\angle 10$ and $\angle 11$; $\angle 3$ and $\angle 8$, $\angle 3$ and $\angle 9$, $\angle 7$ and $\angle 8$, $\angle 7$ and $\angle 9$; $\angle 4$ and $\angle 10$, $\angle 4$ and $\angle 11$, $\angle 6$ and $\angle 10$, $\angle 6$ and $\angle 11$

LESSON 8-7

pages 353–354   Think and Discuss

6b. 28 students do not earn money; in the rectangle outside all the circles; to show that 28 students do not baby-sit, run paper routes, do yard work, or work in an office

7.
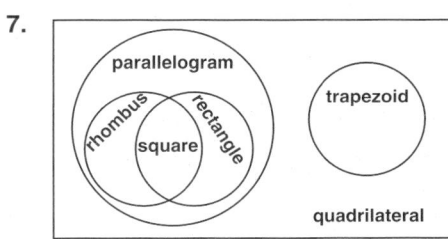

page 378   Assessment

1.
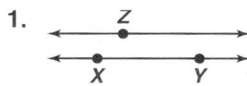

5. 3 diagonals; 4 diagonals; 97 diagonals; the number of diagonals that can be drawn from one vertex is the number of sides of the polygon minus 3, one for each of the two adjacent vertices to which there is no diagonal and one for the vertex from which the diagonals are drawn.

6. Answers may vary. Samples: Triangle AOB is isosceles. $\angle A$ and $\angle B$ are congruent. The radius perpendicular to $\overline{AB}$ bisects $\overline{AB}$, is an angle bisector of $\angle AOB$, and divides the triangle into two congruent right triangles.

10. Answers may vary. Samples are given.

a.
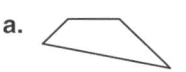

b.
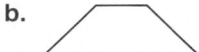

c.
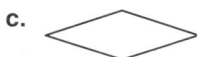

d.

11.
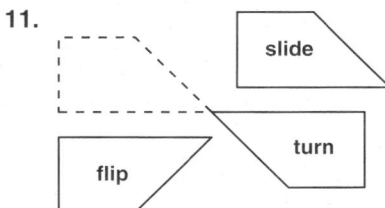

CHAPTER 9

LESSON 9-1

pages 384–385   On Your Own

14
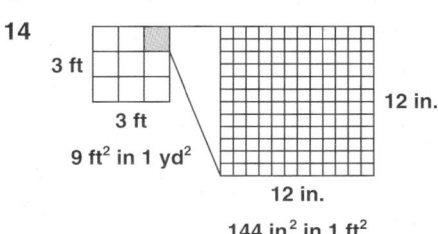

CHAPTER 10

LESSON 10-2

pages 440–441   On Your Own

1.
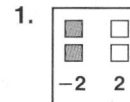

2.
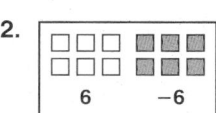

3.
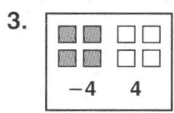

4.
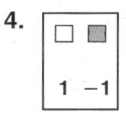

5.
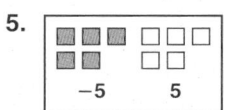

6.
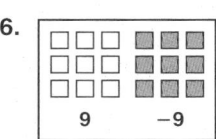

15. Different colored tiles represent positive and negative integers. Each yellow tile represents a positive unit. Each red tile represents a negative unit. To find the number represented by a set of tiles, subtract the number of red tiles from the number of yellow tiles. For example, 3 yellow and 5 red tiles represent $3 - 5 = -2$.

16.
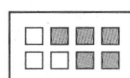

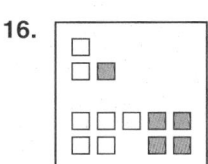

17.
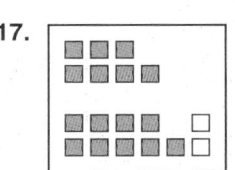

Additional Answers

18.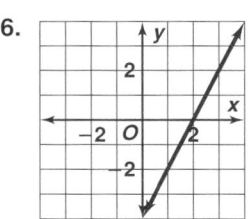

19.

20.

21.

page 462   Math Toolbox

11.

12.

13.

14.

15.

16.

pages 474–475   Wrap Up

24b.
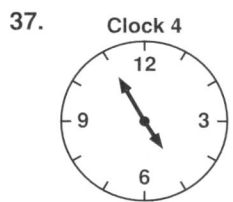
Cost of Telephone Calls

Extend the graph to include 8 min on the horizontal axis. Go up until you reach the graph. Go left to find the cost on the vertical axis.

37.   Clock 4
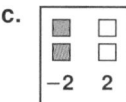

page 476   Assessment

3a.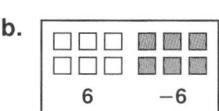

b.

c.

d.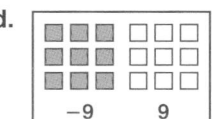

8b.
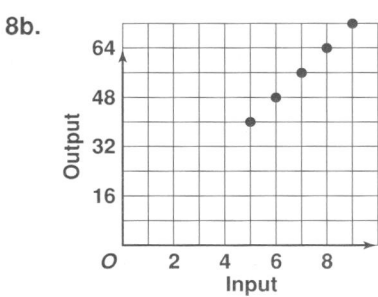

9.
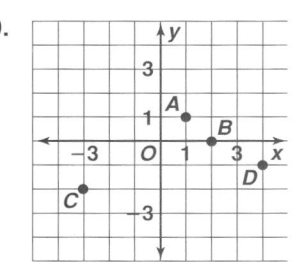

CHAPTER 11

LESSON 11-7

pages 507–509   Think and Disucss

5a.
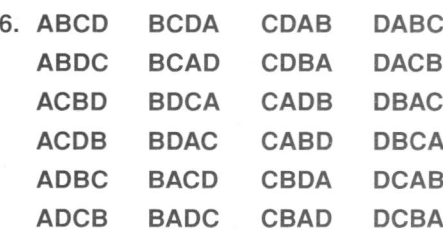

6.

ABCD	BCDA	CDAB	DABC
ABDC	BCAD	CDBA	DACB
ACBD	BDCA	CADB	DBAC
ACDB	BDAC	CABD	DBCA
ADBC	BACD	CBDA	DCAB
ADCB	BADC	CBAD	DCBA

T566

19–24.

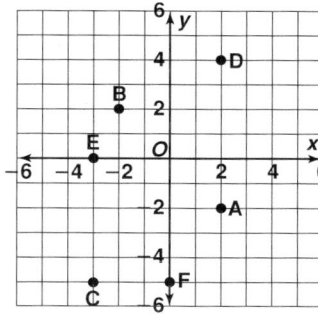

page 520   Assessment

6a.   Outcomes

R   R   R   RRR
           G   RRG
    G   R   RGR
           G   RGG
   G   R   R   GRR
           G   GRG
    G   R   GGR
           G   GGG

7b.

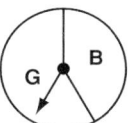

Additional Answers

Index

O

N

T576

W

X

Y

Z

Acknowledgments

Cover Design
Bruce Bond; Martucci Studio

Cover Photos
Martucci Studio

Book Design
Olena Serbyn; Brown Publishing Network

Page Design and Design Management
Brown Publishing Network

Technical Illustration
GTS Graphics; Brown Publishing Network

Illustration
Annie Bissett: 216, 309, 452
Dan Brawner: 313, 445
Tom Klare: 34, 140, 485
Tom Lochray: 186, 287, 305
Karen Minot: 24, 48, 72, 250, 398, 501
Michael Moran: 437
Ortelius Design: 239, 451, 466
Outlook/ANCO: 6, 93, 152, 160, 197, 205, 207, 383, 390
Steve Pica: 62, 91, 164
Matthew Pippin: 64, 525
Gary Torrisi: 98, 277, 278, 387
Camille Venti: 105, 107, 162, 235, 269, 297, 327, 338, 350, 360, 361, 362, 492, 495, 499
Rose Zgodzinski: 15, 89, 110, 118, 194, 197, 301, 315, 414, 424, 460

Photography
Photo Research: Brown Publishing Network

Front Matter: vii, David Ball/The Picture Cube; **viii,** Joanne Ernst/David Madison; **ix,** Steve Sutton/Duomo; **x,** Paul Barton/The Stock Market; **xi,** David Woods/The Stock Market; **xii,** Michael Newman/Photo Edit; **xiii,** Mark Newman/Photo Edit; **xiv,** Corel; **xv,** Tony Freeman/Photo Edit; **xvi,** Prentice Hall photo by Tracy Wheeler; **xvii,** Courtesy of Milton Bradley Company; **xviii,** Lawrence Migdale; **xixt,** Prentice Hall photo by Irene Perlman; **xixc,** Bob Daemmrich/The Image Works; **xx,** Uniphoto; **xxiii,** John Yurka/The Picture Cube; **xxv,** Breck Kent/Animals, Animals; **xxvi,** Will & Deni McIntyre/Photo Researchers; **xxvii,** Bob Daemmrich/Stock Boston; **xxviii,** David Young-Wolff/Photo Edit

Chapter 1: 2–3, Arthur Tilley/FPG; **5,** Alan Carey/The Image Works; **9,** The Stock Market; **13,** Archive Photos; **14,** C.C. Lockwood; **16,** Prentice Hall photo by Russ Lappa; **18,** Prentice Hall photo by Ken O'Donoghue; **21,** Bob Daemmrich/The Image Works; **23,** Arnold Johnson Kaplan/The Picture Cube; **25,** David Ball/The Picture Cube; **27,** Lynn M. Stone/Animals, Animals; **28,** The Image Finders; **30,** U.S. Postal Service; **30,** U.S. Postal Service; **33,** Alice Grulich-Jones; **36,** Robert Clay/Monkmeyer

Chapter 2: 42–43, Bill Horseman/Stock Boston; **45,** Tom McHugh/Photo Researchers; **48,** David Young-Wolff/Photo Edit; **49,** Frederick McKinney/FPG; **51,** David Young-Wolff/Photo Edit; **53,** Lisa Law/Image Works; **53,** Lisa Law/The Image Works; **54,** Richard Hutchings/Photo Edit; **56,** Melancholis Durer/Art Resource; **57,** Prentice Hall photo by Russ Lappa; **57,** Prentice Hall photo by Russ Lappa; **60,** Joanne Ernst/David Madison; **66,** Mehau Kulyk/Science Photo Library/Photo Researchers; **67,** Prentice Hall photo by Ken O'Donoghue; **69,** Mark Greenberg/Visions; **69,** Mark Greenberg/Visions; **75,** L. Kolvoord/The Image Works

Chapter 3: 82–83, Bob Daemmrich; **85,** Gary Gengozian; **87,** Superstock; **93,** Richard Gross/The Stock Market; **94,** John Chumack/Photo Researchers; **96,** Prentice Hall photo by Irene Perlman; **96,** Prentice Hall photo by Russ Lappa; **98,** Prentice Hall photo by Russ Lappa; **104,** E. R. Degginger/Earth Scenes; **109,** Steven Sutton/Duomo; **113,** Prentice Hall photo by Ken O'Donoghue; **114,** Werner Forman Archive/Art Resource; **117,** Tony Freeman/Photo Edit; **119,** Bob Daemmrich; **119,** CC Studio/Science Source Library/Photo Researchers; **119,** Tom Bean/The Stock Market; **120,** Runk/Schoenberg/Grant Heilman; **123,** Archive Photos/American Stock

Chapter 4: 132–33, Prentice Hall photo by Tracy Wheeler; **135,** Chinastock; **137,** Paper House, Rockport, MA; **137,** Paper House, Rockport, MA; **142,** Paul Barton/The Stock Market; **144,** Shelby Thorner/David Madison; **147,** Corbis-Bettmann; **151,** Bonnie Kamin/Photo Edit; **153,** Felicia Martinez/Photo Edit; **159,** Nicole Katano/Tony Stone Images; **161,** Superstock; **162,** Gamma Liaison; **169,** The Stock Market

Chapter 5: 180–81, Uniphoto; **182,** Bob Daemmrich/Uniphoto; **183,** Museo Capitolino, Rome, Italy/AGE Fotostock/ SuperStock; **184,** Vic Bider/Photo Edit; **189,** Superman is a trademark of DC Comics © 1938. All rights reserved. Used with permission; **191,** David R. Frazier/Photo Researchers; **191,** Kent Wood/Peter Arnold; **194,** Greg Anderson/San Gabriel Valley; **202,** Mark Burnett/Stock Boston; **203,** Prentice Hall photo by Russ Lappa; **203,** Prentice Hall photo by Russ Lappa; **205,** Uniphoto; **206,** Elena Rooraid/Photo Edit; **210,** Lance Nelson/The Stock Market; **214,** Bill Aron/Photo Edit; **219,** David Woods/The Stock Market; **220,** Rhoda Sidney/Stock Boston; **225,** Lou Jacobs/Grant Heilman

Chapter 6: 226–27, Superstock; **226,** Prentice Hall photo by Russ Lappa; **228,** Michael Newman/Photo Edit; **236,** LeDuc/Monkmeyer; **237,** Bob Daemmrich; **238,** Prentice Hall photo by Russ Lappa; **243,** Art Wolff; **249,** Lena/Photo Edit; **251,** Tony Freeman/ Photo Edit; **255,** Jeff Greenberg/Photo Edit; **256,** Prentice Hall photo by Russ Lappa; **258,** Prentice Hall photo by Russ Lappa; **261,** Jeffrey Sylvester/FPG; **263,** David Young-Wolff/Photo Edit

Chapter 7: 276–77, Frank Zullo/Science Source/Photo Researchers; **278,** Mark Newman/Photo Edit; **283,** Courtesy of The White House; **283,** Courtesy of The White House; **285,** Superstock; **286,** Prentice Hall photo by Ken O'Donoghue; **290,** Kent Knudson/Uniphoto; **301,** Uniphoto; **306,** Prentice Hall photo by Ken O'Donoghue; **309,** M. Bridwell/Photo Edit; **311,** Superstock

Chapter 8: 324–25, Bob Daemmrich; **328,** Prentice Hall photo by Ken O'Donoghue; **330,** Superstock; **331,** David J. Sams/Stock Boston; **332,** Brady/Monkmeyer; **339,** "Oblique House" interior, Mary Lucier; **341,** Prentice Hall photos by Russ Lappa; **342,** Rob Crandall/Stock Boston; **343,** Philip Habib/Tony Stone Images; **345,** Superstock; **347,** Raphael Gaillarde/Gamma Liaison; **348,** Superstock; **355,** Ledru/Sygma; **357,** J. Messerschmidt/Bruce Coleman; **360,** Corel; **364,** Superstock; **373,** Prentice Hall photo by Russ Lappa

Chapter 9: 380–81, Ullman/Monkmeyer; **383,** Superstock; **388,** Superstock; **390,** From the Cardinal Spellman Philatelic Museum, photo by George McLean; **393,** Darrell Gulin/Tony Stone Images; **400,** Tony Freeman/Photo Edit; **404,** David Madison; **404,** Victor R. Boswell, Jr./National Geographic Society; **408,** Scott Berber/Picture Cube; **411,** R. M. Arakaki/ International Stock; **411,** Tony Freeman/Photo Edit; **411,** Superstock; **411,** Tony Freeman/Photo Edit; **412,** Jeff Greenberg/Unicorn; **418,** Prentice Hall photo by Russ Lappa

Chapter 10: 432–33, Lawrence Migdale; **435,** Mary Kate Denny/Photo Edit; **443,** Stephen Dalton/Animals, Animals; **449,** Breck Kent/Animals, Animals; **454,** Michael Dwyer/Stock Boston; **457,** Cary Wollinsky/Stock Boston; **463,** Prentice Hall photo by Tracy Wheeler; **468,** John Elk/Stock Boston; **468,** Image Works; **472,** Mark Burnett/Photo Researchers

Chapter 11: 478–79, David Young-Wolff/Photo Edit; **480,** David Young-Wolff/Photo Edit; **487,** Superstock; **488,** Bob Daemmrich/The Image Works; **498,** Jeff Greenberg/Photo Edit; **503,** David Young-Wolff/Photo Edit; **506,** Courtesy of Milton Bradley Co.; **508,** Jose Carillo/Photo Edit; **510,** David Young-Wolff/Photo Edit; **512,** Robert Shater/Tony Stone International

Teacher's Edition
Editorial Services: Publishers Resource Group, Inc.
Design Coordination: Susan Gerould/Perspectives